Alkaline Solutions

a. *Stock sodium hydroxide*, NaOH. 15N (for preparation of 6N, 1N 0.1N solutions): Cautiously [...] g solid NaOH in 800 ml [...] to form 1 l of solution. Re[...] carbonate precipitate from [...] by keeping it at the boiling [...] few hours in a hot water bath [...] ting the particles settle for at least 48 hr in an alkali-resistant container (wax-lined or polyethylene) protected from atmospheric carbon dioxide with a soda lime tube. Use the supernate for the preparation of the dilute solutions listed in Table B.

Alternatively, prepare the dilute solutions by dissolving the weight of solid NaOH indicated in Table B in carbon-dioxide-free distilled water and diluting to 1,000 ml.

Table B: Preparation of Uniform Sodium Hydroxide Solutions

Normality of NaOH Solution	Required Weight of NaOH to Prepare 1,000 ml of Solution g	Required Volume of 15N NaOH to Prepare 1,000 ml of Solution ml
6	240	400
1	40	67
0.1	4	6.7

Store the NaOH solutions in polyethylene (rigid, heavy type) bottles with polyethylene screw caps, paraffin-coated bottles with rubber or neoprene stop-pers, or p[...] bottles with rubber or ne-op[...]. Check the solutions pe-[...]ct them by attaching a [...]oxide-absorbing granu-[...] as soda lime, Asca-[...]r equivalent. Use at [...]of rubber tubing to mini-[...] vapor diffusion from the bottle. Replace the absorption tube before it becomes exhausted. Withdraw the solution by a siphon to avoid opening the bottle.

b. *Ammonium hydroxide solutions*, NH₄OH: Prepare 5N, 3N, and 0.2N ammonium hydroxide solutions by diluting 333 ml, 200 ml, and 13 ml, respectively, of the concentrated reagent (sp gr 0.90, 29.0%, 15N) to 1,000 ml with distilled water.

Indicator Solutions

a. *Phenolphthalein indicator solution:* Use either the aqueous (1) or alcoholic (2) solution.

1) Dissolve 5 g phenolphthalein disodium salt in distilled water and dilute to 1 l.

2) Dissolve 5 g phenolphthalein in 500 ml 95% ethyl or isopropyl alcohol and add 500 ml distilled water.

If necessary, add 0.02N NaOH dropwise until a faint pink color appears in solution 1) or 2).

b. *Methyl orange indicator solution:* Dissolve 500 mg methyl orange powder in distilled water and dilute to 1 l.

*Fisher Scientific Co.
†A. H. Thomas Co.

Standard Methods

For the Examination of Water and Wastewater

FOURTEENTH EDITION

Standard Methods

For the Examination of Water and Wastewater

FOURTEENTH EDITION

Prepared and published jointly by:
AMERICAN PUBLIC HEALTH ASSOCIATION
AMERICAN WATER WORKS ASSOCIATION
WATER POLLUTION CONTROL FEDERATION

Joint Editorial Board

M.C. RAND, WPCF, Chairman
ARNOLD E. GREENBERG, APHA
MICHAEL J. TARAS, AWWA

MARY ANN FRANSON
 Managing Editor

Publication Office:
 American Public Health Association
 1015 Eighteenth Street NW
 Washington, DC 20036

25M3/76
Library of Congress Catalog Number: 55-1979 rev
International Standard Book Number: 0-87553-078-8

Library of Congress Cataloging in Publication Data

Main entry under title:

Standard Methods for the Examination of Water and Wastewater

Includes index.

1. Water—analysis.	2. Sewage—analysis	I. Title
QD142.A5	543.3	55-1979 rev

Printed and bound in the United States of America
Typography: Bru-El Graphic Inc., Springfield, VA
Set in: *Janson*
Text: John D. Lucas Co., Baltimore MD
Binding: Optic Bindery, Inc., Glen Burnie MD

Cover Design: Donya Melanson Assoc., Boston MA

PREFACE TO THE FOURTEENTH EDITION

The first edition of *Standard Methods* was published in 1905. Each subsequent edition has presented significant improvements of methodology and has enlarged its scope to include technics suitable for examination of many types of samples encountered in the assessment and control of water quality and water pollution.

A brief history of *Standard Methods* is of interest because of its contemporary relevance. A movement for "securing the adoption of more uniform and efficient methods of water analysis" led in the 1880's to the organization of a special committee of the Chemical Section of the American Association for the Advancement of Science. A report of this committee, published in 1889, was entitled: A Method, in Part, for the Sanitary Examination of Water, and for the Statement of Results, Offered for General Adoption.* Five topics were covered: (1) "free" and "albuminoid" ammonia; (2) oxygen-consuming capacity; (3) total nitrogen as nitrates and nitrites; (4) nitrogen as nitrites; and (5) statement of results.

In 1895, members of the American Public Health Association, recognizing the need for standard methods in the bacteriologic examination of water, sponsored a convention of bacteriologists to discuss the problem. As a result, an APHA committee was appointed "to draw up procedures for the study of bacteria in a uniform manner and with special references to the differentiation of species." Submitted in 1897,† the procedures found wide acceptance.

In 1899, APHA appointed a Committee on Standard Methods of Water Analysis, charged with the extension of standard procedures to all methods involved in the analysis of water. The report of this committee, published in 1905, constituted the first edition of *Standard Methods* (then entitled *Standard Methods of Water Analysis*). Physical, chemical, microscopic, and bacteriologic methods of water examination were included. In its letter of transmittal, the Committee stated:

> The methods of analysis presented in this report as "Standard Methods" are believed to represent the best current practice of American water analysts, and to be generally applicable in connection with the ordinary problems of water purification, sewage disposal and sanitary investigations. Analysts working on widely different problems manifestly cannot use methods which are identical, and special problems obviously require the methods best adapted to them; but, while recognizing these facts, it yet remains true that sound progress in analytical work will advance in proportion to the general adoption of methods which are reliable, uniform and adequate.
>
> It is said by some that standard methods within the field of applied science tend to stifle investigations and that they retard true progress. If such standards are used in the proper spirit, this ought not to be so. The Committee strongly desires that every effort shall be continued to improve the techniques of water analysis and especially to compare current methods with those herein recommended, where different, so that the results obtained may be still more accurate and reliable than they are at present.

Revised and enlarged editions were published by APHA under the title *Standard Methods of Water Analysis* in 1912 (Second Edition), 1917 (Third), 1920 (Fourth), and 1923 (Fifth). In 1925, the American Water Works Association

---

*J. Anal. Chem. 3:398 (1889).
†Proc. Amer. Pub. Health Ass. 23:56 (1897).

joined APHA in publishing the Sixth Edition, which had the broader title, *Standard Methods of the Examination of Water and Sewage*. Joint publication was continued in the Seventh Edition, dated 1933.

In 1935, the Water Pollution Control Federation (then the Federation of Sewage Works Associations) issued a committee report, "Standard Methods of Sewage Analysis."‡ With minor modifications, these methods were incorporated into the Eighth Edition (1936) of *Standard Methods,* which was thus the first to provide methods for the examination of "sewages, effluents, industrial wastes, grossly polluted waters, sludges, and muds." The Ninth Edition, appearing in 1946, likewise contained these methods, and in the following year the Federation became a full-fledged publishing partner. Since 1947, the work of the *Standard Methods* committees of the three associations—APHA, AWWA, and WPCF—has been coordinated by a Joint Editorial Board, on which all three are represented.

The Tenth Edition (1955) included methods specific for the examination of industrial wastewaters; this was reflected by a new title: *Standard Methods for the Examination of Water, Sewage and Industrial Wastes.* In order to describe more accurately and concisely the contents of the Eleventh Edition (1960), the title was shortened to *Standard Methods for the Examination of Water and Wastewater.* It remained unchanged for the Twelfth Edition (1965), the Thirteenth Edition (1971), and the Fourteenth Edition (1976).

The Fourteenth Edition

In the Fourteenth Edition, the separation of test methods for water from those for wastewater is discontinued. Recent developments such as advanced wastewater treatment and reuse of effluents have made the distinction obsolete. All methods for a given component or characteristic now appear under a single heading. This trend was started in the previous edition by combining the methods for industrial wastewaters with those for other polluted samples. The integration of all test methods is now complete.

To accomplish this consolidation, it was necessary to change the organization that had been in effect since 1947. In the past several editions, the major divisions were designed to correspond with the areas of principal interest of the sponsoring societies. Each society accepted primary responsibility for certain major parts of the manual, setting up subcommittees to handle individual methods. The present arrangement required much more interaction among the societies in the early stages of the work. For each test of interest to more than one society, a Joint Task Group was established, to which each interested society could appoint members. The Chair, selected by the Joint Editorial Board, was authorized to appoint additional members or advisors.

The coordination of methods is reflected in the revised numbering system. Although based on that used in the Thirteenth Edition, it has been changed to accommodate the new arrangement of the subject matter and to include two major sec-

‡*Sewage Works J.* 7:444 (1935).

tions that consist almost entirely of new material. The major divisions of the Fourteenth Edition are as follows:

Part 100—General Introduction
Part 200—Physical Examination
Part 300—Determination of Metals
Part 400—Determination of Inorganic Nonmetallic Constituents
Part 500—Determination of Organic Constituents
Part 600—Automated Laboratory Analyses
Part 700—Examination of Water and Wastewater for Radioactivity
Part 800—Bioassay Methods for Aquatic Organisms
Part 900—Microbiological Examination of Water
Part 1000—Biological Examination of Water

Changes, revisions, and improvements in the methods are too numerous for individual listing in this preface. Many changes resulted from consolidation of the former separate sections on water and contaminated samples. Many others represent advances in precision and accuracy, in sensitivity, or in applicability of previously existing technics, while still others are improved technics replacing older methods. For a number of components and characteristics, methods appear in this edition for the first time.

The Fourteenth Edition retains the General Introduction (Part 100) containing important information concerning proper execution of the procedures. The Joint Editorial Board strongly urges that every reader carefully study the General Introduction and the introductions to the individual parts. Each introduction discusses vital matters of wide application within its specific province to minimize repetition in the succeeding text. The success of the analysis may well rest on the manner in which the recommendations are adhered to as set forth in the introductions. The same precaution holds true for individual determinations. The complete discussion of each procedure, embracing selection of method, sampling and storage, general discussion, and interferences, should be read and fully understood before an analysis is undertaken.

Part 200 now includes a procedure for the determination of oxygen transfer. An added method for measurement of salinity has been adapted from the discontinued publication, *Recommended Procedures for Examination of Sea Water and Shellfish* (American Public Health Association). This method is included in Part 200, as are the reversing thermometer and thermograph methods for measuring temperature, from the same source. Section 213, Tests on Activated Sludge, presents methods for determining oxygen consumption rate and zone settling rate, neither of which has appeared in earlier editions.

In Determination of Metals (Part 300), relatively few new components appear because previous editions were quite complete in this respect. Methods applicable to a large number of metals, including atomic absorption spectrophotometry and polarography, have been consolidated in Section 301. The Fourteenth Edition includes the flameless atomic absorption method for mercury, which has not appeared previously. Atomic absorption technics have been extended in accordance with advances in the capability of these methods. Wherever possible, these procedures have been extended to samples of more or less polluted water, in addition to their former applications to relatively clean samples.

Determination of Inorganic Nonmetallic Constituents (Part 400) has undergone extensive editorial revision in many sections. The syringaldazine method for residual chlorine has been introduced and the methyl orange method and all acid orthotolidine methods have been deleted. In Section 419, Nitrogen (Nitrate), the electrode method appears for the first time as a screening method, and the phenoldisulfonic acid method, and the zinc reduction method of the Thirteenth Edition have been deleted. Procedures for cyanides amenable to chlorination also are new.

In Determination of Organic Constituents (Part 500), the distillation method for volatile acids has been reinstated. A new "miniature" method for determination of total organic contaminants by activated carbon adsorption has been added. The section on organic pesticides has been amplified by inclusion of methods for chlorinated phenoxy acids, organophosphates, and carbamates. The Thirteenth Edition method for tannin and lignin has been replaced by a new, improved technic. For determination of grease and oil, previously presented technics have undergone substantial modification. Infrared determination is recommended for low concentrations of highly volatile oils, while gravimetric readout is retained where applicable. The Soxhlet extraction procedure and liquid-liquid extraction are retained, but the semiwet procedure has been deleted. Silica gel has replaced activated alumina for the separation of polar lipids from nonpolar compounds.

Completely new divisions deal with automated laboratory analyses (Part 600) and with bioassay methods (Part 800). Each of these areas represents a substantial extension of the scope of these standards. Each embraces a type of laboratory testing that is already important and that is expected to become even more so in the future. With the exception of the fish toxicity bioassay, all the material in these sections is new.

Part 700, dealing with the determination of radioactivity, has been changed relatively little from the Thirteenth Edition. Part 900 has been revised, updated, and expanded to include procedures for *Klebsiella*, pathogenic leptospires, fungi, actinomycetes, and nematodes. The material on iron and sulfur bacteria now appears in Part 900. Part 1000 likewise has been revised and updated.

Selection and Approval of Methods

For each new edition, both the technical criteria for selection of methods and the formal procedures for their approval and inclusion are reviewed critically. In regard to the approval procedures, it is considered particularly important to assure that the methods presented have been reviewed and supported by the largest possible number of qualified persons, in order that they may represent a true consensus of expert opinion.

It has been mentioned that for the Fourteenth Edition a Joint Task Group was established for each test. Appointment of an individual member to a Joint Task Group generally was based on the expressed interest of the individual or his recognized expertise. The effort in every case was to assemble a group having maximum available expertise in the test methods of concern.

Each Joint Task Group was charged with reviewing the pertinent methods in the Thirteenth Edition along with other methods from the literature, recommending the methods to be included in the Fourteenth Edition, and presenting those methods in the form of a proposed manuscript section. Subsequently, each section of the manuscript was ratified by vote of the membership of the pertinent committees of the societies. Every negative vote and every comment submitted in the balloting was reviewed by the Joint Editorial Board. All relevant suggestions were referred to the appropriate Joint Task Groups for resolution.

The methods presented here, as in previous editions, are believed to be the best available and generally accepted procedures for the analysis of water, wastewaters, and related materials. They represent the recommendations of specialists, ratified by a large number of analysts and others of more general expertise, and as such are truly consensus standards, offering a valid and recognized basis for control and evaluation.

The technical criteria for selection of methods were applied by the Joint Task Groups and by the individuals reviewing their recommendations, with the Joint Editorial Board providing only general guidelines. In addition to the classical concepts of precision, accuracy, and minimum detectable concentration, selection of a method must also recognize such considerations as the time required to obtain a result, needs for specialized equipment and for special training of the analyst, and other factors related to the cost of the analysis and the feasibility of its widespread use.

Status of Methods

All methods in the Fourteenth Edition are "standard" unless designated "tentative". No other categories are used. Methods with "standard" status have been studied extensively and accepted as applicable within the limits of sensitivity, precision, and accuracy given. "Tentative" methods are those still under investigation that have not yet been evaluated fully or are not considered sufficiently tested at present to be designated "standard".

Technical progress makes advisable the establishment of a program to keep *Standard Methods* abreast of advances in research and general practice. The Joint Editorial Board has developed the following procedure for effecting interim changes in methods between editions:

1. Any method given "tentative" status in the current edition may be elevated to "standard" by action of the Joint Editorial Board, on the basis of adequate published data supporting such a change as submitted to the Board by the appropriate Joint Task Group. Notification of such a change in status shall be accomplished by publication in the official journals of the three associations sponsoring *Standard Methods*.

2. No method having "standard" status may be abandoned or reduced to "tentative" status during the interval between editions.

3. A new method may be adopted as "tentative" or "standard" by the Joint Editorial Board between editions, such action being based on adequate published data as submitted by the Joint Task Group concerned. Upon adoption, the details of the method, together with a resume of the supporting data, must be published in the official journal of any one of the three sponsoring associations, and reprints shall be made available at a nominal charge. Notice of such publication and of the availability of reprints shall appear in the official journals of the other two sponsors.

Even more important to maintaining the current status of these standards is the intention of the sponsors and the Joint Editorial Board that subsequent editions will appear regularly at intervals of approximately two years.

Acknowledgments

For the major portion of the work in preparing and revising the methods in the Fourteenth Edition, the Joint Editorial Board gives full credit to the Standard Methods Committees of the American Water Works Association and of the Water Pollution Control Federation, and to the Subcommittee on Standard Methods for the Examination of Water and Wastewater, and the Committee on Laboratory Standards and Practices of the American Public Health Association. Members of these committees chair and serve as members of the Joint Task Groups. They were assisted in many cases by advisors, not formally members of the committees, and in many cases not members of the sponsoring societies. To the advisors, special gratitude is extended in recognition of their efforts. A list of the committee members and advisors follows these pages.

The Joint Editorial Board expresses its appreciation to James R. Kimmey, M.D., and William H. McBeath, M.D., past and present Executive Director, respectively, American Public Health Association, to Eric F. Johnson, Executive Director, American Water Works Association, and to Robert A. Canham, Executive Secretary, Water Pollution Control Federation, for their continuous cooperation and helpful advice. James B. Ramsey, Director of Standards, American Water Works Association, has acted as secretary to the Joint Editorial Board for this edition and has provided an endless variety of helpful services as well as useful advice. In the final stages of compiling the manuscript, obtaining approval of every section, and readying it for printing, Mr. Ramsey and the Joint Editorial Board were assisted most ably by Paul A. Schulte, Deputy Director of Standards, American Water Works Association. Special recognition for her valuable services is due to Mary Ann H. Franson, Managing Editor of the Fourteenth Edition, who has discharged most efficiently the extensive and detailed responsibilities on which a complete volume depends.

Joint Editorial Board
Arnold E. Greenberg, American Public Health Association
Michael J. Taras, American Water Works Association
M.C. Rand, Water Pollution Control Federation (Chairman)

JOINT EDITORIAL BOARD

M. C. RAND, Water Pollution Control Federation, *Chairman*
ARNOLD E. GREENBERG, American Public Health Association
MICHAEL J. TARAS, American Water Works Association

COMMITTEES FOR THE FOURTEENTH EDITION
American Public Health Association

Task force on *Standard Methods for the Examination of Water and Wastewater* of the Committee on Laboratory Standards and Practices

ARNOLD E. GREENBERG, *Chairman*
NORMAN A. CLARKE, *Vice Chairman*
WARREN LITSKY, *Vice Chairman*
G. WOLFGANG FUHS
EDWIN E. GELDREICH

HERBERT W. JACKSON
ROBERT L. MORRIS
HUGH D. PUTNAM
ROBERT M. SCOTT
CORNELIUS I. WEBER

American Water Works Association

Committee on *Standard Methods for Examination of Water and Wastewater*

M.J. TARAS, *Chairman*
CHARLES W. AMAN
CLAYTON M. BACH
ROBERT A. BAKER
DWIGHT G. BALLINGER
E. ROBERT BAUMANN
ELWOOD L. BEAN
DEAN C. BECKER
ROBERT J. BECKER
GERALD BERG
A.P. BLACK
ROBERT L. BOOTH
MAXEY BROOKE
J.R. CARVER
RUSSELL CHRISTMAN
JAMES A. CLARK
NORMAN A. CLARKE
W.R. CONLEY
JOSEPH J. CONNORS
N.J. DAVOUST

JOSEPH J. DELFINO
ALBERT DRAGON
CARLTON M. DUKE
DARYL W. EBERT
JOSEPH F. ERDEI
HOWARD W. FIEDELMAN
MARVIN FISHMAN
RUSSELL E. FRAZIER
MADELAINE R. GIGLIOTTI
WALTER GINSBURG
TERRY GLORIOD
KATHRYN L. GLYNN
EUGENE GOLDMAN
A.L. GOODENKAUF
BEN L. GRIMES
C. EUGENE HAMILTON
SIDNEY A. HANNAH
ROBERT H. HARRIS
PIERCE HAYWARD
JOHN D. HEM

DON E. HENLEY
LAUREL M. HENLEY
CLARENCE R. HENRY
ALAN F. HESS
HUGH W. HETZER
JAMES J. HICKEY
J.H. HUBBLE
JOSEPH V. HUNTER
A.Y. HYNDSHAW
ROBERT S. INGOLS
HERBERT W. JACKSON
J. DONALD JOHNSON
ROGER M. JORDEN
ROBERT A. JUNG
R. KAPLAN
FLOYD KEFFORD
BERNARD A. KENNER
STEPHEN R. KIN
RILEY KINMAN
KENNETH F. KNOWLTON

Water Pollution Control Federation

Committee on *Standard Methods for the Examination of Water and Wastewater*

P.A. Krenkel
L.E. Lancy
T.E. Larson
G.W. Lawton
G.F. Lee
D.V. Libby
L.L. Louden
M.D. Lubratovich
F.J. Ludzack
T.E. Maloney
E.F. McFarren
J.J. McKeown
B.W. Mercer, Jr.
E.J. Middlebrooks
E.F. Mohler, Jr.
A.H. Molof
R.L. Morris
A.I. Mytelka
J.K. Nelson

R.J. Nogaj
R. Patrick
W.O. Pipes, Jr.
F.G. Pohland
J.L. Puntenney
R.D. Pomeroy
D. B. Porcella
H.D. Putnam
C.W. Randall
D.J. Reish
J.A. Roeber
A.A. Rosen
F.M. Saunders
J.W. Scherfig
K.L. Schulze
W.B. Schworm
K.E. Shull
P.C. Singer
F.W. Sollo, Jr.

P.C. Soltow, Jr.
C.A. Sorber
R.G. Spicher
O.J. Sproul
R.M. Stewart
H.G. Swope
C.M. Tarzwell
M.M. Varma
D.R. Washington
C.H. Wayman
C.M. Weiss
F.K. West
W.C. Westgarth
G.P. Whittle
A.J. Winter
J.D. Wolszon
C.C. Wright
N.S. Zaleiko

ADVISORS
American Public Health Association

Microbiological Examination:

Gerald Berg
Robert Bordner
Francis T. Brezenski
Victor J. Cabelli
Shih L. Chang
James A. Clark
Wm. Bridge Cooke
Jack Delaney

Lou Estella
Martin S. Favero
Walter Ginsburg
N. Bruce Hanes
Hugh W. Hetzer
William F. Hill, Jr.
Walter Jakubowski
Bernard A. Kenner

Ronald F. Lewis
J.A. Martucci
Romola Popper
John J. Redys
Robert S. Safferman
B.F. Shema
J. Edward Singley
Hugh T. Victoreen

Biological Examination:

Cornelius I. Weber, *General Cochairman and Sub-chairman for Periphyton*
Herbert W. Jackson, *General Cochairman and Sub-chairman for Introduction and Identification of Types of Aquatic Organisms*
C.M. Fetterolf, *Subchairman for Macrophytes*
B.G. Isom, *Subchairman for Macroinvertebrates*

ix

B.G. Johnson, *Subchairman for Plankton*
E. Karvelis, *Subchairman for Fish*

M.L. Allen	R. Patrick	J.H. Tackett
J. Cairns, Jr.	H. Putnam	C. Tarzwell
W. Ginsburg	B.F. Shema	L. Tebo

Radiological Examination:

James W. Mullins   George S. Uyesugi

American Water Works Association

R.G. Allen	S.D. Faust	D.H.A. Price
Ervin Bellack	Roy C. Hoather	Floyd Robinson
H. Bernhardt	Barry E. Hunt	F.F. Ross
H.J. Boorsma	David Jenkins	C.H. Schmiege
J.J. Bouquiaux	Wm. L. Klein	C.M. Tarzwell
Henry F. Bruner	F.J. Ludzack	E.W. Taylor
C.T. Bryant	Willy Masschelein	William W. Ullmann
Norman G. Bunton	D.H. Matheson	Erik Vasseur
Arnold K. Cherry	D. Mercer	R.J. Wells
Barbara L. Cole	R. Packham	P.W. West
D.I. Coomber	A.H. Paessler	T.J. Williams
N.M. DeJarnette	A.T. Palin	John A. Winter
A.L. Downing	Franklyn Pogge	Nicholas Zaleiko
J. Dvir		

Water Pollution Control Federation

M.L. Allen	A. Calabrese	C. Fremling
B. Anderson	R.S. Caldwell	A.R. Gaufin
R.L. Anderson	G.H. Carleu	J.H. Gentile
J.W. Arthur	N.L. Clesceri	J.G. Gonzalez
E. Berry	N.R. Cooley	T.B. Hoover
K. Biesinger	J. Costolow	J.R. Hubschman
F.B. Birkner	G.J. Crits	J. Hughes
F.C. Blanc	J.C. Davis	R. Johannes
I.B. Blumenthal	J.W. Eichelberger	E.T. Johnson
W.H. Bouma	J.G. Eaton	W.W. Johnson
W. Breeze	S.D. Faust	P. Jokiel
P.L. Brezonik	L.B. Fournier	B.M. Jones
P. Butler	J.V. Fuess	E. Kindemann

x

W. Klein
R.E. Kreider
J. Kushner
G. LaRoche
J.J. Lichtenberg
L.W. Little
W. Litsky
L.B. Lobring
J.I. Lowe
C.Z. Machler
N.J. Maluez
L.W. Marking
F.L. Mayer
G. N. McDermott
J.M. McKim

D.A. McLean
D. Middaugh
W.E. Miller
C.R. Mock
J. Morrow
G.E. Morrison
D.R. Nimmo
W.E. Oatess
J.M. Pappenhagen
P.R. Parrish
A.G. Payne
T.B.S. Prakasam
S.A. Rose
E.M. Sallee

H. Sanders
R. Schleser
L.L. Smith
A. Spacie
J. Sprague
C.E. Stephan
N.E. Stewart
P.D. Uttermark
H. Van Der Schalie
F.J. Vernberg
G.E. Walsh
R.A. White
C.E. Woelke
L.A. Woods

TABLE C. INTERNATIONAL RELATIVE ATOMIC WEIGHTS, 1975

Scaled to the relative atomic mass. $A_r(^{12}C) = 12$

The atomic weights of many elements are not invariant but depend on the origin and treatment of the material. The footnotes to this table elaborate the types of variation to be expected for individual elements. The values of $A_r(E)$ given here apply to elements as they exist naturally on earth and to certain artificial elements. When used with due regard to the footnotes they are considered reliable to ±1 in the last digit or ±3 when followed by an asterisk*. Values in parentheses are used for certain radioactive elements whose atomic weights cannot be quoted precisely without knowledge of origin: the value given is the atomic mass number of that element of longest known half life.

Name	Symbol	Atomic number	Atomic weight	Footnotes
Actinium	Ac	89	(227)	
Aluminium	Al	13	26.98154	
Americium	Am	95	(243)	
Antimony	Sb	51	121.75*	
Argon	Ar	18	39.948*	a
Arsenic	As	33	74.9216	
Astatine	At	85	(210)	
Barium	Ba	56	137.33*	
Berkelium	Bk	97	(247)	
Beryllium	Be	4	9.01218	
Bismuth	Bi	83	208.9804	
Boron	B	5	10.81	b, c, d, g
Bromine	Br	35	79.904	a
Cadmium	Cd	48	112.41	
Caesium	Cs	55	132.9054	
Calcium	Ca	20	40.08	c, d, e
Californium	Cf	98	(251)	c
Carbon	C	6	12.011	a
Cerium	Ce	58	140.12	
Chlorine	Cl	17	35.453	g
Chromium	Cr	24	51.996	
Cobalt	Co	27	58.9332	b, d
Copper	Cu	29	63.546*	
Curium	Cm	96	(247)	c
Dysprosium	Dy	66	162.50*	a
Einsteinium	Es	99	(254)	c, d

Name	Symbol	Atomic number	Atomic weight	Footnotes
Mercury	Hg	80	200.59*	
Molybdenum	Mo	42	95.94*	
Neodymium	Nd	60	144.24*	c, e
Neon	Ne	10	20.179*	f
Neptunium	Np	93	237.0482	
Nickel	Ni	28	58.70	
Niobium	Nb	41	92.9064	a
Nitrogen	N	7	14.0067	b, c
Nobelium	No	102	(255)	
Osmium	Os	76	190.2	g
Oxygen	O	8	15.9994*	b, c, d
Palladium	Pd	46	106.4	
Phosphorus	P	15	30.97376	a
Platinum	Pt	78	195.09*	
Plutonium	Pu	94	(244)	
Polonium	Po	84	(209)	
Potassium	K	19	39.0983*	a
Praseodymium	Pr	59	140.9077	
Promethium	Pm	61	(145)	
Protactinium	Pa	91	231.0359	f
Radium	Ra	88	226.0254	f, g
Radon	Rn	86	(222)	
Rhenium	Re	75	186.207	
Rhodium	Rh	45	102.9055	a
Rubidium	Rb	37	85.4678*	c
Ruthenium	Ru	44	101.07*	c

Element	Symbol	At. No.	At. Weight	Notes	Element	Symbol	At. No.	At. Weight	Notes
Erbium	Er	68	167.26*		Samarium	Sm	62	150.4	
Europium	Eu	63	151.96		Scandium	Sc	21	44.9559	a
Fermium	Fm	100	(257)		Selenium	Se	34	78.96*	d
Fluorine	F	9	18.998403		Silicon	Si	14	28.0855*	c
Francium	Fr	87	(223)		Silver	Ag	47	107.868	a
Gadolinium	Gd	64	157.25*	a	Sodium	Na	11	22.98977	
Gallium	Ga	31	69.72		Strontium	Sr	38	87.62	g
Germanium	Ge	32	72.59*		Sulfur	S	16	32.06	d
Gold	Au	79	196.9665	a	Tantalum	Ta	73	180.9479*	b
Hafnium	Hf	72	178.49*		Technetium	Tc	43	(97)	
Helium	He	2	4.00260	b, c	Tellurium	Te	52	127.60*	
Holmium	Ho	67	164.9304	a	Terbium	Tb	65	158.9254	a
Hydrogen	H	1	1.0079	b, d	Thallium	Tl	81	204.37*	
Indium	In	49	114.82		Thorium	Th	90	232.0381	f, g
Iodine	I	53	126.9045	a	Thulium	Tm	69	168.9342	a
Iridium	Ir	77	192.22		Tin	Sn	50	118.69*	
Iron	Fe	26	55.847*		Titanium	Ti	22	47.90*	
Krypton	Kr	36	83.80	e	Tungsten (Wolfram)	W	74	183.85*	b, c, e, g
Lanthanum	La	57	138.9055*	b	Uranium	U	92	238.029	b, c
Lawrencium	Lr	103	(260)		Vanadium	V	23	50.9414*	
Lead	Pb	82	207.2	d, g	Xenon	Xe	54	131.30	e
Lithium	Li	3	6.941*	c, d, e, g	Ytterbium	Yb	70	173.04*	
Lutetium	Lu	71	174.97		Yttrium	Y	39	88.9059	a
Magnesium	Mg	12	24.305	c, g	Zinc	Zn	30	65.38	
Manganese	Mn	25	54.9380	a	Zirconium	Zr	40	91.22	
Mendelevium	Md	101	(258)						

a Element with only one stable nuclide.

b Element with one predominant isotope (about 99 to 100 percent abundance); variations in the isotopic composition or errors in its determination have a correspondingly small effect on the value of A_r(E).

c Element for which the value of A_r(E) derives its reliability from calibrated measurements (i.e. from comparisons with synthetic mixtures of known isotopic composition).

d Element for which known variations in isotopic composition in terrestrial material prevent a more precise atomic weight being given; A_r(E) values should be applicable to any 'normal' material.

e Element for which substantial variations in A_r from the value given can occur in commercially available material because of inadvertent or undisclosed change of isotopic composition.

f Element for which the value of A_r is that of the most commonly available long-lived isotope.

g Element for which geological specimens are known in which the element has an anomalous isotopic composition.

Source: International Union of Pure and Applied Chemistry.

TABLE OF CONTENTS

TABLES

FIGURES

PLATES

Black and White plates of aquatic organisms

PART 100

GENERAL

INTRODUCTION

101 APPLICATIONS

The procedures described in these standards are intended for the examination of waters within a wide range of quality. These waters include water suitable for domestic or industrial supplies, surface waters, groundwaters, cooling or circulating water, boiler water, boiler feed water, wastewater effluents after varying degrees of treatment, and untreated municipal or industrial wastewaters. With higher standards of effluent quality and the increasing use of natural waters for receiving treated effluents, the distinction, emphasized in previous editions, between polluted and unpolluted waters has been abandoned in favor of a unified treatment that reflects growing realization of the unity of the fields of water supply, receiving water quality, and wastewater treatment and disposal.

An effort has been made to present methods that apply as generally as possible, and where alternative methods are necessary for samples of different composition, to present as clearly as possible the basis for selecting the most appropriate method. However, samples with extreme concentrations or otherwise unusual compositions may present difficulties that preclude the direct use of these methods. Hence, some modification of a procedure may be necessary in specific instances. Whenever a procedure is modified, the nature of modification must be stated plainly in the report of results.

Certain parts of these standards present procedures that are intended for use with sludges and sediments. Here again, the effort has been to present methods of the widest possible application, but when chemical sludges or slurries, or other samples of highly unusual composition are encountered, the methods of this manual may require modification, or may be wholly inappropriate.

Many water plant laboratories perform analyses on bulk chemicals received for the treatment of water. These standards are not intended to cover such analyses. A committee of the American Water Works Association prepares and issues standards for water treatment chemicals. Each separate standard describes the acceptable physical and chemical characteristics of the material and presents methods for collecting the sample and determining the major components in order to ascertain compliance with the specifications.

102   LABORATORY APPARATUS, REAGENTS, AND TECHNICS

1. Containers

For general laboratory use, the most suitable material for containers is resistant borosilicate glass, commonly called "pyrex."* Special glassware is available with such characteristics as high resistance to alkali attack, low boron content, or exclusion of light. Stoppers, caps, and plugs should be chosen to resist the attack of material contained in the vessel. Cork stoppers wrapped with a relatively inert metal foil are suitable for many samples. Metal screw caps are a poor choice for any sample that will cause them to corrode readily. Glass stoppers are unsatisfactory for strongly alkaline liquids because of their tendency to stick fast. Rubber stoppers are excellent for alkaline liquids but very poor for organic solvents, in which they swell or disintegrate. Teflon or silver plugs may be used for burets that contain strongly alkaline liquids. For particular purposes, other materials such as porcelain, nickel, iron, platinum, stainless steel, and Vycor† can be used to advantage. It is recommended that samples be collected and stored in bottles made of pyrex, hard rubber, plastic, or other inert material.

For relatively short storage periods, or for constituents that are not affected by storage in soft glass, such as calcium, magnesium, sulfate, chloride, and per-

haps others, the 2.5-l acid-bottle "bell closure" is satisfactory. This type of closure holds a glass disk against the ground-glass surface of the bottle lip and insures adequate protection for the sample. If part of the sample is to be analyzed later for silica, sodium, or other substances that would be affected by prolonged storage in soft glass, transfer it to a small plastic bottle, while leaving the remainder of the sample in the soft-glass bottle.

Sample bottles must be cleaned carefully before each use. Rinse glass bottles, except those to be used for chromium or manganese analyses, with a cleaning mixture made by adding 1 l of conc H_2SO_4 slowly, with stirring, to 35 ml saturated sodium dichromate solution, or with an alkaline permanganate solution followed by an oxalic acid solution. Rinsing with other concentrated acids may be used to remove inorganic matter. Detergents are excellent cleansers for many purposes; use either detergents or conc HCl for cleaning hard-rubber and plastic bottles. After the bottles have been cleaned, rinse them thoroughly with tap water and then with distilled water.

For shipment, pack bottles in wooden, metal, plastic, or heavy fiberboard cases, with a separate compartment for each bottle. Boxes may be lined with corrugated fiber paper, felt, or other resilient material, or may be provided with spring-loaded corner strips, to prevent breakage. Lined wicker baskets also may be used. Samples stored in plastic bottles need no protection against breakage by impact or through freezing.

---

*As used in this manual, "pyrex" refers not to a specific brand, but to the general type, such as that manufactured by Corning Glass Works (under the name "Pyrex"), or Kimble Glass Co., Division of Owens-Illinois ("Kimax"), or equivalent.

†A high-silica glass product of Corning Glass Works.

2. Distilled Water

Some of the colorimetric tests described in this manual are sufficiently sensitive to detect even the minute traces of impurities that may be found in ordinary distilled water. In such cases, the use of double- or triple-distilled water may be required. The material of which the still is constructed may contribute impurities to the distillate. Most commercial stills, for example, are constructed in part of copper, and distilled water from them frequently contains 10 to 50 μg/l Cu. For special purposes, distill water from an all-pyrex apparatus or from an apparatus in which the condenser is made of glass, fused quartz, silver, or block tin.

Ordinary distillation of water will not remove ammonia or carbon dioxide; in fact, distilled water is often supersaturated with carbon dioxide because of the decomposition of raw-water bicarbonates to carbonates in the boiler. Remove ammonia by distillation from acid solution or by passing the water through a column of mixed anionic and cationic resins. Remove carbon dioxide by distillation from a solution containing an excess of alkali hydroxide, by boiling for a few minutes, by vigorously aerating the water with a stream of inert gas for a sufficient period, or by passing the water through a column of strong anion-exchange resin in the hydroxide form. Distilled water kept in glass containers slowly leaches the more soluble materials from the glass and the concentration of total dissolved solids increases.

Demineralized water from a mixed-bed ion exchanger is satisfactory for many applications in this manual. However, because ion exchange fails to remove such nonelectrolytes and colloids as plankton, nonionic organic materials, and dissolved air, it is not suitable for determinations where such constituents interfere. Some ion-exchange resins also release traces of organic matter, which make the demineralized water unsuitable for use in certain tests.

A very high-purity water, with less than 0.1 μsiemens/cm conductivity, can be produced by passing ordinary distilled water through a mixed-bed exchanger and discarding the effluent until the desired quality is obtained. Water prepared in this way is often satisfactory for use in the determination of trace cations and anions.

Three types of special distilled water are specified for various methods in this book. For easy reference, the preparation of these waters is described on the inside front cover.

3. Reagents

Use only the best quality of chemical reagents even though this injunction is not repeated in the description of a particular method. Order chemicals for which the American Chemical Society has published specifications in the "ACS grade." Order other chemicals as "analytical reagent grade" or "spectral grade organic solvents." Methods of checking the purity of suspect reagents will be found in books of reagent specifications listed in the bibliography under laboratory reagents.

Unfortunately, many commercial dyes for which the ACS grade has not been established fail to meet exacting analytical requirements because of variations in the color response of different lots. In such cases, dyes certified by the

Biological Stain Commission may be satisfactory for chemical analysis.

Where neither an ACS grade nor a certified Biological Stain Commission dye is available, purify the solid dye through recrystallization.

The following standard substances, each bottle of which is accompanied by a certificate of analysis, are issued by the National Bureau of Standards, Department of Commerce, Washington, D.C., for the purpose of standardizing analytical solutions:

Acidimetric:
   84h —Acid potassium phthalate
   350 —Benzoic acid
Oxidimetric:
   40h —Sodium oxalate
   83c —Arsenic trioxide
  136c —Potassium dichromate
Buffer:
  185e —Acid potassium phthalate
  186Ic —Potassium dihydrogen phosphate
  186IIc —Disodium hydrogen phosphate
  187b —Borax
  188 —Potassium hydrogen tartrate
  189 —Potassium tetroxalate
  191 —Sodium bicarbonate
  192 —Sodium carbonate

Many hundreds of other standards issued by NBS are described in its Special Publication 260.

A successful dithizone test demands reagents of the highest purity. Chloroform and carbon tetrachloride are available in a grade declared to be suitable for the dithizone methods. Select reagents of this quality preferentially for the several dithizone methods described in this manual.

The general availability of the water-soluble sodium salts of the common indicators at nominal cost has resulted in their predominant recommendation for indicator preparation in this edition.

When alcohol or ethyl alcohol is specified for the preparation of such solutions as phenolphthalein indicator, use 95% ethyl alcohol. A similar grade of isopropyl alcohol is a permissible alternate.

Certain organic reagents are somewhat unstable upon exposure to the atmosphere. If the stability of a chemical is limited or unknown, purchase small lots at frequent intervals.

Many of the chemical reagents prescribed in this book should be treated with the utmost care, both in their original state and in the form of solutions. Handle with special discretion chemical reagents bearing commercial labels with the words POISON, DANGER, CAUTION, FLAMMABLE, or comparable warnings. Continuing investigations are revealing the carcinogenic properties of common reagents such as orthotolidine dihydrochloride, 1-naphthylamine hydrochloride, and 3, 3'-diaminobenzidine hydrochloride. These aromatic amines and other suspected amines should be handled with a circumspection that will prevent their inhalation, ingestion, absorption, or contact through the lungs, mouth, or skin. The Occupational Safety and Health Administration has established a list of chemical carcinogens and defined restrictive conditions under which they may be used. In the interest of personal safety, the analyst will be well repaid by a study of the manual entitled *Safety Practice for Water Utilities* published by the American Water Works Association and of the *Guide for Safety in the Chemical Laboratory* prepared by the Manufacturing Chemists Association and detailing the hazards that may occur in the laboratory. Specific restrictions imposed under Occupational Safety and Health Administration (federal and/or state) rules and regulations must be observed.

Dry all anhydrous reagent chemicals required for the preparation of standard calibration solutions and titrants in an oven at 105 to 110 C for at least 1 to 2 hr and preferably overnight. After cooling them to room temperature in an efficient desiccator, promptly weigh the proper amount for dissolution. Should a different drying temperature be necessary, this is specified for the particular chemical. For hydrated salts, milder drying in an efficient desiccator can be substituted for oven-drying.

4. Common Acid and Alkali Solutions

a. Concentration units used: Reagent concentrations are expressed in this manual in terms of normality, molarity, and additive volumes.

A *normal solution (N)* contains one gram equivalent weight of solute per liter of solution.

A *molar solution (M)* contains one gram molecular weight of solute per liter of solution.

In additive volumes $(a+b)$, the first number, a, refers to the volume of the concentrated reagent; the second number, b, refers to the volume of distilled water required for dilution. Thus, "1+9 HCl" denotes that 1 volume of concentrated HCl is to be diluted with 9 volumes of distilled water.

In order to make a solution of exact normality from a chemical that cannot be measured as a primary standard, first prepare a relatively concentrated stock solution and then make an exact dilution of this to the desired strength. Alterna-

tively, make a solution of slightly stronger concentration than that desired, standardize, and then make suitable adjustments in the concentration; or, use the solution as first standardized and modify the factor used in the calculation. This latter procedure is useful especially for solutions that slowly change strength—for example, sodium thiosulfate solution, which must be restandardized frequently. Often, however, adjustment to the exact normality specified is desirable when a laboratory makes a large number of determinations with one standard solution.

As long as the normality of a standard solution does not result in a titration volume so small as to preclude accurate measurement or so large as to cause abnormal dilution of the reaction mixture, and as long as the solution is standardized properly and the calculations are made properly, the determinations are in accord with the instructions in this manual.

b. Preparation and dilution of solutions: If a solution of exact normality is to be prepared by dissolving a weighed amount of a primary standard or by diluting a stronger solution, bring it up to exact volume in a volumetric flask.

Accurately prepare the stock and standard solutions prescribed for the colorimetric determinations in the chemical sections of these standards in volumetric flasks. Where the concentration does not need to be exact, it is easier to mix the concentrated solution or the solid with measured amounts of water, using graduated cylinders for these measurements. There is usually a significant change of volume when strong solutions are mixed, so that the total volume is less than the sum of the volumes used. For approximate dilutions, the volume changes are negligible when concentrations of 6N or less are diluted.

Mix thoroughly and completely when making dilutions. One of the commonest sources of error in analyses using standard solutions diluted in volumetric flasks is failure to attain complete mixing.

c. Storage of solutions: Some standardized solutions alter slowly because of chemical or biological changes. The practical life, required frequency of standardizations, or storage precautions are indicated for such standards. Others, such as dilute hydrochloric acid, are nonreactive. Yet they, too, may change in strength as a result of evaporation that is not prevented by a glass stopper. Changes in temperature cause a bottle to "breathe," thus allowing some evaporation. Do not consider a standard valid for more than a year unless it is restandardized, and it is valid for that length of time only if conditions minimize evaporation. If the bottle is opened often or if it is much less than half full, serious evaporation occurs in a few months.

Where glass bottles are called for, use chemically resistant glass. For standard solutions that do not react with rubber or neoprene, use stoppers of these materials, because they can, if properly fitted, prevent evaporation as long as the bottle is closed. Screw-cap bottles also are effective. If the cap has a gasket of a reasonably resistant material, permissible usage will be about the same as that for rubber stoppers.

d. Hydrochloric and sulfuric acid as alternatives: Dilute standardized sulfuric and hydrochloric acids are called for in various procedures. Often these solutions are interchangeable. Where

one is mentioned, the analyst may use the other if he is certain that the substitution will make no difference.

e. Preparation: Instructions in this manual usually describe the preparation of 1 l of solution. It is often expedient to prepare a smaller or larger volume. The analyst should consider this and not limit the amount to 1 l just because the instructions are so written. Sometimes instructions call for the preparation of 100 ml; the solutions involved either have a short life or are used in small amounts, so that 1 l would be excessive.

A safe general rule to follow in the preparation of solutions is to add the more concentrated acid or alkali to the water, with stirring, in a vessel that can withstand thermal shock, and then to dilute to the final volume after cooling to room temperature.

f. Uniform reagent concentrations: An attempt has been made in these standards to establish a uniform number of common acid and base concentrations that will serve for the adjustment of the acid and alkaline reaction of samples prior to color development or final titration. The following acid concentrations are recommended for general laboratory use: the concentrated reagent of commerce, 6N, 1N, 0.1N, and 0.02N. The preparations of these acid concentrations, as well as the required 15N, 6N, and 1N sodium hydroxide solutions, and 5N, 3N, and 0.2N ammonium hydroxide solutions, are tabulated and described on the inside front cover of this book for easy reference.

5. Volumetric Glassware

Volumetric glassware may be calibrated either by the analyst who will use it or by a competent laboratory that can furnish certificates of accuracy. Volumetric glassware is calibrated either "to contain" (TC) or "to deliver" (TD). Glassware designed "to deliver" will do so with accuracy only when the inner surface is so scrupulously clean that water wets it immediately and forms a uniform film upon emptying. Whenever possible, pyrex glassware should be used.

Approved quantitative technics will yield the best results in the standard procedures. For this reason, careful measurement of weights and volumes is required in the preparation of standard solutions and calibration curves. Observe similar precautions in the measurement of sample volumes. Use volumetric pipets or burets where the volume is designated to two decimal places (X.00 ml) in the text. Use volumetric flasks where the volume is specified as 1,000 ml rather than 1 l and where a volumetric flask is specified.

6. Nessler Tubes

Use nessler tubes of the "tall" form (except when otherwise indicated), made of resistant glass, and selected from uniformly drawn tubing. The glass should be clear and colorless. The bottoms of the nessler tubes should be plane-parallel. When the tubes are filled with liquid and viewed from the top with a light source beneath the tubes, there should be no dark spots nor any lenslike distortion of the transmitted light. The best quality tube is manufactured by fusion-sealing a separately prepared, ground, and polished circle of glass to the tube to form its bottom. Less expensive tubes are manufactured with integral bottoms, which cannot be made perfectly flat, but which may appear to be satisfactory. The tops of the tubes should be flat, preferably fire-polished, and smooth enough to permit cover slips to be cemented on for sealing. Nessler tubes with standard-taper clear glass tops are available commercially. The graduation marks should completely encircle the tubes.

The 100-ml tubes should have a total length of approximately 375 mm. Their inside diameter should approximate 20 mm and the outside diameter 24 mm. The graduation mark should be as near as possible to 300 mm above the inside bottom. Tubes sold in sets should be of such uniformity that this distance does not vary more than 6 mm. (Sets are available commercially in which the maximum difference between tubes is not more than 2 mm.) A graduation mark at 50 ml is permissible.

The 50-ml tubes should have a total length of about 300 mm. Their inside diameter should approximate 17 mm and the outside diameter 21 mm. The graduation mark on the tube should be as near as possible to 225 mm above the inside of the bottom. Tubes sold in sets should be of such uniformity that this distance does not vary more than 6 mm. (Sets are available commercially in which the maximum difference between tubes is not more than 1.5 mm.) A graduation mark at 25 ml is permissible.

Tubes for Jackson candle turbidimeters, in addition to conforming precisely to the measurements given in Section 214, Turbidity, should conform to all the requirements of quality, glass color, and workmanship pertaining to nessler tubes.

7. Colorimetric Equipment and Technic

Many of the procedures in this manual depend upon matching colors, either by eye or with a photometric instrument. In order to obtain the best possible results, the analyst should understand the principles and limitations of these methods, especially because the choice of instrument and of technic is discretionary.

Both visual and photometric methods have their place in water analysis and each method has advantages.

Tall-form nessler tubes provide a 30-cm light path, which is highly desirable when very faint colors are to be compared. Nessler tubes are inexpensive; their use does not require much training; they are not subject to mechanical or electrical failure; and in general they are entirely satisfactory for much of the routine work. Because they are portable and do not require a source of electric light, they can be used in the field.

Photometric instruments are more versatile than nessler tubes; they are generally capable of superior accuracy if used properly, and they do not depend on external lighting conditions or on the analyst's eyesight. Therefore, results obtained with photometric instruments are less subject to personal bias and are more reproducible. Their use often allows corrections to be made for interfering color or turbidity. It is not necessary to prepare a complete set of standards for every single determination if a photometric instrument is used, whereas it is necessary to prepare such a set, or to maintain permanent standards, if nessler tubes are used for visual comparison.

However, photometric methods are not free from specific limitations. An analyst will recognize that something has gone wrong if he sees an off color or turbidity when making a visual comparison, but such a discrepancy easily may escape detection during a photometric reading, for the instrument always will yield some sort of reading, whether meaningful or not. Sensitivity and accuracy must be checked frequently by testing standard solutions, to detect electrical, mechanical, or optical problems in the instrument and its accessories. Testing, maintaining, and repairing such instruments call for specialized skills.

A photometer is not uniformly accurate over its entire scale. At very low transmittances the scale is crowded in terms of concentration, so that a considerable change in the relative concentration of the substance sought will cause only a slight change in the position of the indicator dial or needle. At very high transmittances, slight differences between optical cells, the presence of condensed moisture, dust, bubbles, fingerprints, or a slight lack of reproducibility in positioning the cells can cause as great a change in readings as would a considerable change in concentration. The difficulties are minimized if readings are made to fall between 10% and 80% transmission by diluting or concentrating the sample or varying the light path by selecting cells of appropriate size.

Some suggestions for suitable ranges and light paths are offered under individual methods in this manual, but much reliance necessarily must be placed on the knowledge and judgment of the analyst. Most photometers are capable of their best performance when readings fall in the range of 10% to 80% transmittance (i.e., approximately 1 to 0.1 absorbance) with respect to a blank adjusted to read 100% transmittance or 0 absorbance. The closer the readings approach 0% or 100% transmittance, the less accurate they can be expected to be. If it is impractical to use an optical cell with a sufficiently long light path—as in some commercial instruments—or to concentrate the sample or select a more sensitive color test, then it may be more accurate to compare very faint colors in nessler tubes than to attempt photometric readings close to 100% transmittance.

In general, the best wavelength or filter to select is that which produces the largest spread of readings between a standard and a blank. This usually corresponds to a visual color for the light beam that is complementary to that of the solution—for example, a green filter for a red solution, a violet filter for a yellow solution.

Although the use of a photoelectric instrument makes unnecessary the preparation of a complete set of standards for every single set of samples to be analyzed, it is necessary to prepare a reagent blank and at least one standard in the upper end of the optimum concentration range, along with every group of samples, in order to verify the constancy of the calibration curve. This precaution will reveal any unsuspected changes in the reagents, the instrument, or the technic. At regular intervals, or if at any time results fall under suspicion, a complete set of standards—at least five or six spaced to cover the optimum concentration range—should be prepared in order to check the calibration curve. Also

valuable in this regard is the absorptivity information given in this manual for a number of photometric methods.

Use the utmost care with calibration curves supplied by the instrument manufacturer or in the use of commercial permanent standards of colored liquids or glasses. Verify frequently the accuracy of the curves or permanent standards by comparing with standards prepared in the laboratory, using the same set of reagents, the same instrument, and the same procedure as those used for analyzing samples. Even if permanent calibration curves or artificial standards have been prepared accurately by the manufacturer, they may not be valid under conditions of use. Permanent standards may be subject to fading or color alteration and their validity may depend also on certain arbitrary lighting conditions. Standards and calibration curves may be incorrect because of slight differences between reagents, instruments, or technics at the manufacturer's laboratory and those at the analyst's laboratory.

If a photometer provides readings in terms of absorbance, plot calibration curves on rectangular graph paper; if readings are in terms of percentage transmittance, plot calibration curves on semilogarithmic graph paper, with transmittance on the logarithmic scale and concentration on the arithmetic scale. Usually, such graphs will be straight, or nearly straight, lines.

Photometric compensation can be used to correct for the interference caused by color or turbidity present in a sample and also for impurities in the chemicals and distilled water used in the reagent blank, but not for interfering substances that react with the color-developing reagents to produce a color (i.e., positive interferences). The principle involved is the additivity of absorbances.

If there is a significant reagent blank, but no color or turbidity in the sample, make the necessary correction by adding the color-developing reagents to distilled water and nulling the photometer with the resulting solution.

If there is color or turbidity or both in the sample, but a negligible reagent blank, correct by carrying an additional portion of the sample through the procedure, with the exception that either: (a) one of the essential color-developing reagents is omitted; or, preferably, (b) the color is bleached out after it has been produced, but in such a way that the interfering color or turbidity is not bleached. Use the special blank for nulling the photometer. Take into account any significant change in volume produced by the addition or omission of reagents.

If color or turbidity or both are present in the sample, and if, in addition, the reagent blank is significant, then a slightly more complicated procedure is needed to correct for both interferences: Prepare the calibration curve by setting the photometer to zero absorbance with plain distilled water and read all the standards, including a zero standard or reagent blank, against the distilled water. If the graph is plotted in the recommended manner, and Beer's law holds, a straight line will be obtained; but if there is a measurable reagent blank, this line will not pass through the point of origin.

For each sample, prepare a special blank by either: (a) omitting a reagent, or (b) bleaching out the color as described above. Place each special blank in the photometer in turn, adjust the instrument each time to read zero absorbance, and read each regularly developed sample against its corresponding blank. Interpret the observed absorbances from the calibration graph. As before, consider any significant increase or decrease in volume caused by addition or omission of reagents in the calculations.

In visual color comparison with some instruments, compensation for color and turbidity can be made by the Walpole technic. View the treated sample, after color development, through distilled water, while viewing the color standard through an untreated sample. It is inconvenient to use the Walpole technic when viewing tall-form nessler tubes axially, because of their clumsy length.

Sometimes none of the cited expedients will apply. In such an event, several approaches are available for the separation of turbidity from a sample. The nature of the sample, the size of suspended particles, and the reasons for conducting the analysis will all combine to dictate the method for turbidity removal. The turbidity may be coagulated by the addition of zinc sulfate and an alkali, as is done in the direct nesslerization method for ammonia nitrogen. For samples of relatively coarse turbidity, centrifuging may suffice. In some instances, glass fiber filters, filter paper, or sintered-glass filters of fine porosity will serve the purpose. For very small particle sizes, membrane filters may provide the required retentiveness. Used with discretion, each of these methods will yield satisfactory results in a suitable situation. However, it must be emphasized that no single universally ideal method of turbidity removal is available. Moreover, the analyst should be perpetually alert to adsorption losses possible with any flocculating or filtering procedure.

8. Other Methods of Analysis

The use of an instrumental method of analysis not specifically described in procedures in this manual is permissible provided that the results so obtained are checked periodically, either against a standard method described in this manual or against a standard sample of undisputed composition. Identification of any such instrumental method used must be included in the laboratory report along with the analytical results.

a. Atomic absorption spectroscopy: Atomic absorption spectrophotometry has been applied to the determination of a growing number of metals in water without the need for prior concentration or extensive sample pretreatment. The use of organic solvents coupled with oxyacetylene, oxyhydrogen, or nitrous oxide-acetylene flames enables the determination of metals that form refractory oxides. These standards include atomic absorption methods for many metals, including certain flameless technics.

b. Flame photometry: Flame photometry is used for the determination of sodium, potassium, lithium, and strontium. To a lesser extent it is useful also for the determination of calcium and other ions.

c. Emission spectroscopy: Arc-spark emission spectroscopy is an important analytical tool for water analysis and is proving valuable both for trace analysis and for certain determinations not easily made by any other method. Considerable specialized training and experience with this technic are required to obtain satisfactory results, and frequently it is practical to obtain only semiquantitative results from such methods in water analysis. It should be noted that an arc-spark emission spectrograph is relatively expensive when used exclusively for routine water testing, but its purchase is justified if it can be used as a general laboratory analytical instrument.

d. Polarography and related analytical systems: Polarography is suggested for scanning industrial wastes for various metal ions, especially where the possible interferences in the colorimetric procedures are unknown. Pulse polarography has enabled the determination of seven or more metals at the low microgram-per-liter level when a single 100-ml sample has been ashed with nitric acid. Differential pulse voltammetry and differential pulse anodic stripping voltammetry also have gained acceptance for the determination of heavy metals in water and wastewater.

A method closely allied to polarography is amperometric titration, which is suitable for the determination of residual chlorine, chlorine dioxide, and iodine, and other iodometric methods.

e. Potentiometric titration: Many of the titrimetric methods of these standards can be performed potentiometrically, by using a millivoltmeter or pH meter with suitable electrodes. However, the application to a particular determination should be attempted only when the analyst understands thoroughly the pertinent theoretical and operational considerations.

f. Selective ion electrodes and probes: Selective ion electrodes and probes are available for the rapid estimation of certain constituents in water. These electrodes function best in conjunction with the expanded-scale pH meter or a suitable millivoltmeter. For the most part, the electrodes operate on the ion-exchange principle. The selective ion electrodes available at this time are designed for the measurement of ammonia, cadmium, calcium, divalent copper, divalent hardness, lead, potassium, silver, sodium, total monovalent and total divalent cations, and bromide, chloride, cyanide, fluoride, iodide, nitrate, perchlorate, and sulfide anions, among others. Additional selective ion electrodes undoubtedly will become available in the future.

These devices are subject to varying degrees of interference from other ions in the sample and many must still receive the thorough study that would warrant their adoption as tentative and standard methods. Nonetheless, their value for monitoring activities is readily apparent. To remove all doubt of variations in reliability, check each electrode in the presence of interferences as well as the ion for which it is intended. This manual details the electrode method for fluoride (Section 414).

The commercial dissolved oxygen probes vary considerably in their dependability and maintenance requirements. Despite these shortcomings, they have been applied to the monitoring of dissolved oxygen in a variety of waters and wastewaters. Most probes embody an electrode covered by a thin layer of electrolyte held in place by an oxygen-permeable membrane. The oxygen in solution diffuses through the membrane and electrolyte layer to react at the electrode, inducing a current that is proportional to the activity (and concentration) of the dissolved oxygen. Satisfactory dissolved-oxygen electrodes also are available without a membrane. In either case, the face of the dissolved oxygen sensor should be kept well agitated and temperature compensation should be provided to insure acceptable results.

g. *Gas chromatography:* Considerable work is under way in the development of gas chromatographic methods suitable for water and wastewater analysis. Such methods appear in this manual for the determination of chlorinated hydrocarbon pesticides, for the determination of the components in sludge digester gas, and for the determination of phenols. The skill of the operator and the expense entailed in purchase may limit use of this specialized instrumentation.

h. *Automated analytical instrumentation:* Automated analyses are discussed in Part 600.

i. *Other methods of analysis:* Instrumentation and new methods of analysis are always under development. The analyst will find it to his advantage to keep abreast of current progress. Reviews of each branch of analytical chemistry are published regularly in the periodical *Analytical Chemistry* and the annual literature review published in *Journal Water Pollution Control Federation.*

9. Interferences

Many analytical procedures are subject to interference from substances that may be present in the sample. The more common and obvious interferences are known and information about them has been given in the details of individual procedures. It is inevitable that the analyst will encounter unknown or unexpected interferences. Such occurrences are unavoidable because of the diverse nature of waters and particularly of wastewaters. Therefore, the analyst must be alert to the fact that hitherto untested ions, new treatment compounds—especially complexing agents—and new industrial wastes constitute an ever-present threat to the accuracy of chemical analyses.

Any sudden change in the apparent composition of water that has been rather constant, any off color observed in a colorimetric test or during a titration, any unexpected turbidity, odor, or other laboratory finding is cause for suspicion. Such a change may be due to a normal variation in the relative concentrations of the usual constituents or it may be caused by the introduction of an unforeseen interfering substance.

A few substances—such as chlorine, chlorine dioxide, alum, iron salts, silicates, copper sulfate, ammonium sulfate, and polyphosphates—are so widely used that they deserve special mention as possible causes of interference. Of these, chlorine is probably the worst offender, in that it bleaches or alters the colors of many of the sensitive organic reagents that serve as titration indicators and as color developers for photometric methods. Among the methods that have proved effective in removing chlorine residuals are: the addition of minimal amounts of sulfite, thiosulfate, or arsenite; exposure to sunlight or an artificial ultraviolet source; and prolonged storage.

Whenever interference is encountered or suspected and no specific recommendations are found in this manual for overcoming it, the analyst must endeavor to determine what technic, if any, will eliminate the interference without adversely affecting the analysis itself. If two or more choices of procedure are offered, often one procedure will be less affected than another by the presence of the interfering substance. If different procedures yield considerably different results, it is likely that interference is present. Some inteferences become less severe upon dilution or upon use of smaller samples; any tendency of the results to increase or decrease in a consistent manner with dilution indicates the likelihood of interference effects.

a. Types of interference: Interference may cause the analytical results to be either too high or too low as a consequence of one of the following processes:

1) An interfering substance may react like the substance sought and thus produce a high result—for example, bromide will respond to titration as though it were chloride.

2) An interfering substance may react with the substance sought and thus produce a low result.

3) An interfering substance may combine with the analytical reagent and prevent it from reacting with the substance sought—for example, chlorine will destroy many indicators and color-developing reagents.

Nearly every interference will fit one of these classes. For example, in a photometric method, turbidity may be considered as a "substance" that acts like the one being determined—that is, it reduces the transmission of light. Occasionally, two or more interfering substances, if present simultaneously, may interact in a nonadditive fashion, either canceling or enhancing one another's effects.

b. Counteracting interference: The best way to minimize interference is to remove the interfering substance or to render it innocuous by one of these methods:

1) Either the substance sought or the interfering substance may be removed physically: For example, fluoride and ammonia may be distilled off, leaving interferences behind; chloride may be converted to silver chloride and filtered off, leaving nitrate behind. The interferences may also be adsorbed on an ion-exchange resin, a process described more fully in Section 106.

2) The pH may be adjusted so that only the substance sought will react.

3) The sample may be oxidized or reduced to convert the interfering substance to a harmless form—for example, chlorine may be reduced to chloride by adding thiosulfate.

4) The addition of a suitable agent may complex the interfering substance so that it is innocuous although still present: For example, iron may be complexed with pyrophosphate to prevent it from interfering with the copper determination; copper may be complexed with cyanide or sulfide to prevent interference with the titrimetric hardness determination.

5) A combination of the first four technics may be used: For example, phenols are distilled from an acid solution to prevent amines from distilling; thiosulfate is used in the dithizone method for zinc to prevent most of the interfering metals from passing into the carbon tetrachloride layer.

6) Color and turbidity may sometimes be destroyed by wet or dry ashing or may be removed by use of a flocculating agent. Some types of turbidity may be removed by filtration. These procedures, however, introduce the danger that the desired constituent also will be removed.

c. Compensation for interference: If none of these technics is practical, several methods of compensation can be used:

1) If the color or turbidity initially present in the sample interferes in a photometric determination, it may be possible to use photometric compensation. The technic is described in Section 102.7 preceding.

2) The concentration of interfering substances may be determined and then identical amounts may be added to the calibration standards. This involves much labor.

3) If the interference does not continue to increase as the concentration of interfering substance increases, but tends to level off, then a large excess of interfering substance may be added routinely to all samples and to all standards. This is called "swamping." For example, an excess of calcium is added in the photometric magnesium determination.

4) The presence in the chemical reagents of the substance sought may be accounted for by carrying out a blank determination.

10. Special Requirements

Many of the methods described in the main body of this manual call for apparatus, reagents, and technics that are more or less specific to the particular determination being performed. Such requirements are described under the methods to which they apply. The general considerations presented in this section should also be observed. The requirements of radiological, bacteriological, biological, and bioassay methods tend to differ in many respects from those of chemical and physical tests.

Special attention is directed to the descriptions of apparatus and procedure in the sections dealing with those methods.

103 EXPRESSION OF RESULTS

1. Units

In this text, chemical and physical results are expressed in milligrams per liter (mg/l). Only the significant figures should be recorded. If the concentrations are generally less than 1 mg/l, it may be more convenient to express the results in micrograms per liter (μg/l). Use μg/l when concentrations are less than 0.1 mg/l.

Express concentrations greater than 10,000 mg/l in percent, 1% being equal to 10,000 mg/l when the specific gravity is 1.00. In solid samples and liquid wastes of high specific gravity, make a correction if the results are expressed as parts per million (ppm) or percent by weight:

$$\text{ppm by weight} = \frac{\text{mg/l}}{\text{sp gr}}$$

$$\% \text{ by weight} = \frac{\text{mg/l}}{10,000 \times \text{sp gr}}$$

In such cases, if the result is given as mg/l, the specific gravity must be stated.

The unit grains per gallon (gpg) is encountered occasionally. (1 gpg=17.1 mg/l.) The use of this unit is decreasing, and it is not encouraged.

The unit equivalents per million (epm), or the identical and less ambiguous term milligram-equivalents per liter, or milliequivalents per liter (me/l),

can be valuable for making water treatment calculations and checking analyses by anion-cation balance.

Table 103:I presents the factors for converting concentrations of the common ions found in water from milligrams per liter to milliequivalents per liter, and vice versa. The term milliequivalent used in this table represents 0.001 of an equivalent weight. The equivalent weight, in turn, is defined as the weight of the ion (sum of the atomic weights of the atoms making up the ion) divided by the number of charges normally associated with the particular ion. The factors for converting results from milligrams per liter to milliequivalents per liter were computed by dividing the ion charge by the weight of the ion. Conversely, the factors for converting results from milliequivalents per liter to milligrams per liter were calculated by dividing the weight of the ion by the ion charge.

2. Significant Figures

To avoid ambiguity in reporting results or in presenting directions for a procedure, it is the custom to use "significant figures." All the digits in a reported result are expected to be known definitely, except for the last digit, which may be in doubt. Such a number is said to contain only significant figures. If

Table 103:I. Conversion Factors*
(Milligrams per Liter—Milliequivalents per Liter)

Ion (Cation)	me/l=mg/lX	mg/l=me/lX	Ion (Anion)	me/l=mg/lX	mg/l=me/lX
Al^{3+}	0.1112	8.994	BO_2^-	0.02336	42.81
B^{3+}	0.2775	3.604	Br^-	0.01251	79.91
Ba^{2+}	0.01456	68.67	Cl^-	0.02821	35.45
Ca^{2+}	0.04990	20.04	CO_3^{2-}	0.03333	30.00
Cr^{3+}	0.05770	17.33	CrO_4^{2-}	0.01724	58.00
			F^-	0.05264	19.00
Cu^{2+}	0.03148	31.77	HCO_3^-	0.01639	61.02
Fe^{2+}	0.03581	27.92	HPO_4^{2-}	0.02084	47.99
Fe^{3+}	0.05372	18.62	$H_2PO_4^-$	0.01031	96.99
H^+	0.9921	1.008	HS^-	0.03024	33.07
K^+	0.02557	39.10	HSO_3^-	0.01233	81.07
			HSO_4^-	0.01030	97.07
Li^+	0.1441	6.939	I^-	0.007880	126.9
Mg^{2+}	0.08226	12.16	NO_2^-	0.02174	46.01
Mn^{2+}	0.03640	27.47	NO_3^-	0.01613	62.00
Mn^{4+}	0.07281	13.73	OH^-	0.05880	17.01
Na^+	0.04350	22.99	PO_4^{3-}	0.03159	31.66
NH_4^+	0.05544	18.04	S^{2-}	0.06238	16.03
Pb^{2+}	0.009653	103.6	SiO_3^{2-}	0.02629	38.04
Sr^{2+}	0.02283	43.81	SO_3^{2-}	0.02498	40.03
Zn^{2+}	0.03060	32.69	SO_4^{2-}	0.02083	48.03

* Factors are based on ion charge and not on redox reactions that may be possible for certain of these ions. Cations and anions are listed separately in alphabetical order.

more than a single doubtful digit is carried, the extra digit or digits are not significant. If an analytical result is reported as "75.6 mg/l," the analyst should be quite certain of the "75," but may be uncertain as to whether the ".6" should be .5 or .7, or even .4 or .8, because of unavoidable uncertainty in the analytical procedure. If the standard deviation were known from previous work to be ±2 mg/l, the analyst would have, or at least should have, rounded off the result to "76 mg/l" before reporting it. On the other hand, if the method were so good that a result of "75.61 mg/l" could have been conscientiously reported, then the analyst should not have rounded it off to 75.6.

A report should present only such figures as are justified by the accuracy of the work. The all-too-common practice of requiring that quantities listed in a column have the same number of figures to the right of the decimal point is justified in bookkeeping, but not in chemistry.

a. Rounding off: Round off by dropping the digits that are not significant. If the digit 6, 7, 8, or 9 is dropped, then increase the preceding digit by one unit; if the digit 0, 1, 2, 3, or 4 is dropped, do not alter the preceding digit. If the digit 5 is dropped, round off the preceding digit to the nearest even number: thus 2.25 becomes 2.2 and 2.35 becomes 2.4.

b. Ambiguous zeros: The digit 0 may record a measured value of zero, or it may serve merely as a spacer to locate the decimal point. If the result of a sulfate determination is reported as 420 mg/l, the recipient of the report may be in doubt whether the zero is significant or not, because the zero cannot be deleted. If an analyst calculates a total residue (total solids) content of 1,146 mg/l, but realizes that the 4 is somewhat doubtful and that therefore the 6 has no significance, he will round off the answer to 1,150 mg/l and so report, but here, too, the recipient of the report will not know whether the zero is significant. Although the number could be expressed as a power of 10 (e.g., 11.5×10^2 or 1.15×10^3), this form is not generally used because it would not be consistent with the normal expression of results and might be confusing. In most other cases, there will be no doubt as to the sense in which the digit 0 is used. It is obvious that the zeros are significant in such numbers as 104 and 40.08. In a number written as 5.000, it is understood that all the zeros are significant, or else the number could have been rounded off to 5.00, 5.0, or 5, whichever was appropriate. Whenever the zero is ambiguous, it is advisable to accompany the result with an estimate of its uncertainty.

Sometimes, significant zeros are dropped without good cause. If a buret is read as "23.60 ml," it should be so recorded, and not as "23.6 ml." The first number indicates that the analyst took the trouble to estimate the second decimal place; "23.6 ml" would indicate that he read the buret rather carelessly.

c. The plus-or-minus (±) notation: If a calculation yields as a result "1,476 mg/l" with a standard deviation estimated as ±40 mg/l, report it as 1,480±40 mg/l. But if the standard deviation is estimated as ±100 mg/l, round off the answer still further and report as 1,500±100 mg/l. By this device, ambiguity is avoided and the recipient of the report can tell that the zeros are only spacers. Even if the problem of ambiguous zeros is not present, showing the standard deviation is helpful in that it provides an estimate of reliability.

d. Calculations: As a practical operating rule, the result of a calculation in which several numbers are multiplied or divided together should be rounded off to as few significant figures as are present in the factor with the fewest significant figures. Suppose that the following calculation must be made in order to obtain the result of an analysis:

$$\frac{56 \times 0.003462 \times 43.22}{1.684}$$

A ten-place calculator yields an answer of "4.975740996," but this number must be rounded off to a mere "5.0" because one of the measurements that entered into the calculation, 56, has only two significant figures. It was a waste of time to measure the other three factors to four significant figures because the "56" is "the weakest link in the chain" and limits the accuracy of the answer. If the other factors were measured to only three, instead of four, significant figures, the answer would not suffer and the labor would be less.

When numbers are added or subtracted, the number that has the fewest decimal places, not necessarily the fewest significant figures, puts the limit on the number of places that may justifiably be carried in the sum or difference. Thus the sum

$$
\begin{array}{r}
0.0072 \\
12.02 \\
4.0078 \\
25.9 \\
4,886 \\
\hline
4,927.9350
\end{array}
$$

must be rounded off to a mere "4,928," no decimals, because one of the addends, 4,886, has no decimal places. Notice that another addend, 25.9, has only three significant figures and yet it does not set a limit to the number of significant figures in the answer.

The preceding discussion is necessarily oversimplified. The reader is referred to the bibliography for a more detailed discussion.

104   PRECISION, ACCURACY, AND CORRECTNESS OF ANALYSES

104 A.   Precision and Accuracy

A clear distinction should be made between the terms "precision" and "accuracy" when they are applied to methods of analysis. *Precision* refers to the reproducibility of a method when it is repeated on a homogeneous sample under controlled conditions, regardless of whether or not the observed values are widely displaced from the true value as a result of systematic or constant errors present throughout the measurements. Precision can be expressed by the standard deviation. *Accuracy* refers to the agreement between the amount of a component measured by the test method and the amount actually present. *Relative error* expresses the difference between the measured and the actual amounts, as a percentage of the actual amount. A method may have very high precision but recover only a part of the element being determined; or an analysis, although precise, may be in error because of poorly standardized solutions, inaccurate dilution technics, inaccurate balance weights, or improperly calibrated equipment. On the other hand, a method may be accurate but lack precision because of low instrument sensitivity, variable rate of biological activity, or other factors beyond the control of the analyst.

It is possible to determine both the precision and the accuracy of a test method by analyzing samples to which known quantities of standard substances have been added. It is possible to determine the precision, but not the accuracy, of such methods as those for suspended solids, BOD, and numerous physical characteristics because of the unavailability of standard substances that can be added in known quantities on which percentage recovery can be based.

Precision and accuracy data presented in this volume are explained in Section 104 A.2, below.

1. Statistical Approach

a. Standard deviation (σ): Experience has shown that if a determination is repeated a large number of times under essentially the same conditions, the observed values, *x*, will be distributed at random about an average as a result of uncontrollable or experimental errors. If there is an infinite number of observations from a common universe of causes, a plot of the relative frequency against magnitude will produce a symmetrical bell-shaped curve known as the Gaussian or normal curve (Figure 104:1). The shape of this curve is completely defined by two statistical parameters: (1) the mean or average $\bar{x}$, of *n* observations; and (2) the standard deviation, σ, which fixes the width or spread of the curve on each side of the mean. The formula is:

$$\sigma = \sqrt{\frac{\Sigma\ (x - \bar{x})^2}{n - 1}}$$

The proportion of the total observations lying within any given range about the mean is related to the standard deviation. For example, 68.27% of the observations lie between $\bar{x} \pm 1\ \sigma$, 95.45% between $\bar{x} \pm 2\ \sigma$, and 99.70% between $\bar{x} \pm 3\ \sigma$. These limits do not apply exactly for any finite sample from a normal population; the agreement with them may be expected to be better as the number of observations, *n*, increases.

b. Application of standard deviation: If the standard deviation, σ, for a particular analytical procedure has been determined from a large number of samples, and a set of *n* replicates on a sample gives a mean result $\bar{x}$, there is a 95% chance that the true value of the mean for this sample lies within the values $\bar{x} \pm 1.96\,\sigma\ \sqrt{n}$. This range is known as the 95% confidence interval. It provides an estimate of the reliability of the mean, and may be used to forecast the number of replicates needed to secure suitable precision.

If the standard deviation is not known and is estimated from a single small sample,* or a few small samples, the 95% confidence interval of the mean of *n* observations is given by the equation $\bar{x} \pm t\sigma\sqrt{n}$, where *t* has the following values:

n	t
2	12.71
3	4.30
4	3.18
5	2.78
10	2.26
∞	1.96

The use of *t* compensates for the tendency of small samples to underestimate the variability.

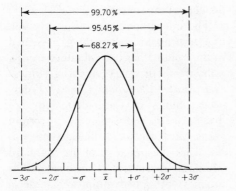

Figure 104:1. Gaussian or normal curve of frequencies.

---

* A "small sample" in statistical discussions means a small number of replicate determinations, *n*, and does not refer to the quantity used for a determination.

c. Range (R): The difference between the smallest and largest of n observations is also closely related to the standard deviation. When the distribution of errors is normal in form, the range, R, of n observations exceeds the standard deviation times a factor d_n only in 5% of the cases. Values for the factor d_n are:

n	d_n
2	2.77
3	3.32
4	3.63
5	3.86
6	4.03

As it is rather general practice to run replicate analyses, use of these limits is very convenient for detecting faulty technic, large sampling errors, or other assignable causes of variation.

d. Rejection of experimental data: Quite often in a series of observations, one or more of the results deviate greatly from the mean whereas the other values are in close agreement with the mean value. At this point, one must decide whether to reject disagreeing values. Theoretically, no results should be rejected, since the presence of disagreeing results shows faulty technics and therefore casts doubt on all the results. Of course the result of any test in which a known error has occurred is rejected immediately. For methods for the rejection of other experimental data, standard texts on analytical chemistry or statistical measurement should be consulted.

2. Evaluation of Methods

Data on precision of methods first appeared in the 10th Edition. In preparation of the 11th Edition, a concerted effort was made to offer an idea of the precision and accuracy with which selected methods can be applied on a broad geographic basis in examination of the relatively simpler water samples. The manner of best expressing the resulting data has remained to this day a matter of continuing study. The 11th and 12th Editions presented both precision and accuracy in terms of mg/l. This practice is retained where such data continue to be cited in this edition. However, more recent experience suggests that data can be presented more briefly and clearly in the form of a percentage. By this system, the standard deviation is expressed as a percentage of the mean and is termed the relative standard deviation or coefficient of variation. It measures the precision or reproducibility of a method, independent of the known concentration of the sample constituent. Similarly, the relative error gives the difference between the mean of a series of test results and the true value, expressed as a percentage of the true value. Thus, the relative error represents the measure of the accuracy of a method. The relative standard deviation and relative error are preferred in quoting the precision and accuracy of a method because they are independent of the concentration.

The information regarding precision and accuracy of the methods presented in this volume has been obtained from a number of sources, and at various times.

a. Water Pollution Control Federation: Some of the oldest data are presented in connection with certain wastewater methods. These were collected on the initiative of the Standard Methods Committee of the Water Pollution Control Federation and some of the data appeared first in the 10th edition of this manual. For many methods, results were obtained from 10 replicate determinations on 10 different days, or when necessary, from 5 replicate samples on 20 days.

Most methods studied were found to be statistically reliable, and the standard deviation given may be used with some confidence in statistical prediction. If a method has been found statistically unreliable, this is indicated in the statements on precision under the method. The standard deviations of unreliable methods cannot be used safely for statistical prediction, but may be of some value for indicating roughly the variation that may be expected.

In expressing the evaluation data on each test, the number of analysts and determinations is given in shorthand form; for example, "n=5; 56×10," which means that 5 different analysts ran 56 separate sets of 10 determinations each, making a total of 560 determinations. Usually the precision is expressed as the standard deviation in original units of measurement—i.e., milligrams or milliliters. In a few instances, the precision is expressed as the coefficient of variation C_v (the ratio of the standard deviation to the average), expressed as a percentage:

$$C_v = \frac{100\sigma}{\bar{x}}$$

The standard deviation given with each method is based on careful laboratory examination. No attempt has been made to obtain the standard deviation under research conditions or with the use of specially calibrated apparatus or glassware. The values given are to be regarded as provisional and subject to change on further study. In general, the standard deviations given may be regarded as being too high rather than too low.

b. *Analytical Reference Service:* For a number of methods applicable to relatively clean water samples, precision and accuracy data are based on results of studies by the Analytical Reference Service, which was conducted formerly by the U. S. Public Health Service.

This activity was devoted to the collaborative study of water chemistry methodology. Nearly 300 agencies, including public, private, and university laboratories, were involved in collaborative testing. The results provide an evaluation of selected analytical methods and supply a factual basis for judgment of the reliability that may be expected in the practical application of these methods.

c. *Environmental Protection Agency:* Currently, the United States Environmental Protection Agency (EPA) is involved in an extensive program for evaluating both analytical methods and the performance of its own laboratories. This activity is directed by the Methods Development and Quality Assurance Research Laboratory of the EPA. Data from these studies have been made available for inclusion in this volume and for a number of methods they have replaced older results.

3. Graphical Representation of Data

Graphical representation of data is one of the simplest methods for showing the influence of one variable on another. Graphs frequently are desirable and advantageous in colorimetric analysis because they show any variation of one variable with respect to the other within specified limits.

a. General: Ordinary rectangular-coordinate paper is satisfactory for most purposes. Twenty lines per inch is often convenient. For some graphs, semilogarithmic paper is preferable.

The five rules listed by Worthing and Geffner for choosing the coordinate scales are useful. Although these rules are not inflexible, they are satisfactory. When doubt arises, common sense should prevail. The rules are:

1) The independent and dependent variables should be plotted on abscissa and ordinate in a manner that can be comprehended easily.

2) The scales should be chosen so that the value of either coordinate can be found quickly and easily.

3) The curve should cover as much of the graph paper as possible.

4) The scales should be chosen so that the slope of the curve approaches unity as nearly as possible.

5) Other things being equal, the variables should be chosen to give a plot that will be as nearly a straight line as possible.

The title of a graph should describe adequately what the plot is intended to show. Legends should be presented on the graph to clarify possible ambiguities. Complete information on the conditions under which the data were obtained should be included in the legend.

b. Method of least squares: If sufficient points are available and the functional relationship between the two variables is well defined, a smooth curve can be drawn through the points. If the function is not well defined, as is frequently the case when experimental data are used, the method of least squares is used to fit a straight line to the pattern.

Any straight line can be represented by the equation $x = my + b$. The slope of the line is represented by the constant m and the slope intercept (on the x axis) is represented by the constant b. The method of least squares has the advantage of giving a set of values for these constants not dependent upon the judgment of the investigator. Two equations in addition to the one for a straight line are involved in these calculations:

$$m = \frac{n \, \Sigma xy - \Sigma x \, \Sigma y}{n \, \Sigma y^2 - (\Sigma y)^2}$$

$$b = \frac{\Sigma y^2 \, \Sigma x - \Sigma y \, \Sigma xy}{n \, \Sigma y^2 - (\Sigma y)^2}$$

n being the number of observations (sets of x and y values) to be summed. In order to compute the constants by this method, it is necessary first to calculate Σx, Σy, Σy^2, and Σxy. These operations are carried out to more places than the number of significant figures in the experimental data because the experimental values are assumed to be exact for the purposes of the calculations.

Example: Given the following data to be graphed, find the best line to fit the points:

Absorbance	Solute Concentration mg/l
0.10	29.8
0.20	32.6
0.30	38.1
0.40	39.2
0.50	41.3
0.60	44.1
0.70	48.7

Let y equal the absorbance values, which are subject to error, and x the accurately known concentration of solute. The first step is to find the summations (Σ) of x, y, y^2, and xy:

x	y	y^2	xy
29.8	0.10	0.01	2.98
32.6	0.20	0.04	6.52
38.1	0.30	0.09	11.43
39.2	0.40	0.16	15.68
41.3	0.50	0.25	20.65
44.1	0.60	0.36	26.46
48.7	0.70	0.49	34.09
$\Sigma = 273.8$	2.80	1.40	117.81

Next substitute the summations in the equations for m and b; $n=7$ because there are seven sets of x and y values:

$$m = \frac{7(117.81) - 2.80(273.8)}{7(1.40) - (2.80)^2} = 29.6$$

$$b = \frac{1.4(273.8) - 2.80(117.81)}{7(1.40) - (2.80)^2} = 27.27$$

To plot the line, select three convenient values of y—say, 0, 0.20, 0.60—and calculate the corresponding values of x:

$$x_0 = 29.6(0) + 27.27 = 27.27$$
$$x_1 = 29.6(0.20) + 27.27 = 33.19$$
$$x_2 = 29.6(0.60) + 27.27 = 45.04$$

When the points representing these values are plotted on the graph, they will lie in a straight line (unless an error in calculation has been made) that is the line of best fit for the given data. The points representing the latter are also plotted on the graph, as in Figure 104:2.

4. Self-Evaluation (Desirable Philosophy for the Analyst)

A good analyst continually tempers his confidence with doubt. Such doubt stimulates a search for new and different methods of confirmation for his reassurance. Frequent self-appraisals should embrace every step—from collecting samples to reporting results.

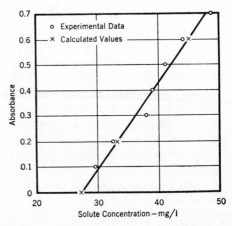

Figure 104:2. **Example of least-squares method.**

The analyst's first critical scrutiny should be directed at the entire sample collection process in order to guarantee a representative sample for the purpose of the analysis and to avoid any possible losses or contamination during the act of collection. Attention should also be given to the type of container and to the manner of transport and storage, as discussed elsewhere in this volume.

A periodic reassessment should be made of the available analytical methods, with an eye to applicability for the purpose and the situation. In addition, each method selected must be evaluated by the analyst himself for sensitivity, precision, and accuracy, because only in this way can he determine whether his technic is satisfactory and whether he has interpreted the directions properly. Self-evaluation on these points can give the analyst confidence in the value and significance of his reported results.

The benefits of less rigid intra-laboratory as well as interlaboratory evaluations deserve serious consideration. The analyst can regularly check standard or unknown concentrations with and without interfering elements and compare results on the same sample with results obtained by other workers in the laboratory. Such programs can uncover weaknesses in the analytical chain and permit improvements to be instituted without delay. The results can disclose whether the trouble stems from faulty sample treatment, improper elimination of interference, poor calibration practices, sloppy experimental technic,

impure or incorrectly standardized reagents, defective instrumentation, or even inadvertent mistakes in arithmetic.

Other checks of an analysis are described in Section 104C and involve anion-cation balance, conductivity, ion exchange, and the recovery of added substance in the sample.

All these approaches are designed to appraise and upgrade the level of laboratory performance and thus inspire greater faith in the final reported results.

104 B.   Quality Control in Chemical Analysis

1. Introduction

Quality assurance in the laboratory has come to mean many things and to some is merely equated with good laboratory operations such as:

1. Adequately trained and experienced personnel,
2. Good physical facilities and equipment,
3. Certified reagents and standards,
4. Frequent servicing and calibration of instruments, and
5. A knowledgeable and understanding management.

While all of these are important, none of them in itself assures the reliability of laboratory data, and obviously something else is needed. This something else can be referred to as analytical quality control. It consists essentially of three programs or conditions: (1) the use only of methods that have been studied collaboratively and found acceptable (this generally implies "Standard Methods"),[1,2] (2) routine analysis of a control sample at least once each day[3] on which

unknown samples are being analyzed, and (3) confirmation of the ability of a laboratory to produce acceptable results by requiring analysis of a few reference samples once or twice a year. The second program may be designated internal quality control or statistical quality control, while the third is external quality control, proficiency testing, or laboratory evaluation. In the following discussion, internal quality control will be emphasized. It is based on a system developed for the control of production processes and product quality, but the same concepts are adapted readily to laboratory operations.

2. Internal Quality Control

a. Control charts: The applicability of control chart technics is based on the assumption that laboratory data approximate a normal distribution like that shown in Figure 104:1. The data from such a system, however, can be presented in a different graphic way by plotting on the vertical scale the units of the test results, and on the horizontal scale the order or sequence in which the results were obtained. The mean and limits of the dispersion in terms of the standard deviation are then calculated and plotted. The result is the control chart of Figure 104:3.

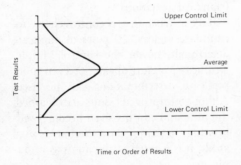

Figure 104:3. Control chart.

For best results make at least 20 determinations on a sample before calculating the standard deviation or plotting a control chart. All these results need not be obtained on the same day; in fact, it is best if they are accumulated as a part of a day-to-day operation. A result may be obtained on a control sample every time an unknown or group of unknowns is analyzed.

For example, consider a collection of results, in milligrams per liter, obtained by analysis of a water sample for copper, as follows:

1. 0.251	11. 0.229
2. 0.250	12. 0.250
3. 0.250	13. 0.283
4. 0.263	14. 0.300
5. 0.235	15. 0.262
6. 0.240	16. 0.270
7. 0.260	17. 0.225
8. 0.290	18. 0.250
9. 0.262	19. 0.256
10. 0.234	20. 0.250

The mean of this series of determinations is 0.256 mg/l, the standard deviation is 0.020 mg/l, and the resulting control chart is that of Figure 104:4.

The upper and lower control limits (UCL and LCL) are set at $+3$ and -3 standard deviations from the mean, respectively, and the upper and lower warning limits (UWL and LWL) at $+2$ and -2 standard deviations.

This is a control chart for individuals, and is most frequently used in chemical analysis. In quality control on a production line, every fifth or tenth item can be measured or tested and returned. Laboratory control requires the addition of known or standard samples to the unknown samples, thus increasing both the cost and time of analysis.

If a result should fall outside the control limits on an individual control chart, the analysis is said to be "out of

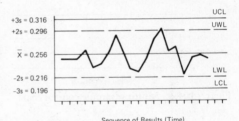

Figure 104:4. Control chart for copper analysis data given in example.

control" and immediate action should be taken to determine the cause of the outlying result. Analytical results obtained for unknown samples on the same day as the erroneous result occurred on the known sample should be considered unreliable and the analyses should be repeated after corrective action has been taken and the procedure is back in control. It is sometimes desirable to take milder action when the results exceed the warning limits, since an unduly high percentage of results exceeding these limits is a warning that the laboratory precision may not be as good as expected, or that the distribution of the results is not normal.

b. Multiple sample control chart: It is advisable to use several control samples that span a range of concentrations. This avoids unintentional bias on the part of an analyst who becomes familiar with the assay value of a single control. When several control samples are used, the control chart must be modified. Instead of plotting the analytical results, plot the deviation of the results from the mean concentration of the corresponding control sample (Figure 104:5). In general,

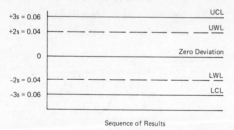

Figure 104:5. Multiple sample control chart.

use such a control chart only for control samples that do not differ widely from each other in concentration. In this case, it can be assumed that the standard deviation is constant over the range of concentrations spanned by the control samples. Set the upper and lower control limits at ±3 standard deviations and the upper and lower warning limits at ±2 standard deviations.

c. The x̄-R control chart: The x̄-R control chart (really two charts but usually treated as one for reasons that will

become evident) is probably the most widely used in industrial applications where large numbers of a product are being sampled because the x̄ chart is more sensitive to change in the mean (which is sometimes referred to as a shift or trend), and the R chart detects changes in the dispersion or variability (standard deviation).

To construct an x̄-R control chart, accumulate at least 20 pairs of duplicate determinations on the control sample. Triplicate, quadruplicate, or even more replicate determinations can be used. Although improved results are obtained, the time and cost involved becomes self-limiting, so that, if the x̄-R chart is used at all, it is limited to the analysis of duplicates.

After collecting 20 pairs of duplicate determinations, compute the averages ($\bar{x}_i$) of each pair of results and the range (R) of each pair. Then calculate the grand mean ($\bar{\bar{x}}$):

$$\bar{\bar{x}} = \Sigma \bar{x}_i / n$$

and the mean range (R):

$$\bar{R} = \Sigma R / n$$

Calculate the upper and lower control limits using Table 104:I, which gives control chart constants (essentially 90% confidence limits for various sample sizes), and the following equations:

Control limits for averages:

$$UCL = \bar{\bar{x}} + A_2 \bar{R}$$
$$LCL = \bar{\bar{x}} - A_2 \bar{R}$$
$$UWL = \bar{\bar{x}} + 2/3 (A_2 \bar{R})$$
$$LWL = \bar{\bar{x}} - 2/3 (A_2 \bar{R})$$

Control limits for ranges:

$$UCL = D_4 \bar{R}$$
$$LCL = D_3 \bar{R}$$
$$UWL = \bar{R} + 2/3 (D_4 \bar{R} - \bar{R})$$

where A_2, D_3, and D_4 are constants depending on subgroup size (Table 104:I):

TABLE 104:I. FACTORS FOR COMPUTING CONTROL CHART LINES[3]

Observations in Subgroup (n)	Factor A_2	Factor D_3	Factor D_4
2	1.88	0	3.27
3	1.02	0	2.58
4	0.73	0	2.28
5	0.58	0	2.12
6	0.48	0	2.00
7	0.42	0.076	1.92
8	0.37	0.136	1.86

As an example, Table 104:II gives an array of data and Figure 104:6 is an $\bar{x}$-R chart for these data.

Once the $\bar{x}$-R chart has been constructed it may be used like the individual control chart in day-to-day operation, with the exception, of course, that duplicate determinations (if the control chart was constructed using duplicates; otherwise whatever number was used) on the control sample must be obtained every time an unknown or group of unknowns is analyzed. Calculate the average and the range of the replicate determinations on the control sample and plot them on the $\bar{x}$-R chart. If either falls

TABLE 104:II. DATA AND COMPUTATIONS FOR CONSTRUCTION OF EXAMPLE $\bar{x}$-R CHART

Sequence of Results	Results x_i	Results x'_i	Average $\bar{x}_i$	Range R
1	0.501	0.491	0.496	0.010
2	0.490	0.490	0.490	0.000
3	0.479	0.482	0.480	0.003
4	0.520	0.512	0.516	0.008
5	0.500	0.490	0.495	0.010
6	0.510	0.488	0.499	0.022
7	0.505	0.500	0.502	0.005
8	0.475	0.493	0.484	0.018
9	0.500	0.515	0.508	0.015
10	0.498	0.501	0.500	0.003
11	0.523	0.516	0.520	0.007
12	0.500	0.512	0.506	0.012
13	0.513	0.503	0.508	0.010
14	0.512	0.497	0.504	0.015
15	0.502	0.500	0.501	0.002
16	0.506	0.510	0.508	0.004
17	0.485	0.503	0.494	0.018
18	0.484	0.487	0.486	0.003
19	0.512	0.495	0.504	0.017
20	0.509	0.500	0.504	0.009
			$\Sigma \bar{x}_i = 10.005$	$\Sigma R = 0.191$

$$\bar{\bar{x}} = \frac{10.005}{20} = 0.500 \qquad \bar{R} = \frac{0.191}{20} = 0.0096 \approx 0.010$$

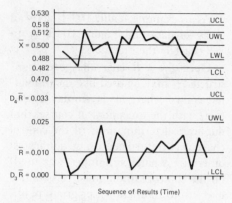

Figure 104:6. $\bar{x}$-R chart.

outside the control limits, take corrective action.

d. Moving averages and ranges: A study of the control chart constants (Table 104:I) shows that the $\bar{x}$-R chart is more efficient for detecting modest changes in the process as the subgroup

size increases. A reasonable compromise between individual values and larger subgroups is the use of moving averages. Such a set of data is given in Table 104:III. The moving average for n samples is the mean of the results for those samples, $\Sigma x/n$, and the moving range is the difference between the extreme results in the group of n samples. The moving average serves to smooth out the variations in the results. The moving range can also be plotted to serve as a measure of the dispersion. Thus, it is possible to obtain nearly the same information from individual determinations on a control sample, while avoiding the additional cost and time involved in making duplicate determinations.

e. Accuracy: Accuracy, in analytical chemistry, is a measure of the difference between the mean of the results and the

TABLE 104:III. MOVING AVERAGE AND RANGE TABLE ($n=2$)

Sample No.	Assay Value	Sample Nos. Included	Moving Average	Moving Range
1	17.09	–	–	–
2	17.35	1–2	17.22	+0.26
3	17.40	2–3	17.38	+0.05
4	17.23	3–4	17.32	−0.17
5	17.09	4–5	17.16	−0.14
6	16.94	5–6	17.02	−0.15
7	16.68	6–7	16.81	−0.26
8	17.11	7–8	16.90	+0.43
9	18.47	8–9	17.79	+1.36
10	17.08	9–10	17.78	−1.39
11	17.08	10–11	17.08	0.00
12	16.92	11–12	17.00	−0.16
13	18.03	12–13	17.45	+1.11
14	16.81	13–14	17.42	−1.22
15	17.15	14–15	16.98	+0.34
16	17.34	15–16	17.25	+0.19
17	16.71	16–17	17.03	−0.73
18	17.28	17–18	17.00	+0.57
19	16.54	18–19	16.91	−0.74
20	17.30	19–20	16.92	+0.76

true value. Most frequently, accuracy is expressed in terms of the mean error:

$$\text{mean error} = \bar{x} - T.V.$$

where:

$\bar{x}$ = mean
$T.V.$ = true value

Accuracy can be determined only if the control sample is a synthetic sample prepared in the laboratory from known amounts of pure reagents (see Section 104B.4, "Preparation of Control Samples," for further details). The accuracy of the determination is then the difference between the mean of the 20 determinations (collected for the construction of the initial control chart) and the true value or known amount of the chemical that was dissolved in the distilled water.

The true value ($T.V.$) can be plotted on the control chart also. Usually it will fall only slightly above or below the mean. If the true value is more than half way between the mean and the upper or lower warning limit (i.e., the mean error is greater than one standard deviation), the method, reagent, glassware, technic, or instruments should be suspected of bias and corrective action should be taken.

3. External Quality Control

The ability of a laboratory to produce acceptable results can be confirmed by requiring analysis once or twice a year of a few reference samples. These reference samples may be no different from the control samples that the laboratory has been preparing for its own use, with the exception that the amount of each substance present is unknown to the analysts.

A check by one laboratory of the proficiency or ability of another laboratory to obtain acceptable results (i.e., an external quality control program) is a check on whether the laboratory being tested has an acceptable internal quality control program. The analysis of an occasional reference sample may, however, serve another useful purpose, that is, it may reveal an error in the preparation of standards or control samples or the use of poor-quality distilled water, reagents, etc., that may be causing extreme variability of results.

In evaluating proficiency testing results, the laboratory issuing the reference samples may use control charts. The control limits are generally larger than those for internal quality control charts because the variation between laboratories is always larger than the variation within one laboratory as a result of the use of different instruments, different pieces of glassware, etc.

If data for use in constructing an external or interlaboratory quality control chart are not available from the results of analysis of the reference sample by many laboratories, then data from collaborative studies of the method may be used to establish control limits.

4. Preparation of Control Samples

Control samples can be natural water samples. In fact, with data obtained by recycling about 20% of the normal stream of samples so as to obtain duplicate determinations one can construct a control chart. However, such a chart will provide information only about the precision of the determination.

In order to obtain information on the accuracy of the determination, prepare a synthetic sample by adding known amounts of a pure chemical or chemicals to distilled water. Such samples may contain substances known to interfere with the determination, thus simulating natural samples. The true value of the constituents of these synthetic samples is the amount added.

Control samples also may be natural water samples or "spiked" samples (natural water with one or more chemicals added) that have been assayed by several "referee" laboratories, preferably by several different methods providing good agreement, so that a "known" value can be assigned to the sample.

One of the most important factors in a quality control program is the availability of an adequate supply of a stable known control. Ideally, prepare enough of the control so that it can be used for as long as 6 months; this will eliminate the need for preparing new quality control charts at more frequent intervals. Samples usually are preserved to prevent changes due to bacterial or mold growths, precipitation, or plating out on the walls of the container.

It has been found that concentrates often are more stable than dilute solutions that resemble natural waters. Therefore, the practice has developed of preparing concentrates that are diluted (5 ml to 1,000 ml) just before use.

In Section 4b, below, the compositions of five synthetic concentrated samples are presented. They are most useful in controlling analysis of potable water. Dilute each of these, 5 ml to 1,000 ml, before use. The concentrates are quite stable and if kept in a cool place out of direct sunlight they may be used for at least 6 months. New dilutions (the working control samples) should be prepared weekly, and preferably each day of use.

a. *Preparation:* Dilute all concentrates (solutions A,B,C,D, and E) 5 ml to 1,000 ml with good-quality distilled water just before use. If several control samples are wanted, prepare by diluting 4 ml or 6 ml (or some other volume) of the concentrate to 1,000 ml with distilled water. Calculate the concentrations in these other dilutions.

b. *Synthetic concentrated samples:*

Solution A

Metal	Salt*	Stock Solutions g/l	ml stock/l concentrate	mg/l concentrate†	mg/l diluted 5 ml/l
Zinc	Zn metal in HNO_3	1.0000	10	10	0.05
Cadmium	$Cd(NO_3)_2 \cdot 4H_2O$	2.7442	4	4	0.02
Lead	$Pb(NO_3)_2$	1.5984	10	10	0.05
Iron	$Fe(NO_3)_3 \cdot 9H_2O$	7.2359	30	30	0.15
Manganese	Mn metal in HNO_3	1.0000	20	20	0.10
Chromium	$K_2Cr_2O_7$	2.8281	10	10	0.05
Silver	$AgNO_3$	1.5748	10	10	0.05
Copper	Cu metal in HNO_3	1.0000	5	5	0.025
Cobalt	$Co(NO_3)_2 \cdot 6H_2O$	4.9383	8	8	0.04
Barium	$Ba(NO_3)_2$	1.9029	30	30	0.15
Mercury	$Hg(NO_3)_2$	1.6184	1.0	1.0	0.005

* All salts must be nitrates because sulfates will precipitate the barium, and chloride will precipitate the silver.

† If necessary, add HNO_3 until the pH of the concentrate is about 2, before making up to a final volume of 1 l.

Solution B

Dry KH_2PO_4 in a desiccator, weigh 54.436 g, and add to this salt in a 1-l volumetric flask, 180.2 ml of 1.0000 N NaOH. Make this solution up to volume (1,000 ml) with distilled water. When diluted 5 ml to 1,000 ml with distilled water this will produce:

Total dissolved solids	293 mg/l
Conductivity	303 μsiemens/cm
pH	6.87

Solution C

Anion	Salt	Stock* Solution g/l	ml stock/l concentrate	mg/l in concentrate	mg/l diluted 5 ml/l
NO$_3$	KNO$_3$	8.1525	undiluted	5,000.0	25.0
SO$_4$	Na$_2$SO$_4$	5.9144	undiluted	4,000.0	20.0
LAS	Standard†		as required	30.0	0.15
Cl	KCl	23.1335	undiluted	11,000.0	55.0
F	NaF	2.2104	240	240.0	1.2

* Preserve with 1 ml/l of a 27.1 g/l solution of $HgCl_2$.
† From Environmental Monitoring and Support Laboratory, U.S. EPA, Cincinnati, Ohio 45268.

Solution D

Standardize a solution of sodium or potassium cyanide containing approximately 2.0 mg CN/ml by titrating with standard silver nitrate that has been standardized the same day with standard sodium chloride. If this stock standard solution is found to contain, for example, 1.89 mg CN/ml, take 42.3 ml of this solution, make up to about 3.5 l, adjust to pH 11.5 with NaOH and dilute to 4,000 ml. This concentrate contains 20.0 mg CN/l, and is quite stable. Dilute 5 ml to 1,000 ml just before use to obtain 0.10 mg CN/l.

Solution E

Metal	Salt	Stock Solution g/l	ml stock/l concentrate	mg/l concentrate	mg/l diluted 5 ml/l
Arsenic	Na$_2$HAsO$_4$•7H$_2$O	4.1653	8.0	8.0	0.04
Selenium	SeO$_2$	1.4052	1.0	1.0	0.005

104 C.   Checking Correctness of Analyses

The following procedures for checking the correctness of analyses are applicable specifically to water samples for which relatively complete mineral analyses are made.

1. Anion-Cation Balance

Theoretically, the sum of the anions, expressed in me/l, must equal exactly the sum of the cations, in me/l, in any sample. In practice, the sums are seldom equal because of unavoidable variations in the analysis. This inequality increases as the ionic concentration increases. A control chart can be constructed so that it will be immediately evident if the difference between the sum of the anions and cations, in me/l, falls between acceptable limits, which have been taken as ±1 standard deviation.

If the difference is plotted against the sum of the anions, the lines showing ±1 standard deviation, that is, the acceptable limits, are given by the equation:

Σ anions$- \Sigma$ cations
$$= \pm(0.1065 + 0.0155 \ \Sigma \ \text{anions})$$

This is shown in Figures 104:7 and

104:8, which represent modified control charts. Values of differences of the sums falling outside of the limits set by the equations indicate that at least one of the determinations should be rechecked.

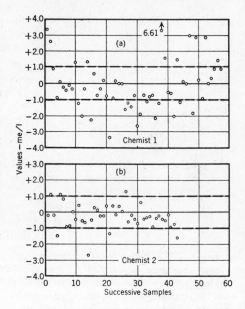

Figure 104:8. Control chart with transformed limits. The vertical scale is plotted:

$$\frac{\Sigma \ \text{anions}-\Sigma \ \text{cations}}{0.1065+0.0155 \ \Sigma \ \text{anions}}$$

A fortuitous combination of erroneous analyses resulting in the balancing of errors (compensating errors) may produce agreement between the sum of the anions and the sum of the cations even though two or more individual analytical results are seriously incorrect. The additional methods of checking that follow are useful for detecting such discrepancies.

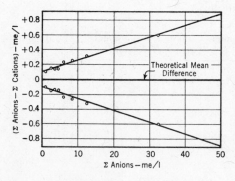

Figure 104:7. Control chart for anion-cation balances.

2. Conductivity

In using conductivity check analyses, two methods of calculation may be used.

a. Rough calculation: In most natural waters it has been found that when conductivity (in μsiemens/cm at 25 C) is multiplied by a factor ordinarily in the range of 0.55 to 0.7, the product is equal to milligrams per liter total filtrable residue. For waters that contain appreciable concentrations of free acid or caustic alkalinity, the factor may be much lower than 0.55 and for highly saline waters it may be much higher than 0.7. An approximate check based on this principle will reveal gross mistakes in analysis.

b. More refined calculations: In order to obtain better results based on electrical conductance it is necessary to dilute the sample so that its conductivity falls within a narrow range and to take into account the contribution of each separate ion to the total measured conductivity. Use distilled water, boiled and cooled, to dilute the sample in a known ratio until the conductivity lies between 90 and 120 μsiemens/cm. Some trial may be necessary to achieve the proper dilution, because the conductivity does not vary in exact ratio to the dilution; if it did, dilution would be unnecessary. The exact dilution ratio, D, must be known:

$$D = \frac{V_s + V_w}{V_s}$$

in which V_s is volume of sample and V_w is volume of distilled water. Determine the conductivity of the distilled water, which should be less than 2 μsiemens/cm. Determine conductivity in the usual way and calculate the "diluted conductivity," K_d, from the equation:

$$K_d = \frac{AD \times 10^6}{R_d} - (D-1)K_w$$

where A = cell constant, R_d = measured resistance, in ohms, of the diluted sample, and K_w = distilled-water conductivity.

Next, compute the diluted conductivity from the chemical analysis by multiplying the concentration found (as either milliequivalents per liter or milligrams per liter) by the appropriate factor in Table 104:IV and summing the products. If the computed diluted conductivity is more than 1.5% greater or more than 2% lower than the measured value of the diluted conductivity, an error probably has been made in the chemical analysis and it should be rechecked.

The diluted-conductivity method of checking is not applicable to samples that have conductivities lower than 90 μsiemens/cm or pH values less than 6 or greater than 9, or to samples that contain significant quantities of ions not listed in Table 104:IV. The con-

TABLE 104:IV. CONDUCTIVITY FACTORS OF IONS COMMONLY FOUND IN WATER

Ion	Conductivity (25 C) $\mu siemens/cm$	
	Per me/l	Per mg/l
Bicarbonate	43.6	0.715
Calcium	52.0	2.60
Carbonate	84.6	2.82
Chloride	75.9	2.14
Magnesium	46.6	3.82
Nitrate	71.0	1.15
Potassium	72.0	1.84
Sodium	48.9	2.13
Sulfate	73.9	1.54

ductivities due to hydrogen ion and hydroxyl ion are much greater than those due to other ions and will cause the method to be invalid for samples outside the pH 6 to 9 range.

3. Ion Exchange

The accuracy of the chemical analysis can also be checked when all the major ionic constituents of a simple natural water are determined quantitatively by means of an ion-exchange method. A serious discrepancy between the cations, me/l, obtained by titration of the sample after ion exchange, and the total cation concentration found by the summation of the determined constituents can uncover a gross error in the water analysis.

The ion-exchange method is based on the replacement of the cations in the original sample with hydrogen ions supplied by a strongly acidic cation-exchange resin. The acid produced by mixing the sample with the resin is titrated with standard sodium hydroxide. The total alkalinity of the original sample must also be ascertained in order to complete the calculation.

The apparatus required for the ion-exchange method consists of a pH meter (line- or battery-operated) or methyl orange indicator, a magnetic or mechanical stirrer provided with a speed control, a 10-ml buret graduated in 0.05-ml steps, and glass wool. The reagents comprise 0.02N standard acid, 0.02N standard sodium hydroxide, a strongly acidic cation-exchange resin such as Amberlite IR-120 (H)* of analytical grade, and distilled water.

---

*Rohm and Haas Company, Philadelphia, Pa.

Pipet a sample of water containing 0.1 to 0.2 me cations into a 250-ml erlenmeyer flask or beaker and add enough distilled water to bring the final volume to 100 ml. Add 2.0 g cation-exchange resin and stir at moderate speed for 15 min. Remove the resin by filtering through a plug of glass wool placed in the neck of a 10-cm (4-in.) pyrex funnel and wash with two 15-ml portions distilled water. Titrate the combined filtrate and washings to pH 4.5 with 0.02N standard sodium hydroxide, using a pH meter or methyl orange as end-point indicator, and stirring the solution during the titration.

The cation exchange can also be performed by the column method described in Section 106.

Determine the alkalinity in the sample, in me/l, by titrating a portion to a pH of 4.5 with 0.02N standard acid, using a pH meter or methyl orange as end-point indicator.

Finally, compute the total cations in the sample $(E$, me/l) by the equation:

$$E = \frac{AB \times 1{,}000}{C} + D \qquad (1)$$

in which A is the volume (ml) of the standard sodium hydroxide used in titrating the filtrate from the ion exchange, B is the normality of the standard sodium hydroxide, C is the volume (ml) of sample taken, and D is the alkalinity (me/l).

The column method of ion exchange is preferred for checking the results of the gravimetric determinations for filtrable residues because less attention to the total milliequivalents of cations in the sample is required.

Determine the filtrable and fixed filtrable residues by multiplying the quantity $(E-D)$ from Equation 1 by a factor—usually found to be between 70 and 90, depending on the water tested and the resin used in the column—and adding $50D$. For more accurate determinations, derive the factors for the type of water tested routinely by subtracting $50D$ from the filtrable residues and dividing the results by the quantity $(E-D)$, thus:

$$\frac{R_{fg}-50D}{E-D} = F_1 \qquad (2)$$

$$\frac{R_{ffg}-50D}{E-D} = F_2 \qquad (3)$$

where R_{fg} and R_{ffg} are the filtrable and fixed filtrable residues determined gravimetrically and F_1 and F_2 are the resulting factors. The equations for calculating the filtrable residues are then:

$$(E-D) F_1 + 50D = R_{fx} \qquad (4)$$
$$(E-D) F_2 + 50D = R_{ffx} \qquad (5)$$

where R_{fx} and R_{ffx} are the filtrable and fixed filtrable residues determined by ion exchange.

Once these factors are derived for the particular water, the filtrable-residue values can be determined by ion exchange and the gravimetric values obtained less frequently, or only when there is a major change in the water being checked.

For approximation purposes, a factor of 80 may be used in either Equation 4 or Equation 5. If the water tested has an unusually high sulfate or bicarbonate content compared to chloride (mg/l), or has unusually high organic content, the factor in Equation 4 approaches 90. If the water tested has an unusually high chloride content compared to sulfate (mg/l), the factor more nearly approximates 70.

4. Recovery

A qualitative estimate of the presence or absence of interfering substances in a particular determination may be made by means of a recovery procedure. Although this method does not enable the analyst to apply any correction factor to the results of an analysis, it does give him some basis for judging the applicability of a particular method of analysis to a particular sample. Furthermore, it enables the analyst to obtain this information without an extensive investigation to determine exactly which substances interfere. It also eliminates the necessity of making separate determinations on the sample for the interfering substances themselves.

A recovery may be performed at the same time as the sample analysis. Recoveries are not run on a routine basis with samples with a known general composition or when using a method of well-established applicability. Recovery methods are tools to remove doubt about the applicability of a method to a sample. In brief, the recovery procedure involves applying the analytical method to a reagent blank; to a series of known standards covering the expected range of concentration of the sample; to the sample itself, in at least a duplicate run; and to the recovery samples, prepared by adding known quantities of the substance sought to separate portions of the sample itself, each portion equal to the size of sample taken for the run. The substance sought should be added in sufficient quantity to overcome the limits of error of the analytical method, but not to cause the total in the sample to exceed the range of the known standards used.

First correct the results by subtracting the reagent blank from each of the other determined values. Graphically represent the resulting known standards. From this graph, determine the amount of sought substance in the sample. Subtract this value from each of the analyses of sample plus known added substance. The resulting amount of substance divided by the known amount added, multiplied by 100, gives the percentage recovery.

The procedure outlined above may be applied to colorimetric or instrumental methods of analysis. It also may be applied in a more simple form to titrimetric, gravimetric, and other types of analyses.

Rigid rules concerning the percentage recoveries required for acceptance of results of analyses for a given sample and method cannot be stipulated. Recoveries in the range of the sensitivity of the method may, of course, be very high or very low and approach a value nearer to

100% as the error of the method becomes small with respect to the amount of substance added. In general, intricate and exacting procedures for trace substances that have inherent errors due to their complexity may give recoveries that would be considered very poor and yet, from the practical viewpoint of usefulness of the result, may be quite acceptable. Poor results may reflect either interferences present in the sample or real inadequacy of the method of analysis in the range in which it is being used.

It must be stressed, however, that the judicious use of recovery methods for the evaluation of analytical procedures and their applicability to particular samples is an invaluable aid to the analyst in both routine and research investigations.

Special methods for the treatment of data from radiological, biological, bacteriological, and bioassay methods are presented in the corresponding sections of this manual.

105 COLLECTION AND PRESERVATION OF SAMPLES

It is an old axiom that the result of any test procedure can be no better than the sample on which it is performed. It is not possible to specify in general terms detailed procedures for the collection of all samples because of the varied purposes and procedures of the tests possible. More detailed information appears in connection with specific methods. This section presents only general considerations.

The objective of sampling is to collect a portion of material small enough in

volume to be conveniently transported to and handled in the laboratory while still accurately representing the material being sampled. This implies, first, that the relative proportions or concentrations of all pertinent components must be the same in the sample as in the material being sampled, and second, that the sample must be handled in such a way that no significant changes in composition occur before the tests are performed. Often, more meaningful results can be obtained if the analyst and the individual who will use the test results confer in advance of sampling about the purpose of the analysis and its effect on the choice of technics for collecting and testing.

1. General Precautions

Take care to obtain a sample that is truly representative of existing conditions and to handle it in such a way that it does not deteriorate or become contaminated before it reaches the laboratory. Before filling, rinse the sample bottle out two or three times with the water being collected. Representative samples of some sources can be obtained only by making composites of samples that have been collected over a period of time or at many different sampling points. The details of collection vary so much with local conditions that no specific recommendations would be universally applicable. Sometimes it will be more informative to analyze numerous separate samples instead of one composite.

Care must be exercised to insure that the analyses are representative of the actual composition of the sample. Important factors affecting the results are the presence of suspended matter or turbidity, the method chosen for its removal, and the physical and chemical changes brought about by storage or aeration. Each sample must be treated individually with regard to the substances to be determined, the amount and nature of the turbidity present, and other conditions that may influence the results.

It is impossible to give directions covering all conditions, and the choice of technic must be left to the analyst's judgment. In general, any significant amount of suspended matter should be

separated by decantation, centrifugation, or an appropriate filtration procedure. Often a slight amount of turbidity can be tolerated if experience shows that it will cause no interference in gravimetric or volumetric tests and that it can be corrected for in colorimetric tests, where it has potentially the greatest interfering effect. When pertinent, a statement of whether or not the sample has been filtered should be made.

Make a record of every sample collected, and identify every bottle, preferably by attaching an appropriately inscribed tag or label. The record should contain sufficient information to provide positive identification of the sample at a later date, as well as the name of the sample collector, the date, hour, and exact location, the water temperature, and any data that may be needed for correlation, such as weather conditions, water level, stream flow, or the like. Fix sampling points by detailed description, by maps, or with the aid of stakes, buoys, or landmarks in a manner that will permit their identification by other persons without reliance on memory or personal guidance.

Cool hot samples collected under pressure while still under pressure (see Section 107.3 and Figure 107:1).

Before samples are collected from distribution systems, flush the lines sufficiently to insure that the sample is representative of the supply, taking into account the diameter and length of the pipe to be flushed and the velocity of flow.

Collect samples from wells only after the well has been pumped sufficiently to insure that the sample represents the groundwater that feeds the well. Sometimes it will be necessary to pump at a specified rate to achieve a characteristic drawdown, if this determines the zones from which the well is supplied. Record the pumping rate and the drawdown as part of the sample record.

When samples are collected from a river or stream, the analytical values may vary with depth, stream flow, and distance from shore and from one shore to the other. If equipment is available, it is best to take an "integrated" sample from top to bottom in the middle of the stream in such a way that the sample is made composite according to the flow. If only a grab or catch sample can be collected, it is best to take it in the middle of the stream and at mid-depth.

Lakes and reservoirs are subject to considerable variations from normal causes such as seasonal stratification, rainfall, runoff, and wind. The choice of location, depth, and frequency of sampling will depend on local conditions and the purpose of the investigation.

These general directions do not provide enough information for collecting samples in which dissolved gases are to be determined. Specific instructions will be found in the sections that describe these determinations.

Use only representative samples for examination. The great variety of conditions under which collections must be made makes it impossible to prescribe a fixed procedure. In general, the sampling procedure should take account both of the tests or analyses to be performed and of the purpose for which the results are needed.

2. Types of Samples

a. Grab or catch samples: Strictly speaking, a sample collected at a particular time and place can represent only the composition of the source at that time and place. However, when a source is known to be fairly constant in composition over a considerable period of time or over substantial distances in all directions, then the sample may be said to represent a longer time period or a larger volume, or both, than the specific point at which it was collected. In such circumstances, some sources may be quite well represented by single grab samples. Examples are some water supplies, some surface waters, and rarely some wastewater streams.

When a source is known to vary with time, grab samples collected at suitable intervals and analyzed separately can be of great value in documenting the extent, frequency, and duration of these variations. Choose sampling intervals on the basis of the frequency with which changes may be expected, which may vary from as little as 5 min to as long as 1 hr or more.

When the composition of a source varies in space rather than time, a set of samples collected from appropriate locations with less emphasis on timing may provide the most useful information.

Use great care in sampling wastewater sludges, sludge banks, and muds. No definite procedure can be given, but every possible precaution should be taken to obtain a representative sample.

b. Composite samples: In most cases, the term composite sample refers to a mixture of grab samples collected at the same sampling point at different times. Sometimes the term time-composite is used when it is necessary to distinguish this type of sample from others. Time-composite samples are most useful for observing average concentrations that are used, for example, in calculating the loading or the efficiency of a wastewater treatment plant. As an alternative to the separate analysis of a large number of samples, followed by computation of average and total results, composite samples of this type represent a substantial saving in laboratory effort and expense. For these purposes, a composite sample representing a 24-hr period is considered standard for most determinations. Under certain circumstances, however, a composite sample representing one shift, or a shorter time period, or a complete cycle of a periodic operation, may be preferable. Evaluation of the effects of special, variable, or irregular discharges and operations may require composite samples representing the period during which such discharges occur.

For determination of components or characteristics subject to significant and unavoidable changes on storage, composite samples cannot be used. Perform such determinations on individual samples as soon as possible after collection and preferably at the sampling point. Analyses for all dissolved gases, residual chlorine, soluble sulfide, temperature, and pH are examples of determinations of this type. Changes in such components as dissolved oxygen or carbon dioxide, pH, or temperature may produce secondary changes in certain inorganic components such as iron, manganese, alkalinity, or hardness. Use time-composite samples only for determining components that can be demonstrated to remain unchanged under the existing conditions of sample collection and preservation.

Take individual portions in a wide-mouth bottle having a diameter of at least 35 mm at the mouth and capacity of at least 120 ml. Collect these portions each hour—in some cases each half hour or even every 5 min—and mix at the end of the sampling period or combine in a single bottle as collected. If preservatives are used, add them to the sample bottle initially so that all portions of the composite are preserved as soon as collected. Analysis of individual samples may sometimes be necessary.

It is desirable, and often absolutely essential, to combine the individual samples in volumes proportional to the volume of flow. A final volume of 2 to 3 l is sufficient for sewage, effluents, and wastes.

Automatic sampling devices are available but should not be used unless the sample is preserved as described below. Clean sampling devices, including bottles, daily to eliminate biological growths and other deposits.

c. Integrated samples: For certain purposes, the information needed is provided best by analysis of mixtures of grab samples collected from different points simultaneously, or as nearly so as possible. Such mixtures sometimes are called integrated samples. An example of the need for such sampling occurs in a river or stream that varies in composition across its width and depth. For evaluation of average composition or total loading, a mixture of samples representing various points in the cross-section, in proportion to their relative flows, may be useful. The need for integrated samples also may exist if combined treatment is proposed for several separate wastewater streams, the interaction of which may have a significant effect on treatability or even the composition of the mixture. Mathematical prediction of the interactions may be inaccurate or impossible and testing of a suitable integrated sample may provide more useful information.

TABLE 105:I. SUMMARY OF SPECIAL SAMPLING OR SAMPLE HANDLING REQUIREMENTS*

Determination	Container†	Minimum Sample Size, ml	Storage and/or Preservation
Acidity	P, G(B)	100	24 hr; refrigerate
Alkalinity	P, G(B)	200	24 hr; refrigerate
BOD	P, G	1,000	6 hr; refrigerate
Boron	P	100	—
Carbon, organic, total	G(brown)	100	Analyze as soon as possible, refrigerate or add HCl to pH $\leq$ 2
Carbon dioxide	P, G	100	Analyze immediately
COD	P, G	100	Analyze as soon as possible; add H_2SO_4 to pH $\leq$ 2
Chlorine dioxide	P, G	500	Analyze immediately
Chlorine, residual	P, G	500	Analyze immediately
Chlorophyll	P, G	500	30 days in dark; freeze
Color	G	500	—
Cyanide	P, G	500	24 hr; add NaOH to pH 12; refrigerate
Fluoride	P	300	—
Grease and oil	G, wide-mouth, calibrated	1,000	Add HCl to pH $\leq$ 2
Iodine	P, G	500	Analyze immediately
Metals	P, G	—	For dissolved metals separate by filtration immediately; add 5 ml conc HNO_3/l
Nitrogen			
Ammonia	P, G	500	Analyze as soon as possible; add 0.8 ml conc H_2SO_4/l; refrigerate
Nitrate	P, G	100	Analyze as soon as possible; add 0.8 ml conc H_2SO_4/l; refrigerate
Nitrite	P, G	100	Analyze as soon as possible; add 40 mg $HgCl_2$/l and refrigerate or freeze at -20 C

Both natural and artificial lakes often show variations of composition with both depth and horizontal location. However, under most conditions, neither total nor average figures are especially significant in these situations. The local variations are of more importance, and the samples are examined separately rather than integrated.

The preparation of integrated samples usually requires special equipment to collect a sample from a known depth, without contamination by the overlying water. Prior knowledge about the volume, movement, and composition of the various parts of the water being sampled usually is required. Therefore, the collection of the integrated samples becomes a complicated and specialized process that cannot be described in complete detail here.

3. Quantity

A 2-l sample should suffice for most physical and chemical analyses. For certain special determinations, larger samples may be necessary. Table 105:I shows the volumes ordinarily required for analyses.

TABLE 105:I. SUMMARY OF SPECIAL SAMPLING OR SAMPLE HANDLING REQUIREMENTS* *Continued*

Determination	Container†	Minimum Sample Size, *ml*	Storage and/or Preservation
Organic	P, G	500	Analyze as soon as possible; refrigerate or add 0.8 ml conc H_2SO_4/l
Odor	G	500	Analyze as soon as possible; refrigerate
Oxygen, dissolved	G, BOD bottle	300	Analyze immediately
Ozone	G	1,000	Analyze immediately
Pesticides (organic)	G(S)	—	—
pH	P, G(B)	—	—
Phenol	G	500	24 hr; add H_3PO_4 to pH$\leq$4.0 and 1 g $CuSO_4\cdot5H_2O$/l; refrigerate
Phosphate	G(A)	100	For dissolved phosphates separate by filtration immediately; freeze at $\leq$-10 C and/or add 40 mg HgCl/l
Residue	P, G(B)	—	—
Salinity	G, wax seal	240	Analyze immediately or use wax seal
Silica	P	—	—
Sludge digester gas	G, gas bottle	—	—
Sulfate	P, G	—	Refrigerate
Sulfide	P, G	100	Add 4 drops 2N zinc acetate/100 ml
Sulfite	P, G	—	Analyze immediately
Taste	G	500	Analyze as soon as possible; refrigerate
Temperature	—	—	Analyze immediately
Turbidity	P, G	—	Analyze same day; store in dark for up to 24 hr

*See text for additional details. For determinations not listed, no special requirements have been set: use glass or plastic containers, preferably refrigerate during storage, and analyze as soon as possible.

†P=plastic (polyethylene or equivalent); G=glass, G(A) or P(A)=rinsed with 1+1 HNO_3; G(B)=glass, borosilicate; G(S)=glass, rinsed with organic solvents.

Do not attempt to use the same sample for chemical, bacteriological, and microscopic examinations because the methods of collection and handling are different.

4. Preservation

Complete and unequivocal preservation of samples, whether domestic wastewater, industrial wastes, or natural waters, is a practical impossibility. Regardless of the nature of the sample, complete stability for every constituent never can be achieved. At best, preservation technics can only retard the chemical and biological changes that inevitably continue after the sample is removed from the source. The changes that take place in a sample are either chemical or biological. In the former case, certain changes occur in the chemical structure of the constituents that are a function of physical conditions.

Some determinations are more likely than others to be affected by storage of samples before analysis. Certain cations are subject to loss by adsorption on, or ion exchange with, the walls of glass containers. These include aluminum, cadmium, chromium, copper, iron, lead, manganese, silver, and zinc, which are best collected in a separate clean bottle and acidified with concentrated hydrochloric or nitric acid to a pH below 2.0 in order to minimize precipitation and adsorption on the walls of the container.

Temperature changes quickly; pH may change significantly in a matter of minutes; dissolved gases may be lost (oxygen, carbon dioxide). For these reasons make determinations of temperature, pH, and dissolved gases in the field. With changes in the pH-alkalinity-carbon dioxide balance, calcium carbonate may precipitate and cause a decrease in the values for calcium and for total hardness.

Iron and manganese form readily soluble compounds in their lower (reduced) valence states and relatively insoluble compounds in their higher (oxidized) valence states; therefore, these cations may precipitate out or they may dissolve out of a sediment, depending upon the redox potential of the sample. Microbiologic activity may be responsible for changes in the nitrate-nitrite-ammonia content, for decreases in phenols and in BOD, or for the reduction of sulfate to sulfide. Residual chlorine is reduced to chloride. Sulfide, sulfite, ferrous iron, iodide, and cyanide may be lost through oxidation. Color, odor, and turbidity may increase, decrease, or change in quality. Sodium, silica, and boron may be leached out of the glass container. Hexavalent chromium may be reduced to the trivalent state.

Biological changes taking place in a sample may change the valence of an element or a radical. Soluble constituents may be converted to organically bound materials in cell structures, or cell lysis may result in release of cellular material into solution. The well-known nitrogen and phosphorus cycles are examples of biological influence on sample composition.

The foregoing discussion is by no means all-inclusive. It is clearly impossible to prescribe absolute rules for the prevention of all possible changes. Some advice will be found in the discussions under individual determinations, but to a large degree the dependability of water analyses must rest on the experience and good judgment of the analyst.

a. Time interval between collection and analysis: In general, the shorter the time that elapses between collection of a sample and its analysis, the more reliable will be the analytical results. For certain constituents and physical values, immediate analysis in the field is required to obtain dependable results because the sample composition may change before it arrives at the laboratory.

It is impossible to state exactly how much time may be allowed to elapse between collection of a sample and its analysis; this depends on the character of the sample, the particular analyses to be made, and the conditions of storage. Changes caused by the growth of organisms are greatly retarded by keeping the sample in the dark and at a low temperature until analysis. Where the interval between sample collection and analysis is long enough to produce changes in either the concentration or the physical state of the constituent to be measured, follow the preservation practices in Table 105:I. Record the time elapsed between sampling and analysis, and which preservative, if any, was added.

b. Preservation methods: Preservation of samples is difficult because almost all preservatives interfere with some of the tests. Immediate analysis is ideal. Storage at low temperature (4 C) is perhaps the best way to preserve most samples until the next day. Use chemical preservatives only when they are shown not to interfere with the examination being made. When they are used, add them to the sample bottle initially so that all portions of the sample are preserved as soon as collected. No single method of preservation is entirely satisfactory; choose the preservative with due regard to the determinations to be made.

All methods of preservation may be inadequate when applied to suspended matter. Formaldehyde affects so many of the determinations that its use is not recommended.

Methods of preservation are relatively limited and are intended generally to retard biological action, retard hydrolysis of chemical compounds and complexes, and reduce volatility of constituents.

Preservation methods are generally limited to pH control, chemical addition, refrigeration, and freezing. Table 105:I lists preservation methods on the basis of the measurements to be performed.

106   ION-EXCHANGE RESINS

Ion-exchange resins provide the chemist with an important analytical tool. In water analysis, ion exchangers can be applied to: (a) remove interfering ions, (b) determine total ion content, (c) indicate the approximate volume of sample for certain gravimetric determinations, (d) concentrate trace quantities of cations, and (e) separate anions from cations. This manual recommends the use of ion-exchange resins for the removal of interference in the sulfate determination and for the determination of total ion content (see 104C.3 above). Inasmuch as the ion-exchange process can be applied in other determinations, a brief description of typical operations will be given here for convenient use

where supplementary applications are warranted.

1. Selection of Method

The batch method of ion exchange is satisfactory for sample volumes of less than 100 ml, while the column method is recommended for larger sample volumes. In the batch method, the resin is agitated with the sample for a given period, after which the resin is removed by filtration. The column method is more efficient in that it provides continuous contact between the sample and the resin, thereby enabling the exchange reaction to go to completion. In this modification, the solution passes slowly through the resin bed and ions are removed quantitatively from the sample. Elution of the resin permits recovery of the exchanged substances.

2. Procedure

Use resins specifically manufactured for analytical applications. Prepare the ion exchanger by rinsing the resin with several volumes of ion-free water (good-quality distilled water) to remove any coloring matter and other leachable material that might interfere with subsequent colorimetric procedures.

a. Batch method for cation removal: Pipet a sample portion containing 0.1 to 0.2 me of cations into a 250-ml erlenmeyer flask or beaker and add enough distilled water to bring the final volume to 75 ml. Add 2.0 g strongly acidic cation-exchange resin and stir the mixture at moderate speed for 15 min. Filter through a plug of glass wool placed in the neck of a 10-cm (4-in.) pyrex funnel. When the filtration is complete, wash the resin with two 10-ml portions of distilled water and make up to 100 ml total volume with distilled water.

Regeneration and storage of resin: Transfer the spent resin from the batch procedure to a flask containing 500 ml $3N$ nitric acid. When sufficient resin has accumulated, wash into a column (Figure 106:1) and regenerate by passing $3N$ nitric acid through the column at a rate of 0.1 to 0.2 ml of acid/ml resin/min. Use about 20 ml $3N$ nitric acid/ml resin in the column. Finally, wash the resin with sufficient distilled water until the pH of the effluent is 5 to 7, using the same rate of flow as in the regeneration step. Remove the resin from the column and store under distilled water in a wide-mouth container. Should the water become colored during storage, decant and replace with fresh distilled water. Before use, filter the resin through a plug of glass wool placed in the neck of a funnel, wash with distilled water, and allow to drain. The resin is then ready for use.

b. Column method for cation removal: Prepare the column as depicted in Figure 106:1 (length of resin bed, 21.5 cm; diameter of column, 1.3 cm; representing approximately 21 ml, or 20 g of resin). Other ion-exchange columns can be used equally well. One of the simplest consists of a buret containing a plug of glass wool immediately above the stopcock. (Whatever type of column is adopted, never allow the liquid level in the column to fall below the upper surface of the resin because the trapped air causes uneven flow rates and poor efficiency of ion exchange.)

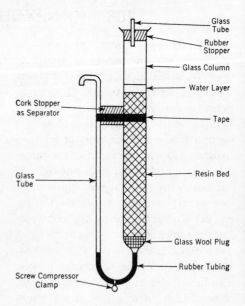

Figure 106:1. Ion-exchange column.

Charge the column by stirring the resin in a beaker with distilled water and then carefully washing the suspension into the column through a funnel. Backwash the column immediately by introducing distilled water at the bottom and passing it upward through the column until all air bubbles and channels are removed from the column. Connect a separatory funnel to the top of the column. Allow the sample to flow through the column at the rate of 0.2 ml solution/ml resin/min. After all of the sample has passed through the column, wash the resin with distilled water until the effluent pH is 5 to 7. Use strips of blue litmus paper or other indicating methods to determine when the column has been washed free of acid. For convenience, when adsorbing cations from a sample of one or more liters start this operation before the close of a workday and allow the exchange process to proceed overnight. The column will not dry because of the curved outlet.

Column elution: After the distilled-water wash, elute the adsorbed cations by passing 100 ml $3N$ nitric acid through the column at a rate of 0.2 ml acid/ml resin/min. Because a volume of 100 ml $3N$ nitric acid quantitatively removes 3 me of cations, use additional increments of 100 ml $3N$ nitric acid for quantities of adsorbed cations in excess of 3 me. After the elution step, rinse the column free of acid with enough distilled water to produce an effluent pH of 5 to 7. Conduct the wash at the same flow rate as the acid elution. The acid elution and wash regenerate the column for future use. The combined acid eluates contain the cations originally present in the sample.

107 EXAMINATION OF INDUSTRIAL WATER SUPPLIES

The following discussion summarizes the reasons for conducting an examination of an industrial water supply. Inasmuch as this section is limited in scope, the reader is urged to refer to comprehensive reference books on industrial water treatment[4-7] for further information on this complex subject.

1. Industrial Needs

Industrial water is water used directly or indirectly in an industrial process. From a volume standpoint, the most important industrial usage is cooling, either on a once-through basis or with cooling towers. Of almost equal importance is industrial water destined for steam generation.

Many industries, particularly those producing foods and beverages, use water as a raw material. Still others, such as the dye industry, take advantage of water's solvent power. One of the newest uses of water is in the nuclear industries, for radiation shielding, reactor modulation, and cooling. Other industries use water to carry matter, as in hydraulic classifiers, or to carry energy, as in high-pressure sprays for debarking timber or descaling steel.

2. Industrial Water Treatment

Natural waters are seldom suitable for industrial use without some treatment. Fortunately, technics exist for fitting any water to any job. The only limitation is economic.

Water treatment may be divided into two phases. Primary, external, or pretreatment is treatment applied to water before it reaches the point of use. Secondary, internal, or post-treatment takes place after the water reaches the point of use.

Although the number of basic water treatment processes and operations is not large, the combinations and variations of these steps are almost infinite. For example, treatment for a boiler feedwater may consist of sedimentation, chlorination, addition of cold lime soda, filtration, ion exchange, acidizing, aeration, and degassing. A discussion of these treatment processes is beyond the scope of this book.

3. Analysis of Industrial Water

The matter of examination assumes great importance during the selection of a proper supply for a specific industrial application or a variety of uses.[8-10]

Diagnosis of existing or potential water problems requires a maximum of information about the particular system involved. Thorough and accurate analyses of makeup water and of water from operating systems, analyses and examination of deposits and sections removed from operating systems, plus full information on the size, design characteristics, and operating conditions of the water system or water-using equipment are all desirable in helping the water treatment specialist to make a decision about the materials that must be re-moved from or added to the water to render it suitable for the intended process. Guidelines are difficult to give in a limited space, except to say that there is no substitute for experience.

Once the most suitable raw water supply has been chosen and a treatment system has been established, start a control testing program to insure adequate treatment rather than expensive over-treatment.[5-7] A control testing schedule can vary from a simple color comparison for chromate in a closed cooling system to an elaborate determination of a dozen or more ions in the microgram-per-liter range for supercritical boiler operations. Tailor the control program for each individual case. For example, analysis for only chloride and phosphate concentrations may be necessary for treatment control in one type of system, whereas in the case of a very high-pressure boiler, alkalinity, chloride, copper, hydrazine or sulfite, iron, morpholine, pH, phosphate, sulfate, and other analyses may be required.

Table 107:I lists the determinations most frequently performed to control the quality of water destined for steam generation, heating, cooling, and other manufacturing processes. The method of analysis for each particular constituent is set forth subsequently in these standards. Procedures for chromate,[11] hydrazine,[12] morpholine,[12] nickel,[12] and octadecylamine[12] are described in the references at the end of this section.

As already indicated, an analysis and the conclusions drawn from it can be no better than the sample on which it is made. Use proper sampling technics for each particular case in order to obtain the specificity or representativeness required (see Section 105 preceding). Give proper attention to flushing sample

TABLE 107:I. ROUTINE AND SPECIAL
DETERMINATIONS ON INDUSTRIAL WATER
SAMPLES

Determination	Applications*
Acidity	B, C, P
Alkalinity:	
Hydroxyl (OH)	B, P
Phenolphthalein (P)	B, C, P
Total, methyl orange or mixed indicator (M)	B, C, P
Ammonia	B, P
Boron	C, P
Calcium	B, C, P
Carbon dioxide	B, P
Chloride	B, C, P
Chlorine, residual	C, P
Chromium, hexavalent	B, C, P
Color	P
Conductivity	B, C, P
Copper	B, C, P
Fluoride	C, P
Hardness	B, C, P
Hydrazine	B
Iron	B, C, P
Lead	P
Magnesium	B, C, P
Manganese	C, P
Morpholine	B
Nickel	B, P
Nitrate	B, C, P
Nitrite	B, C, P
Octadecylamine	B
Oil and grease	B, C, P
Oxygen, dissolved	B, P
pH	B, C, P
Phosphate:	
Ortho	B, C, P
Poly	B, C, P
Residue, total:	
Filtrable	B, C, P
Nonfiltrable	B, C, P
Silica	B, C, P
Sodium	B, C, P
Sulfate	B, C, P
Sulfide	C, P
Sulfite	B, C, P
Tannin and lignin	B, C, P
Turbidity	P
Zinc	B, C, P

* Key: B—boiler water, feedwater, or condensate; C—cooling water, recirculating (open and closed systems) or once-through; P—industrial process applications.

lines, preventing contamination, and making sure the sample is representative.

Obtain samples not collected under pressure in the usual manner. Cool boiler waters collected under pressure to approximately 20 C while still under pressure. Figure 107:1 illustrates typical sampling-cooling installations. Certain determinations demand specialized sampling equipment and procedures and/or analyses conducted immediately after collection of samples. Specific examples include carbon dioxide, dissolved oxygen, dissolved and total iron, hydrogen sulfide, or octadecylamine in condensate. For such determinations, the sampling procedures are generally specified as part of the analytical method.

4. Scale

The occurrence of scale or sludge formation in industrial water systems may induce equipment failures, such as boiler tube ruptures or plugged heat-exchanger tubing. Such occurrences frequently result from increased temperature, evaporation, or aeration, which cause insolubility of some of the ionic combinations present. Common scale deposits may consist of calcium carbonate, phosphate, silicate, or sulfate, or of magnesium hydroxide, phosphate, and silicate. Others may be from oxides, silica, or related substances.

In distribution systems of 0 to 93 C (32 to 200 F) temperature, estimate the tendency of a water supply to form calcium carbonate scale by calculating the Langelier pH of saturation (pH_s) from the alkalinity, calcium, dissolved solids, and temperature of the water (see Section 203, Calcium Carbonate Saturation) and subtracting this pH_s from the actual measured pH of the water. A

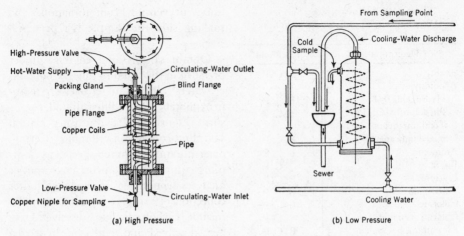

Figure 107:1. Cooling coils for boiler water sampling. These illustrations do not represent standardized equipment, but exemplify the characteristics of the devices that should be used.

positive value indicates scale-forming tendency; a negative value indicates scale-dissolving (or probably corrosive) tendency. A balanced or stable water usually has a zero or slightly positive index. Ryznar[13] has used the same pH_s and calculated a value of $2pH_s-pH$, which he calls a Stability Index and which correlates well with field experience of increasingly heavy scale as the numerical value of this index decreases from about 6.5, and increasingly serious corrosion as the index increases above this value. The literature also offers methods for calculating indices or solubilities of calcium phosphate,[14] calcium sulfate,[15] and magnesium hydroxide.[16]

Scale formation is prevented in boilers[5,17] by ion exchange or other hardness-reduction or solubilizing methods in the feedwater. The residual hardness is then precipitated inside the boiler by the addition of phosphate or carbonate and organic sludge conditioning chemicals, producing a nonadhering sludge rather than a scale; or is reacted with chelating agents to form soluble complexes.

For sludge removal and maintenance of scale-free conditions, and for the control of steam quality, maximum limits are designated for the total dissolved solids. Control is accomplished by blowdown as necessary.

In cooling towers, acid is applied for alkalinity reduction and scale prevention; however, presoftening of makeup water is practiced in some cases. Polyphosphates and other chemicals are also applied to control calcium carbonate, calcium phosphate, and silica deposit formation.[18,19] Proper and adequate bleedoff is an important part of treatment of cooling water.

5. Corrosion

Deterioration of metals caused by corrosion may produce soluble metallic ions in the system, which may redeposit later as oxides. Certain constituents or contaminants in the water, including dissolved oxygen, carbon dioxide, anions (such as chloride and sulfate), and acidity (low pH) increase the corrosive tendency of the water. Microorganisms such as sulfate-reducing or iron bacteria also cause corrosion and/or deposits.

Development of a thin protective layer of calcium carbonate on the metal surfaces often is effective for preventing corrosion of the metal in the water distribution system. The Saturation Index or Ryznar[13] Stability Index may be used to suggest the tendency to dissolve calcium carbonate or the degree of stability or balance.

Another procedure[20] for estimating corrosive tendency is calculation of the ratio

$$\frac{me/l\,(Cl^- + SO_4^{2-})}{me/l\ \text{alkalinity as } CaCO_3}$$

In the neutral pH range (7 to 8) and in the presence of dissolved oxygen, ratios equal to or below about 0.1 indicate general freedom from corrosion, whereas increasingly higher ratios generally indicate more aggressive waters.

Corrosion in boilers is controlled by removal of the oxygen from the feedwater by deaeration and by the reaction of residual oxygen with sodium sulfite or hydrazine. The corrosion of iron is also reduced effectively by the application of alkaline chemicals such as caustic soda and sodium phosphates to provide boiler water pH in the range of 10 to 12. At high boiler pressures [about 105 kg/cm^2 (1,500 psi) and above] it may be preferable to use a "low solids" type of treatment (ammonia, amines, hydrazine) to avoid localized corrosion associated with high pH. Because of the lack of buffer-

ing and softening agents in this treatment, high-quality demineralized water very low in silica is necessary and only minimum condenser leakage can be tolerated.

Carbonate and bicarbonate decompose in the boiler to release carbon dioxide in the steam. This causes formation of carbonic acid in the steam condensate,[21, 22] and corrosion by acid results. The presence of dissolved oxygen accelerates the carbonic acid attack.

Steam condensate corrosion can be minimized by maintaining minimum carbonate content in the boiler water and by the use of low bicarbonate or carbonate makeup waters. Volatile neutralizing amines such as morpholine and cyclohexylamine reduce corrosion in condensate systems by providing higher pH and pH control of condensate. Filming amines such as octadecylamine,[23] which forms a monomolecular film on the walls of the condensate piping to prevent contact with an acidic environment, also is effective in reducing corrosion.

Inhibition of corrosion in cooling towers is provided by the application of corrosion inhibitors such as chromates, phosphates, and silicates, applied singly or in various combinations. Open recirculating cooling systems[17, 18] in which water is continuously saturated with dissolved oxygen pose more difficult corrosion control problems than do closed recirculating systems. The generally low makeup water requirements of closed systems account for the minimum scale and corrosion problems. In the case of excessive makeup water usage due to poor design or leakage, scaling or corrosion may occur unless corrective treatment is used.

6. Special Problems

Fouling is the deposition of a material, normally in suspension, on a surface in contact with the water. Such deposition may cause reduced flow, inefficiency in heat transfer, and localized corrosion. Fouling also may result from reaction of dissolved minerals and water-conditioning chemicals and from the growth of microorganisms.

Sanitation practices to retard the growth of undesirable living organisms may encompass the destruction of pathogenic organisms by heat, as applied in the food industries, or the application of selective biocides to kill slime-forming or sulfate-reducing organisms growing on heat transfer surfaces. Also included is the destruction of algae growing in cooling towers, water plants growing in reservoirs, and mollusks growing in the cooling water pipes of industries using once-through seawater. Because many industries rely on biological methods to treat their wastewater, the applied biocides must not inhibit the growth of desirable organisms in the disposal treatment system and in the stream effluent.

Taste and odor result from organic or inorganic matter in the water. Taste- and odor-forming substances may be removed by adsorption on a number of materials such as activated carbon, or they may also be oxidized by chlorine, chlorine dioxide, oxygen, ozone, and permanganate. In some cases they may be rendered nonoffensive by masking.

A problem of disposal may arise when some industries must reuse water to such a degree that high concentrations of solids or impurities develop. Wastewater injected into a disposal well must be chemically compatible with the aquifer; otherwise the sands will clog and the well will have a short life. Wastewater effluents discharged to surface waters must be chemically, biologically, and thermally compatible with the receiving stream or lake to avert serious upset of the ecological balance.

Water-conditioning, waste disposal, and corrosion control problems are as varied as the industries seeking to solve them.

108   REFERENCES

1. Evaluation of Laboratory Methods for the Analysis of Inorganics in Water. 1968. Advan. Chem. Ser. No. 73, p. 253, American Chemical Soc.

2. McFarren, E.F., R.J. Lishka & J.H. Parker. 1970. Criterion for judging and acceptability of analytical methods. *Anal. Chem.* 42:358.

3. Bennett, C.A. & N.L. Franklin. 1954. Statistical Analysis in Chemistry and the Chemical Industry. John Wiley and Sons, Inc., New York, N.Y.

4. American Society for Testing and Materials. 1969. Manual on Water and Industrial Waste Water, 3rd ed. ASTM Spec. Tech. Publ. 442. Philadelphia, Pa.

5. Boiler water chemistry symposium. 1954. *Ind. Eng. Chem.* 46:953.

6. Nordell, E. 1961. Water Treatment for Industrial and Other Uses, 2nd ed. Reinhold Publishing Corp., New York, N.Y.

7. Hamer, P., J. Jackson & E.F. Thurston. 1961. Industrial Water Treatment Practice. Butterworths, London.

8. U.S. Public Health Service. 1962. Public Health Service Drinking Water Standards, 1962. PHS Publ. No. 956, Washington, D.C.

9. American Water Works Association. 1971. Water Quality and Treatment, 3rd ed. McGraw Hill, Inc., New York, N.Y.

10. California State Water Pollution Control Board. 1963. Water Quality Criteria, 2nd ed. Calif. State Water Pollution Control Board, Sacramento.

11. Furman, N.H., ed. 1962. Standard Methods of Chemical Analysis, 6th ed. D. Van Nostrand Co., Princeton, N.J., Vol. I, pp. 354, 360.

12. American Society for Testing and Materials. 1974. Book of ASTM Standards, Part 23, Water; Atmospheric Analysis. ASTM, Philadelphia, Pa.

13. Ryznar, J.W. 1944. A new index for determining amount of calcium carbonate scale formed by a water. *J. Amer. Water Works Ass.* 36:472.

14. Green, J. & J.A. Holmes. 1947. Calculation of the pH of saturation of tricalcium phosphate. *J. Amer. Water Works Ass.* 39:1090.

15. Denman, W.L. 1961. Maximum re-use of cooling water. *Ind. Eng. Chem.* 53:817.

16. Larson, T.E. et al. 1959. Stabilization of magnesium hydroxides in the solids-contact process. *J. Amer. Water Works Ass.* 51:1551.

17. Applebaum, S.B. & R.J. Zumbrunnen. 1956. Selecting water-treating processes for medium-pressure boilers. Amer. Soc. Mechan. Eng. Paper No. 56–A–191.

18. Lane, R.W. & T.E. Larson. 1963. Role of water treatment in the economic operation of cooling towers. *Amer. Power Conf.* XXV, 687.

19. Applebaum, S.B. 1950. Treatment of cooling water. *Combustion* 22:5 (Nov.), 41.

20. Larson, T.E. & R.V. Skold. 1958. Laboratory studies relating mineral quality of water to corrosion of steel and cast iron. *Corrosion* 14:6, 285t.

21. Collins, L.F. 1943. More information concerning corrosion in steam heating systems. 4th Water Conf., Eng. Soc. Western Pennsylvania 33.

22. Berk, A.A. & J. Nigon. 1948. Amine volatility and alkalinity in relation to corrosion control in steam heating systems. U.S. Bur. Mines Tech. Pap. 714.

23. Wilkes, J.F. et al. 1955. Filming amines— Use and misuse in power plant water-steam cycles. *Amer. Power Conf.* XVII, 527.

109 BIBLIOGRAPHY

General

Welch, P.S. 1948. Limnological Methods. Blakiston Co., Philadelphia, Pa.

Hauck, C.F. 1949. Gaging and sampling waterborne industrial wastes. Amer. Soc. Testing & Materials Bull. (Dec.)

Black, H.H. 1952. Procedures for sampling and measuring industrial wastes. *Sewage Ind. Wastes* 24:45.

Welch, P.S. 1952. Limnology, 2nd ed. McGraw-Hill Book Co., New York, N.Y.

Ministry of Housing and Local Government. 1956. Methods of Chemical Analysis as Applied to Sewage and Sewage Effluents, 2nd ed. Her Majesty's Stationery Office, London.

American Water Works Association. 1958.

Safety Practice for Water Utilities. Manual M6, AWWA, New York, N.Y.

Taylor, E.W. 1958. Examination of Waters and Water Supplies, 7th ed. Little, Brown & Co., Boston, Mass.

Hem, J.D. 1959. Study and interpretation of the chemical characteristics of natural water. U.S. Geol. Surv. Water Supply Pap. No. 1473.

Klein, L. 1959. River Pollution. I. Chemical Analysis. Academic Press, New York, N.Y.

Institute of Water Engineers. 1960. Approved Methods for the Physical and Chemical Examination of Water, 3rd ed. Inst. Water Eng., London.

Rainwater, F.H. & L.L. Thatcher. 1960. Methods for Collection and Analysis of Water Samples. U.S. Geol. Surv. Water Supply Pap. No. 1454.

AMERICAN SOCIETY FOR TESTING AND MATERIALS. 1962. Manual on Industrial Water and Industrial Waste Water, 2nd ed. Spec. Tech. Publ. 148-I, ASTM, Philadelphia, Pa.

U.S. PUBLIC HEALTH SERVICE. 1962. Public Health Service Drinking Water Standards, 1962. PHS Publ. No. 956.

TAYLOR, F.B. 1963. Significance of trace elements in public finished water supplies. J. Amer. Water Works Ass. 55:619.

CAMP, T.R. 1963. Water and Its Impurities. Reinhold Publishing Corp., New York, N.Y.

CALIFORNIA STATE WATER POLLUTION CONTROL BOARD. 1963. Water Quality Criteria, 2nd ed. Calif. State Water Pollution Control Board, Sacramento.

STEERE, N.V., ed. 1967. Handbook of Laboratory Safety. Chemical Rubber Company, Cleveland, Ohio.

SAWYER, C.N. & P.L. McCARTY. 1967. Chemistry for Sanitary Engineers, 2nd ed. McGraw-Hill Book Co., New York, N.Y.

AMERICAN WATER WORKS ASSOCIATION. 1971. Water Quality and Treatment: a Handbook of Public Water Supplies, 3rd ed. McGraw-Hill, New York, N.Y.

WORLD HEALTH ORGANIZATION. 1971. International Standards for Drinking Water, 3rd ed. WHO, Geneva.

MANUFACTURING CHEMISTS' ASSOCIATION, GENERAL SAFETY COMMITTEE. 1972. Guide for Safety in the Chemical Laboratory, 2nd ed. D. Van Nostrand Co., New York, N.Y.

Water Supply Data

LOHR, E.W. & S.K. LOVE. 1954. The industrial utility of public water supplies in the United States. 1952. Parts 1 and 2. U.S. Geol. Surv. Water Supply Pap. No. 1299 and 1300.

Laboratory Reagents

AMERICAN CHEMICAL SOCIETY. 1968. Reagent Chemicals—American Chemical Society Specifications, 4th ed. ACS, Washington, D.C.

ROSIN, J. 1967. Reagent Chemicals and Standards, 5th ed. D. Van Nostrand Co., Princeton, N.J.

The United States Pharmacopeia. 1974. 19th rev. U.S. Pharmacopeial Convention Inc., Rockville, Md.

NATIONAL BUREAU OF STANDARDS. 1975. Catalog of NBS Standard Reference Materials. NBS Spec. Publ. 260.

General Analytical Technics

FOULK, C.W., H.V. MOYER & W.M. MACNEVIN. 1952. Quantitative Chemical Analysis. McGraw-Hill Book Co., New York, N.Y.

WILLARD, H.H., N.H. FURMAN & C.E. BRICKER. 1956. Elements of Quantitative Analysis, 4th ed. D. Van Nostrand Co., Princeton, N.J.

HUGHES, J.C. 1959. Testing of glass volumetric apparatus. Nat. Bur. Standards Circ. No. 602.

WILSON, C.L. & D.W. WILSON, eds. 1959, 1960, 1962. Comprehensive Analytical Chemistry, Vol. 1A, Vol. 1B, Vol. 1C. Elsevier Publishing Co., New York, N.Y.

VOGEL, A.I. 1962. Textbook of Quantitative Inorganic Analysis, Including Elementary Instrumental Analysis, 3rd ed. John Wiley & Sons, New York, N.Y.

WELCHER, F.J., ed. 1963, 1966. Standard Methods of Chemical Analysis, 6th ed. Vol. IIA, & Vol. IIIA. D. Van Nostrand Co., Princeton, N.J.

MEITES, L., ed. 1963. Handbook of Analytical Chemistry. McGraw-Hill Book Co., New York, N.Y.

PECSOK, R. & L.D. SHIELDS. 1968. Modern Methods of Chemical Analysis. John Wiley & Sons, New York, N.Y.

KOLTHOFF, I.M., E.J. MEEHAN, E.B. SANDELL & S. BRUCKENSTEIN. 1969. Quantitative Chemical Analysis, 4th ed. Macmillan Co., New York, N.Y.

Colorimetric Technics

MELLON, M.G. 1947. Colorimetry and photometry in water analysis. J. Amer. Water Works Ass. 39:341.

NATIONAL BUREAU OF STANDARDS. 1947. Terminology and Symbols for Use in Ultraviolet, Visible, and Infrared Absorptiometry. NBS Letter Circ. LC-857 (May 19).

GIBSON, K.S. & M. BALCOM. 1947. Transmission measurements with the Beckman quartz spectrophotometer. J. Res. Nat. Bur. Standards 38:601.

SNELL, F.D. & C.T. SNELL. 1948. Colorimetric Methods of Analysis, 3rd ed. D. Van Nostrand Co., Princeton, N.J., Vol. 1.

MELLON, M.G., ed. 1950. Analytical Absorption Spectroscopy. John Wiley & Sons, New York, N.Y.

DISKANT, E.M. 1952. Photometric methods in water analysis. *J. Amer. Water Works Ass.* 44:625.

BOLTZ, D.F., ed. 1958. Colorimetric Determination of Nonmetals. Interscience Publishers, New York, N.Y.

SANDELL, E.B. 1959. Colorimetric Determination of Traces of Metals, 3rd ed. Interscience Publishers, New York, N.Y.

Emission Spectroscopy

HARRISON, G.R. 1939. Wavelength Tables. John Wiley & Sons, New York, N.Y.

BRODE, W. 1943. Chemical Spectroscopy, 2nd ed. John Wiley & Sons, New York, N.Y.

HARRISON, G.R., R.C. LORD & J.R. LOOFBOUROW. 1948. Practical Spectroscopy. Prentice-Hall, New York, N.Y.

NACHTRIEB, N.H. 1950. Principles and Practice of Spectrochemical Analysis. McGraw-Hill Book Co., New York, N.Y.

HARVEY, C.E. 1950. Spectrochemical Procedures. Applied Research Labs., Glendale, Calif.

SAWYER, R.A. 1951. Experimental Spectroscopy, 2nd ed. Prentice-Hall, New York, N.Y.

TWYMAN, F. 1951. Metal Spectroscopy, 2nd ed. Charles Griffin & Co., London.

AHERNS, L.A. 1954. Quantitative Spectrochemical Analysis of Silicates. Pergamon Press, London.

MEGGERS, W.F. 1949, 1950, 1952, 1954, 1956. Emission spectroscopy. *Anal. Chem.* 21:29; 22:18; 24:23; 26:54; 28:616.

AHRENS, L.H. & S.R. TAYLOR. 1961. Spectrochemical Analysis, 2nd ed. Addison-Wesley Publishing Co., Reading, Mass.

AMERICAN SOCIETY FOR TESTING AND MATERIALS. 1971. Methods for Emission Spectrochemical Analysis, 6th ed. ASTM, Philadelphia, Pa.

Polarography

BUTTS, P.G. & M.G. MELLON. 1951. Polarographic determination of metals in industrial wastes. *Sewage Ind. Wastes* 23:59.

MULLER, O.H. 1951. Polarographic Method of Analysis, 2nd ed. Chemical Education Publishing Co., Easton, Pa.

KOLTHOFF, I.M. & J.J. LINGANE. 1952. Polarography, 2nd ed. Interscience Publishers, New York, N.Y.

Bibliography of Polarographic Literature, 1922-1955. 1956. E.H. Sargent Co., Chicago, Ill.

Potentiometric Titration

FURMAN, N.H. Potentiometric titrations. 1950, 1951, 1954. *Anal. Chem.* 22:33; 23:21; 26:84.

KOLTHOFF, I.M. & H.A. LAITINEN. 1958. pH and Electrotitrations. John Wiley & Sons, New York, N.Y.

WILLARD, H.H., L.L. MERRITT & J.A. DEAN. 1965. Instrumental Methods of Analysis, 4th ed. D. Van Nostrand Co., Princeton, N.J.

Other Methods of Analysis

LOVE, S.K. 1951. Analytical instruments used in the modern water plant laboratory. *J. Amer. Water Works Ass.* 43:725.

BOLTZ, D.F., ed. 1952. Selected Topics in Modern Instrumental Analysis. Prentice-Hall, New York, N.Y.

OSBORN, G.H. 1953. Bibliography on the analytical applications of ion-exchange resins. *Analyst* 78:221.

EWING, G.W. 1954. Instrumental Methods of Chemical Analysis. McGraw-Hill Book Co., New York, N.Y.

LEDERER, E. & M. LEDERER. 1957. Chromatography, 2nd ed. Elsevier Press, Houston, Tex.

BLOCK, R.J., E.L. CURRUM & G. ZWEIG. 1958. A Manual of Paper Chromatography and Paper Electrophoresis, 2nd ed. Academic Press, New York, N.Y.

LINGANE, J.J. 1958. Electroanalytical Chemistry, 2nd ed. Interscience Publishers, New York, N.Y.

SAMUELSON, O. 1963. Ion Exchangers in Analytical Chemistry. John Wiley & Sons, New York, N.Y.

HARLEY, J.H. & S.E. WIBERLEY. 1967. Instrumental Analysis, 2nd ed. John Wiley & Sons, New York, N.Y.

HEFTMANN, E., ed. 1967. Chromatography, 2nd ed. Reinhold Publishing Corp., New York, N.Y.

General Analytical Reviews and Bibliographies
WEIL, B.H. et al. 1948. Bibliography on Water and Sewage Analysis. State Engineering Experiment Station, Georgia Institute of Technology, Atlanta.

Annual reviews of analytical chemistry. 1953-1974. *Anal. Chem.* 25:2; 26:2; 27:574; 28:559; 29:589; 30:553; 31:776; 32:3R; 33.3R; 34:3R; 35:3R; 36:3R; 37:1R; 38:1R; 39:1R; 40:1R; 41:1R; 42:1R; 43:1R; 44:1R; 45:1R; 46:1R.

WATER POLLUTION CONTROL FEDERATION RESEARCH COMMITTEE. 1960-1974. Annual literature review, analytical methods. *J. Water Pollut. Control Fed.* 32:443; 33:445; 34:419; 35:553; 36:535; 37:735; 38:869; 39:867; 40:897; 41:873; 42:863; 43:933; 44:903; 45:979; 46:1031.

Statistics
WORTHING, A.G. & J. GEFFNER. 1943. Treatment of Experimental Data. John Wiley & Sons, New York, N.Y.

AMERICAN SOCIETY FOR TESTING AND MATERIALS. 1950. Symposium on application of statistics. ASTM Spec. Tech. Publ. 103.

AMERICAN SOCIETY FOR TESTING AND MATERIALS. 1951. Manual on quality control of materials. ASTM Spec. Tech. Publ. 15C.

DEAN, R.B. & W.J. DIXON. 1951. Simplified statistics for small numbers of observations. *Anal. Chem.* 23:636.

YOUDEN, W.J. 1951. Statistical Methods for Chemists. John Wiley & Sons, New York, N.Y.

KOLTHOFF, I.M. & E.B. SANDELL. 1952. Textbook of Quantitative Inorganic Analysis, 3rd ed. Macmillan Co., New York, N.Y. Chapter 15.

GORE, W.L. 1952. Statistical Methods for Chemical Experimentation. Interscience Publishers, New York, N.Y.

DIXON, W.J. & F.J. MASSEY, JR. 1957. Introduction to Statistical Analysis, 2nd ed. McGraw-Hill Book Co., New York, N.Y.

DUNCAN, A.J. 1959. Quality Contents Industrial Statistics. Richard R. Irwin, Inc., Homewood, Ill.

Guide for measures of precision and accuracy. 1962. *Anal. Chem.* 34:364R.

HOEL, P.G. 1962. Introduction to Mathematical Statistics. John Wiley & Sons, New York, N.Y.

OSTLE, B. 1963. Statistics in Research. Iowa State Univ. Press, Ames.

YOUDEN, W.J. 1967. Statistical Techniques for Collaborative Tests. Ass. Official Analytical Chemists, Washington, D.C.

GREENBERG, A.E., N. MOSKOWITZ, B.R. TAMPLIN & J. THOMAS. 1969. Chemical reference samples in water laboratories. *J. Amer. Water Works Ass.* 61:599.

Evaluation of Methods
KRAMER, H.P. & R.C. KRONER. 1959. Cooperative studies on laboratory methodology. *J. Amer. Water Works Ass.* 51:607.

KRONER, R.C., D.G. BALLINGER & H.P. KRAMER. 1960. Evaluation of laboratory methods for analysis of heavy metals in water. *J. Amer. Water Works Ass.* 52:117.

MULLINS, J.W. et al. 1961. Evaluation of methods for counting gross radioactivity in water. *J. Amer. Water Works Ass.* 53:1466.

LISHKA, R.J., F.S. KELSO & H.P. KRAMER. 1963. Evaluation of methods for determination of minerals in water. *J. Amer. Water Works Ass.* 55:647.

Checking Analyses
ROSSUM, J.R. 1949. Conductance method for checking accuracy of water analyses. *Anal. Chem.* 21:631.

ROBERTSON, R.S. & M.F. NIELSEN. 1951. Quick test determines dissolved solids. *Power* 95:87 (Feb.).

NAVONE, R. 1954. Sodium determination with ion-exchange resin. *J. Amer. Water Works Ass.* 46:479.

GREENBERG, A.E. & R. NAVONE. 1958. Use of the control chart in checking anion-cation balances in water. *J. Amer. Water Works Ass.* 50:1365.

Collection of Samples
ELLISON, G., H.W. HACKLER & W.A. BUICE. 1932. Effects of age and storage temperatures on growth of bacteria in water samples. *J. Amer. Water Works Ass.* 24:895.

WELCH, P.S. 1948. Limnological Methods. Blakiston Co., Philadelphia, Pa. Chapter 14.

HAUCK, C.F. 1949. Gaging and sampling waterborne industrial wastes. *Amer. Soc. Testing & Materials Bull.* (Dec.), pp. 38-43.

BLACK, H.H. 1952. Procedures for sampling and measuring industrial wastes. *Sewage Ind. Wastes 24:45.*

WELCH, P.S. 1952. Limnology, 2nd ed. McGraw-Hill Book Co., New York, N.Y., Chapter 5.

AMERICAN SOCIETY FOR TESTING AND MATERIALS. 1957. Standard Methods of Sampling Industrial Water. ASTM Publ. D510-57, Philadelphia, Pa.

TAYLOR, E.W. 1958. Examination of Waters and Water Supplies, 7th ed. Little, Brown & Co., Boston, Mass., Chapter 11.

RAINWATER, F.H. & L.L. THATCHER. 1960. Methods for collection and analysis of water samples. U.S. Geol. Surv. Water Supply Pap. No. 1454.

Preservation of Samples

JEWELL, M.E. 1920. Experiments on the preservation of mud samples. *Ill. State Water Surv. Bull.* 16:206.

HATFIELD, W.D. & G.E. PHILLIPS. 1941. Preservation of sewage samples. *Water Works Sewage* 88:285.

Ion Exchange

KUNIN, R. et al. 1949-52, 1954, 1956, 1958, 1960, 1962, 1966, 1968. Ion exchange. *Anal. Chem.* 21:87; 22:64; 23:45; 24:64; 26:104; 28:729; 30:681; 32:67R; 34:101R; 38:176R; 40:136R.

SAMUELSON, O. 1963. Ion Exchange in Analytical Chemistry. John Wiley & Sons, New York, N.Y.

PART 200

PHYSICAL

EXAMINATION

201 INTRODUCTION

This section deals primarily with measurement of the physical properties of a sample, as distinguished from the concentrations of chemical or biological components. Many of the determinations included here, such as color, electrical conductivity, and turbidity, fit this category unequivocally. However, physical properties cannot be divorced entirely from chemical composition, and some of the technics of this section measure collective properties resulting from the presence of a number of constituents. Others, for example, calcium carbonate saturation and oxygen transfer, are related to, or depend on, chemical tests. Also included here are tests for appearance, odor, and taste, which have been classified traditionally among physical properties, although the point could be argued. Finally, Section 213 includes certain tests for which the description "physical" is questionable. However, they are grouped with the other tests used for sludge as a matter of convenience.

With these minor exceptions, the effort has been to keep the content of this section reasonably faithful to its name. Most of the methods included are either inherently or at least traditionally physical, as distinguished from explicitly chemical, radiologial, biological, or bacteriological methods of other sections.

202 APPEARANCE

When it is desirable to record the general physical appearance of the sample, use any terms that best describe the characteristics of the individual sample. No standard methods or standard terminology are recommended.

For liquid samples, supplement or replace the description of appearance by the determination of color. Also, for relatively clear liquid samples, the determination of turbidity may be appropriate.

203 CALCIUM CARBONATE SATURATION

Calculation of the saturation, equilibrium, or undersaturation of water with respect to calcium carbonate requires knowledge of the calcium ion concentration, alkalinity, pH, temperature, and ionic strength or total dissolved solids concentration. Frequently, the degree of oversaturation or undersaturation is described by the Langelier saturation index[1], equal to pH measured – pH saturation. A value of zero indicates calcium carbonate equilibrium, that is, a stable water. A negative value indicates undersaturation or corrosivity, while a positive value indicates oversaturation with respect to calcium carbonate, or scale-forming properties.

1. Calculation

The value of pH saturation can be calculated, with good precision, by using the equilibrium expressions for the solution of calcium carbonate and the second hydrolysis of carbonic acid:

$$CaCO_{3(s)} \leftrightharpoons Ca^{2+} + CO_3^{2-}$$
$$K_s = [Ca^{2+}][CO_3^{2-}] \qquad (1)$$

$$HCO_3^- \leftrightharpoons H^+ + CO_3^{2-}$$
$$K_2 = \frac{[H^+][CO_3^{2-}]}{[HCO_3^-]} \qquad (2)$$

Divide Equation 1 by Equation 2 and rearrange to obtain:

$$[H^+] = \frac{K_2}{K_s}[Ca^{2+}][HCO_3^-] \qquad (3a)$$

or

$$pH_s = p[Ca^{2+}] + p[HCO_3^-] + p(K_2/K_s) \qquad (3b)$$

Values of conditional equilibrium constants may be obtained from the literature.[2-5]

Accounting for the effect of temperature and ionic strength on the equilibrium constants, Larson[5] formulated the expression for the pH at calcium carbonate saturation, pH_s, as:

$$pH_s = A + B - \log(Ca^{2+}) - \log(\text{alkalinity}) \qquad (4a)$$

where calcium ion concentration and alkalinity are expressed in terms of mg/l as $CaCO_3$ equivalent. Values for the constants and logarithms in Equation 4a are given in Tables 203:I through III.

For example, for a water having a calcium ion concentration of 200 mg/l

TABLE 203:I. CONSTANT A AS FUNCTION OF WATER TEMPERATURE

Water Temperature C	A
0	2.60
4	2.50
8	2.40
12	2.30
16	2.20
20	2.10

TABLE 203:II. CONSTANT B AS FUNCTION OF TOTAL DISSOLVED RESIDUE

Total Dissolved Residue mg/l	B
0	9.70
100	9.77
200	9.83
400	9.86
800	9.89
1,000	9.90

TABLE 203:III. LOGARITHMS OF CALCIUM ION AND ALKALINITY CONCENTRATIONS

Ca^{2+} or Alkalinity mg/l as $CaCO_3$ equivalent	log
10	1.00
20	1.30
30	1.48
40	1.60
50	1.70
60	1.78
70	1.84
80	1.90
100	2.00
200	2.30
300	2.48
400	2.60
500	2.70
600	2.78
700	2.84
800	2.90
900	2.95
1000	3.00

as $CaCO_3$, an alkalinity of 60 mg/l as $CaCO_3$, a temperature of 16 C, and a total dissolved residue concentration of 650 mg/l, this equation is solved:

$$pH_s = 2.20 + 9.88 - 2.30 - 1.78 = 8.00 \quad (4b)$$

If the measured pH of this water is 9.0, the saturation index is 9.0–8.0 or +1.0, and the water is supersaturated with respect to calcium carbonate.

The pH_s value of 8.0 means that the water will neither dissolve nor precipitate calcium carbonate at that pH. While it does not specifically indicate anything about the corrosion of any metal in contact with the water, it is widely assumed that maintaining the water pH above the pH_s will result in the deposition of a protective coating of calcium carbonate on distribution system piping. Frequently, this does not occur because of non-uniform deposition or sloughing of materials from pipe walls. The formation of protective calcium carbonate coatings may be further inhibited by the application of polyphosphates as sequestering agents to the finished water.

Additional aids for the calculation of the saturation index are available.[6-11] Particularly useful is the Caldwell-Lawrence diagram,[11] which facilitates estimation of chemical dosages for softening as well as equilibrium conditions.

The pH of stability with respect to calcium carbonate frequently has been estimated experimentally by equilibrating chips of calcium carbonate with a given water (marble test). This test suffers from the facts that equilibrium may not be attained and the partial pressure of carbon dioxide in the atmosphere over the sample may influence the results adversely.

2. References

1. LANGELIER, W.F. 1936. The analytical control of anticorrosion water treatment. *J. Amer. Water Works Ass.* 28:1500.
2. MOORE, E.W. 1938. Calculation of chemical dosages required for the prevention of corrosion. *J. New England Water Works Ass.* 52:311.
3. LARSON, T.E. & A.M. BUSWELL. 1942. Calcium carbonate saturation index and alkalinity interpretations. *J. Amer. Water Works Ass.* 34:1667.
4. LANGELIER, W.F. 1946. Effect of temperature on the pH of natural waters. *J. Amer. Water Works Ass.* 38:179.
5. LARSON, T.E. 1951. The ideal lime-softened water. *J. Amer. Water Works Ass.* 43:649.
6. LANGELIER, W.F. 1946. Chemical equilibria in water treatment. *J. Amer. Water Works Ass.* 38:169.
7. HOOVER, C.P. 1938. Practical application of the Langelier method. *J. Amer. Water Works Ass.* 30:1802.
8. BLACK, A.P. 1948. The chemistry of water treatment. *Water Sewage Works* 95:369.
9. HIRSCH, A.A. 1942. A special slide rule for calcium carbonate equilibrium problems. *Ind. Eng. Chem.*, Anal. Ed. 14:178.
10. HIRSCH, A.A. 1942. A slide rule for carbonate equilibrium and alkalinity in water supplies. *Ind. Eng. Chem.*, Anal. Ed. 14:943.
11. CALDWELL, D.H. & W.B. LAWRENCE. 1953. Water softening and conditioning problems. *Ind. Eng. Chem.* 45:535.
12. STUMM, W. & J.J. MORGAN. 1970. Aquatic Chemistry. Section 5-2, The solubility of oxides, hydroxides and carbonates. Wiley-Interscience, New York, N.Y.

204   COLOR

Color in water may result from the presence of natural metallic ions (iron and manganese), humus and peat materials, plankton, weeds, and industrial wastes. Color is removed in order to make a water suitable for general and industrial applications.

The term "color" is used herein to mean true color—that is, the color of the water from which the turbidity has been removed. The term "apparent color" includes not only the color due to substances in solution, but also that due to suspended matter. Apparent color is determined on the original sample without filtration or centrifugation.

Selection of method: The visual comparison method is applicable to nearly all samples of potable water. Pollution by certain industrial wastes may produce unusual colors that cannot be matched; in this case use one of the instrumental methods. For comparison of color values between laboratories, calibrate the visual method by the instrumental procedures.

204 A.   Visual Comparison Method

1. General Discussion

a. Principle: Color is determined by visual comparison of the sample with known concentrations of colored solutions. Comparison also may be made with special glass color disks if they have been properly calibrated. The platinum-cobalt method of measuring color is given as the standard method, the unit of color being that produced by 1 mg/l platinum in the form of the chloroplatinate ion. The ratio of cobalt to platinum may be varied to match the hue in special cases; the proportion given below is usually satisfactory to match the color of natural waters.

b. Interference: Even a slight turbidity causes the apparent color to be noticeably higher than the true color; therefore it is necessary to remove turbidity before the true color can be approximated by differential reading with different color filters[1] or by differential scattering measurements.[2] Neither of these technics, however, has reached the status of a standard method. The recommended method for the removal of turbidity is described under Instrumental Methods B and C.

The color value of water is extremely pH-dependent, and invariably increases as the pH of the water is raised. For this reason, when reporting a color value, specify the pH at which the color is determined. For research purposes or when color values are to be compared between laboratories, it is advisable to determine the color response of a given water over a wide range of pH values. This procedure has been described by Black and Christman.[3]

c. Field method: Since the platinum-cobalt standard method is not convenient for field use, the color of water may be compared with that of glass disks held at the end of metallic tubes containing glass comparator tubes of the sample and colorless distilled water. Match the color of the sample with the color of the tube of clear water plus the calibrated colored glass when viewed by looking toward a white surface. Calibrate every individual disk to correspond with the colors on the platinum-cobalt scale. The glass disks give results in substantial agreement with those obtained by the platinum-cobalt method, and their use is recognized as a standard field procedure.

d. *Nonstandard laboratory methods:* The use of glass disks or of liquids other than water as standards for laboratory work is permissible only if these have been individually calibrated against platinum-cobalt standards. Waters of highly unusual color, such as those that may occur by mixture with certain industrial wastes, may have hues so far removed from those of the platinum-cobalt standards that comparison by the standard method is difficult or impossible. For such waters, the methods in Sections 204B and C may be used. However, the results so obtained are not directly comparable to those obtained with platinum-cobalt standards.

e. *Sampling:* Collect representative samples in clean glassware. Make the color determination within a reasonable period, because biological or physical changes occurring in storage may affect the color. With naturally colored waters these changes invariably lead to poor results.

2. Apparatus

a. *Nessler tubes*, matched, 50-ml, tall form.

b. *pH meter*, for determining the sample pH as described in pH Value (Section 424). The pH also may be determined colorimetrically.

3. Preparation of Standards

a. If a reliable supply of potassium chloroplatinate cannot be purchased, use chloroplatinic acid, which can be prepared from metallic platinum. Do not use commercial chloroplatinic acid because it is very hygroscopic and therefore may vary in platinum content. Potassium chloroplatinate is not hygroscopic.

b. Dissolve 1.246 g potassium chloroplatinate, K_2PtCl_6 (equivalent to 500 mg metallic platinum) and 1.00 g crystallized cobaltous chloride, $CoCl_2 \cdot 6H_2O$ (equivalent to about 250 mg metallic cobalt) in distilled water with 100 ml conc HCl and dilute to 1,000 ml with distilled water. This stock standard has a color of 500 units.

c. If potassium chloroplatinate is not available, dissolve 500 mg pure metallic platinum in aqua regia with the aid of heat; remove nitric acid by repeated evaporation with fresh portions of conc HCl. Dissolve this product, together with 1.00 g crystallized cobaltous chloride, as directed above.

d. Prepare standards having colors of 5, 10, 15, 20, 25, 30, 35, 40, 45, 50, 60, and 70 by diluting 0.5, 1.0, 1.5, 2.0, 2.5, 3.0, 3.5, 4.0, 4.5, 5.0, 6.0, and 7.0 ml stock color standard with distilled water to 50 ml in nessler tubes. Protect these standards against evaporation and contamination when not in use.

4. Procedure

a. *Estimation of intact sample:* Observe the color of a sample by filling a matched nessler tube to the 50-ml mark with the water to be examined and comparing it with the standards. Look vertically downward through the tubes toward a white or specular surface placed at such an angle that light is reflected upward through the columns of liquid. If turbidity is present and has not been removed by the procedure given below, report the color as "apparent color." If the color exceeds 70 units, dilute the sample with distilled water in known proportions until the color is within the range of the standards.

b. Because the color is related to pH, measure the pH of each sample.

5. Calculation

a. Calculate the color units by means of the following equation:

$$\text{Color units} = \frac{A \times 50}{B}$$

where A = estimated color of a diluted sample and B = ml sample taken for dilution.

b. Report the color results in whole numbers and record as follows:

Color Units	Record to Nearest
1–50	1
51–100	5
101–250	10
251–500	20

c. Report the pH of the water sample.

6. References

1. KNIGHT, A. G. 1951. The photometric estimation of color in turbid waters. *J. Inst. Water Eng.* 5:623.
2. JULLANDER, I. & K. BRUNE. 1950. Light absorption measurements on turbid solutions. *Acta Chem. Scand.* 4:870.
3. BLACK, A. P. & R. F. CHRISTMAN. 1963. Characteristics of colored surface waters. *J. Amer. Water Works Ass.* 55:753.

204 B.   Spectrophotometric Method

1. Apparatus

a. Spectrophotometer, having 10-mm absorption cells, a narrow (10-nm or less) spectral band, and an effective operating range from 400 to 700 nm.

b. Filtration system, consisting of the following (see Figure 204:1):

1) *Filtration flasks,* 250-ml, with side tubes.

2) *Walter crucible holder.*

3) *Micrometallic filter crucible,* average pore size 40 μm.

4) *Calcined filter aid.* *

5) *Vacuum system.*

---

*Celite No. 505 (Johns Manville Corp.) or equivalent.

2. Procedure

a. Preparation of sample: Bring two 50-ml samples to room temperature. Use one sample at the original pH; adjust the pH of the other to 7.6 by using conc H_2SO_4 or NaOH as required. A standard pH is necessary because of the variation of color with pH. Remove excessive quantities of suspended materials by centrifuging. Treat each sample separately, as follows:

Thoroughly mix 0.1 g filter aid in a 10-ml portion of centrifuged sample and filter the slurry to form a precoat in the filter crucible. Direct the filtrate to the waste flask as indicated in Figure 204:1. Mix 40 mg filter aid in a 35-ml portion

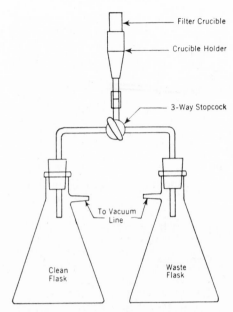

Figure 204:1. Filtration system for color determinations.

water blank and make all determinations with a narrow spectral band.

TABLE 204:I. SELECTED ORDINATES FOR SPECTROPHOTOMETRIC COLOR DETERMINATIONS*

Ordinate No.	X	Y	Z
	Wavelength nm		
1	424.4	465.9	414.1
2*	435.5*	489.5*	422.2*
3	443.9	500.4	426.3
4	452.1	508.7	429.4
5*	461.2*	515.2*	432.0*
6	474.0	520.6	434.3
7	531.2	525.4	436.5
8*	544.3*	529.8*	438.6*
9	552.4	533.9	440.6
10	558.7	537.7	442.5
11*	564.1*	541.4*	444.4*
12	568.9	544.9	446.3
13	573.2	548.4	448.2
14*	577.4*	551.8*	450.1*
15	581.3	555.1	452.1
16	585.0	558.5	454.0
17*	588.7*	561.9*	455.9*
18	592.4	565.3	457.9
19	596.0	568.9	459.9
20*	599.6*	572.5*	462.0*
21	603.3	576.4	464.1
22	607.0	580.4	466.3
23*	610.9*	584.8*	468.7*
24	615.0	589.6	471.4
25	619.4	594.8	474.3
26*	624.2*	600.8*	477.7*
27	629.8	607.7	481.8
28	636.6	616.1	487.2
29*	645.9*	627.3*	495.2*
30	663.0	647.4	511.2
Factors When 30 Ordinates Used			
	0.03269	0.03333	0.03938
Factors When 10 Ordinates Used			
	0.09806	0.10000	0.11814

* Insert in each column the transmittance value (%) corresponding to the wavelength shown. Where limited accuracy is sufficient, only the ordinates marked with an asterisk need be used.

of the centrifuged sample. With the vacuum still on, filter through the precoat and pass the filtrate to the waste flask until clear; then direct the clear-filtrate flow to the clean flask by means of the three-way stopcock and collect 25 ml for the transmittance determination.

b. Determination of light transmission characteristics: Thoroughly clean the 10-mm absorption cells with detergent and rinse with distilled water. Rinse twice with filtered sample, clean the external surfaces with lens paper, and fill the cell with filtered sample.

Determine the transmittance values (in percent) for the sample at each of the visible wavelength values presented in Table 204:I, using the 10 ordinates marked with an asterisk for fairly accurate work and all 30 ordinates for increased accuracy. Set the instrument to read 100% transmittance on the distilled

3. Calculation

a. Tabulate the transmittance values corresponding to the wavelengths shown in Columns X, Y, and Z in Table 204:I. Total each of the transmittance columns and multiply the totals by the appropriate factors (for 10 or 30 ordinates) shown at the bottom of the table, to obtain tristimulus values X, Y, and Z. The tristimulus value Y is the *percent luminance* of the waste.

b. Calculate the trichromatic coefficients x and y from the tristimulus values X, Y, and Z by the following equations:

$$x = \frac{X}{X+Y+Z}$$

$$y = \frac{Y}{X+Y+Z}$$

Locate point (x, y) on one of the chromaticity diagrams in Figure 204:2 and determine the dominant wavelength (in nm) and the purity (in percent) directly from the diagram.

Determine the hue from the dominant-wavelength value, according to the ranges in Table 204:II.

4. Expression of Results

Express the color characteristics (at pH 7.6 and at the original pH) in terms of *dominant wavelength* (nm, to the nearest unit), *hue* (e.g., blue, blue-green, etc.), *luminance* (percent, to the nearest tenth), and *purity* (percent, to the nearest unit). Report the type of instrument (i.e., spectrophotometer), the number of selected ordinates (10 or 30), and the spectral band width (nm) that were used.

TABLE 204:II. COLOR HUES FOR DOMINANT-WAVELENGTH RANGES

Wavelength Range nm	Hue
400–465	violet
465–482	blue
482–497	blue-green
497–530	green
530–575	greenish yellow
575–580	yellow
580–587	yellowish orange
587–598	orange
598–620	orange-red
620–700	red
400–530c	blue-purple
530c–700	red-purple

204 C.   Tristimulus Filter Method

1. General Discussion

Three special tristimulus light filters, combined with a specific light source and photoelectric cell in a filter photometer, may be used to obtain color data suitable for routine control purposes.

The percentage of tristimulus light transmitted by the solution is determined for each of the three filters. The transmittance values are then converted to trichromatic coefficients and color characteristic values.

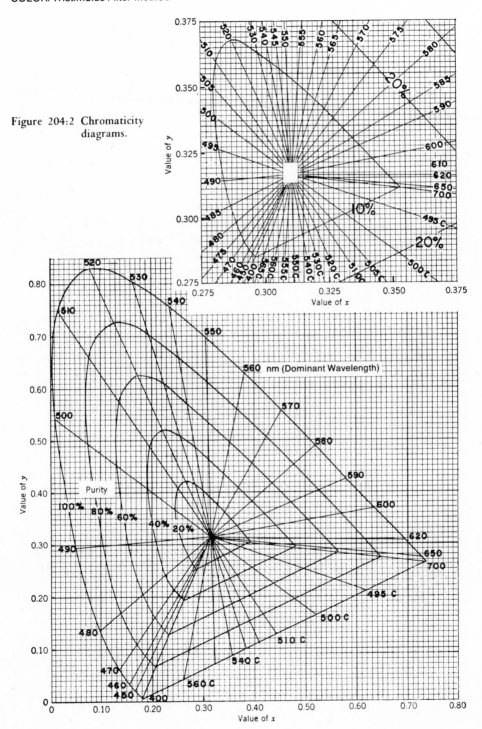

Figure 204:2 Chromaticity diagrams.

2. Apparatus

a. Filter photometer.*

b. Filter photometer light source: Tungsten lamp at a color temperature of 3,000 C.†

c. Filter photometer photoelectric cells, 1 cm.‡

d. Tristimulus filters: Corning CS–3–107 (No. 1), CS–4–98 (No. 2), and CS–5–70 (No. 3).

e. Filtration system: See Section 204 B.1b and Figure 204:1

3. Procedure

a. Preparation of sample: See Section 204 B.2*a*.

b. Determination of light transmission characteristics: Thoroughly clean (with detergent) and rinse the 1-cm absorption cells with distilled water. Rinse each absorption cell twice with filtered sample, clean the external surfaces with lens paper, and fill the cell with filtered sample.

Place a distilled water blank in another cell and use it to set the instrument at

---

*Fisher Electrophotometer or equivalent.

†General Electric lamp No. 1719 (at 6 V) or equivalent.

‡General Electric photovoltaic cell, Type PV-1, or equivalent.

100% transmittance. Determine the percentage of light transmission through the sample for each of the three tristimulus light filters, with the filter photometer lamp intensity switch in a position equivalent to 4 V on the lamp.

4. Calculation

a. Determine the luminance value directly as the percentage transmittance value obtained with the No. 2 tristimulus filter.

b. Calculate the tristimulus values X, Y, and Z from the percentage transmittance (T_1, T_2, T_3) for filters No. 1, 2, 3, as follows:

$$X = T_3 \times 0.06 + T_1 \times 0.25$$
$$Y = T_2 \times 0.316$$
$$Z = T_3 \times 0.374$$

Calculate and determine the trichromatic coefficients x and y, dominant wavelength, hue, and purity in the manner described in Section 204B.3*b* above.

5. Expression of Results

The results are expressed in the manner prescribed in Section 204B.4. Except for very exact work, this method gives results very similar to the more accurate Method B.

204 D.   Bibliography

HAZEN, A. 1892. A new color standard for natural waters. *Amer. Chem. J.* 14:300.

HAZEN, A. 1896. The measurement of the colors of natural waters. *J. Amer. Chem. Soc.* 18:264.

Measurement of Color and Turbidity in Water. 1902. U.S. Geol. Surv., Div. Hydrog. Circ. 8, Washington, D.C.

HARDY, A.C. 1936. Handbook of Colorimetry. Technology Press, Boston, Mass.

OPTICAL SOCIETY OF AMERICA. 1943. Committee Report. The concept of color. *J. Opt. Soc. Amer.* 33:544.

RUDOLFS, W. & W.D. HANLON. 1951. Color in industrial wastes. *Sewage Ind. Wastes* 23:1125.

JONES, H. et al. 1952. The Science of Color. Thomas Y. Crowell Co., New York, N.Y.

JUDD, D.D. 1952. Color in Business, Science, and Industry. John Wiley & Sons, New York, N.Y.

PALIN, A.T. 1955. Photometric determination of the colour and turbidity of water. *Water Water Eng.* 59:341.

CHRISTMAN, R.F. & M. GHASSEMI. 1966. Chemical nature of organic color in water. *J. Amer. Water Works Ass.* 58:723.

GHASSEMI, M. & R.F. CHRISTMAN. 1968. Properties of the yellow organic acids of natural waters. *Limnol. Oceanogr.* 13:583.

205 CONDUCTIVITY

Conductivity is a numerical expression of the ability of a water sample to carry an electric current. This number depends on the total concentration of the ionized substances dissolved in the water and the temperature at which the measurement is made. The mobility of each of the various dissolved ions, their valences, and their actual and relative concentrations affect conductivity.

An aqueous system containing ions will conduct an electric current. In a direct-current field the positive ions migrate toward the negative electrode, while the negatively charged ions migrate toward the positive electrode. Most inorganic acids, bases, and salts (such as hydrochloric acid, sodium carbonate, and sodium chloride) are relatively good conductors. Conversely, molecules of such organic compounds as sucrose and benzene that do not dissociate in aqueous solution conduct a current very poorly, if at all.

Freshly distilled water has a conductivity of 0.5 to 2 μmhos/cm, increasing after a few weeks of storage to 2 to 4 μmhos/cm. This increase is caused mainly by absorption of atmospheric carbon dioxide, and, to a lesser extent, ammonia.

The conductivity of potable waters in the United States ranges generally from 50 to 1,500 μmhos/cm. The conductivity of domestic wastewater reflects to a degree the characteristics of the water supply serving the district. Some industrial wastes may have conductivities well in excess of 10,000 μmhos/cm.

Monitoring equipment is useful for conductivity measurements of water and wastewater. Commercially available instruments provide essentially continuous records of the conductivity of flowing streams. Conductivity can be recorded either by single-parameter instruments or by more elaborate monitors that also measure and record other variables such as dissolved oxygen, pH, and temperature of the stream. The sensor (or cell) may be placed in a tank through which water is pumped continuously, or placed directly in the flowing stream, depending on conditions at the monitoring site.

In order to obtain reliable results, monitoring instruments must be carefully maintained and frequently checked. Procedures for doing so depend on the nature of the streams being monitored and the characteristics of the instruments; they cannot be prescribed here in detail. Periodic comparisons of the indicated conductivity with laboratory determinations will show how frequently the sensor and intake must be cleaned. Most problems in obtaining good records with monitoring equipment are related to electrode fouling and to inadequate circulation of solutions being measured.

A number of practical applications are made of conductivity measurements, as follows:

a. Conductivity is at least as good a criterion of the degree of mineralization as the more commonly used "total dissolved solids" for assessing the effect of diverse ions on chemical equilibria, physiological effect on plants or animals, corrosion rates, etc.

b. The purity of distilled and deionized water can be checked by the determination.

c. Variations in the dissolved mineral concentration of raw water or wastewater samples can be noted quickly. Minor seasonal variations found in reservoir waters contrast sharply with the daily fluctuations in some polluted river waters. Wastewater containing significant trade wastes also may show a considerable daily variation.

d. Conductivity measurements allow an estimate of the sample size that should be used for the common chemical determinations. They also offer a means for checking the results of a chemical analysis, as described in the Introduction, Section 104C.2.

e. Conductivity measurements make possible the determination of the amount of ionic reagent needed in certain precipitation and neutralization reactions, the end point being denoted by a change in the slope of the curve resulting from plotting conductivity against buret readings.

f. The concentration (in mg/l) of dissolved ionic matter in a sample often may be estimated by multiplying the conductivity (in μmhos/cm) by an empirical factor. This factor may vary from 0.55 to 0.9, depending on the soluble components of the water and on the temperature of the measurement. Relatively high factors may be required for saline or boiler waters, whereas lower factors may apply where considerable hydroxide or free acid is present. Even though sample evaporation results in the change of bicarbonate to carbonate, an empirical factor is often derived for a comparatively constant water supply by dividing the dissolved residue by the conductivity. An approximation of the milliequivalents per liter of either cations or anions in some waters may be obtained by multiplying the conductivity (in μmhos/cm) by 0.01.

1. General Discussion

The standard unit of electrical resistance (R) is the ohm (Ω). The standard unit of electrical conductance (G) is its inverse, the siemens (or the mho, $\mho$). Resistivity is the resistance measured between opposite faces of a rectangular prism and is reported in ohms $\times$ unit length. Conductivity is the reciprocal of resistivity and is reported in siemens per unit length. Inasmuch as specific conductance is defined as the conductance of a conductor 1 cm long and 1 cm^2 in cross-sectional area, it is properly reported in siemens and is numerically identical to *conductivity* in mhos/cm. For water analyses, the siemens is inconveniently large, and results are reported in microsiemens. Conductivity may also be expressed in millisiemens/meter, which is equal to 10 μmhos/cm. Report results of water tests as conductivity in terms of micromhos/centimeter.

A conductance cell and a Wheatstone bridge may be used for measuring the electrical resistance of the sample or the conductance may be measured as the ratio of electrical current through the cell to the applied voltage.

Electrolytic conductivity (unlike metallic conductivity) increases with temperature at a rate of approximately 2%/degree C. Significant errors can result from inaccurate temperature measurement. Potassium chloride solutions have a temperature coefficient of conductivity that is lower than that of the typical potable water. Sodium chloride, on the other hand, has a temperature coefficient that closely approximates that found in most waters from wells and surface sources. Note that each ion has a different temperature coefficient; thus, for precise work, the conductivity must be determined at 25.00 C.

2. Apparatus

a. *Self-contained conductance instruments:* These are commercially available. Most of these instruments consist of a source of alternating current, a Wheatstone bridge, a null indicator, and a conductivity cell. Other instruments measure the ratio of alternating current through the cell to voltage across it and have the advantage of a linear reading of conductance. The instrument chosen should be capable of measuring conductivity with an error not exceeding 1% or 1 μmho/cm, whichever is the greater.

b. *Thermometer*, capable of being read to the nearest 0.1 C and covering

the range 23 C to 27 C. An electrical thermometer having a small thermistor sensing element is convenient because of its rapid response.

c. *Conductivity cell*:

1) Platinum-electrode type: Conductivity cells containing platinized electrodes are available in either the pipet or the immersion form. Cell choice will depend on the expected range of conductivity and the resistance range of the instrument. Experimentally check the range for complete instrument assembly by comparing the instrumental results with the true conductances of the potassium chloride solutions listed in Table 205:I. Clean new cells with chromic-sulfuric acid cleaning mixture and platinize the electrodes before use. Subsequently, clean and replatinize them

TABLE 205:I. CONDUCTANCE OF POTASSIUM CHLORIDE SOLUTIONS AT 25 C*

Concen-tration M	Conductance $\mu mhos/cm$	
	Equivalent	Specific
0	149.85	
0.0001	149.43	14.94†
0.0005	147.81	73.90
0.001	146.95	147.0
0.005	143.55	717.8
0.01	141.27	1,413
0.02	138.34	2,767
0.05	133.37	6,668
0.1	128.96	12,900
0.2	124.08	24,820
0.5	117.27	58,640
1	111.87	111,900

*Data drawn from Robinson & Stokes.[1]
†Computed from equation given in Lind et al.[2]

whenever the readings become erratic, when a sharp end point cannot be obtained, or when inspection shows that any of the platinum black has flaked off. To platinize, prepare a solution of 1 g chloroplatinic acid (platinum chloride) and 12 mg lead acetate in 100 ml water. A stronger solution will reduce the time required to platinize electrodes and may be used when time is a factor, e.g., when the cell constant is 1.0/cm or more. Immerse the electrodes in this solution and connect both to the negative terminal of a 1.5-V dry cell battery. Connect the positive side of the battery to a piece of platinum wire and dip the wire into the solution. The amount of current should be such that only a small quantity of gas is evolved. Continue the electrolysis until both cell electrodes are coated with platinum black. The platinizing solution may be saved for subsequent use. Rinse the electrodes thoroughly and when not in use keep them immersed in distilled water.

2) Nonplatinum-electrode type: Conductivity cells containing electrodes constructed from durable common metals (stainless steel among others) are widely used for continuous monitoring and field studies. Calibrate such cells by comparing the conductivity of the water being tested with the results obtained with a laboratory instrument. Determination of the cell constant with KCl may introduce a significant error if the cell and instrument are not properly designed and mated.

3. Reagents

a. Conductivity water: Pass distilled water through a mixed-bed deionizer, discarding the first 1,000 ml. The conductivity of this water should be less than 1 μmho/cm.

b. Standard potassium chloride, 0.0100M; Dissolve 745.6 mg anhydrous KCl in conductivity water and make up to 1,000 ml at 25 C. This is the standard reference solution, which at 25 C has a specific conductance of 1,413 μmhos/cm. It is satisfactory for most waters when using a cell with a constant between 1 and 2. For other cell constants, stronger or weaker potassium chloride solutions listed in Table 205:1 will be needed. Store in glass-stoppered pyrex bottles.

4. Procedure

a. Determination of cell constant: Rinse the conductivity cell with at least three portions of 0.01 *M* KCl solution. Adjust the temperature of a fourth portion to 25.0±0.1 C. Measure the resistance of this portion and note the temperature. Compute the cell constant, C:

$$C = \frac{0.001413\, R_{KCl}}{1+0.0200(t-25)}$$

b. Conductivity measurement: Rinse the cell with one or more portions of the sample to be tested. Adjust the temperature of a final portion of the sample to 25.0±0.1 C. Measure the resistance of the sample and note the temperature.

5. Calculation

The following directions apply to the commonly used Wheatstone bridge instruments. Instruments may be calibrated to read conductivity (or conductance) directly; in that case follow the manufacturer's instructions.

a. The conductivity G, in μmhos /cm, is given by the equation:

$$G = \frac{1{,}000{,}000\, C}{R[1+0.0200(t-25)]}$$

where

R = resistance of the sample, ohms,
C = cell constant, and
t = temperature, degrees C.

6. Precision and Accuracy

Three synthetic unknown samples were tested with the following results:

Conductivity $\mu mhos/cm$	No. of Results	Relative Standard Deviation %	Relative Error %
147.0	117	8.6	9.4
303.0	120	7.8	1.9
228.0	120	8.4	3.0

With satisfactory equipment, a quali-

fied analyst should be able to obtain results within 1% of the true value.

7. References

1. ROBINSON, R. A. & R. H. STOKES. 1959. Electrolyte Solutions, 2nd ed. Academic Press, New York, p. 466.
2. J. E. LIND, J. J. ZWOLENIK & R. M. FUOSS. 1959. Calibration of conductance cells at 25 C with aqueous solutions of potassium chloride. J. Amer. Chem. Soc. 81:1557.

8. Bibliography

JONES, G. & B. C. BRADSHAW. 1933. The measurement of the conductance of electrolytes. V: A redetermination of the conductance of standard potassium chloride solutions in absolute units. J. Amer. Chem. Soc. 55:1780.

206   ODOR

Odor and taste are known as the "chemical senses" since they depend on actual contact of the stimulating substance with the appropriate human receptor cell. No physical or chemical theory adequately describes the mechanism of odor, nor is the purpose of this complex sense in mankind readily apparent.

Odor is recognized[1] as a quality factor affecting water in several ways: acceptability of drinking water (and foods prepared therefrom), tainting of fish and other aquatic organisms, and aesthetics of recreational waters. Most organic and some inorganic chemicals contribute taste or odor. These chemicals may originate from municipal and industrial waste discharges, natural sources (such as decomposition of vegetable matter), or from associated microbial activity. Uncontaminated water could not have an odor or taste because water is a neu-

tral medium always present in the moist membranes where the odor and taste of other chemicals are perceived.

As awareness of the risks to health arising from chemical contaminants is expanded, it becomes prudent to consider whether the chemical senses do not serve mankind as a warning against hazard. This is increasingly significant as there is technological expansion in varieties and quantities of waste materials, more demands for water disposal of former air pollutants, and continuous population growth with consequently increased reuse of available water supplies. Besides domestic consumers, process industries such as food, beverage, and pharmaceutical manufacturers require water essentially free of tastes and odors.

Some substances, such as many inorganic salts, produce taste without odor and are evaluated by a Taste Test (Section 211). Many other sensations ascribed to the sense of taste are actually odors, even though the sensation is not noticed until the material is taken into the mouth. Despite rapid strides in relating sensory qualities to chemical analyses,[2] most odors are too complex and are detectable at concentrations too low to permit their definition by isolating and determining the odor-producing chemicals. The ultimate odor-testing device is the human nose. Odor tests are performed to arrive at qualitative descriptions and approximate quantitative measurements of odor intensity. The method for intensity measurement presented here is the *threshold odor* test, based on a method of limits.[2] *Suprathreshold* methods are not included here.

Taste and odor tests are useful as a check on the quality of raw and finished water for various uses, for control of odor through the treatment plant and the determination of treatment dosages, as a test of the effectiveness of different kinds of treatment, and as a means of tracing the source of contamination.

1. General Discussion

a. Principle: The sample is diluted with odor-free water until a dilution is found that is of the least definitely perceptible odor to each tester. Individuals have widely varying sensitivities to odor, and even the same person will not be consistent in the concentrations detectable from day to day. Panels of not less than five persons, and preferably 10 or more, are recommended to overcome the variability caused by using one observer.[2] Some investigators have sought to overcome the problems involved in

using one or two observers, or to compare the sensitivities of different individuals, by using a calibrating standard odor substance such as *n*-butyl alcohol. Panels with a sufficient number of observers eliminate the necessity for a calibrating standard.

b. Application: This threshold method is applicable to samples ranging from nearly odorless natural waters to industrial wastes with threshold numbers in the thousands. There are no intrinsic difficulties with the highly odorous samples because they are reduced in concentration proportionately before being presented to the test observers.

c. Qualitative descriptions: A satisfactory system for characterizing odor has not been developed despite efforts over more than a century. Previous editions of this book contained a table of odor descriptions proposed as a guide in expressing odor quality. The reader may continue to encounter the obsolete standard abbreviations of that table. The 12th Edition presents an explanation of such terms.

d. Sampling and storage: Collect samples for odor testing in glass bottles with glass or teflon-lined closures. Complete tests as soon as possible after sample collection. If storage is necessary, collect at least 500 ml of sample in a bottle filled to the top; refrigerate, making sure that no extraneous odors can be drawn into this sample when the water cools. Do not use plastic containers for odor samples.

e. Dechlorination: Most tap waters and some wastewaters are chlorinated. It is often desirable to determine the odor of the chlorinated sample as well as that of the same sample after dechlorination. Dechlorinate with arsenite or thiosulfate in exact stoichiometric quantity as described under Nitrogen (Ammonia), Section 418A.3*d*2) and 4). CAUTION—*Do not use arsenic compounds as dechlorinating agents on samples to be tasted.*

f. Temperature: Threshold odor values vary with temperature. For most tap waters and raw water sources, a sample temperature of 60 C will permit the detection of odors that might otherwise be missed; 60 C is the standard temperature for hot threshold tests. For some purposes—because the odor is too fleeting or there is excessive heat sensation—the hot odor test may not be applicable; where experience shows that a lower temperature is needed, use a standard test temperature of 40 C. For special purposes, other temperatures may be used. *Always report the temperature at which observations are made.*

2. Apparatus

To assure reliable threshold measurements, all glassware must be odor-free. Clean the glassware shortly before use with nonodorous soap and acid cleaning solution, and rinse it with odor-free water. Reserve the glassware used in threshold testing for that purpose only. Do not use rubber, cork, or plastic stoppers. Do not use narrow-mouth vessels for running odor tests.

a. Sample bottles, glass-stoppered or with teflon-lined closures, to hold the original samples.

b. Constant-temperature bath: A water bath or electric hot plate capable of temperature control of ±1 C for odor tests at elevated temperatures. The bath must not contribute any odor to the odor flasks.

c. Odor flasks: Glass-stoppered, 500-ml (¶ 32) erlenmeyer flasks, to hold sample dilutions during testing.

d. Pipets:

1) *Transfer and volumetric pipets or graduated cylinders:* 200-, 100-, 50-, and 25-ml.

2) *Measuring pipets:* 10-ml, graduated in tenths.

e. Thermometer: Zero to 110 C, chemical or metal-stem dial type.

3. Odor-Free Water

a. Sources: Prepare odor-free dilution water as needed by filtration through a bed of activated carbon. Most tap waters are suitable for the preparation of odor-free water, except that it is necessary to check the filtered water for residual chlorine, unusual salt concentrations, or unusually high or low pH. All these may affect some odorous samples. Where supplies are adequate use distilled water as a source for odor-free water. A convenient odor-free water generator may be made as shown in Figures 206:1 and 206:2.

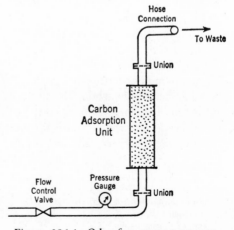

Figure 206:1. Odor-free-water generator.

b. *Odor-free water generator:**

1) *Pyrex pipe*, 3-in. diam, 18-in. length.

2) *Asbestos inserts* (two), for 3-in. pipe.

3) *Flange sets* (two), for 3-in. pipe.

4) *Neoprene gaskets†* (two), 1/4-in. thickness, with 3-in. hole slotted to 3/8-in. depth to take screen. Drill 3 holes, 5/16-in. diam, to match flange.

5) *Stainless-steel screens†* (two), 40-mesh, 3-3/4-in. diam.

6) *Brass plates* (two), 3/16-in. thickness×6-1/4-in. diam. Tap hole in center for 3/4-in. nipple. Score a circular groove (1/16-in. depth×1/16-in. width and 3-3/8-in. diam) into the plate to prevent leakage. Drill 3 holes, 5/16-in. diam, to coincide with the flange.

7) *Galvanized nipples* (two), 3/4-in. ×3 in. Thread nipple into brass plate and weld in place.

8) *Aluminum bolts and nuts* (six), 5/16-in.×2 in., for holding assembly together.

9) *Activated carbon*, such as Nuchar (WV-G 12 to 40 mesh grain size‡ or Filtrasorb 200 14 to 40 mesh grain size.§

Attach the end fittings of the adsorption unit to the glass pipe. Draw up the bolts evenly, holding the brass plate to the glass pipe in order to get a good seal on the gasket. Add carbon. Be sure the unit is full. Tap the cylinder gently but do not tamp the carbon. Attach the end fittings on the adsorption unit and install

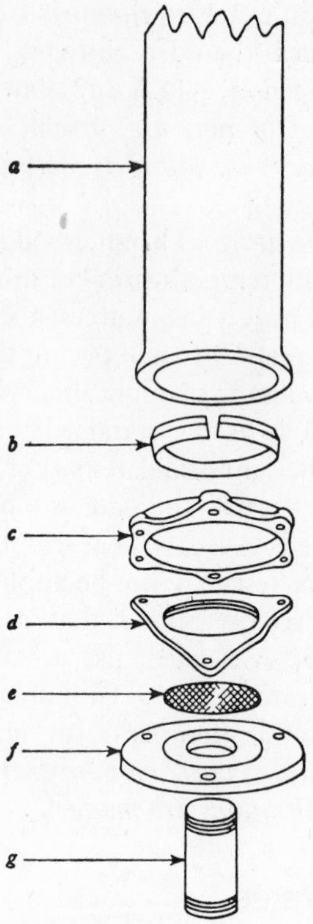

Figure 206:2. End assembly of odor-free-water generator.

on the water source as shown in Figure 206:1.

Avoid organic contaminants in making pipe joints or other plumbing. Use Teflon-type tape or a paste made by mixing red lead powder and water. Clean all new fittings with kerosene and follow with a detergent wash. Rinse thoroughly with clean water.

c. *Generator operation:* Pass tap or distilled water through the odor-free water generator at a rate of 0.1 l/min. When the generator is first started, flush to remove the carbon fines before the odor-free water is used.

---

*For approximate metric dimensions in centimeters multiply dimensions in inches by 2.54.

†Such as can be obtained from Netherland Rubber Co., Cincinnati, Ohio.

‡Westvaco, Covington, Va.

§Calgon Corp., Pittsburgh, Pa.

Check the quality of water obtained from the odor-free water generator daily at 40 C and 60 C before use. The life of the carbon will vary with the condition and amount of the water filtered. Subtle odors of biological origin are often found if moist carbon filters stand idle between test periods. Detection of odor in the water coming through the carbon indicates that a change of carbon is needed.

4. Procedure

a. Precautions: Carefully select by preliminary tests the persons to make taste or odor tests. Although extreme sensitivity is not required, exclude insensitive persons and concentrate on observers who have a sincere interest in the test. Avoid extraneous odor stimuli such as those caused by smoking and eating prior to the test or those contributed by scented soaps, perfumes, and shaving lotions. Insure that the tester is free from colds or allergies that affect odor response. Limit the frequency of tests to a number below the fatigue level by frequent rests in an odor-free atmosphere. Keep the room in which the tests are conducted free from distractions, drafts, and other odor. If necessary, set aside a special odor-free room ventilated by air that is filtered through activated carbon and maintained at a constant comfortable temperature and humidity.[3]

For precise work use a panel of five or more testers. Do not allow the persons making the odor measurements to prepare the samples or to know the dilution concentrations being evaluated. Familiarize testers with the procedure before they participate in a panel test. Present the most dilute sample first to avoid tiring the senses with the concentrated sample. Keep the temperature of the samples during testing within 1 C of the temperature specified for the test.

Since many raw and waste waters are colored or have a decided turbidity that will bias the odor-testing results, use opaque or darkly colored odor flasks, such as red actinic erlenmeyer flasks, to conceal these variations.

b. Characterization: As part of the threshold test or as a separate test, direct each observer to describe in his own words the characteristic odor of the sample tested. Compile the consensus that may appear among the panel members and that affords a clue to the origin of the odorous pollutant. The value of the characterization test increases as the observers become more experienced with a particular category of odor, such as algae, chlorophenol, or mustiness.

c. Threshold measurement:[||] The ratio by which the odor-bearing sample has to be diluted with odor-free water for the odor to be just detectable by the odor test is the "threshold odor number," designated by the abbreviation T. O. N. Bring the total volume of sample and odor-free water to 200 ml in each test. Follow the dilutions and record the corresponding threshold numbers presented in Table 206:I. If a total volume other than the 200 ml specified is

___

[||] There are numerous methods of arranging and presenting samples for odor determinations. The methods offered here are believed to be practical and economical of time and personnel and are adequate for the problems encountered at most water plants. If extensive tests are planned and statistical analysis of data is required, the experimenter should become familiar with the triangle test and the methods that have been used extensively by flavor and allied industries.[4]

TABLE 206:I. THRESHOLD ODOR NUMBERS
CORRESPONDING TO VARIOUS DILUTIONS

Sample Volume Diluted to 200 ml ml	Threshold Odor No.	Sample Volume Diluted to 200 ml ml	Threshold Odor No.
200	1	12	17
140	1.4	8.3	24
100	2	5.7	35
70	3	4	50
50	4	2.8	70
35	6	2	100
25	8	1.4	140
17	12	1.0	200

used, compute the threshold number thus:

$$T. O. N. = \frac{A+B}{A}$$

where A = ml sample and B = ml odor-free water. Place the proper volume of odor-free water in the flask first; then pipet the sample into the water, mix by swirling flask, and proceed as follows:

1) Determine the approximate range of the threshold number by adding 200 ml, 50 ml, 12 ml, and 2.8 ml of sample to separate 500-ml glass-stoppered erlenmeyer flasks containing odor-free water to make a total volume of 200 ml. Use a separate flask containing only odor-free water as the reference for comparison. Heat the dilutions and the reference to the temperature desired for running the test.

2) Shake the flask containing the odor-free water, remove the stopper, and sniff the vapors. Test the sample containing the least amount of odor-bearing water in the same way. If odor can be detected in this dilution, prepare more dilute samples as described in ¶5) below. If odor cannot be detected in the

first dilution, repeat the above procedure, using the sample containing the next higher concentration of the odor-bearing water, and continue this process until odor is clearly detected.

3) Based on the results obtained in the preliminary test, prepare a set of dilutions using Table 206:II as a guide. Prepare the five dilutions shown in the appropriate column, plus the three next most concentrated in the next column to the right in Table 206:II. For example, if odor was first noted in the flask containing 50 ml sample in the preliminary test then prepare flasks containing 50, 35, 25, 17, 12, 8.3, 5.7, and 4.0 ml sample, each diluted to 200 ml with odor-free water. This array is necessary to challenge the range of sensitivities of the entire panel of subjects.

Insert two or more blanks in the series near the expected threshold, but avoid any repeated pattern. Do not let the observer know which dilutions are odorous and which are blanks. Instruct the observer to smell each flask in sequence, beginning with the least concentrated sample, until odor is detected with certainty.

TABLE 206:II. DILUTIONS FOR VARIOUS ODOR
INTENSITIES

Sample Volume in Which Odor First Noted			
200 ml	50 ml	12 ml	2.8 ml
Volume of Sample to be Diluted to 200 ml ml			
200	50	12	(Inter-
140	35	8.3	mediate
100	25	5.7	dilution)
70	17	4.0	
50	12	2.8	

4) Record the observations by indicating whether odor is noted in each test flask. For example:

ml Sample Diluted to 200 ml	12	0	17	25	0	35	50
Response	-	-	-	+	-	+	+

5) If the sample being tested requires more extensive dilution than is provided by Table 206:II, prepare an intermediate dilution consisting of 20 ml sample diluted to 200 ml with odor-free water. Use this dilution for the threshold determination. Multiply the T. O. N. obtained by 10 to correct for the intermediate dilution. In rare cases more than one tenfold intermediate dilution step may be required.

5. Calculation

The threshold odor number is the dilution ratio at which taste or odor is just detectable. In the example above, ¶4) preceding, the first detectable odor occurred when 25 ml sample was diluted to 200 ml. Thus, the threshold is 200 divided by 25, yielding a result of 8. Table 206:I lists the threshold numbers that correspond to common dilutions.

The smallest threshold number that can be observed is 1, as in the case where the odor flask contains 200 ml undiluted sample. If no odor is detected at this concentration, report "No Odor Observed" instead of a threshold number. (In special applications, fractional threshold numbers have been calculated.[5])

Anomalous responses sometimes occur; a low concentration may be called positive and a higher concentration in the series may be called negative. In such a case, the threshold may properly be designated as that point of detection after which no further anomalies occur. For instance:

Increasing   concentration   →

Response: c   c   i   c   i   c   c

↓
Threshold

where:

i signifies incorrect response ("no odor" in sample or "odor" in blank), and

c signifies correct response ("odor" in sample or "no odor" in blank).

Use appropriate statistical methods to calculate the most probable average threshold from large numbers of panel results. For most purposes, the threshold of a group can be expressed as the geometric mean of the individual thresholds.

6. Interpretation of Results

A threshold number is not a precise value. In the case of the single observer, it represents a judgment at the time of testing. Panel results are more meaningful because individual differences have less influence on the result. One or two observers can develop useful data if comparison with larger panels has been made to check their sensitivity. Do not make comparisons of data from time to time or place to place unless all test conditions have been standardized carefully and there is some basis for comparison of observer intensities.

7. References

1. U.S. ENVIRONMENTAL PROTECTION AGENCY. 1973. Proposed Criteria for Water Quality. Vol. 1, Washington, D.C.

2. AMERICAN SOCIETY FOR TESTING AND MATERIALS COMMITTEE E-18. 1968. STP 433, Basic principles of sensory evaluation; STP 434, Manual on sensory testing methods; STP 440. Correlation of subjective-objective methods in the study of odors and taste. ASTM, Philadelphia, Pa.

3. BAKER, R.A. 1962. Critical evaluation of ol-

factory measurement. *J. Water Pollut. Control Fed.* 34:582.

4. Flavor Research and Food Acceptance. 1958. Reinhold Publishing Corp., New York, N.Y.

5. ROSEN, A.A., J.B. PETER & F.M. MIDDLETON. 1962. Odor thresholds of mixed organic chemicals. *J. Water Pollut. Control Fed.* 34:7.

8. Bibliography

HULBERT, R. & D. FEBEN. 1941. Studies on accuracy of threshold odor value. *J. Amer. Water Works Ass.* 33:1945.

SPAULDING, C.H. 1942. Accuracy and application of threshold odor test. *J. Amer. Water Works Ass.* 34:877.

THOMAS, H.A., JR. 1943. Calculation of threshold odor. *J. Amer. Water Works Ass.* 35:751.

MONCRIEFF, R.W. 1946. The Chemical Senses. John Wiley & Sons, New York, N.Y.

CARTWRIGHT, L.C., C.T. SNELL & P.H. KELLY. 1952. Organoleptic panel testing as a research tool. *Anal. Chem.* 24:503.

LAUGHLIN, H.F. 1954. Palatable level with the threshold odor test. *Taste Odor Control J.* 20: No. 8 (Aug.).

SECHENOV, I.M. 1956 and 1958. Problem of hygenic standards for waters simultaneously polluted with harmful substances [in Russian]. *Gig. Sanit.* Nos. 10 and 8.

SHELLENBERGER, R.D. 1958. Procedures for determining threshold odor concentrations in aqueous solutions. *Taste Odor Control J.* 24: No. 5 (May).

Taste and Odor Control in Water Purification, 2nd ed. 1959. West Virginia Pulp & Paper Co. Industrial Chemical Sales Division, New York. [Contains 1,063 classified references.]

BAKER, R.A. 1961. Problems of tastes and odors. *J. Water Pollut. Control Fed.* 33:1099.

LAUGHLIN, H.F. 1962. Influence of temperature in threshold odor evaluation. *Taste Odor Control J.* 28: No. 10 (Oct.).

BAKER, R.A. 1963. Odor effects of aqueous mixtures of organic chemicals. *J. Water Pollut. Control Fed.* 35:728.

ROSEN, A.A., R.T. SKEEL & M.B. ETTINGER. 1963. Relationship of river water odor to specific organic contaminants. *J. Water Pollut. Control Fed.* 35:777.

STAFF REPORT. 1963. The threshold odor test. *Taste Odor Control J.* 29: Nos. 6, 7, 8 (June, July, Aug.).

WRIGHT, R.H. 1964. The Science of Smell. Basic Books, New York, N.Y.

AMERINE, M.A., R.M. PANGBORN & E.B. ROESSLER. 1965. Principles of Sensory Evaluation of Food. Academic Press, New York, N.Y.

ROSEN, A.A. 1970. Report of research committee on tastes and odors. *J. Amer. Water Works Ass.* 62:59.

SUFFET, I.H. & S. SEGALL. 1971. Detecting taste and odor in drinking water. *J. Amer. Water Works Ass.* 63:605.

GELDARD, F.A. 1972. The Human Senses. John Wiley & Sons, New York, N.Y.

STAHL, W.H., ed. 1973. Compilation of Odor and Taste Threshold Values Data. Amer. Soc. Testing & Materials Data Ser. DS 48, Philadelphia, Pa.

AMERICAN SOCIETY FOR TESTING AND MATERIALS. 1973 Annual Book of ASTM Standards. Part 23, D-1292-65, ASTM, Philadelphia, Pa.

207 OXYGEN TRANSFER

In several unit processes, air is introduced into wastewater for the oxidation of a variety of objectionable materials. The rate at which the supplied oxygen is dissolved in the aerating liquid is called oxygen transfer. Several methods for measuring oxygen transfer by steady- and non-steady-state technics have been reported in the literature. Presented here are the common technics used in obtaining the most reliable measurements of oxygen transfer. However, the results are still subject to interpretation because the measurements are affected by many variables such as the type of aeration equipment, aeration tank geometry, power input per unit volume, temperature, barometric pressure, altitude, and various liquid characteristics.

207 A. Oxygen Transfer in Water (TENTATIVE)

1. General Discussion

The fundamental concept of oxygen transfer theory in clean water is defined in the basic transfer equation as:

$$\frac{dc}{dt} = K_L a\ (C_S - C_L) \tag{1}$$

where

$\dfrac{dc}{dt}$ = oxygen transfer rate, mg/l/hr,

$K_L a$ = mass transfer coefficient, hr^{-1},

C_S = oxygen saturation concentration at test temperature and pressure, mg/l, and

C_L = oxygen concentration at time t, mg/l.

The rate at which oxygen enters solution is proportional to the degree of undersaturation, $(C_S - C_L)$, and to the area of the air-water interface per unit volume of water, a. The coefficient $K_L a$ depends on the hydrodynamics of the interfacial area, and increases with increased turbulence at the interface. The standard oxygen transfer rate is defined as the measured oxygen transfer rate when the liquid is clean water, the liquid temperature is 20 C, the initial dissolved oxygen concentration is zero, and the atmospheric pressure is 760 mm Hg.

The equation for the mass transfer coefficient $(K_L a)$ is derived from an integration of Equation 1:

$$K_L a = \frac{\ln(C_S - C_1) - \ln(C_S - C_2)}{t_2 - t_1} \tag{2}$$

The $K_L a$ term is a composite of the liquid film coefficient K_L and the specific interfacial area $(a = \dfrac{A}{V})$ available for mass transfer.

The oxygen saturation concentration C_S varies with the partial pressure of the oxygen in contact with the water and with the composition and temperature of the water. The value of C_S for clean water in contact with wet air at a total atmospheric pressure of 760 mm of mercury is given in Section 422, Oxygen (Dissolved), Table 422:I entitled "Solubility of Oxygen in Water Exposed to Water-Saturated Air." The value of C_S given in the table applies when the atmospheric pressure at the air-water interface is at 760 mm of mercury, which is the average barometric pressure at sea level. For other atmospheric pressures the saturation value is given by:

$$C_S = (C_S)_{760}\ \frac{P - p}{760 - p} \tag{3}$$

where C_S is the solubility at total pressure P mm, and p the saturated water vapor pressure at the temperature of the water. At an altitude of 1,520 m (5,000 ft) above sea level atmospheric pressure is only 84% of that at sea level. For surface aerators, the value of P that should be used is the atmospheric pressure at the particular location. For diffused air systems, the pressure of the air bubbles is greater than the atmospheric pressure, and C_S is commonly taken as the oxygen saturation value corresponding to the average partial pressure of oxygen in the bubbles. This can be taken as the pressure at mid-depth corrected for the reduction in the partial pressure of the oxygen in the bubbles.

The value of K_La depends on water temperature. The value of K_La at any temperature can be calculated from the equation:

$$(K_La)_T = (K_La)_{20} \times (1.024)^{T-20} \qquad (4)$$

where

$(K_La)_T$ = the value of K_La at T C, and
$(K_La)_{20}$ = the value of K_La at 20 C.

The value of K_La is also affected by the type of aeration equipment and the tank geometry. Some observers have discovered empirical relationships between K_La and depth and width or length of tank. However, there are no universally accepted factors that can be applied to all aerators and test conditions to establish a reproducible K_La. As a guide, the power applied to a unit volume ratio is widely used to compare one system to another. An acceptable range is 0.01 to 0.04 kW/cu m (0.05 to 0.20 hp/1,000 gal).

2. Apparatus

a. *Aeration equipment:* Any aeration device that can be operated at a constant power output for the duration of the test is acceptable. The volume of water under aeration should remain constant without any change in aerator submergence.

b. *Six submersible sample pumps* at various depths and at least at two loca-

tions. Small submersible lift pumps with a minimum detention time (5 to 10 sec) between pump and sample withdrawal are required.

c. *Dissolved oxygen meters and membrane electrodes* may be used in conjunction with the liquid samples removed for chemical determination of dissolved oxygen. The DO meter is also helpful as an indicator for starting the actual test and withdrawal of samples.

d. *Mixing tank* for the pre-mixing of chemicals before they are discharged into the aeration tank.

e. *Electrical instruments* such as ammeters and kilowatt meters to measure the drawn power.

f. *Sample bottles,* normally 300-ml BOD bottles. Fifty to 60 bottles are usually sufficient for one test.

g. *Glassware* used in the chemical determination of dissolved oxygen (Section 422).

3. Reagents

a. *Reagents required for the test* for dissolved oxygen (Section 422).

b. *Sodium sulfite,* Na_2SO_3, technical grade, 95 g/cu m (800 lb/mil gal) of water under aeration.

c. *Cobalt chloride,* $CoCl_2 \cdot 6H_2O$ or *cobalt sulfate,* 9.5 g/cu m (80 lb/mil gal) of water.

4. Collection of Samples

Collect samples in 300-ml BOD bottles at specified time intervals and seal them before analysis. Handle sample lines carefully to avoid entraining air bubbles. Begin sampling when the dissolved oxygen has just begun to rise from zero as indicated on the dissolved oxygen meter. Simultaneously withdraw at least six samples representing a cross section through a tank quadrant until the dissolved oxygen level reaches approximately 80 to 90 percent of saturation.

5. Procedure

a. Clean the basin for the aeration device thoroughly and fill it with fresh tap water.

b. Maintain temperature of the fresh water, if possible, at about 20 C.

c. Set the aeration device at the proper operating condition.

d. Install submersible sample pumps at selected locations in the tank. Base the minimum number and the location of the sampling points on the type of aeration device and the size and geometry of the tank. Take samples from all points simultaneously. To insure taking equal volumes of sample from all points, use pumps and lengths of tubing that are identical.

e. Dissolve a catalyst, cobalt chloride or cobalt sulfate, in the tank contents, with the aerator running to insure mixing.

f. While the aeration device is running, release the sodium sulfite solution into the tank contents. For a liquid having an initial dissolved oxygen concentration of 10 mg/l, approximately 95 g/cu m (800 lb/mil gal) of dry sodium sulfite will be required per test.

g. As the DO rises in the tank, draw samples at 1- to 10-min intervals, depending on the horsepower applied per unit of aeration tank volume. Select intervals to obtain at least six sets of samples between 10 and 70% saturation. Determine the DO in accordance with Section 422, and obtain an average for the six samples at each sampling time. A convenient equation for determining the required interval is given by:

$$t = \frac{100w}{OC} \times 1.024^{(20-T)} \qquad (5)$$

where:

t = sampling interval,
w = million pounds water in test tank,
OC = expected oxygenation capacity, lb/hr,
100 = constant for 70% saturation termination (use 133 for 80%), and
T = temperature, C.

h. If the individual DO values at time t are within 0.25 mg/l of the average DO value at time t, then one determination of K_La by a semilog plot of the average dissolved oxygen deficit vs. time is sufficient. If the individual DO values deviate by more than 0.25 mg/l from the average DO value at time t, prepare individual semilog plots for each sampling point and determine the value of K_La for each point. If the plots of the individual sampling points have parallel slopes, the deviation is a result of lag times in the sampling pumps and tubing and the test can be considered valid. Nonparallel slopes, however, indicate incomplete mixing; void the test results.

6. Calculation

Calculate the value of K_La from the equation according to the line of best fit by:

$$K_La = \frac{\ln(C_s-C_1)-\ln(C_s-C_2)}{t_2-t_1} \qquad (6)$$

where:

K_La = mass transfer coefficient, hr^{-1},
C_s = saturation value of water at test temperature and pressure, mg/l,
C_1 = initial oxygen concentration, mg/l, on line of best fit,

C_2 = final oxygen concentration, mg/l, on line of best fit,

t_1 = time (initial), hr, and

t_2 = time (final), hr.

The value of K_La is for temperature t. A correction to 20 C can be made by using Equation 4.

Compute the pounds of oxygen dissolved per unit time at standard conditions of tap water at 20 C and zero dissolved oxygen concentration by multiplying $(K_La)_{20}$ by the saturation in water at 20 C and 760 mm Hg times pounds of water in the tank in which the aerator was tested, with the above product divided by 10^6.

7. Precision and Accuracy

There is no standard against which the accuracy of the oxygen transfer test can be measured. The precision of the dissolved oxygen determination on which the oxygen transfer test is based is defined in Section 422, Oxygen (Dissolved). The application of statistical analysis to typical aeration data shows that a single K_La value is reproducible within ±15% of the established mean for tests involving multiple aerators in a single basin and ±8% for tests involving a single aerator in a single basin.

207 B.　Oxygen Transfer in Waste (Activated Sludge) (TENTATIVE)

1. General Discussion

The oxygen transfer rate under process conditions can be approximated if certain characteristics of the waste are known. Under process conditions, the rate of change of dissolved oxygen is given by the equation:

$$\frac{dc}{dt} = K_La(C_s-C_L)-r \qquad (1)$$

where r is the rate of oxygen utilization. If the process is operating at steady state (the DO is maintained at a constant level ($dc/dt=0$), the equation becomes

$$K_La = \frac{r}{C_s-C_L} \qquad (2)$$

Under wastewater conditions, the K_La is different from its value in clean water. Also, the saturation value, C_s, for

wastewater conditions will be different from clean water. The ratio of K_La for wastewater to that for clean water is designated α and the ratio of C_s for wastewater to that for clean water β.

In an activated sludge system, the mixed liquor solids exert a demand for oxygen. Therefore, the basic equation must be modified to include the uptake rate. The following equation results:

$$\frac{dc}{dt} = \alpha K_La(\beta C_s-C_L)-r \qquad (3)$$

where:

r = oxygen uptake rate, mg/l/hr,

α = ratio of K_La of mixed liquor to K_La at standard conditions, and

β = ratio of C_s in mixed liquor to C_s at standard conditions.

The value of K_La is dependent on the temperature of the waste. The K_La at any temperature can be determined by the equation

$$(K_La)_T = (K_La)_{20} \times (1.024)^{T-20} \quad (4)$$

2. Apparatus

a. *Model aerator suitable for bench-scale tests.* Mechanical or diffused aeration devices may be used. If a diffused air system is used, also use an air measuring rotometer for flow control. When a mechanical surface aerator is used, control the mixing intensity with a variable-speed motor and rheostat.

b. *Dissolved oxygen analyzer and membrane electrode* (self-stirring if desired). See Section 207A.2.

c. *Magnetic stirrer.*

d. *BOD bottles.*

3. Reagents

a. *Reagents required for the Winkler DO analysis* (see Section 422B for azide modification of DO test).

b. *Sodium sulfite and cobalt chloride* in quantities sufficient to deoxygenate the test basin. Nitrogen gas, rather than chemicals, also can be used for oxygen stripping.

4. Collection of Samples

Exercise care when sampling mixed liquor from the aeration tank so that the samples contain a residual dissolved oxygen of at least 0.5 to 1.0 mg/l.

5. Procedure

a. *Determination of uptake rate, r:* Measure the uptake rate, r, by removing a mixed liquor sample from the aeration tank, transferring it to a BOD bottle, and measuring (with a dissolved oxygen membrane electrode and under constant mixing) the change in dissolved oxygen with time.

b. *Determination of alpha, α:* Fill the container with a known volume of tap water and record the temperature. Deoxygenate the water with sodium sulfite and a cobalt catalyst (approximately 8 to 12 mg/l sodium sulfite per mg/l of dissolved oxygen) or preferably by stripping the oxygen from solution with nitrogen. Reaerate the water at a controlled rate. Record the dissolved oxygen concentration at various times at the predetermined level of liquid turbulence. Plot the oxygen deficit on semi-log paper and find the slope, which represents the coefficient K_La. Repeat this step for various mixing intensities and temperatures.

After deoxygenation and reaeration of tap water for the various test conditions, repeat the procedure with the same volume of wastewater. Because the factor is a function of the degree of biological stabilization, make every effort to use a wastewater similar to the mixed liquor anticipated in the prototype aeration basin.

Aerate the wastewater to increase the dissolved oxygen content by several milligrams per liter. The rate of dissolved oxygen increase is given by the equation:

$$\frac{dc}{dt} = (K_LaC_S - r) - K_LaC_L \quad (5)$$

Plot dc/dt versus C, to obtain a straight line with a slope equal to K_La.

Compare the K_La values determined for the wastewater to the K_La values for tap water at the same temperature and mixing conditions, and calculate the ratio. If the straight line on the plot is extrapolated to a C_L value of zero, the value of dc/dt will be equal to $K_L a C_s - r$. From a knowledge of C_s for the waste, compute the value of r. The foregoing procedure is based on the assumption that the uptake rate, r, does not change appreciably during the period of the test.

c. *Determination of beta, β*: Saturate a wastewater settled sample with oxygen by violent hand mixing in a half-full liter jar. Record temperature and withdraw the sample for dissolved oxygen measurement by the Winkler test or membrane electrode methods. Compare the measured dissolved oxygen to the handbook value for clean water at the same temperature to establish the beta factor. Beta factors are seldom less than 0.8.

6. Calculations

Calculate the actual oxygen transfer rate in waste as:

Actual oxygen transfer rate =
$$\frac{r \times \text{weight of liquid under aeration(lb)}}{10^6}$$

This gives pounds of oxygen dissolved per hour. Alternatively, calculate the actual oxygen transfer rate in the wastewater as:

Actual oxygen transfer rate =
$$\frac{(K_L a)_{measured} \times \text{weight of liquid under aeration} \times (C_s - C_L)}{10^6}$$

The two calculations should give comparable results.

7. Precision and Accuracy

The determination of the oxygen transfer rate under process conditions is not exact, and the results are only approximate. Exercise care in the estimation and measurement of all factors involved in the test.

207 C.   Bibliography

1. Aeration in Wastewater Treatment. 1970. Manual of Practice No. 5, Water Pollut. Control Fed., Washington, D.C.
2. GAMESON, A.L.H. & ROBERTSON, K.G. 1955. The solubility of oxygen in pure water and sea water. *J. Appl. Chem.* (Brit.) 5: 502.
3. ECKENFELDER, W.W., JR. & O.C. FORD. 1970. Water Pollution Control. Pemberton Press, New York, N.Y.

4. NOGAJ, R.J. & E. HURWITZ. 1963. Determination of aerator efficiency under process conditions. *Proc. 18th Ind. Waste Conf.*, Purdue Univ., p. 674.
5. GLOPPEN, R.C. & J.A. ROEBER. 1965. Rating and application of surface aerators. *TAPPI* 48: No. 12.

208 RESIDUE

The term "residue" refers to solid matter suspended or dissolved in water or wastewater. Residue may affect water or effluent quality adversely in a number of ways. Waters with high residue generally are of inferior palatability, and may induce an unfavorable physiological reaction in the transient consumer. Highly mineralized waters also are unsuitable for many industrial applications. For these reasons, a limit of 500 mg/l residue is desirable for drinking waters. Waters with very high levels of nonfiltrable residues may be aesthetically unsatisfactory for such purposes as bathing. Water and wastewater treatment processes that remove suspended particles help to minimize these problems.

1. Definitions

"Total residue" is the term applied to the material left in the vessel after evaporation of a sample and its subsequent drying in an oven at a defined temperature. Total residue includes "nonfiltrable residue," that is, the portion of the total residue retained by a filter, and "filtrable residue," the portion of the total residue that passes through the filter.

The earlier used terms "suspended" and "dissolved" (residue) correspond to nonfiltrable and filtrable residue, respectively. The chemical and physical nature of the material in suspension, the pore size of the filter, the area and thickness of the filter mat, and the amount and physical state of the materials deposited on it are the principal factors affecting the separation of nonfiltrable from filtrable residue. A method designed to control all the variables affecting filtration would be too cumbersome for practical use. It must be recognized, therefore, that residue determinations are not subject to the usual criteria of accuracy. The various types of residue are defined arbitrarily by the methods used for their determination, and these in turn represent practical approaches to what would otherwise be exceedingly complex operations.

2. Sources of Error and Variability

Analyses performed for some special purposes may demand deviation from the stated procedures in order to include with the measured residue an unusual constituent. Whenever such variations of technic are introduced they must be recorded and presented with the results.

The results for total, volatile, and fixed residues are subject to considerable error because of losses of volatile compounds during evaporation and of carbon dioxide and volatile minerals during ignition, and also because of the presence of calcium oxide in the ash. Results for residues high in oil or grease content may be of questionable value because of the difficulty of drying to constant weight in a reasonable time. By definition, results will not include materials that are volatile under the conditions of the procedure.

In the interpretation of results, these possible sources of error must be recognized.

The temperature at which the residue is dried has an important bearing on the results, because weight losses due to volatilization of organic matter, mechanically occluded water, water of crystallization, and gases from heat-induced chemical decomposition, as well as weight gains due to oxidation, depend on the temperature and the period of heating. A choice of drying temperatures is provided and the analyst should be familiar with the probable effects of each.

"Fixed residue"—the residue remaining after ignition for 1 hr at 550±50 C—does not distinguish precisely between organic and inorganic residue because the loss on ignition is not confined to organic matter but includes losses due to decomposition or volatilization of certain mineral salts. A better approximation of the organic matter in water can be made by the total organic carbon, biochemical oxygen demand, or chemical oxygen demand methods described in Sections 505, 507, and 508 respectively.

Conductivity measurements are roughly proportional to the filtrable residue and may be used to advantage in selecting the proper size of sample for residue determinations. However, close correlation of results of the two tests should not be expected always.

An additional possibility for checking fixed filtrable residue is the use of ion-exchange procedures described in the Introduction, Section 104C.3.

Selection of drying temperature: The methods described are gravimetric and permit freedom of choice with respect to the temperature of drying.

Residues dried at 103 to 105 C may be expected to retain not only water of crystallization but also some mechanically occluded water. Loss of carbon dioxide will result in the conversion of bicarbonate to carbonate. Loss of organic matter by volatilization will be very

slight at this temperature if it occurs at all. Because removal of occluded water is marginal at 105 C, attainment of constant weight is very slow.

Residues dried at 180±2 C will lose almost all the mechanically occluded water, but some water of crystallization may remain, especially if sulfates are present. Organic matter is reduced by volatilization but is not completely destroyed. Bicarbonate is converted to carbonate and carbonate may be partially decomposed to oxide or basic salts. Some chloride and nitrate salts may be lost. In general, evaporating and drying water samples at 180 C yield values for total residue that conform more closely to those obtained through summation of individually determined mineral salts than do the values for total residue secured through drying at a lower temperature.

The analyst must select the drying temperature best suited to the water. Waters that are low in organic matter and total mineral content and are intended for human consumption may be examined at either temperature, but waters containing considerable organic matter or those with pH over 9.0 should be dried at the higher temperature. In any case, the report should indicate the drying temperature.

3. Sample Handling and Preservation

Begin analysis as soon as possible because of the impracticality of preserving the sample. Exclude unrepresentative particles such as leaves, sticks, fish, and lumps of fecal matter from the sample in Methods A, D, and E.

Water has considerable solvent action on glass, and the mineral content of a sample will increase when the water is stored in a bottle made of nonresistant glass. This effect is especially pronounced with alkaline waters. Resistant-glass bottles are desirable. Plastic bottles are satisfactory provided that the material in suspension in the sample does not adhere to the walls of the container. Store samples likely to contain iron or manganese so that oxygen will not come into contact with the water. Analyze these samples promptly to minimize the possibility of chemical or physical change during storage.

4. Selection of Method

Methods A through F are suitable for the determination of residue in potable, surface, and saline waters, as well as domestic and industrial wastewaters in the range up to 20,000 mg/l.

Method G is applicable to the determination of the volatile and fixed fractions in sediments, suspended matter, and solid and semisolid materials produced during water and wastewater treatment.

The amount and type of suspended matter in the sample, the purpose of the water analysis, and the relative ease of making the determination will dictate whether the nonfiltrable residue is obtained by a direct determination or by calculation of the difference between the total residue and the filtrable residue.

208 A.   Total Residue Dried at 103-105 C

1. General Discussion

a. Principle: A well mixed sample is evaporated in a weighed dish and dried to constant weight in an oven at 103 to 105 C. The increase in weight over that of the empty dish represents the total residue, which is an arbitrary quantity defined by the procedure followed. The determined values may not check with the theoretical value for solids calculated from the chemical analysis of water. Approximate methods for correlating the chemical analysis with the residue are available.[1] Although the results may not represent the weight of actual dissolved and suspended solids in wastewater samples, the determination serves a useful purpose for plant control. In some instances, correlation may be improved by adding 1 N sodium hydroxide to wastewater samples with a pH below 4.3 and maintaining the pH of 4.3 during evaporation. Correct the final calculation for the added sodium.

b. Interferences: Exclude large, floating particles or submerged agglomerates of nonhomogeneous materials from the sample. Disperse visible floating oil and grease with a blender before withdrawing a sample portion for analysis.

2. Apparatus

a. Evaporating dishes: Dishes of 100-ml capacity made of the following materials:

1) Porcelain, 90-mm diam.
2) Platinum—Generally satisfactory for all purposes.

3) Vycor*

b. *Muffle furnace* for operation at 550±50 C.

c. *Steam bath.*

d. *Drying oven*, equipped with a thermostatic control capable of maintaining the temperature within a 2 C range.

e. *Desiccator*, provided with a desiccant containing a color indicator of moisture concentration.

f. *Analytical balance*, 200-g capacity, capable of weighing to 0.1 mg.

3. Procedure

a. Ignite the clean evaporating dish at 550±50 C for 1 hr in a muffle furnace.

b. Cool, desiccate, weigh, and store the dish in a desiccator until ready for use.

c. Transfer the measured sample to the preweighed dish and evaporate to dryness on a steam bath or in a drying oven. Choose a sample volume that will yield a minimum residue of 25 mg to 250 mg. Estimate the volume from the conductivity. If necessary, add successive portions of sample to the same dish. When evaporating in a drying oven,

---

*A product of Corning Glass Works, Corning, N.Y.

lower the temperature to approximately 98 C to prevent boiling and splattering.

d. Dry the evaporated sample for at least 1 hr at 103 to 105 C.

e. Cool the dish in a desiccator and weigh.

f. Repeat the cycle of drying at 103 to 105 C, cooling, desiccating, and weighing until a constant weight is obtained, or until loss of weight is less than 4% of the previous weight, or 0.5 mg, whichever is less.

4. Calculation

$$\text{mg/l total residue} = \frac{(A-B) \times 1,000}{\text{ml sample}}$$

where A = weight of sample + dish and B = weight of dish.

5. Precision and Accuracy

The precision of the method is about ±4 mg or ±5%. When the residue from a 50- to 100-ml sample of raw sewage was weighed, the standard deviation of the weighing was found to be 1.9 mg ($n=3$; 60×10), but the data are considered statistically unreliable because of sampling errors. On settled effluents, a standard deviation of 0.9 mg ($n=1$; 5×20) was found and is statistically reliable.

208 B.   Total Filtrable Residue Dried at 180 C

1. General Discussion

Filtrable residue is material that passes through a standard glass fiber filter disk and remains after evaporation and drying to constant weight at 180 C.

The filtrate from the total nonfiltrable residue (Section 208 D) may be used for the determination of the total filtrable residue.

Interferences: Highly mineralized waters with a considerable calcium, magnesium, chloride, and/or sulfate content may be hygroscopic and require prolonged drying, proper desiccation, and rapid weighing. Samples high in bicarbonate require careful and possibly prolonged drying at 180 C to insure complete conversion of bicarbonate to carbonate.

2. Apparatus

All of the apparatus listed in Section 208 A.2 is required and in addition:

*a. Glass fiber filter disks**, without organic binder.

b. Filtration apparatus suitable for the type of filter disk selected.

1) *Filter holder:* Gooch crucible adapter or membrane filter funnel.

2) *Gooch crucible*, 25-ml capacity, for 2.2-cm-size glass fiber filter.

c. Suction flask, 500-ml capacity.

3. Procedure

a. Preparation of glass fiber filter disk: Place the disk either on the membrane filter apparatus or the bottom of a suitable Gooch crucible. Apply the vacuum and wash the disk with three successive 20-ml volumes of distilled water. Continue the suction to remove all

---

*Reeve Angel type 934A, 984H; Gelman type A; or equivalent.

traces of water from the disk and discard the washings.

b. Preparation of evaporating dish: Ignite the cleaned evaporating dish at 550 ± 50 C for 1 hr in a muffle furnace. Cool and store in desiccator until needed. Weigh immediately before use.

c. Sample analysis: Because excessive residue in the evaporating dish may form a water-entrapping crust, use a sample that yields no more than 200 mg total filtrable residue. Under vacuum, filter 100 ml, or more, of well mixed sample through the glass fiber filter and continue suction for about 3 min after filtration is complete to remove as much water as possible. Transfer 100 ml (or a larger volume if total filtrable residue is low) filtrate to a weighed evaporating dish, and evaporate to dryness on a steam bath. Dry the evaporated sample for at least 1 hr in an oven at 180 ± 2 C, cool in a desiccator, and weigh. Repeat the drying cycle until a constant weight is obtained or until weight loss is less than 0.5 mg.

4. Calculation

$$\text{mg/l total filtrable residue at 180 C} = \frac{(A-B)\times1,000}{C}$$

where A = weight of dried residue + dish, B = weight of dish, and C = ml filtrate used.

208 C.   Total Filtrable Residue Dried at 103-105 C

Follow the procedure described in Section 208 B. Dry the filtrate at 103 to 105 C instead of 180.

Precision and accuracy: In 18 laboratories, a synthetic unknown sample containing 134 mg/l filtrable residue was analyzed at a drying temperature of 103 to 105 C with a standard deviation of ±13 mg/l.

208 D.   Total Nonfiltrable Residue Dried at 103-105 C (Total Suspended Matter)

1. General Discussion

Total nonfiltrable residue is the retained material on a standard glass fiber filter disk after filtration of a well mixed sample of water or wastewater. The residue is dried at 103 to 105 C. If the suspended material clogs the filter and prolongs the filtration time, the difference between the total residue and the total filtrable residue provides an estimate of the total nonfiltrable residue.

2. Apparatus

Apparatus listed in Sections 208 A.2 and 208 B.2 is required.

3. Procedure

a. Preparation of glass fiber filter disk: Place the disk either on the membrane filter apparatus or the bottom of a suitable Gooch crucible. Apply vacuum and wash the disk with three successive 20-ml portions of distilled water. Continue suction to remove all traces of water from the disk, and discard the washings. Remove the filter from the membrane filter apparatus and transfer to an aluminum or stainless steel planchet as a support. Remove the crucible and filter combination if a Gooch crucible is used. Dry in an oven at 103 to 105 C for 1 hr. Store in desiccator until needed. Weigh immediately before use.

b. Sample treatment: Since excessive residue on the filter may entrap water and extend the drying time, take for analysis a sample that will yield no more than 200 mg total nonfiltrable residue. Under vacuum, filter 100 ml (or a larger volume if total nonfiltrable residue is low) well mixed sample. Carefully remove the filter from the membrane filter funnel assembly, and transfer to an aluminum or stainless steel planchet as a support. Remove the crucible and filter combination from crucible adapter if a Gooch crucible is used. Dry for at least 1 hr at 103 to 105 C, cool in a desiccator, and weigh. Repeat the drying cycle until a constant weight is attained or until weight loss is less than 0.5 mg.

4. Calculation

$$\text{mg/l total nonfiltrable residue} = \frac{(A-B) \times 1{,}000}{\text{ml sample}}$$

where A = weight of filter + residue and B = weight of filter.

5. Precision and Accuracy

The precision of the determination varies directly with the concentration of suspended matter in the sample. The standard deviation was ±5.2 mg/l (coefficient of variation 33%) at 15 mg/l, ±24 mg/l (10%) at 242 mg/l, and ±13 mg/l (0.76%) at 1,707 mg/l ($n =$ 2; 4×10). There is no satisfactory procedure for obtaining the accuracy of the method on wastewater samples, because the true concentration of suspended matter is unknown. See Section 208A.5 for other comments.

208   E.   Total Volatile and Fixed Residue at 550 C

1. General Discussion

The volatile and fixed components in the total residue of Method A may be determined by igniting the sample at 550 ± 50 C. The determination is useful in the control of wastewater plant operation because it offers a rough approximation of the amount of organic matter present in the solid fraction of wastewater, activated sludge, industrial wastes, or bottom sediments. Because the result also may reflect loss of water of crystallization, loss of volatile organic matter before combustion, incomplete oxidation of certain complex organics, and decomposition of mineral salts during combustion, it may not yield an accurate measure of organic carbon.

2. Apparatus

See Sections 208 A.2 and 208 B.2.

3. Procedure

Ignite the residue produced by Method A to constant weight in a muffle furnace at a temperature of 550 ± 50 C. Have the furnace up to temperature before inserting the sample. (Usually, 15 to 20 min ignition are required.) Allow the dish to cool partially in air until most of the heat has been dissipated and transfer to a desiccator for final cooling in a dry atmosphere. Do not overload the desiccator. Weigh the dish as soon as it has cooled completely. Report the loss of weight on ignition as total volatile residue and the weighed residue as total fixed residue.

4. Calculation

$$\text{mg/l volatile residue} = \frac{(A-B)\times1{,}000}{\text{ml sample}}$$

$$\text{mg/l fixed residue} = \frac{(B-C)\times1{,}000}{\text{ml sample}}$$

where A = weight of residue+dish before ignition, B = weight of residue+dish after ignition, and C = weight of dish.

5. Precision and Accuracy

Three laboratories examined four samples by means of 10 replicates with a standard deviation of ±11 mg/l at 170 mg/l volatile residue concentration.

208   F.   Settleable Matter

1. General Discussion

Settleable matter in surface and saline waters as well as domestic and industrial wastes may be determined and reported on either a volume (milliliters per liter) or a weight (milligrams per liter) basis.

2. Apparatus

The apparatus listed under Sections 208 A.2 and 208 B.2, and an Imhoff cone, are required for a gravimetric test. The volumetric test requires only an Imhoff cone.

3. Procedure

a. By volume: Fill an Imhoff cone to the liter mark with a thoroughly mixed sample. Settle for 45 min, gently stir the sides of the cone with a rod or by spinning, settle 15 min longer, and record the volume of settleable matter in the cone as milliliters per liter. The practical lower limits is about 1 ml/l/hr. Where a separation of settleable and floating materials occurs, do not estimate the floating material.

b. By weight:

1) Determine the suspended matter (in milligrams per liter) in the sample as in Method D, preceding.

2) Pour a well-mixed sample into a glass vessel not less than 9 cm in diameter. Use a sample of not less than 1 l and sufficient to give a depth of 20 cm. A glass vessel of greater diameter and a larger volume of sample also may be used. Let stand quiescent for 1 hr and, without disturbing the settled or floating material or that which may be floating, siphon 250 ml from the center of the container at a point halfway between the surface of the settled sludge and the liquid surface. Determine the suspended matter (in milligrams per liter) in all or in a portion of this supernatant liquor as directed under Method D. This is the nonsettling matter.

4. Calculation

mg/l settleable matter
= mg/l suspended matter
− mg/l nonsettleable matter

208 G.   Volatile and Fixed Matter in Nonfiltrable Residue and in Solid and Semisolid Samples

1. General Discussion

Occasionally, the fixed and volatile components of suspended matter and associated solid materials must be determined. Ordinarily, the total residue on evaporation and its fixed and volatile fractions are determined in such solid and semisolid samples as river and lake sediments, sludges separated from water and wastewater treatment processes, and sludge cakes from vacuum filtration, centrifugation, or other dewatering treatment of wastewater sludges.

The determination of both total and volatile residue in these materials is subject to negative error due to the loss of ammonium carbonate and volatile organic matter while drying. Although this is true also for wastewater, the effect tends to be more pronounced with sediments, and especially with sludges and sludge cakes.

The mass of organic matter recovered from sludge and sediment requires a period of ignition longer than that specified for the residue from wastewaters, effluents, or polluted waters. The specified ignition time and temperature must be observed carefully in order to control losses of volatile inorganic salts.

All weighings must be performed quickly. Wet samples tend to lose weight by evaporation. After drying or ignition, the residues are often very hygroscopic and rapidly absorb moisture from the air.

2. Apparatus

See Sections 208A.2 and 208B.2.

3. Procedure

a. Solid and semisolid samples:

1) Total residue and moisture—

a) Preparation of evaporating dish—Ignite a clean evaporating dish at 550 ± 50 C for 1 hr in a muffle furnace. Cool in a desiccator, weigh, and store the dish in a desiccator until ready for use.

b) Fluid samples—If the sample contains enough moisture to flow more or less readily, stir to homogenize, then place 25 to 50 g in a prepared evaporating dish and weigh to the nearest 10 mg. Evaporate to dryness on a water bath, dry at 103 C for 1 hr, cool in an individual desiccator containing fresh desiccant, and weigh.

c) Solid samples—If the sample consists of discrete pieces of solid material (dewatered sludge, for example), take cores from each piece with a No. 7 cork borer, or pulverize the entire sample coarsely on a clean surface by hand, using rubber gloves. Place 25 to 50 g in a prepared evaporating dish and weigh to the nearest 10 mg. Place in an oven at 103 C overnight. Cool in an individual desiccator containing fresh desiccant and weigh. Prolonged heating may result in a loss of volatile organic matter and ammonium carbonate, but it is usually necessary in order to dry such samples thoroughly.

2) Volatile residue—Determine volatile residue, which includes organic matter and volatile inorganic salts, on the total residue obtained in 1) above by igniting it in an electric muffle furnace at 550 C for 60 min. Avoid loss of solids by decrepitation. Cool in a desiccator and reweigh. Report results as percent ash (fixed matter) and volatile solids.

b. Nonfiltrable residue (suspended matter):

1) Preparation of glass fiber filter disk—Place a glass fiber filter disk in a membrane filter holder, Hirsch funnel, or Buchner funnel, with the wrinkled surface of the disk facing upward. Apply vaccum to the assembled apparatus to seat the filter disk. With vacuum applied, wash the disk with distilled water. After the water has filtered through, disconnect the vacuum, remove the filter disk from the apparatus, transfer to an aluminum or stainless steel planchet as a support, and dry in an oven at 103 C for 1 hr (30 min in a mechanical convection oven). If volatile matter is not to be determined, cool the filter disk to room temperature in a desiccator and weigh. If volatile matter is to be determined, transfer the disk to a muffle furnace and ignite at 550 C for 15 min. Remove the disk from the furnace, place in a desiccator until cooled to room temperature, and weigh.

2) Treatment of sample—Except for samples that contain high concentrations of suspended matter, or that filter very slowly, select a sample volume≥ 14 ml/ cm^2 filter area.

Place the prepared filter disk in the membrane filter holder, Hirsch funnel, or Buchner funnel, with the wrinkled surface upward. With the vacuum applied, wet the disk with distilled water to seat it against the holder or funnel. Measure the well-mixed sample with a wide-tip pipet, volumetric flask, or graduated cylinder. Filter the sample through the disk, using suction. Leaving the suction on, wash the apparatus three times with 10-ml portions of distilled water, allowing complete drainage between washings. Discontinue suction, remove the filter disk, and dry it at 103 C for 1 hr in an oven (30 min in a mechanical convection oven). After drying, cool the disk to room temperature in a desiccator and weigh on an analytical balance.

3) Filtration with Gooch crucibles— Alternatively, use glass-fiber filter disks of suitable diameter (usually 2.1 or 2.4 cm) with Gooch crucibles, making certain that the disk lies flat in the bottom of the crucible and completely covers the perforations.

Prepare the disk and treat the sample as described in ¶s 1) and 2) above, except that the disk usually is dried, ignited, and weighed along with the Gooch crucible, rather than being handled separately.

4) Ignition—Ignite the filter disk with its nonfiltrable residue (total suspended matter) for 15 min at 550 ± 50 C, transfer to a desiccator, cool to room temperature, and weigh.

4. Calculation

a. Solid and semisolid samples:

$$\% \text{ total residue } = \frac{A \times 100}{B}$$

$$\% \text{ volatile residue } = \frac{(A-C) \times 100}{A}$$

$$\% \text{ fixed residue } = \frac{C \times 100}{A}$$

b. Nonfiltrable residue (suspended matter):

$$\text{mg/l volatile residue } = \frac{(D-E) \times 1,000}{\text{ml sample}}$$

$$\text{mg/l fixed residue } = \frac{C \times 1,000}{\text{ml sample}}$$

where:

A = weight of dried solids,
B = weight of wet sample,
C = weight of ash,
D = weight of residue before ignition, and
E = weight of residue after ignition.

5. Precision and Accuracy

The precision of the determination varies directly with the concentration of suspended matter in the sample. The standard deviation was ±5.2 mg/l (coefficient of variation 33%) at 15 mg/l, ±24 mg/l (10%) at 242 mg/l, and ±13 mg/l (0.76%) at 1,707 mg/l ($n=2; 4\times10$). There is no satisfactory procedure for obtaining the accuracy of the method on wastewater samples because the true concentration of suspended matter is unknown.

208 H.   Reference

1. SOKOLOFF, V.P. 1933. Water of crystalliza-   tion in total solids of water analysis. *Ind. Eng. Chem.*, Anal. Ed. 5:336.

208 I.   Bibliography

THERIAULT, E.J. & H.H. WAGENHALS. 1923. Studies of representative sewage plants. *Pub. Health Bull.* No. 132.

HOWARD, C.S. 1933. Determination of total dissolved solids in water analysis. *Ind. Eng. Chem.*, Anal. Ed. 5:4.

SYMONS, G.E. & B. MOREY. 1941. The effect of drying time on the determination of solids in sewage and sewage sludges. *Sewage Works J.* 13:936.

FISCHER, A.J. & G.E. SYMONS. 1944. The determination of settleable sewage solids by weight. *Water Works Sewage* 91:37.

DEGEN, J. & F.E. NUSSBERGER. 1956. Notes on the determination of suspended solids. *Sewage Ind. Wastes* 28:237.

CHANIN, G., E.H. CHOW, R.B. ALEXANDER & J. POWERS. 1958. Use of glass fiber filter media um in the suspended solids determination. *Sewage Ind. Wastes* 30:1062.

NUSBAUM, I. 1958. New method for determination of suspended solids. *Sewage Ind. Wastes* 30:1066.

SMITH, A.L. & A.E. GREENBERG. 1963. Evaluation of methods for determining suspended solids in wastewater. *J. Water Pollut. Control Fed.* 35:940.

GOODMAN, B.L. 1964. Processing thickened sludge with chemical conditioners. Pages 78 et seq *in* Sludge Concentration, Filtration and Incineration. Univ. Michigan Continued Education Ser. No. 113, Ann Arbor.

WYCKOFF, B.M. 1964. Rapid solids determination using glass fiber filters. *Water Sewage Works* 111:277.

209   SALINITY

Salinity is an important measurement in the analysis of certain industrial wastes and seawater. It is defined as the total solids in water after all carbonates have been converted to oxides, all bromide and iodide have been replaced by chloride, and all organic matter has been oxidized. It is numerically smaller than the filtrable residue and usually is reported as grams per kilogram or parts per thousand (‰).

Associated terms are chlorinity, which includes chloride, bromide, and iodide, all reported as chloride, and chlorosity, which is the chlorinity multiplied by the water density at 20 C. An empirical relationship[1] between salinity and chlorinity is often used:

$$\text{Salinity, } ‰ = 0.03 + 1.805 \text{ (chlorinity, } ‰)$$

Selection of method: Three procedures are presented. The electrical conductivity (A) and hydrometric (B) methods are suited for field use along a shore line or in a small boat. For laboratory or field analysis of estuarine or coastal inlet waters the argentometric method (C) is recommended.

209 A.   Electrical Conductivity Method

See Conductivity, Section 205. Because of the relatively high concentration of ions in seawater and the effect of temperature on conductivity, standardize each instrument against seawater samples of known salinity (as determined by the argentometric method below).

209 B.   Hydrometric Method

1. General Discussion

Principle: Salinity is determined by measuring specific gravity with a hydrometer, correcting for temperature, and converting specific gravity to salinity by means of density salinity tables.

2. Apparatus

a. Hydrometer jar: Use a special jar 400 mm high with 45 mm ID, or a rubber-stoppered transparent plastic tube with the same dimensions, or a 500-ml graduated cylinder.

b. Thermometer, graduated in 0.2 C divisions.

c. Hydrometer, seawater*: For usual work a set of three, with specific gravity ranges of 0.966 to 1.011, 1.010 to 1.021, and 1.010 to 1.031, is needed. Hydrometer divisions should be 0.002. A set should be calibrated by the Na-

*Available from Emil Greiner Co., 20 North Moore St., N.Y., N.Y. 10004.

tional Bureau of Standards for specific gravity of NaCl solutions at 15/4 C.

3. Procedure

a. Fill hydrometer jar 2/3 full of sample.

b. While holding the jar vertically, place the thermometer and hydrometer in the jar.

c. Read and record the temperature.

d. Read and record the specific gravity. Estimate the fourth decimal place.

e. Make temperature corrections for the specific gravity reading from the factors listed in Table 209:I.

4. Calculation

Determine salinity from Table 209:II. Locate corrected density and read salinity from opposite column. Report salinity as parts per thousand (‰).

TABLE 209:I. DIFFERENCES TO CONVERT HYDROMETER READINGS AT ANY TEMPERATURE TO DENSITY AT 15 C

Observed Reading	Temperature of Water in Jar, C												
	—2.0	—1.0	0.0	1.0	2.0	3.0	4.0	5.0	6.0	7.0	8.0	9.0	10.0
0.9960													
0.9970													
0.9980													
0.9990	—1	—2	—3	—4	—5	—5	—6	—6	—6	—6	—6	—5	—5
1.0000	—2	—3	—4	—5	—5	—6	—6	—6	—6	—6	—6	—5	—5
1.0010	—3	—4	—4	—5	—6	—6	—6	—7	—7	—6	—6	—6	—5
1.0020	—3	—4	—5	—6	—6	—7	—7	—7	—7	—7	—6	—6	—5
1.0030	—4	—5	—6	—6	—7	—7	—7	—7	—7	—7	—6	—6	—5
1.0040	—4	—5	—6	—7	—7	—7	—8	—8	—7	—7	—7	—6	—6
1.0050	—5	—6	—6	—7	—8	—8	—8	—8	—8	—7	—7	—6	—6
1.0060	—6	—6	—7	—8	—8	—8	—8	—8	—8	—8	—7	—6	—6
1.0070	—6	—7	—8	—8	—8	—8	—8	—8	—8	—8	—7	—7	—6
1.0080	—7	—8	—8	—9	—9	—9	—9	—9	—8	—8	—7	—7	—6
1.0090	—7	—8	—9	—9	—9	—9	—9	—9	—9	—8	—8	—7	—6
1.0100	—8	—9	—9	—10	—10	—10	—10	—9	—9	—8	—8	—7	—6
1.0110	—9	—9	—10	—10	—10	—10	—10	—10	—9	—9	—8	—7	—6
1.0120	—9	—10	—10	—10	—10	—10	—10	—10	—10	—9	—8	—7	—7
1.0130	—10	—10	—11	—11	—11	—11	—11	—10	—10	—9	—8	—8	—7
1.0140	—10	—11	—11	—11	—11	—11	—11	—11	—10	—10	—9	—8	—7
1.0150	—11	—11	—12	—12	—12	—12	—11	—11	—10	—10	—9	—8	—7
1.0160	—12	—12	—12	—12	—12	—12	—12	—11	—11	—10	—9	—8	—7
1.0170	—12	—12	—12	—13	—13	—12	—12	—12	—11	—10	—9	—8	—7
1.0180	—13	—13	—13	—13	—13	—13	—12	—12	—11	—10	—9	—8	—7
1.0190	—13	—13	—14	—14	—13	—13	—13	—12	—12	—11	—10	—9	—8
1.0200	—14	—14	—14	—14	—14	—13	—13	—12	—12	—11	—10	—9	—8
1.0210	—14	—14	—14	—14	—14	—14	—13	—13	—12	—11	—10	—9	—8
1.0220	—15	—15	—15	—15	—15	—14	—14	—13	—12	—11	—10	—9	—8
1.0230	—15	—15	—15	—15	—15	—15	—14	—13	—12	—12	—10	—9	—8
1.0240	—16	—16	—16	—16	—15	—15	—14	—14	—13	—12	—11	—10	—8
1.0250	—16	—16	—16	—16	—16	—15	—15	—14	—13	—12	—11	—10	—8
1.0260	—17	—17	—17	—16	—16	—16	—15	—14	—13	—12	—11	—10	—8
1.0270	—18	—17	—17	—17	—17	—16	—15	—14	—14	—12	—11	—10	—9
1.0280	—18	—18	—18	—17	—17	—16	—16	—15	—14	—13	—11	—10	—9
1.0290	—19	—18	—18	—18	—17	—17	—16	—15	—14	—13	—12	—10	—9
1.0300	—19	—19	—19	—18	—18	—17	—16	—15	—14	—13	—12	—10	—9
1.0310	—20	—19	—19	—19	—18	—17	—16	—16	—15	—13	—12	—10	—9

TABLE 209:I, CONT.

Observed Reading	Temperature of Water in Jar, C											
	11.0	12.0	13.0	14.0	15.0	16.0	17.0	18.0	18.5	19.0	19.5	20.0
0.9960												
0.9970												
0.9980							3	4	5	6	7	8
0.9990	—4	—3	—2	—1	0	1	3	4	5	6	7	8
1.0000	—4	—3	—2	—1	0	1	3	4	5	6	7	8
1.0010	—4	—3	—2	—1	0	1	3	4	5	6	7	8
1.0020	—4	—3	—2	—1	0	1	3	4	5	6	7	8
1.0030	—4	—3	—2	—1	0	1	3	4	5	6	7	8
1.0040	—5	—4	—3	—1	0	2	3	5	6	6	7	8
1.0050	—5	—4	—3	—1	0	2	3	5	6	7	8	9
1.0060	—5	—4	—3	—1	0	2	3	5	6	7	8	9
1.0070	—5	—4	—3	—2	0	2	3	5	6	7	8	9
1.0080	—5	—4	—3	—2	0	2	3	5	6	7	8	9
1.0090	—5	—4	—3	—2	0	2	3	5	6	7	8	9
1.0100	—5	—4	—3	—2	0	2	3	5	6	7	8	9
1.0110	—5	—4	—3	—2	0	2	3	5	6	7	8	9
1.0120	—6	—4	—3	—2	0	2	3	5	6	7	8	9
1.0130	—6	—4	—3	—2	0	2	4	5	6	7	8	10
1.0140	—6	—4	—3	—2	0	2	4	5	6	8	9	10
1.0150	—6	—4	—3	—2	0	2	4	5	6	8	9	10
1.0160	—6	—5	—3	—2	0	2	4	6	7	8	9	10
1.0170	—6	—5	—3	—2	0	2	4	6	7	8	9	10
1.0180	—6	—5	—3	—2	0	2	4	6	7	8	9	10
1.0190	—6	—5	—3	—2	0	2	4	6	7	8	9	10
1.0200	—6	—5	—3	—2	0	2	4	6	7	8	9	10
1.0210	—6	—5	—3	—2	0	2	4	6	7	8	9	10
1.0220	—7	—5	—3	—2	0	2	4	6	7	8	9	11
1.0230	—7	—5	—4	—2	0	2	4	6	7	8	9	11
1.0240	—7	—5	—4	—2	0	2	4	6	7	8	10	11
1.0250	—7	—5	—4	—2	0	2	4	6	7	8	10	11
1.0260	—7	—5	—4	—2	0	2	4	6	7	9	10	11
1.0270	—7	—5	—4	—2	0	2	4	6	7	9	10	11
1.0280	—7	—6	—4	—2	0	2	4	6	8	9	10	11
1.0290	—7	—6	—4	—2	0	2	4	6	8	9	10	11
1.0300	—7	—6	—4	—2	0	2	4	6	8	9	10	12
1.0310	—8	—6	—4	—2	0	2	4					

TABLE 209:I, CONT.

Observed Reading	Temperature of Water in Jar, C												
	20.5	21.0	21.5	22.0	22.5	23.0	23.5	24.0	24.5	25.0	25.5	26.0	26.5
0.9960											19	20	21
0.9970			10	11	12	14	15	16	17	18	19	20	22
0.9980	9	10	11	12	13	14	15	16	17	18	19	21	22
0.9990	9	10	11	12	13	14	15	16	17	18	20	21	22
1.0000	9	10	11	12	13	14	15	16	17	19	20	21	22
1.0010	9	10	11	12	13	14	15	17	18	19	20	21	23
1.0020	9	10	11	12	13	14	16	17	18	19	20	22	23
1.0030	9	10	11	12	13	15	16	17	18	19	21	22	23
1.0040	9	10	11	12	14	15	16	17	18	20	21	22	23
1.0050	10	11	12	13	14	15	16	17	19	20	21	22	24
1.0060	10	11	12	13	14	15	16	18	19	20	21	23	24
1.0070	10	11	12	13	14	15	17	18	19	20	21	23	24
1.0080	10	11	12	13	14	16	17	18	19	20	22	23	24
1.0090	10	11	12	13	15	16	17	18	19	21	22	23	25
1.0100	10	11	12	14	15	16	17	18	20	21	22	24	25
1.0110	10	12	13	14	15	16	17	19	20	21	22	24	25
1.0120	10	12	13	14	15	16	18	19	20	21	23	24	25
1.0130	11	12	13	14	15	16	18	19	20	22	23	24	26
1.0140	11	12	13	14	15	17	18	19	20	22	23	24	26
1.0150	11	12	13	14	16	17	18	20	21	22	23	25	26
1.0160	11	12	13	14	16	17	18	20	21	22	24	25	26
1.0170	11	12	13	15	16	17	18	20	21	22	24	25	27
1.0180	11	12	14	15	16	17	19	20	21	23	24	25	27
1.0190	11	12	14	15	16	18	19	20	21	23	24	26	27
1.0200	11	13	14	15	16	18	19	20	22	23	24	26	27
1.0210	12	13	14	15	17	18	19	21	22	23	25	26	27
1.0220	12	13	14	15	17	18	19	21	22	23	25	26	28
1.0230	12	13	14	16	17	18	20	21	22	24	25	26	28
1.0240	12	13	14	16	17	18	20	21	22	24	25	27	28
1.0250	12	13	15	16	17	18	20	21	23	24	25	27	28
1.0260	12	13	15	16	17	19	20	22	23	24	26	27	29
1.0270	12	14	15	16	17	19	20	22	23	24	26	27	29
1.0280	12	14	15	16	18	19	20	22	23	25	26	28	29
1.0290	13	14	15	16	18	19	21	22	23				
1.0300	13	14	15	16	18								
1.0310													

TABLE 209:I, CONT.

Observed Reading	Temperature of Water in Jar, C												
	27.0	27.5	28.0	28.5	29.0	29.5	30.0	30.5	31.0	31.5	32.0	32.5	33.0
0.9960	23	24	25	27	28	29	31	32	34	35	37	38	40
0.9970	23	24	26	27	28	30	31	33	34	36	37	39	40
0.9980	23	25	26	27	29	30	31	33	34	36	38	39	41
0.9990	24	25	26	28	29	30	32	33	35	36	38	39	41
1.0000	24	25	26	28	29	31	32	34	35	37	38	40	41
1.0010	24	25	27	28	30	31	32	34	35	37	39	40	42
1.0020	24	26	27	28	30	31	33	34	36	37	39	41	42
1.0030	25	26	27	29	30	32	33	35	36	38	39	41	42
1.0040	25	26	28	29	30	32	33	35	36	38	40	41	43
1.0050	25	26	28	29	31	32	34	35	37	38	40	42	43
1.0060	25	27	28	30	31	32	34	36	37	39	40	42	44
1.0070	26	27	28	30	31	33	34	36	38	39	41	42	44
1.0080	26	27	29	30	32	33	35	36	38	39	41	43	44
1.0090	26	28	29	30	32	33	35	36	38	40	41	43	45
1.0100	26	28	29	31	32	34	35	37	38	40	42	43	45
1.0110	27	28	30	31	32	34	36	37	39	40	42	44	45
1.0120	27	28	30	31	33	34	36	37	39	41	42	44	46
1.0130	27	29	30	32	33	35	36	38	39	41	43	44	46
1.0140	27	29	30	32	33	35	36	38	40	41	43	45	46
1.0150	28	29	31	32	34	35	37	38	40	42	43	45	47
1.0160	28	29	31	32	34	35	37	39	40	42	44	45	47
1.0170	28	30	31	33	34	36	37	39	40	42	44	46	47
1.0180	28	30	31	33	34	36	38	39	41	42	44	46	48
1.0190	29	30	32	33	35	36	38	39	41	43	44	46	48
1.0200	29	30	32	33	35	37	38	40	41	43	45	47	48
1.0210	29	31	32	34	35	37	38	40	42	43	45	47	49
1.0220	29	31	32	34	36	37	39	40	42	44	45	47	49
1.0230	30	31	33	34	36	37	39	41	42	44	46	47	49
1.0240	30	31	33	34	36	37	39	41	42	44	46	48	49
1.0250	30	31	33	35	36	38	39	41	43	44	46	48	50
1.0260	30	32	33	35	37	38	40	41	43	45	46	48	50
1.0270	30	32	34	35	37	38	40						
1.0280	31	32											
1.0290													
1.0300													
1.0310													

SOURCE: ZERBE, W. B. and C. B. TAYLOR. 1953. Sea Water Temperature and Density Reduction Tables. U.S. Dept. Commerce Spec. Publ. No. 298, Washington, D.C.

TABLE 209:II. CORRESPONDING DENSITIES AND SALINITIES*

Density	Salinity	Density	Salinity	Density	Salinity	Density	Salinity
0.9991	0.0	1.0036	5.8	1.0081	11.6	1.0126	17.5
0.9992	0.0	1.0037	5.9	1.0082	11.8	1.0127	17.7
0.9993	0.2	1.0038	6.0	1.0083	11.9	1.0128	17.8
0.9994	0.3	1.0039	6.2	1.0084	12.0	1.0129	17.9
0.9995	0.4	1.0040	6.3	1.0085	12.2	1.0130	18.0
0.9996	0.6	1.0041	6.4	1.0086	12.3	1.0131	18.2
0.9997	0.7	1.0042	6.6	1.0087	12.4	1.0132	18.3
0.9998	0.8	1.0043	6.7	1.0088	12.6	1.0133	18.4
0.9999	0.9	1.0044	6.8	1.0089	12.7	1.0134	18.6
1.0000	1.1	1.0045	6.9	1.0090	12.8	1.0135	18.7
1.0001	1.2	1.0046	7.1	1.0091	12.9	1.0136	18.8
1.0002	1.3	1.0047	7.2	1.0092	13.1	1.0137	19.0
1.0003	1.5	1.0048	7.3	1.0093	13.2	1.0138	19.1
1.0004	1.6	1.0049	7.5	1.0094	13.3	1.0139	19.2
1.0005	1.7	1.0050	7.6	1.0095	13.5	1.0140	19.3
1.0006	1.9	1.0051	7.7	1.0096	13.6	1.0141	19.5
1.0007	2.0	1.0052	7.9	1.0097	13.7	1.0142	19.6
1.0008	2.1	1.0053	8.0	1.0098	13.9	1.0143	19.7
1.0009	2.2	1.0054	8.1	1.0099	14.0	1.0144	19.9
1.0010	2.4	1.0055	8.2	1.0100	14.1	1.0145	20.0
1.0011	2.5	1.0056	8.4	1.0101	14.2	1.0146	20.1
1.0012	2.6	1.0057	8.5	1.0102	14.4	1.0147	20.3
1.0013	2.8	1.0058	8.6	1.0103	14.5	1.0148	20.4
1.0014	2.9	1.0059	8.8	1.0104	14.6	1.0149	20.5
1.0015	3.0	1.0060	8.9	1.0105	14.8	1.0150	20.6
1.0016	3.2	1.0061	9.0	1.0106	14.9	1.0151	20.8
1.0017	3.3	1.0062	9.2	1.0107	15.0	1.0152	20.9
1.0018	3.4	1.0063	9.3	1.0108	15.2	1.0153	21.0
1.0019	3.5	1.0064	9.4	1.0109	15.3	1.0154	21.2
1.0020	3.7	1.0065	9.6	1.0110	15.4	1.0155	21.3
1.0021	3.8	1.0066	9.7	1.0111	15.6	1.0156	21.4
1.0022	3.9	1.0067	9.8	1.0112	15.7	1.0157	21.6
1.0023	4.1	1.0068	9.9	1.0113	15.8	1.0158	21.7
1.0024	4.2	1.0069	10.1	1.0114	16.0	1.0159	21.8
1.0025	4.3	1.0070	10.2	1.0115	16.1	1.0160	22.0
1.0026	4.5	1.0071	10.3	1.0116	16.2	1.0161	22.1
1.0027	4.6	1.0072	10.5	1.0117	16.3	1.0162	22.2
1.0028	4.7	1.0073	10.6	1.0118	16.5	1.0163	22.4
1.0029	4.8	1.0074	10.7	1.0119	16.6	1.0164	22.5
1.0030	5.0	1.0075	10.8	1.0120	16.7	1.0165	22.6
1.0031	5.1	1.0076	11.0	1.0121	16.9	1.0166	22.7
1.0032	5.2	1.0077	11.1	1.0122	17.0	1.0167	22.9
1.0033	5.4	1.0078	11.2	1.0123	17.1	1.0168	23.0
1.0034	5.5	1.0079	11.4	1.0124	17.3	1.0169	23.1
1.0035	5.6	1.0080	11.5	1.0125	17.4	1.0170	23.3

* Density at 15 C. Salinity in parts per 1,000.

TABLE 209:II, CONT.

Density	Salinity	Density	Salinity	Density	Salinity	Density	Salinity
1.0171	23.4	1.0211	28.6	1.0251	33.8	1.0291	39.0
1.0172	23.5	1.0212	28.8	1.0252	34.0	1.0292	39.2
1.0173	23.7	1.0213	28.9	1.0253	34.1	1.0293	39.3
1.0174	23.8	1.0214	29.0	1.0254	34.2	1.0294	39.4
1.0175	23.9	1.0215	29.1	1.0255	34.4	1.0295	39.6
1.0176	24.1	1.0216	29.3	1.0256	34.5	1.0296	39.7
1.0177	24.2	1.0217	29.4	1.0257	34.6	1.0297	39.8
1.0178	24.3	1.0218	29.5	1.0258	34.8	1.0298	39.9
1.0179	24.4	1.0219	29.7	1.0259	34.9	1.0299	40.1
1.0180	24.6	1.0220	29.8	1.0260	35.0	1.0300	40.2
1.0181	24.7	1.0221	29.9	1.0261	35.1	1.0301	40.3
1.0182	24.8	1.0222	30.1	1.0262	35.3	1.0302	40.4
1.0183	25.0	1.0223	30.2	1.0263	35.4	1.0303	40.6
1.0184	25.1	1.0224	30.3	1.0264	35.5	1.0304	40.7
1.0185	25.2	1.0225	30.4	1.0265	35.7	1.0305	40.8
1.0186	25.4	1.0226	30.6	1.0266	35.8	1.0306	41.0
1.0187	25.5	1.0227	30.7	1.0267	35.9	1.0307	41.1
1.0188	25.6	1.0228	30.8	1.0268	36.0	1.0308	41.2
1.0189	25.8	1.0229	31.0	1.0269	36.2	1.0309	41.4
1.0190	25.9	1.0230	31.1	1.0270	36.3	1.0310	41.5
1.0191	26.0	1.0231	31.2	1.0271	36.4	1.0311	41.6
1.0192	26.1	1.0232	31.4	1.0272	36.6	1.0312	41.7
1.0193	26.3	1.0233	31.5	1.0273	36.7	1.0313	41.9
1.0194	26.4	1.0234	31.6	1.0274	36.8	1.0314	42.0
1.0195	26.5	1.0235	31.8	1.0275	37.0	1.0315	42.1
1.0196	26.7	1.0236	31.9	1.0276	37.1	1.0316	42.3
1.0197	26.8	1.0237	32.0	1.0277	37.2	1.0317	42.4
1.0198	26.9	1.0238	32.1	1.0278	37.3	1.0318	42.5
1.0199	27.1	1.0239	32.3	1.0279	37.5	1.0319	42.7
1.0200	27.2	1.0240	32.4	1.0280	37.6	1.0320	42.8
1.0201	27.3	1.0241	32.5	1.0281	37.7		
1.0202	27.5	1.0242	32.7	1.0282	37.9		
1.0203	27.6	1.0243	32.8	1.0283	38.0		
1.0204	27.7	1.0244	32.9	1.0284	38.1		
1.0205	27.8	1.0245	33.1	1.0285	38.2		
1.0206	28.0	1.0246	33.2	1.0286	38.4		
1.0207	28.1	1.0247	33.3	1.0287	38.5		
1.0208	28.2	1.0248	33.5	1.0288	38.6		
1.0209	28.4	1.0249	33.6	1.0289	38.8		
1.0210	28.5	1.0250	33.7	1.0290	38.9		

209 C. Argentometric Method

1. General Discussion

This procedure is similar to that specified for chloride, Section 408 A. It is not as precise as the longer Knudsen method[1] but is less time-consuming.

2. Sample Handling

Collect samples in a 240-ml (8-oz) glass bottle with a No. 6 cork stopper. Pretreat the stopper by soaking in melted paraffin wax for 30 to 40 sec, draining, and drying. Remove excess wax. To collect sample, rinse bottle with water being sampled three times and fill bottle to shoulder. Seal bottle by forcing waxed cork below level of neck. If samples are not examined within 2 days, dip the neck of bottle in melted wax. The sealed sample is stable indefinitely. Titrate unsealed samples within a few minutes of collection; do not hold unsealed samples more than 1 hr before analysis.

3. Apparatus

a. *Automatic 10-ml pipet.*

b. *Automatic zero-adjusting 35-ml buret.* Lubricate with paraffin stopcock grease, never silicone.

c. *Tall-form 200-ml beakers.* Keep clean by periodic soaking in cold 5% sodium hydroxide in methyl alcohol, rinse in nitric acid, then in distilled water.

4. Reagents

a. *Standard seawater.* Standard seawater of known chlorinity ("Eau de Mer Normale") is available from the Depot d'Eau Normale, Laboratory Hy- drographique, Charlottenlund Slot, Copenhagen, Denmark.* A secondary standard may be prepared by filtering seawater (chlorinity about 18‰) collected from the open ocean at a depth of at least 50 m. Stabilize with a few crystals of thymol and seal in standard sample bottles. Use the mean of 10 or more sample titrations as the chlorosity (20 C) of this secondary standard.

b. *Silver nitrate solution,* approximately 0.28 N: Dissolve 48.5 g $AgNO_3$ in 500 ml distilled water and dilute to 1,000 ml. Store in glass-stoppered brown glass bottle at room temperature.

c. *Potassium chromate indicator solution:* Dissolve 63 g K_2CrO_4 in 100 ml distilled water. Add a few drops of 0.28 N $AgNO_3$ until a definite red precipitate persists. Let stand to settle, filter, and store in glass dropping bottle.

d. *Standard sodium chloride:* Dry about 35 g NaCl to constant weight. Cool and weigh out 29.674 g. Dissolve in distilled water and dilute to 1,000 ml. Check this standard against Copenhagen water and periodically against the secondary seawater standard.

Standardization: Place 25.0 ml standard NaCl solution in a 150-ml erlenmeyer flask. Add 6 drops of chromate indicator and titrate with $AgNO_3$ solution in a yellow light until a red precipi-

---

*Other sources are listed in **AMERICAN SOCIETY OF LIMNOLOGY AND OCEANOGRAPHY. COMMITTEE ON APPARATUS AND SUPPLIES.** 1964. Sources of Limnological and Oceanographic Apparatus and Supplies. Spec. Publ. No. 1, 3rd rev. *Limnol. Oceanogr.* 9 (suppl. Apr. 1964).

tate just forms. Stopper flask with rubber stopper and shake vigorously to break curds of AgCl. Wash down stopper and continue titration to brown end point.

$$\text{Normality} = \frac{12.69}{\text{ml AgNO}_3}$$

4. Procedure

Allow sample and $AgNO_3$ titrant to come to same temperature. Use a 25.0-ml sample and titrate as directed above.

5. Calculation

a. Calculate the chlorosity equivalent of 1 ml of $AgNO_3$ solution:

$$ClEq = N \times 0.355$$

where $ClEq$ = chlorosity equivalent and N = normality of $AgNO_3$.

b. Calculate the chlorosity

$$Clo = d \times ClEq \times 40$$

where d = ml titrant used and $ClEq$ = chlorosity equivalent per liter $AgNO_3$.

c. Convert chlorosity to chlorinity by subtracting the appropriate factor given in Table 209:III. Record chlorinity as Cl ‰.

d. Convert chlorinity to salinity by using Table 209:IV. Record salinity, S, as ‰.

6. Precision and Accuracy

This procedure is suitable for salinities ranging from 4 to 40 ‰. It is accurate to between 0.05 and 0.1 ‰ salinity.

TABLE 209:III. CONVERSION OF CHLOROSITY, Clo, AT 20 C TO CHLORINITY, Cl‰

Calculated Chlorosity	Subtract for Chlorinity
9.95—10.35	—0.12
10.36—10.75	—0.13
10.76—11.15	—0.14
11.16—11.46	—0.15
11.47—11.76	—0.16
11.77—12.06	—0.17
12.07—12.46	—0.18
12.47—12.86	—0.19
12.87—13.07	—0.20
13.08—13.37	—0.21
13.38—13.67	—0.22
13.68—14.02	—0.23
14.03—14.27	—0.24
14.28—14.52	—0.25
14.53—14.82	—0.26
14.83—15.09	—0.27
15.10—15.37	—0.28
15.38—15.68	—0.29
15.69—15.87	—0.30
15.88—16.17	—0.31
16.18—16.32	—0.32
16.33—16.62	—0.33
16.63—16.82	—0.34
16.83—17.11	—0.35
17.12—17.32	—0.36
17.33—17.57	—0.37
17.58—17.82	—0.38
17.83—18.02	—0.39
18.03—18.27	—0.40
18.28—18.47	—0.41
18.48—18.67	—0.42
18.68—18.97	—0.43
18.98—19.17	—0.44
19.18—19.32	—0.45
19.33—19.52	—0.46
19.53—19.77	—0.47
19.78—19.97	—0.48

TABLE 209:IV. CONVERSION OF CHLOROSITY TO SALINITY

Conversion of 20 C chlorosity, $Cl/\text{liter}(20)$, to salinity, $S\%_0$, from the expression $S\%_0 = 0.03 +$
$$[1.8050 \times Cl/\text{liter}(20) \times 1/\rho(20)]$$
where $\rho(20)$ is the density of sea water at chlorosity $Cl/\text{liter}(20)$.

$Cl/\text{liter}_{(20)}$	$S\%_0$	$Cl/\text{liter}_{(20)}$	$S\%_0$	$Cl/\text{liter}_{(20)}$	$S\%_0$	$Cl/\text{liter}_{(20)}$	$S\%_0$
2.00	3.64	2.40	4.36	2.80	5.07	3.20	5.79
.01	.66	.41	.37	.81	.09	.21	.81
.02	.68	.42	.39	.82	.11	.22	.82
.03	.69	.43	.41	.83	.13	.23	.84
.04	.71	.44	.43	.84	.14	.24	.86
.05	.73	.45	.45	.85	.16	.25	.88
.06	.75	.46	.46	.86	.18	.26	.90
.07	.77	.47	.48	.87	.20	.27	.91
.08	.78	.48	.50	.88	.22	.28	.93
.09	.80	.49	.52	.89	.24	.29	.95
2.10	3.82	2.50	4.54	2.90	5.25	3.30	5.97
.11	.84	.51	.55	.91	.27	.31	5.99
.12	.86	.52	.57	.92	.29	.32	6.00
.13	.87	.53	.59	.93	.31	.33	.02
.14	.89	.54	.61	.94	.32	.34	.04
.15	.91	.55	.63	.95	.34	.35	.06
.16	.93	.56	.64	.96	.36	.36	.08
.17	.95	.57	.66	.97	.38	.37	.09
.18	.96	.58	.68	.98	.40	.38	.11
.19	3.98	.59	.70	.99	.41	.39	.13
2.20	4.00	2.60	4.71	3.00	5.43	3.40	6.15
.21	.02	.61	.73	.01	.45	.41	.16
.22	.03	.62	.75	.02	.47	.42	.18
.23	.05	.63	.77	.03	.48	.43	.20
.24	.07	.64	.79	.04	.50	.44	.22
.25	.09	.65	.80	.05	.52	.45	.24
.26	.11	.66	.82	.06	.54	.46	.25
.27	.12	.67	.84	.07	.56	.47	.27
.28	.14	.68	.86	.08	.57	.48	.29
.29	.16	.69	.88	.09	.59	.49	.31
2.30	4.18	2.70	4.89	3.10	5.61	3.50	6.33
.31	.20	.71	.91	.11	.63	.51	.34
.32	.21	.72	.93	.12	.65	.52	.36
.33	.23	.73	.95	.13	.66	.53	.38
.34	.25	.74	.97	.14	.68	.54	.40
.35	.27	.75	4.98	.15	.70	.55	.42
.36	.29	.76	5.00	.16	.72	.56	.43
.37	.30	.77	.02	.17	.74	.57	.45
.38	.32	.78	.04	.18	.75	.58	.47
.39	.34	.79	.06	.19	.77	.59	.49

TABLE 209:IV, CONT.

$Cl/liter_{(20)}$	$S‰$	$Cl/liter_{(20)}$	$S‰$	$Cl/liter_{(20)}$	$S‰$	$Cl/liter_{(20)}$	$S‰$
3.60	6.50	4.05	7.31	4.50	8.11	4.95	8.92
.61	.52	.06	.33	.51	.13	.96	.94
.62	.54	.07	.35	.52	.15	.97	.95
.63	.56	.08	.36	.53	.17	.98	.97
.64	.58	.09	.38	.54	.18	.99	.99
.65	.59	4.10	7.40	.55	.20	5.00	9.01
.66	.61	.11	.42	.56	.22	.01	.02
.67	.63	.12	.43	.57	.24	.02	.04
.68	.65	.13	.45	.58	.26	.03	.06
.69	.67	.14	.47	.59	.27	.04	.08
3.70	6.68	.15	.49	4.60	8.29	.05	.10
.71	.70	.16	.51	.61	.31	.06	.11
.72	.72	.17	.52	.62	.33	.07	.13
.73	.74	.18	.54	.63	.35	.08	.15
.74	.76	.19	.56	.64	.36	.09	.17
.75	.77	4.20	7.58	.65	.38	5.10	9.18
.76	.79	.21	.60	.66	.40	.11	.20
.77	.81	.22	.61	.67	.42	.12	.22
.78	.83	.23	.63	.68	.44	.13	.24
.79	.84	.24	.65	.69	.45	.14	.26
3.80	6.86	.25	.67	4.70	8.47	.15	.27
.81	.88	.26	.68	.71	.49	.16	.29
.82	.90	.27	.70	.72	.51	.17	.31
.83	.92	.28	.72	.73	.52	.18	.33
.84	.93	.29	.74	.74	.54	.19	.34
.85	.95	4.30	7.76	.75	.56	5.20	9.36
.86	.97	.31	.77	.76	.58	.21	.38
.87	6.98	.32	.79	.77	.60	.22	.40
.88	7.01	.33	.81	.78	.61	.23	.42
.89	.02	.34	.83	.79	.63	.24	.43
3.90	7.04	.35	.85	4.80	8.65	.25	.45
.91	.06	.36	.86	.81	.67	.26	.47
.92	.08	.37	.88	.82	.69	.27	.49
.93	.10	.38	.90	.83	.70	.28	.50
.94	.11	.39	.92	.84	.72	.29	.52
.95	.13	4.40	7.93	.85	.74	5.30	9.54
.96	.15	.41	.95	.86	.76	.31	.56
.97	.17	.42	.97	.87	.77	.32	.58
.98	.18	.43	7.99	.88	.79	.33	.59
.99	.20	.44	8.01	.89	.81	.34	.61
4.00	7.22	.45	.02	4.90	8.83	.35	.63
.01	.24	.46	.04	.91	.85	.36	.65
.02	.26	.47	.06	.92	.86	.37	.67
.03	.27	.48	.08	.93	.88	.38	.68
.04	.29	.49	.10	.94	.90	.39	.70

Table 209:IV, Cont.

$Cl/liter_{(20)}$	S^0/oo	$Cl/liter_{(20)}$	S^0/oo	$Cl/liter_{(20)}$	S^0/oo	$Cl/liter_{(20)}$	S^0/oo
5.40	9.72	5.85	10.52	6.30	11.32	6.75	12.12
.41	.74	.86	.54	.31	.34	.76	.14
.42	.75	.87	.56	.32	.36	.77	.16
.43	.77	.88	.57	.33	.37	.78	.17
.44	.79	.89	.59	.34	.39	.79	.19
.45	.81	5.90	10.61	.35	.41	6.80	12.21
.46	.83	.91	.63	.36	.43	.81	.23
.47	.84	.92	.64	.37	.44	.82	.24
.48	.86	.93	.66	.38	.46	.83	.26
.49	.88	.94	.68	.39	.48	.84	.28
5.50	9.90	.95	.70	6.40	11.50	.85	.30
.51	.91	.96	.72	.41	.52	.86	.31
.52	.93	.97	.73	.42	.53	.87	.33
.53	.95	.98	.75	.43	.55	.88	.35
.54	.97	.99	.77	.44	.57	.89	.37
.55	9.99	6.00	10.79	.45	.59	6.90	12.39
.56	10.00	.01	.81	.46	.60	.91	.40
.57	.02	.02	.82	.47	.62	.92	.42
.58	.04	.03	.84	.48	.64	.93	.44
.59	.06	.04	.86	.49	.66	.94	.46
5.60	10.07	.05	.88	6.50	11.68	.95	.47
.61	.09	.06	.89	.51	.69	.96	.49
.62	.11	.07	.91	.52	.71	.97	.51
.63	.13	.08	.93	.53	.73	.98	.53
.64	.15	.09	.95	.54	.75	.99	.55
.65	.16	6.10	10.97	.55	.76	7.00	12.56
.66	.18	.11	10.98	.56	.78	.01	.58
.67	.20	.12	11.00	.57	.80	.02	.60
.68	.22	.13	.02	.58	.82	.03	.62
.69	.24	.14	.04	.59	.84	.04	.63
5.70	10.25	.15	.05	6.60	11.85	.05	.65
.71	.27	.16	.07	.61	.87	.06	.67
.72	.29	.17	.09	.62	.89	.07	.69
.73	.31	.18	.11	.63	.91	.08	.71
.74	.32	.19	.12	.64	.92	.09	.72
.75	.34	6.20	11.14	.65	.94	7.10	12.74
.76	.36	.21	.16	.66	.96	.11	.76
.77	.38	.22	.18	.67	11.98	.12	.78
.78	.40	.23	.20	.68	12.00	.13	.79
.79	.41	.24	.21	.69	.01	.14	.81
5.80	10.43	.25	.23	6.70	12.03	.15	.83
.81	.45	.26	.25	.71	.05	.16	.85
.82	.47	.27	.27	.72	.07	.17	.86
.83	.48	.28	.28	.73	.08	.18	.88
.84	.50	.29	.30	.74	.10	.19	.90

TABLE 209:IV, CONT.

$Cl/\text{liter}_{(20)}$	S^0/oo	$Cl/\text{liter}_{(20)}$	S^0/oo	$Cl/\text{liter}_{(20)}$	S^0/oo	$Cl/\text{liter}_{(20)}$	S^0/oo
7.20	12.92	7.65	13.72	8.10	14.51	8.55	15.31
.21	.94	.66	.73	.11	.53	.56	.33
.22	.95	.67	.75	.12	.55	.57	.34
.23	.97	.68	.77	.13	.57	.58	.36
.24	12.99	.69	.79	.14	.58	.59	.38
.25	13.01	7.70	13.80	.15	.60	8.60	15.40
.26	.02	.71	.82	.16	.62	.61	.41
.27	.04	.72	.84	.17	.64	.62	.43
.28	.06	.73	.86	.18	.65	.63	.45
.29	.08	.74	.88	.19	.67	.64	.47
7.30	13.10	.75	.89	8.20	14.69	.65	.48
.31	.11	.76	.91	.21	.71	.66	.50
.32	.13	.77	.93	.22	.72	.67	.52
.33	.15	.78	.95	.23	.74	.68	.54
.34	.17	.79	.96	.24	.76	.69	.56
.35	.18	7.80	13.98	.25	.78	8.70	15.57
.36	.20	.81	14.00	.26	.80	.71	.59
.37	.22	.82	.02	.27	.81	.72	.61
.38	.24	.83	.03	.28	.83	.73	.63
.39	.25	.84	.05	.29	.85	.74	.64
7.40	13.27	.85	.07	8.30	14.87	.75	.66
.41	.29	.86	.09	.31	.88	.76	.68
.42	.31	.87	.11	.32	.90	.77	.70
.43	.33	.88	.12	.33	.92	.78	.71
.44	.34	.89	.14	.34	.94	.79	.73
.45	.36	7.90	14.16	.35	.95	8.80	15.75
.46	.38	.91	.18	.36	.97	.81	.77
.47	.40	.92	.19	.37	14.99	.82	.79
.48	.41	.93	.21	.38	15.01	.83	.80
.49	.43	.94	.23	.39	.03	.84	.82
7.50	13.45	.95	.25	8.40	15.04	.85	.84
.51	.47	.96	.27	.41	.06	.86	.86
.52	.49	.97	.28	.42	.08	.87	.87
.53	.50	.98	.30	.43	.10	.88	.89
.54	.52	.99	.32	.44	.11	.89	.91
.55	.54	8.00	14.34	.45	.13	8.90	15.93
.56	.56	.01	.35	.46	.15	.91	.94
.57	.57	.02	.37	.47	.17	.92	.96
.58	.59	.03	.39	.48	.18	.93	15.98
.59	.61	.04	.41	.49	.20	.94	16.00
7.60	13.63	.05	.42	8.50	15.22	.95	.01
.61	.65	.06	.44	.51	.24	.96	.03
.62	.66	.07	.46	.52	.25	.97	.05
.63	.68	.08	.48	.53	.27	.98	.07
.64	.70	.09	.50	.54	.29	.99	.09

TABLE 209:IV, CONT.

$Cl/liter_{(20)}$	$S\%o$	$Cl/liter_{(20)}$	$S\%o$	$Cl/liter_{(20)}$	$S\%o$	$Cl/liter_{(20)}$	$S\%o$
9.00	16.10	9.45	16.89	9.90	17.69	10.35	18.48
.01	.12	.46	.91	.91	.70	.36	.50
.02	.14	.47	.93	.92	.72	.37	.52
.03	.16	.48	.95	.93	.74	.38	.53
.04	.17	.49	.96	.94	.76	.39	.55
.05	.19	9.50	16.98	.95	.77	10.40	18.57
.06	.21	.51	17.00	.96	.79	.41	.59
.07	.23	.52	.02	.97	.81	.42	.60
.08	.24	.53	.03	.98	.83	.43	.62
.09	.26	.54	.05	.99	.85	.44	.64
9.10	16.28	.55	.07	10.00	17.87	.45	.66
.11	.30	.56	.09	.01	.88	.46	.67
.12	.31	.57	.11	.02	.90	.47	.69
.13	.33	.58	.12	.03	.92	.48	.71
.14	.35	.59	.14	.04	.94	.49	.73
.15	.37	9.60	17.16	.05	.95	10.50	18.74
.16	.38	.61	.18	.06	.97	.51	.76
.17	.40	.62	.19	.07	17.99	.52	.78
.18	.42	.63	.21	.08	18.01	.53	.80
.19	.44	.64	.23	.09	.02	.54	.81
9.20	16.45	.65	.25	10.10	18.04	.55	.83
.21	.47	.66	.26	.11	.06	.56	.85
.22	.49	.67	.28	.12	.08	.57	.87
.23	.51	.68	.30	.13	.09	.58	.88
.24	.53	.69	.32	.14	.11	.59	.90
.25	.54	9.70	17.33	.15	.13	10.60	18.92
.26	.56	.71	.35	.16	.15	.61	.94
.27	.58	.72	.37	.17	.16	.62	.96
.28	.60	.73	.39	.18	.18	.63	.97
.29	.61	.74	.40	.19	.20	.64	18.99
9.30	16.63	.75	.42	10.20	18.22	.65	19.01
.31	.65	.76	.44	.21	.23	.66	.03
.32	.67	.77	.46	.22	.25	.67	.04
.33	.68	.78	.47	.23	.27	.68	.06
.34	.70	.79	.49	.24	.29	.69	.08
.35	.72	9.80	17.51	.25	.30	10.70	19.10
.36	.74	.81	.53	.26	.32	.71	.11
.37	.75	.82	.54	.27	.34	.72	.13
.38	.77	.83	.56	.28	.36	.73	.15
.39	.79	.84	.58	.29	.38	.74	.17
9.40	16.81	.85	.60	10.30	18.39	.75	.18
.41	.82	.86	.62	.31	.41	.76	.20
.42	.84	.87	.63	.32	.43	.77	.22
.43	.86	.88	.65	.33	.45	.78	.24
.44	.88	.89	.67	.34	.46	.79	.25

TABLE 209:IV, CONT.

Cl/liter$_{(20)}$	S‰	Cl/liter$_{(20)}$	S‰	Cl/liter$_{(20)}$	S‰	Cl/liter$_{(20)}$	S‰
10.80	19.27	11.25	20.06	11.70	20.85	12.15	21.64
.81	.29	.26	.08	.71	.87	.16	.66
.82	.31	.27	.10	.72	.89	.17	.68
.83	.32	.28	.11	.73	.90	.18	.69
.84	.34	.29	.13	.74	.92	.19	.71
.85	.36	11.30	20.15	.75	.94	12.20	21.73
.86	.38	.31	.17	.76	.96	.21	.75
.87	.39	.32	.18	.77	.97	.22	.76
.88	.41	.33	.20	.78	20.99	.23	.78
.89	.43	.34	.22	.79	21.01	.24	.80
10.90	19.45	.35	.24	11.80	21.03	.25	.82
.91	.47	.36	.26	.81	.04	.26	.83
.92	.48	.37	.27	.82	.06	.27	.85
.93	.50	.38	.29	.83	.08	.28	.87
.94	.52	.39	.31	.84	.10	.29	.89
.95	.54	11.40	20.33	.85	.11	12.30	21.90
.96	.55	.41	.34	.86	.13	.31	.92
.97	.57	.42	.36	.87	.15	.32	.94
.98	.59	.43	.38	.88	.17	.33	.96
.99	.61	.44	.40	.89	.18	.34	.97
11.00	19.62	.45	.41	11.90	21.20	.35	21.99
.01	.64	.46	.43	.91	.22	.36	22.01
.02	.66	.47	.45	.92	.24	.37	.03
.03	.68	.48	.47	.93	.26	.38	.04
.04	.69	.49	.48	.94	.27	.39	.06
.05	.71	11.50	20.50	.95	.29	12.40	22.08
.06	.73	.51	.52	.96	.31	.41	.09
.07	.75	.52	.54	.97	.33	.42	.11
.08	.76	.53	.55	.98	.34	.43	.13
.09	.78	.54	.57	.99	.36	.44	.15
11.10	19.80	.55	.59	12.00	21.38	.45	.16
.11	.82	.56	.61	.01	.40	.46	.18
.12	.83	.57	.62	.02	.41	.47	.20
.13	.85	.58	.64	.03	.43	.48	.22
.14	.87	.59	.66	.04	.45	.49	.23
.15	.89	11.60	20.68	.05	.47	12.50	22.25
.16	.90	.61	.69	.06	.48	.51	.27
.17	.92	.62	.71	.07	.50	.52	.29
.18	.94	.63	.73	.08	.52	.53	.30
.19	.96	.64	.75	.09	.54	.54	.32
11.20	19.97	.65	.76	12.10	21.55	.55	.34
.21	19.99	.66	.78	.11	.57	.56	.36
.22	20.01	.67	.80	.12	.59	.57	.37
.23	.03	.68	.82	.13	.61	.58	.39
.24	.04	.69	.83	.14	.62	.59	.41

TABLE 209:IV, CONT.

$Cl/\text{liter}_{(20)}$	S^0/oo	$Cl/\text{liter}_{(20)}$	S^0/oo	$Cl/\text{liter}_{(20)}$	S^0/oo	$Cl/\text{liter}_{(20)}$	S^0/oo
12.60	22.43	13.05	23.21	13.50	24.00	13.95	24.79
.61	.44	.06	.23	.51	.02	.96	.80
.62	.46	.07	.25	.52	.03	.97	.82
.63	.48	.08	.27	.53	.05	.98	.84
.64	.50	.09	.28	.54	.07	.99	.85
.65	.51	13.10	23.30	.55	.09	14.00	24.87
.66	.53	.11	.32	.56	.10	.01	.89
.67	.55	.12	.34	.57	.12	.02	.91
.68	.57	.13	.35	.58	.14	.03	.92
.69	.58	.14	.37	.59	.16	.04	.94
12.70	22.60	.15	.39	13.60	24.17	.05	.96
.71	.62	.16	.41	.61	.19	.06	.98
.72	.64	.17	.42	.62	.21	.07	24.99
.73	.65	.18	.44	.63	.23	.08	25.01
.74	.67	.19	.46	.64	.24	.09	.03
.75	.69	13.20	23.48	.65	.26	14.10	25.05
.76	.71	.21	.49	.66	.28	.11	.06
.77	.72	.22	.51	.67	.30	.12	.08
.78	.74	.23	.53	.68	.31	.13	.10
.79	.76	.24	.55	.69	.33	.14	.12
12.80	22.78	.25	.56	13.70	24.35	.15	.13
.81	.79	.26	.58	.71	.37	.16	.15
.82	.81	.27	.60	.72	.38	.17	.17
.83	.83	.28	.62	.73	.40	.18	.19
.84	.85	.29	.63	.74	.42	.19	.20
.85	.86	13.30	23.65	.75	.44	14.20	25.22
.86	.88	.31	.67	.76	.45	.21	.24
.87	.90	.32	.69	.77	.47	.22	.26
.88	.92	.33	.70	.78	.49	.23	.27
.89	.93	.34	.72	.79	.51	.24	.29
12.90	22.95	.35	.74	13.80	24.52	.25	.31
.91	.97	.36	.76	.81	.54	.26	.32
.92	22.99	.37	.77	.82	.56	.27	.34
.93	23.00	.38	.79	.83	.58	.28	.36
.94	.02	.39	.81	.84	.59	.29	.38
.95	.04	13.40	23.83	.85	.61	14.30	25.39
.96	.06	.41	.84	.86	.63	.31	.41
.97	.07	.42	.86	.87	.65	.32	.43
.98	.09	.43	.88	.88	.66	.33	.45
.99	.11	.44	.89	.89	.68	.34	.46
13.00	23.13	.45	.91	13.90	24.70	.35	.48
.01	.14	.46	.93	.91	.72	.36	.50
.02	.16	.47	.95	.92	.73	.37	.52
.03	.18	.48	.96	.93	.75	.38	.53
.04	.20	.49	.98	.94	.77	.39	.55

TABLE 209:IV, CONT.

Cl/liter$_{(20)}$	S‰	Cl/liter$_{(20)}$	S‰	Cl/liter$_{(20)}$	S‰	Cl/liter$_{(20)}$	S‰
14.40	25.57	14.85	26.35	15.30	27.13	15.75	27.91
.41	.59	.86	.37	.31	.15	.76	.93
.42	.60	.87	.39	.32	.17	.77	.95
.43	.62	.88	.40	.33	.18	.78	.97
.44	.64	.89	.42	.34	.20	.79	.98
.45	.66	14.90	26.44	.35	.22	15.80	28.00
.46	.67	.91	.46	.36	.24	.81	.02
.47	.69	.92	.47	.37	.25	.82	.03
.48	.71	.93	.49	.38	.27	.83	.05
.49	.72	.94	.51	.39	.29	.84	.07
14.50	25.74	.95	.53	15.40	27.31	.85	.09
.51	.76	.96	.54	.41	.32	.86	.10
.52	.78	.97	.56	.42	.34	.87	.12
.53	.79	.98	.58	.43	.36	.88	.14
.54	.81	.99	.59	.44	.38	.89	.16
.55	.83	15.00	26.61	.45	.39	15.90	28.17
.56	.85	.01	.63	.46	.41	.91	.19
.57	.86	.02	.65	.47	.43	.92	.21
.58	.88	.03	.66	.48	.44	.93	.23
.59	.90	.04	.68	.49	.46	.94	.24
14.60	25.92	.05	.70	15.50	27.48	.95	.26
.61	.93	.06	.72	.51	.50	.96	.28
.62	.95	.07	.73	.52	.51	.97	.29
.63	.97	.08	.75	.53	.53	.98	.31
.64	25.99	.09	.77	.54	.55	.99	.33
.65	26.00	15.10	26.79	.55	.57	16.00	28.35
.66	.02	.11	.80	.56	.58	.01	.36
.67	.04	.12	.82	.57	.60	.02	.38
.68	.06	.13	.84	.58	.62	.03	.40
.69	.07	.14	.86	.59	.64	.04	.42
14.70	26.09	.15	.87	15.60	27.65	.05	.43
.71	.11	.16	.89	.61	.67	.06	.45
.72	.13	.17	.91	.62	.69	.07	.47
.73	.14	.18	.92	.63	.71	.08	.49
.74	.16	.19	.94	.64	.72	.09	.50
.75	.18	15.20	26.96	.65	.74	16.10	28.52
.76	.19	.21	.98	.66	.76	.11	.54
.77	.21	.22	26.99	.67	.77	.12	.55
.78	.23	.23	27.01	.68	.79	.13	.57
.79	.25	.24	.03	.69	.81	.14	.59
14.80	26.26	.25	.05	15.70	27.83	.15	.61
.81	.28	.26	.06	.71	.84	.16	.62
.82	.30	.27	.08	.72	.86	.17	.64
.83	.32	.28	.10	.73	.88	.18	.66
.84	.33	.29	.12	.74	.90	.19	.68

TABLE 209:IV, CONT.

$Cl/liter_{(20)}$	$S\permil$	$Cl/liter_{(20)}$	$S\permil$	$Cl/liter_{(20)}$	$S\permil$	$Cl/liter_{(20)}$	$S\permil$
16.20	28.69	16.65	29.47	17.10	30.25	17.55	31.03
.21	.71	.66	.49	.11	.27	.56	.04
.22	.73	.67	.51	.12	.28	.57	.06
.23	.75	.68	.52	.13	.30	.58	.08
.24	.76	.69	.54	.14	.32	.59	.10
.25	.78	16.70	29.56	.15	.34	17.60	31.11
.26	.80	.71	.58	.16	.35	.61	.13
.27	.82	.72	.59	.17	.37	.62	.15
.28	.83	.73	.61	.18	.39	.63	.17
.29	.85	.74	.63	.19	.41	.64	.18
16.30	28.87	.75	.65	17.20	30.42	.65	.20
.31	.88	.76	.66	.21	.44	.66	.22
.32	.90	.77	.68	.22	.46	.67	.23
.33	.92	.78	.70	.23	.47	.68	.25
.34	.94	.79	.71	.24	.49	.69	.27
.35	.95	16.80	29.73	.25	.51	17.70	31.29
.36	.97	.81	.75	.26	.53	.71	.30
.37	28.99	.82	.77	.27	.54	.72	.32
.38	29.00	.83	.78	.28	.56	.73	.34
.39	.02	.84	.80	.29	.58	.74	.36
16.40	29.04	.85	.82	17.30	30.60	.75	.37
.41	.06	.86	.84	.31	.61	.76	.39
.42	.07	.87	.85	.32	.63	.77	.41
.43	.09	.88	.87	.33	.65	.78	.42
.44	.11	.89	.89	.34	.66	.79	.44
.45	.13	16.90	29.90	.35	.68	17.80	31.46
.46	.14	.91	.92	.36	.70	.81	.48
.47	.16	.92	.94	.37	.72	.82	.49
.48	.18	.93	.96	.38	.73	.83	.51
.49	.20	.94	.97	.39	.75	.84	.53
16.50	29.21	.95	29.99	17.40	30.77	.85	.55
.51	.23	.96	30.01	.41	.79	.86	.56
.52	.25	.97	.03	.42	.80	.87	.58
.53	.26	.98	.04	.43	.82	.88	.60
.54	.28	.99	.06	.44	.84	.89	.61
.55	.30	17.00	30.08	.45	.85	17.90	31.63
.56	.32	.01	.09	.46	.87	.91	.65
.57	.33	.02	.11	.47	.89	.92	.67
.58	.35	.03	.13	.48	.91	.93	.68
.59	.37	.04	.15	.49	.92	.94	.70
16.60	29.39	.05	.16	17.50	30.94	.95	.72
.61	.40	.06	.18	.51	.96	.96	.74
.62	.42	.07	.20	.52	.98	.97	.75
.63	.44	.08	.22	.53	30.99	.98	.77
.64	.45	.09	.23	.54	31.01	.99	.79

TABLE 209:IV, CONT.

$Cl/liter_{(20)}$	S^0/oo	$Cl/liter_{(20)}$	S^0/oo	$Cl/liter_{(20)}$	S^0/oo	$Cl/liter_{(20)}$	S^0/oo
18.00	31.80	18.45	32.58	18.90	33.36	19.35	34.13
.01	.82	.46	.60	.91	.37	.36	.15
.02	.84	.47	.61	.92	.39	.37	.16
.03	.86	.48	.63	.93	.41	.38	.18
.04	.87	.49	.65	.94	.42	.39	.20
.05	.89	18.50	32.67	.95	.44	19.40	34.22
.06	.91	.51	.68	.96	.46	.41	.23
.07	.92	.52	.70	.97	.48	.42	.25
.08	.94	.53	.72	.98	.49	.43	.27
.09	.96	.54	.73	.99	.51	.44	.28
18.10	31.98	.55	.75	19.00	33.53	.45	.30
.11	31.99	.56	.77	.01	.54	.46	.32
.12	32.01	.57	.79	.02	.56	.47	.34
.13	.03	.58	.80	.03	.58	.48	.35
.14	.05	.59	.82	.04	.60	.49	.37
.15	.06	18.60	32.84	.05	.61	19.50	34.39
.16	.08	.61	.86	.06	.63	.51	.40
.17	.10	.62	.87	.07	.65	.52	.42
.18	.11	.63	.89	.08	.67	.53	.44
.19	.13	.64	.91	.09	.68	.54	.46
18.20	32.15	.65	.92	19.10	33.70	.55	.47
.21	.17	.66	.94	.11	.72	.56	.49
.22	.18	.67	.96	.12	.73	.57	.51
.23	.20	.68	.98	.13	.75	.58	.52
.24	.22	.69	32.99	.14	.77	.59	.54
.25	.23	18.70	33.01	.15	.79	19.60	34.56
.26	.25	.71	.03	.16	.80	.61	.58
.27	.27	.72	.05	.17	.82	.62	.59
.28	.29	.73	.06	.18	.84	.63	.61
.29	.30	.74	.08	.19	.85	.64	.63
18.30	32.32	.75	.10	19.20	33.87	.65	.64
.31	.34	.76	.11	.21	.89	.66	.66
.32	.36	.77	.13	.22	.91	.67	.68
.33	.37	.78	.15	.23	.92	.68	.70
.34	.39	.79	.17	.24	.94	.69	.71
.35	.41	18.80	33.18	.25	.96	19.70	34.73
.36	.42	.81	.20	.26	.97	.71	.75
.37	.44	.82	.22	.27	33.99	.72	.77
.38	.46	.83	.23	.28	34.01	.73	.78
.39	.48	.84	.25	.29	.03	.74	.80
18.40	32.49	.85	.27	19.30	34.04	.75	.82
.41	.51	.86	.29	.31	.06	.76	.83
.42	.53	.87	.30	.32	.08	.77	.85
.43	.55	.88	.32	.33	.09	.78	.87
.44	.56	.89	.34	.34	.11	.79	.89

Table 209:IV, Cont.

$Cl/liter_{(20)}$	$S‰$	$Cl/liter_{(20)}$	$S‰$	$Cl/liter_{(20)}$	$S‰$	$Cl/liter_{(20)}$	$S‰$
19.80	34.90	20.25	35.68	20.70	36.45	21.15	37.22
.81	.92	.26	.70	.71	.47	.16	.24
.82	.94	.27	.71	.72	.48	.17	.25
.83	.95	.28	.73	.73	.50	.18	.27
.84	.97	.29	.74	.74	.52	.19	.29
.85	34.99	20.30	35.76	.75	.53	21.20	37.30
.86	35.01	.31	.78	.76	.55	.21	.32
.87	.02	.32	.80	.77	.57	.22	.34
.88	.04	.33	.82	.78	.59	.23	.36
.89	.06	.34	.83	.79	.60	.24	.37
19.90	35.07	.35	.85	20.80	36.62	.25	.39
.91	.09	.36	.87	.81	.64	.26	.40
.92	.11	.37	.88	.82	.65	.27	.42
.93	.13	.38	.90	.83	.67	.28	.44
.94	.14	.39	.92	.84	.69	.29	.46
.95	.16	20.40	35.93	.85	.71	21.30	37.47
.96	.18	.41	.95	.86	.72	.31	.49
.97	.19	.42	.97	.87	.74	.32	.51
.98	.21	.43	35.99	.88	.76	.33	.53
.99	.23	.44	36.00	.89	.77	.34	.54
20.00	35.25	.45	.02	20.90	36.79	.35	.56
.01	.27	.46	.04	.91	.81	.36	.58
.02	.28	.47	.06	.92	.83	.37	.59
.03	.30	.48	.07	.93	.84	.38	.61
.04	.32	.49	.09	.94	.86	.39	.63
.05	.34	20.50	36.11	.95	.88	21.40	37.65
.06	.35	.51	.12	.96	.89	.41	.66
.07	.37	.52	.14	.97	.91	.42	.68
.08	.39	.53	.16	.98	.93	.43	.70
.09	.40	.54	.18	.99	.94	.44	.71
20.10	35.42	.55	.19	21.00	36.96	.45	.73
.11	.44	.56	.21	.01	36.98	.46	.75
.12	.46	.57	.23	.02	37.00	.47	.77
.13	.47	.58	.24	.03	.01	.48	.78
.14	.50	.59	.26	.04	.03	.49	.80
.15	.51	20.60	36.28	.05	.05	21.50	37.82
.16	.52	.61	.30	.06	.06	.51	.83
.17	.54	.62	.31	.07	.08	.52	.85
.18	.56	.63	.33	.08	.10	.53	.87
.19	.58	.64	.35	.09	.12	.54	.89
20.20	35.59	.65	.36	21.10	37.13	.55	.90
.21	.61	.66	.38	.11	.15	.56	.92
.22	.63	.67	.40	.12	.17	.57	.94
.23	.64	.68	.41	.13	.18	.58	.95
.24	.66	.69	.43	.14	.20	.59	.97

TABLE 209:IV, CONT.

$Cl/\text{liter}_{(20)}$	$S^0/\!oo$	$Cl/\text{liter}_{(20)}$	$S^0/\!oo$	$Cl/\text{liter}_{(20)}$	$S^0/\!oo$	$Cl/\text{liter}_{(20)}$	$S^0/\!oo$
21.60	37.99	21.70	38.16	21.80	38.33	21.90	38.50
.61	38.00	.71	.17	.81	.34	.91	.51
.62	.02	.72	.19	.82	.36	.92	.53
.63	.04	.73	.21	.83	.38	.93	.55
.64	.06	.74	.23	.84	.40	.94	.57
.65	.07	.75	.24	.85	.41	.95	.58
.66	.09	.76	.26	.86	.43	.96	.60
.67	.11	.77	.28	.87	.45	.97	.62
.68	.12	.78	.29	.88	.46	.98	.63
.69	.14	.79	.31	.89	.48	.99	.65
						22.00	38.67

SOURCE: A Manual of Sea Water Analysis. Department of Public Printing and Stationery, Ottawa, Canada.

209 D.   Reference

1. FORD, W.L. & E.S. DEEVEY, JR. 1946. The Determination of Chlorinity by the Knudsen Method. Woods Hole Oceanographic Inst., Woods Hole, Mass.

209 E.   Bibliography

THOMPSON, T.G. 1928. Standardization of silver nitrate solutions used in chemical studies of sea water. *J. Amer. Chem. Soc.* 50:618.

SVERDRUP, H.V., M.W. JOHNSON & R.H. FLEMING. 1942. The Oceans. Prentice-Hall, Inc., Englewood Cliffs, N.J.

ZERBE, W.B. & C.B. TAYLOR. 1953. Sea Water Temperature and Density Reduction Tables. Coast & Geodetic Survey, U.S. Dept. Commerce, Spec. Publ. No. 298. U.S. Govt. Print. Off., Washington, D.C.

VAN ARX, W.S. 1962. Introduction to Physical Oceanography. Addison-Wesley Publ. Co., Reading, Mass.

STRICKLAND, J.D.H. & T.R. PARSONS. 1968. A Practical Handbook of Seawater Analysis. Fisheries Research Board, Ottawa, Canada.

210 SPECIFIC GRAVITY

Specific gravity is determined by comparing the weight of a volume of the sample of mud, sludge, or industrial waste with that of an equal volume of distilled water.

Weigh to the nearest 0.1 g an empty wide-mouth flask or bottle of about 250-ml capacity. Fill completely with distilled water and weigh again.

If the sample flows readily, fill the flask completely with the sample, weigh, and calculate the result:

$$sp\ gr = \frac{weight\ of\ sample}{weight\ of\ distilled\ water}$$

If the sample does not flow readily, add as much of it to the bottle as possible, without exerting pressure, and weigh. Fill the bottle containing the sample with water and weigh again, making sure that all entrained air bubbles have escaped. Determine the weight of added water by difference. Then:

$$sp\ gr = \frac{A}{B - C}$$

where A = weight of sample, B = weight of water to fill bottle, and C = weight of water added to sample.

211 TASTE

Taste, like odor, is one of the chemical senses. Most of the general principles of sensory methods described in Section 206 (Odor) apply equally to the taste determination and should be reviewed as background to this section.

The differences between the two sense modes are reflected in their corresponding measurement methods. Taste and odor differ in the nature and location of the receptor nerve sites: high in the nasal cavity for odor, and primarily on the tongue for taste.[1] The odor sensation is stimulated by vapors without physical contact with a water sample, while taste requires contact of the taste buds with the water sample. Taste is simpler than odor—there may be only four true taste sensations: sour, sweet, salty, and bitter. Dissolved inorganic salts of copper, iron, manganese, potassium, sodium, and zinc[2] can be detected by taste. The taste sense is moderately sensitive. Concentrations producing taste range from a few tenths to several hundred milligrams per liter. The complex sensation experienced in the mouth during the act of tasting is a combination of taste, odor, temperature, and feel; this combination is often called flavor. Taste tests usually have to deal with this complex combination. If a water sample contains no detectable odor and is presented at near body temperature, the resulting sensation is predominantly true taste.

It may not be assumed that a tasteless water is most desirable; it has become almost axiomatic that distilled water is less pleasant to drink than certain high-quality waters. Accordingly, there are two distinct purposes of taste tests. The first is to measure taste intensity by the so-called threshold test. The test results are used to assess treatment or pollution abatement required to convert a water source into a quality drinking water supply or to measure the taste impact of specific contaminants.[3] The second purpose of taste testing is to evaluate the consumer's judgment of the quality of a drinking water. This test involves a panel evaluation of undiluted samples presented as ordinarily consumed.[3] A mean acceptance rating of the sample is determined, based upon a specified rating scale.[4]

Values representing mean thresholds or quality ratings for a laboratory panel are only estimates of these values for the entire consuming population.[5]

Taste tests are performed only on samples known to be safe for ingestion.

Samples that may be contaminated with bacteria, viruses, parasites, or toxic chemicals such as arsenic dechlorinating agents, or that are derived from an unesthetic source, are not used for taste tests. A laboratory performing taste tests must observe all sanitary and esthetic precautions with regard to apparatus and containers contacting the sample. Hospital-level sanitation of these items and of the small containers for the taste sample must be observed scrupulously. Panel taste tests are not performed on wastewaters or similar untreated effluents.

Use the procedures described in Section 206 with respect to purity of taste and odor-free water and use of panels of observers.

211 A.   Taste Threshold Test

1. General Discussion

The threshold test is used when the purpose is quantitative measurement of detectable taste. When odor is the predominant sensation, as in the case of chlorophenols, the threshold odor test of Section 206 takes priority.

2. Apparatus

a. Preparation of dilutions: Use the same dilution system as that described for odor tests in preparing taste samples.

b. For tasting: Present each dilution and blank to the observer in a clean 50-ml beaker filled to the 30-ml level. An automatic dishwasher supplied with water at not less than 60 C is convenient

for sanitizing these beakers between tests.

c. Temperature control: Carefully maintain sample presentation temperature of 40 C by use of a water bath apparatus.

3. Procedure

Prepare a dilution series (including random blanks) as described in Section 206 and bring to the test temperature in the water bath. Present the series of unknown samples to each judge. Pair each sample with a known blank sample, both containing 30 ml of water in the 50-ml beaker. Have the judge taste the sample by taking into the mouth whatever volume of sample is comfortable, holding it for several seconds, and discharging it without swallowing the water. Have the judge compare the sample with the blank and record whether a taste or aftertaste is detectable in the unknown sample. Submit the samples in an increasing order of concentration until the judge's taste threshold has been passed.

Calculate the individual threshold and the threshold of a panel in the manner described for threshold odor tests.

211 B.   Taste Rating Test

1. General Discussion

When the purpose of the test is to estimate taste acceptability, follow the taste rating procedure described below. This procedure has been used with water samples from public sources in laboratory research and consumer surveys in order to recommend standards governing mineral content in drinking water.[6] In this procedure, each judge (tester) is presented with a list of nine statements about the water, ranging on a scale from very favorable to very unfavorable. The tester's task is to select the statement that best expresses his opinion. The scored rating is the scale number of the statement selected. The panel rating is the arithmetic mean of the scale numbers of all judges.

2. Apparatus

a. *Preparation of samples:* Samples for this test usually represent public finished water ready for human consumption; however, experimentally treated water may be used *if the sanitary requirements given in the introductory material of Section 211 are met fully.* Taste- and odor-free water, and a 2,000-mg/l solution of NaCl prepared with taste- and odor-free water, are recommended as reference samples.

b. *For tasting:* Present each sample to the observer in a clean 50-ml beaker filled to the 30-ml level. An automatic dishwasher supplied with water at not less than 60 C is convenient for sanitizing beakers between tests.

c. *Temperature control:* Present samples at a temperature that the judges will find pleasant for drinking water; maintain this temperature by a water bath apparatus. A standard temperature of 15 C is recommended, but in any case, do not allow the test temperature to exceed tap water temperatures that are customary at the time of the test. Always specify the test temperature in the test results.

3. Procedure

For test efficiency, a single rating session may contain up to 10 samples, including the reference samples noted above. Judges will work alone after receiving thorough instructions and trial or orientation sessions followed by questions and discussion of procedures. Select

panel members on the basis of performance in trial sessions. Rating involves the
following steps: *a)* initial tasting of
about half of the sample by taking the
water into the mouth, holding it for several seconds, and discharging it without
swallowing; *b)* forming an initial judgment on the rating scale; *c)* a second
tasting conducted in the same manner as
the first; *d)* a final rating made for the
sample and the result recorded on the
appropriate data form; *e)* rinsing the
mouth with taste- and odor-free water;
and *f)* resting 1 min before repeating
Steps *a* through *e* on the next samples.
Independently randomize sample order
for each judge. Allow at least 30 min of
rest between repeated rating sessions.
Judges should not know the composition
or source of specific samples. Use the following scale for rating and record ratings as integers ranging from one to
nine, with one given the highest quality
rating.

Calculate the mean and standard deviation of all ratings given each sample.

4. Rating Scale

Action tendency scale:

1) I would be very happy to accept this water as my everyday
   drinking water.
2) I would be happy to accept this
   water as my everyday drinking
   water.
3) I am sure that I could accept
   this water as my everyday
   drinking water.
4) I could accept this water as my
   everyday drinking water.
5) Maybe I could accept this water as my everyday drinking
   water.
6) I don't think I could accept this
   water as my everyday drinking
   water.
7) I could not accept this water as
   my everyday drinking water.
8) I could never drink this water.
9) I can't stand this water in my
   mouth and I could never drink
   it.

211 C.   References

1. GELDARD, F.A. 1972. The Human Senses.
   John Wiley & Sons, New York, N.Y.
2. COHEN, J.M., L.J. KAMPHAKE, E.K. HARRIS
   & R.L. WOODWARD. 1960. Taste threshold
   concentrations of metals in drinking water. *J.
   Amer. Water Works Ass.* 52:660.
3. BRUVOLD, W.H., H.J. ONGERTH & R.C.
   DILLEHAY. 1967. Consumer attitudes toward mineral taste in domestic water. *J.
   Amer. Water Works Ass.* 59:547.
4. BRUVOLD, W.H. 1968. Scales for rating the
   taste of water. *J. Appl. Psychol.* 52:245.
5. BRUVOLD, W.H. 1970. Laboratory panel estimation of consumer assessments of taste
   and flavor. *J. Appl. Psychol.* 54:326.
6. BRUVOLD, W.H., H.J. ONGERTH & R.C.
   DILLEHAY. 1969. Consumer assessment of
   mineral taste in domestic water. *J. Amer.
   Water Works Ass.* 61:575.

211 D.   Bibliography

Cox, G.J. & J.W. Nathaus. 1952. A study of the taste of fluoridated water. *J. Amer. Water Works Ass.* 44:940.

Lockhart, E.E., C.L. Tucker & M.C. Merritt. 1955. The effect of water impurities on the flavor of brewed coffee. *Food Res.* 20:598.

Campbell, C.L., R.K. Dawes, S. Deolalkar & M.C. Merritt. 1958. Effect of certain chemicals in water on the flavor of brewed coffee. *Food Res.* 23:575.

Cohen, J.M. 1963. Taste and odor of ABS in water. *J. Amer. Water Works Ass.* 55:587.

Bruvold, W.H. & R.M. Pangborn. 1966. Rat-
ed acceptability of mineral taste in water. *J. Appl. Psychol.* 50:22.

Bruvold, W.H. & W.R. Gaffey. 1969. Rated acceptability of mineral taste in water: II. Combinatorial effects of ions on quality and action tendency ratings. *J. Appl. Psychol.* 53:317.

Bruvold, W.H. & H.J. Ongerth. 1969. Taste quality of mineralized water. *J. Amer. Water Works Ass.* 61:170.

Bryan, P.E., L.N. Kuzminski, F.M. Sawyer & T.H. Feng. 1973. Taste thresholds of halogens in water. *J. Amer. Water Works Ass.* 65:363.

212   TEMPERATURE

1. General Discussion

Temperature readings are used in the calculation of various forms of alkalinity, in studies of saturation and stability with respect to calcium carbonate, in the calculation of salinity, and in general laboratory operations. In limnological studies, water temperatures as a function of depth often are required. Elevated temperatures resulting from heated water discharges may have significant ecological impact. Identification of source of water supply, such as deep wells, often is possible by temperature measurements alone. Industrial plants often require data on water temperature for process use or heat-transmission calculations.

Normally, temperature measurements may be made with any good grade of mercury-filled Celsius thermometer. As a minimum, the thermometer should have a scale marked for every 0.1 C. Markings should be etched on the capillary glass. The thermometer should have a minimal thermal capacity

to permit rapid equilibration. It should be checked against a precision thermometer certified by the National Bureau of Standards,* which should always be used with its certificate and correction chart. For field use a thermometer should be provided with a metal case to prevent breakage.

Depth temperature required for limnological studies may be measured with a reversing thermometer, thermophone, or thermistor. The thermistor is most convenient and accurate; however, higher cost may preclude its use. Any temperature measurement devices should be calibrated with a National Bureau of Standards certified thermometer before field use. Make readings with the thermometer or device immersed in water long enough to permit complete equilibration. Report results to the nearest 0.1 or 1.0 C, depending on need.

---

*Some commercial thermometers may be as much as 3 C in error.

2. Reversing Thermometer

The thermometer commonly used for depth measurements is of the reversing type. It is often mounted on the sample collection apparatus so that a water sample may be obtained simultaneously. Correct readings of reversing thermometers for changes due to differences between temperature at reversal and temperature at time of reading. Calculate as follows:

$$\Delta T = \left[\frac{(T^1-t)(T^1+V_o)}{K} \right]$$
$$\times \left[\frac{1+(T^1-t)(T^1+V_0)}{K} \right] + L$$

where:

ΔT = correction to be added algebraically to uncorrected reading,

T^1 = uncorrected reading at reversal,

t = temperature at which thermometer is read,

V_o = volume of small bulb end of capillary up to 0 C graduation,

K = constant depending on relative thermal expansion of mercury and glass (usual value of K = 6,100), and

L = calibration correction of thermometer depending on T^1.

If series observations are made it is convenient to prepare graphs for a thermometer to obtain ΔT from any values of T^1 and t.

3. Bibliography

WARREN, H.F. & G.C. WHIPPLE. 1895. The thermophone—A new instrument for determining temperatures. *Mass. Inst. Technol. Quart.* 8:125.

SVERDRUP, H.V., M.W. JOHNSON & R.H. FLEMING. 1942. The Oceans. Prentice-Hall, Inc., Englewood Cliffs, N.J.

AMERICAN SOCIETY FOR TESTING AND MATERIALS. 1949. Standard Specifications for ASTM Thermometers. No. E1-58, ASTM, Philadelphia, Pa.

REE, W.R. 1953. Thermistors for depth thermometry. *J. Amer. Water Works Ass.* 45:259.

213   TESTS ON ACTIVATED SLUDGE

The activated sludge process of wastewater treatment is dependent on laboratory control through use of the procedures described in this section. The results obtained from these tests are most useful when the tests are performed daily or more frequently over a period of time. The operator can then learn from experience the normal range of values for the particular type of activated sludge produced in that specific plant and how plant operation best can be adjusted in response to changes in the sludge characteristics.

The results of these tests are also used in design of activated sludge systems. The oxygen consumption rate test can be used to detect toxicity of wastewater components and to determine the oxygen transfer requirements of the aeration system. The sludge volume index can be used to determine the required capacities of pumps and piping for return sludge facilities and waste sludge facilities. The zone settling rate can be used to determine the surface area requirements of the final settling tank.

213 A. Suspended Matter

Determine suspended matter in sludges, aeration tank mixed liquor, and effluent by gravimetric methods (Residue, Section 208).

213 B. Oxygen Consumption Rate

1. General Discussion

This test is used in the determination of the rate of oxygen consumption of a sample of activated sludge. It has been found useful in laboratory and pilot-plant studies as well as in the operation of full-scale treatment plants. When used as a routine plant operation test, it often will detect changes in operating conditions at an early stage.

2. Apparatus

a. Oxygen consumption rate device such as an oxygen-sensitive membrane electrode (polarographic or galvanic) or a manometric device, with appropriate readout and a sample capacity of at least 300 ml. The apparatus should have an oxygen supply capacity greater than the actual oxygen consumption rate. Provide agitation by a suitable stirring mechanism.

b. Stopwatch or other suitable timing device, or recorder.

3. Procedure

a. Calibration of apparatus: Calibrate the apparatus according to the manufacturer's instructions.

b. Mixed liquor solids determination: Determine the volatile suspended solids concentration of the activated sludge to be tested by gravimetric methods (Residue, Section 208).

c. Preparation of activated sludge sample: Before testing, increase the dissolved oxygen concentration of the sample to near saturation. This can be done by shaking the sample in a partially filled bottle or by bubbling air or oxygen through the sample.

d. Measurement of oxygen consumption rate:

1) Fill the sample chamber with an appropriate volume of mixed liquor and drop a magnetic stirring rod into the chamber.

2) If a BOD bottle is used, insert the probe into the bottle as rapidly as possible after filling. The probe should displace enough liquid to fill the flared top of the bottle and seal the probe. Switch on the stirring mechanism. If a manometric device is used, see the manufacturer's instructions for any special directions to initiate the procedure.

3) Thoroughly mix the contents, let the meter reading stabilize, record the dissolved oxygen concentration or manometric reading, and start the timing device. Continue to record data at time intervals of less than 1 min, depending on the rate of consumption. Record oxygen readings over a 15-min period or until the dissolved oxygen concentration becomes limiting. With a probe, a dissolved oxygen concentration of 1.0 mg/l is considered to be limiting. If a manometric device is used, refer to the manufacturer's instructions for the limiting concentration.

4. Calculations

If a probe is used, plot the observed readings versus time on arithmetic graph paper and determine the slope of the line of best fit. The slope is the oxygen uptake rate for the mixed liquor sample (in units of mg/l/min). To calculate the oxygen consumption rate (in units of mg/g/hr), divide the uptake rate by the volatile suspended solids concentration:

$$\text{Oxygen consumption rate} = \frac{\text{uptake rate, mg/l/min} \times 60 \text{ min/hr}}{\text{volatile suspended solids, g/l}}$$

If a manometric apparatus is used, refer to the manufacturer's instructions for the method of calculating the oxygen consumption rate.

5. Precision and Accuracy

This determination is quite sensitive to temperature and has very poor precision unless replicate determinations are made at the same temperature. When oxygen consumption is used as a plant control test, the analyst should run replicate determinations on an activated sludge sample periodically (at least once a month) to establish the precision of the technic. Normal oxygen consumption rates for activated sludge from plants treating municipal wastewaters range between 5 mg/g/hr and 25 mg/g/hr at 20 C. Acceptable precision for a plant control test is ±20% between replicate samples.

213 C.   Settled Volume

Determine the settled volume of activated sludge by collecting a 1-l sample at the outlet of the aeration tank in a 1,000-ml graduated cylinder, or by transferring it quickly to such a cylinder, and allowing the activated sludge to settle at the same temperature as that of the aeration tank. Read the volume occupied by the settled sludge at measured time intervals, for example, 5, 10, 15, 20, 30, 45, and 60 min. For plant control, use a 30-min settled volume or the ratio of the 15min to the 30-min settled volume. Although many types of activated sludge give consistent results, some show a great variation if factors such as temperature, agitation, and the time between sampling and the start of the determination vary. To obtain consistent results, follow exactly the same procedure each time the determination is made.

When a sample of activated sludge is settled, if the suspended-solids concentration is low enough, discrete settling and compaction are observed. If the suspended-solids concentration is in an intermediate range, hindered settling followed by compaction is observed, but the hindered settling is usually completed in less than 10 min. If the suspended-solids concentration is high enough, only compaction is observed. The settled volume test is used by plant operators to determine when to increase or decrease the returned-sludge rate and when to waste sludge. The need to change the returned-sludge rate depends on how well the sludge compacts, not how well it settles. Use of the 30-min settled volume for calculation of the sludge volume index gives a control parameter for the process that has no basis in solid-liquid separation theory but that has been found empirically valuable.

213 D.   Zone Settling Rate

1. General Discussion

The zone settling rate of activated sludges is used in the design of final sedimentation tanks and in the assessment of operating condition changes. Activated sludge zone settling rate varies in response to changes in both process loading level and mixed liquor suspended solids concentration. Zone settling rate also varies with changes in nutrient levels, mixed liquor temperature, pH, turbulence, and the application of flocculents and flocculent aids. Zone settling rate can be a sensitive indicator of process condition changes as well as a useful tool in the design of treatment facilities and the interpretation of routine operating data.

2. Apparatus

a. Settling vessel: One of the following is required:

1) *Graduated cylinder*, 1 l, recalibrated to read in inches and fractions thereof, and fitted with a stirring mechanism.

2) *Cylindrical battery jar*, calibrated in inches and fractions thereof, and having a 2- to 3-l capacity. Stirring mechanisms are not used commonly with a battery jar.

b. Stirring mechanism, with multiple vertical elements long enough to extend to near the cylinder bottom when inserted in a filled graduated cylinder. The stirring mechanism is connected directly to the output shaft of a clock motor or other drive mechanism capable of rotating it 12 rph.

3. Procedure

a. Fill the settling vessel with mixed liquor.

b. Insert a stirring mechanism into the test vessel if a 1-l cylinder is used. Activate the stirring mechanism.

c. Record the height of the sludge-liquid interface at 1-min intervals for at least 10 min or until enough data have been recorded to permit the construction of the required plot.

4. Calculation

Construct an arithmetic plot of sludge-liquid interface height in inches versus time in minutes. Draw a line of best fit through the straight-line portion of the graph. Determine the zone settling rate as the slope of the line. Express the test results in terms of feet per hour, computed as:

$$\text{Zone settling rate} = \frac{\text{Slope, in./min} \times 60 \text{ min/hr}}{12 \text{ in./ft}}$$

5. Precision and Accuracy

Zone settling rate is a function of mixed liquor suspended solids concentration. The reproducibility of zone settling rate determinations at a given solids concentration depends on the type of activated sludge being tested and the skill of the analyst in maintaining constant conditions from one set of tests to another. The zone settling rate of activated sludges having high sludge volume indices (more than 100 ml/g) sometimes will change in an erratic manner while activated sludges with low sludge volume indices usually give acceptable reproducibility.

It is advisable to run zone settling rate determinations in triplicate and average the results. Results of nine replicate determinations on a series of activated sludge samples with low sludge volume indices gave values for the standard deviations that were less than 20% of the respective mean values.

213 E.   Sludge Volume Index

The sludge volume index (SVI) is the volume in milliliters occupied by 1 g of activated sludge after the aerated liquor has settled for 30 min. Collect a 1-l sample at the outlet of the aeration tanks and settle for 30 min in a 1,000-ml graduated cylinder; report the volume occupied by the sludge as percent or milliliters. Thoroughly mix the sample, or take a new sample, determine the suspended solids, and report in percent by weight or milligrams per liter.

$$SVI = \frac{\% \text{ settling by volume}}{\% \text{ suspended matter}}$$

$$SVI = \frac{ml \text{ settled sludge} \times 1,000}{mg/l \text{ suspended matter}}$$

The standard deviation of the sludge volume index was determined as 1.69 on an average index of 72—a coefficient of variation of 2.35% ($n=1$; 10×10).

213 F.   Bibliography

RUDOLFS, W. & I.O. LACY. 1934. Settling and compacting of activated sludge. *Sewage Works J.* 6:647.

FINCH, J. & H. IVES. 1950. Settleability indexes for activated sludge. *Sewage Ind. Wastes* 22:883.

ISENBERG, E. & H. HEUKELEKIAN. 1959. Sludge volume index. *Water Sewage Works* 106:525.

EDDIE, H.J. & W.W. ECKENFELDER, JR. 1968. Theoretical concepts of gravity sludge thickening: Scaling-up laboratory units to prototype design. *J. Water Pollut. Control Fed.* 40:8.

YOUNG, J.C. & E.R. BAUMAN. 1973. Hydrogen peroxide aids in measuring sludge oxygen uptake rates. *Deeds Data*, January 1973:4.

214   TURBIDITY

Clarity of water is important in industries producing products destined for human consumption or for a large number of manufacturing uses. Beverage producers, food processors, and treatment plants drawing on a surface water supply commonly rely on coagulation, settling, and filtration to insure an acceptable product.

Turbidity in water is caused by the presence of suspended matter, such as clay, silt, finely divided organic and inorganic matter, plankton, and other microscopic organisms. Turbidity is an expression of the optical property that causes light to be scattered and absorbed rather than transmitted in straight lines through the sample. Attempts to correlate turbidity with the weight concentration of suspended matter are impractical because the size, shape, and refractive index of the particulate materials are important optically but bear little direct relationship to the concentration and specific gravity of the suspended matter.

The standard method for the determination of turbidity has been based on the Jackson candle turbidimeter. However, the lowest turbidity value that can be measured directly on this instrument is 25 units. With turbidities of treated water generally falling within the range of 0 to 5 units, indirect secondary methods have been required to estimate turbidities on such samples. Unfortunately, no instrument yet devised will duplicate the results obtained on the Jackson candle turbidimeter for all samples. Because of fundamental differences in optical systems, the results obtained with different types of secondary instruments frequently will not check closely with one another, even though the instruments are all precalibrated against the candle turbidimeter.

Most commercial turbidimeters available for measuring low turbidities give comparatively good indications of the intensity of light scattered in one particular direction, predominantly at right angles to the incident light. These nephelometers are relatively unaffected by small changes in design parameters and are therefore specified as the standard instrument for measurement of low turbidities. Other nonstandard turbidimeters, such as the forward-scattering devices, are much more sensitive than the nephelometers to the presence of larger particles and are quite useful for process monitoring.

A further cause of discrepancies in turbidity analysis is the use of suspensions of different types of particulate matter for the preparation of instrumental calibration curves. Like water samples, prepared suspensions have different optical properties depending on the particle size distributions, shapes, and refractive indices. A standard reference suspension having reproducible light-scattering properties is specified for nephelometer calibration.

Since there is no direct relationship between the intensity of light scattered at 90 deg and the Jackson candle turbidity, there is no valid basis for the practice of calibrating a nephelometer in terms of candle units. To distinguish between turbidities derived from the nephelometric and visual methods, the results from the former should be expressed as nephelometric turbidity units (NTU) and from the latter as Jackson turbidity units (JTU).

1. Selection of Method

Its greater precision, sensitivity, and applicability over a wide turbidity range make the nephelometric method preferable to the visual methods. The candle turbidimeter, with a lower limit of 25 turbidity units, has its principal usefulness in examination of highly turbid waters. The bottle standards offer a practical means for checking raw and conditioned water at various stages of the treatment process.

2. Storage of Sample

Determine turbidity on the day the sample is taken. If longer storage is unavoidable, store samples in the dark for up to 24 hr. Prolonged storage before measurement is not recommended because irreversible changes in turbidity may occur. All samples should be shaken vigorously before examination.

214 A.   Nephelometric Method—Nephelometric Turbidity Units

1. General Discussion

a. *Principle:* The method presented below is based on a comparison of the intensity of light scattered by the sample under defined conditions with the intensity of light scattered by a standard reference suspension under the same conditions. The higher the intensity of scattered light, the higher the turbidity. Formazin polymer, which has gained acceptance as the turbidity standard reference suspension in the brewing industry, is used as the reference turbidity standard suspension for water. It is easy to prepare and is more reproducible in its light-scattering properties than the clay or turbid natural water standards previously used. The turbidity of a given concentration of formazin suspension is defined as 40 nephelometric units. This same suspension of formazin has an approximate turbidity of 40 Jackson units when measured on the candle turbidimeter; therefore, nephelometric turbidity units based on the formazin preparation will approximate units derived from the candle turbidimeter but will not be identical to them.

b. *Interference:* Turbidity can be determined for any water sample that is free of debris and rapidly settling coarse sediments. Dirty glassware, the presence of air bubbles, and the effects of vibrations that disturb the surface visibility of the sample will lead to false results. The presence of "true color", that is, the color of the water due to dissolved substances that absorb light, will cause measured turbidities to be low. This effect generally is not significant in the case of treated water.

2. Apparatus

a. Turbidimeter consisting of a neph-elometer with a light source for illuminating the sample and one or more photoelectric detectors with a readout device to indicate the intensity of light scattered at 90 deg to the path of the incident light. The turbidimeter should be so designed that little stray light reaches the detector in the absence of turbidity and it should be free from significant drift after a short warm-up period. The sensitivity of the instrument should permit detection of turbidity differences of 0.02 NTU or less in waters having turbidity of less than 1 NTU. The instrument should measure from 0 to 40 NTU. Several ranges will be necessary to obtain both adequate coverage and sufficient sensitivity for low turbidities.

Differences in physical design of turbidimeters will cause differences in measured values for turbidity even though the same suspension is used for calibration. To minimize such differences, observe the following design criteria:

1) Light source—Tungsten lamp operated between 85% and 100% rated voltage.

2) Distance traversed by incident light and scattered light within the sample tube—Total not to exceed 10 cm.

3) Angle of light acceptance by detector—Centered at 90 deg to the incident light path and not to exceed ±30 deg from 90 deg.

4) Maximum turbidity to be measured, 40 NTU.

b. Sample tubes, clear colorless glass. Keep tubes scrupulously clean, both inside and out, and discard when they become scratched or etched. Never handle them where the light strikes them. Use tubes with sufficient extra length, or with a protective case, so that they may be handled properly. Fill the tubes with samples and standards that have been agitated thoroughly, and allow sufficient time for bubbles to escape.

3. Reagents

a. Turbidity-free water: Pass distilled water through a membrane filter having a pore size no greater than 100 μm, if such filtered water shows a lower turbidity than the distilled water. Discard the first 200 ml collected. If filtration does not reduce turbidity, use distilled water.

b. Stock turbidity suspension:

1) Solution I—Dissolve 1.000 g hydrazine sulfate, $(NH_2)_2 \cdot H_2SO_4$, in distilled water and dilute to 100 ml in a volumetric flask.

2) Solution II—Dissolve 10.00 g hexamethylenetetramine, $(CH_2)_6N_4$, in distilled water and dilute to 100 ml in a volumetric flask.

3) In a 100-ml volumetric flask, mix 5.0 ml Solution I with 5.0 ml Solution II. Allow to stand 24 hr at 25±3 C, then dilute to the mark and mix. The turbidity of this suspension is 400 NTU.

4) Prepare solutions and suspensions monthly.

c. Standard turbidity suspensions: Dilute 10.00 ml stock turbidity suspension to 100 ml with turbidity-free water. Prepare weekly. The turbidity of this suspension is defined as 40 NTU.

d. Dilute turbidity standards: Dilute portions of the standard turbidity suspension with turbidity-free water as required. Prepare weekly.

4. Procedure

a. *Turbidimeter calibration:* Follow the manufacturer's operating instructions. In the absence of a precalibrated scale, prepare calibration curves for each range of the instrument. Check the accuracy of any supplied calibration scales on a precalibrated instrument by the use of appropriate standards. Run at least one standard in each instrument range to be used. On instruments that allow adjustment of sensitivity so that scale values will correspond to turbidities, *do not rely on a manufacturer's solid scattering standard for setting overall instrument sensitivity for all ranges unless the turbidimeter has been shown to be free of drift on all ranges.*

b. *Measurement of turbidities less than 40 NTU:* Thoroughly shake the sample. Wait until air bubbles disappear and pour the sample into the turbidimeter tube. Read the turbidity directly from the instrument scale or from the appropriate calibration curve.

c. *Measurement of turbidities above 40 NTU:* Dilute the sample with one or more volumes of turbidity-free water until the turbidity falls between 30 and 40 NTU. Compute the turbidity of the original sample from the turbidity of the diluted sample and the dilution factor as shown below. For example, if five volumes of turbidity-free water were added to one volume of sample and the diluted sample showed a turbidity of 30 NTU, then the turbidity of the original sample was 180 NTU.

Use the stock turbidity suspension of 400 NTU when turbidity must be calibrated for the continuous monitoring of waters with turbidities greater than 40 NTU. Hold the total distance traversed by incident light and scattered light to the absolute minimum consistent with low background readings if high turbidities are to be determined by the measurement of scattered-light intensities. High turbidities determined by direct measurement are likely to differ appreciably from those determined by the dilution technic.

5. Calculation

Nephelometric turbidity units (NTU) =
$$\frac{A \times (B+C)}{C}$$

where A = NTU found in diluted sample, B = volume of dilution water, ml, and C = sample volume taken for dilution, ml.

6. Interpretation of Results

a. Report turbidity readings in accordance with the following schedule:

Turbidity Range NTU	Record to the Nearest NTU
0–1.0	0.05
1–10	0.1
10–40	1
40–100	5
100–400	10
400–1,000	50
>1,000	100

b. For comparison of water treatment efficiencies, it may be desirable to estimate turbidity more closely than is specified in the above tabulation. However, the uncertainties and discrepancies in turbidity measurements make it unlikely that two or more laboratories will duplicate results on the same sample more closely than specified.

214 B.   Visual Methods—Jackson Turbidity Units

1. General Discussion

a. Principle: Turbidity measurements by the candle turbidimeter are based on the light path through a suspension that just causes the image of the flame of a standard candle to disappear—that is, to become indistinguishable against the general background illumination—when the flame is viewed through the suspension. The longer the light path, the lower the turbidity.

b. Interference: Turbidity can be determined for any water sample that is free of rapidly settling debris and coarse sediments. Dirty glassware, the presence of air bubbles, and the effects of vibrations that disturb the surface visibility of the sample will lead to false results.

2. Apparatus

a. Candle turbidimeter: The instrument consists of a glass tube calibrated according to Table 214:I, a standard candle, and a support that aligns the candle and the tube. The glass tube and the candle are supported in a vertical position so that the center line of the tube passes through the center line of the candle. The candle support consists of a spring-loaded cylinder designed to keep the top of the candle pressed against the top of the support as the candle gradually burns away. The top of the support for the candle is 7.6 cm (3 in.) below the bottom of the glass tube. The glass tube has a flat, polished optical-glass bottom and conforms to the specifications for nessler tubes given in Section 102.6. It is graduated to read directly in JTU. Keep the tube clean and free from scratches. Keep most of the glass tube enclosed within a metal tube when observations are being made, both to protect it against breakage and to exclude extraneous light.

The *candle* is made of beeswax and spermaceti, designed to burn within the limits of 114 to 126 grains/hr. To insure uniform results, keep the flame as near constant size and constant distance from the bottom of the glass tube as possible by frequently trimming the charred portion of the wick and frequently making sure that the candle is pushed to the top of its support. Eliminate all drafts during measurements to prevent the flame from flickering. Do not burn the candle for more than a few minutes at a time, because the flame has a tendency to increase in size. Before lighting the candle each time, remove any portions of the charred wick that can easily be broken off when manipulated with the fingers.

b. Bottles for visual comparison: A matched set of 1-l-capacity, glass-stoppered bottles made of pyrex or other resistant glass.

3. Preparation of Standard Suspensions

a. Turbidity-free water: See Section 214A.3a.

b. Visual comparison standards: Prepare from natural turbid water or kaolin.

1) Natural water—For best results, prepare from the natural turbid water from the same source as that to be tested. Determine turbidity with the candle turbidimeter, then dilute portions of the suspension to the turbidity values desired.

TABLE 214:I. GRADUATION OF CANDLE TURBIDIMETER

Light Path* cm	Jackson Turbidity Units JTU	Light Path* cm	Jackson Turbidity Units JTU
2.3	1,000	11.4	190
2.6	900	12.0	180
2.9	800	12.7	170
3.2	700	13.5	160
3.5	650	14.4	150
3.8	600	15.4	140
4.1	550	16.6	130
4.5	500	18.0	120
4.9	450	19.6	110
5.5	400	21.5	100
5.6	390	22.6	95
5.8	380	23.8	90
5.9	370	25.1	85
6.1	360	26.5	80
6.3	350	28.1	75
6.4	340	29.8	70
6.6	330	31.8	65
6.8	320	34.1	60
7.0	310	36.7	55
7.3	300	39.8	50
7.5	290	43.5	45
7.8	280	48.1	40
8.1	270	54.0	35
8.4	260	61.8	30
8.7	250	72.9	25
9.1	240		
9.5	230		
9.9	220		
10.3	210		
10.8	200		

* Measured from inside bottom of glass tube.

Prepare weekly suspensions of turbidities below 25 units by dilution of a freshly checked, more concentrated suspension.

2) Kaolin—Add approximately 5 g kaolin to 1 l distilled water, thoroughly agitate, and allow to stand for 24 hr. Withdraw the supernatant without disturbing the bottom sediment. Determine turbidity with the candle turbidimeter. Dilute portions of the suspension to the turbidity values desired. Preserve standard suspensions by adding 1 g mercuric chloride/l suspen-

sion. Shake the suspensions vigorously before each reading and check monthly with the candle turbidimeter.

4. Procedure

a. Estimation with candle turbidimeter:

1) Turbidities between 25 and 1,000 JTU—Pour the shaken sample into the glass tube until the image of the candle flame just disappears from view. Make certain that a uniformly illuminated field with no bright spots materializes. Add the sample slowly toward the end. After the image has been made to disappear, remove 1% of the sample with a pipet to make the flame image visible again. Then add small amounts of the removed sample to approach the end point more carefully. Keep the glass tube clean both inside and outside, and avoid scratching the glass. Accumulation of soot or moisture on the bottom of the tube interferes with the accuracy of the results.

2) Turbidities exceeding 1,000 JTU—Dilute the sample with one or more volumes of turbidity-free water until the turbidity falls below 1,000 JTU. Compute the turbidity of the original sample from the turbidity of the diluted sample and the dilution factor. For example, if five volumes of turbidity-free water were added to one volume of sample and the diluted sample showed a turbidity of 500 JTU, the turbidity of the original sample was 3,000 JTU.

b. Estimation with bottle standards: In the range 5 to 100 JTU, compare shaken samples with standard suspensions made by diluting concentrated

standard suspensions with turbidity-free water in known ratios. Place the sample and the standards in bottles of the same size, shape, and type; leave enough empty space at the top of each bottle to allow adequate shaking before each reading. Compare the sample and the standards through the sides of the bottles by looking through them at the same object and noting the distinctness with which such objects as ruled lines or newsprint can be seen. Arrange the artificial lighting above or below the bottles so that no direct light reaches the eye. Record the turbidity of the sample as that of the standard that produces the visual effect most closely approximating that of the sample.

5. Calculation

See Section 214A.5. Report results from visual methods as Jackson turbidity units, JTU.

6. Interpretation of Results

Record the turbidity readings in the following manner:

Turbidity Range JTU	Record to Nearest JTU
0–1.0	0.1
1–10	1
10–100	5
100–400	10
400–700	50
700 or more	100

Identify the visual method (candle turbidimeter or bottle standards) used for the turbidity estimation.

214 C. Bibliography

WHIPPLE, G.C. & D.D. JACKSON. 1900. A comparative study of the methods used for the measurement of turbidity of water. *Mass. Inst. Technol. Quart.* 13:274.

AMERICAN PUBLIC HEALTH ASSOCIATION. 1901. Report of Committee on Standard Methods of Water Analysis. *Pub. Health Papers & Rept.* 27:377.

WELLS, P.V. 1922. Turbidimetry of water. *J. Amer. Water Works Ass.* 9:488.

BAYLIS, J.R. 1926. Turbidimeter for accurate measurement of low turbidities. *Ind. Eng. Chem.* 18:311.

WELLS, P.V. 1927. The present status of turbidity measurements. *Chem. Rev.* 3:331.

BAYLIS, J.R. 1933. Turbidity determinations. *Water Works Sewage* 80:125.

ROSE, H.E. & H.B. LLOYD. 1946. On the measurement of the size characteristics of powders by photo-extinction methods. *J. Soc. Chem. Ind.* (London) 65:52 (Feb.); 65:55 (Mar.).

ROSE, H.E. & C.C.J. FRENCH. 1948. On the extinction coefficient: Particle size relationship for fine mineral powders. *J. Soc. Chem. Ind.* (London) 67:283.

GILLETT, T.R., P.F. MEADS & A.L. HOLVEN. 1949. Measuring color and turbidity of white sugar solutions. *Anal. Chem.* 21:1228.

JULLANDER, I. 1949. A simple method for the measurement of turbidity. *Acta Chem. Scand.* 3:1309.

ROSE, H.E. 1950. Powder-size measurement by a combination of the methods of nephelometry and photo-extinction. *J. Soc. Chem. Ind.* (London) 69:266.

ROSE, H.E., 1950. The design and use of photo-extinction sedimentometers. *Engineering* 169:350, 405.

BRICE, B.A., M. HALWER & R. SPEISER. 1950. Photoelectric light-scattering photometer for determining high molecular weights. *J. Opt. Soc. Amer.* 40:768.

KNIGHT, A.G. 1950. The measurement of turbidity in water. *J. Inst. Water Eng.* 4:449.

HANYA, T. 1950. Study of suspended matter in water. *Bull. Chem. Soc. Jap.* 23:216.

JULLANDER, I. 1950. Turbidimetric investigations on viscose. *Svensk Papperstidn.* 22:1.

ROSE, H.E. 1951. A reproducible standard for the calibration of turbidimeters. *J. Inst. Water Eng.* 5:310.

AITKEN, R.W. & D. MERCER. 1951. Comment on "The measurement of turbidity in water." *J. Inst. Water Eng.* 5:328.

ROSE, H.E. 1951. The analysis of water by the assessment of turbidity. *J. Inst. Water Eng.* 5:521.

KNIGHT, A.G. 1951. The measurement of turbidity in water: A reply. *J. Inst. Water Eng.* 5:633.

STAATS, F.C. 1952. Measurement of color, turbidity, hardness and silica in industrial waters. Preprint 156, Amer. Soc. Testing & Materials, Philadelphia, Pa.

PALIN, A.T. 1955. Photometric determination of the colour and turbidity of water. *Water Water Eng.* 59:341.

SLOAN, C.K. 1955. Angular dependence light scattering studies of the aging of precipitates. *J. Phys. Chem.* 59:834.

CONLEY, W.R. & R.W. PITMAN. 1957. Microphotometer turbidity analysis. *J. Amer. Water Works Ass.* 49:63.

PACKHAM, R.F. 1962. The preparation of turbidity standards. *Proc. Soc. Water Treat. Exam.* 11:64.

BAALSRUD, K. & A. HENRIKSEN. 1964. Measurement of suspended matter in stream water. *J. Amer. Water Works Ass.* 56:1194.

HOATHER, R.C. 1964. Comparison of different methods for measurement of turbidity. *Proc. Soc. Water Treat. Exam.* 13:89.

EDEN, G.E. 1965. The measurement of turbidity in water. A progress report on the work of the analytical panel. *Proc. Soc. Water Treat. Exam.* 14:27.

BLACK, A.P. & S.A. HANNAH. 1965. Measurement of low turbidities. *J. Amer. Water Works Ass.* 57:901.

HANNAH, S.A., J.M. COHEN & G.G. ROBECK. 1967. Control techniques for coagulation-filtration. *J. Amer. Water Works Ass.* 59:1149.

REBHUN, M. & H.S. SPERBER. 1967. Optical properties of diluted clay suspensions. *J. Colloid Interface Sci.* 24:131.

DANIELS, S.L. 1969. The utility of optical parameters in evaluation of processes of flocculation and sedimentation. *Chem. Eng. Progr. Symp. Ser.* No. 97, 65:171.

LIVESEY, P.J. & F.W. BILLMEYER, JR. 1969. Particle-size determination by low-angle light scattering: new instrumentation and a rapid method of interpreting data. *J. Colloid. Interface Sci.* 30:447.

OSTENDORF, R.G. & J.F. BYRD. 1969. Modern monitoring of a treated industrial effluent. *J. Water Pollut. Control Fed.* 41:89.

EICHNER, D.W. & C.C. HACH. 1971. How clear is clear water? *Water Sewage Works* 118:299.

HACH, C.C. 1972. Understanding turbidity measurement. *Ind. Water Eng.* 9:18, No. 2.

SIMMS, R.J. 1972. Industrial turbidity measurement. *ISA Tran.* 11:146, No. 2.

TALLEY, D.G., J.A. JOHNSON & J.E. PILZER. 1972. Continuous turbidity monitoring. *J. Amer. Water Works Ass.* 64:184.

PART 300
DETERMINATION OF
METALS

301 INTRODUCTION

The presence of metals in potable waters, domestic wastewater, industrial effluents, and receiving waters is a matter of serious concern because of the toxic properties of these materials. They may adversely affect water consumers, wastewater treatment systems, or the biological systems of bodies of water.

Metals may be determined satisfactorily by atomic absorption spectroscopy, polarography, or colorimetric methods. The instrumental methods are preferable because they are rapid and do not require extensive separations. Many of the colorimetric methods for determination of individual metals must include procedures for the elimination of interference from other metals present.

Preliminary treatment of the samples is sometimes necessary and appropriate methods are described for each type of analysis. Sample preparation must be carried out carefully to avoid difficulties in the subsequent metals determination.

1. Sampling and Sample Preservation

Serious errors may be introduced during sampling and storage. Errors may occur because of (a) contamination from the sampling device, (b) failure to remove residues of previous samples from the sample container, and (c) loss of metal by adsorption on the sample container. To eliminate such errors, insure that all materials coming in contact with the sample are glass or plastic and that the sample container is thoroughly washed and rinsed with 1+1 nitric acid, then with redistilled water before reuse, and add 5 ml concentrated nitric acid per liter of sample at the time of collection to minimize adsorption of metals on the container walls.

2. General Precautions

Take care to avoid the introduction of contaminating metals from glassware and distilled water. For the preparation of reagents and in the determination of metals, use distilled water that has been redistilled in an all-glass apparatus or passed through a mixed-bed ion-exchange column. Clean all glassware thoroughly, rinse with 1+1 nitric acid, and finally with redistilled water.

3. Bibliography

SERFASS, E.J. et al. 1948-51. Determination of impurities in electroplating solutions. *Plating* 35: 156, 260, 458, 1019 (1948); 36: 254, 818, 1034 (1949); 37: 62, 166, 389, 495, 1057 (1950); 38: 473 (1951).

301 A.   Metals by Atomic Absorption Spectrophotometry

Because the requirements for the determination of metals by atomic absorption spectrophotometry may vary with the metal and/or concentration to be determined, the method is divided into seven sections, as follows:

I. Sample pretreatment.

II. Determination of cadmium, calcium, chromium, cobalt, copper, iron, lead, magnesium, manganese, nickel, silver, and zinc by direct aspiration into an air-acetylene flame.

III. Determination of low concentrations of cadium, chromium, and lead by chelation with ammonium pyrrolidine dithiocarbamate, extraction into methyl isobutyl ketone, and aspiration into an air-acetylene flame.

IV. Determination of aluminum, barium, beryllium, silicon, and vanadium by direct aspiration into a nitrous oxide-acetylene flame.

V. Determination of low concentrations of aluminum and beryllium by chelation with 8-hydroxyquinoline, extraction into methyl isobutyl ketone, and aspiration into a nitrous oxide-acetylene flame.

VI. Determination of mercury by flameless atomic absorption.

VII. Determination of arsenic and selenium by conversion to their hydrides and aspiration into an argon-hydrogen flame.

1. General Discussion

a. Principle: Atomic absorption spectrophotometry resembles emission flame photometry in that a sample is aspirated into a flame and atomized. The major difference is that flame photometry measures the amount of light emitted, whereas in atomic absorption spectrophotometry a light beam is directed through the flame, into a monochromator, and onto a detector that measures the amount of light absorbed by the atomized element in the flame. For many metals difficult to analyze by flame emission, atomic absorption exhibits superior sensitivity. Because each metal has its own characteristic absorption wavelength, a source lamp composed of that element is used; this makes the method relatively free from spectral or radiation interferences. Thus the amount of energy of the characteristic wavelength absorbed in the flame is proportional to the concentration of the element in the sample.

b. Interference: Most metals can be determined by direct aspiration of the sample into an air-acetylene flame. The most troublesome type of interference is termed "chemical" and results from the lack of absorption of atoms bound in molecular combination in the flame. This can occur when the flame is not hot enough to dissociate the molecules (in the case of phosphate interference with magnesium) or when the dissociated atom is oxidized immediately to a compound that will not dissociate further at the temperature of the flame. The interference of phosphate in the magnesium determination can be overcome by the addition of lanthanum. Similarly, the introduction of calcium eliminates silica interference in the determination of manganese. However, silicon and metals such as aluminum, barium, beryllium, and vanadium require the use of the higher-temperature, nitrous oxide-acetylene flame to dissociate their molecules. In addition, barium undergoes ionization in the flame and the ground state (potentially absorbing) population is thereby reduced. The addition of an excess of a cation (sodium or potassium) having a similar or lower ionization potential will overcome this problem. The wavelength of maximum absorption for arsenic is 193.7 nm, and for selenium 196.0 nm. Unfortunately, the air-acetylene flame absorbs intensely at these wavelengths. The sensitivity of the method for these metals can be improved by the use of the argon-hydrogen flame. In the determination of mercury by the cold vapor (flameless) technic, certain volatile organic materials may absorb at 253.7 nm. If this is expected, the sample should be analyzed by the regular procedure and again under oxidizing conditions only, that is, without the addition of stannous chloride. The true mercury concentration can be obtained by subtracting the two values.

c. *Sample handling:* Before collecting a sample, decide on the type of data desired, i.e., dissolved, suspended, total, or extractable metals. This decision will determine whether the sample is to be acidified, with or without filtration, and the kind of digestion required.

Acidify all samples at the time of collection to keep the metals in solution and to minimize their adsorption on the container wall. If only dissolved metals are to be measured, filter the sample through a 0.45-μm membrane before acidification. If possible, filter and acidify in the field at the time of collection. Report the results obtained on this sample as "dissolved." Filtration is not necessary when total or extractable concentrations are required.

Acidify the sample with conc HNO_3 to a pH of 2.0 or less. Usually, 1.5 ml conc HNO_3/l sample will be sufficient for potable waters free from particulate matter. Such samples can be analyzed with no further treatment. However, samples containing suspended materials or organic matter require pretreatment, as described in Section 301A.I below.

2. Apparatus

a. *Atomic absorption spectrophotometer,* consisting of a source of light emitting the line spectrum of an element (hollow cathode lamp), a device for vaporizing the sample (usually a flame), a means of isolating an absorption line (monochromator or filter and adjustable slit), and a photoelectric detector with its associated amplifying and electronic measuring equipment. Both direct current and alternating current systems are used in atomic absorption instruments. The AC or chopped-beam system is preferred because with this system flame emission can be distinguished from lamp emission. For waters high in salt, the use of either a deuterium background corrector or a double-beam instrument that permits the measurement of the absorption at two different wavelengths simultaneously may be helpful.

b. *Burner:* The most common type of burner is known as a premix, which introduces the spray into a condensing chamber for removal of large droplets. The burner may be fitted with a conventional head containing a single slot 7.6 cm (3 in.) long, which is most useful for aspiration when organic solvents are used; a three-slot Boling head, which is preferred for direct aspiration with an air-acetylene flame; or a head containing a single slot 5 cm (2 in.) long for use with nitrous oxide and acetylene.

c. *Recorder:* While most instruments are equipped with either a digital or null meter readout mechanism, a good-quality 10-mV recorder with high sensitivity and a fast response time is needed to record the peaks resulting from the determination of mercury by the cold vapor (flameless) technic and for the determination of arsenic and selenium by aspiration of their gaseous hydrides.

d. Hollow cathode lamps: Use one for each element being measured. Multi-element lamps are available but not recommended because they may require the selection of different operating parameters.

e. Pressure-reducing valves: Maintain the supplies of fuel and oxidant at pressures somewhat higher than the controlled operating pressure of the in-

strument by suitable reducing valves. Use separate reducing valves for each gas.

f. Vent: Place a vent about 15 to 30 cm (6 to 12 in.) above the burner to remove the fumes and vapors from the flame. This precaution protects the laboratory personnel from toxic vapors, prevents the stability of the flame from being affected by room drafts, and protects the instrument from corrosive vapors. A damper or variable-speed blower is also desirable for modulating the air flow and preventing disturbance of the flame.

3. Precision and Accuracy

Some data typical of the precision and accuracy obtainable with the methods discussed are presented in Table 301:I

4. Bibliography

Goon, E., et al. 1953. Fluorometric determination of aluminum by use of 8-quinolinol. *Anal. Chem.* 25:608.

Allan, J.E. 1961. The use of organic solvents in atomic absorption spectrophotometry. *Spectrochim. Acta* 17:467.

Willis, J.B. 1962. Determination of lead and other heavy metals in urine by atomic absorption spectrophotometry. *Anal. Chem.* 34:614.

Willis, J.B. 1965. Nitrous oxide-acetylene flame in atomic absorption spectroscopy. *Nature* 207:715.

Slavin, W. 1968. Atomic Absorption Spectroscopy. John Wiley and Sons, New York, N.Y.

Ramirez-Munoz, J. 1968. Atomic Absorption Spectroscopy and Analysis by Atomic Absorption Flame Photometry. American Elsevier Publishing Co., New York, N.Y.

Kahn, H.L. 1968. Principles and Practice of Atomic Absorption. Advan. Chem. Ser. No. 73, Washington, D.C.

TABLE 301:I. PRECISION AND ACCURACY DATA FOR ATOMIC ABSORPTION METHODS

Metal	Metal Concentration $\mu g/l$	Relative Standard Deviation %	Relative Error %
Direct determination:			
Barium	500	10.0	8.6
Cadmium	50	21.6	8.2
Chromium	50	26.4	2.3
Copper	1,000	11.2	3.4
Iron	300	16.5	0.6
Magnesium	200	10.5	6.3
Manganese	50	13.5	6.0
Silver	550	17.5	10.6
Zinc	500	8.2	0.4
Extracted samples:			
Aluminum	300	22.2	0.7
Beryllium	5	34.0	20.0
Cadmium	50	43.8	13.3
Lead	50	23.5	19.0
Flameless:			
Mercury	0.4	21.2	2.4
As hydride:			
Arsenic	10	6.0	1.0
Selenium	10	11.0	0.0

HATCH, W.R. & W.L. OTT. 1968. Determination of sub-microgram quantities of mercury by atomic absorption spectrophotometry. *Anal. Chem.* 40:2085.

UTHE, J.F., et al. 1970. Mercury determination in fish samples by wet digestion and flameless atomic absorption spectrophotometry. *J. Fish. Res. Board Can.* 27:805.

FERNANDEZ, F.J. & D.C. MANNING. 1971. The determination of arsenic at sub-microgram levels by atomic absorption spectrophotometry. *Atomic Absorption Newsletter* (July-Aug.).

MANNING, D.C. 1971. A high sensitivity arsenic-selenium sampling system for atomic absorption spectroscopy. *Atomic Absorption Newsletter* (Nov.-Dec.).

High Sensitivity Arsenic Determination by Atomic Absorption. 1971. Jarrel-Ash Atomic Absorption Applications Laboratory Bull. No. As-3.

KOPP, J.F., M.C. LONGBOTTOM & L.B. LOBRING. 1972. "Cold vapor" method for determining mercury. *J. Amer. Water Works Ass.* 64:20.

CALDWELL, J.S., R.J. LISHKA & E.F. McFARREN. 1973. Evaluation of a low cost arsenic and selenium determination of microgram per liter levels. *J. Amer. Water Works Ass.* 65:731.

SACHDEV, S.L. & WEST, P.W. 1970. Concentration of trace metals by solvent extraction and their determination by atomic absorption spectrophotometry. *Environ. Sci. Technol.* 4:749.

I. SAMPLE PRETREATMENT

Wastewater and raw water samples are likely to contain suspended materials and to require pretreatment before analysis. Pretreatment may include additional acid to preserve the sample and certainly requires a digestion step to destroy organic matter and bring all metals into solution.

1. Total Metals Analyses

Transfer a representative portion of well-mixed sample (50 to 100 ml) to a beaker and add 5 ml conc HNO_3. Place the beaker on a hot plate and evaporate to nearly dryness, making certain that the sample does not boil. Cool the beaker and add another 5 ml acid. Cover the beaker with a watch glass and return to the hot plate. Increase the temperature until a gentle refluxing action occurs. Continue heating, adding additional acid as necessary until digestion is complete; this is indicated by a light-colored residue. Add 1 to 2 ml conc nitric acid and warm the beaker slightly to dissolve the residue. Wash down the beaker walls and watch glass with distilled water and filter the sample to remove silicate and other insoluble material that could clog the atomizer. Adjust the volume to 50 to 100 ml or some other predetermined volume based on the expected metal concentration. The sample is now ready for analysis. Report results as "total". CAUTION: A special digestion is required for mercury, arsenic, and selenium (see Sections 301A.VI and VII), and some polluted waters may require additionally the use of sulfuric and/or perchloric acid and a reflux condenser for complete digestion.

2. Suspended Metals Analyses

If the concentration of metals in the suspended material is to be measured, use the same digestion procedure after filtering of the sample through a 0.45-μm membrane filter. Digest the filter as well as the material on it and run a filter blank to permit a blank correction. Report the suspended metals as micrograms or milligrams per liter, or weigh the residue and report as micrograms or milligrams per gram. Report the results as "suspended."

3. Extractable Metals Analyses

"Extractable metals" include metals in solution plus metals lightly adsorbed on the suspended material. The results obtained in analyses for extractable metals will be influenced by the kind of acid or acids used in the digestion, the concentration of acid, and the heating time. Unless conditions are controlled rigidly, results will be meaningless and unreproducible. The following procedure determines metals soluble in hot HCl-HNO₃. At the time of collection, acidify the entire sample with 5 ml conc HNO_3/l sample. At the time of analysis, mix the sample, transfer a 100-ml portion to a beaker or flask, and add 5 ml 1+1 redistilled HCl. Heat 15 min on a steam bath. Filter and adjust the volume to 100 ml. The sample is then ready for analysis.

The data approximate the total metals in the sample, although something less than the actual total is measured. Concentrations of metal found, especially in heavily silted samples, will be substantially higher than results obtained on only the soluble fraction. Report as "extractable" metals.

II. DETERMINATION OF CADMIUM*, CALCIUM, CHROMIUM*, COBALT, COPPER, IRON, LEAD*, MAGNESIUM, MANGANESE, NICKEL, SILVER, AND ZINC BY DIRECT ASPIRATION INTO AN AIR-ACETYLENE FLAME†

---

* For low concentrations of cadmium, chromium, and lead (<250, 100, and 500 μg/l, respectively) see Section 301A.III.

† This technic also can be used for sodium, potassium, and strontium but this is not recommended because flame emission produces better results.

1. Apparatus

See Section 301A.2 for a description of the required atomic absorption spectrophotometer and associated equipment. The three-slot Boling burner head is recommended.

2. Reagents

a. Air, cleaned and dried through a suitable filter to remove oil, water, and other foreign substances. The source may be a compressor or commercially bottled gas.

b. Acetylene, standard commercial grade. Acetone, which is always present in acetylene cylinders, can be prevented from entering and damaging the burner head by replacing a cylinder when its pressure has fallen to 7 kg/cm² (100 psig) acetylene.

c. Calcium solution: Dissolve 630 mg calcium carbonate, $CaCO_3$, in 10 ml conc HCl. Add 200 ml water, and if necessary heat the solution and boil gently to obtain complete solution. Cool and dilute to 1,000 ml with deionized distilled water.

d. Deionized distilled water: Use deionized distilled water for the preparation of all reagents and calibration standards and as dilution water.

e. Hydrochloric acid, HCl, conc.

f. Lanthanum solution: Dissolve 58.65 g lanthanum oxide, La_2O_3, in 250 ml conc HCl. Add the acid slowly until the material is dissolved and dilute to 1,000 ml with deionized distilled water.

g. Nitric acid, HNO_3, conc.

h. Standard metal solutions: Prepare a series of standard metal solutions containing 5 to 1,000 μg/l by appropriate dilution of the following stock metal solutions with deionized distilled water containing 1.5 ml conc HNO_3/l.

1) *Calcium:* To 2.4972 g calcium carbonate, $CaCO_3$, add 50 ml deionized water and add dropwise a minimum volume of conc HCl (about 10 ml) to effect complete solution. Dilute to 1,000 ml with deionized distilled water; 1.00 ml = 1.00 mg Ca.

2) *Cadmium:* Dissolve 1.000 g cadmium metal in a minimum volume of 1+1 HCl. Dilute to 1,000 ml with deionized distilled water; 1.00 ml = 1.00 mg Cd.

3) *Chromium:* Dissolve 2.828 g anhydrous potassium dichromate, $K_2Cr_2O_7$, in about 200 ml deionized distilled water, add 1.5 ml conc HNO_3, and dilute to 1,000 ml with deionized distilled water; 1.00 ml = 1.00 mg Cr.

4) *Cobalt:* Dissolve 1.407 g cobaltic oxide, Co_2O_3, in 20 ml hot HCl. Cool and dilute to 1,000 ml with deionized distilled water; 1.00 ml = 1.00 mg Co.

5) *Copper:* Dissolve 1.000 g copper metal in 15 ml of 1+1 HNO_3 and dilute to 1,000 ml with deionized distilled water; 1.00 ml = 1.00 mg Cu.

6) *Iron:* Dissolve 1.000 g iron wire in 50 ml of 1+1 HNO_3 and dilute to 1,000 ml with deionized distilled water; 1.00 ml = 1.00 mg Fe.

7) *Lead:* Dissolve 1.598 g lead nitrate, $Pb(NO_3)_2$, in about 200 ml of water, add 1.5 ml conc HNO_3, and dilute to 1,000 ml with deionized distilled water; 1.00 ml = 1.00 mg Pb.

8) *Magnesium:* Dissolve 10.0135 g magnesium sulfate heptahydrate, $MgSO_4 \cdot 7H_2O$, in 200 ml deionized distilled water, add 1.5 ml conc HNO_3, and make up to 1,000 ml with deionized distilled water; 1.00 ml = 1.00 mg Mg.

9) *Manganese:* Dissolve 3.076 g manganous sulfate monohydrate, $MnSO_4 \cdot H_2O$, in about 200 ml deionized distilled water, add 1.5 ml conc HNO_3, and make up to 1,000 ml with deionized distilled water; 1.00 ml = 1.00 mg Mn.

10) *Nickel:* Dissolve 4.953 g nickelous nitrate hexahydrate, $Ni(NO_3)_2 \cdot 6H_2O$, in about 200 ml deionized distilled water, add 1.5 ml conc HNO_3, and make up to 1,000 ml with deionized distilled water; 1.00 ml = 1.00 mg Ni.

11) *Silver:* Dissolve 1.575 g anhydrous silver nitrate, $AgNO_3$, in deionized distilled water, add 1.5 ml conc HNO_3, and make up to 1,000 ml; 1.00 ml = 1.00 mg Ag.

12) *Zinc:* Dissolve 1.000 g zinc metal in 20 ml 1+1 HCl and dilute to 1,000 ml with deionized distilled water; 1.00 ml = 1.00 mg Zn.

3. Procedure

a. Instrument operation: Because of differences between makes and models of satisfactory atomic absorption spectrophotometers, it is not possible to formulate instructions applicable to every instrument. In general, proceed according to the following steps:

1) Install a hollow cathode lamp of the desired metal in the instrument, set the wavelength dial according to Table 301:II, and align the lamp in accordance with the manufacturer's instructions.

2) Set the slit width according to the manufacturer's suggested setting for the element being measured.

3) Turn on the instrument and apply the amount of current suggested by the

TABLE 301:II. WAVELENGTHS AND SENSITIVITIES
FOR METALS ANALYSES

Metal	Wavelength nm	Sensitivity for 1% Absorption µg/l
Calcium	422.7	70
Cadmium	228.8	25
Chromium	357.9	100
Cobalt	240.7	150
Copper	324.7	100
Iron	248.3	100
Lead	283.3	500
Magnesium	285.2	7
Manganese	279.5	50
Nickel	232.0	100
Silver	328.1	60
Zinc	213.9	15

manufacturer to the hollow cathode lamp.

4) Allow the instrument to warm up until the energy source stablilizes; this process usually requires 10 to 20 min. Readjust the current as necessary after warmup.

5) Install the burner heads.

6) Turn on the air and adjust the flow rate to that specified by the manufacturer to give maximum sensitivity for the metal being measured.

7) Turn on the acetylene, adjust the flow rate to the value specified, and ignite the flame.

8) Atomize deionized distilled water acidified with 1.5 ml conc HNO_3/l, and check the aspiration rate over 1 min. Adjust if necessary to a rate between 3 and 5 ml/min, and zero the instrument.

9) Atomize a standard (usually a 0.5-mg/1 standard is suitable) and adjust the burner both up and down and sideways until a maximum response is obtained.

10) The instrument is now ready to operate. When analyses are finished, ex-

tinguish the flame by turning off first the acetylene and then the air.

b. Standardization:

1) Select at least three concentrations of each of the standard metal solutions (prepared as in 2b above) so as to bracket the expected metal concentration of a sample. Aspirate each in turn into the flame and record the absorbance.

2) For calcium and magnesium calibration, mix 100 ml of standard with 25 ml of lanthanum solution (see 2f above) before aspirating.

3) For iron and manganese calibration mix 100 ml of standard with 25 ml of calcium solution (see 2c above) before aspirating.

4) With some instruments, it may be necessary to convert percent absorption to absorbance by use of a suitable table generally provided by the manufacturer.

5) Prepare a calibration curve by plotting on linear graph paper the absorbance of the standards versus their concentration.

6) Plot calibration curves for iron and manganese based on the original concentrations of the standards before dilution with calcium solution (¶2c).

7) Plot calibration curves for calcium and magnesium based on the original concentration of the standards before dilution with lanthanum solution (¶2f).

8) Recheck the calibration curve by aspirating at least one standard after the completion of the analysis of a group of unknown samples.

c. Analysis of samples:

1) Rinse the atomizer by aspirating deionized distilled water containing 1.5 ml conc HNO_3/l, and zero the instrument.

2) Atomize the sample and determine its absorbance.

3) When determining calcium or magnesium, dilute and mix 100 ml sample with 25 ml lanthanum solution (¶2f) before atomization.

4) When determining iron or manganese, dilute and mix 100 ml sample with 25 ml calcium solution (¶2c) before atomization.

4. Calculations

Calculate the concentration of each metal ion, in micrograms per liter, by referring to the appropriate calibration curve prepared according to 3b 5), 6), and 7).

III. Determination of Low Concentrations of Cadium, Chromium, and Lead by Chelation with Ammonium Pyrrolidine Dithiocarbamate, and Extraction into Methyl Isobutyl Ketone*

1. Apparatus

See Section 301 A.2 for a description of the required atomic absorption spectrophotometer and associated equipment.

a. Burner head, conventional, with single 7.6-cm-(3-in.-) long slot.

b. Separatory funnels: 250 ml, with teflon stopcocks.

2. Reagents

a. Air, cleaned and dried through a

suitable filter to remove oil, water, and other foreign substances. The source may be a compressor or a commercially bottled gas.

b. Acetylene, standard commercial grade.

c. Ammonium pyrrolidine dithiocarbamate solution: Dissolve 4 g ammonium pyrrolidine dithiocarbamate (APDC) in 100 ml deionized distilled water.

d. Deionized distilled water: Use deionized distilled water for the preparation of all reagents, standards, and dilution water.

e. Methyl isobutyl ketone, reagent grade.

f. Nitric acid, HNO₃, conc.

g. Potassium permanganate, 0.1N: Dissolve 3.16 g KMnO₄ in deionized distilled water and dilute to 1,000 ml.

h. Standard metal solutions: Prepare a series of standard metal solutions containing 5 to 1,000 mg/1 by appropriate dilution of the following stock metal solutions with deionized distilled water containing 1.5 ml conc HNO₃/l.

1) Cadmium: Dissolve 1.000 g cadmium metal in a minimum volume 1 + 1 HCl, and dilute to 1,000 ml with deionized distilled water; 1.00 ml = 1.00 mg Cd.

2) Chromium: Dissolve 2.828 g anhydrous potassium dichromate, K₂Cr₂O₇, in about 200 ml of water, add 1.5 ml conc HNO₃, and dilute to 1,000 ml with deionized distilled water; 1.00 ml = 1.00 mg Cr.

3) Lead: Dissolve 1.598 g anhydrous lead nitrate, Pb(NO₃)₂, in about 200 ml deionized distilled water, add 1.5 ml conc HNO₃, and dilute to 1,000 ml with deionized distilled water; 1.00 ml = 1.00 mg Pb.

---

* Cobalt, copper, iron, manganese, nickel, and silver also can be determined by this technic but direct aspiration usually provides sufficient sensitivity.

3. Procedure

a. Instrument operation:

1) See Section 301 A.II 3a.

2) After adjusting the burner position at Step 9), aspirate methyl isobutyl ketone into the flame and gradually reduce the fuel flow until the flame is similar to that before aspiration of the solvent.

3) Adjust the wavelength according to Table 301:II.

b. Standardization:

1) Select at least three standard metal solutions (prepared as in ¶ 2b) so as to bracket the expected metal concentration of a sample and adjust 100 ml of each and 100 ml of a deionized distilled water blank to pH 2.2 to 2.8 by adding 1 N HNO₃ or 1 N NaOH.

2) Transfer each standard solution and blank to an individual 250-ml separatory funnel, add 1 ml ammonium pyrrolidine dithiocarbamate solution and shake to mix.

3) Add 10 ml methyl isobutyl ketone and shake vigorously for 30 sec.

4) Let the contents of each separatory funnel separate into aqueous and organic layers.

5) Drain off aqueous layers and discard. Make sure that none of the aqueous layer remains in the stem of the funnel.

6) Drain the organic layer into a 10-ml glass stoppered graduated cylinder.

7) Aspirate the organic extracts directly into the flame (zeroing the instrument on methyl isobutyl ketone blank) and record the absorbance.

8) With some instruments it may be necessary to convert percent absorption to absorbance by using a suitable table generally provided by the manufacturer.

9) Prepare a calibration curve by plotting on linear graph paper the absorbances of the extracted standards against their concentrations before extraction.

c. Analysis of samples:

1) Rinse the atomizer by aspirating methyl isobutyl ketone.

2) Aspirate extracts of samples [treated as in Section b1) through 6)] and record the absorbances.

3) The above extraction procedure will measure only hexavalent chromium. To determine total chromium, oxidize trivalent to hexavalent chromium by bringing the sample to a boil and adding sufficient potassium permanganate solution dropwise to give a persistent pink color while the solution is boiled for 10 min. Cool and analyze as in 3c 2), above.

4. Calculations

Calculate the concentration of each metal ion in micrograms per liter by referring to the appropriate calibration curve prepared according to 3b 9).

IV. Determination of Aluminum*, Barium, Beryllium*, Vanadium, and Silicon by Direct Aspiration into a Nitrous Oxide Acetylene Flame

1. Apparatus

See Section 301 A.2 for a description of the required atomic absorption spectrophotometer and associated equipment.

a. Nitrous oxide burner head with 5.0-cm (2-in.) slot. A razor blade or

---

* For low concentrations of aluminum and beryllium (<900 and 30 μg/l, respectively) see Section 301 A.V.

equivalent is required to dislodge, about every 20 min, the carbon crust that forms along the slit surface.

b. *T-junction valve* or other switching valve for rapidly changing from nitrous oxide to air, so the flame can be turned on or off with air as oxidant to prevent flashbacks.

2. Reagents

a. *Air,* cleaned and dried through a suitable filter to remove oil, water, and other foreign substances. The source may be a compressor or a commercial bottled gas.

b. *Acetylene,* standard commercial grade.

c. *Deionized distilled water:* Use deionized distilled water for the preparation of all reagents and calibration standards, and as dilution water.

d. *Hydrochloric acid,* HCl, conc.

e. *Nitric acid,* HNO_3, conc.

f. *Nitrous oxide,* commercially available cylinders.

g. *Sodium chloride solution:* Dissolve 250 g NaCl in deionized distilled water and dilute to 1,000 ml.

h. *Standard metal solutions:* Prepare a series of standard metal solutions containing 5 to 1,000 µg/l by appropriate dilution of the following stock metal solutions with deionized distilled water containing 1.5 ml conc HNO_3/l:

1) *Aluminum:* Dissolve 1.000 g aluminum metal in 20 ml conc HCl by heating gently and diluting to 1,000 ml, or dissolve 17.584 g aluminum potassium sulfate (also called potassium alum), $AlK(SO_4)_2 \cdot 12H_2O$, in 200 ml deionized distilled water, add 1.5 ml conc HNO_3 and dilute to 1,000 ml with deionized distilled water; 1.00 ml = 1.00 mg Al.

2) *Barium:* Dissolve 1.7787 g barium chloride dihydrate, $BaCl_2 \cdot 2H_2O$, in about 200 ml of deionized distilled water, add 1.5 ml conc HNO_3, and dilute to 1,000 ml with deionized distilled water; 1.00 ml = 1.00 mg Ba.

3) *Beryllium:* Dissolve 20.7574 g beryllium nitrate trihydrate, $Be(NO_3)_2 \cdot 3H_2O$, in about 200 ml deionized distilled water, add 1.5 ml conc HNO_3, and dilute to 1,000 ml with deionized distilled water; 1.00 ml = 1.00 mg Be.

4) *Silicon:* Dissolve 50.60 g sodium metasilicate nonahydrate, $Na_2SiO_3 \cdot 9H_2O$, in about 600 ml deionized distilled water. Neutralize to a litmus endpoint (or pH 5.0) with 1 : 1 HCl and make up to 1,000 ml with deionized distilled water; 1.00 ml = 1.00 mg Si.

5) *Vanadium:* Dissolve 2.2965 g ammonium metavanadate, NH_4VO_3, in about 800 ml deionized distilled water, add 10 ml conc HNO_3, and dilute to 1,000 ml with deionized distilled water; 1.00 ml = 1.00 mg V.

3. Procedure

a. *Instrument operation:* Because of differences between makes and models of satisfactory atomic absorption spectrophotometers it is not possible to formulate instructions applicable to every instrument. In general, proceed according to the following steps:

1) Install a hollow cathode lamp of the desired metal in the instrument, set the wavelength dial according to Table 301:III, and align the lamp in accordance with the manufacturer's instructions.

2) Set the slit width according to the manufacturer's suggested setting for the element being measured.

TABLE 301:III. WAVELENGTHS AND SENSITIVITIES
FOR METALS ANALYSES

Metal	Wavelength nm	Sensitivity for 1% Absorption μg/l
Aluminum	309.3	900
Barium	553.6	300
Beryllium	234.9	30
Silicon	251.6	2,000
Vanadium	318.4	1,500

3) Turn on the instrument and apply the amount of current suggested by the manufacturer to the hollow cathode lamp.

4) Allow the instrument to warm up until the energy source stabilizes; this process usually requires from 10 to 20 min.

5) Install a nitrous oxide burner head.

6) Turn on the acetylene (without igniting the flame), and adjust the flow rate to the value specified by the manufacturer for a nitrous oxide-acetylene flame.

7) Turn off the acetylene.

8) With both air and nitrous oxide supplies turned on, set the T-junction valve to nitrous oxide and adjust the flow rate according to the specifications of the manufacturer.

9) Turn the switching valve to the air position and verify that the flow rate is the same.

10) Turn the acetylene on and ignite to a bright yellow flame.

11) With a rapid motion, turn the switching valve to nitrous oxide. The flame should become rose-red; if it does not, adjust fuel flow to obtain a red cone in flame.

12) Atomize deionized distilled water containing 1.5 ml conc HNO_3/l and check the aspiration rate. Adjust if necessary to a rate between 3 and 5 ml/min.

13) Atomize a 1-mg/l standard of the desired metal and adjust the burner (both sideways and vertically) in the light path until maximum response is obtained.

14) The instrument is now ready to run standards and samples.

15) To extinguish the flame, turn the switching valve from nitrous oxide to air, and turn off the acetylene. This procedure eliminates the danger of flashback that may occur on direct ignition or shutdown of nitrous oxide and acetylene.

b. Standardization:

1) Select at least three standard metal solutions (prepared as in 2b) so as to bracket the expected metal concentration of a sample, and aspirate each in turn into the flame. Record the absorbances.

2) For barium, add 2 ml sodium chloride solution (¶ 2g) to 100 ml standard before aspiration.

3) With some instruments, it may be necessary to convert percent absorption to absorbance by use of a suitable table generally provided by the manufacturer.

4) Prepare a calibration curve by plotting on linear graph paper the absorbance of the standards versus concentration.

5) Plot calibration curves for barium based on the original concentration of the standard before adding the sodium chloride solution.

c. Analysis of samples:

1) Rinse the atomizer by aspirating deionized distilled water containing 1.5 ml conc HNO_3/l and zero the instrument.

2) Atomize a sample and determine its absorbance.

3) When determining barium, add 2 ml sodium chloride solution to 100 ml sample before atomization.

4. Calculations

Calculate the concentration of each metal ion in micrograms per liter by referring to the appropriate calibration curve prepared according to ¶ 3b.

V. DETERMINATION OF LOW CONCENTRATIONS OF ALUMINUM AND BERYLLIUM BY CHELATION WITH 8-HYDROXYQUINOLINE AND EXTRACTION INTO METHYL ISOBUTYL KETONE

1. Apparatus

See Section 301 A.2 and 301 A.IV 1. In addition, use *separatory funnels,* 250 ml, with teflon stopcocks.

2. Reagents

a. Air, cleaned and dried through a suitable filter to remove oil, water, and other foreign substances. The source may be a compressor or a commercially bottled gas.

b. Acetylene, standard commercial grade.

c. Buffer: Dissolve 300 g ammonium acetate, $NH_4C_2H_3O_2$, and 105 ml conc NH_4OH in deionized distilled water and dilute to 1 l with deionized distilled water.

d. Deionized distilled water: Use deionized distilled water for the preparation of all reagents and calibration standards, and as dilution water.

e. Hydrochloric acid, HCl, conc.

f. 8-Hydroxyquinoline solution: Dissolve 20 g 8-hydroxyquinoline in about 200 ml deionized distilled water, add 60 ml glacial acetic acid, and dilute to 1 l with deionized distilled water.

g. Methyl isobutyl ketone.

h. Nitric acid, HNO_3, conc.

i. Nitrous oxide, commercial cylinders.

j. Standard metal solutions: Prepare a series of standard metal solutions containing 5 to 1,000 $\mu g/l$ by appropriate dilution of the following stock metal solutions with deionized distilled water containing 1.5 ml conc HNO_3/l.

1) *Aluminum:* See Section 301 A.IV 2h1).

2) *Beryllium:* See Section 301 A.IV 2h3).

3. Procedure

a. Instrument operation:

1) See Section 301 A.II 3a.

2) After adjusting the burner position at Step 13), aspirate methyl iosbutyl ketone into the flame and gradually reduce the fuel flow until the flame is similar to that before aspiration of the solvent.

TABLE 301:IV. WAVELENGTHS AND SENSITIVITIES FOR METALS ANALYSES

Metal	Wavelength nm	Sensitivity for 1% Absorption $\mu g/l$
Aluminum	309.3	90
Beryllium	234.9	3

3) Adjust the wavelength setting according to Table 301:IV.

b. Standardization:

1) Select at least three standard metal solutions (prepared as in 2j) so as to

bracket the expected metal concentration of a sample and transfer 100 ml of each (and 100 ml water blank) to four different 250-ml separatory funnels.

2) Add 2 ml 8-hydroxyquinoline solution to each and shake.

3) Add 10 ml ammonium hydroxide-ammonium acetate buffer solution to each and shake again.

4) Add 10.0 ml methyl isobutyl ketone to each and shake vigorously to mix.

5) Let the contents of each separatory funnel separate into aqueous and organic layers.

6) Drain off aqueous layers and discard. Make sure that none of the aqueous layer remains in the stem of the funnel.

7) Drain the organic layer into a 10-ml glass stoppered graduated cylinder.

8) Aspirate the organic extracts directly into the flame (zeroing the instrument on the blank) and record the absorbances.

9) With some instruments, it may be necessary to convert percent absorption to absorbance by use of a suitable table generally provided by the manufacturer.

10) Prepare a calibration curve by plotting on linear graph paper the absorbance of the extracted standards against concentration prior to extraction.

c. Analysis of samples:

1) Rinse the atomizer by aspirating methyl isobutyl ketone.

2) Aspirate the extracts of samples [treated as in b1) to 7)] and record the absorbances.

4. Calculations

Calculate the concentration of each metal ion in micrograms per liter by re-ferring to the appropriate calibration curve prepared according to ¶ 3b10).

VI. Determination of Mercury by Cold Vapor (Flameless) Atomic Absorption*

1. Apparatus

See Section 301 A.2 for a description of the required atomic absorption spectrophotometer and associated equipment.*

a. Absorption cell, a glass or plastic tube approximately 2.5 cm (1 in.) in diameter and as long as the instrument will permit. An 11.4-cm-(4.5-in.-) long tube has been found satisfactory but a 15-cm.-(6-in.-) long tube is preferred. Grind the ends of the tube perpendicular to the longitudinal axis and cement quartz windows in place. Attach gas inlet and outlet ports (6.4 mm diam) 1.3 cm (0.5 in.) from each end.

b. Cell support: Strap the cell to the flat nitrous-oxide burner head or other suitable support and align in the light beam to give maximum transmittance.

c. Air pump: Any peristaltic pump, with electronic speed control, capable of delivering 2 l air/min may be used, but any other regulated compressed air system or cylinder also is satisfactory.

d. Flowmeter, capable of measuring an air flow of 2 l/min.

e. Aeration tubing, a straight glass frit having a coarse porosity for use in the reaction flask.

f. Reaction flask, 250-ml erlenmeyer flask fitted with a rubber stopper to hold the aeration tube.

---

* Instruments specifically designed for the measurement of mercury by the cold vapor technic are available commercially and may be substituted.

g. Drying tube, 150 mm × 18 mm diam, containing 20 g magnesium perchlorate, $MgClO_4$

h. Small reading lamp, with 60-W bulb positioned to shine on the absorption cell to maintain the air temperature in the cell about 10 C above ambient and prevent condensation of moisture. (This may be unnecessary.)

i. Plastic tubing: Use clear vinyl plastic such as Tygon to pass the mercury vapor from the reaction flask to the absorption cell and to interconnect all other components.

2. Reagents

a. Deionized distilled water: Use deionized distilled water for the preparation of all reagents, standards, and dilution water.

b. Stock mercury solution: Dissolve 1.3540 g $HgCl_2$ in about 700 ml deionized distilled water, add 1.5 ml conc HNO_3, and dilute to 1,000 ml with deionized distilled water; 1.00 ml = 1.00 mg Hg.

c. Standard mercury solutions: Prepare a series of standard mercury solutions containing 0 to 5 $\mu g/l$ by appropriate dilution of the stock mercury solution with deionized distilled water containing 1.5 ml conc nitric acid/l. Prepare standards daily.

d. Nitric acid, HNO_3, conc.

e. Potassium permanganate solution: Dissolve 50 g $KMnO_4$ in deionized distilled water and dilute to 1 l with deionized distilled water.

f. Potassium persulfate solution: Dissolve 50 g $K_2S_2O_8$ in deionized distilled water and dilute to 1 l with deionized distilled water.

g. Sodium chloride—hydroxylamine sulfate solution: Dissolve 120 g of NaCl and 120 g $(NH_2OH)_2 \cdot H_2SO_4$ in deionized distilled water and dilute to 1 l with deionized distilled water.

h. Stannous chloride solution: Dissolve 100 g $SnCl_2$ in deionized distilled water containing 12.5 ml conc HCl and dilute to 1 l with deionized distilled water. On aging, this solution decomposes. If a suspension forms stir the reagent continuously during use.

i. Sulfuric acid, H_2SO_4, conc.

3. Procedure

a. Instrument operation: Because of differences between makes and models of satisfactory atomic absorption spectrophotometers, it is not possible to formulate instructions applicable to every instrument. In general, proceed as follows:

1) Install the mercury hollow cathode lamp in the instrument, set the wavelength dial at 253.7 nm, and align the lamp in accordance with the manufacturer's instructions.

2) Set the slit width according to the manufacturer's suggested setting for mercury.

3) Turn on the instrument and apply the amount of current suggested by the manufacturer to the hollow cathode lamp.

4) Allow the instrument to warm up until the energy source stabilizes; this process usually requires 10 to 20 min.

5) Install the absorption cell and align in the light path to give maximum transmission.

6) Connect the associated equipment to the absorption cell with vinyl plastic tubing as indicated in Figure 301:1.

7) Turn on the air and adjust the flow rate to 2 l/min, and allow the air to flow continuously.

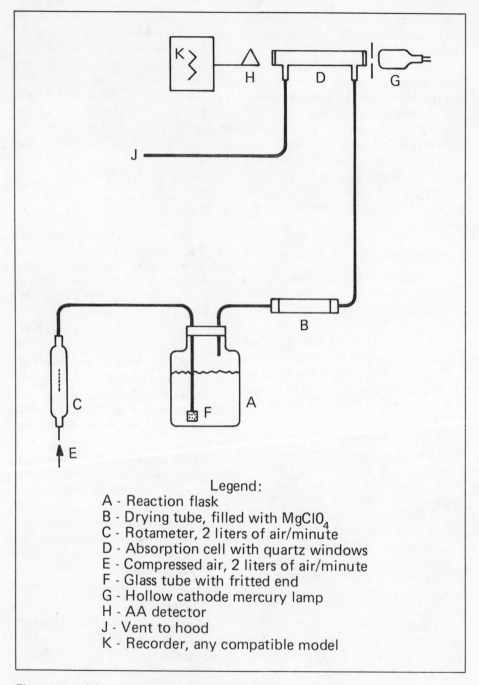

Legend:
A - Reaction flask
B - Drying tube, filled with MgClO$_4$
C - Rotameter, 2 liters of air/minute
D - Absorption cell with quartz windows
E - Compressed air, 2 liters of air/minute
F - Glass tube with fritted end
G - Hollow cathode mercury lamp
H - AA detector
J - Vent to hood
K - Recorder, any compatible model

Figure 301:1. Schematic arrangement of equipment for measurement of mercury by cold vapor atomic absorption technic.

b. Standardization:

1) Transfer 100 ml of each of the mercury standard solutions containing 1.0, 2.0, and 5.0 μg/l, and 100 ml of a deionized distilled water blank to 250-ml erlenmeyer reaction flasks.

2) Add 5 ml conc H_2SO_4 and 2.5 ml conc HNO_3 to each flask.

3) Add 15 ml potassium permanganate solution to each flask and let stand at least 15 min.

4) Add 8 ml potassium persulfate solution to each flask and heat for 2 hr in a water bath at 95 C.

5) Cool to room temperature and add 6 ml sodium chloride-hydroxylamine sulfate solution to reduce the excess permanganate.

6) Treating each flask individually, add 5 ml stannous chloride solution and immediately attach the flask to the aeration apparatus.

7) As the mercury is volatilized and carried into the absorption cell, the absorbance will increase to a maximum within a few seconds.

8) As soon as the recorder returns approximately to base line, remove the stopper holding the frit from the reaction flask and replace with a flask containing deionized water.

9) Flush the system for a few seconds and run the next standard in the same manner.

10) Construct a standard curve by plotting peak height versus micrograms of mercury.

c. Analysis of samples:

Transfer 100 ml sample or portion diluted to 100 ml containing not more than 5.0 μg/l to a reaction flask and treat as in ¶ 3*b*2) through 8).

4. Calculation

Determine the peak height of the sample from the recorder chart and read the mercury value from the standard curve prepared according to ¶ 3*b*10).

VII. DETERMINATION OF ARSENIC AND SELENIUM BY CONVERSION TO THEIR HYDRIDES AND ASPIRATION OF THE GAS INTO THE ARGON-HYDROGEN FLAME

1. Apparatus

See Section 301 A.2 for a description of the required atomic absorption spectrophotometer and associated equipment.

a. Flow meter, capable of measuring 1 l/min, such as that used for auxiliary argon.*

b. Medicine dropper, capable of delivering 1.5 ml, fitted into a size "0" rubber stopper.

c. Reaction flask, a pear-shaped vessel with side arm and 50 ml capacity, both arms having $ 14/20 joint.†

d. Special gas inlet-outlet tube, constructed from a micro cold finger condenser‡ by cutting off the portion below the $ 14/20 ground glass joint.

e. Magnetic stirrer, strong enough to homogenize the zinc slurry described in ¶2*c* below.

f. Drying tube, 100-mm-long polyethylene tube filled with glass wool to keep particulate matter out of the burner.

---

* Gilmont No. 12 or equivalent.
† Scientific Glass JM-5835 or equivalent.
‡ Scientific Glass JM-3325 or equivalent.

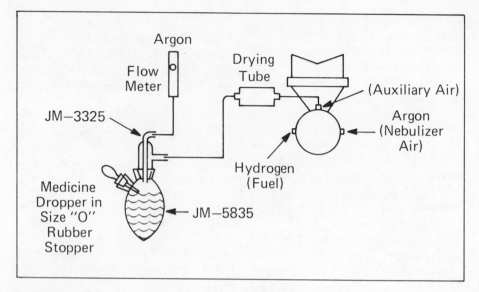

Figure 301:2. Schematic arrangement of equipment for determination of arsenic and selenium.

g. Apparatus setup: Connect the apparatus with the burner of the spectrophotometer as shown in Figure 301:2. Connect the outlet of the reaction vessel to the auxiliary oxidant input of the burner with Tygon tubing. Connect the inlet of the reaction vessel to the outlet side of the auxiliary oxidant (argon supply) control valve of the instrument.

2. Reagents

a. Potassium iodide solution: Dissolve 20 g KI in 100 ml deionized distilled water.

b. Stannous chloride solution: Dissolve 100 g $SnCl_2$ in 100 ml conc HCl.

c. Zinc slurry: Add 50 g zinc metal dust (200 mesh) to 100 ml deionized distilled water.

d. Diluent: Add 100 ml 18N H_2SO_4 and 400 ml conc HCl to 400 ml deionized distilled water in a 1-l volumetric flask and bring to volume with deionized distilled water.

e. Arsenic solutions:

1) *Stock arsenic solution:* Dissolve 1.3209 g arsenic trioxide, As_2O_3, in 100 ml distilled water containing 4 g NaOH and dilute to 1,000 ml with deionized distilled water; 1.00 ml = 1.00 mg As.

2) *Intermediate arsenic solution:* Pipet 1 ml stock arsenic solution into a 100-ml volumetric flask and bring to volume with deionized distilled water containing 1.5 ml conc HNO_3/l; 1.00 ml = 10.0 μg As.

3) *Standard arsenic solution:* Pipet 10 ml intermediate arsenic solution into a 100-ml volumetric flask and bring to volume with deionized distilled water containing 1.5 ml conc HNO_3/l; 1.00 ml = 1 μg As.

f. Selenium solutions:

1) *Stock selenium solution:* Dissolve 1.000 g selenium in 5 ml conc HNO_3.

Warm until the reaction is complete and cautiously evaporate just to dryness. Dilute to 1,000 ml with deionized distilled water; 1.00 ml = 1.00 mg Se.

2) *Intermediate selenium solution:* Pipet 1 ml stock selenium solution into a 100-ml volumetric flask and bring to volume with deionized distilled water containing 1.5 ml conc HNO_3/l; 1.00 ml = 10.0 μg Se.

3) *Standard selenium solution:* Pipet 10 ml intermediate selenium solution into a 100-ml volumetric flask and bring to volume with deionized distilled water containing 1.5 ml conc HNO_3/l; 1.00 ml = 1.00 μg Se.

g. *Perchloric acid,* 70 to 72% $HClO_4$.

3. Procedure

a. *Instrument operation:* Because of differences between makes and models of satisfactory atomic absorption spectrophotometers, it is not possible to formulate instructions applicable to every instrument. In general, proceed as follows:

1) Install a hollow cathode lamp of the desired metal in the instrument, set the wavelength dial according to Table 301:V, and align the lamp in accordance with the manufacturer's instructions.

2) Set the slit width according to the manufacturer's suggested setting for the element being measured.

TABLE 301:V. WAVELENGTHS AND SENSITIVITIES FOR METALS ANALYSES

Metal	Wavelength nm	Approximate Sensitivity $\mu g/l$
Arsenic	193.7	2.5
Selenium	196.0	2.5

3) Turn on the instrument and apply the amount of current suggested by the manufacturer to the hollow cathode lamp.

4) Allow the instrument to warm up until the energy source stabilizes; this process usually requires 10 to 20 min.

5) Install a Boling burner head.

6) Turn on the argon and adjust to a flow rate of about 8 l/min, with the auxiliary argon flow at 1 l/min.

7) Turn on the hydrogen, adjust to a flow rate of about 7 l/min and ignite the flame. The flame is essentially colorless. To determine whether the flame is ignited, pass the hand about 30 cm (1 ft) above the burner to detect the heat emitted.

8) Atomize the standard solution (1.00 ml = 1.00 μg) of the desired metal, and adjust the burner both sideways and vertically in the light path until maximum response is obtained.

9) The instrument is now ready to run standards and samples by the arrangement of Figure 301:2.

b. *Sample preparation:*

1) Inorganic arsenic or selenium— To a 50-ml volumetric flask, add 25 ml sample, 20 ml conc HCl, and 5 ml 18N H_2SO_4.

2) Total (inorganic and organic) arsenic—To 50 ml sample in a 150-ml beaker, add 10 ml conc HNO_3 and 12 ml 18N H_2SO_4. Evaporate to SO_3 fumes (a volume of about 20 ml). To avoid the loss of arsenic, maintain oxidizing conditions at all times by adding small amounts of nitric acid whenever the red-brown NO_2 fumes disappear. Cool slightly, add 25 ml deionized distilled water, 1 ml perchloric acid, and again evaporate to SO_3 fumes. Cool, add 40 ml conc HCl, and bring to a vol-

ume of 100 ml with deionized distilled water.

c. *Preparation of standards:* Transfer 0, 0.5, 1.0, 1.5, and 2.0 ml standard arsenic or selenium solution to 100-ml volumetric flasks and bring to volume with diluent to obtain concentrations of 0, 5, 10, 15, and 20 $\mu g/1$ arsenic or selenium.

d. *Treatment of samples and standards:* Transfer a 25-ml portion of sample prepared as in ¶ *b*1) or *b*2) or standard prepared as in *c* to the reaction vessel, and add 1 ml potassium iodide solution to arsenic samples and standards only. Omit KI for selenium determinations. Add 0.5 ml SnCl₂ solution. Allow at least 10 min for the metal to be reduced to its lowest oxidation state. Attach the reaction vessel to the special gas inlet-outlet glassware. Fill the medicine

dropper with 1.50 ml zinc slurry that has been kept in suspension with the magnetic stirrer. Firmly insert the stopper containing the medicine dropper into the side neck of the reaction vessel. Squeeze the bulb to introduce the zinc slurry into the sample or standard. The metal hydride will produce a peak almost immediately. When the recorder pen returns part way to the base line, remove the reaction vessel.

4. Calculations

Draw a standard curve by plotting peak heights of standards versus concentration of standards. Measure the peak heights of the samples and read the concentration from the curve. Multiply these concentrations by two because the sample was diluted 1 + 1 with acid.

301 B.   Polarographic Method for Cadmium, Copper, Lead, Nickel, and Zinc

1. General Discussion

Colorimetric analysis of metal-bearing wastes and receiving streams is generally difficult and time-consuming. Polarographic technics are preferable to colorimetric methods because of the rapidity of analysis and because the method may be applied simultaneously to a variety of metals. The method has been developed to permit the simultaneous determination of cadmium, copper, lead, nickel, and zinc.

Numerous other metals can be determined polarographically by selecting the proper supporting electrolyte. The sequence of supporting electrolytes used in these procedures was selected to give

maximum information for the least effort and with the least danger of contamination by reagents.

a. *Principle:* Conventional polarography is based on the unique properties displayed by an electrolytic cell consisting of a nonpolarizable reference electrode, a readily polarizable electrode in the form of a mercury drop falling from a capillary, and an electrolytic solution containing small amounts of electroreducible or electro-oxidizable material. When an increasing electromotive force is impressed across such a cell and the resulting current is plotted as a function of the applied voltage (Figure 301:4), a curve is obtained. Its extension along the current axis is directly related to the concentration of the trace material and its inflection point is located at a voltage characteristic of that material.

b. Interference: Iron, chromium, organic matter, turbidity, chlorides, oxidizing and reducing substances, and dissolved oxygen are the major interferences that are likely to be encountered. The pretreatment procedure was designed to eliminate interference of this type and must be used before the polarographic technic described below. Deviation from the procedure may lead either to completely erroneous results or to polarograms that are impossible to interpret. When the recommended procedure is followed, the only significant interferences are from large quantities of other reducible species with half-wave potentials close to that of the metal of interest. The sequence of supporting electrolytes was selected to permit interpretation of the polarograms for each of the five metals of interest even in the presence of large quantities of one or more interfering metals. The method was also tested in the presence of 100 mg/l of chromium, iron, and organic matter, with no detectable effect.

c. Minimum detectable concentrations: The lower limit of detection, using ordinary equipment and the dropping mercury electrode, is about $10^{-6}M$. Therefore, including a 10-to-1 concentration, the lower limits of detection are about 0.1 mg/l.

2. Apparatus

a. Polarograph: Use any commercially available polarograph capable of utilizing applied voltages of 0.00 to −2.0 V. Automatic voltage scanning and recording, although not required, are recommended.

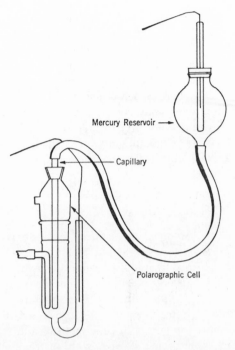

Mercury Reservoir →

Capillary

Polarographic Cell

Figure 301:3. Polarographic cell for use with dropping mercury electrode.

b. Polarographic cell: Figure 301:3 shows the conventional polarographic cell used with the dropping mercury electrode, including the mercury reservoir. In cells of this type, the mercury pool is a reference electrode. The indicator electrode consists of small drops of mercury falling from a capillary attached to a reservoir of mercury. Other types of cells also available commercially permit the use of external standard reference electrodes. In general, selection of the type of cell is left to the discretion of the analyst.

c. Deaeration apparatus: Oxygen is readily reduced at the dropping mercury electrode and must be removed. This is usually accomplished by bubbling nitrogen through the solution. Tank nitrogen, which is usually contaminated by traces of oxygen, can be purified by passing it over copper turnings heated to 450 C. Equipment of this type is available commercially.

d. *Sintered-glass filter*, fine-porosity, with holder. Gooch crucible with glass-fiber filter may be used. (These are needed only for pretreatment.)

NOTE: Rinse all glassware with 1 +1 HNO_3, distilled water, and redistilled water.

3. Reagents

a. *Mercury, redistilled, National Formulary grade:* Used mercury may be purified by using commercially available oxidizers and gold adhesion filters.

b. *Ammonium sulfate solution*, saturated: Neutralize 7M metal-free ammonia solution with conc H_2SO_4, adding the acid slowly with extreme caution. Extract the neutralized solution with a solution of diphenylthiocarbazone in carbon tetrachloride. Wash with carbon tetrachloride to remove all traces of color. Concentrate to a saturated solution by evaporating excess water.

c. *Gelatin*, U.S.P. powder.

d. *Ethylenediaminetetraacetic acid disodium salt*, commercially available grade.

e. *Sulfuric acid*, H_2SO_4, conc.

f. *Nitric acid*, HNO_3, conc and 1 + 1.

g. *Redistilled water:* Distilled water redistilled in all-glass apparatus.

h. *Ammonium hydroxide solution*, NH_4OH, metal-free: Pass tank ammonia gas through a glass-wool trap into chilled redistilled water until the concentration reaches about 7M. Alternatively, distill 900 ml of conc NH_4OH in a 1,500-ml distilling flask into a 1-l polyethylene bottle containing 250 ml of chilled redistilled water until the volume

of liquid in the bottle has increased to 900 ml. Keep the tip of the condenser below the surface of the liquid during the distillation.

e. *Sodium sulfite*, crystals, reagent grade.

4. Procedure

a. *Sample pretreatment:* Add 0.1 ml conc H_2SO_4 to 100 ml of sample in a pyrex erlenmeyer flask and evaporate to dense white fumes. Add conc HNO_3 to the fuming liquid drop by drop until the solution clears and becomes colorless. With some samples it is not possible to remove all the color by this procedure; however, add nitric acid until no further color change can be perceived. Wash down the sides of the flask with glass-distilled water to remove excess HNO_3 and again bring to fumes. Fuming also removes chlorides that interfere.

Neutralize the solution with the metal-free ammonia solution, using pink litmus paper to indicate the completion of neutralization. The resultant solution is about 0.18M in $(NH_4)_2SO_4$. Boil to remove excess ammonia until the odor of ammonia disappears. Filter the solution through a sintered-glass filter and make up to 10 ml with redistilled water.

b. *Instrumental measurement:*

1) Transfer the pretreated sample to the polarographic cell. Add about 10 mg gelatin to suppress maxima that may interfere. Use a fritted-glass bubbler for better dispersion of the nitrogen and more complete deoxygenation. Place a small amount of purified mercury in the bottom of the cell to form the indicator electrode. Insert the dropping mercury electrode into the cell so that

the tip is immersed in the solution. Adjust the height of the mercury reservoir to give a drop time of 4 or 5 sec.

2) Connect the cell to the polarograph and run a polarogram at suitable sensitivity, from 0.00 V to about −1.6 V. While making measurements, remove the nitrogen bubbler from the solution and hold just above the surface to maintain an atmosphere of nitrogen and prevent surface absorption of oxygen.

3) After suitable curves have been run with $(NH_4)_2SO_4$ supporting electrolyte, add sufficient NH_4OH to make the solution about $0.4M$ in NH_3. Usually 4 or 5 drops of the ammonia solution are sufficient.

4) After curves have been run in the presence of free ammonia, add about 300 mg of ethylenediaminetetraacetate disodium salt and repeat.

5. Interpretation of Polarograms

Read half-wave potentials at the halfway point of the rise, as determined by inspection or by rough measurement. It

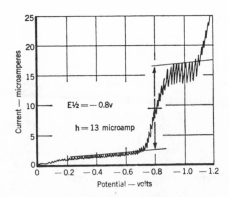

Figure 301:4. Interpretation of polarograms obtained with the the dropping mercury electrode.

is not necessary to correct for current resistance (IR) drop across the resistors in the measuring circuit. Measure heights vertically through the half-wave potentials between straight-line extrapolations of the sections of the polarogram immediately preceding and following the wave. This is illustrated in Figure 301:4.

Half-wave potentials and current concentration ratios of metals at the dropping mercury electrode are given in Table 301:VI. These values identify the

TABLE 301:VI. HALF-WAVE POTENTIALS AND CURRENT CONCENTRATION RATIOS OF METALS AT THE DROPPING MERCURY ELECTRODE

Metal	Supporting Electrolyte					
	$0.18M$ $(NH_4)_2SO_4$		$0.4M$ NH_4OH + $0.18M$ $(NH_4)_2SO_4$		$0.4M$ NH_4OH + EDTA + $0.18M$ $(NH_4)_2SO_4$	
	Half-Wave Potential v	Relative Wave Height*	Half-Wave Potential v	Relative Wave Height*	Half-Wave Potential v	Relative Wave Height*
Copper	0.02 to 0.05	0.0076	0.17	Often not seen	0.47 to 0.51	0.0050
			0.38 to 0.45	0.0040		
Lead	0.37 to 0.40	0.0010	0.43 to 0.47	0.0010	1.13 to 1.17	0.0010
Cadmium	0.57 to 0.59	0.0036	0.67 to 0.74	0.0036	No wave	—
Nickel	1.01 to 1.03	0.0083	0.91 to 0.95	0.0083	No wave	—
Zinc	0.98	0.0083	1.19 to 1.22	0.0083	No wave	—

* $\mu A/$ μg of element.

five metals—cadmium, copper, lead, nickel, and zinc—and provide semi-quantitative results that can be used to eliminate the necessity of analyzing for metals that are absent and to determine

sample size for wet analysis. For quantitative results, a similar table should be prepared by the analyst using his equipment and standard solutions of the metals of interest.

301 C.   Preliminary Treatment of Samples

This section describes general methods for pretreatment of samples in which metals are to be determined according to Sections 302 through 323. Pretreatment is especially important in testing polluted water or wastewater samples that are likely to contain particulate matter or other interferences. The sections describing analytical procedures refer to this section where appropriate.

Section 301 C.I, below, describes pretreatment of samples for the determination of the alkali and alkaline earth metals (Groups I and II of the periodic table). Section 301 C.II, which follows, presents alternative methods of preparing samples for the colorimetric determination of other metals, and includes instructions for preparation of the dithizone solutions used in several of the determinations.

I. Pretreatment for Metals of Groups I and II

The methods described below for pretreatment of samples for the determination of metals in Groups I and II can be applied satisfactorily to the determination of calcium, lithium, magnesium, potassium, sodium, and strontium. This pretreatment eliminates interfering materials, which may prohibit the direct determination of these metals in wastewaters, effluents, and polluted water.

1. General Discussion

If the sample contains considerable organic matter, ashing by either wet or dry methods will be necessary. If the elements of interest are volatile at ashing temperature, wet ashing is preferable. If a sample of sufficient size is ashed and the ash dissolved, suitable portions can be used for individual determinations.

2. Reagents

a. *Nitric acid*, HNO_3, conc.

b. *Hydrogen peroxide*, H_2O_2, 30%.

c. *Hydrochloric acid*, HCl, conc.

d. *Ammonium hydroxide*, NH_4OH, conc.

3. Procedure

Use either digestion with nitric acid (¶ *a* below) or dry ashing (¶ *b* below).

a. *Digestion with nitric acid:* Measure a sample of suitable size into a 250-ml erlenmeyer flask, acidify with nitric acid, and evaporate to dryness on a steam bath. Add approximately 25 ml conc HNO_3 and heat to near boiling. Evaporate the acid to a small volume, taking precautions to prevent spattering. The presence of unoxidized organic matter is indicated by brown fumes. Complete the ashing by repeated additions of nitric acid or nitric acid plus small quantities of hydrogen peroxide.

The residue on final drying should be white unless such elements as iron or copper are present. Proceed to ¶ 3c.

b. Dry ashing: Evaporate a sample of suitable size to dryness on a steam bath in a platinum or Vycor evaporating dish. Transfer the dish to a muffle furnace and heat the sample to a white ash. The ashing temperature to be used depends on the elements to be determined in the sample. If volatile elements are present, keep the temperature at 400 to 450 C for as many hours as required. If sodium only is to be determined, ash the sample at a temperature up to 600 C.

c. Final sample preparation: Dissolve the sample ash in a minimum amount of conc HCl and warm distilled water. Filter the diluted sample, neutralize with conc NH_4OH, and adjust to a known volume.

d. Determinations: After pretreatment, determine calcium, lithium, magnesium, potassium, sodium, and strontium by the methods described for the specific metals. For best results, apply flame photometric methods for the determination of lithium, potassium, sodium, and strontium, and titrimetric, gravimetric, or atomic absorption methods for calcium and magnesium. When applying flame photometric methods, adjust the acid concentrations of the standards to that of the sample being analyzed.

4. Bibliography

WEST, P.W., P. FOLSE & D. MONTGOMERY. 1950. Application of flame spectrophotometry to water analysis, determination of sodium, potassium and calcium. *Anal. Chem.* 22:667.

POLUEKTOVE, N.S. 1961. Techniques in Flame Photometric Analysis. Consultants Bureau, New York, p. 219.

HARLEY, J. 1967. Manual of Standard Procedures. U.S. Atomic Energy Commission Document No. NYO-4700.

II. PRETREATMENT FOR COLORIMETRIC ANALYSIS OF HEAVY METALS

1. General Discussion

Because metals readily form complex ions with organic constituents, it is necessary that organic matter be destroyed by preliminary treatment. The recommended treatment is digestion, either with a mixture of nitric and sulfuric acids, or—when the organic matter is difficult to oxidize—with nitric and perchloric acids. Acid digestion also eliminates possible interference from cyanide, nitrite, sulfide, sulfite, thiosulfate, and thiocyanate.

A single sample of suitable size may be digested and portions of the sample used for determination of the individual metals. The volume of sample to be digested may be estimated by summing the volumes needed for determination of each of the constituents, as given in the directions for the individual determinations.

2. Apparatus

a. Sintered-glass filter crucibles, fine porosity, with holder. Gooch crucibles with glass fiber filters may be used.

Clean all glassware thoroughly, then rinse with $1 + 1$ HNO_3, and finally rinse with glass-redistilled water.

b. Infrared lamp (optional).

3. Reagents

a. Methyl orange indicator solution.

b. Sulfuric acid, H_2SO_4, conc.

c. Nitric acid, HNO₃, conc.

d. Hydrogen peroxide, H₂O₂, 30%.

e. Redistilled water: Distilled water redistilled in all-glass apparatus or passed through a deionizing column. (See Ammonia Nitrogen, Section 418.)

f. Perchloric acid, 60%.

g. Special reagent—ammonium acetate solution: Dissolve 400 g NH₄C₂H₃O₂ in 600 ml redistilled water. Use this solution only if lead is to be determined in the presence of sulfate.

Total iron and heavy-metal impurities in the reagent acids should not exceed 0.0001%. Prepare blanks in any event, but if the metallic impurities are greater than this, the blanks will be too large and variable for precise determinations of small concentrations of the metals. When the amounts of acid specified are used, 0.0001% of heavy-metal impurity will add about 0.03 mg of heavy metals to the sample.

4. Dithizone Solutions

Diphenylthiocarbazone (dithizone) is the colorimetric reagent for the determination of cadmium, lead, and zinc. To insure satisfactory results, purify dithizone solutions to remove the contaminating oxidation product, diphenylthiocarbondiazone. Prepare purified stock solutions of dithizone in chloroform and carbon tetrachloride according to the directions below. Refrigerate the solutions at all times and prepare the working solutions for the specific metal determinations daily.

a. Stock dithizone solution I (chloroform): Dissolve 250 mg dithizone crystals in 50 ml CHCl₃, filter through a small paper, and wash the filter with several small portions of CHCl₃. Transfer the filtrate to a separatory funnel and

extract with portions of 1 + 99 NH₄OH until the CHCl₃ layer is nearly devoid of green color. Discard the CHCl₃ layer and wash the combined extracts with four 15-ml portions of CHCl₃. Discard the CHCl₃ extracts. Precipitate the dithizone by adding 2 ml conc HCl; shake to completely neutralize the ammonia. Extract the precipitated dithizone with 25-ml portions of CHCl₃ and finally dilute the combined extracts with CHCl₃ to a volume of 250 ml. Keep the solution in the refrigerator.

b. Stock dithizone solution II (carbon tetrachloride): Dissolve 125 mg dithizone in 50 ml CHCl₃ and filter through a small filter paper. Wash filter paper with small portions of CHCl₃ and combine all filtrates. Extract the filtrates with 1 + 99 NH₄OH until the CHCl₃ layer is nearly devoid of green color. Wash the aqueous layer with CCl₄ to remove traces of CHCl₃ and any diphenylthiocarbondiazone. Discard the CCl₄ extracts. Neutralize the NH₄OH by shaking well with 2 ml conc HCl. Extract the precipitated dithizone with CCl₄. Dilute the extracts to 500 ml with CCl₄. Keep this solution in a refrigerator. CAUTION: Carbon tetrachloride is a toxic substance. Long-continued exposure to small amounts may be hazardous. While the solvent can be absorbed through the skin, the primary danger is through inhalation of the vapor. Prepare reagents and extract standards and samples with carbon tetrachloride in a well-ventilated hood.

5. Digestion with Nitric and Sulfuric Acids

a. Agitate the sample to obtain a homogeneous suspension. Measure a suitable volume (as determined from the tabulation) with a pipet or volumetric flask and transfer to an evaporating dish or casserole. (If the volume required is greater than 250 ml, transfer in portions as the sample evaporates.)

Concentration mg/l	Volume ml
<1	1,000
1–10	100
10–100	10
100–1,000	1

Acidify to methyl orange with conc H_2SO_4, then add 5 ml conc HNO_3 and 2 ml 30% H_2O_2 to reduce chromate. Evaporate on a steam bath or hot plate to 15 to 20 ml, covering the vessel with a watch glass, when necessary, to avoid loss of material by spattering. An infrared lamp may be placed over the sample to hasten the evaporation.

b. Transfer the evaporated solution, together with any solids remaining in the dish, to a 125-ml conical flask. Add 5 ml conc HNO_3 that was used to rinse the evaporating dish or casserole; 10 ml conc H_2SO_4; and a few glass beads, carborundum chips, or Hengar granules to minimize bumping. Evaporate on a hot plate (in a hood) until dense white fumes of SO_3 just appear in the flask, but do not continue heating beyond this point. If the solution is not clear, add 10 ml HNO_3 and repeat the evaporation to fumes of SO_3. Be sure that all HNO_3 is removed, as indicated by the clarity of the solution and the absence of brownish fumes in the flask.

c. Cool to room temperature and dilute carefully to about 50 ml with redistilled water. Heat nearly to boiling to dissolve slowly soluble salts, and filter through a sintered-glass or porcelain filter crucible into a thoroughly clean filter

flask. Rinse the sample flask with two 5-ml portions of redistilled water, passing them through the crucible to wash any residue on the filter. (A filtering device that allows collection of the filtrate directly in a 100-ml volumetric flask may be used and, if available, is preferable.) Transfer the filtrate to a 100-ml volumetric flask and rinse the filter flask with two 5-ml portions of redistilled water, adding these rinsings to the volumetric flask. Dilute in the volumetric flask to the 100-ml mark and mix thoroughly. The resulting solution is about $3N$ in H_2SO_4. Take portions of it for the determination of the metals. For the determination of lead, also use the solution obtained in the following section:

d. If the sample contains much lead, some of it will be present as $PbSO_4$ in the residue on the filter; this must be dissolved and measured as a part of the lead determination. Add 50 ml ammonium acetate solution to the conical flask in which the digestion was carried out and heat to incipient boiling, rotating the flask occasionally to wet thoroughly all interior areas on which residue might have deposited. Reconnect the filter and draw the hot ammonium acetate solution through it slowly to dissolve the $PbSO_4$. Transfer the filtrate to a 100-ml volumetric flask, allow it to cool to room temperature, dilute to the mark, mix thoroughly, and set aside for the determination of lead.

6. Digestion with Nitric and Perchloric Acids

CAUTION: Heated mixtures of concentrated perchloric acid and organic matter may explode violently. Observe the following precautions: (a) Do not add perchloric acid to a hot solution that may contain organic matter. (*b*) Always pretreat samples containing organic matter with HNO₃ before adding HClO₄. (*c*) Use a mixture of nitric and perchloric acids in starting the digestion step. (*d*) Avoid repeated fumings of perchloric acid in ordinary hoods. For routine operations use hoods of stone or asbestos-cement. Alternatively, for occasional work with HClO₄, use glass fume eradicators* attached to a water pump.

a. Measure a sample, acidify to methyl orange with HNO₃, add another 5 ml conc HNO₃, and evaporate the sample as in ¶ *5a*. Transfer the evaporated sample to a 125-ml conical flask as in ¶ *5b*, cool, and add 5 ml HNO₃ and 10 ml 70% HClO₄. After adding a few boiling chips, heat on a hot plate, and evaporate gently until dense white fumes of HClO₄ just appear. If the solution is not clear, add 10 ml HNO₃, cover the neck of the flask with a watch glass, and keep the solution just barely boiling until it clears.

b. Cool, dilute to about 50 ml with redistilled water, and boil to expel any chlorine or oxides of nitrogen. Then filter the sample as in ¶ *5c*, transfer the filtrate and washings to a 100-ml volumetric flask, cool, dilute to the mark, and mix thoroughly. The resulting solution is about 0.8*N* in HClO₄. Take portions of this solution for the determina-

tion of individual metals just as from the solution obtained in ¶ *5c*.

c. If lead is to be determined, and if sulfate is present in the sample, treat the residue from the filtration as directed in ¶ *5d*.

7. Digestion of Sludges Having High or Refractory Organic Content

Transfer a sample, measured as in ¶ *5a*, to a suitable evaporating dish or casserole and evaporate to 15 to 20 ml on a steam bath. Add 12 ml conc HNO₃ and evaporate on a hot plate to near dryness. Repeat the addition of HNO₃ and evaporation. Using 25 ml 1 + 1 HNO₃, transfer the residue to a 250-ml conical flask (add 10 ml to the residue to assist in the transfer and use the other 15 ml for rinsing the evaporating dish). Add 25 ml 60% HClO₄ and boil until nearly dry or until the solution is clear and white fumes of HClO₄ have appeared. Cool, add 50 ml redistilled water, and proceed with ¶ *6b*.

8. Bibliography

Butts, P. G., A. R. Gahler & M. G. Mellon. 1950. Colorimetric determination of metals in sewage and industrial wastes. *Sewage Ind. Wastes* 22: 1543.

Christie, A. A. et al. 1957. The colorimetric determination of cadmium, chromium, copper, iron, lead, manganese, nickel, and zinc in sewage and industrial wastes. *Analyst* 82:336.

---

* G. F. Smith Chemical Company, Columbus, Ohio, or equivalent.

302 ALUMINUM

Aluminum is the third most abundant element of the earth's crust, occurring in minerals, rocks, and clays. This wide distribution accounts for the presence of aluminum in practically all natural water as a soluble salt, a colloid, or an insoluble compound. Soluble, colloidal, and insoluble aluminum also may appear in treated water or wastewater as a residual from alum coagulation. Recent work indicates that filtered water from a modern rapid sand filtration plant should have an aluminum concentration no greater than 50 μg/l.

Selection of method: The atomic absorption spectrophotometric method is free from such common interferences as fluoride and phosphate, and therefore is preferred. The Eriochrome cyanine R colorimetric method provides a means for estimating aluminum with simpler instrumentation.

302 A. Atomic Absorption Spectrophotometric Method

See Section 301A. IV and V.

302 B. Eriochrome Cyanine R Method (TENTATIVE)

1. General Discussion

a. Principle: Dilute aluminum solutions buffered to a pH of 6.0 produce with Eriochrome cyanine R dye a red to pink complex that exhibits maximum absorption at 535 nm. The intensity of the developed color is influenced by the aluminum concentration, reaction time, temperature, pH, alkalinity, and the concentration of other ions in the sample. To compensate for color and turbidity, the aluminum in one portion of sample is complexed with EDTA to provide a blank. The interference of iron and manganese, two elements often found in water, is eliminated by adding ascorbic acid. The optimum aluminum range lies between 20 and 300 μg/l but can be extended upward by sample dilution.

b. Interference: Negative errors are caused by both fluoride and polyphosphates. When the fluoride concentration is constant, the percentage of error decreases with increasing amounts of aluminum. Because the fluoride concentration is often known or can be determined readily, fairly accurate results can be obtained by adding the known amount of fluoride to a set of standards. If less accuracy can be tolerated, a simpler correction can be determined from the family of curves in Figure 302:1. A procedure is given for the removal of complex phosphate interference. Orthophosphate in concentrations under 10 mg/l does not interfere. The inter-

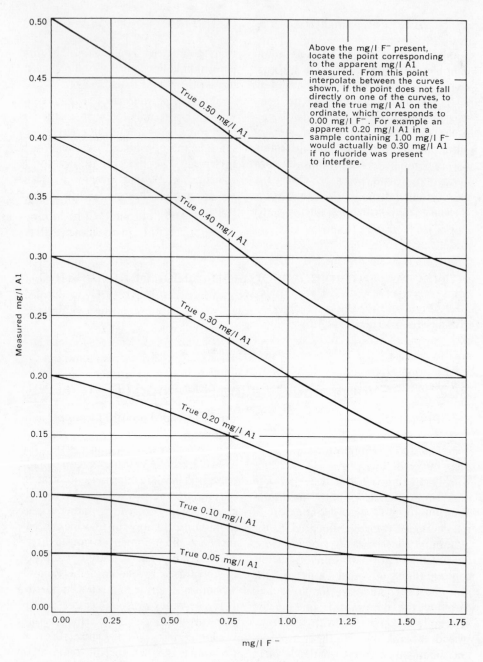

Above the mg/l F⁻ present, locate the point corresponding to the apparent mg/l Al measured. From this point interpolate between the curves shown, if the point does not fall directly on one of the curves, to read the true mg/l Al on the ordinate, which corresponds to 0.00 mg/l F⁻. For example an apparent 0.20 mg/l Al in a sample containing 1.00 mg/l F⁻ would actually be 0.30 mg/l Al if no fluoride was present to interfere.

True 0.50 mg/l Al

True 0.40 mg/l Al

True 0.30 mg/l Al

True 0.20 mg/l Al

True 0.10 mg/l Al

True 0.05 mg/l Al

Measured mg/l Al

mg/l F⁻

Figure 302:1. Correction curves for estimation of aluminum in the presence of fluoride.

ference caused by even small amounts of alkalinity is removed by acidifying the sample just beyond the neutralization point of methyl orange. Sulfate does not interfere up to a concentration of 2,000 mg/l.

c. *Minimum detectable concentration:* The minimum aluminum concentration detectable by this method in the absence of fluorides and complex phosphates is approximately 6 μg/l.

d. *Sample handling:* Collect samples in clean, acid-rinsed bottles, preferably plastic, and examine them as soon as possible after collection. If only soluble aluminum is to be determined, filter a portion of the sample through a 0.45-μm membrane filter; discard the first 50 ml of filtrate and use the succeeding filtrate for the determination. Do not use filter paper, absorbent cotton, or glass wool for filtering any solution that is to be tested for aluminum, because they will remove most of the soluble aluminum.

2. Apparatus

a. *Colorimetric equipment:* One of the following is required:

1) *Spectrophotometer,* for use at 535 nm and utilizing a light path of 1 cm or longer.

2) *Filter photometer,* providing a light path of 1 cm or longer and equipped with a green filter showing maximum transmittance between 525 and 535 nm.

3) *Nessler tubes,* 50-ml, tall form, matched.

b. *Glassware:* Treat all glassware with warm 1 + 1 HCl and rinse with aluminum-free distilled water to avoid errors due to materials absorbed on the glass. Rinse sufficiently to remove all acid.

3. Reagents

Use reagents low in aluminum, and aluminum-free distilled water.

a. *Stock aluminum solution:* Use either the metal (1) or the salt (2) for the preparation of the stock solution, which contains 500 μg Al/1.00 ml:

1) Dissolve 500.0 mg aluminum metal in 10 ml of conc HCl by heating gently. Dilute to 1 l in a volumetric flask with distilled water, or

2) Dissolve 8.792 g aluminum potassium sulfate (also called potassium alum), $AlK(SO_4)_2 \cdot 12H_2O$, in distilled water and dilute to 1 l in a volumetric flask.

b. *Standard aluminum solution:* Dilute 10.00 ml of the stock aluminum solution to 1 l in a volumetric flask with distilled water; 1.00 ml = 5.00 μg Al. Prepare daily.

c. *Sulfuric acid,* 0.02N and 6N.

d. *Ascorbic acid solution:* Dissolve 0.1 g ascorbic acid in distilled water and make up to 100 ml in a volumetric flask. Prepare fresh daily.

e. *Buffer reagent:* Dissolve 136 g sodium acetate, $NaC_2H_3O_2 \cdot 3H_2O$, in distilled water, add 40 ml 1N acetic acid, and dilute to 1 l.

f. *Stock dye solution:* Use any of the following products:

1) *Solochrome cyanine R-200** or *Eriochrome cyanine†:* Dissolve 100 mg in distilled water and dilute to 100 ml in

---

* A product of Arnold Hoffman & Co., Providence, R. I.

† A product of K & K Laboratories, Plainview, N. Y.

a volumetric flask. This solution should have a pH of about 2.9.

2) *Eriochrome cyanine R‡*: Dissolve 300 mg of the dye in about 50 ml distilled water. Adjust the pH from about 9 to about 2.9 with 1 + 1 acetic acid (approximately 3 ml will be required). Dilute with distilled water to 100 ml.

3) *Eriochrome cyanine R§*: Dissolve 150 mg in about 50 ml of distilled water. Adjust the pH from about 9 to about 2.9 with 1 + 1 acetic acid (approximately 2 ml will be required). Dilute with distilled water to 100 ml.

Stock solutions have excellent stability. They can be kept for at least a year.

g. *Working dye solution:* Dilute 10.0 ml of any one of the stock dye solutions to 100 ml in a volumetric flask with distilled water. Working solutions are stable for at least 6 months.

h. *Methyl orange indicator solution*, or the mixed bromcresol green-methyl red indicator solution specified in the total alkalinity determination (Section 403.3d).

i. *0.01M EDTA (disodium ethylenediamine tetraacetate):* Weigh 3.7 g of the reagent, dissolve in distilled water, and dilute to 1 l.

j. *Sodium hydroxide*, 1N and 0.1N.

4. Procedure

a. *Preparation of calibration curve:*
1) Prepare a series of aluminum standards from 0 to 7 μg (0 to 280 μg/l based on a 25-ml sample) by accurately measuring the calculated volumes of standard aluminum solution into 50-ml

‡ A product of Pfaltz & Bauer, Inc., Flushing, N. Y.
§ A product of Hartman-Leddon Co., Philadelphia, Pa.

volumetric flasks or nessler tubes. Add distilled water to a total volume of approximately 25 ml.

Add 1 ml 0.02N sulfuric acid to each standard and mix. Add 1 ml ascorbic acid solution and mix.

2) Add 10 ml buffer solution and mix. With a volumetric pipet, add 5 ml of working dye reagent and mix. Immediately make up to 50 ml with distilled water. Mix and let stand for 5 to 15 min (the color begins to fade after 15 min).

3) Read the transmittance or absorbance on a spectrophotometer, using a wavelength of 535 nm or a green filter providing maximum transmittance between 525 and 535 nm. Adjust the instrument to 100% transmittance or zero absorbance with the standard containing no aluminum.

Plot a calibration curve relating micrograms aluminum to the instrument reading.

b. *Sample treatment in the absence of fluoride and complex phosphates:* Place a 25.0-ml sample, or a portion diluted to 25 ml, in a porcelain dish or flask, add a few drops of methyl orange indicator, and titrate with 0.02N sulfuric acid to a faint pink color. Record reading and discard.

To two similar samples at room temperature add the same amount of 0.02N acid used in the titration and 1 ml in excess.

To one of the samples add 1 ml EDTA solution. This will serve as a blank by complexing any aluminum present and compensating for color and turbidity.

Add 1 ml ascorbic acid to the blank and sample, followed by 10 ml buffer reagent and 5.00 ml working dye reagent as prescribed in ¶ *a2)* above.

Set the instrument to zero absorbance or 100% transmittance using the EDTA blank. After a 5- to 15-min contact time, read the transmittance or absorbance and determine the aluminum concentration from the previously prepared calibration curve.

c. *Visual comparison:* If photometric equipment is not available, prepare and treat the standards and a sample, as described above, in 50-ml nessler tubes. Make up to the mark with distilled water and compare the color of the sample with the standards after a 5- to 15-min contact time. A sample treated with EDTA is not needed when nessler tubes are used. If the sample shows turbidity or color, the use of nessler tubes may result in considerable error.

d. *Removal of phosphate interference:* Add 1.7 ml 6N sulfuric acid to 100 ml of sample in a 200-ml erlenmeyer flask.

Heat on a hot plate for at least 90 min, keeping the solution temperature just below the boiling point.

At the end of the heating period the solution volume should be about 25 ml. Add distilled water whenever necessary to keep it at or above that volume.

After cooling, neutralize the solution to a pH of 4.3 to 4.5 with sodium hydroxide, using 1N hydroxide at the start and 0.1N for the final fine adjustment, and a pH meter.

Make up to 100 ml with distilled water, mix, and use a 25-ml portion for the aluminum test.

Run a blank in the same manner, using 100 ml of distilled water and 1.7 ml 6N sulfuric acid. Subtract blank from the sample or use it to set the instrument to zero absorbance or 100% transmittance before reading the sample.

e. *Sample treatment in the presence of fluoride:* Measure the fluoride concentration of the sample by the SPADNS or electrode method. Either:

1) Add the same amount of fluoride as in the sample to each aluminum standard, or

2) Determine the fluoride correction from the set of curves in Figure 302:1. This method may be used when a slight loss in accuracy can be tolerated.

5. Calculation

$$\text{mg/l Al} = \frac{\mu g \text{ Al}}{\text{ml sample}}$$

6. Precision and Accuracy

A synthetic unknown sample containing 520 μg/l Al and no interference in distilled water was analyzed by the Eriochrome cyanine R method in 27 laboratories with a relative standard deviation of 34.4% and a relative error of 1.7%.

A second synthetic unknown sample containing 50 μg/l Al, 500 μg/l Ba, and 5 μg/l Be in distilled water was analyzed in 35 laboratories with a relative standard deviation of 38.5% and a relative error of 22.0%.

A third synthetic unknown sample containing 500 μg/l Al, 50 μg/l Cd, 110 μg/l Cr, 1,000 μg/l Cu, 300 μg/l Fe, 70 μg/l Pb, 50 μg/l Mn, 150 μg/l Ag, and 650 μg/l Zn in distilled water was analyzed in 26 laboratories with a relative standard deviation of 28.8% and a relative error of 6.2%.

A fourth synthetic unknown sample containing 540 μg/l Al and 2.5 mg/l polyphosphate in distilled water was analyzed in 16 laboratories that hydrolyzed the sample in the prescribed manner with a relative standard deviation of 44.3% and a relative error of 1.3%. In 12 laboratories that applied no corrective measures, the relative standard deviation was 49.2% and the relative error 8.9%.

A fifth synthetic unknown sample containing 480 μg/l Al and 750 μg/l F in distilled water was analyzed in 16 laboratories that relied on the curve to correct for the fluoride content with a relative standard deviation of 25.5%

and a relative error of 2.3%. The 17 laboratories that added fluoride to the aluminum standards showed a relative standard deviation of 22.5% and a relative error of 7.1%.

7. Bibliography

SHULL, K. E. & G. R. GUTHAN. 1967. Rapid modified Eriochrome cyanine R method for determination of aluminum in water. *J. Amer. Water Works Ass.* 59:1456.

303   BARIUM

Barium stimulates the heart muscle. However, a barium dose of 550 to 600 mg is considered fatal to human beings. Afflictions arising from its consumption, inhalation, or absorption involve the heart, blood vessels, and nerves.

Despite a relative abundance in nature (16th in order of rank), barium oc-

curs only in trace amounts in water. The barium concentration of U.S. drinking waters ranges between 0.7 and 900 μg/l, with a mean of 49 μg/l. Therefore, an appreciable presence in a water supply signals undesirable industrial waste pollution.

303 A.   Atomic Absorption Spectrophotometric Method

See Section 301 A. IV.

304   BERYLLIUM

Beryllium and its compounds are exceedingly poisonous and in high concentrations can cause death. Inhalation of beryllium dust can cause a serious disease called berylliosis. Beryllium disease also can take the form of derma-

titis, conjunctivitis (eye disease), acute pneumonitis (lung disease), and chronic pulmonary berylliosis.

In the form of the element, compounds, or alloys, beryllium is used in atomic reactors, aircraft, rockets, and missile fuels. Entry into water can result from the discharges of such industries. Beryllium has been reported to occur in U.S. drinking waters in the range of 0.01 to 0.7 μg/l, with a mean of 0.013 μg/l.

Selection of method: The atomic ab-

sorption spectrophotometric method and the colorimetric method are equally suitable for the determination of beryllium. Personal preference and the equipment available can dictate the method to be used.

304 A.   Atomic Absorption Spectrophotometric Method

See Section 301 A. IV and V.

304 B.   Aluminon Method

1. General Discussion

a. Principle: The addition of a small amount of an ethylenediamine tetraacetic acid complexing solution prevents interference from moderate quantities of aluminum, cobalt, copper, iron, manganese, nickel, titanium, zinc, and zirconium. An aluminon buffer reagent is then added to form a beryllium lake and the color developed is measured at 515 nm.

b. Interference: Under the conditions specified in the method, not more than 10 mg of copper can be tolerated. If more is present, increase the amount of EDTA reagent. The complexed copper absorbs slightly at 515 nm; eliminate this interference by adding an equivalent amount of copper to the standards.

c. Minimum detectable concentration: 5 μg/l.

d. Absorptivity: 900.

2. Sample Handling

Acidify all samples at the time of collection to keep the metals in solution and prevent their plating out on the container wall. With relatively clean waters containing no particulate matter, normally 1.5 ml conc HNO_3/l of sample is sufficient to reduce the pH to 2.0. Surface waters, such as those from streams, lakes, and wastewater treatment plant effluents, which may contain sediment, require more acid. If the sample contains particulate matter and only the "dissolved" metal content is desired, filter the sample through a 0.45-μm membrane filter and acidify the filtrate with 1.5 ml conc HNO_3/l.

3. Apparatus

a. Spectrophotometer, for use at 515 nm, with a light path of 5 cm.

b. Filter photometer, equipped with a light path of 5 cm and a green filter, exhibiting a maximum transmittance near 515 nm.

4. Reagents

a. *Stock beryllium solution:* Dissolve 9.82 g beryllium sulfate tetrahydrate, $BeSO_4 \cdot 4H_2O$, in 100 ml distilled water, filter if necessary, and dilute to 500 ml; 1.00 ml = 1.00 mg Be.

b. *Standard beryllium solution:* Dilute 10.00 ml stock beryllium solution with distilled water to 1,000 ml in a volumetric flask; 1.00 ml = 10.0 μg Be.

c. *EDTA reagent:* Add 30 ml distilled water and a drop of an alcoholic solution of methyl red (50 mg/100 ml) to 2.5 g ethylenediamine tetraacetic acid, also called (ethylenedinitrilo)-tetraacetic acid. Neutralize with ammonium hydroxide, cool, and dilute to 100 ml.

d. *Aluminon buffer reagent:* Transfer 500 g $NH_4C_2H_3O_2$, ammonium acetate, to 1 l distilled water in a 2-l beaker. Add 80 ml conc (glacial) acetic acid and stir until completely dissolved. Filter if necessary. Dissolve 1 g aurintricarboxylic acid ammonium salt (aluminon),* in 50 ml distilled water and add to the buffer solution in the 2-l beaker. Dissolve 3.0 g benzoic acid ($C_7H_6O_2$) in 20 ml methyl alcohol and add to the buffer solution while stirring. Dilute the mixture to 2 l. Transfer 10 g gelatin to 250 ml distilled water in a 400-ml beaker. Place the beaker in a boiling water bath and stir occasionally until the gelatin has dissolved completely. Pour the warm gelatin into a 1,000-ml volumetric flask containing 500 ml distilled water. Cool to room temperature, dilute to the

mark, and mix. Transfer the gelatin solution and buffer solutions to a 4-l chemical-resistant dark glass bottle. Mix and store in a cool dark place. The reagent is stable for at least a month.

5. Procedure

a. *Treatment of sample:* If organic matter is present and it is desired to determine total beryllium, digest the sample with nitric and sulfuric acid as indicated in Section 301C.II 5. If only dissolved beryllium is desired, filter sample through a 0.45-μm membrane filter.

b. *Reaction with aluminon:* Dilute 0.50, 1.00, and 2.00 ml standard beryllium solution to 100 ml in volumetric flasks. Dilute a 50-ml sample, or a portion containing less than 20 μg Be, to 100 ml in a volumetric flask. Add 2 ml EDTA reagent to each flask and dilute with distilled water to approximately 75 ml. Add 15 ml aluminon buffer reagent, dilute to 100 ml with distilled water, and mix thoroughly. Let stand away from the light for 20 min after the aluminon buffer is added. Filter if necessary. Read the absorbancy of the standard and unknown as compared to the blank in a spectrophotometer or filter photometer at a 515-nm wavelength using 5-cm cells. Construct a calibration curve by plotting the absorbancy of the standards versus micrograms of beryllium. Determine the amount of beryllium in the unknown by referring to the corresponding absorbance on the calibration curve.

6. Calculation

-----

* Aurintricarboxylic acid, triammonium salt.

$$mg/l\ Be = \frac{\mu g\ Be}{ml\ sample}$$

7. Precision and Accuracy

In 32 laboratories a synthetic un-known sample of distilled water contain-ing 250 μg/l Be, 40 μg/l As, 240 μg/l B, 20 μg/l Se, and 6 μg/l V, the beryl-lium was determined with a relative standard deviation of 7.13% and a rela-tive error of 12%.

8. Bibliography

LUKE, C. L. & M. E. CAMPBELL. 1952. Photo-metric determination of beryllium in beryl-lium-copper alloys. *Anal. Chem.* 24:1056.

LUKE, C. L. & K. C. BROWN. 1952. Photometric determination of aluminum in manganese, bronze, zinc die casting alloys, and magne-sium alloys. *Anal. Chem.* 24:1120.

305   CADMIUM

Cadmium is highly toxic and has been implicated in some cases of poison-ing through food. Minute quantities of cadmium are suspected of being respon-sible for adverse changes in arteries of human kidneys. A cadmium concentra-tion of 200 μg/l is toxic to certain fish. On the other hand, there is an in-dication that cadmium might be a diet-ary essential. The cadmium concentra-tion of U.S. drinking waters has been reported to vary between 0.4 and 60 μg/l, with a mean of 8.2 μg/l. Cad-mium may enter water as a result of in-dustrial discharges or the deterioration of galvanized pipe.

Selection of method: The atomic ab-sorption spectrophotometric method is preferred. The first of the two dithizone methods is suitable for the determina-tion of cadmium in potable waters while the second is designed for polluted sam-ples.

305 A.   Atomic Absorption Spectrophotometric Method

See Section 301 A. II and III.

305 B.   Dithizone Method I

1. General Discussion

a. Principle: Cadmium ions under suitable conditions react with dithizone to form a pink to red color that can be extracted with chloroform. The chloro-form extracts are measured photometri-cally and the cadmium concentration is obtained from a calibration curve pre-pared from a standard cadmium solu-tion treated in the same manner as the sample.

b. Interference: Under the conditions of this method, concentrations of metal ions normally found in water do not interfere. Lead concentrations up to 6 mg, zinc up to 3 mg, and copper up to 1 mg in the portion analyzed do not interfere. Ordinary room lighting does not affect the cadmium dithizonate color.

c. Minimum detectable quantity: 0.5 μg Cd with a 2-cm light path.

2. Apparatus

a. Colorimetric equipment: One of the following is required:

1) *Spectrophotometer,* for use at 518 nm with a minimum light path of 1 cm.

2) *Filter photometer,* equipped with a green filter having a maximum light transmittance near 518 nm, with a minimum light path of 1 cm.

b. Separatory funnels, 125 to 150 ml, preferably with teflon stopcocks.

c. Glassware: Clean all glassware, including sample bottles, with 1 + 1 HCl and rinse thoroughly with tap water and distilled water.

3. Reagents

a. Stock cadmium solution: Weigh 100.0 mg pure cadmium metal and dissolve in a solution composed of 20 ml distilled water plus 5 ml conc HCl. Use heat to assist dissolution of the metal. Transfer the solution quantitatively to a 1-l volumetric flask and dilute to the mark with distilled water: 1.00 ml = 100 μg Cd. Store in a polyethylene container.

b. Standard cadmium solution: Pipet 10.00 ml stock cadmium solution into a 1-l volumetric flask, add 10 ml conc HCl, and dilute to the mark with dis-

tilled water. Prepare as needed and use the same day; 1.00 ml = 1.00 μg Cd.

c. Sodium potassium tartrate solution: Dissolve 250 g $NaKC_4H_4O_6 \cdot 4H_2O$ in distilled water and make up to 1 l.

d. Sodium hydroxide—potassium cyanide solutions:

1) *Solution I:* Dissolve 400 g NaOH and 10 g KCN in distilled water and make up to 1 l. Store in a polyethylene bottle. This solution is stable for 1 to 2 months.

2) *Solution II:* Dissolve 400 g NaOH and 0.5 g KCN in distilled water and make up to 1 l. Store in a polyethylene bottle. This solution is stable for 1 to 2 months.

CAUTION—*Potassium cyanide is extremely poisonous. Be especially cautious when handling it. Never use mouth pipets to deliver cyanide solutions.*

e. Hydroxylamine hydrochloride solution: Dissolve 20 g $NH_2OH \cdot HCl$ in distilled water and make up to 100 ml.

f. Stock dithizone solution: Dissolve 100 mg diphenylthiocarbazone* in 1 l chloroform, $CHCl_3$. Keep in a brown bottle in the refrigerator until required and use while still cold.

g. Chloroform, ACS grade passed for "suitability for use in dithizone test." Test for a satisfactory chloroform by adding a minute amount of dithizone to a portion of the $CHCl_3$ in a stoppered test tube so that a faint green is produced; the green color should be stable for a day.

h. Tartaric acid solution: Dissolve 20 g $H_2C_4H_4O_6$ in distilled water and

---

* Eastman No. 3092 or equivalent.

make up to 1 l. Keep the solution in the refrigerator; it must be cold when used.

i. Standard dithizone solution: Dilute 100 ml stock dithizone solution to 1 l with CHCl₃. Keep in a brown bottle in the refrigerator and allow to warm to room temperature before using.

j. Hydrochloric acid, HCl, conc.

k. Thymol blue indicator solution: Dissolve 0.4 g thymolsulfonephthalein sodium salt in 100 ml distilled water.

l. Sodium hydroxide, NaOH, 6N.

4. Procedure

a. Preparation of standard curve: Pipet 0 (blank), 2.00, 4.00, 6.00, 8.00, and 10.00 μg Cd into a series of separatory funnels. Add sufficient distilled water to make up to a final volume of 25 ml.

b. Color development, extraction, and measurement: Add reagents in the following order, mixing after each addition: 1 ml sodium potassium tartrate solution, 5 ml NaOH-KCN solution I, 1 ml hydroxylamine hydrochloride solution, and 15 ml stock dithizone solution. Stopper the funnels and shake for 1 min, relieving the vapor pressure in the funnels through the stopper rather than the stopcock. Drain the CHCl₃ layer into a second funnel containing 25 ml cold tartaric acid solution. Add 10 ml CHCl₃ to the first funnel; shake for 1 min and drain into the second funnel again. Do not permit the aqueous layer to enter the second funnel in these operations. Because the time of contact of the CHCl₃ with the strong alkali must be kept to a minimum, perform the two extractions without delay after addition of the dithizone (cadmium dithizonate decomposes on prolonged contact with strong alkali saturated with CHCl₃).

Shake the second funnel for 2 min and discard the CHCl₃ layer. Add 5 ml CHCl₃, shake 1 min, and discard the CHCl₃ layer, making as close a separation as possible. In the following order, add 0.25 ml hydroxylamine hydrochloride solution and 15.0 ml standard dithizone solution. Add 5 ml NaOH-KCN solution II, and *immediately* shake for 1 min. Insert a pledget of cotton in the stem of the funnel and filter the CHCl₃ layer into a dry photometer tube. Read the absorbance at 518 nm against the blank. Plot a calibration curve.

c. Treatment of samples: Pipet the appropriate volume of the sample containing 1 to 10 μg Cd into a separatory funnel and make up to 25 ml with distilled water. In the case of potable water containing 10 μg/l Cd or less, add 0.5 ml conc HCl to 200 ml sample and evaporate to 20 ml. Add a few drops of thymol blue indicator solution and then 6N NaOH solution until the indicator just turns yellow at a pH of approximately 2.8. Make up to 25 ml with distilled water. Adjust similarly the pH of a sample that has undergone acid digestion. Unless the calibration curve is being prepared at the same time, prepare a blank and a standard containing 6.00 μg Cd in a final volume of 25 ml and run it in conjunction with the unknown. Proceed as in ¶ 4*b* above. Obtain the Cd concentration from the calibration curve.

5. Calculation

Use the following equation for calculating the Cd concentration from the absorbance readings:

$$\text{mg/l Cd} = \frac{A_2 \times C}{A_1 \times S}$$

in which A_1 = absorbance of the standard taken, A_2 = absorbance of sample, C = micrograms Cd in standard taken, and S = milliliters of unknown water sample used.

6. Precision and Accuracy

A synthetic unknown sample containing 50 $\mu g/l$ Cd, 500 $\mu g/l$ Al, 110 $\mu g/l$ Cr, 470 $\mu g/l$ Cu, 300 $\mu g/l$ Fe, 70 $\mu g/l$ Pb, 120 $\mu g/l$ Mn, 150 $\mu g/l$ Ag, and 650 $\mu g/l$ Zn was analyzed in 44 labora-tories by the dithizone method with a relative standard deviation of 24.6% and a relative error of 6.0%.

7. Bibliography

SALTZMAN, B. E. 1953. Colorimetric micro-determination of cadmium with dithizone. *Anal. Chem.* 25:493.

GANOTES, J., E. LARSON & R. NAVONE. 1962. Suggested dithizone method for cadmium determination. *J. Amer. Water Works Ass.* 54:852.

305 C.   Dithizone Method II

1. General Discussion

After digestion of the sample with HNO_3-H_2SO_4 or with HNO_3-$HClO_4$ to decompose organic matter, any large amount of silver present is precipitated as AgCl. Copper and mercury, together with remaining silver, are then removed by an extraction with dithizone in chloroform at pH 2. The solution is adjusted to pH 9, and nickel is removed by addition of dimethylglyoxime and extraction with chloroform; any cobalt present is complexed with dimethylglyoxime so that it will not react with dithizone.

The solution is then made strongly basic and cadmium is extracted with dithizone in chloroform. Zinc extracted with the cadmium from this basic solution is removed by washing the chloroform solution with $0.5N$ NaOH. Finally, the cadmium is determined by measuring the absorbance of the cadmium-dithizone complex in chloroform at a wavelength of 515 nm, or with a suitable filter.

b. Interference: When the recommended procedure is used, the major interference is from massive amounts of zinc; if the zinc-cadmium ratio is large (greater than 500:1) it is difficult to extract the last traces of cadmium and low results are obtained. Otherwise, quantities of cadmium from 2.5 to 25 μg can be determined readily in the presence of 0.25 mg each of copper, cobalt, and zinc, and 2.5 mg each of acetate, aluminum, antimony, arsenic, bismuth, chromium, cyanide, iron, lead, manganese, mercury, nickel, phosphate, silver, sulfite, tartrate, thiocyanate, thiosulfate, tin, and other common ions.

c. Minimum detectable concentration: The quantity of cadmium required to give a net absorbance of 0.01 (98% transmittance) at 515 nm in the final chloroform solution is about 0.5 μg when a 1-cm absorption cell is used. When 50 ml of initial sample are taken, this corresponds to 10 $\mu g/l$.

d. Sampling and storage: Because of the great sensitivity of the method and the ready adsorbability of cadmium ions on surfaces, clean sampling vessels very thoroughly. Polyethylene vessels are recommended. After normal cleaning, wash glass vessels with $1+1$ HNO_3 and rinse with redistilled water.

Acidify samples with HNO_3 and add an excess of 5 ml HNO_3/l of sample at the time of collection.

2. Apparatus

a. Volumetric pipets, 5 ml.

b. Colorimetric equipment: One of the following, equipped with absorption cells providing a 1-cm light path and having lids for stoppers, is required:

1) *Spectrophotometer,* for use at 515 nm.

2) *Filter photometer,* equipped with a green filter, exhibiting maximum light transmission near 515 nm.

c. Separatory funnels, 125-ml Squibb form, with ground-glass or teflon stopcocks and stoppers. Amber or low-actinic ware is convenient but not essential. Wash with $1+1$ HNO_3 after normal cleaning and rinse thoroughly with redistilled water.

d. Volumetric flasks, 25-ml, with ground-glass stoppers. Amber or low-actinic ware is desirable but not essential. Clean as described in ¶*c* preceding.

3. Reagents

a. Stock cadmium solution: Dissolve 100.0 mg pure cadmium metal in 20 ml redistilled water and 5 ml conc HCl, and dilute to 1,000 ml with redistilled water. Store this solution in a polyethylene container.

b. Standard cadmium solution: To 5.00 ml stock cadmium solution add 2 ml conc HCl and dilute to 200 ml with redistilled water. Prepare as needed and use the same day; 1.00 ml = 2.50 µg Cd.

c. Redistilled water: Distilled water redistilled in all-glass apparatus.

d. Potassium sodium tartrate solution: In 250 ml distilled water, dissolve 50 g $KNaC_4H_4O_6 \cdot 4H_2O$. Place in a separatory funnel and shake with 50-ml portions of dithizone solution II (*i* below) in CCl_4 to remove heavy-metal impurities. Remove the dithizone and its yellow oxidation product by extraction with portions of $CHCl_3$ until the extracts remain colorless. Finally, extract with CCl_4 to remove any chloroform. Store in a polyethylene bottle.

e. Sodium hydroxide solution, 6N.

f. Carbon tetrachloride, ACS grade or purified as follows: Reflux 500 ml CCl_4 with 100 ml 1.25N NaOH for 2 hr; separate the CCl_4 layer, wash with 100 ml distilled water, dry over anhydrous $CaCl_2$, and distill over CaO. Avoid or redistill CCl_4 that comes in containers with metal or metal-lined caps.

g. Hydrochloric acid, HCl, conc.

h. Dithizone solution I: Use stock dithizone solution ($CHCl_3$), Section 301C.II4a.

i. Dithizone solution II: Dilute 40 ml stock dithizone solution (CCl_4), Section 301C.II4b, to 100 ml with CCl_4. Prepare daily.

j. Chloroform: Avoid or redistill material that comes in containers with metal-lined caps.

k. Ammonium hydroxide, NH_4OH, conc: Place 660 ml redistilled water in a 1-l polyethylene bottle and chill by immersion in an ice bath. Pass ammonia gas from a cylinder through a glass-wool trap into the chilled bottle until the volume of liquid has increased to 900 ml.

Alternatively, place 900 ml conc reagent ammonium hydroxide in a 1,500-ml distillation flask and distill into a chilled 1-l polyethylene bottle initially containing 250 ml redistilled water. Continue distilling until the volume of liquid in the bottle has increased to 900 ml, keeping the condenser tip below the surface of the liquid.

l. Dimethylglyoxime solution: Dissolve 1 g dimethylglyoxime in 100 ml 95% ethyl alcohol.

m. Sodium hydroxide solution, NaOH, 1N: Dissolve 10 g NaOH in 490 ml redistilled water. Store in a polyethylene container.

4. Procedure

a. Preparation of calibration curve: Pipet 1.00- to 10.00-ml portions of the standard cadmium solution into 125-ml separatory funnels (amber). Dilute each to about 15 to 20 ml with redistilled water and add 10 ml potassium sodium tartrate solution and 4.2 ml 6N NaOH. Then continue with ¶s 4b5) and 4b8) of the procedure.

Transfer a suitable portion of each final solution to a 1-cm absorption cell and measure its absorbance at 515 nm or with a green filter having maximum transmission near this wavelength. As reference, use either CCl₄ or a blank prepared by carrying 20 ml redistilled water through the procedure used for the standards. If CCl₄ is used as the reference, correct the absorbance readings of the standards by subtracting the absorbance of a blank prepared as described.

Construct a calibration chart by plotting corrected absorbance values against micrograms of cadmium.

b. Treatment of sample:

1) Pipet a measured portion containing 2.5 to 20 μg Cd from the digested sample, prepared according to directions given in Section 301C.II, into a 150-ml beaker. If a separate sample for cadmium is desired, measure a sample containing 25 to 200 μg Cd, treat it according to directions in Section 301C.II, and use a 10.00-ml portion of the final solution.

Add 0.2 ml conc HCl to precipitate silver, stir, and let stand 2 min. Filter, if necessary, and wash. To the combined filtrate and washings add 5 ml potassium sodium tartrate solution and adjust to pH 2.0 with conc HCl or NH₄OH.

2) Transfer to a 125-ml separatory funnel and extract with 5-ml portions of dithizone solution I in CHCl₃ until the dithizone layer remains green. Discard the extracts. Then wash with 10-ml portions of CHCl₃ until the organic layer remains colorless, discarding the washings. Finally, wash with a 5-ml portion of CCl₄ and discard the washing.

3) Transfer the aqueous solution to a 150-ml beaker, add 5 ml potassium sodium tartrate solution, and adjust to pH 8.5 to 9.0 with conc NH₄OH. Return the solution quantitatively to the separatory funnel.

4) Add 5 ml dimethylglyoxime solution and shake vigorously for 30 sec. Extract with three or more 10-ml portions of CHCl₃ until any white precipitate of excess dimethylglyoxime has been removed. Discard the extract. Wash the aqueous layer with 5 ml CCl₄ and discard the washing.

Note: In the absence of copper, mercury, or silver, ¶ 4b2) may be omitted;

in the absence of nickel or cobalt, ¶ 4b4) may be omitted.

5) Add 4.2 ml 6N NaOH to the aqueous layer in the separatory funnel and mix. Add 5 ml dithizone solution II in CCl₄ and shake thoroughly. Transfer the CCl₄ layer to a clean separatory funnel (amber) and re-extract the aqueous layer with a second 5-ml portion of dithizone solution II in CCl₄. Combine the organic layers. Continue extracting with 3-ml portions of the dithizone in CCl₄ until the organic extracts remain colorless or only slightly yellow, adding these additional extracts to the previous ones.

6) Wash the combined organic extracts twice with 10 ml 1N NaOH plus 10 ml distilled water, then once with 20 ml distilled water; discard the aqueous layer in each instance.

7) Filter the red solution of cadmium-dithizone complex through a small filter paper into a 25-ml volumetric flask. Wash the filter paper with a little CCl₄ and add the washing to the contents of the volumetric flask. Dilute to the mark with CCl₄ and mix well.

NOTE: During extraction of the cadmium [¶s 4b5)-7)], darken the room unless amber or low-actinic glassware is used. Towels may be wrapped around the separatory funnels and volumetric flask to prevent sunlight from accelerating the light-sensitive decomposition of the solution.

8) Transfer a suitable portion of the CCl₄ solution to a 1-cm absorption cell and measure its absorbance within 15 min at a wavelength of 515 nm or with a suitable green filter against a blank of pure CCl₄. From the observed absorbance subtract that of a reagent blank prepared by carrying 10 ml redistilled water through the entire procedure, including initial digestion. From the corrected absorbance determine the cadmium in the sample analyzed by reference to the calibration chart prepared according to Section 305C.4a preceding.

5. Calculation

$$\text{mg/l Cd} = \frac{\mu\text{g Cd}}{\text{ml sample}} \times \frac{100}{\text{ml portion}}$$

6. Bibliography

FISCHER, H. & G. LEOPOLDI. 1937. Determination of small quantities of cadmium with dithizone. *Mikrochim. Acta* 1:30.

SERFASS, E. J. et al. 1948. Determination of impurities in electroplating solutions. *Plating* 35:458.

SHIRLEY, R. L., W. J. BENNE & E. J. MILLER. 1949. Cadmium in biological materials and foods. *Anal. Chem.* 21:300.

SANDELL, E. B. 1959. Colorimetric Determination of Traces of Metals, 3rd ed. Interscience Publishers, New York, N.Y.

306   CALCIUM

The presence of calcium (fifth among the elements in order of abundance) in water supplies results from passage through or over deposits of limestone, dolomite, gypsum, and gypsiferous shale. The calcium content may range from zero to several hundred milligrams per liter, depending on the source and treatment of the water. Small concentrations of calcium carbonate combat corrosion of metallic pipes by laying down a protective coating. Appreciable calcium salts, on the other hand, break down on heating to form harmful scale in boilers, pipes, and cooking utensils. Calcium carbonate saturation is discussed in Section 203.

Calcium contributes to the total hardness of water. Chemical softening treatment or ion exchange is used to reduce the calcium and the associated hardness.

Selection of method: The atomic ab-

sorption method provides an accurate method for the determination of calcium. The permanganate or EDTA titration methods give good results for control and routine applications. The simplicity and rapidity of the EDTA titration procedure makes it the method of choice for general use.

Storage of samples: The customary precautions are sufficient if care is taken to redissolve any calcium carbonate that may precipitate on standing.

306 A.   Atomic Absorption Spectrophotometric Method

See Section 301A. II.

306 B.   Permanganate Titrimetric Method

1. General Discussion

a. Principle: Ammonium oxalate precipitates calcium quantitatively as calcium oxalate. An excess of oxalate overcomes the adverse effects of magnesium. Optimum crystal formation and minimum occlusion are obtained only when the pH is brought slowly to the desired value. This is accomplished in two stages, with intervening digestion to promote seed crystal formation. The precipitated calcium oxalate is dissolved in acid and titrated with permanganate. The amount of permanganate required to oxidize the oxalate is proportional to the amount of calcium.

b. Interference: The sample should be free of interfering amounts of strontium, silica, aluminum, iron, manganese, phosphate, and suspended matter.

Strontium may precipitate as the oxalate and cause high results. In such an event, determine strontium by flame photometry and apply the proper correction to the gravimetric estimate. Eliminate silica interference by the classical dehydration procedure. Precipitate aluminum, iron, and manganese by ammonium hydroxide after treatment with persulfate. Precipitate phosphate as the ferric salt. Remove suspended matter by centrifuging or by filtration through paper, sintered glass, or a cellulose acetate membrane (see Residue, Sections 208B. 2 and 3 and 298G.3*b*.

2. Apparatus

a. Vacuum pump, or other source of vacuum.

b. Filter flasks.

c. *Filter crucibles,* 30-ml. Medium-porosity crucibles are recommended. Use either glass or porcelain crucibles. Paper filters may be used but are not recommended. Crucibles of all-porous construction are difficult to wash quantitatively.

3. Reagents

a. *Methyl red indicator solution:* Dissolve 0.1 g methyl red sodium salt and dilute to 100 ml with distilled water.

b. *Hydrochloric acid,* HCl, 1 + 1.

c. *Ammonium oxalate solution:* Dissolve 10 g $(NH_4)_2C_2O_4 \cdot H_2O$ in 250 ml distilled water. Filter if necessary.

d. *Ammonium hydroxide,* NH_4OH, 3N: Add 240 ml conc NH_4OH to about 700 ml distilled water and dilute to 1 l. Filter before use to remove suspended silica flakes.

e. *Ammonium hydroxide,* 1 + 99.

f. *Special reagents for removal of aluminum, iron, and manganese interference:*

1) *Ammonium persulfate,* solid.

2) *Ammonium chloride solution* Dissolve 20 g NH_4Cl in 1 l of distilled water. Filter if necessary.

g. *Sodium oxalate:* Use primary standard grade $Na_2C_2O_4$. Dry at 105 C overnight and store the dried material in a desiccator.

h. *Sulfuric acid,* H_2SO_4, 1 + 1.

i. *Standard potassium permanganate titrant,* 0.05N. Dissolve 1.6 g $KMnO_4$ in 1 l distilled water. Keep in a brown glass-stoppered bottle and age for at least 1 wk. Carefully decant or pipet the supernate without stirring up any sediment. Standardize this solution frequently by the following procedure (standard potassium permanganate so-

lution, exactly 0.0500N, is equivalent to 1.002 mg Ca/1.00 ml):

Weigh several samples of anhydrous sodium oxalate, $Na_2C_2O_4$, into 400-ml beakers. Weigh to the nearest 0.1 mg samples between 100 and 200 mg. To each beaker, in turn, add 100 ml distilled water and stir to dissolve. Add 10 ml 1 + 1 H_2SO_4 and heat rapidly to 90 to 95 C. Titrate rapidly with the permanganate solution to be standardized, while stirring, to a slight pink endpoint color that persists for at least 1 min. Do not allow the temperature to fall below 85 C. If necessary, warm the beaker contents during the course of titration; 100 mg sodium oxalate will consume about 30 ml permanganate solution. Run a blank on the distilled water and H_2SO_4.

$$\text{Normality of } KMnO_4 = \frac{\text{g } Na_2C_2O_4}{(A - B) \times 0.06701}$$

where A = ml titration for sample and B = ml titration for blank. Average the results of several titrations.

4. Procedure

a. *Pretreatment of polluted water and wastewater samples:* Follow procedure described in Section 301C.1.

b. *Treatment of sample:* Use 200 ml sample, containing not more than 50 mg Ca (or a smaller portion diluted to 200 ml). If interfering substances are present, proceed as follows:

1) Removal of silica interference— Remove interfering amounts of silica from the sample by the gravimetric procedure described in Silica, Section 426 A.4. Discard the silica precipitate and save the filtrate for removal of interfer-

ing amounts of combined oxides described in ¶ *c* below. If combined oxides are absent, proceed to ¶ *d*.

2) Removal of combined oxides interference—Remove interfering amounts of aluminum, iron, and manganese by concentrating the filtrate from the gravimetric silica determination to 120 to 150 ml. Add enough HCl so that the filtrate from the silica removal contains at least 10 ml conc HCl at this point. Add 2 to 3 drops of methyl red indicator and $3N$ NH$_4$OH until the indicator color turns yellow.

Add 1 g ammonium persulfate; when boiling begins, carefully add $3N$ NH$_4$OH until the solution becomes slightly alkaline and the steam bears a distinct but not a strong odor of ammonia. Test the solution with litmus paper. Boil for 1 to 2 min and let stand 10 min, until the hydroxides coagulate, but no longer. Filter the precipitate and wash three or four times with ammonium chloride solution. Treat the filtrate as described in the following.

c. pH adjustment of sample: To 200 ml of the sample, which must not contain more than 0.50 mg Ca, or to a smaller portion diluted to 200 ml, add 2 or 3 drops methyl red indicator solution. Neutralize with 1 + 1 HCl and boil for 1 min. Add 50 ml ammonium oxalate solution and if any precipitate forms, add just enough 1 + 1 HCl to redissolve.

d. Precipitation of calcium oxalate: Keeping the solution just below the boiling point, add $3N$ NH$_4$OH dropwise from a buret, stirring constantly. Continue the addition until the solution is quite turbid (about 5 ml are required.) Digest for 90 min at 90 C. Then filter, preferably through a filter crucible, using suction. Wash at once with 1 + 99

NH$_4$OH. Although it is not necessary to transfer all of the precipitate to the filter crucible, remove all excess ammonium oxalate from the beaker. (If magnesium is to be determined gravimetrically, set aside the combined filtrate and washings for this purpose.)

e. Titration of calcium oxalate: Place the filter crucible on its side in the beaker and cover with distilled water. Add 10 ml H$_2$SO$_4$ and, while stirring, heat rapidly to 90 to 95 C. Titrate rapidly with permanganate titrant to a slightly pink end point that persists for at least 1 min. Do not allow the temperature to fall below 85 C; if necessary, warm the beaker contents during the course of the titration. Agitate the crucible sufficiently to insure reaction of all the oxalate. Run a blank, using a clean beaker and crucible, 10 ml H$_2$SO$_4$, and about the same volume of distilled water as was used in titrating the sample.

5. Calculation

$$\text{mg/l Ca} = \frac{(A-B) \times N \times 20{,}040}{\text{ml sample}}$$

where A = ml titration for sample, B = ml titration for blank, and N = normality of KMnO$_4$.

6. Precision and Accuracy

A synthetic unknown sample containing 108 mg/l Ca, 82 mg/l Mg, 3.1 mg/l K, 19.9 mg/l Na, 241 mg/l chloride, 1.1 mg/l nitrate N, 0.25 mg/l nitrite N, 259 mg/l sulfate, and 42.5 mg/l total alkalinity (contributed by NaHCO$_3$) in distilled water was analyzed in six laboratories by the permanganate titrimetric method, with a relative standard deviation of 3.5% and a relative error of 2.8%.

306 C.   EDTA Titrimetric Method*

1. General Discussion

a. Principle: When EDTA (ethylenediaminetetraacetic acid or its salts) is added to water containing both calcium and magnesium, it combines first with the calcium. Calcium can be determined directly, using EDTA, when the pH is made sufficiently high that the magnesium is largely precipitated as the hydroxide and an indicator is used that combines with calcium only. Several indicators will give a color change when all of the calcium has been complexed by the EDTA at a pH of 12 to 13.

b. Interference: Under conditions of this test, the following concentrations of ions cause no interference with the calcium hardness determination: copper, 2 mg/l; ferrous iron, 20 mg/l; ferric iron, 20 mg/l; manganese, 10 mg/l; zinc, 5 mg/l; lead, 5 mg/l; aluminum, 5 mg/l; tin, 5 mg/l. Orthophosphate will precipitate calcium at the pH of the test. Strontium and barium interfere with the calcium determination and alkalinity in excess of 30 mg/l may cause an indistinct end point with hard waters.

2. Reagents

a. Sodium hydroxide, NaOH, 1N.

b. Indicators: Many indicators are available for the calcium titration. Some are described in the literature (see Bibliography, Section 306 D); others are commercial preparations and also may be used. Murexide (ammonium purpurate) was the first indicator available for the detection of the calcium end point, and directions for its use are presented in this procedure. Individuals who have difficulty recognizing the murexide end point may find the indicator Eriochrome Blue Black R (color index number 202) or Solochrome Dark Blue an improvement because of the color change from red to pure blue. Eriochrome Blue Black R is sodium-1-(2-hydroxy-1-naphthylazo) - 2 - naphthol - 4 - sulfonic acid. Other indicators specifically designed for use as end-point detectors in the EDTA titration of calcium may be used.

1) *Murexide (ammonium purpurate) indicator:* This indicator changes from pink to purple at the end point. Prepare an indicator solution by dissolving 150 mg of the dye in 100 g of absolute ethylene glycol. Water solutions of the dye are not stable for longer than a day. A ground mixture of the dye powder and sodium chloride provides a stable form of the indicator. Prepare by mixing 200 mg of murexide with 100 g of solid NaCl and grinding the mixture to 40 to 50 mesh. Titrate immediately after adding the indicator because it is unstable under alkaline conditions. Facilitate end-point recognition by preparation of a color comparison blank containing 2.0 ml NaOH solution, 0.2 g solid indicator mixture (or 1 to 2 drops if a solution is used), and sufficient standard EDTA titrant (0.05 to 0.10 ml) to produce an unchanging color.

---

* Two United States patents (Nos. 2,583,890 and 2,583,891) have been issued to G. Schwarzenbach disclosing titration and complexometric methods for quantitative determination of water hardness. Nothing contained in this manual is to be construed as granting any right, by implication or otherwise, for manufacture, sale, or use in connection with any method, apparatus, or product covered by patent, nor as insuring anyone against liability for infringement of patent.

2) *Eriochrome Blue Black R indicator*: Prepare a stable form of the indicator by grinding together in a mortar 200 mg powdered dye and 100 g solid NaCl to a 40 to 50 mesh. Store in a tightly stoppered bottle. Use 0.2 g of the ground mixture for the titration in the same manner as murexide indicator. During the course of titration the color changes from red through purple to bluish purple to a pure blue without any trace of reddish or purple tint. The pH of some (not all) waters must be raised to 14 (rather than 12 to 13) by the use of 8N NaOH in order to get a good color change.

c. Standard EDTA titrant, 0.01M: Prepare the standard EDTA titrant as described for the EDTA total-hardness method (Hardness, Section 309B.2d following). Standard EDTA titrant, exactly 0.0100M, is equivalent to 400.8 μg Ca/1.00 ml.

3. Procedure

a. Pretreatment of polluted water and wastewater samples: Follow the procedure described in Section 301 C.1.

b. Sample preparation: Because of the high pH used in this procedure, titrate immediately after the addition of the alkali. Use 50.0 ml of sample, or a smaller portion diluted to 50 ml so that the calcium content is about 5 to 10 mg. Analyze hard waters with alkalinity higher than 300 mg/l $CaCO_3$ by taking a smaller portion and diluting to 50 ml, or by neutralizing the alkalinity with acid, boiling 1 min, and cooling before beginning the titration.

c. Titration: Add 2.0 ml NaOH solution or a volume sufficient to produce a pH of 12 to 13. Stir. Add 0.1 to 0.2 g of the indicator mixture selected (or 1 to 2 drops if a solution is used). Add EDTA titrant slowly, with continuous stirring to the proper end point. When using murexide, check the end point by adding 1 to 2 drops of titrant in excess to make certain that no further color change occurs.

4. Calculation

$$\text{mg/l Ca} = \frac{A \times B \times 400.8}{\text{ml sample}}$$

$$\frac{\text{Calcium hardness}}{\text{as mg/l } CaCO_3} = \frac{A \times B \times 1,000}{\text{ml sample}}$$

where A = ml titration for sample and B = mg $CaCO_3$ equivalent to 1.00 ml EDTA titrant at the calcium indicator end point.

5. Precision and Accuracy

A synthetic unknown sample containing 108 mg/l Ca, 82 mg/l Mg, 3.1 mg/l K, 19.9 mg/l Na, 241 mg/l chloride, 1.1 mg/l nitrate N, 0.25 mg/l nitrite N, 259 mg/l sulfate, and 42.5 mg/l total alkalinity (contributed by $NaHCO_3$) in distilled water was analyzed in 44 laboratories by the EDTA titrimetric method, with a relative standard deviation of 9.2% and a relative error of 1.9%.

306 D. Bibliography

Permanganate Titrimetric Methods

KOLTHOFF, I.M., E.J. MEEHAN, E.B. SANDELL & S. BRUCKENSTEIN. 1969. Quantitative Chemical Analysis, 4th ed. Macmillan Co., New York, N.Y.

EDTA Titrimetric Method

BETZ, J.D. & C.A. NOLL. 1950. Further studies with the direct colorimetric hardness titration. *J. Amer. Water Works Ass.* 42:749.

KNIGHT, A.G. 1951. Estimation of calcium in water. *Chem. & Ind.* (London), No. 49 (Dec. 22), p. 1141.

DIEHL, H. & J.L. ELLINGBOE. 1956. Indicator for titration of calcium in the presence of magnesium using disodium dihydrogen ethylenediamine tetraacetate. *Anal. Chem.* 28:882.

PATTON, J. & W. REEDER. 1956. New indicator for titration of calcium with (ethylenedinitrilo) tetraacetate. *Anal. Chem.* 28:1026.

HILDEBRAND, G.P. & C.N. REILLEY. 1957. New indicator for complexometric titration of calcium in the presence of magnesium. *Anal. Chem.* 29:258.

SCHWARZENBACH, G. 1957. Complexometric Titrations. Interscience Publishers, New York, N.Y.

GOETZ, C.A. & R.C. SMITH. 1959. Evaluation of various methods and reagents for total hardness and calcium hardness in water. *Iowa State J. Sci.* 34:104.

WELCHER, F.J. 1961. The Analytical Uses of Ethylenediamine Tetra-acetic Acid. D. Van Nostrand Co., Inc., Princeton, N.J.

FURMAN, N.H. 1962. Scotts Standard Methods of Chemical Analysis, 6th ed. D. Van Nostrand Co., Inc., Princeton, N.J.

KATZ, H. & R. NAVONE. 1964. Method for simultaneous determination of calcium and magnesium. *J. Amer. Water Works Ass.* 56:121.

307 CHROMIUM

The hexavalent chromium concentration of U.S. drinking waters has been reported to vary between 3 and 40 μg/l with a mean of 3.2 μg/l. Chromium salts are used extensively in industrial processes and may enter a water supply through the discharge of wastes. Chromate compounds are frequently added to cooling water for corrosion control. Chromium may exist in water supplies in both the hexavalent and the trivalent state although the trivalent form rarely occurs in potable water.

1. Selection of Method

Use the colorimetric method for the determination of hexavalent chromium in a natural or treated water intended for potable uses. Use the atomic absorption spectrophotometric and colorimetric methods for the determination of total chromium in water and wastewater samples.

2. Sample Handling

Acidify all samples at the time of collection to keep the metals in solution and prevent their plating out on the container wall. With relatively clean waters containing no particulate matter, 1.5 ml conc HNO_3/l of sample will be sufficient to lower the pH to 2.0. Surface waters, such as those from streams, lakes, and wastewater treatment plant effluents, which may contain sediment, will require more acid. If the sample contains particulate matter and only the "dissolved" metal content is desired, filter the sample through a 0.45-μm membrane filter. After filtration, acidify the filtrate with 1.5 ml conc HNO_3/l.

307 A.   Atomic Absorption Method for Total Chromium

See Section 301A. II and III.

307 B.   Colorimetric Method

1. General Discussion

a. Principle: Dissolved hexavalent chromium, in the absence of interfering amounts of substances such as molybdenum, vanadium, and mercury, may be determined colorimetrically by reaction with diphenylcarbazide in acid solution. A red-violet color of unknown composition is produced. The reaction is very sensitive, the absorbancy index per gram atom of chromium being about 40,000 at 540 nm. If dissolved trivalent plus hexavalent chromium is to be determined it will be necessary to oxidize the trivalent chromium with potassium permanganate before reacting with diphenylcarbazide. If organic matter is present and total chromium is to be determined, the sample first must be digested with a sulfuric-nitric acid mixture to decompose the organic matter and then the trivalent chromium oxidized to the hexavalent state with potassium permanganate. Excess permanganate is reduced with sodium azide. Addition of an excess of diphenylcarbazide yields the red-violet product and its absorbance is measured photometrically at 540 nm.

b. Interferences: The reaction with diphenylcarbazide is nearly specific for chromium. Hexavalent molybdenum and mercury salts will react to form color with the reagent, but the intensities are much lower than that for chromium at the specified pH. Concentrations of molybdenum and mercury up to 200 mg/l can be tolerated. Vanadium interferes strongly but concentrations up to 10 times that of chromium will not cause trouble. Potential interference from permanganate is eliminated by the prior reduction with azide. Iron in concentrations greater than 1 mg/l may produce a yellow color but the ferric ion color is not strong and no difficulty is encountered normally if the absorbance is measured photometrically at the appropriate wavelength. Interfering amounts of molydenum, vanadium, iron, and copper can be removed by extraction of the cupferrates of these metals into chloroform. A procedure for this extraction is provided, but should not be used unless necessary, because residual cupferron and chloroform in the aqueous solution complicate the later oxidation. Therefore, the extraction is followed by additional treatment with acid fuming in order to decompose these compounds.

2. Apparatus

a. Colorimetric equipment: One of the following is required:

1) *Spectrophotometer*, for use at 540 nm, providing a light path of 1 cm or longer.

2) *Filter photometer*, providing a light path of 1 cm or longer and equipped with a greenish yellow filter having maximum transmittance near 540 nm.

b. *Separatory funnels*, 125-ml, Squibb form, with glass or teflon stopcock and stopper.

3. Reagents

a. *Stock chromium solution:* Dissolve 141.4 mg $K_2Cr_2O_7$ in redistilled water and dilute to 1,000 ml; 1.00 ml = 50.0 μg Cr.

b. *Standard chromium solution:* Dilute 10.00 ml stock chromium solution to 100 ml; 1.00 ml = 5.00 μg Cr.

c. *Nitric acid*, HNO_3, conc.

d. *Sulfuric acid*, H_2SO_4, 1 + 1.

e. *Methyl orange indicator solution.*

f. *Hydrogen peroxide*, H_2O_2, 30%.

g. *Redistilled water:* Distilled water redistilled in all-glass apparatus.

h. *Ammonium hydroxide*, NH_4OH, conc.

i. *Potassium permanganate solution:* Dissolve 4 g $KMnO_4$ in 100 ml redistilled water.

j. *Sodium azide solution:* Dissolve 0.5 g NaN_3 in 100 ml redistilled water.

k. *Diphenylcarbazide solution:* Dissolve 250 mg 1,5-diphenylcarbazide in 50 ml acetone. Store in a brown bottle. Discard when the solution becomes discolored.

l. *Chloroform:* Avoid or redistill material that comes in containers with metal or metal-lined caps.

m. *Cupferron solution:* Dissolve 5 g $C_6H_5N(NO)ONH_4$ in 95 ml redistilled water.

4. Procedure

a. *Preparation of calibration curve:* To compensate for possible slight losses of chromium during digestion or other operations of the analysis, treat the chromium standards by the same procedure as the sample. Accordingly, pipet measured volumes of standard chromium solution (5 μg/ml) ranging from 2.00 to 20.0 ml, to give standards for 10 to 100 μg Cr, into 250-ml beakers or conical flasks. Depending on the pretreatment method used in ¶b below proceed with the subsequent treatment of the standards just as if they were samples, also carrying out cupferron treatment of the standards if this is required for the samples.

Develop the color as for the samples, transfer a suitable portion of each colored solution to a 1-cm absorption cell, and measure the absorbance at 540 nm. As reference, use distilled water. Correct the absorbance readings of the standards by subtracting the absorbance of a reagent blank carried through the method.

Construct a calibration curve by plotting corrected absorbance values against micrograms of chromium.

b. *Treatment of sample:* To determine total chromium, digest the sample with nitric and sulfuric acid as in Section 301C.II5. If interfering amounts of molybdenum, vanadium, copper, or iron are present, proceed as in 4c below; otherwise, start with 4d. If only dissolved (trivalent plus hexavalent) chromium is desired, filter the sample through a 0.45-μm membrane filter and start with 4e.

c. *Separation of molybdenum, vanadium, iron, and copper with cupferron:* Pipet a portion of digested sample containing 10 to 100 μg chromium into a 125-ml separatory funnel. Dilute to about 40 ml with distilled water and chill in an ice bath. Add 5 ml ice-cold cupferron solution, shake well, and let stand in the ice bath for 1 min. Extract the solution in the separatory funnel with three successive 5-ml portions of chloroform; shake each portion thoroughly with the aqueous solution, let the layers separate, and withdraw and discard the chloroform extract. Transfer the extracted aqueous solution to a 125-ml conical flask. Wash the separatory funnel with a small amount of distilled water and add the wash water to the flask. Boil for about 5 min to volatilize the chloroform, and cool. Add 5 ml HNO₃ and sufficient H₂SO₄ to have about three ml present. Boil samples to the appearance of SO₃ fumes. Cool slightly, carefully add 5 ml HNO₃, and again boil to fumes to complete the decomposition of organic matter. Cool, wash sides of flask, and boil once more to SO₃ fumes to eliminate all HNO₃. Cool and add 25 ml water.

d. Oxidation of trivalent chromium: If ¶4c has been omitted, pipet a portion of digested sample containing 10 to 100 µg chromium into a 125-ml conical flask. Using methyl orange as indicator, add conc NH₄OH until the solution in the flask is just basic. Then add 1 + 1 H₂SO₄ dropwise until it is acidic, plus 1 ml (20 drops) in excess. Adjust volume to about 40 ml, add a boiling chip, and heat to boiling. Add 2 drops KMnO₄ solution to give a dark red color. If fading occurs, add KMnO₄ dropwise to maintain an excess of about 2 drops. Boil the solution for 2 min longer. Add 1 ml sodium azide solution and continue boiling gently. If the red color does not fade completely after boiling for approximately 30 sec, add another 1 ml sodium azide solution. Continue boiling for 1 min after the color has faded completely, then cool. Add 0.25 ml (5 drops) H₃PO₄.

e. Color development and measure- *ment:* Transfer the cooled solution to a 100-ml volumetric flask, dilute to 100 ml, and mix. Add 2.0 ml diphenylcarbazide solution, mix, and let stand 5 to 10 min for full color development. Transfer an appropriate portion of the solution to a 1-cm absorption cell and measure its absorbance at 540 nm. Use distilled water as reference. Correct the absorbance reading of the sample by subtracting the absorbance of a blank carried through the method (see also note below). From the corrected absorbance, determine the micrograms of chromium present by reference to the calibration curve.

NOTE: If the solution is turbid after dilution to 100 ml in ¶e above, take an absorbance reading before addition of the carbazide reagent and correct absorbance reading of the final colored solution by subtracting the absorbance measured previously.

5. Calculation

$$\text{mg/l Cr} = \frac{A \times 100}{B \times C}$$

where A = µg Cr, B = ml original sample, and C = ml portion from 100 ml digested sample.

6. Precision and Accuracy

The dissolved (trivalent plus hexavalent) chromium was determined in 31 laboratories in a synthetic unknown sample containing 110 µg/l Cr, 500 µg/l Al, 50 µg/l Cd, 470 µg/l Ca, 300 µg/l Fe, 70 µg/l Pb, 120 µg/l Mn, 150 µg/l Ag, and 650 µg/l Zn in distilled water, with a relative standard deviation of 47.8% and a relative error of 16.3%.

7. Bibliography

ROWLAND, G. P., JR. 1939. Photoelectric colorimetry—Optical study of permanganate ion
and of chromium-diphenylcarbazide system. *Anal. Chem.* 11:442.

SALTZMAN, B. E. 1952. Microdetermination of
chromium with diphenylcarbazide by permanganate   oxidation.   *Anal.   Chem.*
24:1016.

URONE, P. F. 1955. Stability of colorimetric reagent for chromium, s-diphenylcarbazide,
in various solvents. *Anal. Chem.* 27:1354.

ALLEN, T. L. 1958. Microdetermination of chromium with 1,5-diphenylcarbohydrazide.
Anal. Chem. 30:447.

SANDELL, E. B. 1959. Colorimetric Determination of Traces of Metals, 3rd ed. Interscience Publishers, New York, N.Y.

308   COPPER

Copper salts are used in water supply systems for controlling biological growths in reservoirs and distribution pipes and for catalyzing the oxidation of manganese. The corrosion of copper-containing alloys in pipe fittings may introduce measurable amounts of copper into the water in a localized pipe system.

Copper is essential to humans and the adult daily requirement has been estimated at 2.0 mg.

1. Selection of Method

The atomic absorption spectrophoto-metric and the neocuproine methods are recommended because of their high degree of freedom from interferences. The bathocuproine method may be used for potable water samples.

2. Sampling and Storage

Copper ion tends to be absorbed on the surface of the sample container. Therefore, analyze samples as soon as possible after collection. If storage is necessary, use 0.5 ml 1 + 1 HCl/100 ml of sample to prevent "plating out."

308 A.   Atomic Absorption Spectrophotometric Method

See Section 301 A. II.

308 B.   Neocuproine Method

1. General Discussion

a. Principle: Cuprous ion in neutral or slightly acidic solution reacts with 2,9-dimethyl-1,10-phenanthroline ("neocuproine") to form a complex in which 2 moles of the neocuproine are bound by 1 mole of Cu^+ ion. The complex can be extracted by a number of organic liquids, including a chloroform-methanol mixture, to give a yellow solution with a molar absorbancy index of about 8,000 at 457 nm. The reaction is virtually specific for copper; the color system follows Beer's law up to a concentration of 0.2 mg Cu/25 ml of organic solvent; full color development is obtained with the pH of the aqueous system between 3 and 9; the color system is stable in chloroform-methanol for several days.

The sample is treated with hydroxylamine-hydrochloride to reduce copper to the cuprous condition, and with sodium citrate to complex metallic ions that might give precipitates when the pH is raised. The pH is adjusted to 4 to 6 by the addition of ammonia, a solution of neocuproine in methanol is added, and the resultant complex is extracted into chloroform. After dilution of the chloroform to an exact volume with methanol, the absorbance of the solution is measured at 457 nm.

b. Interference: Determination of copper by the recommended procedure is substantially free from interference by other metal ions. Large amounts of chromium and tin may interfere. Potential interference from chromium can be avoided by addition of sulfurous acid to reduce chromate and complex chromic ion. In the presence of much tin or excessive amounts of other oxidizing ions, use up to 20 ml additional hydroxylamine.

Cyanide and sulfide produce strong interference but are removed during the digestion procedure, as are organic materials that might lead to difficulties.

c. Minimum detectable concentration: For the recommended procedure the minimum detectable concentration, corresponding to 0.01 absorbance or 98% transmittance, is 3 μg Cu when a 1-cm cell is used and 0.6 μg Cu when a 5-cm cell is used.

2. Apparatus

a. Colorimetric equipment—One of the following is required:

1) *Spectrophotometer,* for use at 457 nm, providing a light path of 1 cm or longer.

2) *Filter photometer,* providing a light path of 1 cm or longer and equipped with a narrow-band violet filter having maximum transmittance in the range 450 to 460 nm.

b. Separatory funnels, 125-ml, Squibb form, with glass or teflon stopcock and stopper.

3. Reagents

a. Redistilled water, copper-free: Most ordinary distilled water contains detectable amounts of copper. Use redistilled water, prepared by distillation of singly distilled water in a resistant-glass still, or distilled water passed through an ion-exchange unit for the preparation of all reagents and for all dilutions or other operations.

b. *Stock copper solution:* To 200.0 mg polished electrolytic copper wire or foil in a 250-ml conical flask, add 10 ml redistilled water and 5 ml conc HNO_3. After the reaction has slowed, warm gently to complete dissolution of the copper and then boil to expel oxides of nitrogen, using precautions to avoid loss of copper. Cool, add about 50 ml redistilled water, transfer quantitatively to a 1-l volumetric flask, and dilute to the mark with redistilled water; 1 ml = 200 μg Cu.

c. *Standard copper solution:* Dilute 50.00 ml stock copper solution to 500 ml with redistilled water; 1.00 ml = 20.0 μg Cu.

d. *Sulfuric acid,* H_2SO_4, conc.

e. *Hydroxylamine-hydrochloride solution:* Dissolve 50 g $NH_2OH\cdot HCl$ in 450 ml redistilled water.

f. *Sodium citrate solution:* Dissolve 150 g $Na_3C_6H_5O_7\cdot 2H_2O$ in 400 ml redistilled water. Add 5 ml hydroxylamine hydrochloride solution and 10 ml neocuproine reagent. Extract with 50 ml chloroform to remove copper impurities, and discard the chloroform layer.

g. *Ammonium hydroxide,* NH_4OH, 5N: Dilute 330 ml conc NH_4OH (28-29%) to 1,000 ml with distilled water. Store in a polyethylene bottle.

h. *Congo red paper,* or other pH test paper showing a color change in the pH range 4 to 6.

i. *Neocuproine reagent:* Dissolve 100 mg 2,9-dimethyl-1,10-phenanthroline hemihydrate* in 100 ml methyl alcohol. This solution is stable under ordinary storage conditions for a month or more.

_____

* G. F. Smith Chemical Company, Columbus, Ohio, or equivalent.

j. *Chloroform:* Avoid or redistill material that comes in containers with metal-lined caps.

k. *Methyl alcohol.*

l. *Nitric acid,* HNO_3, conc.

m. *Hydrochloric acid,* HCl, conc.

4. Procedure

a. *Preparation of calibration curve:* Pipet 50 ml redistilled water into a 125-ml separatory funnel for use as a reagent blank. Prepare standards by pipetting 1.00 to 10.00 ml (20.0 to 200 μg Cu) standard copper solution into a series of 125-ml separatory funnels, then dilute to 50 ml with redistilled water. Add 1 ml conc H_2SO_4 and proceed according to ¶s 4b 2) and 3) below.

Construct a calibration curve by plotting absorbance value against micrograms of copper.

To prepare a calibration curve for smaller amounts of copper, dilute 10.0 ml standard copper solution to 100 ml. Then carry 1.00- to 10.00-ml volumes of this diluted standard through the previously described procedure, but use 5-cm cells for measurements of absorbance.

b. *Treatment of sample:*

1) Transfer 100 ml sample to a 250-ml beaker, add 1 ml conc H_2SO_4 and 5 ml conc HNO_3. Add a few boiling chips and cautiously evaporate to dense white SO_3 fumes on a hot plate. If the solution remains colored, cool and add an additional 5 ml conc HNO_3 and again evaporate to dense white fumes. Repeat, if necessary, until the solution becomes colorless.

To the cooled beaker after the H_2SO_4 treatment, add about 80 ml redistilled water, and bring to a boil. Cool and filter into a 100-ml volumetric flask.

Make up to 100-ml mark with redistilled water using mostly beaker and filter washings.

2) Pipet exactly 50.0 ml, or other suitable portion containing 4 to 200 μg Cu, from the solution obtained from preliminary treatment, into a 125-ml separatory funnel. Dilute to 50 ml with redistilled water if a smaller portion has been used. Add 5 ml hydroxylamine-hydrochloride solution and 10 ml sodium citrate solution and mix thoroughly. Adjust the pH to approximately 4 by adding 1-ml increments of NH₄OH until congo red paper is just definitely red or other suitable pH test paper indicates a value between 4 and 6.

3) Add 10 ml neocuproine reagent and 10 ml CHCl₃. Stopper and shake vigorously for 30 sec or more to extract the copper-neocuproine complex into the chloroform. Let the mixture separate into two layers and withdraw the lower chloroform layer into a 25-ml volumetric flask, taking care not to transfer any of the aqueous layer. Repeat the extraction of the water layer with an additional 10 ml CHCl₃ and add this extract to the previous one. Dilute the combined extracts exactly to the 25-ml mark with methyl alcohol, stopper, and mix thoroughly.

4) Transfer an appropriate portion of the final organic solution to a suitable absorption cell (1 cm for 40 to 200 μg Cu; 5 cm for lesser amounts) and measure the absorbance at 457 nm or with a filter for 450 to 460 nm. As reference, use a sample blank prepared by carrying 50 ml redistilled water through the complete digestion and subsequent procedure.

Determine the micrograms of copper in the final solution by reference to the appropriate calibration curve.

5. Calculation

$$\text{mg/l Cu} = \frac{\mu\text{g Cu}}{\text{ml portion taken in } 4b\ 2)}$$

308 C.   Bathocuproine Method

I. General Discussion

a. *Principle:* Cuprous ions form a water-soluble orange-colored chelate with bathocuproine disulfonate (2,9-dimethyl-4,7-diphenyl-1,10-phenanthrolinedisulfonic acid, disodium salt). Despite the fact that the color forms over the pH range of 3.5 to 11.0, the recommended pH range is between 4 and 5.

The sample is buffered at a pH of about 4.3 and reduced with hydroxylamine hydrochloride. The absorbance is measured at 484 nm. The method can be applied to copper concentrations up to at least 5 mg/l with a sensitivity of 20 μg/l.

b. *Interference:* The following ions and substances can be tolerated with an error of less than ±2%:

Ion	mg/l
Cations	
Aluminum	100
Beryllium	10
Cadmium	100
Calcium	1,000
Chromium (III)	10
Cobalt (II)	5
Iron (II)	100
Iron (III)	100
Lithium	500
Magnesium	100
Manganese (II)	500
Nickel (II)	500
Sodium	1,000
Strontium	200
Thorium (IV)	100
Zinc	200
Anions	
Chlorate	1,000
Chloride	1,000
Fluoride	500
Nitrate	200
Nitrite	200
Orthophosphate	1,000
Perchlorate	1,000
Sulfate	1,000
Compounds	
Residual chlorine	1
Linear alkylate sulfonate (LAS)	40

Cyanide, thiocyanate, persulfate, and EDTA also can interfere.

c. Minimum detectable concentration: 20 μg/l when a 5-cm cell is used in a spectrophotometer.

2. Apparatus

a. Colorimetric equipment: One of the following, equipped with absorption cells and providing light paths of 1 to 5 cm (the latter is recommended), is required:

1) *Spectrophotometer,* for use at 484 nm.

2) *Filter photometer,* equipped with a blue-green filter exhibiting maximum light transmission near 484 nm.

3) *Nessler tubes,* matched, 100-ml, tall form.

b. Acid-washed glassware: Rinse all glassware with conc HCl and then with copper-free water.

3. Reagents

a. Copper-free water: Use redistilled or deionized distilled water.

b. Standard copper solution: Prepare as directed in Method B, ¶3*b* and 3*c* preceding, to obtain 1.00 ml=20.00 μg Cu. Take 250 ml of this solution and make up to 100 ml to obtain 1 ml= 5.00 μg ml. Prepare daily.

c. Hydrochloric acid, HCl, 1+1. Use copper-free water.

d. Hydroxylamine hydrochloride solution: Dissolve 100 g $NH_2OH \cdot HCl$ in 900 ml copper-free water.

e. Sodium citrate solution: Dissolve 300 g $Na_3C_6H_5O_7 \cdot 2H_2O$ in copper-free water and make up to 1 l.

f. Disodium bathocuproine disulfonate solution: Dissolve 1.000 g $C_{12}H_4N_2(CH_3)_2(C_6H_4)_2(SO_3Na)_2$ in copper-free water and make up to the mark in a 1-l volumetric flask.

4. Procedure

Pipet 50.0 ml sample, or a suitable portion diluted to 50.0 ml, into a 250-ml erlenmeyer flask. In separate 250-ml erlenmeyer flasks, prepare a 50.0-ml copper-free water blank and a series of 50.0-ml copper standards containing 5.0, 10.0, 15.0, 20.0, and 25.0 μg Cu. To sample, blank, and standards add, mixing after each addition, 1.00 ml 1+ 1 HCl, 5.00 ml hydroxylamine hydrochloride solution, 5.00 ml sodium citrate solution, and 5.00 ml disodium bathocuproine disulfonate solution. Transfer to cells and read the absorbance of the sample against the blank at 484 nm. Plot absorbance against micrograms Cu in standards for the calibration curve. Estimate the copper concentration of the sample from the calibration curve.

5. Calculation

$$\text{mg/l Cu} = \frac{\mu\text{g Cu}}{\text{ml sample}}$$

6. Precision and Accuracy

A synthetic unknown sample containing 1,000 μg/l Cu, 500 μg/l Al, 50 μg/l Cd, 110 μg/l Cr, 300 μg/l Fe, 70 μg/l Pb, 50 μg/l Mn, 150 μg/l Ag, and 650 μg/l Zn was analyzed in 33 laboratories by the bathocuproine method, with a relative standard deviation of 4.1% and a relative error of 0.3%.

308 D.   Bibliography

Neocuproine Method

SMITH, G. F. & W. H. McCURDY. 1952. 2,9-Dimethyl-1,10-phenanthroline: New specific in spectrophotometric determination of copper. *Anal. Chem.* 24:371.

LUKE, C. L. & M. E. CAMPBELL. 1953. Determination of impurities in germanium and silicon. *Anal. Chem.* 25:1586.

GAHLER, A. R. 1954. Colorimetric determination of copper with neocuproine. *Anal. Chem.* 26:577.

FULTON, J. W. & J. HASTINGS. 1956. Photometric determinations of copper in aluminum and lead-tin solder with neocuproine. *Anal. Chem.* 28:174.

FRANK, A. J., A. B. GOULSTON & A. A. DEACUTIS. 1957. Spectrophotometric determination of copper in titanium. *Anal. Chem.* 29:750.

Bathocuproine Method

SMITH, G. F. & D. H. WILKINS. 1953. New colorimetric reagent specific for copper. *Anal. Chem.* 25:510.

BORCHARDT, L. G. & J. P. BUTLER. 1957. Determination of trace amounts of copper. *Anal. Chem.* 29:414.

ZAK, B. 1958. Simple procedure for the single sample determination of serum copper and iron. *Clinica Chim. Acta* 3:328.

BLAIR, D. & H. DIEHL. 1961. Bathophenanthrolinedisulfonic acid and bathocuproinedisulfonic acid, water soluble reagents for iron and copper. *Talanta* 7:163.

309   HARDNESS

Originally, the hardness of a water was understood to be a measure of the capacity of the water for precipitating soap. Soap is precipitated chiefly by the calcium and magnesium ions commonly present in water, but also may be precipitated by ions of other polyvalent metals, such as aluminum, iron, manganese, strontium, and zinc, and by hydrogen ions. Because only the first two are usually present in significant concentrations in natural waters, hardness is defined as a characteristic of water that represents the total concentration of just

310   IRON

In filtered samples of oxygenated surface waters iron concentrations seldom reach 1 mg/l. Some ground waters and acid surface drainage may contain considerably more iron. Iron in water can cause staining of laundry and porcelain, and also a bittersweet astringent taste detectable by some persons at levels above 1 or 2 mg/l.

Under reducing conditions, iron exists in the ferrous state. In the absence of complex-forming ions, ferric iron is not significantly soluble unless the pH of the water is very low. On exposure to air or addition of oxidants, ferrous iron is oxidized to the ferric state and may hydrolyze to form insoluble hydrated ferric oxide. This is the predominant form of iron found in most laboratory samples unless the samples are collected under anoxic conditions to avoid oxidation.

The form of iron present in water also may undergo alteration as a result of the growth of bacteria in the sample during storage or shipment (see Section 918A). In acid wastes at pH less than 3.5, ferric iron state also may be soluble.

Iron may be in true solution, in a colloidal state that may be peptized by organic matter, in the inorganic or organic iron complexes, or in relatively coarse suspended particles. It may be either ferrous or ferric, suspended or filtrable.

Silt and clay in suspension may contain acid-soluble iron. Iron oxide particles are sometimes collected with a water sample as a result of flaking of rust from pipes. Iron may come from a metal cap used to close the sample bottle.

1. Selection of Method

For natural and treated waters, the orthophenanthroline method has attained the greatest acceptance for simplicity and reliability. The atomic absorption spectrophotometric method is relatively easy and accurate. The precision and accuracy data developed by a collaborative study of the atomic absorption method for iron showed results that were superior to those of the colorimetric methods.

It is difficult to distinguish between dissolved and suspended iron because, on exposure to air, soluble ferrous iron can be oxidized rapidly by dissolved oxygen and hydrolyzed at neutral pH values to insoluble ferric oxides. Dissolved iron can be determined (¶ 310A.4b) by subsequent analysis of a portion of the sample that has been filtered and acidified immediately after collection at the sampling site. This procedure may suffer from possible oxidation of ferrous iron and hydrolysis during filtration to yield low results.

A rigorous quantitative distinction between ferrous and ferric iron may be obtained with a special procedure using bathophenanthroline.[1,2] Both the orthophenanthroline and the tripyridine reagents tend to shift the soluble ferric-ferrous equilibrium to ferrous iron. The suggested procedure (¶ 310A.4d) has limited application and requires a large excess of orthophenanthroline (mole ratio to ferrous plus ferric greater than 30). The sample is stabilized with hydrochloric rather than acetic acid because the latter does not provide a sufficiently low pH to stabilize the ferrous iron. However, care should be taken while using an acid for stabilizing ferrous iron in the presence of ferric iron. Ferric iron might interfere through photochemical reduction if an acidified sample is exposed to light before the addition of bathophenanthroline and/or after the extraction of the colored complex.[1-2] Of the colorimetric methods, only the phenanthroline procedure and its extraction modification are outlined here.

Further information on methods other than the phenanthroline method is given elsewhere.[3-10]

2. Sampling and Storage

Plan methods of collecting, storing, and pretreating samples in advance. Clean the sample container with acid and rinse with distilled water. Equipment for membrane filtration of samples in the field may be required to determine iron in solution (filtrable iron). The value of the determination depends greatly on the care taken to obtain a representative sample. Iron in well water or tap samples may vary in concentration and form with duration and degree of flushing before and during sampling. When taking the portion of the sample for the determination of iron in suspension, shake the sample bottle often and vigorously to obtain a uniform suspension of the precipitated iron. Use particular care when colloidal iron adheres to the sample bottle. This problem can be acute with plastic bottles.

For a precise determination of total iron, use a separate container for sample collection. Treat with acid at the time of collection to place the iron in solution and prevent adsorption or deposition on the walls of the sample container.

310 A.   Phenanthroline Method

1. General Discussion

a. Principle: Iron is brought into solution, reduced to the ferrous state by boiling with acid and hydroxylamine, and treated with 1,10-phenanthroline at pH 3.2 to 3.3. Three molecules of phenanthroline chelate each atom of ferrous iron to form an orange-red complex. The colored solution obeys Beer's law; its intensity is independent of pH from 3 to 9. A pH between 2.9 and 3.5 insures rapid color development in the presence of an excess of phenanthroline. Color standards are stable for at least 6 months.

In the presence of excessive amounts of organic constituents, the sample first may be digested with H_2SO_4 to destroy organic complexes and to ensure complete dissolution of the iron. The resulting solution is made 7 to $8N$ in HCl and the iron is separated from interfering substances by extraction of $FeCl_3$ into isopropyl ether. After re-extraction of the iron into water, it is reduced with hydroxylamine.

b. Interference: Among the interfering substances are strong oxidizing agents, cyanide, nitrite, and phosphates (polyphosphates more so than orthophosphate), chromium, zinc in concentrations exceeding 10 times that of iron, cobalt and copper in excess of 5 mg/l, and nickel in excess of 2 mg/l. Bismuth, cadmium, mercury, molybdate, and silver precipitate phenanthroline. The initial boiling with acid converts polyphosphates to orthophosphate and removes cyanide and nitrite, which would otherwise interfere. The addition of excess hydroxylamine will eliminate errors caused by excessive concentrations of strong oxidizing reagents. In the presence of interfering metal ions, a larger excess of phenanthroline is required to replace that complexed by the interfering metals. Where excessive concentrations of interfering metal ions are present, the extraction method may be used.

If noticeable amounts of color or organic matter are present, it may be necessary to evaporate the sample, gently ash the residue, and redissolve in acid. The ashing may be carried out in silica, porcelain, or platinum crucibles that have been boiled for several hours in 1+1 HCl.

c. Minimum detectable concentration: Total, dissolved, or ferrous iron concentrations between 0.02 and 4.0 mg/l can be determined directly, and higher concentrations can be determined by the use of smaller samples or dilutions. The minimum detectable quantity is 50 μg with a spectrophotometer (510 nm) with a 1-cm cell.

2. Apparatus

a. Colorimetric equipment: One of the following is required:

1) *Spectrophotometer,* for use at 510 nm, providing a light path of 1 cm or longer.

2) *Filter photometer,* providing a light path of 1 cm or longer and equipped with a green filter having maximum transmittance near 510 nm.

3) *Nessler tubes,* matched, 100 ml, tall form.

b. Acid-washed glassware: Wash all glassware with conc HCl and rinse with distilled water before use to remove deposits of iron oxide.

c. Separatory funnels: 125 ml, Squibb form, with ground-glass or Teflon stopcocks and stoppers.

3. Reagents

All reagents must be low in iron. Use iron-free distilled water. Store reagents in glass-stoppered bottles. The hydrochloric acid and ammonium acetate solutions are stable indefinitely if tightly stoppered. The hydroxylamine, phenanthroline, and stock iron solutions are stable for several months. The standard iron solutions are not stable; prepare daily as needed by diluting the stock solution. Visual standards in nessler tubes are stable for several months if protected from light.

a. Hydrochloric acid, HCl, conc., containing less than 0.00005% iron.

b. Hydroxylamine solution: Dissolve 10 g $NH_2OH \cdot HCl$ in 100 ml distilled water.

c. Ammonium acetate buffer solution: Dissolve 250 g $NH_4C_2H_3O_2$ in 150 ml distilled water. Add 700 ml conc (glacial) acetic acid. Because even a good grade of $NH_4C_2H_3O_2$ contains a significant amount of iron, prepare new reference standards with each buffer preparation.

d. Sodium acetate solution: Dissolve 200 g $NaC_2H_3O_2 \cdot 3H_2O$ in 800 ml distilled water.

e. Phenanthroline solution: Dissolve 100 mg 1,10-phenanthroline monohydrate, $C_{12}H_8N_2 \cdot H_2O$, in 100 ml distilled water by stirring and heating to 80 C. Do not boil. Discard the solution if it darkens. Heating is unnecessary if 2 drops conc HCl are added to the distilled water. (NOTE: One milliliter of this reagent is sufficient for no more than 100 μg Fe.)

f. Stock iron solution: Use metal (1) or the salt (2) for preparing the stock solution, which contains 200 μg Fe/1.00 ml.

1) Use electrolytic iron wire, or "iron wire for standardizing," to prepare the solution. If necessary, clean the wire with fine sandpaper to remove any oxide coating and to produce a bright surface. Weigh 200.0 mg wire and place in a 1-l volumetric flask. Dissolve in 20 ml $6N$ H_2SO_4 and dilute to the mark with iron-free distilled water. Each 1.00 ml will contain 200 μg Fe.

2) If ferrous ammonium sulfate is preferred, add slowly 20 ml conc H_2SO_4 to 50 ml distilled water and dissolve 1.404 g $Fe(NH_4)_2(SO_4)_2 \cdot 6H_2O$. Add $0.1N$ $KMnO_4$ dropwise until a faint pink color persists. Dilute to 1,000 ml with iron-free distilled water and mix. Each 1.00 ml will contain 200 μg Fe.

g. Standard iron solutions: Prepare daily for use.

1) Pipet 50.00 ml stock solution into a 1-l volumetric flask and dilute to the mark with iron-free distilled water; 1.00 ml = 10.0 μg Fe.

2) Pipet 5.00 ml stock solution into a 1-l volumetric flask and dilute to the mark with iron-free distilled water; 1.00 ml = 1.00 μg Fe.

h. Diisopropyl or isopropyl ether.

4. Procedure

a. Preparation of calibration curves:

1) Range 0 to 100 μg Fe/100 ml final solution—Pipet 2.0, 4.0, 6.0, 8.0, and 10.0 ml standard iron solution into 100-ml volumetric flasks. Add 1.0 ml $NH_2OH \cdot HCl$ solution and 1 ml sodium acetate solution to each flask. Dilute each to about 75 ml with distilled water, add 10 ml phenanthroline solution, dilute to volume, mix thoroughly, and let stand for 10 min. Measure the absorbance of each solution in a 5-cm cell at 508 nm against a reference blank prepared by treating distilled water with the specified amounts of all reagents except the standard iron solution. Alternatively, if distilled water is used as a reference, correct the absorbance values for standard concentrations of iron by subtracting the absorbance for a reagent blank against that for distilled water. From the data obtained, construct a calibration curve for absorbance against milligrams of iron.

2) Range 50 to 500 μg Fe/100 ml final solution—Follow the procedure specified in the preceding paragraph, but use 10.0, 20.0, 30.0, 40.0, and 50.0 ml standard iron solution and measure the absorbance values in 1-cm cells.

b. Total iron: Mix the sample thoroughly and measure 50.0 ml into a 125-ml erlenmeyer flask. (If the sample contains more than 2 mg/l Fe, dilute an accurately measured portion containing not more than 100 μg to 50 ml, or use more phenanthroline and a 1- or 2-cm light path.) Add 2 ml conc HCl and 1 ml hydroxylamine solution. Add a few glass beads and heat to boiling. To insure dissolution of all the iron, continue boiling until the volume is reduced to 15 to 20 ml. (If the sample is ashed as described in ¶ 1b, take up the residue in 2 ml conc HCl and 5 ml distilled water.) Cool to room temperature and transfer to a 50- or 100-ml volumetric flask or nessler tube. Add 10 ml ammonium acetate buffer solution and 2 ml phenanthroline solution, and dilute to the mark with distilled water. Mix thoroughly and allow at least 10 to 15 min for maximum color development.

c. *Filtrable iron:* Immediately after collection filter the sample through a 0.45-μm membrane filter into a vacuum flask containing 1 ml conc HCl/100 ml sample. Analyze the filtrate for total filtrable iron (¶ 4b) and/or filtrable ferrous iron (¶ 4d below). (This procedure also can be used in the laboratory, with the understanding that normal exposure of the sample to air during shipment may result in the precipitation of iron.)

Calculate suspended iron by subtracting filtrable iron from total iron.

d. *Ferrous iron:* To determine ferrous iron, acidify a separate sample with 2 ml conc HCl/100 ml sample at the time of collection to prevent oxidation. Fill the bottle directly from the sampling source and stopper. Immediately before analysis, withdraw a 50-ml portion of the acidified sample and add 20 ml phenanthroline solution and 10 ml ammonium acetate solution with vigorous stirring. Dilute to 100 ml and measure the color intensity within 5 to 10 min. Do not expose to sunlight. (Color development is rapid in the presence of excess phenanthroline. The phenanthroline volume given is suitable for less than 50 μg total iron; if larger amounts are present, use a correspondingly larger

volume of phenanthroline or a more concentrated reagent.)

Calculate ferric iron by subtracting ferrous iron from total iron.

e. *Color measurement:* Prepare a series of standards by accurately pipetting calculated volumes of standard iron solutions (use the weaker solution to measure the 1- to 10- μg portions) into 125-ml erlenmeyer flasks, diluting to 50 ml, and carrying out the steps in ¶ 4b.

For visual comparison, prepare a set of at least 10 standards, ranging from 1 to 100 μg Fe in the final 100-ml volume. Compare the colors in 100-ml tall-form nessler tubes.

TABLE 310:I. SELECTION OF LIGHT PATH LENGTH FOR VARIOUS IRON CONCENTRATIONS

Fe μg		
50-ml Final Volume	100-ml Final Volume	Light Path cm
50-200	100-400	1
25-100	50-200	2
10-40	20-80	5
5-20	10-40	10

For photometric measurement, use Table 310:I as a rough guide for the selection of the proper light path. Read the standards against distilled water set at 100% transmittance (zero absorbance) and plot a calibration curve, including a blank (see ¶ 3c and General Introduction, Section 102.7).

If the samples are colored or turbid, carry a second set of samples through all the steps of the procedure without adding phenanthroline. Instead of distilled water, use the prepared blanks to set the photometer to 100% transmittance, and read each developed sample with phenanthroline against the corresponding blank without phenanthroline. Translate the observed photometer readings into iron values by means of the calibration curve. This procedure does *not* compensate for the presence of interfering ions. If color and turbidity are absent, it is quicker and equally satisfactory to read the samples, as well as the standards, against distilled water.

f. Samples containing organic interferences: Digest samples containing organic substances in substantial amounts according to the directions given in "Pretreatment for Colorimetric Analysis of Heavy Metals", Section 301C.II5 or 6.

1) If a digested sample has been prepared according to the directions given in Section 301C.II5 or 6, pipet 10.0 ml or other suitable portion containing 20 to 500 μg Fe into a 125-ml separatory funnel. If the volume taken is less than 10 ml, add distilled water to make up to 10 ml. To the separatory funnel add 15 ml conc HCl for a 10-ml aqueous volume; or, if the portion taken was greater than 10.0 ml, add 1.5 ml conc HCl/ml of sample. Mix, cool, and proceed with 4*f*3) below.

2) To prepare a sample solely for determination of iron, measure a suitable volume of sewage or waste containing 20 to 500 μg Fe and carry it through either of the digestion procedures described in Section 301C.II5 or 6. However, use only 5 ml H_2SO_4 or $HClO_4$ and omit the H_2O_2. When digestion is complete, cool, dilute with 10 ml distilled water, heat almost to boiling to dissolve slowly soluble salts, and, if the sample is still cloudy, filter through a glass-fiber, sintered-glass, or porcelain filter, washing with 2 to 3 ml distilled

water. Quantitatively transfer the filtrate or the clear solution to a 25-ml volumetric flask or graduate and make up to 25 ml with distilled water. Empty the flask or graduate into a 125-ml separatory funnel, rinse with 5 ml conc HCl that is added to the funnel, and add 25 ml conc HCl measured with the same graduate or flask. Mix and cool to room temperature.

3) Extract the iron from the HCl solution in the separatory funnel by shaking for 30 sec with 25 ml isopropyl ether. Draw off the lower acid layer into a second separatory funnel. Extract the acid solution again with 25 ml isopropyl ether, drain the acid layer into a suitable clean vessel, and combine the two portions of isopropyl ether. Pour the acid layer back into the second separatory funnel and extract once more with 25 ml isopropyl ether. Withdraw and discard the acid layer and then add the ether layer to the lower layers in the original funnel. Persistence of a yellow color in the HCl solution after three extractions does not signify incomplete separation of iron because copper, which is not extracted, gives a similar yellow color.

Shake the combined ether extracts with 25 ml distilled water to return the iron to the aqueous phase and transfer the lower aqueous layer to a 100-ml volumetric flask. Repeat the extraction with a second 25-ml portion of distilled water, adding this to the first aqueous extract. Discard the ether layer.

4) Add to the combined aqueous extract 1 ml $NH_2OH{\cdot}HCl$ solution, 10 ml phenanthroline solution, and 10 ml sodium acetate solution. Dilute to 100 ml with distilled water, mix thoroughly, and let stand for 10 min. Measure the

absorbance at 510 nm using a 5-cm absorption cell for amounts of iron less than 100 μg or 1-cm cell for quantities from 100 to 500 μg. As reference, use either distilled water or a sample blank prepared by carrying the specified quantities of acids through the entire analytical procedure. If distilled water is used as reference, correct the absorbance of the sample by subtracting the absorbance of a sample blank.

Determine the micrograms of iron in the sample used from the absorbance (corrected, if necessary) by reference to the calibration curve prepared according to ¶ 4d above.

5. Calculation

When the sample has been treated according to 4b, c, d, e, or 4f2):

$$mg/l\, Fe = \frac{\mu g\, Fe}{ml\, sample}$$

When the sample has been treated according to 4f1):

$$mg/l\, Fe = \frac{\mu g\, Fe}{ml\, sample} \times \frac{100}{ml\, portion}$$

Report details of sample collection, storage, and pretreatment if they are pertinent to interpretation of the results.

6. Precision and Accuracy

a. Precision and accuracy depend on the method of sample collection and storage, the method of color measurement, the iron concentration, and the presence of interfering color, turbidity, and foreign ions. In general, optimum reliability of visual comparison in nessler tubes is not better than 5% and often only 10%, whereas, under optimum conditions, photometric measurement may be reliable to 3% or 3 μg, whichever is greater. The sensitivity limit for visual observation in nessler tubes is approximately 1 μg Fe. The variability and instability of the sample may limit the precision and accuracy of this determination more than will the errors of the analysis itself. Serious divergences have been found in reports of different laboratories because of variations in methods of collecting and treating samples.

b. A synthetic unknown sample containing 300 $\mu g/l$ Fe, 500 $\mu g/l$ Al, 50 $\mu g/l$ Cd, 110 $\mu g/l$ Cr, 470 $\mu g/l$ Cu, 70 $\mu g/l$ Pb, 120 $\mu g/l$ Mn, 150 $\mu g/l$ Ag, and 650 $\mu g/l$ Zn in distilled water was analyzed in 44 laboratories by the phenanthroline method, with a relative standard deviation of 25.5% and a relative error of 13.3%.

310 B.   Atomic Absorption Spectrophotometric Method

See Section 301A. II.

310 C.   References

1. LEE, G. F. & W. STUMM. 1960. Determination of ferrous iron in the presence of ferric iron using bathophenanthroline. *J. Amer. Water Works Ass.* 52:1567.

2. GHOSH, M. M., J. T. O'CONNOR & R. S. ENGELBRECHT. 1967. Bathophenanthroline method for the determination of ferrous iron. *J. Amer. Water Works Ass.* 59:878.

3. SHAPIRO, J. 1966. On the measurement of ferrous iron in natural waters. *Limnol. Oceanogr.* 11:293.

4. McMAHON, J. W. 1967. The influence of light and acid on the measurement of ferrous iron in lake water. *Limnol. Oceanogr.* 12:437.

5. McMAHON, J. W. 1969. An acid-free bathophenanthroline method for measuring dissolved ferrous iron in lake water. *Water Res.* 3:743.

6. SEITZ, W. R. & D. M. HERCULES. 1972. Determination of trace amounts of iron (II) using chemiluminescence analysis. *Anal. Chem.* 44:2143.

7. Moss. M. L. & M. G. MELLON. 1942. Colorimetric determination of iron with 2,2'-bipyridine and with 2,2',2"-tripyridine. *Ind. Eng. Chem.*, Anal. Ed. 14:862.

8. WELCHER, F. J. 1947. Organic Analytical Reagents. D. Van Nostrand Co., Princeton, N.J., Vol. 3, pp. 100–104.

9. MORRIS, R. L. 1952. Determination of iron in water in the presence of heavy metals. *Anal. Chem.* 25:1376.

10. DOIG, M. T., III, & D. F. MARTIN. 1971. Effect of humic acids on iron analyses in natural water. *Water Res.* 5:689.

310 D.   Bibliography

Phenanthroline Method

FORTUNE, W. B. & M. G. MELLON. 1938. Determination of iron with o-phenanthroline: A spectrophotometric study. *Ind. Eng. Chem.*, Anal. Ed. 10:60.

CHRONHEIM, G. & W. WINK. 1942. Determination of divalent iron (by o-nitrosophenol). *Ind. Eng. Chem.*, Anal. Ed. 14:447.

MEHLIG, R. P. & R. H. HULETT. 1942. Spectrophotometric determination of iron with o-phenanthroline and with nitro-o-phenanthroline. *Ind. Eng. Chem.*, Anal. Ed. 14:869.

Moss, M. L. & M. G. MELLON. 1942. Color reactions of 1,10-phenenthroline derivatives. *Ind. Eng. Chem.*, Anal. Ed. 14:931.

HALLINAN, F. J. 1943. Determination of iron in water. *Ind. Eng. Chem.*, Anal. Ed. 15:510.

CALDWELL, D. H. & R. B. ADAMS. 1946. Colorimetric determination of iron in water with o-phenanthroline. *J. Amer. Water Works Ass.* 38:727.

Standard Methods for the Examination of Water and Sewage, 9th ed. 1946. American Public Health Association, New York, N.Y. p. 51.

WELCHER, F. J. 1947. Organic Analytical Reagents. D. Van Nostrand Co., Princeton, N.J., Vol. 3, pp. 85–93.

KOLTHOFF, I. M., T. S. LEE & D. L. LEUSSING. 1948. Equilibrium and kinetic studies on the formation and dissociation of ferroin and ferrin. *Anal. Chem.* 20:985.

RYAN, J. A. & G. H. BOTHAM. 1949. Iron in aluminum alloys: Colorimetric determination using 1,10-phenanthroline. *Anal. Chem.* 21:1521.

REITZ, L. K., A. S. O'BRIEN & T. L. DAVIS. 1950. Evaluation of three iron methods using a factorial experiment. *Anal. Chem.* 22:1470.

SANDELL, E. B. 1959. Colorimetric Determination of Traces of Metals, 3rd ed. Interscience Publishers, New York, N.Y. Chapter 22.

RAINWATER, F. H. & L. L. THATCHER. 1960. Methods of collection and analysis of water samples. U. S. Geol. Surv. Water Supply Pap. No. 1454.

311 LEAD

Lead is a serious cumulative body poison. Natural waters seldom contain more than 20 $\mu g/l$, although values as high as 400 $\mu g/l$ have been reported. Lead in a water supply may come from industrial, mine, and smelter discharges, or from the dissolution of old lead plumbing. Tap waters that are soft, acid, and not suitably treated may contain lead resulting from an attack on the lead service pipes.

Selection of method: The atomic absorption spectrophotometric method entails fewer operations and is adaptable for multiple screening determinations. The dithizone method also yields satisfactory results.

311 A.   Atomic Absorption Spectrophotometric Method

See Section 301 A. II and III.

311 B.   Dithizone Method

1. General Discussion

a. Principle: Lead forms a pink complex, lead dithizonate, with dithizone in carbon tetrachloride solution. Interfering metals are removed by preliminary extraction at pH 2 to 3.

After removal of the interfering elements, tartrate is added to prevent the formation of hydroxide and the solution is brought to pH 8 to 9 with ammonium hydroxide and sodium cyanide. Lead is then extracted with a dilute solution of dithizone. Because an excess of dithizone is used, the pink color of the lead dithizonate is masked by the intense green color of the excess dithizone. This excess is removed from the carbon tetrachloride layer with alkaline cyanide solution, leaving the lead dithizonate in the organic solvent. The solution of lead dithizonate is diluted to a given volume and the color intensity determined by a colorimeter or spectrophotometer, or by comparison with standards.

The use of hydrazine acetate as the reducing agent may cause some difficulties inasmuch as the reduction of ferric and stannic ions proceeds quite slowly. The preliminary reduction must be carried out carefully in accordance with the procedure.

b. Interference: The elements that interfere with the extraction of lead in cyanide medium at pH 8 to 9 are bismuth, stannous tin, and thallium. Thallium is encountered very rarely. Bismuth, and particularly tin, occur quite frequently.

The sample is first fumed with perchloric and nitric acids to remove organic compounds and then is reduced with hydrazine acetate to lower the oxidation state of elements and compounds capable of oxidizing dithizone. The reduction assures that tin and iron exist in the lower valence state. At pH 2 to 3, dithizone forms complexes with bismuth, copper, mercury, silver, and tin. Thus, both bismuth and tin are removed so that they cannot interfere with the lead extraction at pH 8 to 9. Because there may be relatively large quantities of bismuth, tin, or copper, a strong solution of dithizone in chloroform is needed to extract these elements.

c. Application: The method was developed to determine 0 to 75 μg Pb in the presence of 100 μg of each of the following ions: Ag, Hg, Bi, Cu, Cd, As, Sb, Sn, Fe, Al, Cr, Ni, Co, Mn, Zn, Ca, Sr, Ba, Mg, Na, K, and NH₄.

With preliminary digestion this method is suitable for the determination of lead in wastewaters high in organic matter. Normally, with drinking water and other waters low in organic matter and in the absence of tin and bismuth, the preliminary digestion and extraction steps can be eliminated.

d. Sample handling: Acidify all samples at the time of collection to keep the metals in solution and prevent their plating out on the container wall. With relatively clean waters containing no particulate matter 1.5 ml conc HNO₃/l sample will be sufficient to lower the pH to 2.0. Surface waters, such as those from streams, lakes, and wastewater treatment plant effluents that may contain sediment will require more acid. If the sample contains particulate matter and only the "dissolved" metal content is desired, filter the sample through a 0.45-μm membrane filter. After filtra-

tion, acidify the filtrate with 1.5 ml conc HNO₃/l.

2. Apparatus

a. Colorimetric equipment: One of the following is required:

1) *Spectrophotometer,* for use at 520 nm, providing a light path of 1 cm or longer.

2) *Filter photometer,* providing a light path of 1 cm or longer and equipped with a green filter having maximum transmittance near 520 nm.

b. pH meter.

c. Separatory funnels, 125-ml, Squibb form, with ground-glass stoppers.

d. Glassware: Clean all glassware, including sample bottles, with 1+1 HNO₃ and rinse thoroughly with lead-free water.

3. Reagents

a. Lead-free water: Redistill distilled water in all-glass apparatus. Alternatively, pass distilled water through a mixed bed ion-exchange resin.

b. Stock lead solution: Dissolve 100.0 mg pure lead metal in a mixture of 2 ml conc HNO₃ and 2 ml redistilled water. Heat gently if necessary. Dilute to 1,000 ml with redistilled water. Store in polyethylene bottles; 1.00 ml = 100 μg Pb.

c. Standard lead solution: Dilute 10.00 ml stock lead solution to 100 ml with redistilled water; 1.00 ml = 10.0 μg Pb. Dilute 2.00 ml stock lead solution to 100 ml with redistilled water; 1.00 ml = 2.0 μg Pb. Prepare standard lead solutions as needed and use the same day.

d. Phenolphthalein indicator solution.

e. Special reagent—ammonium acetate solution: In 600 ml redistilled water, dissolve 400 g $NH_4C_2H_3O_2$. This solution is required only if lead is to be determined in the presence of sulfate.

Total iron and heavy-metal impurities in the reagent acids should not exceed 0.0001%. Prepare blanks in any event, but if the metallic impurities are greater than this, the blanks will be too large and variable for precise determinations of small concentrations of the metals. When the amounts of acid specified are used, 0.0001% of heavy-metal impurity will add about 0.03 mg of heavy metals to the sample.

f. Ammonium hydroxide, NH_4OH, conc. Prepare as in 305C.3*k*.

g. Ammonium hydroxide, 1+1.

h. Hydrazine acetate solution: Mix 15 ml lead-free hydrazine hydrate (64% hydrazine)* with 50 ml conc acetic acid and dilute to 100 ml with redistilled water.

i. Sodium tartrate solution: Dissolve 10 g $Na_2C_4H_4O_6 \cdot 2H_2O$ in 100 ml redistilled water. To purify, shake with dithizone solution II (below) in CCl_4 until the organic solvent layer appears pure green. Wash away the traces of dithizone by extraction with $CHCl_3$ until the solution is water white. Then extract twice with CCl_4.

j. Tartaric acid solution: Dissolve 50 g $H_2C_4H_4O_6$ in 100 ml redistilled water.

k. Stock dithizone solution I (chloroform): See Section 301C.II 4*a*.

l. Stock dithizone solution II (carbon tetrachloride): See Section 301 C.II 4*b*.

m. Chloroform: Treat all chloroform, especially the reclaimed solvent, as follows: Drain off all water. Wash 1,000 ml of solvent repeatedly with 50 to 100 ml of conc H_2SO_4 until the solvent and the acid layers are clear and colorless. Shake the solvent with a dilute solution of sodium bicarbonate and wash thoroughly with water. Add calcium oxide to dry the solvent. Separate from the CaO and add 2% of its volume of pure absolute methyl alcohol. Distill the solvent slowly while keeping a pellet of CaO in the still. Reject the first 50 to 100 ml; do not allow the still to go to dryness.

n. Carbon tetrachloride: If ACS grade is not available, treat commercial-grade and solvent to be reclaimed as follows: Shake 1,000 ml solvent with 50 ml 50% aqueous solution of KOH. Repeat several times. Wash the CCl_4 with 25- to 50-ml portions of conc H_2SO_4 several times. The final washing with the acid should show no discoloration. Wash the CCl_4 with a dilute solution of sodium bicarbonate; wash repeatedly with water until the washings are neutral to litmus paper. Dry overnight with $CaCl_2$ and distill, or instead of drying overnight, distill about 10% of the solvent and then collect the clear distillate. Do not distill the last 50 to 100 ml after collecting the main fraction.

o. Thymol blue indicator solution: Dissolve 0.4 g indicator in 100 ml redistilled water.

p. Potassium cyanide solution: Dissolve 10 g KCN in 100 ml distilled water. (CAUTION: *Toxic—take care to avoid ingestion.*)

q. Alkaline potassium cyanide solution: To 175 ml pure conc NH_4OH add 15 ml potassium cyanide solution and 7.5 ml lead-free sodium sulfite solution (10 g in 100 ml water). Dilute to

---

* Matheson Scientific, Inc., or equivalent.

500 ml with redistilled water. To remove the lead from sodium sulfite, dissolve 10 g Na_2SO_3 in 100 ml redistilled water and extract with dithizone solution I until the color of the organic layer is pure green. Remove traces of $CHCl_3$ by 4 to 5 extractions with CCl_4.

r. *Hydrochloric acid,* HCl, conc. If necessary, distill in a pyrex apparatus. The distillate will be approximately 22% HCl.

4. Procedure

a. *Treatment of sample:* If organic matter is present and total lead is to be determined, digest the sample with nitric and sulfuric acid as directed in Section 301C.II5. If interfering amounts of tin and bismuth are present, proceed as in 4c and 4d below. If only dissolved lead is to be determined, filter the sample through a 0.45-μm membrane filter and start with 4e, provided that tin and bismuth are absent. With drinking water, the analysis usually can be started with 4e.

b. *Preparation of calibration standards:* Prepare a series of standards ranging from 1 to 10 ml solution (1.00 ml = 2.0 μg Pb or 1.00 ml = 10.0 μg Pb) and carry these standards, together with a redistilled water blank, through the same procedure as the sample.

c. *Preliminary reduction:* Dilute the sample with 10 ml redistilled water. Add 10 to 15 drops (0.5 to 0.75 ml) phenolphthalein indicator solution and neutralize with 1+1 NH_4OH. Add 20 ml hydrazine acetate solution and heat to 90 to 95 C in a water bath for at least 10 min. Cool.

In the absence of tin and bismuth, proceed to ¶f below.

d. *Removal of bismuth and tin interference:* Add 20 ml sodium tartrate solution. Adjust pH to about 2.5, using a pH meter, by adding either 1+1 NH_4OH or tartaric acid solution. Transfer to a separatory funnel.

Extract the solution in the funnel with 3-ml portions of dithizone solution I until the organic layer has a pure green color. Shake well each time and carefully drain off and discard the chloroform layer.

Extract the solution with two 5-ml portions of chloroform to remove the entrained dithizone. Discard the chloroform layers. Remove the remaining chloroform by extracting with 5 ml CCl_4. Discard the CCl_4 layer.

e. *Extraction of lead:* Add 10 ml sodium tartrate solution and 5 drops thymol blue indicator solution. If necessary, add conc NH_4OH to make the indicator turn blue.

Add 10 ml KCN solution. Adjust the pH to 8.5 by adding tartaric acid solution or 1+1 NH_4OH until the indicator turns green.

Extract with 5 ml dithizone solution II. Shake well and carefully transfer the solvent layer to another separatory funnel.

Successively extract the aqueous phase with 2-ml portions of dithizone solution II until the green color of dithizone persists for at least two extractions. Combine all these extractions with the one from the previous step. When multiple samples are run, as with a calibration curve, use the same amount of dithizone solution for all extractions. The color of the blank increases somewhat as the number of extractions increases. Extract the aqueous phase with 5 ml CCl_4 and add it to the other extracts.

To the combined CCl₄ extracts, add 20 ml alkaline KCN solution and shake well. Drain off the CCl₄ layer into a 25- or 50-ml volumetric flask. Extract the aqueous phase with two 2-ml portions of CCl₄. Combine all the extracts and discard the aqueous layer.

Dilute the extracts in the volumetric flask to the mark by adding CCl₄ and shake well.

f. Color measurement: Filter the CCl₄ solution through small dry papers to remove suspended droplets of water. Read the absorbance of this solution at 520 nm using CCl₄ as a reference. Subtract the absorbance of the blank from that of the sample readings.

5. Calculation

$$\text{mg/l Pb} = \frac{\mu g\ Pb}{ml\ sample} \times \frac{100}{ml\ portion}$$

6. Bibliography

Wichmann, H. J. 1939. Isolation and determination of traces of metals—dithizone system. *Ind. Eng. Chem.*, Anal. Ed. 11:66.

Bricker, L. G. & K. L. Proctor. 1945. Application of colorimetry to the analysis of corrosion-resistant steels: Determination of lead. *Ind. Eng. Chem.*, Anal. Ed. 17:511.

Serfass, E. J. & W. S. Levine. 1946. *Monthly Rev. Amer. Electroplaters Soc.* 33:1079.

Association of Official Agricultural Chemists. 1975. Official Methods of Analysis, 12th ed. AOAC, Washington, D.C.

312 LITHIUM

A minor constituent of minerals, lithium is present in fresh waters in concentrations below 10 mg/l. Brines and thermal waters may contain higher lithium levels. The use of lithium or its salts in dehumidifying units, medicinal waters, metallurgical processes, and the manufacture of some types of glass and storage batteries may contribute to its presence in wastes. Lithium hypochlorite is available commercially as a source of chlorine and may be used in swimming pools.

312 A. Flame Photometric Method

1. General Discussion

a. Principle: Like its sister elements, sodium and potassium, lithium can be determined in trace amounts by flame photometric methods. The measurement can be made at a wavelength of 671 nm.

b. Interference: Barium, strontium, and calcium interfere in the flame photometric determination of lithium and can be removed by the addition of a sodium sulfate-sodium carbonate solution that precipitates BaSO₄, SrCO₃, and CaCO₃. The content of either sodium or magnesium individually must not exceed 10 mg in the portion taken for analysis.

c. Minimum detectable concentration: The minimum lithium concentration detectable by the flame photometric method is about 0.1 mg/l.

d. Sampling and storage: Collect the sample in a pyrex bottle. Do not use polyethylene bottles because contamination may result from the occasional use of lithium chloride as a catalyst in the manufacture of polyethylene.

2. Apparatus

Flame photometer: Perkin-Elmer Model 52-C flame photometer; or a Beckman Model DU spectrophotometer equipped with photomultiplier tube and flame accessory; or the equivalent.

3. Reagents

a. Sodium sulfate and sodium carbonate reagent: Dissolve 5 g Na_2SO_4 and 10 g Na_2CO_3 in distilled water and dilute to 1 l.

b. Stock lithium solution: Dissolve 610.9 mg anhydrous lithium chloride, LiCl, in distilled water and dilute to 1,000 ml; 1.00 ml = 100 μg Li. Dry the salt overnight in an oven at 105 C. Weigh the LiCl very rapidly because the salt is highly deliquescent.

c. Standard lithium solution: Dilute 20.00 ml stock lithium chloride solution to 1,000 ml with distilled water. This solution contains 2.0 μg Li/ml.

4. Procedure

a. Pretreatment of polluted water and wastewater samples: See Section 301C.I.

b. Removal of interference from sample: Take a sample of 50.0 ml or less, containing not more than 10 mg Na and 10 mg Mg. Add 5.0 ml Na_2SO_4—Na_2CO_3 reagent. Bring the

solution to a boil to coagulate the precipitate of $BaSO_4$, $SrCO_3$, $CaCO_3$, and possibly $MgCO_3$. Allow enough time for complete precipitation; otherwise a feathery precipitate of $BaSO_4$ will appear after filtration. Pass the sample through Whatman No. 42 filter paper, wash with distilled water, and dilute to 50.0 ml for the flame photometric measurement.

c. Treatment of standard solution: Add 5.0 ml Na_2SO_4—Na_2CO_3 reagent to 50.0 ml of the standard lithium solution. (Boiling is unnecessary because no precipitation occurs in the standard. When boiling is avoided, the treated standard contains 1.8 μg Li/ml.)

d. Flame photometric measurement: Determine the unknown lithium concentration by direct intensity measurements at a wavelength of 671 nm. (The bracketing method can be used with some instruments, while the construction of a calibration curve is necessary with other photometric instruments.) Run the sample, distilled water (0 mg/l Li), and the lithium standard as nearly simultaneously as possible. For best results, take the average of several readings on each solution. In many cases, the calibration readings on distilled water and the lithium standard will suffice. Follow the manufacturer's instructions for operation of the instrument used in the determination.

5. Calculation

$$\text{mg/l Li} = \frac{\mu\text{g Li}}{\text{ml sample}}$$

6. Accuracy

The lithium concentration can be de-

314 B.   Persulfate Method

1. General Discussion

a. Principle: Persulfate oxidation of soluble manganous compounds to form permanganate is carried out in the presence of silver nitrate.[1] The resulting color is stable for at least 24 hr if excess persulfate is present and organic matter is absent.

b. Interference: As much as 0.1 g NaCl is prevented from interfering by the addition of mercuric sulfate to form slightly dissociated complexes. Only minute amounts of bromide and iodide may be present. The persulfate procedure can be used for potable water with trace to small amounts of organic matter if the period of heating is increased after more persulfate has been added.

For wastewaters containing organic matter, preliminary digestion with nitric acid is essential (see Section 301C.II). If large amounts of chloride also are present, the boiling with nitric acid helps to remove the chloride ion. Interfering traces of chloride are eliminated by using mercuric sulfate in the special reagent.

Colored solutions from other inorganic ions are compensated for in the final colorimetric step.

Samples that have been exposed to air may give low results due to precipitation of manganese dioxide. Adding 1 drop of 30% hydrogen peroxide to the sample, after addition of the special reagent, redissolves precipitated manganese.

c. Minimum detectable concentration: The absorbency index of permanganate per gram-atom of manganese at 525 nm is about 2,300. The minimum detectable quantity is 30 μg Mn when a 1-cm cell is used for photometric comparison or 5 μg Mn when a 5-cm cell is used (98% transmittance). If the volume of sample used is 100 ml, these quantities correspond to 300 and 50 μg/l, respectively.

2. Apparatus

Colorimetric equipment: One of the following is required:

a. Spectrophotometer, for use at 525 nm, providing a light path of 1 cm or longer.

b. Filter photometer, providing a light path of 1 cm or longer and equipped with a green filter having maximum transmittance near 525 nm.

c. Nessler tubes, matched, 100-ml, tall form.

Visual comparison is recommended only in the range of 5 to 100 μg Mn (in the 100-ml final solution). For photometric measurement, the following tabulation shows the length of light path appropriate for various concentrations of manganese in the 100-ml final solution:

Mn Range μg	Light Path cm
5–200	15
20–400	5
50–1,000	2
100–1,500	1

3. Reagents

a. Special reagent: Dissolve 75 g mercuric sulfate, $HgSO_4$, in 400 ml conc HNO_3 and 200 ml distilled water. Add 200 ml 85% phosphoric acid,

H_3PO_4, and 35 mg silver nitrate, $AgNO_3$. Dilute the cooled solution to 1 l.

b. *Ammonium persulfate*, $(NH_4)_2S_2O_3$, solid.

c. *Standard manganese solution:* Prepare a $0.1N$ $KMnO_4$ solution by dissolving 3.2 g $KMnO_4$ in distilled water and making up to 1 l. Age for several weeks in sunlight or heat for several hours near the boiling point, then filter through a fritted-glass filter crucible and standardize against sodium oxalate. [The standard $KMnO_4$ solution prepared for the titrimetric calcium determination (Section 306B.3*i* above) may be used.] Calculate the volume of this solution necessary to prepare 1 l of solution of such strength that 1.00 ml $= 50.0$ μg Mn, as follows:

$$\text{ml } KMnO_4 = \frac{4.55}{\text{normality } KMnO_4}$$

To this volume add 2 to 3 ml conc H_2SO_4 and sodium bisulfite solution (10 g $NaHSO_3$ plus 100 ml distilled water) dropwise, with stirring, until the permanganate color disappears. Boil to remove excess SO_2, cool, and dilute to 1,000 ml with distilled water. Dilute this solution further in order to measure small amounts of manganese.

d. *Hydrogen peroxide*, H_2O_2, 30%.

e. *Nitric acid*, HNO_3, conc.

f. *Sulfuric acid*, H_2SO_4, conc.

g. *Perchloric acid*, 60%.

h. *Sodium nitrite solution*, 5.0 g $NaNO_2$ in 95 ml distilled water.

4. Procedure

a. *Treatment of sample:* If a digested sample has been prepared according to directions for reducing organic matter and/or excessive chlorides in Section 301C.II, pipet a portion containing 0.05 to 2.0 mg Mn into a 250-ml conical flask. Add distilled water, if necessary, to have 50 ml and proceed as in *b*.

b. To a suitable aliquot of the sample, add 5 ml special reagent. Concentrate to 90 ml by boiling or dilute to 90 ml. Add 1 g ammonium persulfate, bring to boiling, and boil for 1 min. Do not heat on a water bath. Remove from the heat source, let stand 1 min, then cool under the tap. (Too long a boiling time results in decomposition of excess persulfate and subsequent loss of permanganate color; too slow a cooling has the same effect.) Dilute to 100 ml with distilled water free from reducing substances and mix. Compare visually or measure photometrically, using standards containing 0, 5.00, ... 1,500 μg (etc.) Mn, prepared by treating various amounts of the standard Mn solution in the same way. Make the photometric measurements against a distilled-water blank.

c. *Correction for turbidity or interfering color:* Avoid filtration because of possible retention of some permanganate on the filter paper. If visual comparison is used, the effect of turbidity only can be estimated and no correction can be made for the effect of interfering colored ions. When photometric measurements are made, use the following "bleaching" method, which also corrects for interfering color: As soon as the photometer reading has been made, add 0.05 ml hydrogen peroxide solution directly to the sample in the optical cell. Mix and, as soon as the permanganate color has faded completely and no bubbles remain, read again. Convert the readings to absorbances and make the proper deduction. Alternatively, read the values from the calibration curve as "apparent" manganese and interferences as manganese, and make the proper deduction.

5. Calculation

a. $mg/l\ Mn = \dfrac{\mu g\ Mn}{ml\ sample}$

b. When the sample has been pretreated according to Section 301C.II:

$$mg/l\ Mn = mg\ Mn \times \frac{1,000}{ml\ sample} \times \frac{100}{ml\ aliquot}$$

6. Precision and Accuracy

A synthetic unknown sample containing 120 $\mu g/l$ Mn, 500 $\mu g/l$ Al, 50 $\mu g/$ l Cd, 110 $\mu g/l$ Cr, 470 $\mu g/l$ Cu, 300 $\mu g/l$ Fe, 70 $\mu g/l$ Pb, 150 $\mu g/l$ Ag, and 650 $\mu g/l$ Zn in distilled water was analyzed in 33 laboratories by the persulfate method, with a relative standard deviation of 26.3% and a relative error of 0%.

A second synthetic unknown sample, similar in all respects except for 50 $\mu g/l$ Mn and 1,000 $\mu g/l$ Cu, was analyzed in 17 laboratories by the persulfate method, with a relative standard deviation of 50.3% and a relative error of 7.2%.

7. Reference

1. NYDAHL, F. 1949. Determination of manganese by the persulfate method. *Anal. Chem. Acta* 3:144.

314 C.   Periodate Method for Potable Water

1. General Discussion

a. Principle: With periodate as the oxidizing agent acting upon soluble manganous compounds to form permanganate, Beer's law holds closely up to 15 mg Mn. The intensity of the color is not affected by variation in acid or periodate concentration and the color is stable for many months. To obtain complete oxidation of small amounts of manganese (10 μg or less), silver nitrate is added and the heating time increased.

b. Interference: Reducing substances capable of reacting with periodate or permanganate must be removed or destroyed before the periodate oxidation is attempted. Although chloride in small amounts can be oxidized by periodate, removal by evaporation with sulfuric acid is preferred, especially when the sample contains only a small amount of manganese. This treatment, however, usually results in the dehydration of silica and the production of turbidity. Interference from other oxidizable substances, including organic materials, is eliminated by boiling the sample with nitric acid. Phosphoric acid is added to decolorize ferric iron by complex formation and prevent possible precipitation of periodates or iodates of manganese. Foreign metals, with a few exceptions, do not interfere, except those having colored ions; for these a method of correction is described.

c. Minimum detectable quantity: 5 μg Mn.

2. Apparatus

See Section 314B.2*a-c* above.

3. Reagents

a. *Sulfuric acid,* HNO_3, conc.

b. *Nitric acid,* HNO_3, conc.

c. *Phosphoric acid,* H_3PO_4, syrupy, 85%.

d. *Periodate:* Use either 1) the potassium or 2) the sodium salt.

1) *Potassium metaperiodate,* KIO_4, solid.

2) *Sodium paraperiodate,* $Na_3H_2IO_6$ (also called trisodium periodate [para]), solid.

e. *Silver nitrate,* $AgNO_3$.

f. *Standard manganese solution:* Prepare as described in Section 314B.3*c* preceding.

g. *Hydrogen peroxide,* H_2O_2, 30%.

4. Procedure

a. *Pretreatment of samples:* To remove chloride or other oxidizable substances such as organic matter, add to a sample 5 ml conc H_2SO_4 and 5 ml conc HNO_3, mixing between additions. Evaporate to SO_3 fumes. Cool, add 85 ml distilled water, and cool again. Add 5 ml HNO_3 and 5 ml H_3PO_4, and mix. Treat as described in ¶*b* below, beginning with "... add 0.3 g KIO_4."

b. *Oxidation:* To a suitable portion, add 5 ml conc H_2SO_4, mix, and cool. Add 5 ml HNO_3 and 5 ml H_3PO_4, and mix. Concentrate to about 90 ml by boiling. Cool; add 0.3 g KIO_4 or 0.5 g $Na_3H_2IO_6$. If the amount of Mn is 10 μg or less, also add 20 mg $AgNO_3$. Heat to boiling while stirring, and keep at or slightly below the boiling point for 10 min (or at least 1 hr for very small amounts of Mn). Cool, dilute to 100 ml with distilled water free from reducing substances, and mix. Compare visually or measure photometrically, using standards containing 0, 5.00, ... 1,500 μg Mn, prepared by treating the various amounts of standard Mn solution in the same way. Make the photometric measurements against a distilled-water blank.

c. *Correction for turbidity or interfering color:* Follow the procedure described in Section 314B.4*b* above.

5. Calculation

$$\text{mg/l Mn} = \frac{\mu g \text{ Mn}}{\text{ml sample}}$$

6. Precision and Accuracy

A synthetic unknown sample containing 120 $\mu g/l$ Mn, 500 $\mu g/l$ Al, 50 $\mu g/l$ Cd, 110 $\mu g/l$ Cr, 470 $\mu g/l$ Cu, 300 $\mu g/l$ Fe, 70 $\mu g/l$ Pb, 150 $\mu g/l$ Ag, and 650 $\mu g/l$ Zn in distilled water was analyzed in 14 laboratories by the periodate method with a relative standard deviation of 36.0% and a relative error of 25.0%.

314 D.   Bibliography

Persulfate Method

RICHARDS, M.B. 1930. Colorimetric determination of manganese in biological material. *Analyst* 55:554.

NYDAHL, F. 1949. Determination of manganese by the persulfate method. *Anal. Chem. Acta* 3:144.

MILLS, S.M. 1950. Elusive manganese. *Water Sewage Works* 97:92.

SANDELL, E.B. 1959. Colormetric Determination of Traces of Metals, 3rd ed. Interscience Publishers, New York, N.Y., Chapter 26.

Periodate Method

MEHLIG, J.P. 1939. Colorimetric determination of manganese with periodate. *Ind. Eng. Chem.*, Anal. Ed. 11:274.

ROWLAND, G.P., JR. 1939. Photoelectric colorimetry: An optical study of permanganate ion and of the chromium-diphenyl carbazide system. *Ind. Eng. Chem.*, Anal. Ed. 11:442.

COOPER, M.D. 1953. Periodate method for manganese and effect of band width. *Anal. Chem.* 25:411.

315   MERCURY

Organic and inorganic mercury salts are very toxic and their presence in the environment, especially in water, should be monitored constantly.

Selection of method: The flameless atomic absorption method is the method of choice for all samples, while the dithizone method can be used for potable waters.

315 A.   Flameless Atomic Absorption Method

See Section 301 A.VI.

315 B.   Dithizone Method

1. General Discussion

a. Principle: Mercury ions react with a dithizone solution in chloroform to form an orange color. The various shades of orange are measured in a spectrophotometer and unknown concentrations are estimated from a standard curve.

b. Interference: Copper, gold, palladium, divalent platinum, and silver react with dithizone in acid solution. Copper is separated during the procedure by remaining in the organic phase while the mercury is left in the aqueous phase. The other contaminants usually are not present.

The mercury dithizonate should be measured quickly because it is photosensitive.

c. Minimum detectable quantity: 1 μg Hg in a double-beamed spectrophotometer. A single-beam instrument should also respond satisfactorily.

2. Apparatus

a. Spectrophotometer, for measurements at 490 nm, providing a light path of 1 cm or longer.

b. Separatory funnels: 250 and 1,000 ml, with Teflon stopcocks.

c. Glassware: Clean all glassware with potassium dichromate-sulfuric acid cleaning solution.

3. Reagents

a. Mercury-free water: Use redistilled or deionized distilled water for the preparation of all reagents and dilutions.

b. Stock mercury solution: Dissolve 135.4 mg mercuric chloride, $HgCl_2$, in about 700 ml mercury-free water, add 1.5 ml conc HNO_3, and make up to 1,000 ml with mercury-free water; 1.00 ml=100 μg Hg.

c. Standard mercury solution: Dilute 10.00 ml stock solution to 1,000 ml with mercury-free water; 1.00 ml = 1.00 μg Hg. Prepare immediately before use.

d. Potassium permanganate solution: Dissolve 5 g $KMnO_4$ in 100 ml mercury-free water.

e. Sulfuric acid, H_2SO_4, conc.

f. Potassium persulfate solution: Dissolve 5 g $K_2S_2O_8$ in 100 ml mercury-free water.

g. Hydroxylamine hydrochloride solution: Dissolve 50 g $NH_2OH \cdot HCl$ in 100 ml mercury-free water.

h. Dithizone solution: Dissolve 6 mg in 1 l chloroform.

i. Sulfuric acid, 0.25N: Dilute 250 ml of 1N H_2SO_4 to 1 l with mercury-free water.

j. Potassium bromide solution: Dissolve 40 g KBr in 100 ml mercury-free water.

k. Chloroform, $CHCl_3$.

l. Phosphate-carbonate buffer solution: Dissolve 150 g disodium hydrogen phosphate dodecahydrate, $Na_2HPO_4 \cdot 12H_2O$, and 38 g anhydrous potassium carbonate, K_2CO_3, in 1 l mercury-free water. Extract with 10-ml portions of dithizone until the last portion remains blue. Wash with $CHCl_3$ to remove excess dithizone.

m. Sodium sulfate, Na_2SO_4, anhydrous.

4. Procedure

a. Preparation of calibration curve: Pipet 0 (blank), 2.00, 4.00, 6.00, 8.00, and 10.00 μg mercury into separate beakers. To each beaker, add 500 ml mercury-free water (or any other volume selected for sample), 1 ml $KMnO_4$ solution, and 10 ml conc H_2SO_4. Stir and bring to a boil. If necessary, add more $KMnO_4$ until a pink color persists. After boiling has ceased, cautiously add 5 ml $K_2S_2O_8$ solution and allow to cool for 0.5 hr. Add one or more drops $NH_2OH \cdot HCl$ solution to discharge the pink color. When cool, transfer each solution to individual 1-l separatory funnels. Add about 25 ml dithizone solution. Shake the funnel vigorously and transfer each organic layer to a 250-ml funnel. Repeat this extraction at least three times, making sure that the color in the last dithizone layer is as intense a blue as that of the original dithizone solution. Wash the accumulated dithizone extracts in the 250-ml separatory funnel by shaking with 50 ml of 0.25 N sulfuric acid. Transfer the washed dithizonate extract to another 250-ml funnel. Add 50 ml of 0.25 N sulfuric acid and 10 ml KBr solution and shake vigorously to transfer the mercury dithizonate from the organic layer to the aqueous layer. Discard the lower dithizone layer. Wash the aqueous layer with a small volume of $CHCl_3$ and discard the $CHCl_3$. Transfer 20 ml phosphate-carbonate buffer solution to each separatory funnel and add 10 ml standard dithizone solution. Shake thoroughly, and, after separation, transfer the mercury dithizone to beakers. The final dithizone extract should be slightly blue. Dry the contents with anhydrous sodium sulfate. Transfer the mercury dithizonate solution to a cuvette and record the absorbance at 490 nm. On linear graph paper, plot absorbance or optical density versus micrograms of mercury.

b. Treatment of samples: Samples containing 1.5 ml conc HNO_3/l do not usually affect the dithizone, although strong solutions of nitric acid will oxidize dithizone. Use a 500-ml sample to increase optical density readings, and prepare an absorbance blank consisting of all reagents. When necessary, filter the samples through glass wool into the separatory funnel after the oxidation step. Complete the procedure as described under ¶ 4*a* above. Read the mercury content from the calibration curve.

5. Calculation

Use the following equation for calculating the mercury concentration from the absorbance readings:

$$mg/l\,Hg = \frac{A_2 \times C}{A_1 \times S}$$

where A_1 = absorbance of the standard taken, A_2 = absorbance of sample, C = μg Hg in standard taken, and S = ml sample used.

6. Precision and Accuracy

Five portions of inorganic mercury and five portions of organic mercury as methyl mercuric chloride each yielded a 95% recovery. Two of the ten samples were spiked with bayou water.

7. Bibliography

SANDELL, E.B. 1959. Colorimetric Determination of Traces of Metals, 3rd. ed. Interscience Publishers, New York, N.Y., pp. 637-638.

316   NICKEL

Selection of method: The atomic absorption spectrophotometric method is the method of choice for all samples. The heptoxime or dimethylglyoxime method can be used where atomic absorption equipment is not available.

316 A.   Atomic Absorption Spectrophotometric Method

See Section 301A.II.

316 B.   Heptoxime Method (TENTATIVE)

I. Principle

After preliminary digestion with HNO_3-H_2SO_4 mixture, iron and copper are removed by extraction of the cupferrates with chloroform. The nickel is separated from other ions by extraction of the nickel heptoxime complex with chloroform, reextracted into the aqueous phase with hydrochloric acid, and determined colorimetrically in the acidic solution with heptoxime in the presence of an oxidant.

2. Apparatus

a. Colorimetric equipment: One of the following is required:

1) *Spectrophotometer,* for use at 445 nm, providing a light path of 1 cm or longer.

2) *Filter photometer,* providing a light path of 1 cm or longer and equipped with a violet filter with maximum transmittance near 445 nm.

b. Separatory funnels, 125-ml, Squibb form, with ground-glass stoppers.

3. Reagents

a. Standard nickel sulfate solution: Dissolve 447.9 mg $NiSO_4$•$6H_2O$ in 1,000 ml distilled water; 1.00 ml=100 μg Ni.

b. Hydrochloric acid, HCl, 1.0N.

c. Bromine water: Saturate distilled water with bromine.

d. Ammonium hydroxide, NH_4OH, conc.

e. Heptoxime reagent: Dissolve 0.1 g 1,2-cycloheptanedionedioxime* (hep-

---

* Hach Chemical Company, Ames, Iowa, or equivalent.

toxime) in 100 ml 95% ethyl alcohol.

f. Ethyl alcohol, 95%.

g. Sodium tartrate solution: Dissolve 10 g $Na_2C_4H_4O_6$•$2H_2O$ in 90 ml distilled water.

h. Methyl orange indicator solution.

i. Sodium hydroxide, 6N.

j. Acetic acid, conc.

k. Cupferron solution: Dissolve 1 g cupferron in 100 ml distilled water. Store in a refrigerator or make up fresh for each series of determinations.

l. Chloroform, $CHCl_3$.

m. Hydroxylamine-hydrochloride solution: Dissolve 10 g NH_2OH•HCl in 90 ml distilled water. Make up daily.

4. Procedure

a. Preparation of calibration curve: Pipet portions of the standard nickel sulfate solution into 100-ml volumetric flasks. The series should cover from 50 to 250 μg Ni if 1-cm cells are used. Add 25 ml 1.0N HCl and 5 ml bromine water. Cool with cold running tap water and add 10 ml conc NH_4OH. Immediately add 20 ml heptoxime reagent and 20 ml ethyl alcohol. Dilute to volume with distilled water and mix.

Measure absorbance at 445 nm 20 min after addition of the reagent, using a reagent blank as reference.

b. Treatment of sample:

1) Separation of copper and iron— Take a portion of the original sample, prepared by digesting with HNO_3-H_2SO_4 mixture as directed in Section 301 C.II5, containing from 50 to 250 μg Ni, place in a separatory funnel, and add 10 ml sodium tartrate solution, 2 drops (0.1 ml) methyl orange indicator,

and enough $6N$ NaOH to make the solution basic to the indicator.

Add 1 ml acetic acid and cool by placing the separatory funnel under cold running tap water. Add 4 ml fresh cupferron reagent and extract any precipitate formed with 10 ml CHCl₃. Let the layers separate and add more cupferron until a white silky precipitate forms, indicating that an excess of cupferron is present.

Shake the mixture, allow the layers to separate, and discard the CHCl₃ layer. Extract again with 10 ml CHCl₃ and discard the CHCl₃ layer. Add 1 ml fresh NH₂OH•HCl solution, mix, and let stand a few minutes.

2) Separation of nickel—Add 10 ml heptoxime reagent and extract the nickel complex with one 15-ml and then two 10-ml portions of CHCl₃. If the CHCl₃ layer in the third extraction is not colorless, continue extracting with CHCl₃ until it is. Collect the CHCl₃ layers in a separatory funnel. Extract the nickel from the CHCl₃ by shaking with 15 ml $1.0N$ HCl. Let the layers separate, draw off the CHCl₃ layer into another separatory funnel, rinse with 10 ml $1.0N$ HCl, and add to the 15-ml portion of HCl.

Determine the absorbance of the solution as directed in ¶ 4a.

5. Calculation

$$\text{mg/l Ni} = \frac{\mu\text{g Ni}}{\text{ml sample}} \times \frac{100}{\text{ml portion}}$$

316 C.   Dimethylglyoxime Method

Dimethylglyoxime may be used instead of heptoxime to develop the color with nickel. The conditions of color formation are identical, but separate curves must be prepared. The rate of color development is slightly different for the two reagents so that, with dimethylglyoxime, readings are taken exactly 10 min after addition of the reagent, whereas, with heptoxime, readings are taken exactly 20 min after addition of the reagent. Both systems are measured at 445 nm. The heptoxime system is more stable. Dimethylglyoxime cannot be substituted for heptoxime in the extraction process, Section 316B.4b2), under the conditions prescribed.

The calculation is the same as in the heptoxime method preceding.

316 D.   Bibliography

BUTTS, P.G., A.R. GAHLER & M.G. MELLON. 1950. Colorimetric determination of metals in sewage and industrial wastes. *Sewage Ind. Wastes* 22: 1543.

FERGUSON, R.C. & C.V. BANKS. 1951. Spectrophotometric determination of nickel using 1,2-cycloheptanedionedioxime (heptoxime). *Anal. Chem.* 23: 448, 1486.

SERFASS, E.J. & R.F. MURACA. 1954. Procedures for Analyzing Metal Finishing Wastes. Ohio River Valley Water Sanitation Commission, Cincinnati, Ohio.

317   POTASSIUM

Potassium ranks seventh among the elements in order of abundance, yet its concentration in most drinking waters seldom reaches 20 mg/l. However, occasional brines may contain more than 100 mg/l potassium.

1. Selection of Method

Two methods for the determination of potassium are given. The flame photometric method (A) is more rapid, sensitive, and accurate but requires a special instrument and much preliminary work before samples can be run routinely. It is the recommended method. The colorimetric method (B) is usually inadvisable for potassium levels below 10 mg/l because the determination would then entail more than a tenfold concentration of the sample by evaporation.

2. Storage of Sample

Do not store samples in soft-glass bottles because of the possibility of contamination from leaching of the glass. Use polyethylene or pyrex bottles.

317 A.   Flame Photometric Method

1. General Discussion

a. Principle: Trace amounts of potassium can be determined in either a direct-reading or internal-standard type of flame photometer at a wavelength of 768 nm. The principles, applications, and interferences are described in Section 320A. Because much of the information pertaining to sodium applies equally to the potassium determination, carefully study the entire discussion dealing with the flame photometric determination of sodium (Section 320A) before making a potassium determination.

b. Interference: Remove burner-clogging particulate matter from the sample by filtration through a quantitative filter paper of medium retentiveness. Inclusion of a nonionic detergent into the lithium standard may assure proper aspirator function. Interference in the internal-standard method may occur at sodium-to-potassium ratios of 5:1 or greater. Calcium may interfere if the calcium-to-potassium ratio is 10:1 or more. Magnesium begins to interfere when the magnesium-to-potassium ratio exceeds 100.

c. Minimum detectable concentration: Potassium levels of approximately 0.1 mg/l can be determined in the better flame photometers.

2. Apparatus

See Sodium, Section 320A.2.

3. Reagents

To minimize potassium pickup, store all solutions in plastic bottles. Use small containers to reduce the amount of dry element that may be picked up from the bottle walls when the solution is

c. Centrifuge for 12- or 15-ml tubes (optional).

3. Reagents

a. Stock selenium solution: Place an accurately weighed pellet of ACS-grade metallic selenium into a small beaker. Add 5 ml conc HNO₃. Warm until the reaction is complete and cautiously evaporate just to dryness. Dilute to 1,000 ml with distilled water.

b. Standard selenium solution: Dilute an appropriate volume of stock selenium solution with distilled water; 1.00 ml = 1.00 μg Se.

c. Methyl orange indicator solution.

d. Hydrochloric acid, HCl, 0.1 N.

e. Calcium chloride solution: Dissolve 30 g CaCl₂·2H₂O in distilled water and dilute to 1 l.

f. Potassium permanganate, 0.1N: Dissolve 3.2 g KMnO₄ in 1,000 ml distilled water.

g. Sodium hydroxide, NaOH, 0.1 N.

h. Hydrochloric acid, HCl, conc.

i. Ammonium chloride solution: Dissolve 250 g NH₄Cl in 1 l distilled water.

j. EDTA-sulfate reagent: Dissolve 100 g disodium ethylenediamine tetraacetate dihydrate, also called (ethylenedinitrilo) tetraacetic acid disodium salt, and 200 g sodium sulfate in 1 l distilled water. Add conc NH₄OH dropwise while stirring until the dissolution is complete.

k. Ammonium hydroxide, NH₄OH, 5N: 1+2.

l. Diaminobenzidine solution: Dissolve 100 mg 3,3'-diaminobenzidine hydrochloride in 10 ml distilled water. Prepare no more than 8 hr before use because this solution is unstable. (Cau-

TION—*Handle this reagent with extreme care.*)

m. Toluene.

n. Sodium sulfate, Na₂SO₄, anhydrous: Required if no centrifuge is available.

4. Procedure

a. Oxidation to selenate: Prepare standards containing 0, 10.0, 25.0, and 50.0 μg Se in 500-ml erlenmeyer flasks. Dilute to approximately 250 ml, add 10 drops methyl orange indicator solution, 2 ml 0.1N HCl, 5 ml CaCl₂ solution, 3 drops 0.1N KMnO₄, and a 5-ml measure of glass beads to prevent bumping. Boil vigorously for approximately 5 min.

To a 1,000-ml sample in a 2-l beaker add 10 drops methyl orange indicator solution. Titrate to the methyl orange end point with 0.1N HCl and add 2 ml excess. Add 3 drops KMnO₄, 5 ml CaCl₂ solution, and a 5-ml measure of glass beads to prevent bumping. Heat to boiling, adding KMnO₄ as required to maintain a purple tint. Ignore a precipitate of MnO₂ because it will have no adverse effect. Reduce the volume to approximately 250 ml and transfer quantitatively to a 500-ml erlenmeyer flask.

b. Evaporation: Add 5 ml 0.1N NaOH to each flask and evaporate to dryness. Avoid prolonged heating of the residue.

c. Reduction to selenite: Cool the flask, add 5 ml conc HCl and 10 ml NH₄Cl solution. Heat in a boiling water bath or steam bath for 10±0.5 min.

d. Formation of piazselenol: Transfer the warm solution and ammonium chloride precipitate, if present, to a beaker and wash the flask with 5 ml EDTA-sulfate reagent and 5 ml 5N NH$_4$OH. Adjust the pH to 1.5±0.3 with NH$_4$OH, using a pH meter. The precipitate of EDTA will not interfere. Add 1 ml diaminobenzidine solution and heat in a boiling water bath or steam bath for approximately 5 min.

e. Extraction of piazselenol: Cool and then add NH$_4$OH to adjust the pH to 8±1; the precipitate of EDTA will dissolve. Pour the sample into a 50-ml graduate and adjust the volume to 50±1 ml with washings from the beaker. Pour the contents of the graduate into a 250-ml separatory funnel. Add 10 ml toluene and shake for 30±5 sec. Discard the aqueous layer and transfer the organic phase to a 12- or 15-ml centrifuge tube. Centrifuge briefly to clear the toluene of water droplets. If a centrifuge is not available, filter the organic phase through a dry filter paper to which approximately 0.1 g anhydrous Na$_2$SO$_4$ has been added.

f. Determination of absorbance: Read the absorbance at approximately 420 nm, using toluene to establish zero absorbance. The piazselenol color is stable but evaporation of toluene concentrates the color to a marked degree in a few hours. Beer's law is obeyed up to 50 μg.

5. Calculation

$$mg/l\ Se\ =\ \frac{\mu g\ Se}{ml\ sample}$$

6. Precision and Accuracy

A synthetic unknown sample containing 20 μg/l Se, 40 μg/l As, 250 μg/l Be, 240 μg/l B, and 6 μg/l V in distilled water was analyzed in 35 laboratories by the diaminobenzidine method, with a relative standard deviation of 21.2% and a relative error of 5.0%.

318 B.   Distillation and Diaminobenzidine Method

1. General Discussion

a. Principle: Selenium is quantitatively separated from most other elements by distillation of the volatile tetrabromide from an acid solution containing bromine. The bromine is generated by the reaction of bromide with hydrogen peroxide in order to avoid the inconvenience of handling the element. Selenium tetrabromide, along with a minimum of excess bromine, is absorbed in water. The excess bromine is removed by precipitation as tribromophenol and the quadrivalent selenium is determined with diaminobenzidine as in Method A.

b. Interference: No substances are known to interfere.

c. Minimum detectable quantity: 1 μg Se with a 4-cm light path.

2. Apparatus

All of the apparatus in Section 318 A.2a-c plus:

Distillation assembly, all-pyrex, for use with 500-ml erlenmeyer flasks with interchangeable ground-glass necks.

Figure 318:1 shows another suitable apparatus.

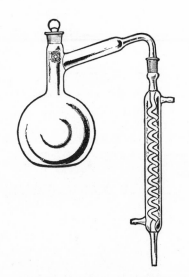

Figure 318:1. Distillation apparatus for ammonia, phenol, selenium, and fluoride determinations.

3. Reagents

All the reagents described in Section 318A.3 are needed except reagents b through k. The following are also required:

a. Potassium bromide-acid reagent: Dissolve 10 g KBr in 25 ml distilled water. Cautiously add 25 ml conc H_2SO_4, mixing and cooling under tap water as each increment of acid is added. Prepare immediately before use, because $KHSO_4$ will precipitate on cooling. Reheating to dissolve this salt will drive off some HBr.

b. Hydrogen peroxide, H_2O_2, 30%.

c. Phenol solution: Dissolve 5 g phenol in 100 ml distilled water.

d. Ammonium hydroxide, NH_4OH, conc.

e. Hydrochloric acid, HCl, 1 + 1.

4. Procedure

a. Oxidation to selenate: Proceed as in Section 318A.4a, but use glass-stoppered erlenmeyer flasks.

b. Evaporation: Add 5 ml 0.1N NaOH to each flask and evaporate to dryness. Avoid prolonged heating of the residue.

c. Distillation: Add 50 ml KBr-H_2SO_4 reagent to the cool flask. Add 1 ml 30% H_2O_2 and immediately fit the flask to the condenser. Distill under the fume hood until the color of bromine is gone from the flask. Use as a receiver a beaker suitable for use in subsequent pH adjustment and containing just enough distilled water to immerse the tip of the condenser. Wash the small amount of distillate remaining in the condenser into the beaker with 5 ml distilled water.

d. Formation of piazselenol: Add phenol solution dropwise until the color of bromine is discharged. A white precipitate of tribromophenol will form, but a small proportion of the yellow tetrabromophenol causes no trouble. Adjust the pH to 1.5±0.3 using conc NH_4OH and 1+1 HCl. Add 1 ml diaminobenzidine solution and heat in a boiling water bath or steam bath for approximately 5 min.

e. Extraction of piazselenol: Cool and then add conc NH_4OH to adjust the pH to 8±1. Pour the sample into a 50-ml graduate, and adjust the volume to 50±1 ml with washings from the beaker. Pour the contents of the graduate into a 250-ml separatory funnel. Add 10 ml toluene and shake for 30±5 sec. Discard the aqueous layer and transfer the organic phase to a 12- or 15-ml centrifuge tube. Centrifuge briefly to clear the toluene of water droplets. If a centrifuge is not available, filter the organic phase through a dry filter paper to which approximately 100 mg anhydrous Na_2SO_4 have been added.

f. Determination of absorbance: Read the absorbance at approximately 420 nm, using toluene to establish zero absorbance. Make the absorbance readings

within 2 hr after extraction because the phenol used in ¶4*d* above causes the yellow piazselenol color slowly to acquire a greenish tint.

5. Calculation

See Section 318A.5.

6. Precision and Accuracy

See Section 318A.6.

318 C.   Atomic Absorption Spectrophotometric Method

See Section 301A.VII.

318 D.   Bibliography

HOSTE, J. & J. GILLIS. 1955. Spectrophotometric determination of traces of selenium with 3,3'-diaminobenzidine. *Anal. Chem. Acta* 12:158.

CHENG, K. 1956. Determination of traces of selenium. *Anal. Chem.* 28:1738.

MAGIN, G.B. et al. 1960. Suggested modified method for colorimetric determination of selenium in natural water. *J. Amer. Water Works Ass.* 52:1199.

ROSSUM, J.R. & P.A. VILLARRUZ. 1962. Suggested methods for determining selenium in water. *J. Amer. Water Works Ass.* 54:746.

319   SILVER

Silver can cause argyria, a permanent, blue-gray discoloration of the skin and eyes that imparts a ghostly appearance. Concentrations in the range of 0.4 to 1 mg/l have caused pathologic changes in the kidneys, liver, and spleen of rats. The silver concentration of U.S. drinking waters has been reported to vary between 0 and 2 μg/l with a mean of 0.13 μg/l. Relatively small quantities of silver are bactericidal or bacteriostatic

and find limited use for the disinfection of swimming pool waters.

1. Selection of Method

The atomic absorption spectrophotometric method is preferred. The dithizone method is useful in the absence of sophisticated instrumentation. The spectrographic method also may be used.

2. Sampling and Storage

Acidify all samples at the time of collection to keep the metals in solution and prevent their plating out on the container wall. With relatively clean waters containing no particulate matter, 1.5 ml conc HNO_3/l of sample will be sufficient to lower the pH to 2.0. Surface waters, such as those from streams, lakes, and wastewater treatment plant effluents, which may contain sediment, will require more acid. If the sample does contain particulate matter and only the "dissolved" metal content is to be determined, filter the sample through a 0.45-μm membrane filter. After filtration, acidify the filtrate with 1.5 ml conc HNO_3/l.

319 A.　Atomic Absorption Spectrophotometric Method

See Section 301A.II.

319 B.　Dithizone Method

1. General Discussion

a. Principle: Twenty metals can react with dithizone to produce colored coordination compounds. Under the proper conditions or upon the removal of all interferences, the reaction can be made selective for a desired substance. In this mixed-color method, a separation of the two colors is not attempted; either the green color of the dithizone or the yellow color of the silver dithizonate can be measured. In view of the sensitivity of the reaction and the numerous interferences among the common metals, the method is somewhat empirical and demands careful adherence to the procedure. The final color evaluation can be made visually or photometrically. The visual finish has been found as accurate as, and more efficient than, the photometric measurement because it circumvents the extra handling involved with a photometer. The use of cells having a volume greater than 1 ml requires final dilution with carbon tetrachloride or the selection of a larger sample.

b. Interference: Ferric ion, residual chlorine, and other oxidizing agents convert dithizone to a yellow-brown color. However, extraction of the silver along with other metals in a carbon tetrachloride solution of dithizone overcomes such oxidation interference. The silver is then removed selectively from the other carry-over metals by the use of an ammonium thiocyanate solution. The extreme sensitivity of the method, as well as silver's affinity for being adsorbed, makes it desirable to prepare and segregate glassware for this determination and to take unusual precautions at every step in the procedure. The necessity for checking and preventing contamination at all points cannot be overemphasized.

Dithizone and silver dithizonate both decompose rapidly in strong light; therefore, do not leave them in the light beam of the photometer for a longer period than is necessary. Avoid direct sunlight at all times.

c. Minimum detectable quantity: 0.2 μg Ag.

2. Apparatus

a. Colorimetric equipment: One of the following is required:

1) *Spectrophotometer* for measurements at either 620 nm or 462 nm, and providing a light path of 1 cm.

2) *Filter photometer* providing a light path of 1 cm and equipped with a red filter having maximum transmittance at or near 620 nm or a blue filter having maximum transmittance at or near 460 nm.

3) *Micro test tubes,* 10-ml capacity, 1×7.5-cm size.

b. Separatory funnels, with a capacity of 500 ml or larger, and also funnels with a capacity of 60 ml, preferably with inert teflon stopcocks.

c. Glassware: Treat all glassware, dishes, and crucibles with a sulfuric-chromic acid mixture and wash in 1+1 HNO$_3$ to dissolve any trace of chromium or silver adsorbed on the glassware. Thoroughly rinse with silver-free water and apply "Desicote"* or a similar silicone coating fluid to establish a repellent surface. Omission of these extremely important steps will result in serious errors. Glassware can be dried in an oven. Avoid acetone rinses because this solvent frequently contains enough interferences to affect the determination.

d. Vycor dishes or silica crucibles.

3. Reagents

a. Silver-free water: Use redistilled or deionized distilled water for the preparation of all reagents and dilutions.

b. Sulfuric acid, H$_2$SO$_4$, conc.

c. Carbon tetrachloride CCl$_4$, Store in a glass container and do not allow contact with any metals before use. If this reagent contains traces of an interfering metal, redistill in an all-pyrex apparatus.

d. Stock dithizone solution: Dissolve without heating 100 mg diphenylthiocarbazone† in 100 ml CCl$_4$ in a separatory funnel. Free the solution from copper as follows. To the solution contained in the separatory funnel, add 100 ml silver-free water and 5 ml conc NH$_4$OH and shake vigorously. Discard the CCl$_4$ layer and wash the alkaline liquid with two 5-ml portions CCl$_4$. Add 200 ml CCl$_4$ and then 1+1 hydrochloric acid in small portions until the aqueous layer is colorless after being shaken. Remove the CCl$_4$ layer and store in the dark in a brown glass bottle. This solution contains 0.5 mg dithizone/ml.

e. Dithizone solution I: Dilute 50 ml stock dithizone solution to 500 ml with CCl$_4$ and store in the dark in a brown glass bottle. This solution contains 50 μg dithizone/ml.

f. Dithizone solution II: Dilute 2.00 ml dithizone solution I to 250.0 ml with CCl$_4$. Store in the dark in a brown glass bottle. This solution contains 0.4 μg dithizone/ml.

g. Ammonium thiocyanate reagent: Dissolve 10 g NH$_4$CNS in silver-free water to which 5 ml conc H$_2$SO$_4$ have been added and dilute to 500 ml with silver-free water. Store this solution in a

---

* Beckman Instruments, Inc.

† Eastman No. 3092 or equivalent.

bottle containing 25 ml dithizone solution I.

h. Nitric acid, HNO₃, 1 N.

i. Urea solution: Dissolve 10 g (NH₂)₂CO in silver-free water and dilute to 100 ml. Store in a bottle containing 25 ml dithizone solution I. Discard the solution upon the formation of a red film, which makes the pipeting of a clear solution impossible.

j. Hydroxylamine sulfate solution: Dissolve 20 g (NH₂OH)₂•H₂SO₄ in silver-free water and dilute to 100 ml. Store in a bottle containing 25 ml dithizone solution I.

k. Sulfuric acid, H₂SO₄, 1N.

l. Stock silver solution: Dissolve 157.4 mg anhydrous silver nitrate, AgNO₃, in silver-free water to which 14 ml conc H₂SO₄ have been added and dilute to 1,000 ml with silver-free water; 1.00 ml = 100 µg Ag.

m. Standard silver solution: Immediately before use, dilute 10.00 ml stock solution to 1,000 ml with silver-free water; 1.00 ml = 1.00 µg Ag.

4. Procedure

a. Pretreatment of sample: If organic matter is present and total silver is to be determined, digest the sample with nitric and sulfuric acid as directed in Section 301C.II5. If only dissolved silver is to be determined, filter sample through a 0.45-µm membrane filter.

b. Preliminary extraction. To 100 ml sample in a 500-ml separatory funnel add 11 ml conc H₂SO₄. Extract the silver by adding 5 ml dithizone solution I and shaking for 1 min. Collect the organic phase and any scum in a 25-ml centrifuge tube. Transfer the scum formed to the centrifuge tube because it

may contain an appreciable amount of silver. Repeat the extraction twice more with 5-ml portions of dithizone solution I and add the extracts and scum to the centrifuge tube. Reject the aqueous phase. If a larger sample is required, use two centrifuge tubes to collect the dithizone extracts. For a 500-ml sample, use at least two 5-ml portions dithizone solution I. Centrifuge, discard the aqueous phase, and add 2 ml silver-free water. Recentrifuge and discard the aqueous phase. Transfer the silver dithizonite layer to a 60-ml separatory funnel. Add 4 ml ammonium thiocyanate reagent to the centrifuge tube to collect any remaining extract, gently agitate, and transfer quantitatively to the separatory funnel. Shake for 1 min and with a suction pipet transfer as much of the aqueous phase as possible to a Vycor dish. Repeat the addition of 4 ml ammonium thiocyanate reagent, gently agitate, and transfer the aqueous phase two more times. Run off the organic layer and add the last few drops of the aqueous phase to the dish. Add 1.5 ml conc H₂SO₄ and evaporate to dryness by first evaporating to fumes by heating from above with an infrared lamp and then by heating the sample from below with a hot plate and above with an infrared lamp. Keep the heating temperature low enough to prevent bumping. Add 0.6 ml 1N HNO₃ and warm to dissolve all the solid residue. Add 1 ml each of urea and hydroxylamine sulfate solutions and digest for 5 min near the boiling point, adding silver-free water dropwise to prevent caking. Let cool to room temperature. Transfer the solution to a 10-ml micro test tube, rinsing the Vycor dish twice with 2-ml portions 1N H₂SO₄.

c. Extraction of silver: Add 1 ml dithizone solution II and extract the silver by mixing for 2 min with the aid of a thin glass rod flattened at the bottom. If the organic phase has a greenish hue, the amount of silver is less than 1.5 μg. If the organic phase is a clear yellow (showing that there is no excess of dithizone), add further 1-ml portions dithizone solution II and repeat the extraction until a mixed color is obtained. Record the total volume, *A*, of dithizone solution II used.

d. Visual colorimetric estimation: Prepare standards by placing in each of the nine micro test tubes 1 ml dithizone solution II and then 0, 0.20 . . . 1.60 ml standard silver solution, and 3.0, 2.8 . . . 1.4 ml 1*N* H_2SO_4. Extract the silver as described in ¶ *4d* above, starting with the solution of lowest concentration.

e. Photometric measurement: Prepare a standard curve by adding known amounts of silver in the range 0.20 to 1.50 μg to 0.3 ml 1*N* HNO_3, and 1 ml each of urea and hydroxylamine sulfate solutions. Add 1 ml dithizone solution II and extract the silver, using the same method as with the samples. Measure the absorbance at or near 620 nm, using special cells of 1-cm light path but of reduced width so as to contain, when full, no more than about 1 ml. Zero the spectrophotometer on a cell containing dithizone solution II at an absorbance reading of 1.0 (or 10% transmittance) and read the samples and standards against this setting. Because the samples and standards will give a lesser absorbance reading, plot the difference between the constant absorbance of 1.0 for the dithizone and the absorbance readings for each standard and sample in order to obtain a positive-sloping standard curve.

f. Subtract the blank value obtained by carrying 100 ml silver-free water through the entire process.

5. Calculation

$$\text{mg/l Ag} = \frac{\mu\text{g Ag}}{\text{ml sample}} \times A$$

where *A* = total volume of dithizone solution II used to extract the silver for the final colorimetric measurement.

6. Precision and Accuracy

A synthetic unknown sample containing 150 μg/l Ag, 500 μg/l Al, 50 μg/l Cd, 110 μg/l Cr, 470 μg/l Cu, 300 μg/l Fe, 70 μg/l Pb, 120 μg/l Mn, and 650 μg/l Zn in distilled water was analyzed in 14 laboratories by the dithizone method with a relative standard deviation of 61.0% and a relative error of 66.6%.

319 C.   Spectrographic Method (TENTATIVE)

1. General Discussion

a. Principle: A sample of potable water is diluted with lithium sulfate solution and a palladium solution is added as an internal standard. Standards are made by adding appropriate amounts of silver to a potable-water blank with less than 0.5 μg/l silver and diluting this with the lithium sulfate spectrobuffer solution and the palladium internal-standard solution. The diluted sample is evaporated in a glass beaker to dryness in a 150 C oven. The residue is scraped loose and crushed to homogeneity with a spatula, and a portion is transferred to a platform graphite electrode and arced to completion. Spectrogram densitometer readings are made on the Ag 3280.7 and the Pd 3242.7 line transmittances, and are converted to a ratio of line intensities from emulsion calibration data. The Ag/Pd intensity ratio is converted to micrograms Ag per liter from the standard working curve. The method is suitable for the determination of silver in the concentration range 10 to 500 μg/l.

b. Interference: No elements in the concentrations encountered in potable water interfere.

c. Minimum detectable concentration: 0.2 μg Ag. With a 20-ml sample this represents 10 μg/l Ag. The 20-ml Li_2SO_4 solution produces 114 mg residue at 150 C. A 20-ml sample for most potable waters produces about 7 mg residue or a 6% contribution to the matrix. If a sample with half the total residue is determined, 40 ml can be taken and 5 μg/l Ag can be determined. The upper concentration limit can be extended by diluting the sample appropriately with a low-silver (less than 0.5 μg/l Ag) potable-water blank, such as the water used to make up the standards.

2. Apparatus

Any commercially available spectrographic equipment meeting the following specifications is satisfactory:

a. Excitation: Excitation is provided by an ARL Multisource * Model No. 5700, or equivalent, adjusted to give a

fully rectified DC arc discharge, 13 amp at 300 V.

b. Spectrograph: The ARL 1.5-m grating spectrograph, or equivalent, with a reciprocal linear dispersion of 0.7 nm/ml over the 230- to 450-nm spectral range. For this method, use only the 320- to 330-nm region.

c. Electrode system: The lower sample electrode (anode) is a 6.35-mm-(1/4-in.-) diam, high-purity graphite preform, 30-degree angle platform with center post,† and the upper is a 6.35-mm-(1/4-in.-) diam (a slightly smaller diameter in the upper electrode may be preferable in instances of trouble caused by arc wandering), high-purity graphite preform with center post and 2.38-mm-(3/32-in.-) diam undercut. The analytical gap is maintained at 5 mm.

d. Recording equipment: Record the spectrum on Eastman SA No. 2 film or plates, or No. 1 film or plates, or equivalent.

e. Densitometer: Measure transmittance readings of spectral lines with the ARL No. 5400 film densitometer or equivalent.

f. Developing equipment: Develop films in a thermostatically controlled, rocking developing machine, wash in a film washer, and dry in a stream of warm air.

g. Calculating equipment: Use a sliding-scale calculating board to convert transmittance readings to intensity ratios based on film calibration data.

h. Beakers, 250-ml, tall electrolytic type, Corning No. 1140, or equivalent.

i. Balance, capable of weighing to 0.1 mg.

---

* Manufactured by Applied Research Labs., Glendale, Calif.

† United Carbon Products, Bay City, Mich., Nos. 104U and 104L, or National Carbon Co., New York, N.Y., Nos. L3948 and L3963.

3. Reagents

a. Palladium internal-standard solution: Dissolve 66.7 mg palladium chloride, $PdCl_2$, in 10 ml $0.1N$ HCl by heating up to 60 C. Dilute with distilled water to 1,000 ml; 1,000 ml=40 mg Pd.

b. Lithium sulfate solution: Dissolve 5.5 g $Li_2SO_4 \cdot H_2O$ in 1 l distilled water. This solution contains 4.75 g/l Li_2SO_4 and yields a residue of 5.7 mg/ml at 150 C.

c. Cementing solution: Dissolve 39 g sucrose in 300 ml absolute methyl alcohol and 100 ml distilled water.

d. Stock silver solution: Dissolve 126.0 mg anhydrous silver nitrate, $AgNO_3$, in distilled water and dilute to 1,000 ml. This solution contains 80.0 mg/l Ag.

e. Standard silver solution: Dilute 5.00 ml stock silver solution to 1,000 ml with distilled water. Store overnight to allow the plating-out process to reach equilibrium. Discard this dilute solution and make again in the same flask just before using. 1.00 ml=0.40 μg Ag.

f. Low-silver potable-water blank: Use a potable water with about 250 to 450 mg/l total residue containing less than 0.5 μg/l Ag to make up the silver standards. Determine the silver concentration in the blank water by a semiquantitative spectrographic method. This range of total residue enables samples of potable water with approximately 150 to 800 mg/l total residue to be analyzed within 5% from the same standard working curve. When markedly different types of waters are to be analyzed, use a similar type of blank water to make the standard working curve.

4. Procedure

a. Preparation of sample for arcing: Take a sample containing 10 to 500 μg/l Ag and 150 to 800 mg/l total residue. See ¶s 1c and 3f for the analysis of other waters.

1) Determination of total residue—Determine total residue in 20.0 ml of sample either by weighing the residue on evaporation of 20 ml at 150 C or by multiplying its conductivity by 0.62×0.020. (Example: If the conductivity is 646 μsiemens, then $646 \times 0.62 \times 0.020 = 8.0$ mg total residue.)

2) Sample treatment and evaporation—Add 1.0 ml Pd internal-standard solution and 20 ml Li_2SO_4 solution to 20.0 ml sample in a 250-ml tall-type electrolytic beaker and evaporate to dryness in a 150 C oven. When the volume is down to about 5 to 10 ml, swirl the beaker slightly to redissolve the salts that have dried on its sides, thus concentrating the residue on the bottom.

3) Preparation of residue—Scrape the residue in the beaker loose from the glass and grind to a homogeneous powder against the side of the beaker with a small stainless steel spatula or a silver-free monel spatula.

4) Transfer of residue to electrode—Weigh a 5.0-mg sample of the ground residue, transfer to the sample electrode, add 3 drops of the cementing solution, and heat over a spirit lamp or small burner until caramelized (until further heating does not produce steam and the residue smells like caramel). Sometimes it is easier to transfer the residue to the electrode if the electrode is first wetted with 1 drop of cementing solution.

b. Preparation of standards for arc-

ing: Prepare exactly as the regular samples except that a standard sample is substituted for the 20.0 ml of sample to be analyzed [see ¶ 4*a*2)]. Make the standard samples by adding 0.50, 2.00, 8.00, and 25.0 ml, respectively, of the standard silver solution to each of four 20-ml aliquots of the low-silver potablewater blanks, corresponding respectively to 10, 40, 160, and 500 µg/l Ag.

c. Spectrograph operations: Properly adjust the electrode system and operate the spectrograph and its accessories according to the manufacturer's instructions. Treat the sample and standards in the same manner.

1) Excitation—Set the following arc discharge-circuit constants for Multisource (see ¶ 2*a*): voltage, 300 V; capacitance, 62 microfarads; inductance, 460 microhenries; resistance, 20 ohms (10+10); average current, 13 amp on short, 11 to 12 amp during run.

2) Exposure conditions—In the spectral region of 230 to 450 nm, use 320 to 330 nm. The slit width and length depend on the spectrograph and densitometer used; however, a 55-µm width has been found satisfactory. Burn the sample and standards to completion (until the platform is gone). Use filters or sectors to expose to background (7.5% of total light has proved satisfactory).

d. Photographic processing: Develop and fix the film as follows: emulsion, Eastman SA No. 2 or equivalent; developer, Eastman D-19 or equivalent, rocked 3 min at 20 C; stop bath, 50 ml conc (glacial) acetic acid diluted to 1 l, 10 sec; fixing, Eastman F-5 or equivalent, 3 min; washing, running water, 3 min; drying, blower and heater, 5 min.

e. Estimation of silver concentration: Read the transmittance of the spectral lines Ag 328.07 nm and Pd 324.27 nm with the film densitometer. Convert the transmittance readings to intensity ratios based on film calibration data. Convert the Ag/Pd intensity ratio to milligrams Ag per liter from the standard working curve.

f. Standard working curve: Plot mg Ag against the intensity ratio of Ag 328.07 to Pd 324.27 on log-log paper (2×2 cycles) with data from standard samples. Once the working curve is established, use it unless samples differ markedly (more than 100% in total residue) from the low-silver potable-water blank used to make up the standard samples.

5. Precision and Accuracy

Based on the fit of standard samples with the working curve and the precision of independent determinations, the accuracy of the method is estimated to be within about 10% of the true value.

319 D.   Bibliography

General

WEST, F. K., P. W. WEST & F. A. IDDINGS. 1966. Adsorption of traces of silver on container surfaces. *Anal. Chem.* 38:1566.

DYCK, W. 1968. Adsorption of silver on borosilicate glass. Effect of pH and time. *Anal. Chem.* 40:454.

Dithizone Method

PIERCE, T. B. 1960. Determination of trace quantities of silver in trade effluents. *Analyst* 85:166.

Spectrographic Method

HARVEY, C. E. 1947. A Method of Semiquantitative Spectrographic Analysis. Applied Research Laboratories, Glendale, Calif.

UMAN, G. A. 1963. Spectrochemical method for silver. *J. Amer. Water Works Ass.* 55:205.

320   SODIUM

Sodium ranks sixth among the elements in order of abundance; therefore, it is present in most natural waters. The levels may vary from negligible to appreciable. Relatively high concentrations may be found in brines and hard waters softened by the sodium exchange process. The ratio of sodium to total cations is important in agriculture and human pathology. Soil permeability has been harmed by a high sodium ratio. Persons afflicted with certain diseases require water with low sodium concentration. A limiting concentration of 2 to 3 mg/l is recommended in feedwaters destined for high-pressure boilers. When necessary, sodium is removed by the hydrogen-exchange process or by distillation.

1. Selection of Method

The flame photometric method (A) is more rapid and sensitive and generally more accurate than the gravimetric method, especially for sodium concentrations below 10 mg/l; but a special instrument and much preliminary work are required before samples can be run routinely. The gravimetric method (B) is used for potable water if a flame photometer is not available or if a check on the flame photometric result by an independent method is desired.

2. Storage of Sample

Store alkaline samples or samples containing low sodium concentrations in polyethylene bottles to eliminate the possibility of contamination of the sample due to leaching of the glass container. Solutions attack glass and consequently become contaminated with sodium.

320 A.   Flame Photometric Method

1. General Discussion

a. Principle: Trace amounts of sodium can be determined in either a direct-reading or an internal-standard-type flame photometer at a wavelength of 589 nm. The sample is sprayed into a gas flame and excitation is carried out under carefully controlled and reproducible conditions. The desired spectral line is isolated by the use of interference filters or by a suitable slit arrangement in light-dispersing devices such as prisms or gratings. The intensity of light is then measured by a phototube potentiometer or other appropriate circuit. The intensity of light at 589 nm is approximately proportional to the concentration of the element. The calibration curve may be linear but has a tendency to level off in the upper reaches. The optimum lithium concentration may vary among individual flame photometers operating on the internal-standard principle and therefore must be ascertained for the instrument used. If the alignment of the wavelength dial with the prism is not precise in the available photometer, the exact wavelength setting, which may be slightly more or less than 589 nm, can be determined from the maximum needle deflection and then used for the emission measurements.

b. Interference: Remove burner-clogging particulate matter from the sample by filtration through a quantitative filter paper of medium retentiveness. Incorporate a nonionic detergent in the lithium standard to assure proper aspirator function.

Interference can be minimized by the following approaches:

1) Operation in the lowest practical sodium range.

2) Use of the internal-standard or standard-addition technic.

3) Addition of radiation buffers.

4) Introduction of identical amounts of the same interfering substances into the calibration standards that are present in the sample.

5) Preparation of a family of calibration curves embodying added concentrations of a common interference.

6) Application of an experimentally determined correction in those instances where the sample contains a single important interference.

7) Removal of the interfering ions.

The standard-addition approach is described in the flame photometric method for strontium. Its use involves the addition of an identical portion of the sample of each standard and determination of the sample concentration by mathematical or graphical evaluation of the calibration data.

Potassium and calcium interfere with the sodium determination by the internal-standard method if the potassium-to-sodium ratio is $\geq 5:1$ and the calcium-to-sodium ratio is $\geq 10:1$. When these ratios are exceeded, measure the calcium and potassium first so that the approximate concentration of interfering ions may be added, if necessary, to the sodium calibration standards. Magnesium interference does not appear until the magnesium-to-sodium ratio exceeds 100, rare occurrence. Among the common anions capable of causing radiation interference are chloride, sulfate, and bicarbonate in relatively large amounts.

c. Minimum detectable concentration: The better flame photometers can be used to determine sodium levels approximating 100 $\mu g/l$. With proper modifications in technic the sodium level can be extended to 10 $\mu g/l$ or lower.

2. Apparatus

a. Flame photometer, either direct-reading or internal-standard type.

b. Glassware: Rinse all glassware with 1+15 nitric acid followed by several portions of deionized distilled water to avoid contamination errors.

3. Reagents

To minimize sodium pickup, store all solutions in plastic bottles. Use small containers to reduce the amount of dry element that may be picked up from the bottle walls when the solution is poured. Shake each container thoroughly to wash the accumulated salts from the walls before pouring solution.

a. Deionized distilled water: Use deionized distilled water for the preparation of all reagents and calibration standards, and as dilution water.

b. Stock sodium solution: Dissolve 2.542 g NaCl dried at 140 C and dilute to 1,000 ml with deionized distilled water; 1.00 ml = 1.00 mg Na.

c. Intermediate sodium solution: Dilute 10.00 ml stock sodium solution with deionized distilled water to 100.0 ml; 1.00 ml = 100 μg Na. Use this intermediate solution for preparing the calibration curve in the sodium range of 1 to 10 mg/l.

d. Standard sodium solution: Dilute 10.00 ml intermediate sodium solution with deionized distilled water to 100 ml; 1.00 ml = 10.0 μg Na. Use this solution for preparing the calibration curve in the sodium range of 0.1 to 1.0 mg/l.

e. Standard lithium solution: Use either lithium chloride (1) or lithium nitrate (2) for preparing the standard lithium solution containing 1.00 mg Li/ 1.00 ml.

1) Dry LiCl overnight in an oven at 105 C. Weigh rapidly 6.109 g, dissolve in deionized distilled water, and dilute to 1,000 ml.

2) Dry LiNO$_3$ overnight in an oven at 105 C. Weigh rapidly 9.935 g, dissolve in deionized distilled water, and dilute to 1,000 ml.

Prepare a new calibration curve whenever the standard lithium solution is changed. Where circumstances warrant, alternatively prepare a standard lithium solution containing 2.00 mg or even 5.00 mg Li/1.00 ml.

4. Procedure

a. Pretreatment of polluted water and wastewater samples: Follow the procedure described in Section 301 C.

b. Precautions: Locate the flame photometer in an area away from direct sunlight or the constant light emitted by an overhead fixture and free of drafts, dust, and tobacco smoke. Guard against contamination arising from corks, filter paper, perspiration, soap, cleansers, cleaning mixtures, and inadequately rinsed apparatus.

c. Instrument operation: Because of the differences between the makes and models of satisfactory flame photometers, it is impossible to formulate detailed instructions applicable to every instrument. Follow the manufacturer's recommendation for the selection of the proper photocell and wavelength, the adjustment of the slit width and sensitivity, the appropriate fuel and air or oxygen pressures, and the steps for warm-up, correcting for flame background, rinsing of the burner, igniting sample, and measuring emission intensity.

d. Direct-intensity measurement: Prepare a blank and sodium calibration standards in stepped amounts in any of the following applicable ranges: 0 to 1.0, 0 to 10, or 0 to 100 mg/l. Starting with the highest calibration standard and working toward the most dilute, measure the emission at 589 nm. Repeat the operation with both the calibration standards and the samples a sufficient number of times to secure a reliable average reading for each solution. Construct a calibration curve from the sodium standards. Determine the sodium concentration of the sample from the calibration curve. Where a large number of samples must be run routinely, use of the calibration curve provides sufficient accuracy. If greater precision and accuracy are desired and time is available, use the bracketing approach described in ¶ 4f below.

e. *Internal-standard measurement:* To a carefully measured volume of the sample (or a diluted portion), each sodium calibration standard, and a blank, add, with a volumetric pipet, an appropriate volume of standard lithium solution. Then follow all the steps prescribed in ¶ 4d above for the direct-intensity measurement.

f. *Bracketing approach:* From the calibration curve, select and prepare the sodium standards that immediately bracket the emission intensity of the sample. Determine the emission intensities of the bracketing standards (one sodium standard slightly less and the other slightly greater than the sample) and the sample as nearly simultaneously as possible. Repeat the determination on both the bracketing standards and the sample. Calculate the sodium concentration by the equation presented in ¶

5b, and average the findings for a final result.

5. Calculation

a. For direct reference to the calibration curve:

$$\text{mg/l Na} = (\text{mg/l Na in portion}) \times D$$

b. For the bracketing approach:

$$\text{mg/l Na} = \left(\frac{(B-A)(s-a)}{(b-a)} + A \right) D$$

in which:

B = mg/l Na in upper bracketing standard,
A = mg/l Na in lower bracketing standard,
b = emission intensity of the upper bracketing standard,
a = emission intensity of the lower bracketing standard,
s = emission intensity of the sample, and
D = dilution ratio
$= \dfrac{\text{ml sample} + \text{ml distilled water}}{\text{ml sample}}$

6. Precision and Accuracy

A synthetic unknown sample containing 19.9 mg/l Na, 108 mg/l Ca, 82 mg/l Mg, 3.1 mg/l K, 241 mg/l chloride, 0.25 mg/l nitrite N, 1.1 mg/l nitrate N, 259 mg/l sulfate, and 42.5 mg/l total alkalinity (contributed by $NaHCO_3$) was analyzed in 35 laboratories by the flame photometric method, with a relative standard deviation of 17.3% and a relative error of 4.0%.

320 B.   Gravimetric Method

1. General Discussion

a. Principle: Sodium is precipitated as sodium zinc uranyl acetate hexahydrate, $NaC_2H_3O_2 \cdot Zn(C_2H_3O_2)_2 \cdot 3UO_2(C_2H_3O_2)_2 \cdot 6H_2O$, by adding a large volume of zinc uranyl acetate reagent, previously saturated with the sodium salt, to a small volume of the concentrated sample. To precipitate sodium quantitatively, at least 10 ml of reagent must be added for every 1 ml of sample and the mixture must be allowed to stand for at least 60 min. Because the solubility of sodium zinc uranyl acetate hexahydrate in water is fairly great, the precipitate, after being collected in a filter crucible, is first washed with successive small portions of the reagent solution saturated with the triple salt and then with 95% ethyl alcohol, also saturated with the triple salt. Next, the precipitate is washed with diethyl ether to remove the alcohol, and finally a stream of air is drawn through the crucible to evaporate the ether. The precipitate is weighed in the air-dry state.

b. Interference: Lithium interferes by forming a slightly soluble salt with the reagent. Potassium interferes if there are more than 25 mg in the 1-ml solution being tested. Organic acids, such as oxalic, citric, and tartaric, interfere, as do anions such as phosphate that give precipitates with the reagent. Sulfate must be absent when much potassium is present because potassium sulfate is only slightly soluble in the reagent. If the potassium and sulfate concentrations are known, the maximum possible error due to the precipitation of K_2SO_4 can be calculated. Usually this error will be negligible because the potassium concentration in potable water is low and also because the calculation factor, 0.01495, for converting weight of sodium is very small. Upon evaporation of the sample, silica may become partially dehydrated and precipitate out. Except in extreme cases, the error caused by silica will be negligible because: (*a*) the precipitation of silica is not complete; (*b*) some of the dehydrated silica adheres strongly to the glass surface of the beaker and is not transferred to the crucible to be weighed with the sodium salt; (*c*) the high ratio of the weight of the triple salt to that of sodium and the slight increase in the weight of precipitate due to precipitated silica has a relatively small effect on the calculated sodium concentration. A method for compensation of errors caused by precipitation of uranyl phosphate and silica is described in the procedure.

2. Apparatus

a. Beakers, 20-ml, pyrex.

b. Fritted-glass crucibles, 30-ml, pyrex, of medium porosity; or porous porcelain crucibles.

c. Vacuum pump or aspirator, with manifold and individual petcocks.

3. Reagents

a. Zinc uranyl acetate reagent: Mix 2.7 ml conc (glacial) acetic acid with 100 ml distilled water. Add 10 g uranyl acetate dihydrate, $UO_2(C_2H_3O_2)_2 \cdot 2H_2O$, and 30 g zinc acetate dihydrate, $Zn(C_2H_3O_2)_2 \cdot 2H_2O$, and warm to dissolve. On cooling, add 2 to 3 mg NaCl, let stand for 24 hr or more, and filter off the precipitate of sodium zinc uranyl acetate, thus leaving the reagent saturated with the triple salt. Store in a pyrex bottle.

b. Ethyl alcohol wash solution: Saturate 95% ethyl alcohol with pure sodium zinc uranyl acetate and decant or filter the solution just before use. Prepare the sodium zinc uranyl acetate by adding 25 ml zinc uranyl acetate reagent to 2 ml sodium chloride solution (10 mg NaCl), stirring, collecting the precipitate in a sintered-glass crucible, and washing three times with conc acetic acid and finally three times with diethyl ether.

c. Diethyl ether.

4. Procedure

If necessary, remove any suspended matter from the potable water sample by filtration. Select a sample volume containing less than 8 mg Na and less than 25 mg K. Pipet the clear sample into a 20- or 50-ml pyrex beaker and evaporate to dryness on a steam or hot water bath. Cool the residue to room temperature, add 1.0 ml distilled water, and rub with a stirring rod. If the residue fails to dissolve, add more 1.0-ml increments of distilled water to dissolve it. Ignore a feathery turbidity of $CaSO_4$ because of its subsequent solubility in the zinc uranyl acetate reagent.

Treat with zinc uranyl acetate reagent in the ratio of 10 ml reagent for each 1.0-ml increment of distilled water required to dissolve the residue. Mix, cover the beaker, and let stand for 1 hr. Stir periodically to prevent the formation of a supersaturated solution. Collect the precipitate under suction in a weighed medium-porosity sintered-glass crucible. Substitute a porous-bottomed porcelain filtering crucible if desired. Drain the filter as dry as possible under suction. Wash the beaker, crucible, and precipitate five to eight times with 2-ml portions of zinc uranyl acetate reagent. Drain the crucible completely after the last wash to remove traces of the zinc uranyl acetate reagent. Wash five times with 2-ml portions of ethyl alcohol wash solution. Conclude the washing with three small portions of diethyl ether.

Continue suction for a few minutes until the diethyl ether is volatilized and the precipitate is dry. Wipe the outside and inner bottom ring of the crucible with a cloth if salts have crystallized there. Transfer the crucible to the balance case and weigh after 10 to 15 min, and again 10 min later to check on the constancy of the weight. Return the crucible to the suction apparatus and dissolve the sodium zinc uranyl acetate by passing 100 ml warm distilled water in small portions through the filter. Dry the crucible with ethyl alcohol wash solution and diethyl ether, as previously directed, and reweigh. The difference in the weight before and after the distilled water treatment represents the weight of the sodium zinc uranyl acetate.

5. Calculation

$$\text{mg/l Na} = \frac{A \times 14.95}{\text{ml sample}}$$

where A = mg triple-salt precipitate.

6. Precision and Accuracy

A synthetic unknown sample containing 19.9 mg/l Na, 108 mg/l Ca, 82 mg/l Mg, 3.1 mg/l K, 241 mg/l chloride, 0.25 mg/l nitrite N, 1.1 mg/l nitrate N, 259 mg/l sulfate, and 42.5 mg/l total alkalinity (contributed by

$NaHCO_3$) was analyzed in four laboratories by the gravimetric method, with a relative standard deviation of 11.3% and a relative error of 0.5%.

320 C. Bibliography

Flame Photometric Method

BARNES, R.B. et al. 1945. Flame photometry: A rapid analytical method. *Ind. Eng. Chem.*, Anal. Ed. 17:605.

BERRY J.W., D.G. CHAPPELL & R.B. BARNES. 1946. Improved method of flame photometry. *Ind. Eng. Chem.*, Anal. Ed. 18:19.

PARKS, T.D., H.O. JOHNSON & L. LYKKEN. 1948. Errors in the use of a model 18 Perkin-Elmer flame photometer for the determination of alkali metals. *Anal. Chem.* 20:822.

BILLS, C. E. et al. 1949. Reduction of error in flame photometry. *Anal. Chem.* 21:1076.

GILBERT, P.T., R.C. HAWES & A.O. BECKMAN. 1950. Beckman flame spectrophotometer. *Anal. Chem.* 22:772.

WEST, P.W., P. FOLSE & D. MONTGOMERY. 1950. Application of flame spectrophotometry to water analysis. *Anal. Chem.* 22:667.

FOX, C.L. 1951. Stable internal-standard flame photometer for potassium and sodium analyses. *Anal. Chem.* 23:137.

AMERICAN SOCIETY FOR TESTING AND MATERIALS. 1952. Symposium on flame photometry. Spec. Tech. Publ. 116, ASTM, Philadelphia, Pa.

COLLINS, C.G. & H. POLKINHORNE. 1952. An investigation of anionic interference in the determination of small quantities of potassium and sodium with a new flame photometer. *Analyst* 77:430.

WHITE, J.U. 1952. Precision of a simple flame photometer. *Anal. Chem.* 24:394.

MAVRODINEANU, R. 1956. Bibliography on analytical flame spectroscopy. *Appl. Spectrosc.* 10:51.

MELOCHE, V.W. 1956. Flame photometry. *Anal. Chem.* 28:1844.

BURRIEL-MARTI, F. & J. RAMIREZ-MUNOZ. 1957. Flame Photometry: A Manual of Methods and Applications. D. Van Nostrand Co., Princeton, N.J.

DEAN, J.A. 1960. Flame Photometry. McGraw-Hill Publishing Co., New York, N.Y.

Gravimetric Method

BARBER, H.H. & I.M. KOLTHOFF. 1928 and 1929. A specific reagent for the gravimetric determination of sodium. *J. Amer. Chem. Soc.* 50:1625; 51:3233.

KOLTHOFF, I.M., E.J. MEEHAN, E.B. SANDELL & S. BRUCKENSTEIN. 1969. Quantitative Chemical Analysis, 4th ed. Macmillan Co., New York, N.Y.

321   STRONTIUM

A typical alkaline-earth element, strontium chemically resembles calcium and causes a positive error in gravimetric and titrimetric methods for the determination of calcium. Because strontium has a tendency to accumulate in bone, radioactive strontium 90, with a half-life of 28 yr, presents a well-recognized peril to health. Naturally occurring strontium is not radioactive. For this reason, the determination of strontium in a water supply should be supplemented by a radiological measurement to exclude the possibility that the strontium content may originate from radioactive contamination (see Section 704).

Although most potable supplies contain little strontium, some well waters in the midwestern part of the United States have levels as high as 39 mg/l.

321 A.   Flame Photometric Method

1. General Discussion

a. Principle: The flame photometric method makes possible the determination of strontium in the small concentrations prevalent in natural water supplies. The strontium emission is measured at a wavelength of 460.7 nm. Because the background intensity at a wavelength of 454 nm equals that at 460.7 nm and is unaffected by the variable strontium concentration, the difference in readings obtained at these two wavelengths allows an estimate of the light intensity emitted by strontium.

b. Interference: The emission intensity is a linear function of the strontium concentration and the concentration of other constituents present. The standard addition technic distributes the same ions throughout the standards and the sample, thereby equalizing the radiation effect of possible interfering substances.

c. Minimum detectable concentration: Strontium levels of about 0.2 mg/l can be detected by the flame photometric method without prior concentration of the sample by evaporation.

d. Sampling and storage: Polyethylene bottles are preferable for sample storage, although pyrex containers also may be used. Make analyses as soon as possible after sample collection.

2. Apparatus

*Spectrophotometer,** equipped with photomultiplier tube and flame accessories.

3. Reagents

a. Stock strontium solution: Weigh into a 500-ml erlenmeyer flask 1.685 g anhydrous $SrCO_3$ powder. Place a funnel in the neck of the flask and add, a little at a time, 1+1 HCl until all the $SrCO_3$ has dissolved. Add 200 ml distilled water and boil for a few minutes to expel the CO_2. Cool, add a few drops of methyl red indicator, and adjust to the

---

* Beckman Model DU or equivalent.

intermediate orange color by adding $3N$ NH_4OH or $1+1$ HCl as required. Transfer quantitatively to a 1-l volumetric flask and dilute to the mark with distilled water; 1.00 ml=1.00 mg Sr.

b. Standard strontium solution: Dilute 25.00 ml stock strontium solution to 1,000 ml with distilled water; 1.00 ml=25.0 μg Sr. Use this solution for preparing Sr standards in the 1- to 25-mg/l range.

c. Nitric acid, HNO₃, conc.

4. Procedure

a. Pretreatment of polluted water and wastewater samples: Follow the procedure described in Section 301 C.I.

b. Preparation of strontium standards: Add 25.0 ml of sample containing less than 10 mg calcium or barium and less than 1 mg strontium to 25.0 ml of each of a series of strontium standards. Use a minimum of four strontium standards from 0 mg/l to a concentration exceeding that of the sample. For most natural waters 0, 2.0, 5.0, and 10.0 mg/l Sr standards are sufficient. Brines may require a strontium series containing 0, 25, 50, and 75 mg/l. Dilute the brine sufficiently to eliminate burner splatter and clogging. Best results are obtained when the strontium concentration of the sample is less than 100 mg/l.

c. Concentration of low-level strontium samples: Concentrate samples containing less than 2 mg/l Sr. Add 3 to 5 drops conc HNO₃ to 250 ml sample and evaporate to about 25 ml. Cool and make up to 50.0 ml with distilled water. Proceed as in ¶ *b* above. The HNO₃ concentration in the sample prepared for atomization can approach 0.2 ml/25 ml without producing interference.

d. Flame photometric measurement: Measure the emission intensity of the prepared samples (standards plus sample) at wavelengths of 460.7 and 454 nm. Follow the manufacturer's instructions for correct operation of the instrument.

5. Calculation

a. Plot the net intensity (reading at 460.7 nm minus reading at 454 nm) against the strontium concentration added to the sample. Because the plot forms a straight calibration line that intersects the ordinate, the unknown strontium concentration can be computed from the equation:

$$mg/l\ Sr\ =\ \frac{A-B}{C\ ||}\times\frac{D}{E}$$

where A=sample emission-intensity reading at 460.7 nm, B=background radiation reading at 454 nm, C=slope

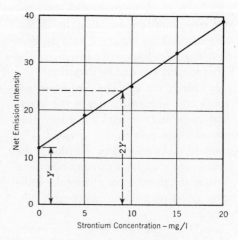

Figure 321:1. Graphical method of computing strontium concentration.

of calibration line. Use the ratio D/E only when E ml of sample are evaporated to form a concentrate of 25.0 ml, the value for D.

b. Graphical method: Strontium concentration also can be evaluated by the graphical method illustrated in Figure 321:1. Plot the net intensity against the strontium concentration added to the sample. The calibration line in the example intersects the ordinate at 12. Thus, $Y=12$ and $2Y=24$. Find the strontium concentration of the unknown sample by locating the abscissa value of the point on the calibration line having an ordinate value of 24. In the example, the strontium concentration is 9.0 mg/l.

c. Report a strontium concentration below 10 mg/l to the nearest 0.1 mg/l and one above 10 mg/l to the nearest whole number.

6. Accuracy

Strontium concentrations in the range 12.0 to 16.0 mg/l can be determined with an accuracy within ±1 to 2 mg/l.

321 B.   Bibliography

Chow, T. J. & T. G. Thompson. 1955. Flame photometric determination of strontium in sea water. *Anal. Chem.* 27:18.

Nichols, M. S. & D. R. McNall. 1957. Strontium content of Wisconsin municipal waters. *J. Amer. Water Works Ass.* 49:1493.

Horr, C. A. 1959. A survey of analytical methods for the determination of strontium in natural water. U.S. Geol. Surv. Water Supply Pap. No. 1496A.

322   VANADIUM

Laboratory and epidemiological evidence suggests that vanadium may play a beneficial role in the prevention of heart disease. In New Mexico, which has a low incidence of heart disease, vanadium has been found in concentrations of 20 to 150 μg/l. In a state where incidence of heart disease is high, vanadium was not found in the water supplies. However, vanadium pentoxide dust causes gastrointestinal and respiratory disturbances. The mean concentration found in U.S. drinking waters is 6 μg/l. Industrial applications of vanadium include dyeing, ceramics, ink, and catalyst manufacture. Discharges from such sources can contribute to its presence in a water supply.

Selection of method: Both the atomic absorption spectrophotometric method and the gallic acid method are suitable for potable water samples. The atomic absorption spectrophotometric method is preferable for polluted samples but may be used for potable water.

322 A.   Atomic Absorption Spectrophotometric Method

See Section 301A.IV.

322 B.   Gallic Acid Method

1. General Discussion

a. Principle: The concentration of trace amounts of vanadium in water is determined by measuring the catalytic effect it exerts on the rate of oxidation of gallic acid by persulfate in acid solution. Under the given conditions of concentrations of reactants, temperature, and reaction time, the extent of oxidation of gallic acid is proportional to the concentration of vanadium. Vanadium is determined by measuring the absorbance of the sample at 415 nm and comparing it with that of standard solutions treated identically.

b. Interference: The substances listed in Table 322:I will interfere in the determination of vanadium if the specified concentrations are exceeded. This is not a serious problem for chromium, cobalt, molybdenum, nickel, silver, and uranium because the tolerable concentration is greater than that commonly encountered in fresh water. However, in some samples the tolerable concentration of copper and iron may be exceeded. Because of the high sensitivity of the method, interfering substances in concentrations only slightly above tolerance limits can be rendered harmless by dilution.

Traces of bromide and iodide interfere seriously and dilution alone will not

TABLE 322:I. CONCENTRATION AT WHICH VARIOUS IONS INTERFERE IN THE DETERMINATION OF VANADIUM

Ion	Concentration *mg/l*
Chromium (VI)	1.0
Cobalt (II)	1.0
Copper (II)	0.05
Iron (II)	0.3
Iron (III)	0.5
Molybdenum (VI)	0.1
Nickel (II)	3.0
Silver	2.0
Uranium (VI)	3.0
Bromide	0.1
Chloride	100.0
Iodide	0.001

always reduce the concentration below tolerance limits. Mercuric ion may be added to complex these halides and minimize their interference; however, the mercuric ion itself interferes if in excess. The addition of 350 μg of mercuric nitrate per sample permits the determination of vanadium in the presence of up to 100 mg/l chloride ion and 250 $\mu g/l$ each of bromide and iodide. Samples containing high concentrations of these ions must be diluted below the above values and mercuric nitrate must be added.

c. Minimum detectable quantity: 0.025 μg.

2. Apparatus

a. *Water bath,* capable of temperature control to 25 ± 0.5 C.

b. *Colorimetric equipment:* One of the following is required:

1) *Spectrophotometer,* for measurements at 415 nm, with a light path of 1 to 5 cm.

2) *Filter photometer,* providing a light path of 1 to 5 cm and equipped with a violet filter exhibiting maximum transmittance near 415 nm.

3. Reagents

a. *Stock vanadium solution:* Dissolve 229.6 mg ammonium metavanadate, NH_4VO_3, in a volumetric flask containing approximately 800 ml distilled water and 15 ml of $1+1$ HNO_3. Dilute to the 1,000-ml mark; 1.00 ml = 100 μg V.

b. *Intermediate vanadium solution:* Dilute 10.00 ml stock vanadium solution with distilled water to 1,000 ml in a volumetric flask; 1.00 ml = 1.00 μg V.

c. *Standard vanadium solution:* Dilute 10.00 ml intermediate vanadium solution with distilled water to 1,000 ml in a volumetric flask; 1.00 ml = 0.010 μg V.

d. *Mercuric nitrate solution:* Dissolve 350 mg $Hg(NO_3)_2 \cdot H_2O$ in 1,000 ml distilled water.

e. *Ammonium persulfate-phosphoric acid reagent:* Dissolve 2.5 g $(NH_4)_2$-S_2O_8 in 25 ml distilled or demineralized water. Bring just to a boil, remove from heat, and add 25 ml conc H_3PO_4. Let stand approximately 24 hr before use. Discard after 48 hr.

f. *Gallic acid solution:* Dissolve 2 g $H_6C_7O_5$ in 100 ml warm distilled water, heat to a temperature just below boiling, and filter through Whatman No. 42 paper or equivalent. Prepare a fresh solution for each set of samples.

4. Procedure

a. *Preparation of standards and sample:* Prepare both blank and sufficient standards by diluting 0- to 8.0-ml portions (0- to 0.08- μg V) of the standard vanadium solution to 10 ml with distilled or demineralized water. Pipet sample (10.00 ml maximum) containing less than 0.08 μg V into a suitable container and adjust the volume to 10.0 ml with distilled or demineralized water. Decolorize or filter colored or turbid samples. Add 1.0 ml mercuric nitrate solution to each of the blanks, standards, and samples. Place the containers in a water bath regulated to 25 ± 0.5 C and allow 30 to 45 min for the samples to come to the temperature of the bath.

b. *Color development and measurement:* Add 1.0 ml ammonium persulfate-phosphoric acid reagent (temperature equilibrated), swirl to mix thoroughly, and return to the water bath. Add 1.0 ml gallic acid solution (temperature equilibrated), swirl to mix thoroughly, and return to the water bath. Add the gallic acid to successive samples at intervals of 30 sec or longer to permit accurate control of the reaction time. Exactly 60 min after addition of the gallic acid, remove the sample from the water bath and measure its absorbance at 415 nm, using distilled water as a reference. Subtract the absorbance of the blank from the absorbance of each standard and sample. Construct a calibration curve by plotting the absorbance values of standards versus micrograms of vanadium. Determine the amount of vanadium in a sample by referring to the corresponding absorbance on the calibration curve. Prepare a calibration curve with each set of samples.

5. Calculation

$$\text{mg/l V} = \frac{\mu\text{g V}}{\text{ml sample}}$$

6. Precision and Accuracy

In a synthetic unknown sample containing 6 μg/l V, 40 μg/l As, 250 μg/l Be, 240 μg/l B, and 20 μg/l Se in distilled water, vanadium was measured in 22 laboratories with a relative standard deviation of 20% and no relative error.

7. Bibliography

FISHMAN, M. J. & M. V. SKOUGSTAD. 1964. Catalytic determination of vanadium in water. *Anal. Chem.* 36:1643.

323 ZINC

Zinc is an essential and beneficial element in body growth. However, concentrations above 5 mg/l can cause a bitter astringent taste and an opalescence in alkaline waters. The zinc concentration of U.S. drinking waters varies between 0.06 and 7.0 mg/l, with a mean of 1.33 mg/l. Zinc most commonly enters the domestic water supply from the deterioration of galvanized iron and the dezincification of brass. In such cases the presence of lead and cadmium also may be suspected, because they are impurities of the zinc used in galvanizing. Zinc also may result from industrial waste pollution.

1. Selection of Method

Where the equipment is available, the atomic absorption spectrophotomet-ric method is preferred for the determination of zinc. The dithizone and zincon colorimetric methods are useful in the absence of the sophisticated instrumentation. Dithizone method I is intended for unpolluted waters, and II for polluted waters or wastewater.

2. Sampling and Storage

Analyze samples within 6 hr after collection. The addition of HCl will preserve the metallic ion content but requires that: (*a*) the acid be zinc-free; (*b*) the sample bottles be rinsed with acid before use; and (*c*) the samples be evaporated to dryness in silica dishes to remove the excess HCl before analysis.

323 A.   Atomic Absorption Spectrophotometric Method

See Section 301A.II.

323 ℞ Dithizone Method I

1. General Discussion

a. Principle: Nearly 20 metals are capable of reacting with diphenylthiocarbazone (dithizone) to produce colored coordination compounds. These dithizonates are extractable into organic solvents such as carbon tetrachloride. Most interferences in the zinc-dithizone reaction can be overcome by adjusting the solution to pH 4.0 to 5.5 and by the addition of sufficient sodium thiosulfate. Zinc also forms a weak thiosulfate complex that tends to retard the slow and incomplete reaction between zinc and dithizone. For this reason, the determination is empirical and demands the use of an identical technic in standard and sample analysis. The duration and vigor of shaking, the volumes of sample, sodium thiosulfate, and dithizone, and the pH should all be kept constant.

b. Interference: Interference from bismuth, cadmium, cobalt, copper, gold, lead, mercury, nickel, palladium, silver, and stannous tin in the small quantities found in potable waters is eliminated by complexing with sodium thiosulfate and by pH adjustment. Ferric iron, residual chlorine, and other oxidizing agents convert dithizone to a yellow-brown color. The zinc-dithizone reaction is extremely sensitive, and unusual precautions must be taken to avoid contamination. Experience has shown that high and erratic blanks are often traceable to glass containing zinc oxide, surface-contaminated glassware, rubber products, stopcock greases, reagent-grade chemicals, and distilled water. The extreme sensitivity of the reaction makes it desirable to prepare and segregate glassware especially for this determination and to extract reagents with dithizone solution to remove all traces of zinc and contaminating metals. Dithizone and dithizonates decompose rapidly in strong light. Perform analyses in subdued light and do not expose the solutions to the light of the photometer for a longer period than is necessary. Avoid direct sunlight at all times.

c. Minimum detectable quantity: 1 μg Zn.

2. Apparatus

a. Colorimetric equipment: Use one of the following, although it is also possible to make visual comparisons directly in separatory funnels:

1) *Spectrophotometer,* for use at either 535 or 620 nm, providing a light path of 2 cm.

2) *Filter photometer,* providing a light path of 2 cm and equipped with either a green filter having maximum transmittance near 535 nm or a red filter having maximum transmittance near 620 nm.

3) *Nessler tubes,* matched.

b. Separatory funnels, capacity 125 to 150 ml, Squibb form, preferably with inert teflon stopcocks. If the funnels are of identical size and shape, visual color comparisons may be made directly in them.

c. Glassware: Rinse all glassware with 1 + 1 HNO_3 and zinc-free water.

d. pH meter.

3. Reagents

a. Zinc-free water: Use redistilled or deionized distilled water for rinsing apparatus and the preparation of solutions and dilutions.

b. Stock zinc solution: Dissolve 100.0 mg 30-mesh zinc metal in a slight excess of 1+1 HCl; about 1 ml is required. Dilute to 1,000 ml with zinc-free water; 1.00 ml = 100 μg Zn.

c. Standard zinc solution: Dilute 10.00 ml zinc stock solution to 1,000 ml with zinc-free water; 1.00 ml = 1.00 μg Zn.

d. Hydrochloric acid, HCl, 0.02N: Dilute 1.0 ml conc HCl to 600 ml with zinc-free water. If high blanks are traced to this reagent, dilute conc HCl with an equal volume of distilled water and redistill in an all-pyrex still.

e. Sodium acetate, 2N: Dissolve 68 g $NaC_2H_3O_2 \cdot 3H_2O$ and dilute to 250 ml with zinc-free water.

f. Acetic acid, 1+7. Use zinc-free water.

g. Acetate buffer solution: Mix equal volumes of 2N sodium acetate solution and 1+7 acetic acid solution. Extract with 10-ml portions of dithizone solution I until the last extract remains green; then extract with carbon tetrachloride to remove excess dithizone.

h. Sodium thiosulfate solution: Dissolve 25 g $Na_2S_2O_3 \cdot 5H_2O$ in 100 ml zinc-free water. Purify by dithizone extraction as in ¶ 3g above.

i. Dithizone solution I: Dissolve 100 mg diphenylthiocarbazone* in 1 l CCl_4. Store in a brown glass-stoppered bottle in a refrigerator. If the solution is of doubtful quality or has been stored for a long time, test for deterioration as follows: Shake 10 ml with 10 ml 1+99 NH_4OH. If the lower, CCl_4, layer is

only slightly yellow, the reagent is in good condition.

j. Dithizone solution II: Dilute 1 volume of dithizone solution I with 9 volumes of CCl_4. If stored in a brown glass-stoppered bottle in a refrigerator, this solution is good for several weeks.

k. Carbon tetrachloride, CCl_4. CAUTION: Carbon tetrachloride is a toxic substance. Long-continued absorption of small amounts may be hazardous. While the solvent can be absorbed through the skin, the primary danger is through inhalation of the vapor. Prepare reagents and extract standards and samples with carbon tetrachloride in a well-ventilated hood.

l. Sodium citrate solution: Dissolve 10 g $Na_3C_6H_5O_7 \cdot 2H_2O$ in 90 ml zinc-free water. Purify by dithizone extraction as in ¶ 3g preceding. Use this reagent in the final cleansing of glassware.

4. Procedure

a. Preparation of colorimetric standards: To a series of 125-ml Squibb separatory funnels, thoroughly cleansed as described in ¶ 2c above, add 0, 1.00, 2.00, 3.00, 4.00, and 5.00 ml standard zinc solution equivalent, respectively, to provide 0, 1.00, 2.00, 3.00, 4.00, and 5.00 μg Zn. Bring each volume up to 10.0 ml by adding zinc-free water. To each funnel add 5.0 ml acetate buffer and 1.0 ml sodium thiosulfate solution, and mix. The pH should be between 4 and 5.5 at this point. To each funnel add 10.0 ml dithizone solution II, stopper, and shake vigorously for 4.0 min. Let the layers separate, dry the stem of the funnel with strips of filter paper, and run the lower (CCl_4) layer into a clean *dry* absorption cell.

---

* Eastman No. 3092 or equivalent.

b. Photometric measurement: Measure either the red color of the zinc dithizonate at 535 nm, or the green color of the unreacted dithizone at 620 nm.

Set the photometer at 100% transmittance with the blank if the 535-nm wavelength is selected. If 620 nm is used, set the blank at 10.0% transmittance. Plot a calibration curve. Run a new calibration curve with each set of samples.

c. Treatment of samples: If the zinc content is not within the working range, dilute the sample with zinc-free water or concentrate it in a silica dish. If the sample has been preserved with acid, evaporate a portion to dryness in a silica dish to remove the excess acid. Do not neutralize with sodium or ammonium hydroxide because these alkalis usually contain excessive amounts of zinc. Using a pH meter and accounting for any dilution, adjust the sample to pH 2 to 3 with HCl. Transfer 10.0 ml to a separatory funnel. Complete the analysis as described in ¶ 4*a*, beginning with the words "To each funnel add 5.0 ml acetate buffer" and continuing to the end of the paragraph.

d. Visual comparison: If a photometric instrument is not available, run the samples and standards at the same time. Compare the CCl4 layers directly in the separatory funnels if these match in size and shape; otherwise transfer to matched test tubes or nessler tubes. The range of colors obtained with various amounts of zinc are roughly these:

Zinc μg	Color
0 (blank)	green
1	blue
2	blue-violet
3	violet
4	red-violet
5	red-violet

5. Calculation

$$\text{mg/l Zn} = \frac{\mu g\ \text{Zn}}{\text{ml sample}}$$

6. Precision and Accuracy

A synthetic unknown sample containing 650 μg/l Zn, 500 μg/l Al, 50 μg/l Cd, 110 μg/l Cr, 470 μg/l Cu, 300 μg/l Fe, 70 μg/l Pb, 120 μg/l Mn, and 150 μg/l Ag in distilled water was analyzed in 46 laboratories by the dithizone method with a relative standard deviation of 18.2% and a relative error of 25.9%.

323 C.   Dithizone Method II

I. Principle

Zinc is separated from other metals by extraction with dithizone and is then determined by measuring the color of the zinc-dithizone complex in carbon tetrachloride. Specificity in the separation is achieved by extracting from a nearly neutral solution containing bis(2-hydroxyethyl)dithiocarbamyl ion and cyanide ion, which prevents moderate concentrations of cadmium, copper, lead, and nickel from reacting with dithizone. If excessive amounts of these metals are present, follow the special procedure given in ¶ 4*b*2) below.

The color reaction is extremely sensitive; avoid introducing extraneous zinc during the analysis. Contamination may arise from water, reagents, and glassware, such as beakers and separatory funnels, on which zinc has been adsorbed during previous use. Appreciable blanks are generally found and the analyst must satisfy himself that these blanks are representative and reproducible.

2. Apparatus

a. Colorimetric equipment: One of the following is required:

1) *Spectrophotometer*, for use at 535 nm, providing a light path of 1 cm or longer.

2) *Filter photometer*, providing a light path of 1 cm or longer and equipped with a greenish yellow filter with maximum transmittance near 535 nm.

b. Separatory funnels, 125-ml, Squibb form, with ground-glass stoppers.

3. Reagents

a. Standard zinc solution: Dissolve 1,000 g zinc metal in 10 ml 1+1 HNO_3. Dilute and boil to expel oxides of nitrogen. Transfer to a 1,000-ml volumetric flask and dilute to volume; 1.00 ml = 1.00 mg Zn.

b. Redistilled water: Distilled water redistilled in all-glass apparatus.

c. Methyl red indicator: Dissolve 0.1 g methyl red sodium salt and dilute to 100 ml with distilled water.

d. Sodium citrate solution: Dissolve 10 g $Na_3C_6H_5O_7 \cdot 2H_2O$ in 90 ml water. Shake with 10 ml dithizone solution I to remove zinc, then filter.

e. Ammonium hydroxide, NH_4OH, conc: Prepare according to directions in Section 305C.3*k*.

f. Potassium cyanide solution: Dissolve 5 g KCN in 95 ml redistilled water. (CAUTION: *Toxic—take care to avoid ingestion.*)

g. Acetic acid, conc.

h. Carbon tetrachloride, CCl_4, zinc-free. CAUTION: Carbon tetrachloride is a toxic substance. Long-continued absorption of small amounts may be hazardous. While the solvent can be absorbed through the skin, the primary danger is through inhalation of the vapor. Prepare reagents and extract standards and samples with carbon tetrachloride in a well-ventilated hood.

i. Bis (2-hydroxyethyl) dithiocarbamate solution: Dissolve 4.0 g diethanolamine and 1 ml CS_2 in 40 ml methyl alcohol. Prepare every 3 or 4 days.

j. Dithizone solution: Dilute 50 ml stock dithizone II solution (carbon tetrachloride), prepared in accordance with Section 301C.II4*b*, to 250 ml with CCl_4. Prepare fresh daily.

k. Sodium sulfide solution I: Dissolve 3.0 g $Na_2S \cdot 9H_2O$ or 1.65 g $Na_2S \cdot 3H_2O$ in 100 ml zinc-free water.

l. Sodium sulfide solution II: Prepare just before use by diluting 4 ml sodium sulfide solution I to 100 ml.

m. Nitric acid, HNO_3, 6N.

n. Hydrogen sulfide, H_2S.

4. Procedure

a. Preparation of calibration curve:

1) Prepare, just before use, a zinc solution containing 2.0 μg Zn/ml by diluting 5 ml standard zinc solution to 250 ml, then diluting 10 ml of the latter solution to 100 ml with redistilled water. Pipet 5.00, 10.00, 15.00, and 20.00 ml, containing 10 to 40 μg Zn, into separate 125-ml separatory funnels

and adjust the volumes to about 20 ml. Set up another funnel containing 20 ml zinc-free water as a blank.

2) Add 2 drops methyl red indicator and 2.0 ml sodium citrate solution to each funnel. If the indicator is not yellow, add conc NH_4OH a drop at a time until it just turns yellow. Add 1.0 ml potassium cyanide solution and then acetic acid, a drop at a time, until the indicator just turns a neutral peach color.

3) Extract the methyl red by shaking with 5 ml CCl_4. Discard the yellow CCl_4 layer. Add 1 ml dithiocarbamate solution. Extract with 10 ml dithizone solution, shaking for 1 min.

Draw off the CCl_4 layer into another separatory funnel and repeat the extraction with successive 5-ml portions of dithizone solution until the last one shows no change from the green dithizone color. Discard the aqueous layer.

4) Shake the combined dithizone extracts with a 10-ml portion of sodium sulfide solution II, separate the layers, and repeat the washing with further 10-ml portions of Na_2S solution until the unreacted dithizone solution has been removed completely, as shown by color of the aqueous layer, which remains colorless or very pale yellow; usually three washings are sufficient.

Remove water adhering to the stem of the funnel with a cotton swab and drain the pink CCl_4 solution into a dry 50-ml volumetric flask. Use a few milliliters of fresh CCl_4 to rinse the last droplets from the funnel and dilute to the mark with fresh CCl_4.

5) Determine the absorbance of the zinc dithizonate solutions at 535 nm, using CCl_4 as a reference. Plot an absorbance-concentration curve after subtracting the absorbance of the blank.

The calibration curve is linear if monochromatic light is used.

6) Clean separatory funnels by shaking several minutes successively with HNO_3, distilled water, and finally a mixture of 5 ml sodium citrate and 5 ml dithizone, to minimize the large or erratic blanks that result from the adsorption of zinc on the glass surface. If possible, reserve separatory funnels exclusively for the zinc determination and do not use for other purposes.

b. Treatment of sample:

1) Digest sample as directed under Preliminary Treatment, Section 301C.II. Transfer a portion containing 10 to 40 μg Zn to a clean 125-ml separatory funnel and adjust the volume to about 20 ml. Determine the zinc in this solution exactly as described in the preceding procedure for preparing the calibration curve.

If more than 30 ml of dithizone solution is needed to extract the zinc completely, the portion taken contains too much zinc or the quantity of other metals that react with dithizone exceeds the amount that can be withheld by the complexing agent. In the latter case, follow the procedure in ¶ 4b2) below.

2) Separation of excessive amounts of cadmium, copper, and lead—When the quantity of these metals, separately or jointly, exceeds 2 mg in the portion taken, in a 100-ml beaker adjust the volume to about 20 ml. Adjust acidity to 0.4 to $0.5N^*$ by adding dilute HNO_3 or NH_4OH as necessary. Pass H_2S into the cold solution for 5 min. Filter off the

---

* The normalities of the solutions obtained in the preliminary treatment are approximately $3N$ for the HNO_3-H_2SO_4 digestion and approximately $0.8N$ for the HNO_3-$HClO_4$ digestion.

precipitated sulfides using a sintered-glass filter and wash the precipitate with two small portions of hot water. Boil the filtrate 3 to 4 min to remove H_2S, cool, transfer to a separatory funnel, and determine the zinc as described in ¶ 4b1) et seq.

5. Calculation

$$mg/l\,Zn = \frac{\mu g\,Zn}{ml\,sample} \times \frac{100}{ml\,portion}$$

323 D.   Zincon Method*

1. General Discussion

a. Principle: Zinc forms a blue complex with 2-carboxy-2'-hydroxy-5'-sulfoformazyl benzene (zincon) in a solution buffered to pH 9.0. Other heavy metals likewise form colored complexes. Heavy metals, including zinc, are complexed by cyanide. Chloral hydrate is added specifically to free the zinc from its cyanide complex. The zinc-zincon complex is measured before other heavy metal-cyanide complexes are destroyed by chloral hydrate. Sodium ascorbate reduces the interference of manganese. The final solutions are unstable and the procedure is designed to minimize the effects of color fading.

b. Interference: The following ions interfere in concentrations exceeding those listed:

Ion	mg/l	Ion	mg/l
Cd (II)	1	Cr (III)	10
Al (III)	5	Ni (II)	20
Mn (II)	5	Cu (II)	30
Fe (III)	7	Co (II)	30
Fe (II)	9	CrO$_4$ (II)	50

c. Minimum detectable quantity: 1 μg Zn.

2. Apparatus

Colorimetric equipment: One of the following is required:

a. Spectrophotometer, for measurements at 620 nm, providing a light path of 1 cm or longer.

b. Filter photometer, providing a light path of 1 cm or longer and equipped with a red filter having maximum transmittance near 620 nm. Deviation from Beer's law occurs when the filter band pass exceeds 20 nm.

3. Reagents

a. Zinc-free water, for rinsing of apparatus and preparation of solutions and dilutions. Prepare as directed in Section 323C.3*a*.

b. Stock zinc solution: Prepare as directed in Section 323C.3*b*.

c. Standard zinc solution: Dilute 10.00 ml stock zinc solution to 100 ml with zinc-free water; 1.00 ml = 10.0 μg Zn.

d. Sodium ascorbate, fine granular powder.†

e. Potassium cyanide solution: Dissolve 1.00 g KCN in 50 ml zinc-free water and dilute to 100 ml. This solution is stable for approximately 60 days.

---

* This method, with modifications, is identical in source and substance to ASTM D1691-67.

† Hoffman-LaRoche or equivalent.

CAUTION: *Poison—potassium cyanide is extremely poisonous. Observe more than customary precautions in its handling. Never use mouth pipets to deliver volumes of cyanide solution.*

f. Buffer solution, pH 9.0: Prepare 1N NaOH by dissolving 40 g sodium hydroxide in 500 ml zinc-free water and diluting to 1,000 ml. Dilute 213 ml 1N NaOH to approximately 600 ml with zinc-free water. Dissolve 37.8 g KCl and 31.0 g H₃BO₃ in the solution and dilute to 1 l.

g. Zincon reagent: Grind the entire supply of zincon powder and make a uniform mixture. Dissolve 130 mg powdered 2-carboxy-2′-hydroxy-5′-sulfoformazyl benzene (zincon) in 100 ml methyl alcohol (methanol). Let stand overnight or use a magnetic stirrer in a closed flask to complete solution.

h. Chloral hydrate solution: Dissolve 10.0 g chloral hydrate in 50 ml zinc-free water and dilute to 100 ml. Filter if necessary.

i. Hydrochloric acid, HCl, conc.

j. Sodium hydroxide, NaOH, 6N.

4. Procedure

a. Preparation of colorimetric standards: To a series of thoroughly cleansed 50-ml erlenmeyer flasks, add 0, 0.25, 0.50, 1.00, 3.00, 5.00, and 7.00 ml standard zinc solution equivalent, to provide 0, 2.50, 5.00, 10.0, 30.0, 50.0, and 70.0 μg Zn, respectively. Bring each volume to 10.0 ml by adding zinc-free water. To each flask add, in sequence, mixing thoroughly after each addition, 0.5 g sodium ascorbate, 1.0 ml KCN solution, 5.0 ml buffer solution, and 3.0 ml zincon solution. Add 3.0 ml chloral hydrate solution, note the time, and mix. Transfer to the absorption cell

and measure the absorbance at 620 nm exactly 5 min after adding the chloral hydrate solution. Use the treated blank as the reference solution for initial balancing of the photometer. For greater accuracy in the range below 10 μg Zn, prepare a separate calibration curve.

b. Treatment of samples: If dissolved zinc is to be determined, filter the sample. If total zinc is to be determined, add 1 ml conc HCl to 50 ml thoroughly mixed sample and mix well. Filter and adjust to pH 7 with 6N NaOH. Transfer a 10.0-ml portion of sample containing not more than 70 μg Zn to a 50-ml erlenmeyer flask. Complete the analysis as described in ¶ 4a above, beginning with the words "To each flask add, in sequence . . . ," and continue to the end of the paragraph.

Prepare as a reference solution a sample portion treated as above, except that 3.0 ml zinc-free water is substituted for the 3.0 ml chloral hydrate. Use this to compensate for color, turbidity, or interference not eliminated by the procedure. Prepare as nearly simultaneously as possible with the sample portion.

5. Calculation

$$\text{mg/l Zn} = \frac{\mu\text{g Zn}}{\text{ml sample}}$$

6. Precision and Accuracy

A synthetic unknown sample containing 650 μg/l Zn, 500 μg/l Al, 50 μg/l Cd, 110 μg/l Cr, 470 μg/l Cu, 300 μg/l Fe, 70 μg/l Pb, 120 μg/l Mn, and 150 μg/l Ag in distilled water was analyzed in four laboratories by the zincon method with a relative standard deviation of 13.9% and a relative error of 17.4%.

323 E. Bibliography

Dithizone Methods

HIBBARD, P. L. 1937. A dithizone method for measurement of small amounts of zinc. *Ind. Eng. Chem.*, Anal. Ed. 9:127.

SANDELL, E. B. 1937. Determination of copper, zinc, and lead in silicate rocks. *Ind. Eng. Chem.*, Anal. Ed. 9:464.

HIBBARD, P. L. 1938. Estimation of copper, zinc, and cobalt (with nickel) in soil extracts. *Ind. Eng. Chem.*, Anal. Ed. 10:615.

WICHMAN, H. J. 1939. Isolation and determination of traces of metals: The dithizone system. *Ind. Eng. Chem.*, Anal. Ed. 11:66.

COWLING, H. & E. J. MILLER. 1941. Determination of small amounts of zinc in plant materials: A photometric dithizone method. *Ind. Eng. Chem.*, Anal. Ed. 13:145.

ALEXANDER, O. R. & L. V. TAYLOR. 1944. Improved dithizone procedure for determination of zinc in foods. *J. Ass. Offic. Agr. Chem.* 27:325.

SERFASS, E. J. et al. 1947. *Chem. Anal.* 35:55.

SERFASS, E. J. et al. 1947. Research Report Serial No. 3, American Electroplaters Society, Newark, N.J., p. 22.

SERFASS, E. J. et al. 1949. Determination of impurities in electroplating solutions. *Plating* 36:254, 818.

SNELL, F. D. & C. T. SNELL. 1949. Colorimetric Methods of Analysis, 3rd ed. D. Van Nostrand Co., Princeton, N.J., Vol. 2, pp. 1-7, 412-419.

BUTTS, P. G., A. R. GAHLER & M. G. MELLON. 1950. Colorimetric determination of metals in sewage and industrial wastes. *Sewage Ind. Wastes* 22:1543.

BARNES, H. 1951. The determination of zinc by dithizone. *Analyst* 76:220.

COOPER, S. S. & M. L. SULLIVAN. 1951. Spectrophotometric studies of dithizone and some dithizonates. *Anal. Chem.* 23:613.

SERFASS, E. J. & R. F. MURACA. 1954. Procedures for Analyzing Metal Finishing Wastes. Ohio River Valley Water Sanitation Commission, Cincinnati, Ohio.

SANDELL, E. B. 1959. Colorimetric Determination of Traces of Metals, 3rd ed. Interscience Publishers, New York, N.Y.

Zincon Method

PLATTE, J. A. & V. M. MARCY. 1959. Photometric determination of zinc with zincon. *Anal. Chem.* 31:1274.

AMERICAN SOCIETY FOR TESTING AND MATERIALS. 1969. Book of ASTM Standards, Part 23. Water; Atmospheric analysis. ASTM, Philadelphia, Pa.

PART 400
DETERMINATION OF INORGANIC
NONMETALLIC CONSTITUENTS

401 INORGANIC NON-METALS—INTRODUCTION

The measurements included in this section range from collective measurements such as acidity and alkalinity to specific analyses for individual components such as the various forms of chlorine, nitrogen, and phosphorus. The measurements are conducted for the assessment and control of potable and receiving water quality and for determining process efficiency in waste treatment. Each test procedure contains in its introduction reference to any special field sampling conditions, desirable sample containers, and preservation and storage methods.

402   ACIDITY

Acidity of a water is its quantitative capacity to neutralize a strong base to a designated pH. The measured value may vary significantly with the end point pH used in the determination. Acidity is a measure of a gross property of a water and can be interpreted in terms of specific substances only when the chemical composition of the sample is known. Strong mineral acids, weak acids such as carbonic and acetic, and hydrolyzing salts such as ferrous or aluminum sulfates may contribute to the measured acidity according to the method of determination.

Acidity of water is significant because acids contribute to corrosiveness and influence certain chemical and biological processes. It is a measure of the amount of base required to neutralize a given sample to a specific pH. The measurement also reflects changes in the quality of the source water.

1. General Discussion

a. Principle: Hydrogen ions present in a sample as a result of dissociation or hydrolysis of solutes are neutralized by titration with standard alkali. The acidity thus depends on the end point pH or indicator used. The construction of a titration curve by recording the sample pH after successive small measured additions of titrant permits identification of inflection points and buffering capacity, if any, and allows the acidity to be determined with respect to any pH of interest.

In the titration of a single acidic species, as in the standardization of reagents, the most accurate end point is obtained from the inflection point of a titration curve. The inflection point is the point at which the slope of the curve (pH change per milliliter of added reagent) changes sign. It may be located by special plotting procedures. (See, for example, Gran's Plot paper, or the procedure in Section 203 C.4*a* and 4*b*, 13th edition Standard Methods.)

Because accurate identification of inflection points may be difficult or impossible in buffered or complex mixtures, the titration in such cases is carried to an arbitrary end point pH based on practical considerations. For routine control titrations or rapid preliminary estimates of acidity, the color change of an indicator may be used for the end point. Samples of industrial wastes, acid mine drainage, or other sources that contain appreciable amounts of hydrolyzable metal ions such as iron, aluminum, or manganese are treated with hydrogen peroxide to ensure oxidation of any reduced forms of polyvalent cations, and boiled to hasten the hydrolysis reaction.

b. End points: Ideally the end point of the acidity titration should correspond to the stoichiometric equivalence point for the neutralization of acids in the sample. The pH at the equivalence point will depend on the nature of the sample and the intended use of the data.

Dissolved carbon dioxide is usually the major acidic component of unpolluted surface waters; samples from such sources must be handled carefully to minimize the loss of dissolved gases. In a sample containing only carbon dioxide-bicarbonates-carbonates, titration to pH 8.3 at 25 C corresponds to stoichiometric neutralization of carbonic acid to bicarbonate. Since the color change of phenolphthalein indicator is close to pH 8.3, this value is generally accepted as a standard end point for the titration of total acidity, including carbon dioxide and most other weak acids.

For more complex mixtures or buffered solutions the selection of an inflection point may be subjective. Consequently, fixed end points of pH 3.7 and pH 8.3 are used for standard acidity determinations in wastewaters and natural waters where the simple carbonate equilibria discussed above cannot be assumed. The resulting titrations are identified as "methyl orange acidity" (pH 3.7), and "phenolphthalein acidity" (pH 8.3) whether or not colored indicators are used in the determination.

c. Interferences: Dissolved gases contributing to acidity or alkalinity, such as carbon dioxide, hydrogen sulfide, or ammonia, may be lost or gained during sampling, storage, or titration. Such effects can be minimized by titrating to the end point promptly after opening the sample container, avoiding vigorous shaking or mixing, and protecting the sample from the atmosphere during the titration.

In the potentiometric titration, oily matter, suspended solids, precipitates, or other waste matter may coat the glass electrode and cause a sluggish response. Difficulty from this source is likely to be revealed in an erratic titration curve. Do *not* remove the interferences from the sample, because they may contribute to its acidity. Pause between titrant additions to allow the electrode to come to equilibrium.

In samples that contain oxidizable or hydrolyzable ions such as ferrous or ferric iron, aluminum, and manganese, the rates of these reactions may be slow enough at room temperature to cause drifting end points.

Do not use indicator titrations with colored or turbid samples that may obscure the color change at the end point. Free available residual chlorine in the sample may bleach the indicator. Eliminate this source of interference by treating the sample with 1 drop of 0.1 N sodium thiosulfate.

d. Selection of method: Determine the acidity of a sample from the volume of standard alkali required to titrate a portion of the sample to a pH of 8.3 ("phenolphthalein acidity") or pH 3.7 ("methyl orange acidity" of wastewaters and grossly polluted waters). Titrate at room temperature using a properly calibrated pH meter, electrically operated titrator, or color indicators.

Construct a titration curve for the standardization of reagents.

Use the hot peroxide procedure to pretreat samples known or suspected to contain hydrolyzable metal ions or reduced forms of polyvalent cation, such as iron pickle liquors, acid mine drainage, and other industrial wastes. Cool to room temperature before titration.

Color indicators may be used for routine and control titrations in the absence of interfering color and turbidity and for preliminary titrations to select sample size and strength of titrant (see below).

e. Sample size: The range of acidities found in wastewaters is so large that a single sample size and normality of base used as titrant cannot be specified. Use a sufficiently large volume of titrant (20 ml or more from a 50-ml buret) to obtain relatively good volumetric precision while keeping the volume of the portion sufficiently small to permit sharp end points. For samples having acidities less than about 1,000 mg/l as $CaCO_3$, select a volume such that less than 50 mg $CaCO_3$ equivalent acidity is present and titrate with 0.02 N NaOH. For acidities greater than about 1,000 mg/l as $CaCO_3$ use a portion containing acidity equivalent to less than 250 mg $CaCO_3$ and titrate with 0.1 N NaOH. If necessary, make a preliminary titration to de-

termine the optimum sample size and/ or normality of titrant.

f. Sampling and storage: Collect samples in polyethylene or borosilicate glass (Pyrex or equivalent) bottles and store at a low temperature. Fill bottles completely and cap them tightly. Because waste samples may be subject to microbial action and to loss or gain of carbon dioxide or other gases when exposed to air, analyze samples without delay, preferably within 1 day. Avoid sample agitation and prolonged exposure to air.

2. Apparatus

a. Electrometric titrator: Use any commercial pH meter or electrically operated titrator that uses a glass electrode and can be read to 0.05 pH unit. Standardize and calibrate the instrument according to the manufacturer's instructions. Pay special attention to temperature compensation and electrode care. If automatic temperature compensation is not provided, make the titrations at 25 ± 2 C.

b. Titration vessel: The size and form will depend on the electrodes and the size of sample. Keep the free space above the sample as small as practicable, but allow room for the titrant and full immersion of the indicating portions of the glass and reference electrodes. For conventional-sized electrodes, use a 200-ml, tall-form Berzelius beaker without a spout. Fit the beaker with a stopper having three holes, to accommodate the two electrodes and the buret. With a miniature combination glass-reference electrode use a 125-ml or 250-ml erlenmeyer flask with a two-hole stopper.

c. Magnetic stirrer.

d. Pipets, volumetric.

e. Flasks, volumetric, 1,000-, 200-, 100-ml.

f. Burets, Pyrex, 50-, 25-, 10-ml.

g. Polyolefin bottle.

3. Reagents

a. Carbon dioxide-free water: Prepare all stock and standard solutions and dilution water for the standardization procedure with distilled or deionized water that has been freshly boiled for 15 min and cooled to room temperature. The final pH of the water should be ≥ 6.0 and its conductivity should be <2 μsiemens/cm.

b. Potassium biphthalate solution, approximately 0.05 N: Crush 15 to 20 g primary standard potassium biphthalate, $KHC_8H_4O_4$, to about 100 mesh and dry at 120 C for 2 hr. Cool in a desiccator. Weight 10.0 ± 0.5 g (to the nearest mg), transfer to a 1-l volumetric flask, and fill to the mark with CO_2-free water.

c. Standard sodium hydroxide titrant, 0.1 N: Dissolve 11 g NaOH in 10 ml distilled water, cool, and filter through a Gooch crucible or hardened filter paper. Dilute 5.45 ml clear filtrate to 1 l with CO_2-free water and store in a polyolefin bottle protected from atmospheric CO_2 by a soda lime tube or tight cap. Standardize by titration of 40.00 ml $KHC_8H_4O_4$ solution (*3b*), using a 25-ml buret. Titrate to the inflection point, which should be close to pH 8.7. Calculate the normality of the NaOH:

$$\text{Normality} = \frac{A \times B}{204.2 \times C}$$

where:

A = g $KHC_8H_4O_4$ weighed into 1 l (section *3b*),

B = ml $KHC_8H_4O_4$ solution taken for titration, and

C = ml NaOH solution used.

Use the measured normality in further calculations or adjust to exactly 0.1000 N. A 0.1000 N solution = 5.00 mg $CaCO_3$/ml.

d. Standard sodium hydroxide titrant, 0.02 N: Dilute 200 ml 0.1 N NaOH to 1 l and store in a polyolefin bottle protected from atmospheric CO_2 by a soda lime tube or tight cap. Standardize against potassium biphthalate as directed in *¶3c*, using 15.00 ml $KHC_8H_4O_4$ solution and a 50-ml buret for the NaOH. Calculate the normality as above (*¶3c*). 0.0200 N solution = 1.00 mg $CaCO_3$/ml.

e. Hydrogen peroxide, H_2O_2, 30% solution.

f. Methyl orange indicator solution.

g. Phenolphthalein indicator solution.

h. Sodium thiosulfate, 0.1 N: Dissolve 25 g $Na_2S_2O_3 \cdot 5H_2O$ and dilute to 1 l with distilled water.

4. Procedure

a. Color change: Select sample size and normality of titrant according to the criteria of *¶1e*. Adjust the sample to room temperature, if necessary, and with a pipet discharge the sample into an erlenmeyer flask, while keeping the tip of the pipet near the bottom of the flask. If free residual chlorine is present add 0.05 ml (1 drop) 0.1 N sodium thiosulfate solution, or destroy with ultraviolet radiation. Add 0.1 ml (2 drops) of indicator solution and titrate over a white surface to a persistent color change characteristic of the equivalence point.

b. Potentiometric titration curve: Rinse the electrodes and titration vessel with distilled water and drain. Select sample size and normality of titrant according to the criteria of ¶1e. Adjust the sample to room temperature, if necessary, and with a pipet discharge the sample while keeping the tip of the pipet near the bottom of the titration vessel.

Measure the pH of the sample. Add standard alkali in increments of 0.5 ml or less. After each addition, mix thoroughly but gently with a magnetic stirrer. Avoid splashing. Record the pH when a constant reading is obtained. Continue adding titrant and measure pH until pH 9 is reached. Construct the titration curve by plotting the observed pH values against the cumulative milliliters titrant used. A smooth curve showing one or more inflections should be obtained. A ragged or erratic curve may indicate that equilibrium was not reached between successive additions. Determine the acidity relative to a particular pH from the curve.

c. Potentiometric titration to pH 3.7 or 8.3: Prepare the sample and titration assembly as specified in ¶4b. Titrate to the preselected end point pH (¶1d) without recording intermediate pH values. As the end point is approached make smaller additions of alkali and be sure that pH equilibrium is reached before the next addition is made.

d. Hot peroxide treatment*: Pipet a suitable sample (see ¶1e) into the titration flask. Measure the pH. If the pH is above 4.0, add 5-ml increments of 0.02 N H_2SO_4 (Section 403.3c) to lower the pH to 4 or less. Remove the electrodes. Add 5 drops 30% H_2O_2 and boil for 2 to 5 min. Cool to room temperature and titrate with standard alkali to pH 8.3 according to the procedure of ¶4c.

---

* This procedure is intended to be equivalent to ASTM D1067, Method E.

5. Calculation

Acidity, as mg/l $CaCO_3$ =
$$\frac{(A \times B - C \times D) \times 50{,}000}{ml\ sample\ portion}$$

where:

A = ml NaOH titrant used,
B = normality of NaOH,
C = ml of H_2SO_4 used (¶4d), and
D = normality of H_2SO_4.

Report the pH of the end point used, as follows: "The acidity to pH _____ = _____ mg/l $CaCO_3$." A negative value signifies alkalinity.

6. Precision

No general statement can be made about precision because of the great variation in the sample characteristics. The precision of the titration is likely to be much greater than the uncertainties involved in sampling and in handling the sample before analysis.

Forty analysts in 17 laboratories analyzed synthetic water samples containing increments of bicarbonate equivalent to 20 mg/l $CaCO_3$. Titration according to the procedure of ¶4c gave a standard deviation of 1.8 mg/l $CaCO_3$, with negligible bias.

6. Bibliography

Winter, J.A. & M.R. Midgett. 1969. FWPCA Method Study 1. Mineral and Physical Analyses. FWPCA, Washington, D.C.

Brown, E., M.W. Skougstad & M.J. Fishman. 1970. Methods for collection and analysis of water samples for dissolved minerals and gases. Chapter A1 in Book 5, Techniques of Water-Resources Investigations of United States Geological Survey. U.S. Geol. Surv., Washington, D.C.

403 ALKALINITY

The alkalinity of a water is its quantitative capacity to neutralize a strong acid to a designated pH. The measured value may vary significantly with the end point pH used in the determination. Alkalinity is a measure of a gross property of water and can be interpreted in terms of specific substances only when the chemical composition of the sample is known.

Alkalinity is significant in many uses and treatments of natural and wastewaters. Because the alkalinity of many surface waters is primarily a function of carbonate, bicarbonate, and hydroxide content, the alkalinity is taken as an indication of the concentration of these constitutents. The measured values may include contributions from borates, phosphates, or silicates if these are present. The alkalinity in excess of alkaline earth concentrations is significant in determining the suitability of a water for irrigation. Alkalinity measurements are used in the interpretation and control of water and wastewater treatment processes. Raw domestic wastewater has an alkalinity only slightly greater than that of the water supply. Properly operating anaerobic digesters typically have supernatant alkalinities in the range of 2,000 to 4,000 mg/l as $CaCO_3$.[1] For industrial wastes, the measurement can indicate change in quality if the source of the sample is known to have generally stable levels of alkalinity.

1. General Discussion

a. Principle: Hydroxyl ions present in a sample as a result of dissociation or hydrolysis of solutes are neutralized by titration with standard acid. The alka-

linity thus depends on the end point pH used. For methods of determining inflection points from titration curves and the rationale for titrating to fixed pH end points, see Section 402.1a.

For samples of low alkalinity (less than 20 mg/l $CaCO_3$) use an extrapolation technic based on the near proportionality of the concentration of hydrogen ions to the excess of titrant beyond the equivalence point. The amount of standard acid required to lower the pH exactly 0.30 pH unit is carefully measured. Because this change in pH corresponds to an exact doubling of the hydrogen ion concentration, a simple extrapolation can be made to the equivalence point.[2, 3]

b. End points: When the alkalinity of a water is due entirely to hydroxide, carbonate, or bicarbonate content, the pH at the equivalence point of the titration is determined by the concentration of CO_2 present at that stage. The CO_2 concentration depends in turn on the total carbonate species originally in the sample and any losses that may have occurred during the titration. The following pH values are suggested as the equivalence points for the corresponding alkalinity concentrations as calcium carbonate:

	End point pH	
	Total	Phenolphthalein
Alkalinity, mg/l:		
30	5.1	8.3
150	4.8	8.3
500	4.5	8.3
Silicates, phosphates known or suspected	4.5	8.3
Industrial waste or complex system	3.7	8.3

c. Interferences: Soaps, oily matter, suspended solids, or precipitates may coat the glass electrode and cause a sluggish response. Allow additional time between titrant additions to let the electrode come to equilibrium. Do not filter, dilute, concentrate, or alter the sample in any way.

d. Selection of method: Determine the alkalinity of the sample from the volume of standard acid required to titrate a portion of the sample to a designated pH taken from the table of ¶1*b*. Titrate at room temperature with a properly calibrated pH meter or electrically operated titrator, or color indicators.

Report an alkalinity less than 20 mg/l CaCO₃ only if it has been determined by the low alkalinity method of ¶4*c*.

Construct a titration curve for the standardization of reagents.

Color indicators may be used for routine and control titrations in the absence of interfering color and turbidity and for preliminary titrations to select the sample size and strength of titrant (see below).

e. Sample size: See Section 402.1*e* for the selection of the sample size to be titrated and the normality of titrant, substituting 0.02 *N* or 0.1 *N* H₂SO₄ (or HCl) for the standard alkali of that method. For the low alkalinity method, titrate a 200-ml sample with 0.02 *N* H₂SO₄ from a 10-ml buret.

f. Sampling and storage: See Section 402.1*f*.

2. Apparatus

See Section 402.2.

3. Reagents

a. Sodium carbonate solution, approximately 0.05 N: Dry 3 to 5 g primary standard Na₂CO₃ at 250 C for 4 hr and cool in a desiccator. Weigh 2.5±0.2 g (to the nearest mg), transfer to a 1-l volumetric flask, and fill to the mark with distilled water.

b. Standard sulfuric acid or hydrochloric acid, 0.1 N: Dilute 3.0 ml conc H₂SO₄ or 8.3 ml conc HCl to 1 l with distilled or deionized water. Standardize against 40.00 ml 0.05 *N* Na₂CO₃ solution, with about 60 ml water, in a beaker by titrating potentiometrically to pH of about 5. Lift out electrodes, rinse into the same beaker, and boil gently for 3 to 5 min under a watch glass cover. Cool to room temperature, rinse the cover glass into the beaker, and finish the titration to the pH inflection point. Calculate the normality according to

$$\text{Normality, } N = \frac{A \times B}{53.00 \times C}$$

where A = g Na₂CO₃ weighed into 1 l, B = ml Na₂CO₃ solution taken for titration, and C = ml acid used. Use measured normality in calculations or adjust to exactly 0.1000 *N*. A 0.1000 *N* solution = 5.00 mg CaCO₃/ml.

c. Standard sulfuric acid or hydrochloric acid, 0.02 N: Dilute 200.00 ml 0.1000 *N* standard acid to 1,000 ml with distilled or deionized water. Standardize by potentiometric titration of 15.00 ml 0.05 *N* Na₂CO₃ according to the procedure of ¶3*b*. 0.0200 *N* solution = 1.00 mg CaCO₃/ml.

d. Mixed bromcresol green-methyl red indicator solution: Use either the aqueous or the alcoholic solution:

1) Dissolve 20 mg methyl red sodium salt and 100 mg bromcresol green sodium salt in 100 ml distilled water.

2) Dissolve 20 mg methyl red and

100 mg bromocresol green in 100 ml 95% ethyl alcohol or isopropyl alcohol.

   e. *Methyl orange solution.*

   f. *Phenolphthalein solution.*

   g. *Sodium thiosulfate*, 0.1 *N:* See Section 402.3*h.*

4. Procedure

   a. *Color change:* See Section 402.4*a.* The color response of the mixed bromcresol green-methyl red indicator is approximately as follows: above pH 5.2, greenish blue; pH 5.0, light blue with lavender gray; pH 4.8, light pink-gray with bluish cast; and pH 4.6, light pink. Check the color changes against the reading of a pH meter under the conditions of the titration.

   b. *Potentiometric titration curve:* Follow the procedure for the determination of acidity (Section 402.4*b*), substituting the appropriate normality of standard acid solution for the standard NaOH, and continue the titration to pH 3.7 or lower. Do not filter, dilute, concentrate, or alter the sample in any way.

   c. *Potentiometric titration to pre-selected pH:* Determine the appropriate end point pH according to ¶1*b.* Prepare the sample and titration assembly (Section 402.4*b*). Titrate to the end point pH without recording intermediate pH values and without undue delay. As the end point is approached make smaller additions of acid and be sure that pH equilibrium is reached before adding more titrant.

   d. *Potentiometric titration of low alkalinity:* For alkalinities less than 20 mg/l titrate 100 to 200 ml according to the procedure of ¶4*c*, above, using a 10-ml microburet and 0.02 *N* standard acid solution. Stop the titration at a pH in

the range 4.3 to 4.7 and record the volume and exact pH. Very carefully add additional titrant to lower the pH of the solution exactly 0.30 pH unit and again record the volume. Precise standardization of the pH meter is unnecessary for this determination.

5. Calculations

   a. *Potentiometric titration to end point pH:*

Alkalinity, mg/l $CaCO_3$ =
$$\frac{A \times N \times 50{,}000}{\text{ml sample}}$$

where A = ml standard acid used and N = normality of standard acid, or

Alkalinity, mg/l $CaCO_3$ =
$$\frac{A \times T \times 1{,}000}{\text{ml sample}}$$

where T = titer of standard acid, mg $CaCO_3$/ml.

   Report the pH of the end point used as follows: "The alkalinity to pH _____ = _____ mg/l $CaCO_3$" and indicate clearly if this pH corresponds to an inflection point of the titration curve.

   b. *Potentiometric titration of low alkalinity:*

Total alkalinity, mg/l $CaCO_3$ =
$$\frac{(2B-C) \times N \times 50{,}000}{\text{ml sample}}$$

where B = ml of titrant to first recorded pH, C = total ml of titrant to reach pH 0.3 unit lower, and N = normality of acid.

   c. *Calculation of alkalinity relationships:* The results obtained from the phenolphthalein and total alkalinity determinations offer a means for the stoichiometric classification of the three principal forms of alkalinity present in many water supplies. The classification ascribes the entire alkalinity to bicarbonate, carbonate, and hydroxide, and assumes the absence of other (weak) acids of inorganic or organic composition, such as silicic, phosphoric, and boric acids. It further presupposes the incompatibility of hydroxide and bicarbonate alkalinities. Since the calculations are made on a stoichiometric basis, ion concentrations in the strictest sense are not represented in the results. According to this scheme:

1) Carbonate alkalinity is present when the phenolphthalein alkalinity is not zero but is less than the total alkalinity.

2) Hydroxide alkalinity is present if the phenolphthalein alkalinity is more than half the total alkalinity.

3) Bicarbonate alkalinity is present if the phenolphthalein alkalinity is less than half the total alkalinity. These relationships may be calculated by the following scheme, where P is the phenolphthalein alkalinity and T is the total alkalinity (¶1b):

Select the smaller value of P or (T-P). Then, carbonate alkalinity equals twice the smaller value. When the smaller value is P, the balance (T-$2P$) is bicarbonate. When the smaller value is (T-P), the balance ($2P$-T) is hydroxide. All results are expressed as $CaCO_3$. The mathematical conversion of the results is shown in Table 403:I.

Alkalinity relationships also may be computed nomographically (see Carbon Dioxide, Section 407). Accurately measure the pH of the water, calculate the OH^- concentration as milligrams

TABLE 403:I. ALKALINITY RELATIONSHIPS*

Result of Titration	Hydroxide Alkalinity as $CaCO_3$	Carbonate Alkalinity as $CaCO_3$	Bicarbonate Alkalinity as $CaCO_3$
$P=0$	0	0	T
$P<\frac{1}{2}T$	0	2P	T-2P
$P=\frac{1}{2}T$	0	2P	0
$P>\frac{1}{2}T$	2P-T	2(T-P)	0
$P=T$	T	0	0

*Key: P—phenolphthalein alkalinity; T—total alkalinity.

per liter $CaCO_3$, and calculate the concentrations of CO_3^{2-} and HCO_3^- as milligrams per liter $CaCO_3$ from the OH^- concentration, and the phenolphthalein and total alkalinities by the following equations:

$$CO_3^{2-} = 2P-2[OH^-]$$
$$HCO_3^- = T-2P+[OH^-]$$

Similarly, if difficulty is experienced with the phenolphthalein end point, or if a check on the phenolphthalein titration is desired, calculate the phenolphthalein alkalinity as $CaCO_3$ from the results of the nomographic determinations of the carbonate (CO_3^{2-}) and hydroxide (OH^-) ion concentrations:

$$P = 1/2 \ [CO_3^{2-}]+[OH^-]$$

6. Precision and Accuracy

No general statement can be made about precision because of the great variation in sample characteristics. The precision of the titration is likely to be much greater than the uncertainties involved in sampling and handling the sample before the analysis.

In the range of 10 to 500 mg/l, where the alkalinity is due entirely to carbonates or bicarbonates, a standard deviation of 1 mg/l can be achieved. Forty analysts in 17 laboratories analyzed synthetic water samples containing increments of bicarbonate equivalent to 120 mg/l CaCO₃. The titration procedure of ¶4b was used, with an end point pH of 4.5. The standard deviation was 5 mg/l and the average bias (lower than the true value) was 9 mg/l.[4]

7. References

1. POHLAND, F.G. & D.E. BLOODGOOD. 1963. Laboratory studies on mesophilic and thermophilic anaerobic sludge digestion. *J. Water Pollut. Control Fed.* 35:11.
2. LARSON, T.E. & L.M. HENLEY. 1955. Determination of low alkalinity or acidity in water. *Anal. Chem.* 27:851.
3. THOMAS, J.F.J. & J.J. LYNCH. 1960. Determination of carbonate alkalinity in natural waters. *J. Amer. Water Works Ass.* 52:259.
4. WINTER, J.A. & M.R. MIDGETT. 1969. FWPCA Method Study 1. Mineral and Physical Analyses. FWPCA, Washington, D.C.

8. Bibliography

AMERICAN SOCIETY FOR TESTING & MATERIALS. 1970. Standard Methods for Acidity or Alkalinity of Water. ASTM Publ. D1067-70, Philadelphia, Pa.
BROWN, E., M.W. SKOUGSTAD & M.J. FISHMAN. 1970. Methods of collection and analysis of water sample for dissolved minerals and gases. Chapter A1 in Book 5, Techniques of Water-Resources Investigation of the United States Geological Survey. U.S. Geol. Surv., Washington, D.C.

404   ARSENIC

Severe poisoning can arise from the ingestion of as little as 100 mg arsenic; chronic effects can appear from its accumulation in the body at low intake levels. Carcinogenic properties have also been imputed to arsenic. The arsenic concentration of most potable waters seldom exceeds 10 $\mu g/l$, although values as high as 100 $\mu g/l$ have been reported. Arsenic may occur in water as a result of mineral dissolution, industrial discharges, or the application of insecticides.

Selection of method: Use the silver diethyldithiocarbamate method when greater precision and accuracy are desired than that possible with the mercuric bromide stain method. Although its minimum detectable quantity is 1 μg As, use the mercuric bromide stain method only for qualitative or semiquantitative (± 5 μg) determinations. Successful application of either method often requires considerable practice. Arsenic also may be determined by the atomic absorption spectrophotometric method.

404 A.   Silver Diethyldithiocarbamate Method

1. General Discussion

a. Principle: Inorganic arsenic is reduced to arsine, AsH_3, by zinc in acid solution in a Gutzeit generator. The arsine is then passed through a scrubber containing glass wool impregnated with lead acetate solution and into an absorber tube containing silver diethyldithiocarbamate dissolved in pyridine. In the absorber, arsenic reacts with the silver salt, forming a soluble red complex suitable for photometric measurement.

b. Interference: Although certain metals—chromium, cobalt, copper, mercury, molybdenum, nickel, platinum, and silver—interfere in the generation of arsine, the concentrations of these metals normally present in water

do not interfere significantly in the method. Antimony salts in the sample form stibine, which may interfere with color development by yielding a red color with maximum absorbance at 510 nm.

c. Minimum detectable quantity: 1 μg As.

2. Apparatus

a. Arsine generator and absorption tube: See Figure 404:1.*

b. Photometric equipment:

1) *Spectrophotometer,* for use at 535 nm with 1-cm cells.

2) *Filter photometer,* with green filter having a maximum transmittance in the range 530 to 540 nm, with 1-cm cells.

3. Reagents

a. Hydrochloric acid, HCl, conc.

b. Potassium iodide solution: Dissolve 15 g KI in 100 ml distilled water. Store in a brown bottle.

c. Stannous chloride reagent: Dissolve 40 g arsenic-free $SnCl_2 \cdot 2H_2O$ in 100 ml conc HCl.

d. Lead acetate solution: Dissolve 10 g $Pb(C_2H_3O_2)_2 \cdot 3H_2O$ in 100 ml distilled water.

e. Silver diethyldithiocarbamate reagent: Prepare this reagent as described in either 1) or 2):

1) Dissolve 410 mg 1-ephedrine in 200 ml chloroform, add 625 mg $AgSCN(C_2H_5)_2$, and adjust the volume to 250 ml with additional $CHCl_3$. Filter the reagent and store in brown bottle.

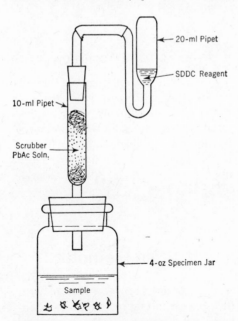

— 20-ml Pipet

— SDDC Reagent

10-ml Pipet

Scrubber
PbAc Soln.

— 4-oz Specimen Jar

Sample

Figure 404:1. Arsine generator and absorber assembly.

*Fisher Scientific Co., No. 1-405 or equivalent apparatus.

2) Dissolve 1 g $AgSCSN(C_2H_5)_2$ in 200 ml pyridine. Store in brown bottle.

f. Zinc: 20 to 30 mesh, arsenic-free.

g. Stock arsenic solution: Dissolve 1.320 g arsenic trioxide, As_2O_3, in 10 ml distilled water containing 4 g NaOH, and dilute to 1,000 ml with distilled water; 1.00 ml = 1.00 mg As. (CAUTION: Toxic—take care to avoid ingestion of arsenic solutions.)

h. Intermediate arsenic solution: Dilute 5.00 ml stock solution to 500 ml with distilled water; 1.00 ml = 10.0 µg As.

i. Standard arsenic solution: Dilute 10.00 ml intermediate solution to 100 ml with distilled water; 1.00 ml = 1.00 µg As.

4. Procedure

a. Treatment of sample: Pipet 35.0 ml sample into a clean generator bottle. Add successively, with thorough mixing after each addition, 5 ml conc HCl, 2 ml KI solution, and 8 drops (0.40 ml) $SnCl_2$ reagent. Allow 15 min for reduction of arsenic to the trivalent state.

b. Preparation of scrubber and absorber: Impregnate the glass wool in the scrubber with lead acetate solution. Do not make too wet because water will be carried over into the reagent solution. Pipet 4.00 ml silver diethyldithiocarbamate reagent into the absorber tube.

c. Arsine generation and measurement: Add 3 g zinc to the generator and connect the scrubber-absorber assembly immediately. Make certain that all connections are tightly fitted.

Allow 30 min for complete evolution of arsine. Warm the generator slightly to make sure that all arsine is released. Pour the solution from the absorber directly into a 1-cm cell and measure the absorbance of the solution at 535 nm, using the reagent blank as the reference.

d. Preparation of standard curve: Treat portions of the standard solution containing 0, 1.0, 2.0, 5.0, and 10.0 µg As as described in this section, ¶s *a* through *d*. Plot absorbance versus concentration of arsenic in the standard.

5. Calculation

$$mg/l\,As = \frac{\mu g\,As}{ml\,sample}$$

6. Precision and Accuracy

A synthetic unknown sample containing 40 µg/l As, 250 µg/l Be, 240 µg/l B, 20 µg/l Se, and 6 µg/l V in distilled water was analyzed in 46 laboratories by the silver diethyldithiocarbamate method, with a relative standard deviation of 13.8% and a relative error of 0%.

404 B.   Mercuric Bromide Stain Method

1. General Discussion

a. Principle: After concentration of the sample, arsenic is liberated as arsine, AsH_3, by zinc in acid solution in a Gut-

zeit generator. The generated arsine is then passed through a column containing a roll of cotton moistened with lead acetate solution. The generated arsine produces a yellow-brown stain on test paper strips impregnated with mercuric bromide. The length of the stain is roughly proportional to the amount of arsenic present.

b. Interference: Antimony interferes by giving a similar stain if present in quantities greater than 0.10 mg.

c. Minimum detectable quantity: 1 μg As.

2. Apparatus

Arsine generator: See Figure 404:2.

3. Reagents

a. Sulfuric acid, H_2SO_4, 1+1.

b. Nitric acid, HNO_3, conc.

c. Roll cotton: Cut a roll of dentist's cotton into 25-mm lengths.

d. Lead acetate solution: Prepare as directed in Method A, ¶3*d*.

e. Mercuric bromide paper: Use commercial arsenic papers cut uniformly into strips about 12 cm long and 2.5 mm wide (papers can be obtained already cut and sensitized). Soak strips for at least 1 hr in filtered solution prepared by dissolving 3 to 6 g $HgBr_2$ in 95% ethyl or isopropyl alcohol; dry by waving in air. Store in dry dark place. For best results, make up papers just before use.

f. Potassium iodide solution: Prepare as directed in Method A, ¶3*b*.

g. Stannous chloride reagent: Prepare as directed in Method A, ¶3*c*.

h. Zinc, 20 to 30 mesh, arsenic-free.

i. Standard arsenic solution: Prepare as directed in Method A, ¶3*i*.

4. Procedure

a. Concentration of sample and oxidation of organic matter: To a suitable

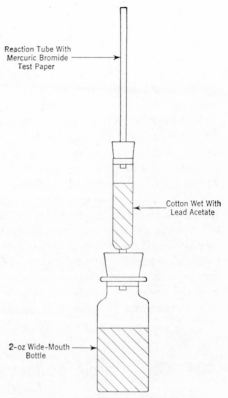

Figure 404:2. Generator used with mercuric bromide stain method.

sample containing from 2 to 30 μg As, add 7 ml 1+1 H_2SO_4 and 5 ml conc HNO_3. Evaporate to SO_3 fumes. Cool, add about 25 ml distilled water, and again evaporate to SO_3 fumes to expel oxides of nitrogen. Maintain an excess of HNO_3 until the organic matter is destroyed. Do not let solution darken while organic matter is being destroyed because arsenic is likely to be reduced and lost.

b. Preparation of guard column and reaction tube: Dip one end of the 2.5-cm length of cotton into the lead acetate solution and introduce into the glass column. Then put the dried narrow glass tube in place and insert the $HgBr_2$ test paper. Make sure the paper strip is straight.

c. *Treatment of sample concentrate:* To the 25-ml sample concentrate in the generator, add 7 ml 1+1 H_2SO_4 and cool. Add 5 ml KI solution, 4 drops $SnCl_2$ reagent, and 2 to 5 g zinc. Immediately connect the reaction tube to the generator. Immerse the apparatus to within 2.5 cm of the top of the narrow tube in a water bath kept at 20 to 25 C and allow evolution to proceed for 1.5 hr. Remove the strip and compute the average length of stains on both sides. Using a calibration curve, the preparation of which is described below, estimate the amount of arsenic present.

d. *Preparation of calibration curve:*

Prepare a blank and standards at 3-μg intervals in the 0- to 30- μg As range with 14 ml 1+1 H_2SO_4 and bring the total volume to 25 ml. Place in the generator and treat in the manner described for the sample concentrate. Remove the strip and compute the average length, in millimeters, of stains on both sides. Plot the length in millimeters against micrograms of arsenic and use as a standard curve.

5. Precision and Accuracy

A synthetic unknown sample containing 50 μg/l As, 400 μg/l Be, 180 μg/l B, and 50 μg/l Se in distilled water was analyzed in five laboratories by the mercuric bromide stain method with a relative standard deviation of 75.0% and a relative error of 60.0%.

404   C.   Atomic Absorption Spectrophotometric Method

See Section 301A.VII.

404   D.   Bibliography

Silver Diethyldithiocarbamate Method

VASAK, V. & V. SEDIVEC. 1952. Colorimetric determination of arsenic. *Chem. Listy* 46:341.

STRATTON, G. & H. C. WHITEHEAD, 1962. Colorimetric determination of arsenic in water with silver diethyldithiocarbamate. *J. Amer. Water Works Ass.* 54:861.

BALLINGER, D. C., R. J. LISHKA & M. E. GALES.
1962. Application of silver diethyldithiocarbamate method to determination of arsenic. *J. Amer. Water Works Ass.* 54:1424.

Mercuric Bromide Stain Method

FURMAN, N. H., ed. 1962. Standard Methods of Chemical Analysis, 6th ed. Vol. I. D. Van Nostrand Co., Princeton, N. J., pp. 118–124.

405 BORON

Although it is an element essential for plant growth, boron in excess of 2.0 mg/l in irrigation water is deleterious to certain plants, and some plants may be affected adversely by concentrations as low as 1.0 mg/l (or even less in commercial greenhouses). Drinking waters rarely contain more than 1 mg/l boron, and generally less than 0.1 mg/l, concentrations considered innocuous for human consumption. Boron may occur naturally in some waters or may find its way into a watercourse through cleaning compounds and industrial waste effluents.

The ingestion of large amounts of boron can affect the central nervous system, and protracted ingestion may result in a clinical syndrome known as borism.

1. Selection of Method

The curcumin method (A) is applicable in the 0.10- to 1.0-mg/l range, while the carmine method (B) is suitable for the determination of boron concentrations in the 1- to 10-mg/l range. The range of these methods can be extended by dilution or concentration of the original sample. Phosphate does not interfere with the colorimetric methods. However, the curcumin method fails in the presence of nitrate nitrogen exceeding 20 mg/l.

2. Sampling and Storage

Store samples in polyethylene bottles or alkali-resistant, boron-free glassware.

405 A. Curcumin Method

1. General Discussion

a. Principle: When a sample of water containing boron is acidified and evaporated in the presence of curcumin, a red-colored product called rosocyanine is formed. The rosocyanine is taken up in a suitable solvent and the red color is compared with standards visually or photometrically.

b. Interference: Nitrate nitrogen concentrations above 20 mg/l interfere. Significantly high results are possible when the total of calcium and magnesium hardness exceeds 100 mg/l as $CaCO_3$. Moderate hardness levels also can cause a considerable percentage error in the low boron range. The interference springs from the insolubility of the hardness salts in 95% ethanol and consequent turbidity in the final solution. Filter the final solution or pass the original sample through a column of strongly acidic cation-exchange resin in the hydrogen form to remove the interfering cations. The latter procedure enables application of the method to waters and effluents of high hardness or solids content.

c. Minimum detectable quantity: 0.2 μg B.

2. Apparatus

a. Colorimetric equipment: One of the following is required:

1) *Spectrophotometer*, for use at 540 nm, with a minimum light path of 1 cm.

2) *Filter photometer*, equipped with a green filter having a maximum transmittance near 540 nm, with a minimum light path of 1 cm.

b. *Evaporating dishes*, 100- to 150-ml capacity, of Vycor glass,* platinum, or other suitable material.

c. *Water bath*, set at 55 ± 2 C.

d. *Glass-stoppered volumetric flasks*, 25- and 50-ml capacity.

e. *Ion-exchange column*, 50 cm long by 1.3 cm in diameter.

3. Reagents

a. *Stock boron solution:* Dissolve 571.6 mg anhydrous boric acid, H_3BO_3, in distilled water and dilute to 1,000 ml; 1.00 ml = 100 μg B. Because H_3BO_3 loses weight on drying at 105 C, use a reagent meeting ACS specifications and keep the bottle tightly stoppered to prevent the entrance of atmospheric moisture.

b. *Standard boron solution:* Dilute 10.00 ml stock boron solution to 1,000 ml with distilled water; 1.00 ml = 1.00 μg B.

c. *Curcumin reagent:* Dissolve 40 mg finely ground curcumin† and 5.0 g oxalic acid in 80 ml of 95% ethyl alcohol. Add 4.2 ml conc HCl and make the solution up to 100 ml with ethyl alcohol in a 100-ml volumetric flask (isopropyl alcohol, 95%, may be used in place of ethyl alcohol). This reagent will be stable for several days if stored in a refrigerator.

---

*A product of Corning Glass Works.
†Eastman No. 1179 or equivalent.

d. *Ethyl or isopropyl alcohol*, 95%.

e. *Reagents for removal of high hardness and cation interference:*

1) *Strongly acidic cation exchange resin.*

2) *Hydrochloric acid*, HCl, 1+5.

4. Procedure

a. *Precautions:* Exercise close control of such variables as volumes and concentrations of reagents, as well as time and temperature of drying. Use evaporating dishes identical in shape, size, and composition to insure equal evaporation time. Increasing the time of evaporation results in intensification of the resulting color.

b. *Preparation of calibration curve:* Pipet 0 (blank), 0.25, 0.50, 0.75, and 1.00 μg boron into evaporating dishes of the same type, shape, and size. Add distilled water to each standard to bring the total volume to 1.0 ml. Add 4.0 ml curcumin reagent to each and swirl each dish gently to mix contents thoroughly. Float the dishes on a water bath set at 55 ± 2 C and let them remain for 80 min, which is usually sufficient for complete drying and removal of HCl. Keep drying time constant for standards and samples. After the dishes cool to room temperature, add 10.0 ml 95% ethyl alcohol to each dish, stirring gently with a polyethylene rod to insure complete dissolution of the red-colored product.

Wash the contents of each dish into a 25-ml volumetric flask, using 95% ethyl alcohol. Make up to the mark with 95% ethyl alcohol and mix thoroughly by inverting. Read the transmittance or absorbance of the standards and samples at a wavelength of 540 nm after setting the reagent blank at 100% transmittance, or zero absorbance. The calibration curve is linear from 0 to 1.00 μg boron. Make the photometric readings within 1 hr of drying the samples.

c. *Sample treatment:* For waters containing 0.10 to 1.00 mg/l boron, use 1.00 ml of sample. For waters containing more than 1.00 mg/l boron, make an appropriate dilution with boron-free distilled water, so that a 1.00-ml portion contains approximately 0.50 μg boron.

Pipet 1.00 ml of sample or dilution into an evaporating dish. Unless the calibration curve is being determined at the same time, prepare a blank and a standard containing 0.50 μg boron and run in conjunction with the unknown. Proceed as in ¶*b* preceding, beginning with "Add 4.0 ml curcumin reagent. . . ." If the final solution is turbid, filter through filter paper (Whatman No. 30 or equivalent) before reading the absorbance. Obtain the boron content from the calibration curve.

d. *Visual comparison:* The photometric method may be adapted to visual estimation of low boron concentrations, from 50 to 200 μg/l, as follows: Dilute standard boron solution so that 1.00 ml equals 0.20 μg boron. Pipet 0, 0.05, 0.10, 0.15, and 0.20 μg boron into the evaporating dishes as indicated in ¶4*b*. At the same time add an appropriate volume of sample (1.00 ml or portion diluted to 1.00 ml) to an identical evaporating dish. The total boron should be between 0.5 and 0.20 μg. Proceed as in ¶4*b*, beginning with "Add 4.0 ml curcumin reagent. . . ." Compare the color of the unknowns with the standards within 1 hr after dissolution of the red color in the alcohol.

e. *Removal of high hardness and cation interference:* Prepare an ion-exchange column of the type illustrated in Figure 106:1 and described in the Introduction, Section 107, ¶2*b*. Charge the column with a strongly acidic cation exchange resin. Backwash the column with distilled water to remove the entrained air bubbles. Henceforth, make certain that the resin remains covered with liquid at all times. Pass 50 ml 1+5 HCl through the column at a rate of 0.2 ml acid/ml resin in column per min and then wash it free of acid with distilled water.

Pipet 25 ml sample, or a smaller sample of known high boron content diluted to 25 ml, onto the resin column. Adjust the rate of flow through the column to about 2 drops/sec and collect the effluent in a 50-ml volumetric flask. Wash the column with small portions of distilled water until the flask is full to the mark. Mix the contents of the flask and transfer 2.00 ml into the evaporating dish. Add 4.0 ml curcumin reagent and complete the analysis as described in ¶4*b* preceding.

5. Calculation

The following equation may be used in calculating the boron concentration from the absorbance readings:

$$\text{mg/l B} = \frac{A_2 \times C}{A_1 \times S}$$

where A_1=absorbance of the standard, A_2=absorbance of sample, C=micrograms boron in standard taken, and S= milliliters sample.

6. Precision and Accuracy

A synthetic unknown sample containing 240 μg/l B, 40 μg/l As, 250 μg/l

Be, 20 $\mu g/l$ Se, and 6 $\mu g/l$ V in distilled water was analyzed in 30 laboratories by the curcumin method with a relative standard deviation of 22.8% and a relative error of 0%.

405 B.   Carmine Method

1. General Discussion

a. Principle: In the presence of boron, a solution of carmine or carminic acid in concentrated sulfuric acid changes from a bright red to a bluish red or blue, depending on the concentration of boron present.

b. Interference: The ions more commonly found in water and wastewater do not interfere in this method.

c. Minimum detectable quantity: 2 μg B.

2. Apparatus

Colorimetric equipment: One of the following is required:

a. Spectrophotometer, for use at 585 nm, with a minimum light path of 1 cm.

b. Filter photometer, equipped with an orange filter having a maximum transmittance near 585 nm, with a minimum light path of 1 cm.

3. Reagents

Store all reagents in polyethylene or boron-free containers.

a. Standard boron solution: Prepare as directed in Method A, ¶3*b*.

b. Hydrochloric acid, HCl, conc and 1+11.

c. Sulfuric acid, H_2SO_4, conc.

d. Carmine reagent: Dissolve 920 mg carmine N.F. 40, or carminic acid, in 1 l conc H_2SO_4.

e. Sodium hydroxide, NaOH, 1N.

4. Procedure

a. Preliminary sample treatment: If the sample contains less than 1 mg/l B, pipet a portion containing 2 to 20 μg B into a platinum dish, make alkaline with 1N NaOH plus a slight excess, and evaporate to dryness on a steam or hot water bath. If necessary, destroy any organic material by ignition to 500 to 550 C. Acidify the cooled residue (ignited or not) with 2.5 ml 1+11 HCl and triturate with a rubber policeman to dissolve. Centrifuge if necessary to obtain a clear solution. Pipet 2.00 ml clear concentrate into a small flask or 30-ml test tube. Treat reagent blank identically.

b. Color development: Prepare a series of boron standard solutions (100, 250, 500, 750, and 1,000 μg) in 100 ml with distilled water. Pipet 2.00 ml of each standard solution into a small flask or 30-ml test tube.

Treat the blank and calibration standards exactly as the sample throughout the procedure. Add 2 drops (0.1 ml) conc HCl, then carefully introduce 10.0

ml conc H_2SO_4, mix, and let cool to room temperature. Add 10.0 ml carmine reagent, mix well, and after 45 to 60 min measure the absorbance at 585 nm in a cell of 1-cm or longer light path, using the blank as the reference.

To avoid error, make sure that no bubbles are present in the optical cell while making the photometric readings. The bubbles may appear as a result of the incomplete mixing of the reagents. Because the carmine reagent deteriorates, check the calibration curve daily.

5. Calculation

$$mg/l\ B = \frac{\mu g\ B}{ml\ sample}$$

6. Precision and Accuracy

A synthetic unknown sample containing 180 $\mu g/l$ B, 50 $\mu g/l$ As, 400 $\mu g/l$ Be, and 50 $\mu g/l$ Se in distilled water was analyzed in nine laboratories by the carmine method with a relative standard deviation of 35.5% and a relative error of 0.6%.

405 C. Bibliography

Curcumin Colorimetric Method

SILVERMAN, L. & K. TREGO. 1953. Colorimetric microdetermination of boron by the curcumin-acetone solution method. *Anal. Chem.* 25:1264.

DIBLE, W.T., E. TRUOG & K.C. BERGER. 1954. Boron determination in soils and plants—Simplified curcumin procedure. *Anal. Chem.* 26:418.

LUKE, C.L. 1955. Determination of traces of boron in silicon, germanium, and germanium dioxide. *Anal. Chem.* 27:1150.

LISHKA, R.J. 1961. Comparison of analytical procedures for boron. *J. Amer. Water Works Ass.* 53:1517.

BUNTON, N.G. & B.H. TAIT. 1969. Determination of boron in waters and effluents using curcumin. *J. Amer. Water Works Ass.* 61:357.

Carmine Colorimetric Method

HATCHER, J.T. & L.V. WILCOX. 1950. Colorimetric determination of boron using carmine. *Anal. Chem.* 22:567.

406 BROMIDE

Bromide may occur in varying amounts in well supplies in coastal areas as a result of seawater intrusion. The bromide content of some groundwater supplies has been ascribed to connate water. Industrial discharges may contribute the bromide found in some freshwater streams. Under normal circumstances, the bromide content of most drinking waters is negligible, seldom exceeding 1 mg/l.

1. General Discussion

a. Principle: Phenol red undergoes a color change from yellow to red over the pH range 6.4 to 8.0. With dilute hypobromite, phenol red forms an indicator of the bromphenol blue type, which changes from yellow to blue-purple over the pH range of 3.2 to 4.6. The oxidation of the bromide and the bromination of the phenol red take place readily in the presence of chloramine-T (sodium toluene-p-sulfonchloramide). If the color comparison is made at a pH of 5.0 to 5.4, the brominated compound will be reddish to violet, depending upon its concentration. Thus, a sharp differentiation can be made between varying quantities of bromide. The concentration of chloramine-T and the timing of the reaction before dechlorination are critical.

b. Interference: Materials present in ordinary tap water do not interfere.

c. Minimum detectable concentration: 100 μg/l Br.

2. Apparatus

a. Colorimetric equipment: One of the following is required:

1) *Spectrophotometer,* for use at 590 nm, providing a light path of 2.54 cm.

2) *Filter photometer,* providing a 2.54 cm light path and equipped with an orange filter having a maximum transmittance near 590 nm.

3) *Nessler tubes,* matched, 100 ml, tall form.

b. Acid-washed glassware: Wash all glassware with 1+6 HNO_3 and rinse with distilled water to remove all trace of adsorbed bromide.

3. Reagents

a. Acetate buffer solution: Dissolve 68 g sodium acetate trihydrate, $NaC_2H_3O_2 \cdot 3H_2O$, in distilled water. Add 30 ml conc (glacial) acetic acid and make up to 1 l. The pH should be 4.6 to 4.7.

b. Phenol red indicator solution: Dissolve 21 mg phenolsulfonephthalein sodium salt and dilute to 100 ml with distilled water.

c. Chloramine-T solution: Dissolve 500 mg chloramine-T and dilute to 100 ml with distilled water. Store in a dark bottle and refrigerate.

d. Sodium thiosulfate. 2M. Dissolve 49.6 g $Na_2S_2O_3 \cdot 5H_2O$ or 31.6 g $Na_2S_2O_3$ and dilute to 100 ml with distilled water.

e. Stock bromide solution: Dissolve 744.6 mg anhydrous potassium bromide, KBr, in distilled water and make up to 1,000 ml; 1.00 ml = 500 μg Br.

f. Standard bromide solution: Dilute 10.00 ml stock bromide solution to 1,000 ml with distilled water; 1.00 ml = 5.00 μg Br.

4. Procedure

a. Treatment of sample: To 50.0 ml of sample containing 0.1 to 1.0 mg/l Br, add 2 ml buffer solution, 2 ml phenol red solution, and 0.5 ml chloramine-T solution. Mix thoroughly. Exactly 20 min after the chloramine-T addition, dechlorinate by adding, with mixing, 0.5 ml sodium thiosulfate solution. Compare visually in nessler tubes against bromide standards prepared simultaneously, or preferably read in a photometer at 590 nm, and determine the bromide values from a calibration curve.

b. Preparation of bromide standards: In addition to a reagent blank, prepare at least six standards at 0.2-mg/l intervals by diluting portions of the standard bromide solution to 50.0 ml; 1.00 ml of the standard solution diluted to 50.0 ml = 0.1 mg/l Br. Use this interval for both visual estimations and the construction of a photometric calibration curve. Read standards at 590 nm on a spectrophotometer or a filter photometer against a reagent blank. A 2.54-cm light path yields a 0.36 absorbance value at 1 mg/l Br.

5. Calculation

$$mg/l\ Br = \frac{\mu g\ Br}{ml\ sample}$$

6. Bibliography

STENGER, V.A. & I.M. KOLTHOFF. 1935. Detection and colorimetric estimation of microquantities of bromide. *J. Amer. Chem. Soc.* 57:831.

HOUGHTON, G.U. 1946. The bromide content of underground waters. *J. Soc. Chem. Ind.* (London) 65:227.

GOLDMAN, E. & D. BYLES. 1959. Suggested revision of phenol red method for bromide. *J. Amer. Water Works Ass.* 51:1051.

407   CARBON DIOXIDE

Surface waters normally contain less than 10 mg/l free carbon dioxide, while some groundwaters may easily exceed that concentration. The carbon dioxide content of a water may contribute significantly to corrosion. The recarbonation of a supply during the last stages of water softening is a recognized treatment process. The subject of saturation with respect to calcium carbonate is discussed in Section 203.

Selection of method: A nomographic and a titrimetric method are described for the estimation of free carbon dioxide in drinking water. The titration may be performed potentiometrically or with phenolphthalein indicator. Properly conducted, the more rapid, simple indicator method is satisfactory for field tests and for control and routine applications if it is understood that the method gives, at best, only an approximation.

The nomographic method (A) usually gives a closer estimation of the total free carbon dioxide when the pH and alkalinity determinations are made immediately and correctly at the time of sampling. The pH measurement preferably should be made with an electrometric pH meter, properly calibrated with standard buffer solutions in the pH range of 7 to 8. The error resulting from inaccurate pH measurements grows with an increase in the total alkalinity. For example, an inaccuracy of 0.1 in the pH determination causes a carbon dioxide error of 2 to 4 mg/l in the pH range of 7.0 to 7.3 and a total alkalinity of 100 mg/l as $CaCO_3$. In the same pH range, the error approaches 10 to 15 mg/l when the total alkalinity is 400 mg/l as $CaCO_3$.

Under favorable conditions, agreement between the titrimetric and nomographic methods is reasonably good. When the agreement is not precise and the carbon dioxide determination is of particular importance, state the method used.

The calculation of the total carbon dioxide, free and combined, is given in Method C.

407 A.   Nomographic Determination of Free Carbon Dioxide and the Three Forms of Alkalinity*

1. General Discussion

Diagrams and nomographs enable the rapid calculation of the carbon dioxide, bicarbonate, normal carbonate, and hydroxide content of natural and treated waters. These graphical presentations are based on equations relating the ionization equilibria of the carbonates and water. If the pH, total alkalinity, temperature, and total mineral content are known, any or all of the alkalinity forms and carbon dioxide can be determined nomographically.

A set of charts, Figures 407:1 through 4, is presented for use where their accuracy for the individual water

*See also Alkalinity, Section 403 preceding.

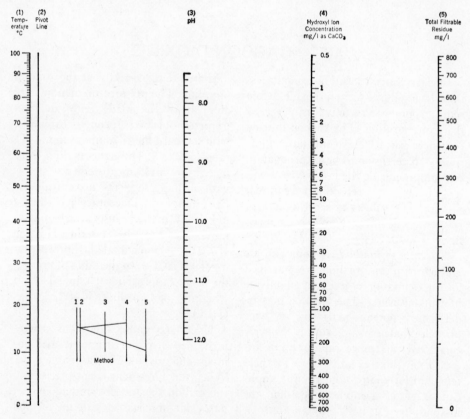

Figure 407:1. **Nomograph for evaluation of hydroxide ion concentration.†** To use: align temperature (Scale 1) and total filtrable residue (Scale 5); pivot on Line 2 to proper pH (Scale 3); read hydroxide ion concentration, as mg/l CaCO₃, on Scale 4.

† Copies of the nomographs in Figures 407:1–4, enlarged to 2.5 times the size shown here, may be obtained from The American Water Works Association, 6666 West Quincy Ave., Denver, Colorado 80235, at nominal cost.

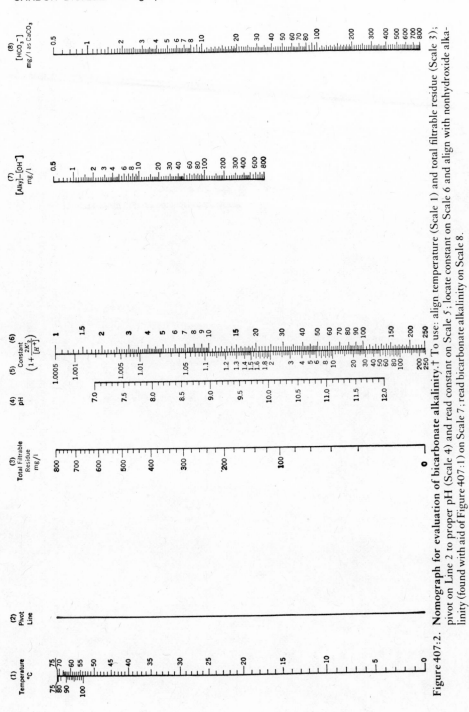

Figure 407:2. Nomograph for evaluation of bicarbonate alkalinity.† To use: align temperature (Scale 1) and total filtrable residue (Scale 3); pivot on Line 2 to proper pH (Scale 4) and read constant on Scale 5; locate constant on Scale 6 and align with nonhydroxide alkalinity (found with aid of Figure 407:1) on Scale 7; read bicarbonate alkalinity on Scale 8.

† See note to Figure 407:1.

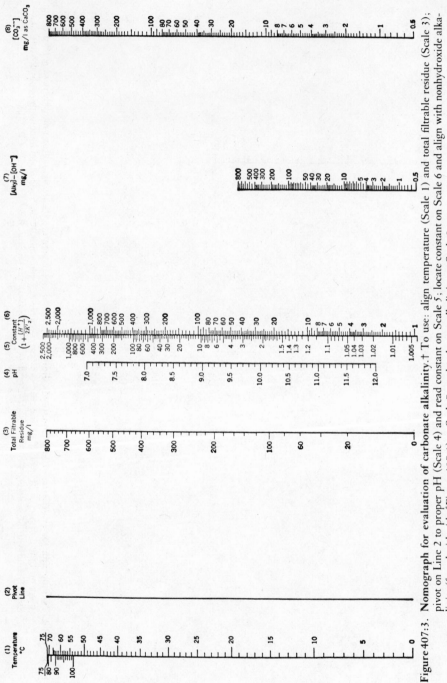

Figure 407:3. Nomograph for evaluation of carbonate alkalinity.† To use: align temperature (Scale 1) and total filtrable residue (Scale 3); pivot on Line 2 to proper pH (Scale 4) and read constant on Scale 5; locate constant on Scale 6 and align with nonhydroxide alkalinity (found with aid of Figure 407:1) on Scale 7; read carbonate alkalinity on Scale 8.

† See note to Figure 407:1.

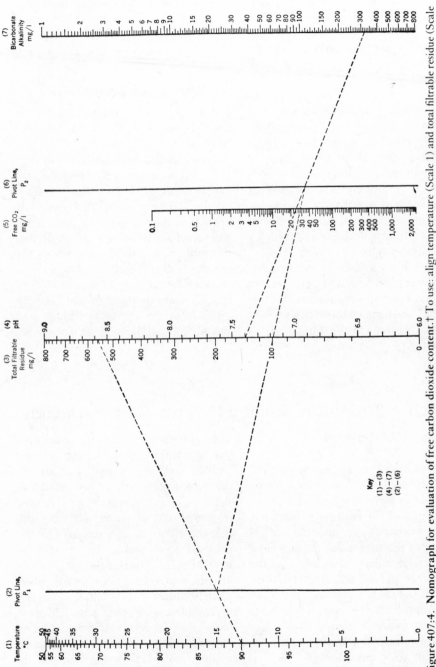

Figure 407:4. Nomograph for evaluation of free carbon dioxide content.† To use: align temperature (Scale 1) and total filtrable residue (Scale 3), which determines Point P₁ on Line 2; align pH (Scale 4) and bicarbonate alkalinity (Scale 7), which determines Point P₂ on Line 6; align P₁ with P₂ and read free carbon dioxide on Scale 5. (Example: for 13 C temperature, 560 mg/l total filtrable residue, pH 7.4, and 320 mg/l alkalinity, the free carbon dioxide content is found to be 28 mg/l.)

† See note to Figure 407:1.

supply is confirmed. The nomographs and the equations on which they are based are valid only where the salts of weak acids other than carbonic acid are absent or present in extremely small amounts.

Some treatment processes, such as superchlorination and coagulation, can significantly affect the pH and total-alkalinity values of a poorly buffered water of low alkalinity and low total-dissolved-mineral content. In such instances, the concentration of chloride and sulfate may overshadow the concentration of carbonic acid salts, thereby invalidating the applicability and accuracy of the nomographs.

Where the variables of temperature, total mineral content, and pH, alone or severally, exert an insignificant effect on the final result, the Moore charts[1] may be used. However, the limitations of these charts must be understood and their applicability to the given water supply thoroughly demonstrated.

2. Precision and Accuracy

The precision possible with the nomographs depends on the size and range of the scales. With practice, the recommended nomographs can be read with a precision of 1%. However, the overall accuracy of the results is limited by the accuracy of the analytical data applied to the nomographs and by the validity of the theoretical equations and the numerical constants on which the nomographs are based. An approximate check of the accuracy of the calculations can be made by the summation of the three forms of alkalinity. Their sum should be equal the total alkalinity.

407 B.   Titrimetric Method for Free Carbon Dioxide

I. General Discussion

a. Principle: Free carbon dioxide reacts with sodium carbonate or sodium hydroxide to form sodium bicarbonate. Completion of the reaction is indicated potentiometrically or by the development of the pink color characteristic of phenolphthalein indicator at the equivalence pH of 8.3. An $0.01N$ sodium bicarbonate solution containing the recommended volume of phenolphthalein indicator is a suitable color standard until familiarity is obtained with the color prevalent at the end point.

b. Interference: Cations and anions that quantitatively disturb the normal carbon dioxide-carbonate equilibrium interfere with the determination. Aluminum, chromium, copper, and iron are some of the metals with salts that contribute to high results. The ferrous-ion level should not exceed 1.0 mg/l. Positive errors also are caused by amines, ammonia, borate, nitrite, phosphate, silicate, and sulfide. Mineral acids and salts of strong acids and weak bases affect the determination and therefore should be absent. The titrimetric method for carbon dioxide is inapplicable to samples containing acid mine wastes and effluent from acid-regenerated cation exchangers. Negative errors may be introduced by high total dissolved solids, such as those encountered in seawater, or by adding excess indicator. Fortunately the concentration of these interferences is low in many supplies of potable water.

c. Sampling and storage: Even with a careful collection technic, some loss in free carbon dioxide can be expected in the storage and transit of the sample. This occurs more frequently when the gas is present in large amounts. Occasionally a sample may show an increase in free carbon dioxide content on standing. Consequently, the field determination of free carbon dioxide immediately at the point of sampling is advisable. Where a field determination is impractical, fill a bottle to the top for laboratory examination. Keep the sample, until tested, at a temperature lower than that at which the water was collected. Make the laboratory examination as soon as possible to minimize the effect of carbon dioxide changes.

2. Apparatus

a. Daylight fluorescent lamps have proved satisfactory and may be used in identifying the end point because they provide uniform lighting conditions at all times, and, in particular cases, accentuate certain indicator color changes.

b. Electrically operated titrators or pH meters, suitably calibrated: Where such devices are available, make the titrations with the same standard solutions given in the indicator method. Gentle agitation with a magnetic stirrer is recommended, as well as insulation of the sample from the heat of the mixer motor by means of a sheet of 3-mm (1/8-in.) asbestos paper. Titrate to selected pH values appropriate for the temperature and total-dissolved-solids content of the samples.[2] Identify the equivalence point by inflection of the titration curve or by the differential method of calculation. The potentiometric method is free from residual chlorine interference, the influence of color and turbidity, and individual visual idiosyncrasies.

3. Reagents

a. Phenolphthalein indicator solution: Use carbon dioxide-free distilled water for the preparation of this solution.

b. Standard aklali titrant: Use either $0.0454N$ Na_2CO_3 or $0.0227N$ NaOH solution. One equivalent of NaOH or two equivalents of Na_2CO_3 (1 mol) are required to convert 1 mol of CO_2 to the bicarbonate end point. For both titrants, 1.00 ml = 1.00 mg CO_2.

1) Standard sodium carbonate titrant, 0.0454N: Dissolve 2.407 g anhydrous Na_2CO_3 (primary standard grade), oven-dried at 140 C, and dilute to the mark of a 1-l volumetric flask with distilled water that has been freshly boiled for at least 15 min to expel the carbon dioxide and cooled to room temperature. Prepare the solution daily or protect from atmospheric carbon dioxide in a pyrex bottle.

2) Standard sodium hydroxide titrant, 0.0227N: Dilute 22.7 ml 1N NaOH (prepare as directed in Acidity, Section 402.3d) to 1 l with CO_2-free distilled water. Prepare the reagent daily and protect from atmospheric carbon dioxide in a pyrex bottle. Standard-

ize as described in Acidity, Section 402.3*d* preceding.

c. Sodium bicarbonate, 0.01N: Dissolve approximately 0.1 g anhydrous $NaHCO_3$ and dilute to 100 ml with CO_2-free distilled water. Prepare immediately before use.

4. Procedure

a. Field determination:

1) Collect the sample by means of rubber tubing discharging at the bottom of a 100-ml graduated cylinder or nessler tube. Allow the sample to overflow for a few minutes and withdraw the tubing while the sample is flowing. Flick the cylinder to throw off excess sample above the 100-ml mark.

2) Add 5 to 10 drops phenolphthalein indicator (always use the same volume of indicator for the sample as for the standardization procedure). If the sample turns red, free CO_2 is absent. If the sample remains colorless, titrate rapidly into the cylinder with standard alkali solution, stirring gently with a stirring rod until a definite pink color persists for 30 sec when viewed through the depth of the sample. This color change is the end point. For best results, use a color comparison standard prepared by adding the identical volume of phenolphthalein indicator to 100 ml sodium bicarbonate solution in a similar graduated cylinder or nessler tube.

3) Where the free carbon dioxide contents of the water sample is high, some loss of carbon dioxide to the atmosphere may occur even with this titra-

tion technic. To check this possibility obtain a second sample in the recommended manner and immediately run in the full amount of standard alkali solution used in the first titration. Add 5 to 10 drops phenolphthalein indicator and, if the sample remains colorless, add sufficient extra alkali solution to titrate to the proper end point. The second result is the more reliable.

b. Laboratory determination: Collect the sample in a 500-ml pyrex bottle as described in ¶4*a*1), completely filling the bottle and leaving no air space. At the laboratory, siphon the sample into a 100-ml graduated cylinder or nessler tube, allowing overflow to occur. Proceed as in ¶4*a*2).

5. Calculation

If the titrant is Na_2CO_3:

$$mg/l\ CO_2 = \frac{A \times N \times 22{,}000}{ml\ sample}$$

If the titrant is NaOH:

$$mg/l\ CO_2 = \frac{A \times N \times 44{,}000}{ml\ sample}$$

where A = ml titrant and N = normality of Na_2CO_3 or NaOH.

6. Precision and Accuracy

Precision and accuracy of the titrimetric method are on the order of ±10% of the known carbon dioxide concentration.

407 C.   Total Carbon Dioxide by Calculation

The total carbon dioxide in a water is the sum of the free carbon dioxide and the carbon dioxide in the form of bicarbonate and carbonate ions as determined nomographically; or the free carbon dioxide and the carbonate and bicarbonate alkalinities as determined stoichiometrically by titration.

Compute the total carbon dioxide from the concentrations of free carbon dioxide, bicarbonate alkalinity, and carbonate alkalinity by the following equation, using alkalinities expressed as $CaCO_3$:

$$\text{mg/l total } CO_2 = \text{mg/l free } CO_2 + 0.88\,(A+B)$$

where $A = $ mg/l bicarbonate alkalinity and $B = 1/2$ (mg/l carbonate alkalinity).

407 D.   References

1. MOORE, E.W. 1939. Graphic determination of carbon dioxide and the three forms of alkalinity. *J. Amer. Water Works Ass.* 31:51.
2. DYE, J.F. 1958. Correlation of the two principal methods of calculating the three kinds of alkalinity. *J. Amer. Water Works Ass.* 50:812.

407 E.   Bibliography

Nomographic Method
LANGELIER, W.F. 1936. The analytical control of anticorrosion water treatment. *J. Amer. Water Works Ass.* 28:1500.
DEMARTINI, F.E. 1938. Corrosion and the Langelier calcium carbonate saturation index. *J. Amer. Water Works Ass.* 30:85.
LARSON, T.E. & A.M. BUSWELL. 1942. Calcium carbonate saturation index and alkalinity interpretations. *J. Amer. Water Works Ass.* 34:1667.
DYE, J.F. 1944. The calculation of alkalinities and free carbon dioxide in water by the use of nomographs. *J. Amer. Water Works Ass.* 36:895.

DYE, J.F. 1952. Calculation of effect of temper-
ature on pH, free carbon dioxide, and the
three forms of alkalinity. *J. Amer. Water
Works Ass.* 44:356.
Titrimetric Method
Standard Methods for the Examination of Water
and Sewage, 8th ed. 1936. APHA &
AWWA, New York, N.Y. pp. 69, 122

Approved Methods for the Physical and Chem-
ical Examination of Water, 3rd ed. 1960.
Inst. Water Engineers, Royal Inst. Chem-
istry, & Soc. Pub. Analysts & Other Anal.
Chem., London, p. 40.
NORDELL, E. 1961. Water Treatment for Indus-
trial and Other Uses, 2nd ed. Reinhold
Publ. Corp., New York, N.Y. pp. 87–98.

408   CHLORIDE

Chloride, in the form of Cl ion, is one of the major inorganic anions in water and wastewater. In potable water, the salty taste produced by chloride concentrations is variable and dependent on the chemical composition of the water. Some waters containing 250 mg/l chloride may have a detectable salty taste if the cation is sodium. On the other hand, the typical salty taste may be absent in waters containing as much as 1,000 mg/l when the predominant cations are calcium and magnesium.

The chloride concentration is higher in wastewater than in raw water because sodium chloride is a common article of diet and passes unchanged through the digestive system. Along the sea coast, chloride may be present in high concentrations because of leakage of salt water into the sewerage system. It may also be increased by industrial processes.

A high chloride content harms metallic pipes and structures, as well as agricultural plants.

Selection of method: Four methods are presented for the determination of chlorides. Since the first two are similar in most respects, selection is largely a matter of preference. The argentometric method (A) is suitable for use in relatively clear waters when 0.15 to 10 mg Cl are present in the portion of sample titrated. The mercuric nitrate method (B) has an easier end point. The potentiometric method (C) is suitable for colored or turbid samples in which color-indicated end points might be difficult to observe. The potentiometric method can be used without a pretreatment step for samples containing ferric ions (if not present in an amount greater than the chloride concentration), chromic phosphate, and ferrous and other heavy metal ions. The ferricyanide method, given in Part 602, is an automated modification which, although used routinely by many laboratories, is listed for the first time as a tentative method.

408 A.   Argentometric Method

I. General Discussion

a. *Principle:* In a neutral or slightly alkaline solution, potassium chromate can indicate the end point of the silver nitrate titration of chloride. Silver chloride is precipitated quantitatively before red silver chromate is formed.

b. *Interference:* Substances in amounts normally found in potable waters will not interfere. Bromide, iodide, and cyanide register as equivalent chloride concentrations. Sulfide, thiosulfate, and sulfite ions interfere but can be removed by treatment with hydrogen peroxide. Orthophosphate in excess of 25 mg/l interferes by precipitation as silver phosphate. Iron in excess of 10 mg/l interferes by masking the end point.

2. Reagents

a. *Chloride-free water:* If necessary, use redistilled or deionized distilled water.

b. *Potassium chromate indicator solution:* Dissolve 50 g K_2CrO_4 in a little distilled water. Add silver nitrate solution until a definite red precipitate is formed. Let stand 12 hr, filter, and dilute to 1 l with distilled water.

c. *Standard silver nitrate titrant,* 0.0141N: dissolve 2.395 g $AgNO_3$ in distilled water and dilute to 1,000 ml. Standardize against 0.0141N NaCl by the procedure described in ¶3b below. Store in a brown bottle. Standard silver nitrate solution 0.0141N = 500 μg Cl/ 1.00 ml.

d. *Standard sodium chloride,* 0.0141N: Dissolve 824.1 mg NaCl (dried at 140 C) in chloride-free water

and dilute to 1,000 ml; 1.00 ml = 500 μg Cl.

e. *Special reagents for removal of interference:*

1) *Aluminum hydroxide suspension:* Dissolve 125 g aluminum potassium sulfate or aluminum ammonium sulfate, $AlK(SO_4)_2 \cdot 12H_2O$ or $AlNH_4(SO_4)_2 \cdot 12H_2O$, in 1 l distilled water. Warm to 60 C and add 55 ml conc NH_4OH slowly with stirring. Let stand about 1 hr, transfer the mixture to a large bottle, and wash the precipitate by successive additions, with thorough mixing and decantations of distilled water, until free from chloride. When freshly prepared, the suspension occupies a volume of approximately 1 l.

2) *Phenolphthalein indicator solution.*

3) *Sodium hydroxide,* NaOH, 1N.

4) *Sulfuric acid,* H_2SO_4, 1N.

5) *Hydrogen peroxide,* H_2O_2, 30%.

3. Procedure

a. *Sample preparation:* Use a 100-ml sample or a suitable portion diluted to 100 ml.

If the sample is highly colored, add 3 ml $Al(OH)_3$ suspension, mix, let settle, filter, wash, and combine filtrate and washing.

If sulfide, sulfite, or thiosulfate is present, add 1 ml H_2O_2 and stir for 1 min.

b. *Titration:* Titrate samples in the pH range 7 to 10 directly. Adjust samples not in this range with H_2SO_4 or NaOH solution. Add 1.0 ml K_2CrO_4 indicator solution. Titrate with standard silver nitrate titrant to a pinkish yellow end point. Be consistent in end-point recognition.

Standardize the silver nitrate titrant and establish the reagent blank value by the titration method outlined above. A blank of 0.2 to 0.3 ml is usual for the method.

4. Calculation

$$mg/l\ Cl\ =\ \frac{(A-B)\times N\times 35,450}{ml\ sample}$$

where A = ml titration for sample, B = ml titration for blank, and N = normality of $AgNO_3$.

$$mg/l\ NaCl = mg/l\ Cl \times 1.65$$

5. Precision and Accuracy

A synthetic unknown sample containing 241 mg/l chloride, 108 mg/l Ca, 82 mg/l Mg, 3.1 mg/l K, 19.9 mg/l Na, 1.1 mg/l nitrate N, 0.25 mg/l nitrite N, 259 mg/l sulfate, and 42.5 mg/l total alkalinity (contributed by $NaHCO_3$) in distilled water was analyzed in 41 laboratories by the argentometric method, with a relative standard deviation of 4.2% and a relative error of 1.7%.

408 B.   Mercuric Nitrate Method*

1. General Discussion

a. Principle: Chloride can be titrated with mercuric nitrate because of the formation of soluble, slightly dissociated mercuric chloride. In the pH range 2.3 to 2.8, diphenylcarbazone indicates the end point of this titration by formation of a purple complex with the excess mercuric ions. The error in titration is about 1% of the volume of titrant used per change of 0.1 pH unit in the pH range 2.1 to 2.8. Because exact pH adjustment is not feasible except by use of a pH meter, it is felt that keeping within a range of ±0.1 pH unit is sufficient for

most water analyses. Therefore, in this method, a specific mixture of nitric acid and diphenylcarbazone is added to a water sample, adjusting the pH of most potable waters to pH 2.5±0.1. A third substance in this alcoholic mixture, xylene cyanol FF, is used as a pH indicator and as a background color to facilitate end-point detection. The introduction of 10 mg sodium bicarbonate to both the blank and the standard titration provides a pH of 2.5±0.1 when 1.0 ml indicator-acidifier reagent [¶2d1)] is added. Increasing the strength of the titrant and modifying the indicator mixture enable determination of the higher chloride concentrations common in wastewater.

b. Interference: Bromide and iodide are titrated with mercuric nitrate in the same manner as chloride. Chromate, ferric, and sulfite ions interfere when present in excess of 10 mg/l.

---

* United States Patent No. 2,784,064 has been issued to F.E. Clarke, relative to the mercurimetric titration of chloride. Nothing contained in this manual is to be construed as granting any right, by implication or otherwise, for manufacture, sale, or use in connection with any method, apparatus or product covered by patent, nor as insuring anyone against liability for infringement of patent.

2. Reagents

a. Standard sodium chloride 0.0141 *N*. See Method A, ¶2*d* above.

b. Nitric acid, HNO_3, 0.1*N*.

c. Sodium hydroxide, NaOH, 0.1*N*.

d. Reagents for low-chloride titrations:

1) *Indicator-acidifier reagent:* The nitric acid concentration of this reagent is an important factor in the success of the determination and can be varied as indicated in a) or b) to suit the alkalinity range of the sample being titrated. Reagent a) contains sufficient nitric acid to neutralize a total alkalinity of 150 mg/l as $CaCO_3$ to the proper pH in a 100-ml sample.

a) Dissolve, in the order named, 250 mg s-diphenylcarbazone, 4.0 ml conc HNO_3, and 30 mg xylene cyanol FF in 100 ml of 95% ethyl alcohol or isopropyl alcohol. Store in a dark bottle in a refrigerator. This reagent is not stable indefinitely. Deterioration causes a slow end point and high results.

b) Because pH control is critical in this method, adjust the pH of highly alkaline or acid samples to 2.5±0.1 with 0.1*N* HNO_3 or NaOH, not with Na_2CO_3. Use a pH meter with a non-chloride type of reference electrode for the pH adjustment. If only the usual chloride-type reference electrode is available for pH adjustment, determine the amount of acid or alkali required to achieve a pH of 2.5±0.1 and discard this sample portion. Treat a separate sample portion with the determined amount of acid or alkali and continue the analysis to its prescribed end. Under these circumstances, omit the nitric acid from the indicator reagent to maintain the proper sample pH. Alternatively, vary the nitric acid concentration of the indicator-acidifier reagent to accommodate conditions wherein water samples of very high or very low alkalinity are being analyzed.

2) *Standard mercuric nitrate titrant*, 0.0141*N*: Dissolve 2.3 g $Hg(NO_3)_2$ or 2.5 g $Hg(NO_3)_2 \cdot H_2O$ in 100 ml distilled water containing 0.25 ml conc HNO_3. Dilute to just under 1 l. Make a preliminary standardization by following the procedure described in ¶3*a*. Use replicates containing 5.00 ml standard NaCl solution and 10 mg $NaHCO_3$ diluted to 100 ml with distilled water. Adjust the mercuric nitrate titrant to exactly 0.0141*N* and make a final standardization. Store away from the light in a dark bottle. Standard mercuric nitrate titrant, exactly 0.0141*N*, is equivalent to 500 μg Cl/1.00 ml.

e. Reagents for high-chloride titrations:

1) *Mixed indicator reagent:* Dissolve 5 g diphenylcarbazone powder and 0.5 g bromphenol blue powder in 750 ml 95% ethyl or isopropyl alcohol and dilute to 1 l with ethyl or isopropyl alcohol.

2) *Strong standard mercuric nitrate titrant*, 0.141*N*: Dissolve 25 g $Hg(NO_3)_2 \cdot H_2O$ in 900 ml distilled water containing 5.0 ml conc HNO_3. Dilute to just under 1 l, and perform a preliminary standardization by following the procedure described in ¶3*b*. Use replicates containing 25.00 ml standard NaCl solution and 25 ml distilled water. Adjust the titrant to 0.141*N* and make a final standardization. The chloride equivalence of the titrant is 5.00 mg/1.00 ml.

3. Procedure

a. Titration of low chloride concentrations: Use a 100-ml sample or smaller portion so that the chloride content is less than 10 mg.

Add 1.0 ml of indicator-acidifier reagent to the sample. (The color of the solution should be green-blue at this point. A light green indicates a pH of less than 2.0; a pure blue indicates a pH of more than 3.8. For most potable waters, the pH after this addition will be 2.5±0.1. For highly alkaline or acid waters, adjust pH to about 8 before adding the indicator-acidifier reagent.)

Titrate the treated sample with 0.0141*N* mercuric nitrate titrant to a definite purple end point. The solution will turn from green-blue to blue a few drops from the end point.

Determine the blank by titrating 100 ml distilled water containing 10 mg NaHCO₃.

b. Titration of high chloride concentrations: Place 50.0 ml sample in a 150-ml beaker (5.00 ml sample may be used when more than 5 ml titrant are needed). Add approximately 0.5 ml mixed indicator reagent and mix well. The color should be purple. Add 0.1*N*

HNO₃ dropwise until the color just turns yellow. Titrate with 0.141*N* mercuric nitrate titrant to the first permanent dark purple. Titrate a distilled water blank using the same procedure.

4. Calculation

$$\text{mg/l Cl} = \frac{(A-B) \times N \times 35{,}450}{\text{ml sample}}$$

where A = ml titration for sample, B = ml titration for blank, and N = normality of $Hg(NO_3)_2$.

$$\text{mg/l NaCl} = \text{mg/l Cl} \times 1.65$$

5. Precision and Accuracy

A synthetic unknown sample containing 241 mg/l chloride, 108 mg/l Ca, 82 mg/l Mg, 3.1 mg/l K, 19.9 mg/l Na, 1.1 mg/l nitrate N, 0.25 mg/l nitrite N, 259 mg/l sulfate, and 42.5 mg/l total alkalinity (contributed by NaHCO₃) in distilled water was analyzed in 10 laboratories by the mercurimetric method, with a relative standard deviation of 3.3% and a relative error of 2.9%.

408 C.   Potentiometric Method

1. General Discussion

a. Principle: Chloride is determined by potentiometric titration with silver nitrate solution with a glass and silver–silver chloride electrode system. During titration an electronic voltmeter is used to detect the change in potential between the two electrodes. The end point of the

titration is that instrument reading at which the greatest change in voltage has occurred for a small and constant increment of silver nitrate added.

b. Interference: Iodide and bromide also are titrated as chloride. Ferricyanide causes high results and must be removed. Chromate and dichromate interfere and should be reduced to the chromic state or removed. Ferric iron interferes if present in an amount that is substantially higher than the amount of chloride. Chromic ion, ferrous ion, and phosphate do not interfere.

Grossly contaminated samples usually require pretreatment. Where contamination is minor, some contaminants can be destroyed simply by the addition of nitric acid.

2. Apparatus

a. Glass and silver–silver chloride electrodes: Prepare in the laboratory or purchase a silver electrode coated with silver chloride for use with specified instruments. Instructions on the use and care of the electrodes are supplied by the manufacturer.

b. Electronic voltmeter, to measure the potential difference between the electrodes: A pH meter may be converted to this use by substitution of the appropriate electrode.

c. Mechanical stirrer, with plastic-coated or glass impeller.

3. Reagents

a. Standard sodium chloride solution, 0.0141N: Dissolve 8.243 g NaCl, dried at 105 C, in distilled water and dilute to exactly 500 ml. Dilute 50.0 ml of this solution to 1,000 ml; 1.00 ml=0.500 mg Cl.

b. Nitric acid, HNO_3, conc.

c. Standard silver nitrate titrant, 0.014N: Dissolve 2.40 g $AgNO_3$ in distilled water and dilute to 1,000 ml. Standardize this solution by titrating exactly 10.0 ml standard NaCl solution by the procedure described in ¶4a. Adjust the $AgNO_3$ titrant to the same normal-

ity as the NaCl solution; 1.00 ml= 0.500 mg Cl.

$$\text{Normality of AgNO}_3 = \frac{10.0 \times 0.0141}{\text{ml AgNO}_3}$$

d. Special reagents for pretreatment:
1) *Sulfuric acid,* H_2SO_4, 1+1.
2) *Hydrogen peroxide,* H_2O_2, 30%.
3) *Sodium hydroxide,* NaOH, 1N.

4. Procedure

a. Standardization: The various instruments that can be used in this determination differ in operating details; follow the manufacturer's instructions. Make necessary mechanical adjustments. Then, after allowing sufficient time for warm-up (10 min), balance the internal electrical components to give an instrument setting of 0 mV or, if a pH meter is used, a pH reading of 7.0.

2) Place 10.0 ml standard NaCl solution in a 250-ml beaker, dilute to about 100 ml, and add 2.0 ml conc HNO_3. Immerse the stirrer and the electrodes in the solution.

3) Set the instrument to the desired range of millivolts or pH units. Start the stirrer.

4) Add standard $AgNO_3$ titrant, recording the scale reading after each addition. At the start, large increments of $AgNO_3$ may be added; then, as the end point of the reaction is approached, add smaller and equal increments (0.1 or 0.2 ml) at longer intervals, so that the exact end point can be determined. Determine the volume of $AgNO_3$ used at the point at which there is the greatest change in instrument reading per unit addition of $AgNO_3$.

5) Plot a differential titration curve if the exact end point cannot be deter-

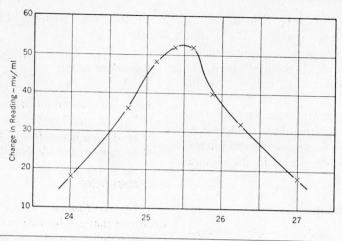

Experimental Data Plotted Above								
Volume, *ml*	23.50	24.50	25.00	25.25	25.50	25.75	26.00	26.50	27.50
Change, *mV/ml*	18	36	48	52	52	40	32	18

Figure 408:1. Example of differential titration curve (end point is 25.5 ml).

mined by inspection of the data. Plot the change in instrument reading for equal increments of $AgNO_3$ against the volume of $AgNO_3$ added, using the average of the buret readings before and after each addition. The procedure is illustrated in Figure 408:1.

b. Sample analysis:

1) Pipet exactly 100.0 ml of sample, or a portion containing not more than 10 mg chloride, into a 250-ml beaker. In the absence of interfering substances, proceed with ¶3) below.

2) In the presence of organic compounds, sulfite, or other interferences (such as large amounts of ferric iron, cyanide, or sulfide), acidify the sample with H_2SO_4, using litmus paper. Boil for 5 min to remove volatile compounds. Add more H_2SO_4, if necessary, to keep the solution acidic. Add 3 ml H_2O_2 and boil for 15 min, adding chloride-free

distilled water to keep the volume above 50 ml. Dilute to 100 ml, add NaOH solution dropwise until alkaline to litmus, then 10 drops in excess. Boil for 5 min, filter into a 250-ml beaker, and wash the precipitate and paper several times with hot distilled water.

3) Add conc HNO_3 dropwise until acidic to litmus paper, then 2.0 ml in excess. Cool and dilute to 100 ml if necessary. Immerse the stirrer and the electrodes in the sample and start the stirrer. Make any necessary adjustments of the instrument according to the manufacturer's instructions and set the selector switch to the appropriate setting for measuring the difference of potential between the electrodes.

4) Complete the determination by titrating according to ¶4*a*4). If an endpoint reading has been established from previous determinations for similar

samples and conditions, use this pre-determined end point. For the most accurate work, make a blank titration by carrying chloride-free distilled water through the procedure.

5. Calculation

$$\text{mg/l Cl} = \frac{(A-B) \times N \times 35.45 \times 1,000}{D}$$

where A = ml $AgNO_3$, B = ml blank, N = normality of titrant, and D = ml sample.

6. Precision and Accuracy

In the absence of interfering substances, the precision and accuracy are estimated to be about 0.12 mg for 5 mg Cl, or 2.5% of the amount present. When pretreatment is required for removal of interfering substances, the precision and accuracy are reduced to about 0.25 mg for 5 mg Cl, or 5% of the amount present.

409 CHLORINE (RESIDUAL)

The chlorination of water supplies and polluted waters serves primarily to destroy or deactivate disease-producing microorganisms. A secondary benefit is the overall improvement in water quality resulting from the reaction of chlorine with ammonia, iron, manganese, sulfide, and some organic substances.

Chlorination may produce adverse effects by intensifying the taste and odor characteristics of phenols and other organic compounds present in a water supply. Combined chlorine formed on chlorination of ammonia- or amine-bearing waters affects some forms of aquatic life adversely. To promote the primary purpose of chlorination and to minimize any adverse effects, it is essential that proper testing procedures be used with a fore-knowledge of the limitations of the analytical determination.

Chlorine applied to water in its elemental or hypochlorite form initially undergoes hydrolysis to form free available chlorine consisting of aqueous molecular chlorine, hypochlorous acid, and hypochlorite ion. The relative proportion of these free chlorine forms is pH-dependent, and at the pH of most waters the hypochlorous acid and hypochlorite ion will predominate.

Free chlorine reacts readily with ammonia and certain nitrogenous compounds to form combined available chlorine. With ammonia, chlorine reacts to form the chloramines: monochloramine, dichloramine, and nitrogen trichloride. The presence and concentrations of these combined forms depend on many conditions, chiefly pH, temperature, and the initial chlorine-to-nitrogen ratio. Both free and combined chlorine may be present simultaneously. Combined chlorine in water supplies may be formed in the treatment of raw waters containing ammonia, by the addition of ammonium salts in pre-chlorination, or by producing a combined chlorine residual in the distribution system. Chlorinated wastewater effluents, as well as certain chlorinated industrial effluents, normally contain only combined chlorine forms. Historically, the principal analytical problem has been to distinguish between free and combined forms.

In two separate but related studies, designated Study No. 1 and 2, respectively, samples were prepared and distributed to participating laboratories for the purpose of evaluating the residual chlorine methods.

In Study No. 1, three solid synthetic unknowns were prepared: One powdered unknown was compounded of 70% calcium hypochlorite* and NaCl filler to yield a free available chlorine concentration of 800 $\mu g/l$ upon dissolution in chlorine-demand-free distilled water; the second was compounded of 70% calcium hypochlorite* and NaCl filler to yield a total available chlorine concentration of 640 $\mu g/l$ upon dissolution and mixing with an aqueous ammonium buffer solution in chlorine-demand-free distilled water; and the third was prepared from Halazone,† p-(N,N-dichlorosulfamyl) benzoic acid, to yield a total available chlorine concentration of 1,830 $\mu g/l$ upon dissolution in chlorine-demand-free distilled water. The results obtained by the participating laboratories are summarized in Table 409:I.

In Study No. 2, each participating laboratory received four sealed glass ampoules of concentrated solution (three hypochlorite solutions of different concentrations and one ammonium chloride borate buffer solution) which, when diluted according to instructions, provided two samples containing free chlo-

rine and one containing combined chlorine. Sample No. 1 contained 440 $\mu g/l$ free chlorine, a concentration likely to be encountered in analysis of treated potable water. Sample No. 2 contained 980 $\mu g/l$ free chlorine, the maximum concentration likely to be encountered in analysis of treated potable water. Sample No. 3 contained only combined chlorine at a concentration of 660 $\mu g/l$ to simulate an insufficiently chlorinated water having no free chlorine residual. To facilitate statistical computations, a value of 50 $\mu g/l$ free chlorine was selected as the "true" value rather than the theoretical 0.0 $\mu g/l$. In Study No. 2, the data were treated statistically according to a total error term defined as

$$\text{Total error} = 100 \times \frac{\text{Absolute value of mean error} + 2\,(\text{Std. Dev.})}{\text{True value}}$$

The results obtained by the participating laboratories are summarized in Tables 409:II through IV. In the last column of these tables all data on Sample No. 1 are omitted because of sample instability, and therefore the results can be used only for comparative purposes and not as a measure of the overall precision or accuracy. Free chlorine data also were omitted in Column 3 because the stated free chlorine content is an artifact and actually was zero.

Because of poor accuracy and precision and a high overall (average) total error in comparison with other available methods, the orthotolidine procedures that have been so widely used have been deleted as standard methods. The methyl orange technic also has been deleted because of the poor precision (lack

---

* Olin Matheson Chemical Corp., HTH (granular).

† Abbott Laboratories.

TABLE 409:I. PRECISION AND ACCURACY DATA FOR RESIDUAL CHLORINE METHODS IN STUDY No. 1

Method	Residual Chlorine Concentration		Number of Laboratories	Relative Standard Deviation %	Relative Error %
	Free µg/l	Total µg/l			
Titrimetric (iodine)		840	32	27.0	23.6
		640	30	32.4	18.5
		1,830	32	23.6	16.7
Amperometric	800		23	42.3	25.0
		640	24	24.8	8.5
		1,830	24	12.5	8.8
Orthotolidine	800		15	64.6	42.5
		640	17	37.3	20.2
		1,830	18	31.9	41.4
Orthotolidine-arsenite	800		20	52.4	42.3
		640	21	28.0	14.2
		1,830	23	35.0	49.6
Stabilized neutral orthotolidine	800		15	34.7	12.8
		640	16	8.0	2.0
		1,830	17	26.1	12.4
Ferrous DPD	800		19	39.8	19.8
		640	19	19.2	8.1
		1,830	19	9.4	4.3
DPD Colorimetric	980		26	20.7	15.6
		660	25	27.6	15.6
Leuco crystal violet	800		17	32.7	7.1
		640	17	34.4	0.9
		1,830	18	32.4	18.6
Methyl orange	800		26	43.0	22.0
		640	26	30.1	14.2
		1,830	26	19.9	7.2

TABLE 409:II. SUMMARY OF OVERALL ACCURACY IN STUDY NO. 2 (AVERAGE MEAN ERROR IN MG/L)

Method	Sample 1		Sample 2		Sample 3		Over-all Average	Omitting all Data on Sample 1 and Free on Sample 3
	Free	Total	Free	Total	Free	Total		
Methyl orange	−0.219	−0.171	−0.044	−0.006	−0.006	+0.029	0.079	0.026
Leuco crystal violet	−0.250	−0.209	−0.085	−0.070	−0.050	−0.007	0.112	0.054
SNORT	−0.241	−0.198	−0.113	−0.107	−0.048	−0.032	0.123	0.084
DPD-titrimetric	−0.259	−0.198	−0.192	−0.059	−0.038	−0.031	0.130	0.094
DPD-colorimetric	−0.263	−0.213	−0.153	−0.097	−0.014	+0.103	0.140	0.117
Amperometric	−0.241	−0.189	−0.230	−0.119	−0.012	−0.108	0.150	0.152
OTA	−0.282	−0.253	−0.198	−0.102	+0.114	−0.092	0.174	0.130

TABLE 409:III. SUMMARY OF OVERALL PRECISION IN STUDY NO. 2
(AVERAGE STANDARD DEVIATION IN MG/L)

Method	Sample 1		Sample 2		Sample 3		Over-all Average	Omitting all Data on Sample 1 and Free on Sample 3
	Free	Total	Free	Total	Free	Total		
Leuco crystal violet	0.085	0.055	0.042	0.015	0.000	0.089	0.048	0.049
SNORT	0.093	0.092	0.120	0.142	0.004	0.110	0.094	0.124
Amperometric	0.106	0.072	0.206	0.137	0.040	0.171	0.122	0.171
DPD-colorimetric	0.102	0.100	0.171	0.152	0.057	0.210	0.132	0.177
DPD-titrimetric	0.110	0.103	0.298	0.205	0.019	0.121	0.143	0.208
Methyl orange	0.143	0.162	0.315	0.301	0.055	0.143	0.187	0.253
OTA	0.090	0.098	0.335	0.325	0.195	0.218	0.210	0.293

TABLE 409:IV. SUMMARY OF OVERALL (AVERAGE) TOTAL ERROR IN STUDY NO. 2

Method	Sample 1		Sample 2		Sample 3		Over-all Average	Omitting all Data on Sample 1 and Free on Sample 3
	Free	Total	Free	Total	Free	Total		
Leuco crystal violet	95.31	72.59	17.24	10.20	100.00	28.00	53.90	18.52
SNORT	97.04	87.00	35.95	39.97	112.40	38.15	68.42	38.02
DPD-titrimetric	108.86	91.77	80.51	47.89	153.40	41.33	87.29	56.64
Amperometric	102.95	75.63	65.46	40.14	182.80	68.21	89.20	57.94
DPD-colorimetric	106.18	94.00	50.57	40.83	256.40	79.33	104.55	56.90
Methyl orange	114.86	112.59	68.83	62.12	232.00	47.75	106.36	59.56
OTA	104.95	101.90	88.57	76.81	1007.80	79.93	243.33	81.77

of reproducibility) inherent in a bleaching technic in which operator skill and environmental factors such as temperature are critical.

The results presented in Tables 409:I through IV are valuable only for comparison of the methods tested. Many factors, such as analytical skill, recognition of known interferences, and inherent limitations, determine the reliability of any given method.

Some oxidizing agents, including free halogens other than chlorine, will appear quantitatively as free chlorine; this is also true of chlorine dioxide. Some nitrogen trichloride may be measured as free chlorine. The actions of interfering substances should be familiar to the analyst because they affect a particular method.

1. Selection of Method

a. Natural and treated waters: The iodometric methods (A and B) are suitable for measuring chlorine concentrations greater than 1 mg/l, but are not accurate at lower concentrations or in the presence of interferences.

The amperometric titration method (C) is a standard of comparison for the determination of free or combined chlorine. It is affected little by common oxidizing agents, temperature variations, turbidity, and color. The method is not as simple as the colorimetric methods and requires greater operator skill to obtain the best reliability.

The ferrous DPD method (E) provides a titrimetric procedure for determining free available chlorine and for estimating free and combined chlorine fractions present together.

The stabilized neutral orthotolidine (SNORT) and the DPD colorimetric methods (Methods D and F, respectively) are applicable to the determination of free available chlorine. Procedures are given for estimating the combined fractions. Increasing concentrations of monochloramine are likely to produce an increased interference with the free chlorine determination. In addition, the SNORT and DPD methods are subject to interference by oxidized forms of manganese.

The leuco crystal violet (LCV) method (G) makes possible the determination of free available chlorine, total chlorine, and combined chlorine by difference. The LCV method exhibits a relatively minimal interference as monochloramine concentrations are increased in the determination of free available chlorine; however, nitrite and monochloramine in combination, as well as oxidized forms of manganese, will produce interference in determining free available chlorine.

The amperometric, LCV, DPD, and SNORT methods are unaffected by dichloramine concentrations in the range of 0 to 9 mg/l (as Cl_2) in the determination of free chlorine. Nitrogen trichloride, if present, reacts partially as free available chlorine in the amperometric, DPD, and SNORT methods. Nitrogen trichloride does not interfere with the LCV procedure for free chlorine.

The free available chlorine test, syringaldazine (Method H, Tentative) was developed as a procedure specific for free available chlorine. It is unaffected by significant concentrations of monochloramine, dichloramine, nitrate, nitrite, and oxidized forms of manganese.

Sample color and turbidity may interfere in all colorimetric procedures unless they are compensated for.

Organic contaminants may produce a false free chlorine reading in most colorimetric methods (see ¶1b below).

b. *Polluted waters:* The determination of residual chlorine in samples containing organic matter presents special problems. Because of the presence of organic compounds, particularly organic nitrogen, the residual chlorine exists in a combined state. A considerable residual may exist in this form, but at the same time there may be appreciable unsatisfied chlorine demand. The addition of the reagents in the determination may change these relationships so that residual chlorine is lost during the analysis. In wastewater, the differentiation between free available chlorine and combined available chlorine is not ordinarily made because wastewater chlorination is seldom carried far enough to produce free available chlorine.

The determination of residual chlorine in industrial wastes is similar to that in sewage when the waste contains organic matter, but may be similar to the determination in water when the waste is low in organic matter.

Although the methods given below are useful for the determination of residual chlorine in wastewaters and treated effluents, selection in accordance with the composition of the sample being tested is necessary. Some industrial wastes, or mixtures of wastes with domestic wastewater, may require special precautions and modifications to obtain satisfactory results.

Free chlorine in a wastewater can be determined by any of the methods presented in Sections 409 A through 409 H, provided that known interfering substances are absent or compensated for. The amperometric method (C) is the method of choice because it is not subject to interference from color, turbidity. iron, manganese, or nitrite nitrogen. The DPD and SNORT methods are subject to interference from high concentrations of monochloramine unless these are compensated for by addition of arsenite immediately after reagent addition. The LCV method (G) is significantly less affected by high monochloramine concentrations and an arsenite addition will produce a minimum interference. The presence of oxidized forms of manganese will interfere in most colorimetric procedures and, in addition, the combination of monochloramine and nitrite will seriously interfere with the LCV procedure.

The tentative syringaldazine method (H) is unaffected by concentrations of monochloramine, dichloramine, nitrite, nitrogen, iron, manganese, and other interfering compounds normally found in domestic wastewaters.

For total available chlorine in samples containing significant amounts of organic matter, the iodometric back titration method (B) should be used to prevent contact between the full concentration of liberated iodine and the sample. Either the amperometric or the starch-iodide end point may be used. In the absence of the interference, the two modifications give concordant results. The amperometric end point is inherently more accurate and is free of interference from color and turbidity, which can cause difficulty with the starch-iodide end point. On the other hand, certain metals and complex anions in some industrial wastes interfere in the amperometric titration and indicate the use of another method for such wastewaters. Silver in the form of soluble silver cyanide complex, in concentrations as low as 1.0 mg/l silver, poisons the cell at pH 4.0 but not at 7.0. The silver ion, in the absence of the cyanide complex, gives extensive response in the current at pH 4.0 and gradually poisons the cell at all pH levels. Cuprous copper in the soluble copper cyanide ion, in concentrations as low as 5 mg/l copper or less, poisons the cell at pH 4.0 and 7.0. Although manganese, iron, and nitrite may interfere with this method, the interference is minimized by buffering to pH 4.0 before addition of KI. An unusually high content of organic matter may cause some uncertainty in the end point. Whenever manganese, iron, and nitrites are definitely absent, this uncertainty can be reduced and precision improved by buffering below pH 4.0—even as low as pH 3.0.

Regardless of the method of endpoint detection, either phenylarsine oxide or thiosulfate may be used as the standard reducing reagent. The former is more stable and is preferred.

The SNORT colorimetric, DPD titrimetric and colorimetric, and the LCV methods (D, E, F, and G, respectively) are applicable to the determination of total available chlorine in polluted waters. In addition, both DPD procedures and the amperometric titration and SNORT methods allow for the estimation of the monochloramine and dichloramine fractions. Since these methods depend on the stoichiometric production of iodine, polluted waters containing iodine-reducing substances may not be analyzed accurately by these methods.

In all of the colorimetric procedures, compensate for color and turbidity by use of color and turbidity "blanks" in visual or spectrophotometric determinations.

2. Sampling and Storage

Chlorine in aqueous solution is not stable, and the chlorine content of samples or solutions, particularly weak solutions, will decrease rapidly. Exposure to sunlight or other strong light or agitation will accelerate the reduction of chlorine. Therefore, start chlorine determinations immediately after sampling, avoiding excessive light and agitation. Do not store samples to be analyzed for chlorine.

409 A.   Iodometric Method I

1. General Discussion

a. Principle: Chlorine will liberate free iodine from potassium iodide solutions at pH 8 or less. The liberated iodine is titrated with a standard solution of sodium thiosulfate, with starch as the indicator. The reaction is preferably carried out at pH 3 to 4.

b. Interference: Although the neutral titration minimizes the interfering effect of ferric, manganic, and nitrite ions, the acid titration is preferred; it is most accurate for determination of total available residual chlorine. Use acetic acid for the acid titration; use sulfuric acid only when interfering substances are absent; *never use hydrochloric acid.*

c. Minimum detectable concentration: The minimum detectable concentration approximates 40 $\mu g/l$ Cl if $0.01N$ sodium thiosulfate is used with a 500-ml sample.

2. Reagents

a. Acetic acid, conc (glacial).

b. Potassium iodide, KI, crystals.

c. Standard sodium thiosulfate, $0.1N$: Dissolve 25 g $Na_2S_2O_3 \cdot 5H_2O$ in 1 l freshly boiled distilled water and standardize the solution against potassium biniodate or potassium dichromate after at least 2 wk storage. Use boiled distilled water and add a few milliliters $CHCl_3$ to minimize bacterial decomposition of the thiosulfate solution.

Standardize the $0.1N$ sodium thiosulfate by one of the following procedures:

1) Biniodate method—Dissolve 3.249 g anhydrous potassium biniodate, $KH(IO_3)_2$, of primary standard qual-

ity,* in distilled water and dilute to 1,000 ml to yield a $0.1000N$ solution. Store in a glass-stoppered bottle.

To 80 ml distilled water, add, with constant stirring, 1 ml conc H_2SO_4, 10.00 ml $0.1000N$ $KH(IO_3)_2$ and 1 g KI. Titrate immediately with $0.1N$ $Na_2S_2O_3$ titrant until the yellow color of the liberated iodine is almost discharged. Add 1 ml starch indicator solution and continue titrating until the blue color disappears.

2) Dichromate method—Dissolve 4.904 g anhydrous potassium dichromate, $K_2Cr_2O_7$, of primary standard quality, in distilled water and dilute to 1,000 ml to yield a $0.1000N$ solution. Store in a glass-stoppered bottle.

Proceed as in the biniodate method, with the following exceptions: Substitute 10.00 ml $0.1000N$ $K_2Cr_2O_7$ for the $KH(IO_3)_2$ and let the reaction mixture stand 6 min in the dark before titrating with the $0.1N$ $Na_2S_2O_3$ titrant.

$$\text{Normality } Na_2S_2O_3 = \frac{1}{\text{ml } Na_2S_2O_3 \text{ consumed}}$$

d. Standard sodium thiosulfate titrant, $0.01N$ or $0.025N$: Improve the stability of $0.01N$ or $0.025N$ $Na_2S_2O_3$ by diluting an aged $0.1N$ solution, made as directed above, with freshly boiled distilled water. Add a few milliliters $CHCl_3$ or 0.4 g sodium borate and 10 mg mercuric iodide/l solution. For accurate work, standardize this solution daily in accordance with the directions given above, using $0.01N$ or $0.025N$ $KH(IO_3)_2$ or $K_2Cr_2O_7$. To speed up

---

* G. F. Smith Chemical Company, Columbus, Ohio, or equivalent.

operations where many samples must be titrated use an automatic buret of a type in which rubber does not come in contact with the solution. Standard sodium thiosulfate titrants, $0.0100N$ and $0.0250N$, are equivalent, respectively, to 354.5 μg and 886.3 μg available Cl/ 1.00 ml.

e. Starch indicator solution: To 5 g starch (potato, arrowroot, or soluble), add a little cold water and grind in a mortar to a thin paste. Pour into 1 l of boiling distilled water, stir, and let settle overnight. Use the clear supernate. Preserve with 1.25 g salicylic acid, 4 g zinc chloride, or a combination of 4 g sodium propionate and 2 g sodium azide/l starch solution. Some commercial starch substitutes are satisfactory.

f. Standard iodine, 0.1 *N:* Refer to Method C, ¶3*a*2).

g. Dilute standard iodine, 0.0282*N:* Refer to Method C, ¶3*a*3).

3. Procedure

a. Volume of sample: Select a sample volume that will require no more than 20 ml $0.01N$ $Na_2S_2O_3$. Thus, for residual chlorine concentrations of 1 mg/l or less, take a 1,000-ml sample; for a chlorine range of 1 to 10 mg/l, a 500-ml sample; and above 10 mg/l, proportionately less sample.

b. Preparation for titration: Place 5 ml acetic acid, or enough to reduce the pH to between 3.0 and 4.0, in a flask or white porcelain casserole. Add about 1 g KI estimated on a spatula. Pour in the sample and mix with a stirring rod. Add chlorine-demand-free distilled water if a larger volume is preferred for titration.

c. Titration: Titrate away from direct sunlight. Add 0.025*N* or 0.01*N* thiosul-

fate from a buret until the yellow color of the liberated iodine is almost discharged. Add 1 ml starch solution and titrate until the blue color is discharged.

If the titration is made with 0.025*N* thiosulfate instead of 0.01, then, with a 1-l sample, 1 drop is equivalent to about 50 μg/l. It is not possible to discern the end point with greater accuracy. If a 500-ml sample is titrated, 1 drop will correspond to about 100 μg/l, which is within the limit of sensitivity. Hence, use of 0.025*N* solution is acceptable. Many laboratories have this on hand.

d. Blank titration: Correct the result of the sample titration by determining the blank contributed by such reagent impurities as: (*a*) the free iodine or iodate in the potassium iodide that liberates extra iodine; or (*b*) the traces of reducing agents that might reduce some of the iodine liberated.

Take a volume of distilled water corresponding to the sample used for titration in ¶s 3*a-c*, add 5 ml acetic acid, 1 g KI, and 1 ml starch solution. Perform either Blank Titration A or B, whichever applies.

1) Blank titration A—If a blue color develops, titrate with 0.01*N* or 0.025*N* sodium thiosulfate to the disappearance of the blue and record the result.

2) Blank Titration B—If no blue color occurs, titrate with 0.0282*N* iodine solution until a blue color appears. Back-titrate with 0.01*N* or 0.025*N* sodium thiosulfate and record the difference as Titration B.

Before calculating the chlorine, subtract Blank Titration A from the sample titration; or, if necessary, add the net equivalent value of Blank Titration B.

4. Calculation

For standardizing chlorine solution for temporary standards:

$$mg/ml \ Cl \ = \ \frac{(A \pm B) \times N \times 35.45}{ml \ sample}$$

For the determination of total available residual chlorine in a water sample:

$$mg/l \ Cl \ = \ \frac{(A \pm B) \times N \times 35,450}{ml \ sample}$$

where A = ml titration for sample, B = ml titration for blank, which may be positive or negative, and N = normality of $Na_2S_2O_3$.

5. Precision and Accuracy

See Tables 409:I through IV preceding and the general introduction to Section 409.

409 B.   Iodometric Method II

1. General Discussion

a. Principle: In this method, used for wastewater analysis, the end-point signal is reversed because the unreacted standard reducing agent remaining in the sample is titrated with standard iodine or standard iodate, rather than directly titrating the iodine released. This indirect procedure is necessary regardless of the method of end-point detection, in order to avoid any contact between the full concentration of liberated iodine and the wastewater.

b. Interference: Manganese, iron, and nitrite interference may be minimized by buffering to pH 4.0 before the addition of KI. An unusually high content of organic matter may cause some uncertainty in the end point. Whenever manganese, iron, and nitrite are definitely absent, this uncertainty can be reduced and precision improved by acidification to pH 1.0.

2. Apparatus

For a description of the amperometric end-point detection apparatus and a discussion of its use, refer to Section 409 C.

3. Reagents

a. Standard phenylarsine oxide solution, 0.00564N: Dissolve approximately 0.8 g phenylarsine oxide powder in 150 ml 0.3N NaOH solution. After settling, decant 110 ml into 800 ml distilled water and mix thoroughly. Bring to pH 6 to 7 with 6N HCl and dilute to 950 ml with distilled water.

Standardization—Accurately measure 5 to 10 ml freshly standardized 0.0282N iodine solution into a flask and add 1 ml KI solution. Titrate with phenylarsine oxide solution, using starch solution as an indicator. Adjust to 0.00564N and recheck against the standard iodine solution; 1.00 ml = 200 μg available chlorine. (CAUTION: *Toxic—take care to avoid ingestion.*)

b. *Standard sodium thiosulfate solution, 0.1N:* Dissolve at least 25 g $Na_2S_2O_3 \cdot 5H_2O$ in 1 l freshly boiled distilled water. Avoid bacterial decomposition by adding 5 ml $CHCl_3$ or 1 g NaOH/l. Store for at least 2 wk before standardizing.

Standardization—To 80 ml distilled water add, with constant stirring, 1 ml conc H_2SO_4, 10.0 ml of either 0.1N potassium biniodate solution containing 3.250 g/l $KH(IO_3)_2$ or 0.1N potassium dichromate solution containing 4.904 g/l $K_2Cr_2O_7$, and 15 ml KI solution. Let stand 6 min in subdued light at laboratory temperature and then dilute to 400 ml if $K_2Cr_2O_7$ was used or to 200 ml if biniodate was used. Titrate the liberated iodine with the thiosulfate solution being standardized, adding starch solution toward the end of the titration. Exactly 10.00 ml of thiosulfate should be required if the solutions under comparison are of equal strength.

Standard sodium thiosulfate solution, 0.00564N: Prepare by dilution of 0.1N sodium thiosulfate (see ¶b preceding). For maximum stability of the dilute solution, prepare it by diluting an aged 0.1N solution with freshly boiled distilled water (to minimize bacterial action) and add 10 mg HgI_2 and 4 g $Na_4B_4O_7$/l. Standardize this thiosulfate solution daily. Use an automatic buret of a type in which rubber does not come in contact with the solution. 1.00 ml= 200 μg available chlorine.

d. *Potassium iodide*, KI, crystals.

e. *Acetate buffer solution*, pH 4.0: Dissolve 146 g anhydrous $NaC_2H_3O_2$, or 243 g $NaC_2H_3O_2 \cdot 3H_2O$, in 400 ml distilled water, add 480 g conc acetic

acid, and dilute to 1 l with distilled water.

f. *Standard arsenite solution, 0.1N:* Accurately weigh a stoppered weighing bottle containing approximately 4.95 g arsenic trioxide, As_2O_3. Transfer without loss to a 1-l volumetric flask and again weigh the bottle. Do not attempt to brush out the adhering oxide. Moisten the As_2O_3 with water and add 15 g NaOH and 100 ml distilled water. Swirl the contents of the flask gently to dissolve the As_2O_3. Dilute to 250 ml with distilled water and saturate the solution with CO_2, thus converting all the NaOH to sodium bicarbonate. Dilute to the mark, stopper the flask, and mix thoroughly. A solution thus prepared will preserve its titer almost indefinitely. (CAUTION: *Toxic—take care to avoid ingestion.*)

$$Normality = \frac{g\ As_2O_3}{49.455}$$

g. *Standard iodine solution, 0.1N:* Dissolve 40 g KI in 25 ml distilled water, add 13 g resublimed iodine, and stir until dissolved. Transfer to a 1-l volumetric flask and dilute to the mark.

Standardization—Accurately measure 40 to 50 ml 0.1N arsenite solution into a flask and titrate with the 0.1N iodine solution, using starch solution as indicator. To obtain accurate results, it is absolutely necessary that the solution be saturated with CO_2 at the end of the titration. A current of CO_2 may be passed through the solution for a few minutes just before the end point is reached, or a few drops of HCl may be added to liberate sufficient CO_2 to saturate the solution.

h. *Standard iodine titrant, 0.0282N:*

Dissolve 25 g KI in a little distilled water in a 1-l volumetric flask, add the correct amount of 0.1N iodine solution exactly standardized to yield a 0.0282N solution, and dilute to 1 l. For accurate work, standardize this solution daily in accordance with directions given in ¶3g above, using 5 to 10 ml of arsenite solution. Store in amber bottles or in the dark; protect the solution from direct sunlight at all times and keep it from all contact with rubber.

i. Starch indicator: Either the aqueous solution or soluble starch powder mixtures may be used for detection of the iodine end point.

To prepare the aqueous solution, place 5 g starch (potato, arrowroot, or soluble) in a mortar, add a little cold water, and grind to a thin paste. Pour into 1 l of boiling distilled water, stir, and let settle overnight. Use the clear supernate. Preserve with 1.25 g salicylic acid or with 4 g zinc chloride/l.

j. Standard iodate titrant, 0.00564N: Dissolve 201.2 mg primary standard grade KIO_3,* which has previously been dried 1 hr at 103 C, in distilled water and dilute to 1 l.

k. Phosphoric acid solution, 1+9.

4. Procedure

a. Amperometric end point:

1) Volume of sample—For residual chlorine concentrations of 10 mg/l or less, titrate 200 ml. For greater residual chlorine concentrations, use proportionately less sample. Use a sample of such size that not more than 10 ml phenylarsine oxide solution is required.

---

* Mallinckrodt No. 1093 or equivalent.

2) Preparation for titration—To a beaker suitable for use with the apparatus add 5.0 ml 0.00564N phenylarsine oxide solution or 0.00564N thiosulfate solution, KI in excess (approximately 1 g), and 4 ml acetate buffer solution or enough to reduce the pH to between 3.5 and 4.2. Add 200 ml of sample and mix thoroughly. Because 1 ml phenylarsine oxide reagent consumed by a 200-ml sample represents 1 mg/l available chlorine, use 5 ml reagent solution for residual chlorine concentrations up to 5 mg/l and 10 ml reagent solution for residual chlorine concentrations of 5 to 10 mg/l. The following is suggested as a dilution method: Add 10.0 ml reagent solution, excess KI (approximately 1 g), and 4 ml acetate buffer solution or enough to reduce the pH to between 3.5 and 4.2 to the beaker or graduate. Dilute to 100 ml with distilled water and then add 100 ml of sample.

3) Titration—Add 0.0282N iodine titrant in small increments from a 1-ml pipet or a 1-ml buret. Observe the response of the meter needle as iodine is added to the sample: The pointer remains practically stationary until the end point is approached, whereupon each iodine increment causes a temporary deflection of the microammeter, with the pointer dropping back to its original position. Stop the titration at the end point when a small increment of iodine titrant gives a definite pointer deflection upscale and the pointer does not return promptly to its original position. Record the volume of iodine titrant used to reach the end point.

b. Starch-iodide end point:

1) Volume of sample—For residual chlorine concentrations of 10 mg/l or

less, take a 200-ml sample for titration. For greater residual chlorine concentrations, use proportionately less sample.

2) Titration with standard iodine— Place 5.00 ml 0.00564N phenylarsine oxide solution or 0.00564N thiosulfate solution in a flask or white porcelain casserole. Add excess KI (approximately 1 g) and 4 ml acetate buffer solution, or enough to reduce the pH to between 3.5 and 4.2. Pour in the sample and mix with a stirring rod. Just before titration with 0.0282N iodine, add 1 ml starch solution for each 200 ml of sample. Titrate to the first appearance of blue color that persists after complete mixing. Because 1 ml 0.00564N reagent solution consumed by a 200-ml sample represents 1 mg/l available chlorine, use 5 ml reagent for residual chlorine concentrations up to 5 mg/l, 10 ml reagent for residual chlorine concentrations of 5 to 10 mg/l, and proportionately larger volumes of reagent for higher concentrations.

3) Titration with standard iodate— To 200 ml distilled water add, with agitation, 5.00 ml 0.00564N thiosulfate solution, an excess of KI (approximately 0.5 g), 2 ml 10% phosphoric acid solution, and 1 ml starch solution in the order given, and titrate immediately* with 0.00564N iodate solution to the first appearance of a blue color that persists after complete mixing. Designate the volume of iodate solution used as A. Repeat the procedure, substituting 200 ml sample for the 200 ml distilled water. If the sample is colored or turbid, titrate to the first change in color, using for comparison another portion of sample with phosphoric acid added. Designate the volume of iodate solution used in titrating the sample as B. Because 1 ml 0.00564N reagent solution consumed by a 200-ml sample represents 1 mg/l available chlorine, use 5 ml thiosulfate solution for residual chlorine concentrations up to 5 mg/l, 10 ml thiosulfate solution for residual chlorine concentrations of 5 to 10 mg/l, and proportionately larger volumes of thiosulfate solution for higher concentrations.

5. Calculation

a. Titration with standard iodine:

$$\text{mg/l Cl} = \frac{(A-5B)\times200}{C}$$

where A = ml 0.00564N reagent, B = ml 0.0282N I_2, and C = ml sample.

b. Titration with standard iodate:

$$\text{mg/l Cl} = \frac{(A-B)\times200}{C}$$

where A and B are as given in ¶4b3) above and C = ml sample.

---

* Titration may be delayed up to 10 min without appreciable error if the phosphoric acid is not added until immediately before the titration.

409 C.   Amperometric Titration Method

1. General Discussion

Amperometric titration requires a higher degree of skill and care than the colorimetric methods. Chlorine residuals over 2 mg/l are best measured by means of smaller samples, or by dilution with water that neither is chlorinated nor has a chlorine demand. The method can be used to determine total residual chlorine and can also differentiate between free and combined available chlorine. A further differentiation into monochloramine and dichloramine fractions is possible by control of the potassium iodide concentration and pH.

a. Principle: The amperometric method is a special adaptation of the polarographic principle. Free available chlorine is titrated at a pH between 6.5 and 7.5, a range in which the combined chlorine reacts slowly. The combined chlorine, in turn, is titrated in the presence of the proper amount of potassium iodide in the pH range 3.5 to 4.5. When free chlorine is determined, the pH must not be greater than 7.5 because the reaction becomes sluggish at higher pH values, nor less than 6.5 because at lower pH values some combined chlorine may react even in the absence of iodide. When combined chlorine is determined, the pH must not be less than 3.5 because substances such as oxidized manganese interfere at lower pH values, nor greater than 4.5 because the reaction is not quantitative at higher pH values. The tendency of monochloramine to react more readily with iodide than does dichloramine provides a means for further differentiation. The addition of a small amount of potassium iodide in the neutral pH range enables the estimation of monochloramine content. Lowering the pH into the acid range and increasing the potassium iodide concentration allows the separate determination of dichloramine.

Phenylarsine oxide is stable even in dilute solution and each mole reacts with two equivalents of halogen. A special amperometric cell is used to detect the end point of the residual chlorine-phenylarsine oxide titration. The cell consists of a nonpolarizable reference electrode that is immersed in a salt solution and a readily polarizable noble-metal electrode that is in contact both with the salt solution and with the sample being titrated. Another approach to end point detection uses dual platinum electrodes, a mercury cell with voltage divider to impress a potential across the electrodes, and a micro-ammeter. If there is no chlorine residual in the sample, the microammeter reading will be comparatively low because of cell polarization. The greater the residual in the sample, the greater the micro-ammeter reading. The meter acts merely as a null-point indicator—that is, the actual meter reading is not important, but rather the relative readings as the titration proceeds. The gradual addition of phenylarsine oxide causes the cell to become more and more polarized because of the decrease in available chlorine. The end point is recognized when no further decrease in meter reading can be obtained by adding more phenylarsine oxide.

b. Interference: Accurate determinations of free chlorine cannot be made in the presence of nitrogen trichloride or chlorine dioxide, which titrate partly as free chlorine. When present, nitrogen trichloride can titrate partly as free available chlorine and partly as dichloramine, contributing a positive error in both fractions. Organic chloramines also can be titrated in each step. Monochloramine can intrude into the free chlorine fraction and dichloramine can interfere in the monochloramine fraction especially at high temperatures and prolonged titration times. Free halogens other than chlorine also will titrate as free chlorine. Combined chlorine reacts with bromide and iodide ions to produce bromine and iodine. When titration for free available chlorine follows a combined chlorine titration, which requires addition of Kl, erroneous results may occur unless the measuring cell is rinsed thoroughly with distilled water between titrations. Interference from copper has been noted in samples after heavy copper sulfate treatment of reservoirs, with metallic copper plating out on the electrode. Silver ions also poison the electrode. Interference also occurs in some highly colored waters, but the interfering substance has not been identified. Very low temperatures slow the response of the measuring cell and longer time is required for the titration, but the precision is not affected. A reduction in reaction rate is also caused by pH values above 7.5, but this is overcome by buffering all samples to pH 7.0 or less. On the other hand, some substances, such as manganese, nitrite, and iron, do not interfere. Stirring can lower chlorine values by volatilization. When dilution is used for samples containing high chlorine content, care must be exercised that the dilution water is free of residual chlorine and ammonia and possesses no chlorine demand.

2. Apparatus

a. End-point detection apparatus, consisting of a cell unit connected to a microammeter, with the necessary electrical accessories. The cell unit includes a noble-metal electrode of sufficient surface area, a salt bridge to provide an electrical connection without diffusion of electrolyte, and a reference electrode of silver-silver chloride in a saturated sodium chloride solution connected into the circuit by means of the salt bridge.

Keep the noble-metal electrode free of deposits and foreign matter. Vigorous chemical cleaning generally is unnecessary. Occasional mechanical cleaning with a suitable abrasive is usually sufficient. Keep the salt bridge in good operating condition; do not allow it to become plugged nor permit appreciable flow of electrolyte through it. Keep the solution surrounding the reference electrode free of contamination and maintain it at constant composition by insuring an adequate supply of undissolved salt at all times. A cell with two metal electrodes polarized by a small DC potential also may be used. (See bibliography.)

b. Agitator, designed to give the greatest possible degree of agitation at the noble-metal electrode surface in order to insure proper sensitivity. Thoroughly clean the agitator and the exposed electrode system to remove all chlorine-consuming contaminants by immersing them in water containing 1 to 2 mg/l free available residual chlorine for a few minutes. Add KI to the same water and allow the agitator and electrodes to remain immersed for 5 min. After thorough rinsing with chlorine-demand-free water or the sample to be tested, the sensitized electrodes and agitator are ready for use.

c. Buret: A convenient form is made from a 1-ml pipet with 0.01-ml graduations. Connect to a delivery tube with a finely drawn tip with suitable plastic tubing. Insert glass beads in the plastic tubing to act as valves.

d. Glassware, exposed to water containing at least 10 mg/l residual chlorine for 3 hr or more before use and rinsed with chlorine-demand-free water.

3. Reagents

a. Standard phenylarsine oxide titrant: See Method B, ¶3*a.*

b. Phosphate buffer solution, pH 7: Dissolve 25.4 g anhydrous potassium dihydrogen phosphate, KH_2PO_4, and 34.1 g anhydrous disodium hydrogen phosphate, Na_2HPO_4, in 800 ml distilled water. Add 2 ml sodium hypochlorite solution containing 1% available chlorine and mix thoroughly. Protect from sunlight for several days and then expose to sunlight until no residual chlorine remains. If necessary, carry out the final dechlorination with a sodium sulfite solution, leaving just a trace of chlorine as shown by a qualitative stabilized neutral orthotolidine (SNORT) test. Dilute to 1 l with distilled water and filter if any precipitate is present.

c. Potassium iodide solution: Dissolve 50 g KI and dilute to 1 l with freshly boiled and cooled distilled water. Store in a brown glass-stoppered bottle, preferably in the refrigerator. Discard the solution when a yellow color has developed.

d. Acetate buffer solution, pH 4: See Method B, ¶3*e.*

4. Procedure

a. Sample volume: Select a sample volume requiring no more than 2 ml phenylarsine oxide titrant. Thus, for residual chlorine concentrations of 2 mg/l or less, take a 200-ml sample; for chlorine levels in excess of 2 mg/l, 100 ml or proportionately less.

b. Free available chlorine: Unless the pH of the sample is known to lie between 6.5 and 7.5, add 1 ml pH 7 phosphate buffer solution to produce a pH of 6.5 to 7.5. Titrate with standard phenylarsine oxide titrant, observing the current changes on the microammeter. Add the titrant in progressively smaller increments until all needle movement ceases. Make successive buret readings when the needle action becomes sluggish, signaling the approach of the end point. Subtract the last very small increment, which causes no needle response due to overtitration.

Continue the titration for combined available chlorine as described in ¶4*c* below or for the separate monochloramine and dichloramine fractions as detailed in ¶s 4*e* and 4*f.*

c. Combined available chlorine: To the sample remaining from the free-chlorine titration add 1.00 ml KI iodide solution and 1 ml acetate buffer solution, in that order. Titrate with phenylarsine oxide titrant to an end point, as above. Do not refill the buret but simply continue the titration after recording the figure for free available chlorine. Again subtract the last increment, which gives the amount of titrant actually used in the reaction with the chlorine. (If the titration was continued without refilling the buret, this figure represents the total residual chlorine. Subtracting the free available chlorine from the total gives the combined residual chlorine.) Wash the apparatus and sample cell thoroughly to remove iodide ion in order to avoid inaccuracies when the titrator is used subsequently for a free available chlorine determination.

d. Separate samples: If desired, determine the total residual chlorine and the free available chlorine on separate samples. If total available chlorine alone is required, treat the sample immediately with 1 ml KI solution followed by 1 ml acetate buffer solution, and titrate with phenylarsine oxide titrant as described in ¶4c preceding.

e. Monochloramine: After the titration for free available chlorine, add 0.2 ml KI solution to the same sample and, without refilling the buret, continue the titration with phenylarsine oxide titrant to the recognized end point. Subtract the last increment to obtain the net volume of titrant consumed by the monochloramine.

f. Dichloramine: Add 1 ml acetate buffer solution and 1 ml KI solution to the same sample and titrate the final dichloramine fraction as described for the previous two chlorine components.

5. Calculation

Convert the individual titrations for free available chlorine, combined available chlorine, total available chlorine, monochloramine, and dichloramine into mg/l by the following equation:

$$\text{mg/1 Cl} = \frac{A \times 200}{\text{ml sample}}$$

where $A = $ ml phenylarsine oxide titration.

6. Precision and Accuracy

See Tables 409: I through IV preceding and the general introduction to Section 409.

409 D.   Stabilized Neutral Orthotolidine (SNORT) Method

1. General Discussion

a. Principle: Orthotolidine is quite stable in the reduced form when stored in brown bottles in the presence of hydrochloric acid. However, the stability of oxidized orthotolidine decreases as the pH increases. For this reason, orthotolidine usually has been used at a pH of 1.3 or less. As the pH increases, the rate of reaction of orthotolidine with combined chlorine, iron, and nitrite becomes slower and their interference essentially disappears at pH 7. Anionic surface-active agents stabilize the color developed by free chlorine and orthotolidine at pH 7.0. "Aerosol OT,"* sodium di(2-ethyl-hexyl) sulfosuccinate, is the best stabilizing reagent. The optimum concentration of stabilizer is 40 mg for each 100 ml of sample plus reagents.

---

* A trademark of the American Cyanamid Co.

The ratio by weight of orthotolidine dihydrochloride to chlorine must be at least 8 to 1. With the concentration of orthotolidine recommended in the procedure, the chlorine concentration must not exceed 6 mg/l.

The pH of the final solution must be between 6.5 and 7.5 to minimize low-pH interference and high-pH fading. If the pH of the sample is less than 5 or greater than 9, and the alkalinity is greater than 150 or the acidity greater than 200 mg/l, check the final pH of the solution. If the alkalinity is high and the final pH does not lie within the range of 6.5 to 7.5, adjust the sample pH to this range before analysis.

To insure correct color development, minimum interference, a pH of 6.5 to 7.5, and a ratio of orthotolidine to free chlorine of at least 8 to 1, the sample must be added to the reagents.

The reaction time and temperature are much less important in this method than in other colorimetric methods for chlorine determination. Nevertheless, for extremely large combined chlorine to free chlorine ratios, high temperature and long waiting times are undesirable. At 35 C a 1-mg/l monochloramine solution produces a false free chlorine residual of 0.01 mg/l per min. At high temperature and for long waiting times, color fading may become important, especially at levels below 0.1 mg/l of free chlorine. A 1-mg/l solution of free chlorine fades at the rate of 0.005 mg/l per min at 35 C.

Iodide can be added in neutral solution to measure monochloramine and in acidic solution to measure dichloramine. The reaction of iodide and chloramine yields a concentration of iodine equivalent to the chloramine. In the color-imetric procedure, orthotolidine is present with the chloramine when iodide is added and the iodine produced by the chloramine is immediately reduced back to iodide and acts as a catalyst in generating an amount of blue orthotolidine equivalent to the original chloramine present. Because of this catalytic effect, lesser amounts of iodide are required than in amperometric titration; this improves the separation of the monochloramine and dichloramine fractions.

b. Interference: When orthotolidine or any other chromogenic reagent is used to measure residual chlorine, strong oxidizing agents of any kind interfere. Such interferences include bromine, chlorine dioxide, iodine, manganic compounds, and ozone. However, the reduced forms of these compounds—bromide, chloride, iodide, manganous ion, and oxygen—do not interfere. Reducing agents such as ferrous compounds, hydrogen sulfide, and oxidizable organic matter do *not* interfere in the analytical method but may interfere in maintaining chlorine residuals by reducing the chlorine residual by reaction with the chlorine to produce chloride ion, that is, acting simply as chlorine demand.

Turbidity and color also interfere unless the background turbidity or color is compensated for by using a blank. Concentrations of 55 mg/l iron, 92 mg/l nitrite, and 6,000 mg/l chloride do not interfere. The interference of combined chlorine is insignificant in the determination of free chlorine except (as noted before) at high temperature and long waiting times. Manganic compounds produce up to stoichiometric interference but can be compensated for by using a blank. In the presence of more than 10 $\mu g/l$ manganic manganese, a blank is prepared by adding 5 ml sodium arsenite to a 100-ml sample. This sample is added to the reagents, as usual, and this blank is used as a reference in measuring the free chlorine present, either by zeroing the photometer with this blank or by using the blank as a reference when making color comparison.

If nitrogen trichloride is present, half reacts as free available chlorine but the remainder does not interfere in the monochloramine and dichloramine measurements. Many different organic chloramines are possible. The extent to which these organic chloramines interfere in the monochloramine or dichloramine steps depends on the nature of the organic compound; they may appear in either or both fractions.

c. *Minimum detectable concentration:* Approximately 10 $\mu g/l$ free chlorine.

2. Apparatus

Colorimetric equipment: One of the following is required:

a. *Filter photometer,* providing a light path of 1 cm or longer for ≤ 1 mg/l free chlorine residual, or a light path from 1 to 10 mm for free chlorine residual > 1.5; also equipped with a red filter having maximum transmission in the range of 600 to 650 nm.

b. *Spectrophotometer,* for use at 625 nm, providing a light path noted in the paragraph above.

3. Reagents

a. *Chlorine-demand-free distilled water:* Add sufficient chlorine to distilled water to destroy the ammonia and nitrite. The amount of chlorine required will be about 10 times the amount of ammonia nitrogen present; produce an initial residual of more than 1.0 mg/l free chlorine. Let the chlorinated distilled water stand overnight or longer; then expose to direct sunlight until all residual chlorine is discharged.

b. *Neutral orthotolidine reagent:* Add 5 ml conc HCl to 100 ml chlorine-demand-free distilled water. Add 10 ml of this acid solution, 20 mg mercuric chloride, $HgCl_2$, 30 mg disodium ethylenediamine tetraacetate dihydrate, also called (ethylenedinitrilo)-tetraacetic acid sodium salt, and 1.5 g orthotolidine dihydrochloride to chlorine-demand-free distilled water and dilute to 1 l. Store in a brown bottle or in the dark at room temperature. Protect at all times from direct sunlight. Use no longer than 6 months. Avoid contact with rubber. Do not let the temperature fall below 0 C because the resulting crystallization of orthotolidine can lead to deficient subsequent color development.

CAUTION: *Handle this chemical with extreme care. Never use a mouth pipet for dispensing this reagent, but rely on an automatic dropping or safety pipet to measure the necessary volumes. Avoid inhalation or exposure to the skin.*

c. *Buffer-stabilizer reagent:* Dissolve 34.4 g dipotassium hydrogen phosphate, K_2HPO_4, 12.6 g potassium dihydrogen phosphate, KH_2PO_4, and 8.0 g "Aerosol OT," 100% solid di(2-ethylhexyl)sulfosuccinate, in a solution of 500 ml chlorine-demand-free water and 200 ml diethylene glycol monobutyl ether. Dilute to 1 l with chlorine-demand-free water.

d. *Potassium iodide solution:* Dissolve

0.4 g KI in chlorine-demand-free distilled water and dilute to 100 ml. Store in a brown glass-stoppered bottle, preferably in a refrigerator. Discard when a yellow color develops.

e. *Sulfuric acid solution:* Cautiously add 4 ml conc H_2SO_4 to chlorine-demand-free distilled water and dilute to 100 ml.

f. *Sodium carbonate solution:* Dissolve 5 g Na_2CO_3 in chlorine-demand-free distilled water and dilute to 100 ml.

g. *Sodium arsenite solution:* Dissolve 5.0 g $NaAsO_2$ in distilled water and dilute to 1 l. (CAUTION: *Toxic—take care to avoid ingestion.*)

4. Procedure

a. *Calibration of photometer:* Construct a calibration curve by making dilutions of standardized hypochlorite solution prepared as directed under Chlorine Demand, Section 410A.3a. Take special precautions when diluting to low concentrations because of possible consumption of small amounts of chlorine by trace impurities. Use chlorine-demand-free water in making the dilutions. Expose all glassware to be used in the dilutions to water containing at least 10 mg/l of chlorine and leave it in contact for a few hours. Rinse with chlorine-demand-free water. Develop and measure the colors as described below for the sample.

b. *Color development of free chlorine:* Use 0.5 ml neutral orthotolidine and 0.5 ml stabilizer-buffer reagent with 10-ml samples; 5 ml neutral orthotolidine and 5 ml stabilizer-buffer reagent with 100 ml!; and the same ratio for other volumes. Place the neutral orthotolidine and stabilizer-buffer mixture in the photometer tube or a 250-ml beaker on a magnetic stirrer. Mix the reagent slightly and add the sample to the reagents with gentle stirring. Measure the percent transmittance and convert to absorbance at 625 nm. The value obtained (A) from the calibration curve represents the free chlorine residual. To minimize possible interference from high concentrations of combined chlorine and high-temperature fading, complete mixing of the sample with the reagents and reading on the photometer within approximately 2 min.

c. *Monochloramine:* Return any portion used for measuring free chlorine in ¶4b to the sample. Add, with stirring, 0.5 ml KI solution to each 100-ml sample, or a similar ratio for other sample volumes. Again measure the transmittance of the residual free chlorine plus the monochloramine and obtain the value (B) from the calibration curve.

d. *Dichloramine:* Return any portion used for measuring the monochloramine in ¶4c to the sample. Add, with stirring, 1 ml H_2SO_4 solution to each 100-ml sample, or a similar ratio for other sample volumes. After 30 sec for color development add 1 ml sodium carbonate solution slowly with stirring or until a pure blue solution returns. Measure the transmittance of the total residual chlorine—free chlorine, monochloramine, and dichloramine—and obtain the value (C) from the calibration curve with a slight dilution correction.

e. *Compensation for interferences:* Compensate for the presence of natural color or turbidity as well as manganic compounds by adding 5 ml arsenite to 100 ml sample. Add this blank sample to the reagents as above. Use the color of the blank to set 100% transmittance or zero absorbance on the photometer. Measure all samples in relation to this blank. Read from the calibration curve the concentrations of chlorine present in the sample.

5. Calculation

mg/l free residual chlorine
   $= A$, including ½ trichloramine if present

mg/l monochloramine $= B-A$, as mg/l Cl
mg/l dichloramine $= 1.03\ C-B$, as mg/l Cl
mg/l total chlorine $= 1.03\ C$, as mg/l Cl

6. Precision and Accuracy

See Tables 409: I through IV preceding and the general introduction to Section 409.

409 E.   DPD Ferrous Titrimetric Method

1. General Discussion

a. Principle: N,N-diethyl-p-phenylenediamine (DPD) is superior to neutral orthotolidine as an indicator in the ferrous method. The colors produced are more stable, fewer reagents are required, and a full response in neutral solution is obtained from dichloramine. In the titrimetric procedure, decolorization by standard ferrous ammonium sulfate (FAS) titrant is instantaneous, thereby enabling each step to be performed more rapidly. Where complete differentiation is not required, the procedure may be simplified further to give only free and combined available chlorine or total residual available chlorine.

In the absence of iodide ion, free available chlorine reacts instantly with the N,N-diethyl-p-phenylenediamine (DPD) indicator to produce a red color. Subsequent addition of a small amount of iodide ion acts catalytically to cause monochloramine to produce color. Further addition of iodide ion to excess evokes a rapid response from dichloramine. Unlike the reaction with neutral orthotolidine, any nitrogen trichloride present no longer displays color with

free available chlorine but is included with dichloramine. However, if iodide ion is added before DPD, a proportion of the nitrogen trichloride appears with free available chlorine. A supplementary procedure based on this alteration of the order of adding the reagents thus permits the estimation of nitrogen trichloride.

Chlorine dioxide appears, to the extent of one-fifth of its total available chlorine content, with free available chlorine. A full response from chlorine dioxide, corresponding to its total available chlorine content, may be obtained if the sample first is acidified in the presence of iodide ion and subsequently is brought back to an approximately neutral pH by the addition of bicarbonate ion. Bromine, bromamine, and iodine react with DPD indicator and appear with free available chlorine. DPD procedures for the determination of these halogens and related compounds have been developed.

b. pH control: For accurate results careful pH control is essential. At the proper pH of 6.2 to 6.5, the red colors produced may be titrated to sharp colorless end points. *Carry out the titration as* soon as the red color is formed in each step. Too low a pH in the first step will tend to make the monochloramine show in the free-chlorine step and the dichloramine in the monochloramine step. Too high a pH may cause dissolved oxygen to give a color.

c. *Temperature control:* In all methods for differentiating free chlorine from chloramines, the higher the temperature the greater the tendency for the chloramines to react with the reagents and thus lead to increased apparent free-chlorine results after a fixed time interval. Exceptions to this are the titration methods, probably because of the speed with which the titration is completed compared with the 2 to 3 min required for the colorimetric measurement to be made. The DPD methods are among those least affected by temperature.

d. *Interference:* The only interfering substance likely to be encountered in water is oxidized manganese. To correct for this, place 5 ml buffer solution, one small crystal of potassium iodide, and 0.5 ml sodium arsenite solution (500 mg $NaAsO_2$ plus 100 ml distilled water) in the titration flask. Add 100 ml sample and mix. Add 5 ml DPD indicator solution, mix, and titrate with standard ferrous ammonium sulfate titrant until any red color is discharged. Subtract the reading from reading *A* obtained by the normal procedure as described in ¶3*a*1) of this method or from the total available chlorine reading obtained in the simplified procedure as given in ¶3*a*4). If the combined reagent in powder form (see below) is used, add the potassium iodide and arsenite first to the sample and mix, then add the combined buffer-indicator reagent afterwards.

Interference by copper up to approximately 10 mg/l copper is overcome by the EDTA incorporated in the reagents. The presence of EDTA enhances the stability of the DPD indicator solution by retarding deterioration due to oxidation, and in the test itself provides virtually complete suppression of dissolved oxygen errors by prevention of trace metal catalysis.

2. Reagents

a. *Phosphate buffer solution:* Dissolve 24 g anhydrous disodium hydrogen phosphate, Na_2HPO_4, and 46 g anhydrous potassium dihydrogen phosphate, KH_2PO_4, in distilled water. Combine with 100 ml distilled water in which 800 mg disodium ethylenediamine tetraacetate dihydrate, also called (ethylenedinitrilo) tetraacetic acid sodium salt, have been dissolved. Dilute to 1 l with distilled water and add 20 mg $HgCl_2$ to prevent mold growth and to prevent interference in the free available chlorine test caused by any trace amounts of iodide in the reagents.

b. *N,N-Diethyl-p-phenylenediamine (DPD) indicator solution:* Dissolve 1 g DPD Oxalate,* or 1.5 g p-amino-N:N-diethylaniline sulfate,† in chlorine-free distilled water containing 8 ml 1+3 H_2SO_4 and 200 mg disodium ethylenediamine tetraacetate dihydrate, also called (ethylenedinitrilo)tetraacetic acid sodium salt. Make up to 1 l, store in a brown glass-stoppered bottle, and discard when discolored. (The buffer and indicator sulfate are commercially

---

* Eastman chemical No. 7102, or equivalent.

† British Drug House chemical available from Gallard-Schlesinger Chemical Mfg. Corp., 584 Mineola Avenue, Carle Place, N.Y. 11514.

available as a combined reagent in stable powder form.) CAUTION: *The oxalate is toxic—take care to avoid ingestion.*

c. *Standard ferrous ammonium sulfate (FAS) titrant:* Dissolve 1.106 g Mohr's salt, $Fe(NH_4)_2(SO_4)_2 \cdot 6H_2O$ in distilled water containing 1 ml of $1+3$ H_2SO_4 and make up to 1 l with freshly boiled and cooled distilled water. This primary standard may be used for 1 month, and the titer checked by potassium dichromate. The FAS titrant is equivalent to 100 μg Cl/1.00 ml.

d. *Potassium iodide,* KI, crystals.

e. *Potassium iodide solution:* Dissolve 500 mg KI and dilute to 100 ml, using freshly boiled and cooled distilled water. Store in a brown glass-stoppered bottle, preferably in a refrigerator. Discard the solution when a yellow color develops.

3. Procedure

The quantities given below are suitable for concentrations of total available chlorine up to 4 mg/l. Where the total chlorine exceeds 4 mg/l, use a smaller sample and dilute to a total volume of 100 ml. Mix the usual volumes of buffer reagent and DPD indicator solution, or the usual amount of DPD powder, with distilled water before adding sufficient sample to bring the total volume to 100 ml.

a. *Free available chlorine or chloramine:* Place 5 ml each of buffer reagent and DPD indicator solution in the titration flask and mix (or use about 500 mg of DPD powder). Add 100 ml sample and mix.

1) Free available chlorine—Titrate rapidly with standard FAS titrant until the red color is discharged (reading A).

2) Monochloramine—Add one very small crystal of KI and mix; or if the dichloramine concentration is expected to be high, add 0.1 ml (2 drops) KI solution and mix. Continue titrating until the red color is again discharged (reading B).

3) Dichloramine—Add several crystals KI (about 1 g) and mix to dissolve. Let stand for 2 min and continue titrating until the red color is again discharged (reading C). In the case of very high dichloramine concentrations, let stand 2 min more if color driftback indicates slightly incomplete reaction. When dichloramine concentrations are not expected to be high, use half the specified amount of KI.

4) Simplified procedure for free and combined available chlorine or total available chlorine—Omit step 2) above in order to obtain monochloramine and dichloramine together as combined available chlorine. To obtain total available chlorine in one reading, add the full amount of KI at the start, with the specified amounts of buffer reagent and DPD indicator, and titrate after 2 min standing.

b. *Nitrogen trichloride:* The absence of color in the first step indicates the absence of nitrogen trichloride (and of chlorine dioxide). Nitrogen trichloride, readily identified by its distinctive odor, may be estimated by the following procedure: Place a small crystal of KI in a titration flask. Add 100 ml sample and mix. Then add the contents to a second flask containing 5 ml each of buffer reagent and DPD indicator solution (or about 500 mg DPD powder direct to the first flask). Titrate rapidly with standard FAS titrant until the red color is discharged (reading D).

Monochloramine is unlikely to be present with nitrogen trichloride. If high concentrations of dichloramine are present, use KI solution as in ¶3a2) in place of a KI crystal.

4. Calculation

For a 100-ml sample, 1.00 ml standard FAS titrant=1.00 mg/l available residual chlorine.

Reading	NCl₃ Absent	NCl₃ Present
A	free Cl	free Cl
$B\text{-}A$	NH_2Cl	NH_2Cl
$C\text{-}B$	$NHCl_2$	$NHCl_2+$
		$\frac{1}{2}NCl_3$
D	—	free Cl+
		$\frac{1}{2}NCl_3$
$2(D\text{-}A)$	—	NCl_3
$C\text{-}D$	—	$NHCl_2$

Should monochloramine be present with nitrogen trichloride, which is un-

likely, it will be included in reading D, in which case NCl₃ is obtained from $2(D\text{-}B)$.

Chlorine dioxide, if present, is included in reading A to the extent of one-fifth of its total available chlorine content.

In the simplified procedure for free and combined available chlorine, only reading A (free Cl) and reading C (total Cl) are required. Combined available chlorine is obtained from $C\text{-}A$.

The result obtained in the simplified total available chlorine procedure corresponds to reading C.

5. Precision and Accuracy

See Tables 409:I through IV preceding and the general introduction to Section 409.

409 F.   DPD Colorimetric Method

1. General Discussion

Principle: This is a colorimetric version of the DPD method and is based on the same principles. Instead of titration with standard ferrous ammonium sulfate (FAS) solution as in the Ferrous Method, a colorimetric procedure is used.

2. Apparatus

Colorimetric equipment: One of the following is required:
a. *Spectrophotometer*, for use at a wavelength of 515 nm and providing a light path of 1 cm or longer.

b. *Filter photometer*, equipped with a filter having maximum transmission in the wavelength range of 490 to 530 nm and providing a light path of 1 cm or longer.

3. Reagents

See Section 409E.2a, b, and d.

4. Procedure

a. *Calibration of photometer or colorimeter:* Calibrate the available instrument with chlorine (1) or potassium permanganate (2) solutions.

1) Chlorine solutions—Prepare chlorine standards in the range of 0.05 to 4 mg/l from chlorine water standardized as directed in Section 410A.3a and chlorine-demand-free distilled water. Develop the color by first placing 5 ml phosphate buffer solution and 5 ml DPD indicator reagent in a flask and then adding 100 ml chlorine standard with thorough mixing as described in ¶s b and c below. Fill the photometer or colorimeter cell from the flask and read the color at 515 nm. Return the contents of the cell to the flask and titrate the solution with standard ferrous ammonium sulfate (FAS) titrant as a check on the chlorine concentration.

2) Potassium permanganate solutions—Prepare a stock solution containing 891 mg $KMnO_4$/1,000 ml. Dilute 10.00 ml stock solution to 100 ml with distilled water in a volumetric flask. When 1 ml of this solution is diluted to 100 ml with distilled water a chlorine equivalent of 1.00 mg/l will be produced in the DPD reaction. Prepare a series of permanganate standards covering the chlorine equivalent range of 0.05 to 4 mg/l. Develop the color by first placing 5 ml phosphate buffer and 5 ml DPD indicator reagent in a flask and then adding 100 ml standard with thorough mixing as described in ¶s b and c below. Fill the photometer or colorimeter cell from the flask and read the color at 515 nm. Return the contents of the cell to the flask and titrate the solution with standard ferrous ammonium sulfate (FAS) titrant as a check on any absorption of permanganate by the distilled water.

b. Volume of sample: Use a sample volume appropriate to the available photometer or colorimeter. Since the following procedure is based on the use of 10-ml volumes, adjust the quantities of reagents proportionately for other sample volumes. Dilute the sample when the total available chlorine exceeds 4 mg/l.

c. Free chlorine: Place 0.5 ml each of buffer reagent and DPD indicator reagent in a test tube or photometer cell. Add 10 ml sample and mix. Read the color immediately (reading A).

d. Monochloramine: Continue by adding one very small crystal of KI and mix. If the dichloramine concentration is expected to be high, instead of the small crystal add 0.1 ml (2 drops) freshly prepared KI solution (0.1 g/100 ml). Read the color immediately (reading B).

e. Dichloramine: Continue by adding a few crystals of KI (about 0.1 g) and mix to dissolve. Let stand about 2 min and read the color (reading C).

f. Nitrogen trichloride: Absence of color in ¶4c (free chlorine) indicates the absence of nitrogen trichloride. Otherwise proceed as follows: Place a very small crystal of KI in a clean test tube or photometer cell. Add 10 ml sample and mix. Add 0.5 ml each of buffer and indicator reagents, and mix. Read the color immediately (reading D).

5. Calculation

Reading	NCl₃ Absent	NCl₃ Present
A	free Cl	free Cl
B-A	NH₂Cl	NH₂Cl
C-B	NHCl₂	NHCl₂+ ½NCl₃
D	—	free Cl+ ½NCl₃
2(D-A)	—	NCl₃
C-D	—	NHCl₂

Should monochloramine be present with nitrogen trichloride, which is unlikely, it will be included in reading D, in which case NCl_3 is obtained from $2(D\text{-}B)$.

409 G.   Leuco Crystal Violet Method

1. General Discussion

The leuco crystal violet method measures separately the free and the total available chlorine. The combined available chlorine may be determined by difference. The residual chlorine in an unknown sample may be determined by visual comparison with chlorine standards or by reference to a standard calibration curve.

a. Principle: The compound 4,4',4"-methylidynetris (N,N-dimethylaniline), also known by the common name of leuco crystal violet, reacts instantaneously with free chlorine to form a bluish color. Interference from combined available chlorine can be avoided by completing the test within a 5-min interval. The correct color development in the free chlorine-leuco crystal violet reaction depends on the following factors and conditions: (*a*) The solution must be buffered in the pH range of 3.6 to 4.3; (*b*) a mercuric chloride solution must be added to the sample either before the addition of a leuco crystal violet solution or more conveniently in the form of a mixed indicator; (*c*) the ratio, by weight, of leuco crystal violet to chlorine must be at least 30 to 1; (*d*) the free chlorine concentration should not exceed 2.0 mg/l; (*e*) the mixed indicator solution should be added to the sample in a standardized procedure as described in ¶4a1); (*f*) the test should be completed within 5 min after the mixed indicator addition; (*g*) the sample temperature should not exceed 40 C.

The total chlorine determination involves the reaction of the free and combined chlorine with iodide ion to produce hypoiodous acid, which in turn reacts instantaneously with leuco crystal violet to form the dye crystal violet. The color is stable for days and follows Beer's law over a wide range of total chlorine. The extreme sensitivity of the determination may necessitate dilution of the sample with chlorine-demand-free water to bring the chlorine concentration to the desired range of 2.0 mg/l total chlorine. The following factors are important in the total chlorine determination: (*a*) The solution must be at pH 3.6 to 4.3 during the reaction period; (*b*) there must be an initial contact of at least 60 sec between chlorine and iodide ion; (*c*) the initial iodide concentration must not exceed 40 mg/l; (*d*) the total chlorine concentration should not exceed 2.0 mg/l. Semipermanent color standards for the total chlorine determination can be prepared from crystal violet dye for visual matching of samples and standards in nessler tubes or test tubes.

Leuco crystal violet is available commercially in a very pure form that readily dissolves in water acidified with orthophosphoric acid. The concentration of orthophosphoric acid must produce a pH of 1.5 or less in the final indicator reagent. The dissolution of leuco crystal violet with orthophosphoric acid must be carried out in the darkness of brown glass and the final solution stored in brown glass or opaque plastic containers to minimize reagent deterioration. Both leuco crystal violet and the developed crystal violet dye are relatively inert nontoxic substances, and no special precautions are required.

The preparation and handling of the saturated mercuric chloride solution require special precautions because of its poisonous and corrosive nature. The mixed indicator system, although containing a considerably diluted mercuric chloride solution, also should be handled with care.

Improved accuracy in the determination of residual chlorine with leuco crystal violet is possible through photometric measurements.

The importance of using only chlorine-demand-free water and scrupulously cleaned glassware is self-evident because the presence of ammonia in the dilution water or of organic matter on the glassware can consume chlorine and may result in low chlorine values.

b. *Interference:* No significant interference from combined available chlorine occurs when the free chlorine content is determined within 5 min after indicator addition. Fifteen minutes after indicator addition the apparent error in the free chlorine determination is of the order of 0.04 mg/l at 25 C in a sample containing 5.0 mg/l combined residual chlorine.

For combined chlorine concentrations in excess of 5.0 mg/l, use the given arsenite addition procedure to minimize interference. The major interference in the determination of free residual chlorine is manganic ion, which increases the apparent residual chlorine reading. When manganic ion is known to be present, use the given photometric procedure in which the absorbance due to manganic ion is determined separately and subtracted from the total absorbance to yield that produced by free chlorine alone.

Ferric and nitrate compounds do not interfere and nitrite ion does not interfere in the absence of monochloramine. Where nitrite ion and monochloramine are present together, as in certain wastewaters, serious interference will occur in the determination of free chlorine. The arsenite addition will minimize but not entirely eliminate this interference.

If suspended matter or organic color is present, compensate by incorporating appropriate turbidity or color blanks into the visual or photometric procedures.

c. *Minimum detectable concentration:* 10 μg/l free available chlorine; 5 μg/l total available chlorine.

2. Apparatus

a. *Illumination:* Make all readings by looking through the samples against an illuminated white surface. This surface may be opaque and illuminated by reflection, or it may be an opal diffusing glass illuminated from behind. Since chlorine determinations are made both day and night in plant control, make all comparisons with a standard artificial light. The permanent standards give greater accuracy when used with either of the two artificial light sources specified, both of which are close approximations of average "north" daylight.

b. *Colorimetric equipment:* One o. the following is required:

1) *Nessler tubes*, matched, 50- and 100-ml, tall form.

2) *Test tubes*, matched, with a capacity of at least 10 ml of sample when the sample surface is near the top of the test tube.

3) *Volumetric flasks*, 100-ml, with plastic caps or ground-glass stoppers.

4) *Filter photometer*, providing a light path of 1 cm or longer and equipped with an orange filter having maximum transmittance near 592 nm.

5) *Spectrophotometer*, for use at 592 nm, providing a light path of 1 cm or longer.

c. Glassware: All glassware or plastic containers, including containers for storage of reagent solutions, must be entirely free of organic matter. Use either the chlorination (1) or the chromic acid (2) method after the glassware has been thoroughly cleaned with suitable detergent and rinsed with distilled water. The chromic acid method requires less total time, but care is necessary to protect laboratory personnel from contact with the cleaning mixture.

1) Chlorination—Expose all glassware or plastic containers to water containing at least 10 mg/l chlorine for 3 hr or more before use and rinse with chlorine-demand-free water. After rinsing, oven- or air-dry in an atmosphere free from organic fumes.

2) Chromic acid—Add 1 l conc H_2SO_4 to 35 ml saturated sodium dichromate solution in a 2-l beaker. Stir the mixture carefully until all the sodium dichromate has dissolved. When cleaning glassware, carefully heat a suitable volume of chromic acid solution to approximately 50 C (CAUTION: *Use rubber gloves, safety goggles, and protective clothing in handling this cleaning agent.*) and carefully pour the chromic acid solution into the glassware to be cleaned so that contact is made with the entire inside surface of the container. Let the cleaning solution remain in the glassware for 2 to 3 min or longer. Drain the chromic acid solution and rinse thoroughly with chlorine-demand-free water. Oven- or air-dry the glassware away from organic or other chlorine-consuming fumes.

3. Reagents

a. Chlorine-demand-free water: Chlorine-demand-free water can be made by the chlorination or ion-exchange method. In either case, best results are obtained when distilled water is used as the primary source.

1) Chlorination—Add sufficient chlorine to distilled water to destroy the ammonia. The amount of chlorine required will be about 10 times the amount of ammonia nitrogen present; in no event should the initial residual be less than 1.0 mg/l free chlorine. Let the chlorinated water stand overnight or longer; then expose to direct sunlight until all residual chlorine is discharged.

2) Ion exchange—Prepare a 1-m (3-ft) column of approximately 2.5 to 5 cm diam containing strongly acid cation and strongly basic anion exchange resins. Several commercial mixed-bed resins, analytical grade, are available, but the analyst should satisfy himself that ammonia, chloramines, or other compounds that react with chlorine are removed. Pass the distilled water at a relatively slow rate through the resin bed and collect in a scrupulously cleaned receiver that will protect the treated water from undue exposure to the atmosphere.

3) Prepare all *reagent solutions* and dilute all *samples* with the chlorine-demand-free water.

b. *Stock chlorine solution:* Prepare the stock chlorine or hypochlorite solution from commercial solutions * containing approximately 1% available chlorine (or household bleach), or by bubbling chlorine gas from a small lecture-size cylinder into distilled water. Adjust the chlorine concentration to approximately 100 $\mu g/ml$ of solution. Standardize the stock solution by titrating a suitable portion with standard sodium thiosulfate titrant as described in the iodometric method, Section 409A.3b and c, or by the amperometric titration method. Section 409C.4.

c. *Chlorine solutions for temporary total chlorine standards:* For measurements of combined residual chlorine, mix an ammonium sulfate solution with chlorine solution in an ammonia-to-chlorine ratio of at least 20 to 1. In distilled water, dissolve 3.89 g $(NH_4)_2SO_4$ and dilute to 1,000 ml; 1.0 ml = 1.0 mg NH_3. To approximately 800 ml chlorine-demand-free water, add 2.0 ml $(NH_4)_2SO_4$ solution for each 1.0 ml stock chlorine solution that contains 100 μg $Cl/1.0$ ml and dilute to 1,000 ml. Standardize the combined chlorine solution and express the concentration as milligrams per liter total Cl. Use immediately for calibration.

d. *Buffer solution for free chlorine determination*, pH 4.0:

1) *Potassium hydroxide, 4M:* Dissolve 224.4 g KOH and dilute to 1 l with chlorine-demand-free water.

2) *Citric acid, 2M:* Dissolve 384.3 g $C_6H_8O_7$, or 420.3 g $C_6H_8O_7 \cdot H_2O$,

and dilute to 1 l with chlorine-demand-free water.

3) *Potassium citrate solution:* To 350 ml 4M KOH add, with stirring, 700 ml 2M citric acid. If desired, prepare smaller volumes in the ratio of 1 volume KOH to 2 volumes of citric acid. Use immediately to prepare final buffer solution (5) and discard the remainder of the solution.

4) *Acetate solution:* Dissolve 161.2 g conc (glacial) acetic acid and 49.5 g sodium acetate, $NaC_2H_3O_2$ or 82.1 g $NaC_2H_3O_2 \cdot 3H_2O$ and dilute to 1 l with chlorine-demand-free water.

5) *Final buffer solution:* Mix equal volumes of potassium citrate solution (3) with acetate solution (4) to make the final pH 4.0 buffer solution. Add 20 mg $HgCl_2/l$ solution to prevent mold growth.

e. *Stock leuco crystal violet reagent:* Measure 500 ml chlorine-demand-free water and 14.0 ml 85% orthophosphoric acid into a brown glass container of at least 1-l capacity. Introduce a magnetic stirring bar into the container and mix the acidified water at moderate speed. Add 3.0 g 4,4′,4″-methylidyne-tris-(N,N-dimethylaniline)† and with a small amount of water wash down any reagent adhering to the neck or sides of the container.

Continue agitation until dissolution is complete. Finally, add 500 ml chlorine-demand-free water. Store in the brown bottle at room temperature away from direct sunlight. Discard after 6 months. If a rubber stopper must be used, wrap with plastic wrapping material to protect from contact with the reagent.

f. *Saturated mercuric chloride solu-*

---

* Zonite, a product of Zonite Products Corp.

† Eastman chemical No. 3651 or equivalent.

tion: To 20 g $HgCl_2$ contained in a 300-ml glass-stoppered flask, add 200 ml chlorine-demand-free water. Gently agitate for a few minutes and let stand for 24 hr. (CAUTION: *Label the container with the warning that mercuric chloride is poisonous and corrosive.*)

g. *Mixed indicator:* To 600 ml stock leuco crystal violet reagent in a brown bottle, add 50 ml saturated $HgCl_2$ solution and swirl to insure complete mixing. If desired, prepare smaller volumes of mixed indicator in the ratio of 12 volumes stock leuco crystal violet reagent to 1 volume saturated $HgCl_2$ solution. Follow the storage directions prescribed in ¶3e above.

b. *Buffer solution for total chlorine determination,* pH 4.0: Dissolve 480 g glacial acetic acid and 146 g sodium acetate, $NaC_2H_3O_2$ or 243 g $NaC_2H_3O_2 \cdot 3H_2O$ in 400 ml chlorine-demand-free water and dilute to 1 l. Transfer the solution to a brown bottle. Add 3.0 g KI to the bottle and mix to dissolve the salt. Store in the brown bottle and avoid undue exposure to the air.

i. *Solutions for preparation of semipermanent total chlorine standards:*

1) *Buffer solution,* pH 4.0: Use solution b above.

2) *Crystal violet solution:* Dissolve 40.0 mg crystal violet in 500 ml chlorine-demand-free water containing 20 ml pH 4.0 buffer solution [¶3i 1) preceding]. Stir for 30 min or more to completely dissolve and dilute to 1,000 ml with chlorine-demand-free water.

j. *Sodium hydroxide,* 1N: Dissolve 40 g NaOH in chlorine-demand-free water and dilute to 1 l.

k. *Dilute sodium arsenite solution:*

Dissolve 26 mg $NaAsO_2$ in chlorine-demand-free water and dilute to 100 ml.

l. *Sodium arsenite solution:* Dissolve 5.0 g $NaAsO_2$ in chlorine-demand-free water and dilute to 1 l. (CAUTION: *Toxic—take care to avoid ingestion.*)

m. *Potassium peroxymonosulfate solution:* Obtain this reagent, $KHSO_5$, as the commercial product Oxone,‡ a stable powdered mixture containing 42.8% $KHSO_5$ by weight and a mixture of $KHSO_4$ and K_2SO_4. Dissolve 1.0 g Oxone in chlorine-demand-free water and dilute to 1 l.

4. Procedure

a. *Temporary chlorine standards:* Temporary standards are recommended for photometric calibration as well as for visual comparison. Two separate sets of temporary chlorine standards are mandatory because of the divergent colors developed by free and combined residual chlorine. Semipermanent color standards for the total chlorine determination can be prepared from crystal violet dye and have a longevity approaching 3 months. The color system produced with free residual chlorine, on the other hand, differs from the normal crystal violet shade and is stable for only a few days.

Commercially prepared standards are available in test kits for free chlorine determination.

1) Preparation of temporary free chlorine standards—Thoroughly clean all glassware as described in ¶2c et seq and air- or oven-dry before use. Prepare

‡ A product of E.I. du Pont de Nemours and Co., Inc., Wilmington, Del.

temporary chlorine standards from a suitable volume of stock chlorine solution added to 2 l chlorine-demand-free water contained in a brown glass bottle. For visual comparison studies, set up a chlorine series in the range of 0.1 to 2.0 mg/l at increments of 0.1 or 0.2 mg/l. Standardize the dilute chlorine solutions by the sodium thiosulfate or amperometric titration methods.

After standardization, measure 50.0 ml dilute chlorine solution into a 100-ml glass-stoppered volumetric flask, taking care to introduce the chlorine solution with a minimum of agitation into the volumetric flask. Using a Mohr pipet, add 1.0 ml pH 4.0 buffer solution, ¶3d 5), and gently swirl the flask to mix. With another measuring pipet, add 1.0 ml mixed indicator, ¶3g. Standardize the mixed indicator addition in the following manner: After filling the measuring pipet to the mark, position the pipet tip inside the neck of the volumetric flask so that the tip makes contact with the inside glass surface and let the mixed indicator flow down the inside glass surface to the sample, with a minimum of initial agitation. Remove the pipet from the flask and swirl the contents with a quick firm motion to effect intimate contact between the mixed indicator and the sample. These steps produce the highest and most consistent absorbance values. *Do not dilute the sample to 100 ml after the addition of mixed indicator* in order to obtain the maximum absorbance values.

Transfer the colored temporary standards to 50-ml nessler tubes for visual comparison or prepare a photometric calibration curve.

Visual comparison: If the temporary standards are prepared directly in 50-ml nessler tubes, stopper the tube after addition of the mixed indicator and mix quickly by inverting the tube several times. If a smaller sample volume is taken, as, for example, 10 ml contained in a test tube, reduce the quantity of pH 4.0 buffer and mixed indicator to 0.2 ml each.

Photometric calibration: Transfer the colored temporary standards to cells of 1-cm light path or longer, and read the absorbance in a photometer at a wavelength of 592 nm against a distilled water reference. Plot the absorbance values versus chlorine concentrations to construct a curve. Beer's law is followed in the lower free chlorine range but there is a slight curvature with higher free chlorine concentrations.

2) Preparation of temporary total chlorine standards—Prepare standardized total chlorine solutions as prescribed in ¶3c above in the total chlorine range of 0.1 to 2.0 mg/l. Pipet a 50-ml sample into a 100-ml volumetric flask or 100-ml nessler tube. Add 0.5 ml total chlorine buffer, ¶3h, mix, and allow a contact period of at least 60 sec. Add 1.0 ml mixed indicator, mix to develop the color, and dilute to 100 ml. No special precautions are necessary in the addition and mixing of these solutions.

Photometric calibration: Construct a calibration curve by measuring the absorbance values of the temporary total chlorine standards at 592 nm, preferably in 1-cm cells.

b. Semipermanent total chlorine standards: The variable composition of commercially available crystal violet dye necessitates reconciling the absorbance of the semipermanent standards with the photometric calibration curve. Adjust the final semipermanent standards to agree with the calibration absorbance values obtained on temporary total chlorine standards.

Add the specified volume of crystal violet solution to a 200-ml volumetric flask containing 100 ml distilled water and 4.0 ml pH 4.0 buffer solution, ¶3*i* 1). Dilute to volume with distilled water and compare the absorbance at 592 nm with the suggested values given in Table 409:V or with the photometric calibration curve. Protect the standards from direct sunlight and exposure to air to maintain stability for approximately 3 months. Seal the standards in glass ampuls for maximum protection.

TABLE 409:V. PREPARATION OF SEMIPERMANENT CRYSTAL VIOLET STANDARDS FOR VISUAL DETERMINATION OF RESIDUAL CHLORINE

Total Chlorine Standard *mg/l*	Crystal Violet Solution *ml*	Absorbance of Final 200-ml Standard at 592 nm in 1-cm cell
0.1	2.84	0.131
0.2	5.80	0.268
0.3	8.60	0.396
0.4	11.60	0.530
0.5	14.40	0.660
0.6	17.30	0.790
0.7	20.00	0.925
0.8	23.20	1.060
0.9	26.60	1.192
1.0	28.80	1.320

c. Color development of free chlorine sample: Measure a 50-ml sample into the same type of flask or tube used to prepare the temporary standards in ¶4*a* 1). Add 1.0 ml pH 4.0 buffer, ¶3*d* 5), and 1.0 ml mixed indicator, ¶3*g*. Add the mixed indicator to the sample in the same uniform manner prescribed for the temporary standards in ¶4*a* 1). Match the test sample visually with the temporary standards or read the absorbance photometrically and refer to the standard calibration curve for the free chlorine equivalent. Complete the determination within 5 min of adding the mixed indicator to obviate interference from combined residual chlorine manifested by a slow increase in color. For free chlorine concentrations greater than 2.0 mg/l, dilute the sample with chlorine-demand-free water to contain 2.0 mg/l or less and proceed with the determination as previously described.

The color development due to combined chlorine residuals is negligible at sample temperatures as high as 40 C and is slightly accelerated at higher temperatures. The color with free chlorine develops instantaneously, and, in the absence of combined residual chlorine, is stable for several days.

d. Color development of total chlorine samples:

1) Concentrations below 2.0 mg/l— Measure a 50-ml sample into a suitable flask or tube and add 0.5 ml total chlorine buffer, ¶3*b*. Mix and wait at least 60 sec. Add 1.0 ml mixed indicator, ¶ 3*g*, mix, and dilute to 100 ml. Visually match with standards or read the absorbance photometrically and compare with the calibration curve.

2) Concentrations above 2.0 mg/l— Place approximately 30 ml chlorine-demand-free water in a flask or tube calibrated to contain at least 100 ml. Add 0.5 ml total chlorine buffer, ¶3*b*, and a measured volume of 20 ml or less of the sample. After mixing, let stand for at least 60 sec. Add 1.0 ml mixed indicator, ¶3*g*, mix, and dilute to the

mark with chlorine-demand-free water. Match visually with standards or read the absorbance photometrically and compare with the calibration curve. Select one of the following sample volumes in order to remain within the optimum chlorine range:

Total Chlorine mg/l	Sample Volume Required ml
2.0–4.0	20.0
4.0–8.0	10.0
8.0–10.0	5.0

The total chlorine color develops instantaneously and remains stable for days. Dilute the final color, if too intense for visual matching, with chlorine-demand-free water buffered at pH 4.0, then match with standards and estimate the initial total chlorine by applying the dilution factor.

e. *Elimination of interference from high concentrations of combined chlorine:* For the determination of free chlorine in the presence of high concentrations of combined chlorine, immediately add 5.0 ml sodium arsenite solution, ¶ 3l, after adding and mixing 1.0 ml mixed indicator, ¶3g. Compare visually or photometrically with standards prepared by adding 5.0 ml distilled water after adding mixed indicator to compensate for dilution by sodium arsenite solution.

f. *Compensation for manganic [Mn(IV)] manganese:* For free chlorine determination, follow the procedure as in ¶4c and record the absorbance as A_1. To a second sample of 50-ml volume, add 0.4 ml of 1 N NaOH to adjust pH to approximately 11.0. Add 1.0 ml dilute sodium arsenite solution, ¶3k, and

let react for 2 min. Add 2.0 ml Oxone solution, ¶3m, and wait 1.0 min. Add 2.0 ml pH 4.0 buffer, ¶3d 5), and 1.0 ml mixed indicator, ¶3g, mix, and record absorbance as A_2. Calculate the absorbance, A_3, due to free chlorine alone as follows:

$$A_3 = A_1 - 1.084\ A_2$$

Refer absorbance A_3 to the free chlorine standard curve to obtain free chlorine concentration.

For total chlorine determination, make the total chlorine test as in ¶4d 1) and record absorbance as B_1. To a second 50-ml sample, add 1 N sodium hydroxide (approximately 0.4 ml) to adjust to pH 11.0. Add dilute sodium arsenite, Oxone, pH 4.0 buffer, and mixed indicator solutions as in ¶4f. Dilute final solution to 100 ml and record absorbance as B_2. Calculate absorbance, B_3, due to total chlorine alone as follows:

$$B_3 = B_1 - B_2$$

Refer absorbance B_3 to total chlorine standard curve to obtain total chlorine concentration.

g. *Compensation for turbidity and color:* Compensate for the interference by natural color or turbidity as follows:

1) Visually—View the sample and standard horizontally after placing an untreated sample of the same thickness behind the standard and the same thickness of clean water behind the sample.

2) Photometrically—Measure the absorbance at 592 nm of the sample and subtract this reading from the absorbance of the treated free or total chlorine sample.

5. Calculation

$$\text{mg/l Total Cl} = \frac{A \times 50}{\text{ml sample}}$$

$$\text{mg/l Combined Cl} = B - C$$

where A = total chlorine in mg/l measured in the diluted sample, B = total chlorine in mg/l in the sample, and C = free chlorine in mg/l.

6. Precision and Accuracy

See Tables 409:I through 409:IV and the general introduction to Section 409.

409 H. Syringaldazine (FACTS) Method (TENTATIVE)

1. General Discussion

a. Principle: The free available chlorine test, syringaldazine (FACTS) measures free available chlorine over the range of 0.1 to 10 mg/l. A saturated solution of syringaldazine (3,5-dimethoxy-4-hydroxybenzaldazine) is used. Syringaldazine is stable when stored as a solid or as a solution in 2-propanol. It is oxidized by free available chlorine on a 1:1 molar basis to produce a colored product with an absorption maximum of 530 nm. The color product is only slightly soluble in water; therefore, at chlorine concentrations greater than 1 mg/l, the final reaction mixture must contain 2-propanol to prevent product precipitation and color fading.

The optimum color and solubility (minimum fading) is obtained in a solution having a pH between 6.5 and 6.8. At a pH less than 6, color development is slow and reproducibility is poor. At a pH greater than 7, the color develops rapidly but fades quickly. Therefore, a buffer is required to maintain the reaction mixture pH at approximately 6.7. Care should be taken with waters of high acidity or alkalinity to assure that the added buffer maintains the proper pH.

Temperature has a minimal effect on the color reaction. The maximum error observed at temperature extremes of 5 and 35 C is ±10%.

This procedure is relatively new and has not received extensive testing; however, it has been demonstrated to be the most specific colorimetric test available for measuring free available chlorine. Although the syringaldazine solution can be used to determine combined forms of chlorine with a potassium iodide step similar to that used with the amperometric procedure, details have yet to be developed.

b. Interferences: Interferences common to other methods for determining free available chlorine do not affect the FACTS procedure. Monochloramine concentrations up to 18 mg/l (as Cl), dichloramine concentrations up to 10 mg/l (as Cl) and manganese concentrations (oxidized forms) up to 1 mg/l do not interfere. Very high concentrations of monochloramine (≥ 35 mg/l) and oxidized manganese (≥ 2.6 mg/l) will produce a color with syringaldazine slowly. Ferric iron can react with syringaldazine; however, concentrations up to 10 mg/l do not interfere with the FACTS procedure. Nitrite (≤ 250 mg/

l), nitrate (≤ 100 mg/l), sulfate ($\leq$ 1,000 mg/l), and chloride ($\leq 1,000$ mg/l) do not interfere. Waters with high hardness (≥ 500 mg/l) will produce a cloudy solution although they will not interfere with the test results.

Other strong oxidizing agents such as iodine, bromine, and ozone will produce a color.

c. Minimum detectable concentration: The FACTS procedure is sensitive to free available chlorine concentrations of 0.1 mg/l or less.

2. Apparatus

Colorimetric equipment: One of the following is required:

a. Filter photometer, providing a light path of 1 cm for chlorine concentrations ≤ 1 mg/l, or a light path from 1 to 10 mm for chlorine concentration above 1 mg/l; also equipped with a filter having a band pass of 500 to 560 nm.

b. Spectrophotometer, for use at 530 nm, providing the light paths noted in the paragraph above.

3. Reagents

a. Chlorine-demand-free water: Add sufficient chlorine to distilled water to destroy the ammonia and nitrite. The amount of chlorine required will be about 10 times the amount of ammonia nitrogen present; produce an initial residual of more than 1.0 mg/l free chlorine. Let the chlorinated distilled water stand overnight or longer; then expose to direct sunlight until all residual chlorine is discharged.

b. Syringaldazine indicator: Dissolve 115 mg of 3,5-dimethoxy-4-hydroxybenzaldazine* in 1 l 2-propanol.

c. Buffer: Dissolve 17.01 g KH_2PO_4 and 1 g sodium benzoate in 200 ml water. Adjust the pH to 6.6 with conc NaOH and dilute to 250 ml with chlorine-demand-free water.

4. Procedure

a. Calibration of photometer: Prepare a calibration curve by making dilutions of a standardized hypochlorite solution prepared as directed under chlorine demand, Section 410A.3*a*. Develop and measure the colors as described in ¶4*b*, below.

b. Free available chlorine analysis: Add 3 ml sample and 0.1 ml buffer to a 5-ml capacity test tube. Add 1 ml syringaldazine indicator, cap the tube, and invert twice to mix. Transfer the sample to a photometer tube or spectrophotometer cell and measure the percent transmittance. Convert percent transmittance to absorbance. Compare the absorbance value obtained with the calibration curve and report the corresponding value as milligrams per liter free available chlorine.

5. Precision and Accuracy

This method has not received extensive testing; however, it has been shown to be the most specific colorimetric test for measuring free available chlorine. The accuracy and precision are comparable to those of the DPD, SNORT, and leuco crystal violet methods.

---

* Aldrich No. 17, 753-9, Aldrich Chemical Company, Inc., Cedar Knolls, N.J. 07927.

409 I. Bibliography

General

Water Chlorine (Residual) No. 1. 1969. Analytical Reference Service Rep. No. 35, EPA, Cincinnati, Ohio.

Water Chlorine (Residual) No. 2. 1971. Analytical Reference Service Rep. No. 40, EPA, Cincinnati, Ohio.

GUTER, W.J., W.J. COOPER & C.A. SORBER. 1974. Evaluation of existing field test kits for determining free chlorine residuals in aqueous solutions. *J. Amer. Water Works Ass.* 66:38.

WHITTLE, G.P. & A. LAPTEFF, JR. 1973. New analytical techniques for the study of water disinfection. In: Chemistry of Water Supply, Treatment, and Distribution. p. 63. Ann Arbor Science Publishers, Ann Arbor, Mich.

Iodometric Method

LEA, C. 1933. Chemical control of sewage chlorination: The use and value of orthotolidine test. *J. Soc. Chem. Ind.* (London) 52:245T.

AMERICAN WATER WORKS ASSOCIATION. 1943. Committee report. Control of chlorination. *J. Amer. Water Works Ass.* 35:1315.

MARKS, H.C., R. JOINER & F.B. STRANDSKOV. 1948. Amperometric titration of residual chlorine in sewage. *Water Sewage Works* 95:175.

STRANDSKOV, F.B., H.C. MARKS & D.H. HORCHIER. 1949. Application of a new residual chlorine method to effluent chlorination. *Sewage Works J.* 21:23.

NUSBAUM, I. & L.A. MEYERSON. 1951. Determination of chlorine demands and chlorine residuals in sewage. *Sewage Ind. Wastes* 23:968.

MARKS, H.C., D.B. WILLIAMS & G.U. GLASGOW. 1951. Determination of residual chlorine compounds. *J. Amer. Water Works Ass.* 43:201.

MARKS, H.C. & N.S. CHAMBERLIN. 1953. Determination of residual chlorine in metal finishing wastes. *Anal. Chem.* 24:1885.

Amperometric Titration

FOULK, C.W. & A.T. BAWDEN. 1926. A new type of endpoint in electrometric titration and its application to iodimetry. *J. Amer. Chem. Soc.* 48:2045.

MARKS, H.C. & J.R. GLASS. 1942. A new method of determining residual chlorine. *J. Amer. Water Works Ass.* 34:1227.

HALLER, J.F. & S.S. LISTEK. 1948. Determination of chlorine dioxide and other active chlorine compounds in water. *Anal. Chem.* 20:639.

MAHAN, W.A. 1949. Simplified amperometric titration apparatus for determining residual chlorine in water. *Water Works Sewage* 96:171.

MARKS, H.C., D.B. WILLIAMS & G.U. GLASGOW. 1951. Determination of residual chlorine compounds. *J. Amer. Water Works Ass.* 43:201.

KOLTHOFF, I.M. & J.J. LINGANE. 1952. Polarography, 2nd ed. Interscience Publishers, New York, N.Y.

MORROW, J.J. 1966. Residual chlorine determination with dual polarizable electrodes. *J. Amer. Water Works Ass.* 58:363.

Stabilized Neutral Orthotolidine (SNORT) Method

KRUTZSCH, W. 1944. Wasser Kohle Öl, 4th ed. Otto Elsner Verlagsgesellschaft, p. 36.

AITKEN, R.W. & D. MERCER. 1951. Photometric measurement of residual chlorine and chloramine in water using neutral orthotolidine. *J. Inst. Water Eng.* 5:321.

PALIN, A.T. 1954. Determining residual chlorine in water by neutral orthotolidine methods—A progress report. *Water Sewage Works* 101:74.

JOHNSON, J.D., R. OVERBY & D.A. OKUN. 1965. Analysis of chlorine, monochloramine and dichloramine with stabilized neutral orthotolidine. 85th Annual Conf., Amer. Water Works Ass., Portland, Ore., June 28.

JOHNSON, J.D. & R. OVERBY. 1969. Stabilized neutral orthotolidine, SNORT, colorimetric method for chlorine. *Anal. Chem.* 41:1744.

Ferrous DPD Method

PALIN, A.T. 1957. The determination of free and combined chlorine in water by the use of diethyl-p-phenylene diamine. *J. Amer. Water Works Ass.* 49:873.

PALIN, A.T. 1961. The determination of free residual bromine in water. *Water Sewage Works* 108:461.

NICOLSON, N.J. 1965. An evaluation of the methods for determining residual chlorine in water. Part I. Free chlorine. *Analyst* 90:187.

NICOLSON, N.J. 1963, 1965, 1966. Determination of chlorine in water, Parts 1, 2 and 3. Water Res. Ass. Tech. Pap. Nos. 29, 47, and 53.

DPD Colorimetric Method

PALIN, A.T. 1960. Colorimetric determination of chlorine dioxide in water. *Water Sewage Works* 107:457.

PALIN, A.T. 1967. Methods for the determination, in water, of free and combined available chlorine, chlorine dioxide and chlorite, bromine, iodine, and ozone using diethyl-p-phenylenediamine (DPD). *J. Inst. Water Eng.* 21:537.

PALIN, A.T. Determination of nitrogen trichloride in water. 1968. *J. Amer. Water Works Ass.* 60:847.

Leuco Crystal Violet Method

BLACK, A.P. & G.P. WHITTLE. 1967. New methods for the colorimetric determination of halogen residuals. Part II. Free and total chlorine. *J. Amer. Water Works Ass.* 59:607.

FACTS Method

BAUER, R. & C. RUPE. 1971. Use of syringaldazine in a photometric method for estimating "free" chlorine in water. *Anal. Chem.* 43:421.

GUTER, K.J., W.J. COOPER & C.A. SORBER. 1974. Evaluation of existing field test kits for determining free chlorine residuals in aqueous solutions. *J. Amer. Water Works Ass.* 66:38.

COOPER, W.J., C.A. SORBER & E.P. MEIER. 1974. A Rapid, Free, Available Chlorine Test with Syringaldazine (FACTS). 94th Annual Conf., Amer. Water Works Ass., Boston, Mass., June 19.

410 CHLORINE DEMAND

The chlorine demand of a water is caused by such inorganic reductants as ferrous, manganous, nitrite, sulfide, and sulfite ions. Ammonia and cyanide consume considerable chlorine during the free residual chlorination process. Chlorine substitutes on phenols and other aromatic compounds to form chloro derivatives, but also may oxidize the aromatic compounds when larger amounts of chlorine are added. It also may react with ammonia and naturally occurring amino compounds to form chloramines with an active or oxidizing chlorine atom. Destruction of the chloramine compounds can be achieved by the addition of more chlorine and subsequently, with the addition of enough chlorine, a free available residual (hypochlorous acid or hypochlorite) may be attained.

The chlorine demand of water is the difference between the amount of chlorine applied and the amount of free, combined, or total available chlorine remaining at the end of the contact period. The chlorine demand of water varies with the amount of chlorine applied, time of contact, pH, and temperature. For comparative purposes, *all test conditions must be stated.* The smallest amount of residual chlorine considered significant is 0.1 mg/l Cl. Presented here are a method for laboratory use and a field procedure that gives less exact results.

410 A.   Laboratory Method

1. Discussion

The laboratory method is designed to determine the so-called immediate demand as well as other demands at longer contact periods. Chlorine demand is measured to determine the amount of chlorine that must be applied to a water to produce a specific free, combined, or total available chlorine residual after a selected period of contact. If the amount of chlorine applied to waters containing ammonium or organic nitrogen compounds is not sufficient to reach what is termed the "breakpoint," chloramines and certain other chloro derivatives that react as combined available residual chlorine are produced. When sufficient chlorine has been added to reach the breakpoint, which depends on pH, ratio of chlorine to nitrogenous compounds present, and other factors, subsequent additions of chlorine remain in the free available state.

2. Apparatus

Colorimetric equipment: One of the following is required:

a. Spectrophotometer or filter photometer, for use in the wavelength range suitable for the method selected for determination of residual chlorine.

b. Comparator, color- and turbidity-compensating.

c. French square bottles, capacity 30 to 60 ml (1 or 2 oz).

3. Reagents

a. Standard chlorine solution: Obtain a suitable solution from the chlorinator solution hose or by bubbling chlorine gas through distilled water. Improve the stability of the chlorine solution by storing in the dark or in brown glass-stoppered bottles. Standardize it each day that it is used. Alternatively, dilute household hypochlorite solution, which contains about 30,000 to 50,000 mg/l chlorine equivalent. This is more stable than a chlorine solution, but do not use it for more than 1 wk without restandardizing. Use the same kind of chlorine solution as is actually applied in plant treatment to determine the chlorine demand. The preparation of temporary standards for calibrating a photometer entails the fewest problems with hypochlorite. Depending on the intended use, a suitable strength of chlorine solution usually will be between 100 mg/l and 1,000 mg/l. If used for chlorine demand determination, it should be sufficiently strong that the volume of treated portions will not be increased more than 5% by addition of the chlorine solution.

Standardization—Place 2 ml acetic acid and 10 to 25 ml distilled water in a flask. Add about 1 g KI. Measure into the flask a suitable volume of the chlorine solution. In choosing a convenient volume, note that 1 ml of 0.025N thiosulfate titrant to be used for titrating is equivalent to about 0.9 mg chlorine.

Titrate with standardized 0.025N sodium thiosulfate titrant until the yellow iodine color is almost gone. Add 1 to 2 ml starch indicator solution and continue the titration to disappearance of the blue color.

Determine the blank by adding identical quantities of acid, KI, and starch indicator to a volume of distilled water corresponding to the sample used for titration.

$$mg/ml\ Cl\ =\ \frac{(A \pm B) \times N \times 35.45}{ml\ sample}$$

where A = ml titration for sample, B = ml titration for blank (positive or negative), and N = normality of $Na_2S_2O_3$.

    b. Acetic acid, conc (glacial).

    c. Potassium iodide, KI, crystals.

    d. Standard sodium thiosulfate titrant, 0.025N: Prepare as directed in Residual Chlorine, Section 409A.2*d* preceding.

    e. Starch indicator solution: Prepare as directed in Section 409A.2*e* preceding.

    f. Appropriate reagents for estimating residual chlorine by one of the standard methods described in Section 409.

4. Procedure

    a. Volume of sample: Measure at least 10 equal portions of the sample, preferably into brown glass-stoppered bottles or erlenmeyer flasks of ample capacity to permit mixing. If the object of the test is to determine chlorine demand, measure 200-ml portions; if it is to relate chlorine demand to bacterial removal, the effect on taste and odor, or the chemical constituents of the water, use portions of 500 ml or more. Properly sterilize all glassware for bacteriological use.

    b. Addition of chlorine water: Add an amount of chlorine to the first portion that leaves no chlorine residual at the end of the contact period. Add increasing amounts of chlorine to the successive portions in the series. Increase the dosage between portions in increments of 0.1 mg/l for determining low demands and up to 1.0 mg/l or more for higher demands. Mix while adding. Dose the portions of the sample according to a staggered schedule that will permit the determination of chlorine residuals at the predetermined contact time.

    c. Contact time: The usual purpose of a chlorine demand test is to determine the amount of chlorine required to produce a specific free, combined, or total available chlorine residual after a definite time interval that may vary from a few minutes to many hours. Carry out the test over the desired contact period. If the objective of the test is to duplicate in the laboratory the temperature and the plant contact time, make several preliminary chlorine determinations during different reaction periods, such as 15, 30, and 60 min, in order to determine the chlorine consumption with respect to time—information that can be valuable in treatment plant control. Record the contact time. Protect the chlorinated samples from strong daylight throughout the test.

    d. Examination of samples: At the end of the contact period, determine the free and/or combined available residual chlorine by one of the standard methods described in Section 409. Plot the residual chlorine or the amount consumed versus the dosage to aid in studying the results. If necessary, remove samples for bacteriological examination at desired intervals.

    e. Taste and odor: Observe the taste and odor of the treated samples at ordinary temperatures with or without dechlorination. For odor observation at elevated temperatures, dechlorinate the samples before heating. Choose the dechlorinating agent with due regard to its effect on the odor in the water under examination. Generally, sodium sulfite is satisfactory if only a slight stoichiometric excess is used.

410 B.   Field Method

1. General Discussion

The test below is designed for the measurement of chlorine demand in the plant or field when facilities or personnel are not adequate to use the more exact method. Results obtained in this test are approximations only.

2. Apparatus

a. Chlorine comparator, color- and turbidity-compensating.

b. Medicine dropper that will deliver 20 drops/ml. When a dropper is used for measurement, it is essential that the end of the dropper be well cleaned so that water adheres all around the periphery, and that the dropper be held in a strictly vertical position, with the drops being formed slowly.

c. Ten flasks of approximately 1 l capacity, marked at the 500-ml level.

d. Ten 60-ml (2-oz) bottles, marked at the 20-ml level.

e. Glass stirring rod.

f. Glass-stemmed thermometer.

3. Reagents

a. Standard chlorine solution: Dilute a 5% household bleaching solution 1+4. Standardize as directed in Method A, ¶3*a*, but take 20 drops of the diluted hypochlorite solution as the sample to be titrated; use the same dropper that will be used in the procedure. For each drop:

$$\text{mg available Cl} = \frac{A \times N \times 35}{20}$$

where A = ml titration for sample and N = normality of $Na_2S_2O_3$.

Adjust this solution to 10 mg/ml (0.5 mg chlorine/drop) so that 1 drop added to a 500-ml water sample will represent a dosage of 1 mg/l.

b. Test reagent: Use the appropriate reagents for estimating residual chlorine by one of the methods described in Section 409.

4. Procedure

a. Measurement of samples: Fill each container to the 500-ml mark with sample. Record the temperature.

b. Addition of chlorine: While stirring constantly, add 1 drop of chlorine solution to the water in the first flask, 2 drops to that in the second flask, 3 drops to that in the third flask, etc.

c. Contact time: Follow directions given in Method A, ¶4*c* above.

d. Examination of samples: At the end of the contact period, remove a portion from each sample and determine the residual chlorine by one of the methods described in Section 409.

5. Calculation

mg/l Cl demand
= mg/l Cl added–mg/l residual Cl

6. Interpretation of Results

This chlorine demand refers only to the particular dosage, contact time, and temperature used in this test. Plotting the residual chlorine or the amount consumed versus the chlorine added will aid in studying the results.

410 C. Bibliography

GRIFFIN, A.E. & N.S. CHAMBERLIN. 1941. Relation of ammonia-nitrogen to breakpoint chlorination. *Amer. J. Pub. Health* 31:803.

AMERICAN WATER WORKS ASSOCIATION. 1943. Committee report. Control of chlorination. *J. Amer. Water Works Ass.* 35:1315.

PALIN, A.T. 1950. Chemical aspects of chlorination. *J. Inst. Water Eng.* 4:565.

TARAS, M.J. 1953. Effect of free residual chlorination on nitrogen compounds in water. *J. Amer. Water Works Ass.* 45:47.

411   CHLORINE DIOXIDE

Because the physical and chemical properties of chlorine dioxide resemble those of chlorine in many respects, the entire discussion of Residual Chlorine (Section 409) should be read before a chlorine dioxide determination is attempted.

Chlorine dioxide is applied to water supplies to combat tastes and odors due to phenolic-type wastes, actinomycetes, and algae, as well as to oxidize soluble iron and manganese to a more easily removable form. It acts as a disinfectant, and some results suggest that it may be stronger than free chlorine or hypochlorite. However, the difficulties of generation, handling, and storage have limited both application and experimentation.

Chlorine dioxide is a deep yellow, volatile, and unpleasant-smelling gas usually produced at the site of application by reacting a solution of sodium chlorite with a strong chlorine solution. An excess of chlorine over the theoretical amount is needed so that the final mixture consists of chlorine and chlorine dioxide. When the source of chlorine is a hypochlorite compound, an acid must be added to insure the production of chlorine dioxide.

The reaction between sodium chlorite and chlorine is inhibited at pH values above 4 in dilute solutions. Therefore, chlorine dioxide solutions are prepared for laboratory studies by acidifying a sodium chlorite solution to a pH of 2.5. The evolved chlorine dioxide is scrubbed with sodium chlorite solution to remove free-chlorine impurity and then is passed into distilled water by means of a smooth current of air when a pure chlorine dioxide solution is desired.

1. Selection of Method

The iodometric method (A) gives a very precise measure of the total available strength of a solution in terms of its ability to liberate iodine from iodide. However, chlorine dioxide, chlorine, chlorite, and hypochlorite are not distinguished easily by this technic. It is designed primarily, and best used, for standardizing the chlorine dioxide solutions needed for the preparation of temporary standards. Temporary standards are valuable for checking the permanent color standards, for the construction of photometric calibration curves required in the OTO method (B), and for securing evidence on the accuracy of the amperometric method (C). Method A cannot be used to check chlorine dioxide residuals after running a chlorine dioxide demand test because of the presence of the chlorite ion.

The orthotolidine-oxalic acid colorimetric method (B), generally abbreviated OTO, is a flash test that finds greatest application in the routine determination of chlorine dioxide both in the control laboratory and in the field. The method requires common reagents and the simplest of operations once the visual standards or the photometric calibration curve have been prepared. Although the OTO method may lack precision in polluted samples, reasonable accuracy can be expected when the proper precautions governing orthotolidine reactions are observed.

The amperometric method (C) is useful when a knowledge of the various chlorine fractions in a water sample is desired. It distinguishes the various chlorine compounds of interest with good accuracy and precision, but requires specialized equipment and considerable analytical skill.

2. Sampling and Storage

Make chlorine dioxide determinations promptly after collecting the sample. Avoid exposing the sample to sunlight or strong artificial light and to agitation that aerates the sample excessively. Minimum chlorine dioxide losses will occur when the determination is completed immediately at the site of the sample collection.

411 A.   Iodometric Method

1. General Discussion

a. Principle: A pure solution of chlorine dioxide is prepared by slowly adding dilute sulfuric acid to a sodium chlorite solution, removing any contaminants such as chlorine by means of a sodium chlorite scrubber, and passing the gas into distilled water by means of a steady stream of air.

Chlorine dioxide releases free iodine from a potassium iodide solution acidified with acetic or sulfuric acid. The liberated iodine is titrated with a standard solution of sodium thiosulfate, with starch as the indicator.

b. Interference: There is little interference in this method, but temperature and strong light affect the stability of the solution. Minimize chlorine dioxide losses by storing the stock chlorine dioxide solution in a dark refrigerator and by preparing and titrating the dilute chlorine dioxide solutions for standardization purposes at the lowest practicable temperature and in subdued light.

c. *Minimum detectable concentration:* One drop (0.05 ml) of $0.01N$ sodium thiosulfate is equivalent to 20 $\mu g/l$ chlorine dioxide (or 40 $\mu g/l$ in terms of available chlorine) when a 500-ml sample is titrated.

2. Reagents

All the reagents listed for the determination of residual chlorine in Section 409A.2a-g are required. Also needed are the following:

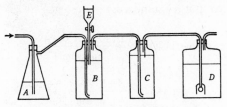

Figure 409:1. **Chlorine dioxide generation and absorption system.**

a. *Stock chlorine dioxide solution:* Prepare a gas generating and absorbing system similar to the one illustrated in Figure 409:1. Connect aspirator flask A of 500-ml capacity by means of rubber tubing to a source of compressed air. Let the air bubble through a layer of 300 ml of distilled water in flask A and then pass over and down through a glass tube to within 5 mm of the bottom of the 1-l gas-generating bottle B. Conduct the evolved gas via glass tubing through a scrubber bottle C containing saturated sodium chlorite solution or a tower packed with flaked sodium chlorite, and finally, via glass tubing, into a 2-l pyrex collecting bottle D, where the gas is absorbed in 1,500 ml distilled water. Provide an air outlet tube on bottle D for escape of the moving air. Select for gas generation a bottle constructed of strong pyrex glass and having a mouth wide enough to permit the insertion of three separate glass tubes: the first leading almost to the bottom for admitting air, the second reaching below the liquid surface for the gradual introduction of the H_2SO_4, and the third near the top for exit of the evolved gas and air. Fit to the second tube a graduated cylinder, E, for containing H_2SO_4. If possible, locate this system in a fume hood with an adequate shield.

Dissolve 10 g sodium chlorite, $NaClO_2$, in 750 ml distilled water and place in bottle B.

Carefully add 2 ml conc H_2SO_4 to 18 ml distilled water and mix. Transfer to cylinder E.

Connect flask A to bottle B and the latter to bottles C and D. Pass a smooth current of air through the system, as evidenced by the bubbling rate in all bottles.

Introduce 5-ml increments of sulfuric acid from cylinder E into bottle B at 5-min intervals.

Continue the air flow for 30 min after the last portion of acid has been added.

Store the yellow stock solution in a dark refrigerator. The concentration of the chlorine dioxide thus prepared may vary between 250 and 600 mg/l, corresponding to approximately 600 to 1,600 mg/l available chlorine.

b. *Standard chlorine dioxide solution:* Use this solution for preparing the desired temporary chlorine dioxide standards. Dilute the required volume of stock chlorine dioxide solution to the desired strength with chlorine-demand-free water prepared as described in Section 409D.3a. Standardize the solution by titrating with standard $0.01N$ or $0.025N$ sodium thiosulfate titrant in the presence of KI, acid, and starch indicator by following the procedure given in ¶3 below. A full or nearly full bottle of chlorine or chlorine dioxide solution retains its titer longer than a half-full one. If repeated withdrawals reduce the volume to a critical level, standardize the solution at the beginning, midway in the series of withdrawals, and at the end of the series. Shake the contents thoroughly before drawing off the needed solution from the middle of the glass-stoppered dark-colored bottle. Prepare this solution frequently.

3. Procedure

Select the volume of sample, prepare the sample for titration, and titrate the sample and the blank as described in Section 409A.3. The only exception is the following: *Allow the chlorine dioxide to react in the dark with the acid and the potassium iodide for 5 min before starting the titration.*

4. Calculations

Express chlorine dioxide concentrations in terms of chlorine dioxide alone or available chlorine content. The available chlorine is defined as the total oxidizing power of the chlorine dioxide measured by titrating the iodine released by the chlorine dioxide from an acidic solution of KI. Calculate the result in terms of chlorine itself.

For standardizing chlorine dioxide solution:

$$\text{mg/ml ClO}_2 = \frac{(A \pm B) \times N \times 13.49}{\text{ml sample titrated}}$$

$$\text{mg/ml Cl} = \frac{(A \pm B) \times N \times 35.45}{\text{ml sample titrated}}$$

For determining chlorine dioxide in temporary standards:

$$\text{mg/l ClO}_2 = \frac{(A \pm B) \times N \times 13,490}{\text{ml sample}}$$

$$\text{mg/l Cl} = \frac{(A \pm B) \times N \times 35,450}{\text{ml sample}}$$

where A = ml titration for sample, B = ml titration for blank (positive or negative), and N = normality of $Na_2S_2O_3$.

411 B.   Orthotolidine-Oxalic Acid (OTO) Method

1. General Discussion

a. Principle: After the sample has been treated with oxalic acid to eliminate the residual chlorine, acidic orthotolidine reagent is added to produce a yellow color. Sodium arsenite serves to minimize interference and arrest color development. Chlorine dioxide produces less yellow color than residual chlorine, the intensity corresponding to approximately one-half that of a similar concentration of residual chlorine when the result is reported in terms of chlorine dioxide itself. However, the color developed by chlorine dioxide is one-fifth that of the available chlorine content.

The yellow orthotolidine color can be measured by visual or photometric methods. Best results are obtained with photometric instruments that have been calibrated with known chlorine dioxide solutions. Visual comparison is satisfactory for routine determinations in the control laboratory.

b. Precautions: The same attention should be paid to details as in the residual chlorine determinations. Because the amounts of chlorine dioxide normally applied to water supplies are quite small, the following instructions are important: Keep all glassware used in the determinations scrupulously clean. Make an average of two or three determinations to avoid questionable values. The fact that the readings are multiplied by 2 or 5 to obtain the final results makes such practices both desirable and prudent.

c. Interferences: When orthotolidine is used to measure residual chlorine, be sure of the presence and amount of interfering substances in the sample to be tested. Such interferences include ferric, manganic, and nitrite compounds, and possibly organic iron compounds, lignocellulose, and algae. These substances increase the apparent residual chlorine content of the sample.

Suspended matter interferes; remove it by centrifuging before testing, or, if the turbidity is not high, use a compensating colorimeter that corrects for existing color turbidity in the sample. Alternatively, compensate for color and turbidity by adding 1 or 2 drops of a reducing reagent containing an oxidizable sulfur group (mercaptosuccin acid, $0.1N$ sodium thiosulfate, or sodium sulfite solution) and stirring until the color disappears. This simple procedure is particularly suited to photometric measurements and for use with samples containing acid-soluble turbidity such as alum floc.

In chlorinated water containing no more than 300 $\mu g/l$ iron, 10 $\mu g/l$ manganic manganese, and 100 $\mu g/l$ nitrite nitrogen, accept development of the characteristic yellow color with orthotolidine as being due to chlorine. If iron and manganese are present in more than the above concentrations, do not accept the development of the characteristic yellow color with orthotolidine as being due to chlorine alone. If nitrite is present in an interfering concentration, develop color in total darkness to minimize interference. Significant amounts of nitrite will not exist in water containing free available chlorine but may exist in the presence of chloramines. In addition, the calcium in hard waters may precipitate after introduction of the saturated oxalic acid solution. Although chlorite ion reacts slowly with orthotolidine, the chlorite ion may react with the oxalic acid solution during the standing period and subsequently with the hydrochloric acid of the orthotolidine reagent to form chlorous acid, which in turn can disproportionate to chlorine dioxide.

d. Minimum detectable concentration: The minimum detectable concentration depends on the terms in which the chlorine dioxide result is reported. If the result is reported as chlorine dioxide, a minimum of 20 $\mu g/l$ can be detected. When the result is reported in terms of available chlorine content, the minimum becomes 50 $\mu g/l$.

2. Apparatus

Colorimetric equipment: One of the following is required:

a. Spectrophotometer or filter photometer, for use in the wavelength range of 400 to 490 nm and providing a light path of 1 cm or longer.

b. Comparator, color- and turbidity-compensating.

c. French square bottles, capacity 30 to 60 ml (1 or 2 oz).

3. Reagents

a. Orthotolidine reagent.

1) Preparation—Dissolve 1.35 g orthotolidine dihydrochloride in 500 ml distilled water. Add this solution, with constant stirring, to a mixture of 350 ml distilled water and 150 ml conc HCl. Do not use orthotolidine base in the preparation of this reagent.

2) Storage—Store the orthotolidine solution in brown bottles or in the dark. Protect at all times from direct sunlight. Use no longer than 6 months. Avoid contact with rubber. Store at room temperature and do not let the temperature fall below 0 C because the resulting crystallization of orthotolidine can lead to deficient color development.

CAUTION—*Handle this reagent with extreme care. Never use a mouth pipet for dispensing this reagent, but use an automatic, dropping, or safety pipet to measure the necessary volume. Avoid inhalation or exposure to the skin.*

b. Sodium arsenite solution: Dissolve 5.0 g $NaAsO_2$ in distilled water

and dilute to 1 l. (CAUTION: *Toxic— take care to avoid ingestion.*)

c. Permanent chlorine standards: Precision in the preparation of the buffer solutions is absolutely necessary; therefore, follow the directions explicitly.

1) *Phosphate buffer stock solution,* 0.5M: Dry anhydrous disodium hydrogen phosphate, Na_2HPO_4, and anhydrous potassium dihydrogen phosphate, KH_2PO_4, overnight at 105 to 110 C, and store in a desiccator. Dissolve 22.86 g Na_2HPO_4 and 46.16 g KH_2PO_4 in distilled water and dilute to 1 l. Let the solution stand for several days to allow any precipitate to form. Filter before using.

2) *Phosphate buffer solution,* 0.1M: This is a standard buffer, pH 6.45. Filter the stock solution prepared above and dilute 200 ml to 1 l with distilled water.

3) *Strong chromate-dichromate solution:* Dissolve 1.55 g potassium dichromate, $K_2Cr_2O_7$, and 4.65 g potassium chromate, K_2CrO_4, in 0.1M phosphate buffer and dilute to 1 l with 0.1M phosphate buffer. This solution corresponds to the color produced by 10 mg/l chlorine in the standard orthotolidine procedure when viewed through a depth of 24 to 30 cm.

4) *Dilute chromate-dichromate solution:* Dissolve 155 mg $K_2Cr_2O_7$ and 465 mg K_2CrO_4 in 0.1M phosphate buffer and dilute to 1 l with 0.1M phosphate buffer. Alternatively, prepare the solution by diluting 100 ml of strong chromate-dichromate solution to 1 l with 0.1M phosphate buffer. This solution corresponds to the color produced by 1 mg/l chlorine in the standard orthotolidine procedure when viewed through all cell depths.

TABLE 411:I. LOW-RANGE CHLORINE
STANDARDS—0.01 TO 1.0 MG/L*

Chlorine mg/l	Chromate-Dichromate Solution ml/100 ml	Chlorine mg/l	Chromate-Dichromate Solution ml/100 ml
0.01	1	0.35	35
0.02	2	0.40	40
0.05	5	0.45	45
0.07	7	0.50	50
0.10	10	0.60	60
0.15	15	0.70	70
0.20	20	0.80	80
0.25	25	0.90	90
0.30	30	1.00	100

* These standards are very close visual matches of the chlorine-orthotolidine color and are preferable to temporary standards, which are difficult to prepare accurately.

5) *Low-range permanent chlorine standards*, 0.01 to 1.0 mg/l: Pipet the volumes of dilute chromate-dichromate solution indicated in Table 411:I for the range of cell depths given into 100-ml tubes of any uniform length and diameter or into 100-ml volumetric flasks. Make the volume up to the 100-ml mark with 0.1M phosphate buffer solution. These standards can be read at any cell depth up to 30 cm.

6) *High-range permanent chlorine standards*, 1.0 to 10.0 mg/l. Pipet the volumes of strong chromate-dichromate solution given in Table 411:II for the range of cell depths given into 100-ml tubes of any uniform length and diameter or into 100-ml volumetric flasks. Make the volume up to the 100-ml mark with 0.1M phosphate buffer solution. Prepare standards for other cell depths or for other concentrations by interpolating between the values in Tables 411:I and 411:II.

7) Comparison tube specifications—Variations in the viewing depth in any set of color comparison tubes, cells, or bottles used in this determination must not be more than ±3%.

8) Protection of standards—Seal on microcover glasses with collodion, Canada balsam, or similar material to protect the tubes from dust and evaporation. Apply the material to the top of the nessler tube with a camel's hair brush and put the cover glass into position promptly with forceps. After it is spot-sealed, reinforce the circumference with additional brush-applied sealing material until the joining of the tube and cover glass is complete. Do not use rubber stoppers. If desired, use nessler tubes with special ground-glass caps that permit optical comparison. Do not store or use the standards in direct sunlight. Prepare new standards whenever turbidity appears.

TABLE 411:II. HIGH-RANGE CHLORINE
STANDARDS—1.0 TO 10.0 MG/L*

Chlorine mg/l	Cell Depth cm			
	2.5–5	10	20	24–30
	Chromate-Dichromate Solution ml			
1	10.0	10.0	10.0	10.0
1.5	15.0	15.0	15.0	15.0
2	19.5	19.5	19.7	20.0
3	27.0	27.5	29.0	30.0
4	34.5	35.0	39.0	40.0
5	42.0	43.0	48.0	50.0
6	49.0	51.0	58.0	60.0
7	56.5	59.0	68.0	70.0
8	64.0	67.0	77.5	80.0
9	72.0	75.5	87.0	90.0
10	80.0	84.0	97.0	100.0

* These standards are very close visual matches of the chlorine-orthotolidine color and are preferable to temporary standards, which are difficult to prepare accurately.

9) Commercial standards—Commercially prepared permanent standards may be used for routine tests, provided that they are checked for accuracy.

4. Procedure

a. Visual comparison:

1) Label two comparator cells or French square bottles "D" and "E." Use 0.5 ml orthotolidine reagent in 10-ml cells, 0.75 ml in 15-ml cells, and the same ratio for other volumes of sample. Use the same volume of sodium arsenite solution as orthotolidine reagent.

2) To the sample in Cell D add 1 ml oxalic acid saturated solution. Mix well and let stand 10 min in the dark. Depending on the volume of sample used, next add the appropriate volume of orthotolidine reagent. Mix quickly, and immediately (within 5 sec) add sodium arsenite solution. Mix quickly again and compare with color standards as rapidly as possible. Record the result, D, which represents approximately one-half the chlorine dioxide and all of the interfering colors. (If it is desired to report the results in terms of available chlorine, the value D represents one-fifth the available chlorine and all of the interfering colors.)

3) To Cell E, containing sodium arsenite solution and 1 ml oxalic acid saturated solution, add sample. Mix quickly, and immediately add orthotolidine reagent. Mix quickly again and compare with color standards as rapidly as possible. Record the result, B_3, which represents the interfering colors present in the sample.

b. Photometric measurement: Measure photometrically the colors developed by following the directions in the preceding paragraphs. Convert the absorbance readings to the proper chlorine dioxide readings by referring to a calibration curve prepared by treating known chlorine dioxide concentrations in the same manner as the unknown samples.

5. Calculations

$$\text{mg/l } ClO_2 \text{ as } ClO_2 = (D-B_3) \times 1.9$$
$$\text{mg/l } ClO_2 \text{ as available chlorine} = (D-B_3) \times 5$$

Inasmuch as chlorine dioxide and residual chlorine coexist in many samples, the residual chlorine determinations can be performed as described in Section 409 and the following calculations then made in terms of available chlorine:

Free available
   residual chlorine $= (A-B_1)-(D-B_3)$

Combined available
   residual chlorine $= (C-B_2)-(A-B_1)$

411 C.   Amperometric Method

1. General Discussion

a. Principle: The amperometric titration of chlorine dioxide is an extension of the amperometric method for residual chlorine. By performing four titrations with phenylarsine oxide, free chlorine (including hypochlorite and hypochlorous acid), chloramines, chlorite, and chlorine dioxide may be separately determined. In stage one the chlorine dioxide is converted to chlorite and chlorate through the addition of sufficient sodium hydroxide to produce a pH of 12, followed by neutralization to a pH of 7 and titration of the free chlorine. When potassium iodide is added to a sample that has been treated similarly with alkali and the pH readjusted to 7, titration yields free chlorine and monochloramine. The third stage involves the addition of potassium iodide and pH adjustment to 7, followed by titration of the free chlorine, monochloramine, and one-fifth of the available chlorine dioxide. The addition of sufficient sulfuric acid to lower the pH to 2 enables all of the available chlorine dioxide and chlorite, as well as the total available chlorine, to liberate an equivalent amount of iodine from the added potassium iodide, and thus be titrated.

b. Precautions: In order to minimize the effects of pH and the time and temperature of reaction, standardize all conditions. Titrate all samples at pH 7. Use a reaction period of 10 min or longer on the samples treated with NaOH at a pH of 12, as well as those treated with H₂SO₄ at a pH of 2. A 10-min reaction period is suggested even though the reaction rate is faster in warm samples.

c. Interference: The same interferences apply in the case of chlorine dioxide as those described in Section 409C.1*b.*

2. Apparatus

The same apparatus is required as in Section 409C.2*a* through *d.*

3. Reagents

All reagents listed for the determination of residual chlorine in Section 409C.3 are required. Also needed are the following:

a. Sodium hydroxide, NaOH, 6*N.*

b. Sulfuric acid, H₂SO₄, 6*N,* 1+5.

4. Procedure

a. Titration of free available chlorine (hypochlorite and hypochlorous acid): Add sufficient 6*N* NaOH to raise the sample pH to 12. After 10 min, add 6*N* H₂SO₄ to lower the pH to 7. Titrate with standard phenylarsine oxide titrant to the amperometric end point as given in Section 409C. Record the result as *A.*

b. Titration of free available chlorine and chloramine: Add 6*N* NaOH to raise the sample pH to 12. After 10 min, add 6*N* H₂SO₄ to reduce the pH to 7. Add 1 ml KI solution. Titrate with standard phenylarsine oxide titrant to the amperometric end point. Record the result as *B.*

c. Titration of free available chlorine, chloramine, and one-fifth of the available chlorine dioxide: Adjust the sample pH to 7 with pH 7 phosphate buffer solution. Add 1 ml KI solution. Titrate with standard phenylarsine oxide titrant to the amperometric end point. Record the result as C.

d. Titration of free available chlorine, chloramines, chlorine dioxide, and chlorite: Add 1 ml potassium iodide solution to the sample. Add sufficient $6N$ sulfuric acid solution to lower the sample pH to 2. After 10 min, add sufficient $6N$ sodium hydroxide solution to raise the pH to 7. Titrate with standard phenylarsine oxide titrant to the amperometric end point. Record the result as D.

5. Calculation

Convert the individual titrations (A, B, C, and D) into mg/l Cl by the following equation:

$$mg/l\ chlorine\ =\ \frac{E \times 200}{ml\ sample}$$

where $E =$ ml phenylarsine oxide titration for each individual sample A, B, C, or D.

Calculate the chlorine dioxide and the individual chlorine fractions as follows:

mg/l ClO_2 as chlorine dioxide $= 1.9\ (C-B)$
mg/l ClO_2 as chlorine $= 5\ (C-B)$
mg/l free available residual chlorine $= A$
mg/l chloramine as chlorine $= B-A$
mg/l chlorite as chlorine $= 4B-5C+D$

411 D.   Bibliography

General

INGOLS, R.S. & G.M. RIDENOUR. 1948. Chemical properties of chlorine dioxide in water treatment. *J. Amer. Water Works Ass.* 40:1207.

HODGDEN, H.W. & R.S. INGOLS. 1954. Direct colorimetric method for determination of chlorine dioxide in water. *Anal. Chem.* 26:1224.

PALIN, A.T. 1960. Colorimetric determination of chlorine dioxide in water. *Water Sewage Works* 107:457.

FEUSS, J.V. 1964. Problems in determination of chlorine dioxide residuals. *J. Amer. Water Works Ass.* 56:607.

MASSCHELEIN, W. 1966. Spectrophotometric determination of chlorine dioxide with acid chrome violet K. *Anal. Chem.* 38:1839.

MASSCHELEIN, W. 1969. Les Oxydes de Chlore et le Chlorite de Sodium. Dunod, Paris, Chapter XI.

Iodometric Method

POST, M.A. & W.A. MOORE. 1959. Determination of chlorine dioxide in treated surface waters. *Anal. Chem.* 31:1872.

Orthotolidine-Oxalic Acid (OTO) Method

ASTON, R.N. 1950. Developments in the chlorine dioxide process. *J. Amer. Water Works Ass.* 42:151.

Amperometric Method

HALLER, J.F. & S.S. LISTEK. 1948. Determination of chlorine dioxide and other active chlorine compounds in water. *Anal. Chem.* 20:639.

412   CHLORINE REQUIREMENT

"Chlorine demand," as defined in Section 410, is of little significance in relation to some objectives of chlorination. "Chlorine requirement" is a more applicable term.

The chlorine requirement is defined as the amount of chlorine that must be added per unit volume to produce the desired result under stated conditions. The result (i.e., the purpose of chlorination) may be based on any of a number of criteria, such as a stipulated coliform density, a specified residual chlorine concentration, the destruction of a chemical constituent, or others. In each instance a definite chlorine dosage will be necessary. This dosage is the chlorine requirement.

In those cases where the desired result is a specified residual chlorine concentration, residuals may be determined by any of the methods of Section 409. It is important that the same method be used for both laboratory testing and operational control.

In reporting results, the following information must be included: (a) the conditions of chlorination, such as pH, contact time, and temperature; (b) the result achieved; (c) the method used for determining the result; and (d) the chlorine dosage required to produce the desired result (i.e., the chlorine requirement).

412 A.   Method for Control of Disinfection

1. General Discussion

For control of the disinfection process the chlorine requirement can be determined on either a plant or a laboratory scale. In plant tests the flow of wastewater, quantity of chlorine used, contact time, residual chlorine concentration, and bacteriological results are determined. Sufficient replication may establish a correlation between bacteriological results and residual chlorine concentration. If so, operational control may then be based on residual chlorine determinations as is permitted now by the EPA Drinking Water Standards. Perform bacteriological tests periodically to verify the correlation.

In plant studies, conduct the test with the minimum and average contact times corresponding to different flow conditions, to determine the average and the variations from the average of the number of organisms in the effluent. Similarly, in laboratory studies, use more than one contact time to establish minimum and average chlorine requirements compatible with the stipulated microbial densities and permissible variations.

Chlorine requirement is not an absolute value that can be used to compare the results from place to place and from time to time. Rather, it is a practical and realistic approach to the control of chlorination, for disinfection or any other purpose.

The chlorine requirement for disinfection of a given effluent is the amount of chlorine that must be added per unit volume of waste to produce the desired residual chlorine concentration after a definite contact time. Residual chlorine and contact time will have been chosen to give a stipulated result in terms of coliform density or other characteristic.

2. Reagents

All the reagents necessary for the determination of residual chlorine by the selected method are required, and in addition:

a. *Standard chlorine solution:* Pass chlorine gas through distilled water or tap water until the solution contains approximately 1.0 mg Cl/ml. Because this solution is not stable, prepare fresh daily or standardize it each time it is used, according to directions in Section 410A.3a, by using 5 ml chlorine water and 0.025N thiosulfate solution. Calculate the strength as follows:

$$\text{mg/ml Cl} = \frac{(A \pm B) \times N \times 35.45}{\text{ml sample}}$$

where A = ml titration for sample, B = ml titration for blank (positive or negative), and N = normality of $Na_2S_2O_3$.

b. *Sodium sulfite solution:* Dissolve 10 g anhydrous Na_2SO_3 in 100 ml distilled water and heat to boiling to sterilize. Prepare daily.

3. Procedure

a. *Measurement of samples:* In each of a series of 1-l beakers, jars, or flasks, place a 500-ml sample.

b. *Addition of chlorine:* Select dosages and increments of chlorine suited to the type and concentration of the sample and to the purpose of chlorination. Use a range of dosages that includes at least one believed certain to produce the desired result. With gentle and constant stirring, add the selected quantities of chlorine to the samples.

c. *Determination of residual chlorine:* At the end of the stipulated contact times, determine residual chlorine on each portion by one or more of the procedures given in Section 409.

NOTE: In following the procedure for Method B, it is permissible, after completing preparations for titration, to set the samples aside until portions have been removed for other tests.

d. *Determination of degree of disinfection:* Immediately after the portions have been removed for determination of residual chlorine, add 0.5 ml sodium sulfite solution to each of the sample portions and estimate the number of organisms surviving by the appropriate procedure(s) given in Part 900.

4. Calculation

The chlorine requirement is the amount of chlorine that must be added per unit volume to produce the stipulated bacteriological quality.

5. Precision

The precision of this test on a single sample is poor because of the inaccuracies in enumeration of surviving organisms. In order to establish the chlorine requirement for a given coliform density with suitable precision, repeat the test at least 10 times on different samples using otherwise identical conditions.

412 B.   Methods for Purposes Other Than Disinfection Control

When chlorine is used for such purposes as odor control, BOD reduction, slime and insect control on trickling filters, and control of activated-sludge bulking, chlorine requirement is defined as the quantity of chlorine that must be added to produce the desired result. In most of the cases mentioned, chlorine requirement is best determined on a plant basis. Occasionally, laboratory tests may be more suitable, as in BOD reduction. If residual chlorine tests are to be used for control, any of the methods of Section 409 may be used.

When industrial wastes are to be chlorinated for such purposes as the destruction of chemicals or the reduction of undesirable qualities in effluents, the same general concept of chlorine requirement as developed for disinfection purposes can be applied. pH values may be varied according to the conditions and purposes of the chlorine treatment. Instead of using bacteriological examination as the criterion of chlorine requirement, the requirement is based on the objective for which chlorine is applied. For example, if chlorine is applied for phenol destruction, the chlorine requirement is based on the actual phenol concentration desired. Contact times may be varied in conjunction with the quantity of chlorine applied, compatible with the accomplishment of the objective. All conditions of the test should be specified.

The procedure is analogous to the one given for disinfection control (Section 412A.3). The determination of bacteriological quality (412A.3*d*) is replaced by a suitable determination of the constituent controlled by the chlorination.

413   CYANIDE

1. General Discussion

"Cyanide" refers to all of the CN groups in cyanide compounds that can be determined as the cyanide ion, CN^-, by the methods used. The cyanide compounds in which cyanide can be obtained as CN^- are classed as simple and complex cyanides.

The simple cyanides are represented by the formula $A(CN)_x$, where A is an alkali (sodium, potassium, ammonium) or a metal, and x, the valence of A, is the number of CN groups. In the soluble compounds, particularly the simple alkali cyanides, the CN group is present as CN^-.

The complex cyanides have a variety of formulas, but the alkali-metallic cyanides normally can be represented by $A_yM(CN)_x$. In this formula, A represents the alkali present y times, M the heavy metal (ferrous and ferric iron, cadmium, copper, nickel, silver, zinc, or others), and x the number of CN groups; x is equal to the valence of A taken y times plus that of the heavy metal. In these soluble alkali-metallic cyanides, the anion is not the CN group but the radical $M(CN)_x$.

The toxic effect of even low concentrations of cyanide on aquatic life and on the biota of wastewater treatment is well established.[1,2] Doudoroff and colleagues found that the toxicity of complex cyanides is due to molecular hydrogen cyanide formation caused by the dissociation of the metal cyanide complexes.[3,4]

The dissociation constants of the various metal complexes are different and therefore great differences in toxic effects exist. The alkali metal cyanides and the complexes of zinc, cadmium, and lead dissociate readily. The dissociation of copper is less; even lower dissociation is found with the silver, gold, nickel, and cobalt complexes. No measurable dissociation occurs with the iron cyanide complexes. This is reflected in results of toxicological studies, showing reduced toxicity for nickel and cobalt and no toxicity for the iron cyanides.[3-6]

However, decomposition of iron cyanides by sunlight releases hydrogen cyanide.[7] Because this reaction depends on time, mixing, clarity, flow rate of the receiving water, and bacterial decomposition of cyanide concurrently with photodecomposition of iron cyanide, regulatory distinction can be made and analytical distinction is possible.[8-12]

Historically, the generally accepted industrial waste treatment of the cyanide compounds is alkaline chlorination:

$$NaCN + Cl_2 \rightarrow CNCl + NaCl \qquad (1)$$

The first reaction product on chlorination is cyanogen chloride, a highly toxic gas with limited solubility. The toxicity of cyanogen chloride may exceed the toxicity of equal concentrations of cyanide.[2,13] At an alkaline pH, cyanogen chloride hydrolyzes to the cyanate ion with only limited toxicity (100 mg/l). There is no known natural reduction reaction that may convert cyanate to cyanide.[14] On the other hand, the breakdown of the toxic cyanogen chloride is pH- and time-dependent. At pH 9, with no excess chlorine present, cyanogen chloride may persist for 24 hr.[15]

$$CNCl + 2NaOH \rightarrow NaCNO + NaCl + H_2O \qquad (2)$$

Cyanate can be oxidized further with chlorine at a nearly neutral pH to carbon dioxide and nitrogen:

$$2NaCNO + 4NaOH + 3Cl_2 \rightarrow 6NaCl + 2CO_2 + N_2 + 2H_2O \qquad (3)$$

Cyanate also will be converted on acidification to ammonia:

$$2NaCNO + H_2SO_4 + 4H_2O \rightarrow (NH_4)_2SO_4 + 2NaHCO_3 \qquad (4)$$

The alkaline chlorination of cyanide compounds is relatively fast, but depends equally on the dissociation constant, which also governs the toxicity. Metal cyanide complexes, such as nickel, cobalt, silver, and gold, dissociate slowly. The chlorination reaction therefore requires more time and a significant chlorine excess.[16,17] Iron cyanides, because they do not dissociate to any degree, are not oxidized by chlorination. The lack of toxicity and the refractory properties of the noted complexes overlap.

Thus there is a need to differentiate between *total cyanides* and *cyanides amenable to chlorination.* For total cy-anides, both dissociable and non-dissociable forms of cyanide are being measured. Cyanides amenable to chlori-nation are potentially dissociable, and therefore only toxic forms of cyanide are measured. The chlorination test proce-dures are carried out in a manner repre-senting the most rigorous conditions for the formation of dissociable forms of cy-anide.

The *cyanogen chloride* procedure is common with the colorimetric test for cyanides amenable to chlorination. This test is based on the addition of chlora-mine-T and subsequent color complex formation with barbituric acid. Without the addition of chloramine, only the existing cyanogen chloride is measured. Cyanogen chloride is a gas that hydro-lyzes to cyanate; preservation of the sample is not possible. Because of this, spot test estimation of cyanogen chloride levels may be the best means for testing. This procedure can be adapted and used when the sample is collected.

There may be analytical require-ments for the determination of cyanate, even though the reported toxicity level is >100 mg/l. On acidification, cyanate decomposes to ammonia, and under cer-tain conditions, ammonia toxicity is sig-nificant (>2 mg/l).[2]

Thiocyanate (CNS⁻) itself is not tox-ic to aquatic life. However, upon chlori-nation, toxic cyanogen chloride is formed, as discussed in connection with the products of chlorination of the cya-nide compounds.[13] Where subsequent chlorination is anticipated, the analyti-cal determination of thiocyanate is desir-able.

2. Cyanide in Solid Waste

a. Soluble cyanide: Determination of soluble cyanide requires leaching of the sample with distilled water until solubil-ity equilibrium is established. One hour stirring in distilled water should be satis-factory. Low cyanide concentration in the leachate (<5 mg/l) will indicate the relatively low solubility of insoluble metal cyanides. The cyanide content of the leachate is indicative of the residual solubility of the insoluble metal cyanides in the waste.

High levels of cyanide in the leachate indicate soluble cyanide in the solid waste. When 500 ml distilled water are stirred into a 500-mg solid waste sample, the cyanide concentration (mil-ligrams per liter) of the leachate multi-plied by 1,000 will give the solubility levels of the cyanide content of the solid waste in milligrams per kilogram. This cyanide determination on the leachate may be for total cyanide and/or cyanide amenable to chlorination.

b. Insoluble cyanide: The insoluble cyanide content of the solid waste can be determined with the total cyanide method by placing a 500-mg sample with 500 ml distilled water into the dis-tillation flask and in general following the procedure from this step forward. The calculations should include a multi-plication by 1,000 to give the cyanide content of the solid waste sample in mil-ligrams per kilogram. Insoluble iron cy-anides in the solid waste can be leached out previously by stirring a weighed sample for 12 to 16 hr in a 10% caustic soda solution. The leachate and wash waters of the solid waste will give the iron cyanide content of the sample with the distillation procedure. A previous chlorination will have eliminated all cyanide amenable to chlorination from the sample. Do not expose the sample to sunlight.

3. Selection of Method

a. Total cyanide after distillation: After removal of interfering substances, the metal cyanide is converted to hydrogen cyanide gas, which is distilled and absorbed in a caustic soda solution.[18] Only the cobalticyanide complex is not recovered completely. This is due to the catalytic decomposition of cyanide in the presence of cobalt at high temperature in a strong acid solution.[19, 20] The distillation also separates the cyanide from other color-producing and possibly interfering organic or inorganic contaminants. Subsequent analysis is for the simple salt, sodium cyanide. Some organic cyanide compounds, such as nitriles, are decomposed under the distillation conditions. Aldehydes convert cyanide to nitrile. The absorption liquid is analyzed using either a titrimetric, colorimetric, or cyanide ion selective electrode procedure:

1) The Titration Method is suitable for cyanide concentrations above 1 mg/l.

2) The Colorimetric Method is suitable for cyanide concentration to a low limit of 20 μg/l. Higher concentrations may be analyzed by taking a portion and diluting the sample.

3) The Ion Selective Electrode Method using the cyanide ion electrode is applicable in the concentration range of 0.05 to 10 mg/l.

b. Cyanide amenable to chlorination:

1) Distillation of two samples is required, one that has been chlorinated to destroy all the amenable cyanide present and the other unchlorinated. The absorption liquids from those tests are analyzed for total cyanide. The observed difference equals cyanides amenable to chlorination.

2) The Colorimetric Method, by conversion of the amenable cyanide and thiocyanate to cyanogen chloride and developing the color complex with barbituric acid, is used for the total cyanide determinations.

c. Cyanogen Chloride Method:

1) The Colorimetric Method, same as for amenable cyanide but omitting the chloramine-T addition, is suitable.

2) The Spot Test also may be used.

d. Spot test for sample screening: This procedure allows a quick screening of the sample to establish if more than 50 μg/l cyanide amenable to chlorination is present. The test also may be used to estimate the cyanogen chloride content at the time of sampling.

e. Cyanate Method: The cyanate ion is converted to ammonium carbonate by acid hydrolysis at elevated temperature. Ammonia is determined before the conversion of the cyanate and again afterwards. The cyanate content is estimated from the difference of ammonia found in the two tests.[21-23] The ammonia may be measured by either:

1) The Ion Selective Electrode Method, using the ammonia electrode.

2) The Colorimetric Method, using the direct nesslerization or the phenate method for ammonia. (Section 418B or C)

f. Thiocyanate Method: Use the colorimetric determination with ferric nitrate as a color-producing compound.

413 A. Preliminary Treatment of Samples

CAUTION—*Exercise care in the manipulation of cyanide samples because of their toxicity. Process them in a hood or other well-ventilated area. Avoid contact, inhalation, or ingestion.*

1. General Discussion

The nature of the preliminary treatment will vary according to the interfering substance present. Sulfides, fatty acids, and oxidizing agents are removed by special procedures. Most other interfering substances are removed by distillation. The importance of the distillation procedure cannot be overemphasized.

2. Preservation of Samples

Because most cyanides are very reactive and unstable, analyze samples as soon as possible. If the sample cannot be analyzed immediately, add NaOH pellets or a strong NaOH solution to raise the pH of the sample to 12 or above and store in a closed, dark bottle in a cool place.

To analyze for cyanogen chloride, collect a separate sample and omit the NaOH addition because cyanogen chloride is converted rapidly to cyanate at high pH. Make colorimetric estimation immediately after sampling.

Oxidizing agents such as chlorine decompose most of the cyanides. Test 2 drops of sample with 2 drops of orthotolidine reagent (Section 411B.3*a*) on a spot plate. Yellow to orange color indicates the need for treatment. Add ascorbic acid, a few crystals at a time, until 2 drops of sample produce no color with the spot test. Then add an additional 0.06 g of ascorbic acid for each liter of sample. If possible, carry out this reducing procedure before preserving sample as described in the preceding paragraph.

Sulfide in the sample will convert CN^- to SCN^- rapidly, especially at high pH. Test for sulfides and remove as directed in ¶3*b* before raising the pH to stabilize the sample.

3. Interferences

a. Oxidizing agents destroy most of the cyanide during storage and manipulation. Add ascorbic acid as directed in Section 413A.2 above.

b. Sulfide will distill over with the cyanide and, therefore, adversely affect the colorimetric and titrimetric procedures. Place a drop of the sample on lead acetate test paper previously moistened with acetic acid buffer solution (pH 4). Darkening of the paper indicates the presence of sulfide. Treat 25 ml more of the stabilized sample (pH>12) than will be required for the cyanide determination with powdered cadmium nitrate. Yellow cadmium sulfide precipitates if the sample contains sulfide. Repeat this operation until a drop of the treated sample does not darken the acidified lead acetate test paper. Filter through a dry filter paper into a dry beaker, and from the filtrate measure the sample to be used for analysis. Avoid a large excess of cadmium and a long contact time in order to minimize a loss by complexation or occlusion of cyanide on the precipitated material.

c. Fatty acids, which distill and form soaps under alkaline titration conditions, make the end point almost impossible to detect. Remove fatty acids by extraction.[24] Acidify the sample with acetic acid (1+9) to pH 6.0 to 7.0. (CAUTION—*Perform this operation in a hood and leave the sample there until it can be made alkaline again after extraction.*) Extract with iso-octane, hexane, or chloroform (preference in order named) with a solvent volume equal to 20% of the sample volume. One extraction usually is adequate to reduce the fatty acid concentration below the interference level. Avoid multiple extractions or a long contact time at low pH in order to keep the loss of HCN at a minimum. When the extraction is completed, immediately raise the pH to >12 with NaOH solution.

d. Other possible interferences include substances that might contribute color or turbidity. In most cases, the distillation procedure will remove these.

e. Aldehydes convert cyanide to nitrile under the distillation conditions. Only the direct titration without distillation can be used, which reveals only the non-complex cyanides. The formaldehyde interference is noticeable in concentrations exceeding 0.5 mg/l; eliminate by addition of silver nitrate to the sample. Use the spot test to establish the absence or presence of aldehydes (detection limit 0.05 mg/l), as follows:

1) Reagents—

a) *MBTH indicator solution*—Dissolve 0.05 g 3-methyl, 2-benzothiazolone hydrazone hydrochloride in 100 ml water. Filter if turbid.

b) *Ferric chloride oxidizing solution* —Dissolve 1.6 g sulfamic acid and 1 g ferric chloride in 100 ml water.

c) *Silver nitrate solution, 0.1N*— Dissolve 17.0 g silver nitrate ($AgNO_3$) crystals in water and dilute to 1 l.

d) *EDTA solution, 0.1M*—Dissolve 37.2 g of the sodium salt of ethylene-diamine-tetraacetic acid in water and dilute to 1 l.

2) Procedure—Place 1 drop of sample and 1 drop of distilled water for a blank in a separate cavity of a white spot plate. Add 1 drop of MBTH solution and subsequently 1 drop of ferric chloride oxidizing solution to each spot. Allow 10 min for color development. The color change will be from a faint green to a deeper color, tending to blue-green at higher concentrations. Add 0.1N silver nitrate solution dropwise and retest on the spot plate. For each drop of silver nitrate, add also 2 drops of the EDTA solution. One mg/l formaldehyde in a 100-ml sample will require approximately 2 drops of silver nitrate solution and 4 drops of EDTA solution.

f. Thiocyanates at concentrations higher than 0.5 mg/l may interfere when the distillation is carried out with the cuprous chloride reagent. To avoid the thiocyanate interference in these cases, use the magnesium chloride reagent.

413 B.   Total Cyanide after Distillation

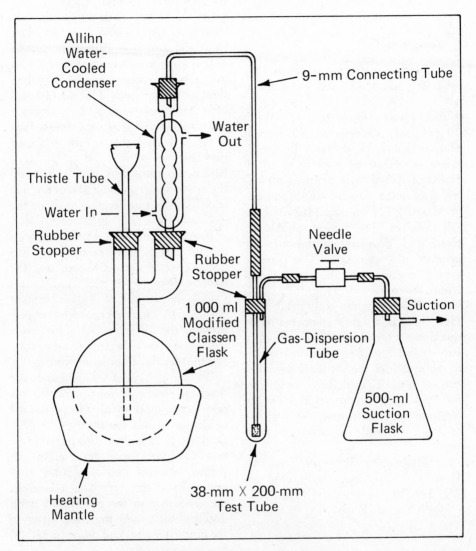

Figure 413:1. Cyanide distillation apparatus.

1. Apparatus

The apparatus setup is shown in Figure 413:1. It includes:

a. Boiling flask, 1 l, with inlet tube and provision for water-cooled condenser.

b. Gas absorber or *Fisher-Milligan scrubber.*

c. Heating element, adjustable.

d. Ground glass 〒 joints, teflon-sleeved or with an appropriate lubricant for the boiling flask and condenser are preferred.

2. Reagents

a. Sodium hydroxide solution: Dissolve 50 g NaOH in water and dilute to 1 l.

b. Cuprous chloride reagent: Weigh 20 g of finely powdered Cu_2Cl_2 into an 800-ml beaker. Wash twice, by decantation, with 250-ml portions of 1+49 H_2SO_4 and then twice, gently, with water. Add about 250 ml water and approximately 125 ml conc HCl until the salt dissolves. The reagent should be clear; dark discoloration indicates the presence of cupric salts. The metallic copper inserted into the reagent will reduce the cupric ions. Dilute to 1 l with water. If precipitation occurs add more HCl. Store in a tightly stoppered bottle containing a few lengths of pure copper wire or rod extending from the bottom to the mouth of the bottle. If a smaller reagent bottle is used, keep completely filled and tightly stoppered. Refill to the top from the stock solution after each use to avoid air oxidation of the cuprous salt.

c. Magnesium chloride reagent: Dissolve 510 g magnesium chloride, $MgCl_2 \cdot 6H_2O$, in water and dilute to 1 l.

d. Sulfuric acid, 1+1.

3. Procedure

a. Add the sample, containing not more than 500 mg CN (diluted if necessary to 250 to 500 ml with distilled water), to the boiling flask. Add 50 ml NaOH solution to the gas washer and dilute, if necessary, with distilled water

to obtain an adequate depth of liquid in the absorber. Connect the train, consisting of boiling flask air inlet, flask, condenser, gas washer, suction flask trap, and aspirator. Adjust the suction so that approximately one bubble of air per second enters the boiling flask through the air inlet. This air rate will carry HCN gas from flask to absorber and usually will prevent a reverse flow of HCN through the air inlet. If the air rate does not prevent the sample from backing up in the delivery tube, increase the air-flow rate to two bubbles per second. If the air rate becomes too high, the gas washer will not trap all the HCN.

b. Add 50 ml 1+1 H_2SO_4 through the air inlet tube. Rinse the tube with distilled water and let the air mix the flask contents for 3 min. Add 10 ml Cu_2Cl_2 or 20 ml of $MgCl_2$ reagent (thiocyanate interference in sample) through the air inlet and wash down with a stream of water. A precipitate that may form redissolves on heating.

c. Heat with rapid boiling, but do not flood the condenser inlet or permit vapors to rise more than halfway into the condenser. Reflux for at least 1 hr. Discontinue heating but continue the air flow. Cool for 15 min and drain the gas washer contents into a separate container. Rinse the connecting tube from the condenser to the gas washer with distilled water, add the rinse water to the drained liquid, and dilute to 250 ml in a volumetric flask.

d. Determine the cyanide content by the titration method (C) if the cyanide concentration is greater than 1 mg/l as CN or by the colorimetric method (D) if the cyanide concentration is less. If the cyanide concentration is unknown, titrate 200 ml of the distillate by Method

C. If the cyanide value is below the desired limit of 1 mg/l as CN, dilute the remaining 50 ml of the distillate if necessary, and examine by Method D. Alternatively, use the cyanide ion selective electrode in the concentration range 0.05 to 10 mg/l CN, Method E.

e. Distillation gives quantitative recovery of even the refractory cyanides such as the iron complexes. To obtain complete recovery of cobalticyanide use ultraviolet radiation pretreatment.[25, 26] If incomplete recovery is suspected, distill again by refilling the gas washer with a fresh charge of NaOH solution and refluxing for another hour. The cyanide from the second reflux, if any, will indicate completeness of recovery.

413 C.   Titrimetric Method

1. General Discussion

a. Principle: The CN^- in the alkaline distillate from the preliminary treatment procedure is titrated with a standard $AgNO_3$ titrant to form the soluble cyanide complex, $Ag(CN^-)_2$. As soon as all the CN has been complexed and a small excess of Ag^+ has been added, the excess Ag^+ is detected by the silver-sensitive indicator, paradimethylaminobenzalrhodanine, which immediately turns from a yellow to a salmon color.[27] The indicator is sensitive to about 0.1 mg/l Ag. If the titration shows that CN^- is below 1 mg/l, another portion is examined colorimetrically. By collecting the CN^- in a smaller volume of NaOH absorption liquid, the useful range of the titration method can be extended downward. The calculation should be adjusted for the absorption volume used.

2. Apparatus

Koch microburet, 5-ml capacity.

3. Reagents

a. Sodium hydroxide solution, NaOH, 1N.

b. Indicator solution: Dissolve 20 mg paradimethylaminobenzalrhodanine in 100 ml acetone.

c. Standard silver nitrate titrant, 0.0192N: Dissolve 3.27 g $AgNO_3$ in 1 l distilled water. Standardize against standard NaCl solution, using the argentometric method with K_2CrO_4 indicator, as directed in Chloride, Section 408A.2 and 3; 1.00 ml of this solution is equivalent to 1.00 mg CN.

4. Procedure

a. If preliminary treatment has included distillation, take a portion of the distillate without adjusting pH. If the sample has not been distilled, adjust the pH to 11.0 or above with 1N NaOH solution. Dilute to 250 ml or some other convenient volume to be used for all titrations. Add 0.5 ml indicator solution.

b. Titrate with standard $AgNO_3$ titrant to the first change in color from a canary yellow to a salmon hue. Titrate a blank containing the same amount of alkali and water.

Adjust the sample size or the strength of $AgNO_3$ titrant so that the titration requires 2 to 10 ml. Use the amount of indicator that gives the best result for all titrations. As the analyst becomes accustomed to the end point, blank titrations decrease from the high values usually experienced in the first few trials to 1 drop or less, with a corresponding improvement in precision.

5. Calculation

$$\text{mg/l CN} = \frac{(A-B) \times 1,000}{\text{ml original sample}} \times \frac{250}{\text{ml sample}}$$

where A = ml standard AgNO₃ for sample and B = standard AgNO₃ for blank.

6. Precision and Accuracy

For samples containing more than 1 mg/l CN that have been distilled or for relatively clear samples without significant interference, the coefficient of variation* is 2%. Extraction and removal of sulfide or oxidizing agents tend to increase the variation to a degree determined by the amount of manipulation and the type of sample. The limit of sensitivity is approximately 0.1 mg/l CN, but at this concentration the end point is indistinct. At 0.4 mg/l the coefficient of variation is four times that at CN concentration levels >1.0 mg/l.

---

* See Introduction, Section 104A.2.

413 D.   Colorimetric Method

1. General Discussion

a. Principle: The CN⁻ in the alkaline distillate from the preliminary treatment procedure is converted to cyanogen chloride, CNCl, by reaction with chloramine-T at a pH less than 8 without hydrolyzing to the cyanate.[28] (CAUTION: *Cyanogen chloride is a toxic gas; avoid inhalation.*) After the reaction is complete, the CNCl forms a redblue dye on the addition of a pyridinebarbituric acid reagent. If the dye is kept in an aqueous solution, the absorbance is read at 578 nm. To obtain colors of comparable intensity, it is essential to have the same salt content in both the sample and the standards.

b. Interference: All interferences are eliminated or reduced to a minimum by distillation.

2. Apparatus

Colorimetric equipment: One of the following is required:

a. Spectrophotometer, for use at 578 nm, providing a light path of 1 cm.

b. Filter photometer, providing a light path of 1 cm and equipped with a red filter having maximum transmittance at 570 to 580 nm.

3. Reagents

a. Chloramine-T solution: Dissolve 1.0 g white, water-soluble powder in 100 ml water. Prepare weekly and store in refrigerator.

b. Stock cyanide solution: Dissolve approximately 2 g KOH and 2.51 g KCN in 1 l distilled water. CAUTION— *Because KCN is highly toxic, avoid con-*

tact or inhalation. Standardize against standard AgNO₃ titrant as described in Section 413C.4, using 25 ml KCN solution. Check the titer each week, because the solution loses strength gradually. 1 ml=1 mg CN.

c. *Standard cyanide solution:* Dilute a calculated volume (approximately 10 ml) of the stock KCN solution based on the determined concentration (¶3*b*) to 1,000 ml with 0.25*N* NaOH to contain exactly 10 μg CN/ml. Mix thoroughly. Make a second dilution of 10 ml diluted to 100 ml with 0.25*N* NaOH. Prepare this solution fresh daily and keep in a glass-stoppered bottle. (CAUTION: *Toxic—take care to avoid ingestion.*)

d. *Pyridine-barbituric acid reagent:* Place 15 g barbituric acid in a 250-ml volumetric flask and add just enough water to wash the sides of the flask and wet the barbituric acid. Add 75 ml pyridine and mix. Add 15 ml conc HCl, mix, and cool to room temperature. Dilute to the mark with water and mix.

e. *Sodium dihydrogen phosphate,* 1*M:* Dissolve 138 g NaH₂PO₄·H₂O in 1 l distilled water. Refrigerate.

f. *Sodium hydroxide solution,* 0.25*N.* Dissolve 10 g NaOH in 1 l distilled water.

4. Procedure

a. *Preparation of calibration curve:* From the standard KCN solution prepare a blank and a series of standards containing from 0.2 to 6 μg CN in 20 ml solution using 0.25*N* NaOH for all dilutions. Treat the standards in accordance with ¶*b* below. Plot the absorbance of the standards against CN concentration in micrograms.

On the basis of the first calibration curve, prepare additional standards containing less than 0.2 and more than 6 μg of cyanide to determine the limits measurable with the photometer being used.

b. *Color development:* Take a portion of the absorption liquid obtained in Method B, such that the CN concentration falls in the measurable range, and dilute to 20 ml with 0.25*N* NaOH. Place the portion in a 50-ml volumetric flask. Add 15 ml phosphate buffer and mix thoroughly. Add 2.0 ml chloramine-T solution and swirl to mix. *Immediately* add 5 ml pyridine-barbituric acid solution and again swirl to mix. Dilute to the mark with water; mix well by inversion. Allow 8 min for color development.

Measure the absorbance of the developed color with the photometer at 578 nm in a 1.0-cm cell within 15 min from the time at which the pyridine-barbituric acid reagent is added. Using the calibration curve and the formula in 5*a*, determine the cyanide concentration in the original sample.

5. Calculations

$$CN,\ mg/l\ =\ \frac{A \times B}{C \times D}$$

where $A = $ μg CN read from calibration curve, $B = $ total ml absorbing solution used in the distillation (B.3), $C = $ ml original sample used in the distillation, and $D = $ ml absorbing solution used.

6. Precision

The analysis of a mixed cyanide solution containing sodium, zinc, copper, and silver cyanides in tap water gave a precision within the designated range as follows:

$$S_T = 0.115X + 0.031$$

where S_T = overall precision, and X = concentration of cyanide in mg/l.

413 E.   Cyanide-Ion-Selective Electrode Method

1. General Discussion

The CN^- in the alkaline distillate from the preliminary treatment procedures can be determined potentiometrically by the known addition technic using a cyanide-ion-selective electrode in combination with a double-junction reference electrode and a pH meter having an expanded millivolt scale, or a specific ion meter. This method can be used to determine the cyanide concentration in place of either the colorimetric or titrimetric procedures in the concentration range of 0.05 to 10 mg/l CN. If the cyanide-ion-selective electrode method is used, the previously described titration screening step can be omitted.

2. Apparatus

a. *Expanded-scale pH meter* or *specific-ion meter.*

b. *Cyanide-ion-selective electrode.**

c. *Reference electrode*, double-junction.

d. *Magnetic mixer* with TFE fluorocarbon-coated stirring bar.

3. Reagents

a. *Stock standard cyanide solution:* See Section 413 D.3 *b.*

---

* Orion Model 94-06A or equivalent.

b. *Sodium hydroxide diluent:* Dissolve 25 g NaOH in water and dilute to 1 l.

c. *Intermediate standard cyanide solution:* Dilute a calculated volume (approximately 100 ml) of the stock KCN solution based on the determined concentration to 1,000 ml with NaOH diluent to contain exactly 100 μg CN/ml. Mix thoroughly.

d. *Dilute standard cyanide solution:* Dilute 100.0 ml intermediate standard CN solution to 1,000 ml with NaOH diluent; 1.00 ml = 10.0 μg CN. Prepare daily and keep in dark, glass-stoppered bottles.

e. *Potassium nitrate solution:* Dissolve 100 g KNO_3 in water and dilute to 1 l. Adjust to pH 12 with KOH. This is the outer filling solution for the double junction reference electrode.

4. Procedure

a. *Instrument calibration:* Use the dilute and intermediate standard CN solutions and the NaOH diluent to prepare a series of three standards, 0.1, 1.0, and 10.0 mg/l CN. Transfer approximately 100 ml of these three standard solutions into 250-ml beakers prerinsed with a small portion of the standard being tested. Immerse the cyanide and double-junction reference electrodes in the solutions. Mix well on a magnetic stirrer at 25 C and maintain as closely as possible the same stirring rate for all solutions.

After equilibrium is reached (at least 5 min and not more than 10 min), record millivolt readings, and plot the CN concentrations versus millivolt readings on semilogarithmic graph paper. A straight line with a slope of 59 mV indicates that the instrument and electrodes are operating properly.

Table 413:I has been developed for analyses at 25 C with an electrode having a 59-mV slope. The electrode slope may not be always Nernstian because of differences due to manufacturing. The correction factor may be supplied by using a constant-temperature bath; a temperature correction factor will correct the electrode slope. If at 25 C an electrode had a 58-mV slope, the analysis would be performed at 30 C. If at 25 C an electrode displayed a 60-mV slope, the analysis would be performed at 20 C.

b. Instrumental measurement of sample: Place 100 ml of the absorption liquid obtained in Section B.3 into a 250-ml beaker. When measuring low CN concentrations, first rinse the beaker and electrodes with a small volume of sample. Immerse the cyanide and double-junction reference electrodes and mix on a magnetic stirrer at the same stirring rate used for the calibration standards. After equilibrium is reached (at least 5 min and not more than 10 min), record the millivolt reading (A).

With a pipet, add 1.0 or 2.0 ml of an appropriate CN standard (3a, 3c, or 3d). Select the standard and the volume added so that an 11- to 50-mV change is observed. Determine the standard CN solution to be added by observing the millivolt reading after equilibrium has been reached and referring to the calibration curve established in ¶4a. By using the curve, establish the approximate CN concentration. If the concentration of CN is 0.05 to 0.25 mg/l, use the dilute CN standard. If the concentration of CN is 0.20 to 3.50 mg/l, use the intermediate standard. For higher concentrations use the stock standard.

Allow sufficient time for equilibration to occur (at least 5 min and not more than 10 min) and record the new millivolt reading (B).

5. Calculations

To simplify calculations for the method of known additions, use Table 413:I. The table is based on the fact that for each millivolt, the antilog expression is constant.

a. Calculate the change in millivolt reading as follows:

$$\Delta mV = (B-A)$$

where ΔmV = millivolt change due to the known addition, B = reading after standard CN addition, mV, and A = reading before addition, mV.

b. Calculate the change in concentration:

$$C_\Delta = \frac{C_s \, (ml_s)}{ml_d + ml_s}$$

where:

C_Δ = change in CN concentration, mg/l,
C_s = concentration of standard CN solution added, mg/l,

TABLE 413:1. VALUES OF ANTILOG EXPRESSION FOR CALCULATING ION CONCENTRATION IN THE KNOWN ADDITION METHOD

ΔmV	Antilog Expression	ΔmV	Antilog Expression	ΔmV	Antilog Expression	ΔmV	Antilog Expression
11.00	1.871	21.00	0.791	31.00	0.427	41.00	0.254
11.20	1.830	21.20	0.780	31.20	0.422	41.20	0.252
11.40	1.791	21.40	0.769	31.40	0.418	41.40	0.250
11.60	1.752	21.60	0.759	31.60	0.413	41.60	8.247
11.80	1.716	21.80	0.749	31.80	0.409	41.80	0.245
12.00	1.680	22.00	0.738	32.00	0.404	42.00	0.242
12.20	1.645	22.20	0.729	32.20	0.400	42.20	0.240
12.40	1.612	22.40	0.719	32.40	0.395	42.40	0.238
12.60	1.580	22.60	0.709	32.60	0.391	42.60	0.235
12.80	1.549	22.80	0.700	32.80	0.387	42.80	0.233
13.00	1.518	23.00	0.691	33.00	0.383	43.00	0.231
13.20	1.489	23.20	0.682	33.20	0.379	43.20	0.229
13.40	1.461	23.40	0.673	33.40	0.375	43.40	0.227
13.60	1.433	23.60	0.664	33.60	0.371	43.60	0.224
13.80	1.406	23.80	0.656	33.80	0.367	43.80	0.222
14.00	1.380	24.00	0.647	34.00	0.363	44.00	0.220
14.20	1.355	24.20	0.639	34.20	0.359	44.20	0.218
14.40	1.331	24.40	0.631	34.40	0.355	44.40	0.216
14.60	1.307	24.60	0.623	34.60	0.352	44.60	0.214
14.80	1.284	24.80	0.615	34.80	0.348	44.80	0.212
15.00	1.261	25.00	0.608	35.00	0.344	45.00	0.210
15.20	1.239	25.20	0.600	35.20	0.314	45.20	0.208
15.40	1.218	25.40	0.593	35.40	0.337	45.40	0.206
15.60	1.197	25.60	0.585	35.60	0.334	45.60	0.204
15.80	1.177	25.80	0.578	35.80	0.330	45.80	0.202

Table 413:1. (Continued)

ΔmV	Antilog Expression	ΔmV	Antilog Expression	ΔmV	Antilog Expression	ΔmV	Antilog Expression
16.00	1.157	26.00	0.571	36.00	0.327	46.00	0.200
16.20	1.138	26.20	0.564	36.20	0.324	46.20	0.199
16.40	1.120	26.40	0.557	36.40	0.320	46.40	0.197
16.60	1.101	26.60	0.551	36.60	0.317	46.60	0.195
16.80	1.084	26.80	0.544	36.80	0.314	46.80	0.193
17.00	1.066	27.00	0.538	37.00	0.311	46.00	0.191
17.20	1.049	27.20	0.531	37.20	0.307	47.20	0.190
17.40	1.033	27.40	0.525	37.40	0.304	47.40	0.188
17.60	1.017	27.60	0.519	37.60	0.301	47.60	0.186
17.80	1.001	27.80	0.513	37.80	0.298	47.80	0.184
18.00	0.985	28.00	0.507	38.00	0.295	48.00	0.183
18.20	0.970	28.20	0.501	38.20	0.292	48.20	0.181
18.40	0.956	28.40	0.495	38.40	0.289	48.40	0.179
18.60	0.941	28.60	0.489	38.60	0.286	48.60	0.178
18.80	0.927	28.80	0.484	38.80	0.284	48.80	0.176
19.00	0.913	29.00	0.478	39.00	0.281	49.00	0.175
19.20	0.900	29.20	0.473	39.20	0.278	49.20	0.173
19.40	0.887	29.40	0.467	39.40	0.275	49.40	0.171
19.60	0.874	29.60	0.462	39.60	0.273	49.60	0.170
19.80	0.861	29.80	0.457	39.80	0.270	49.80	0.168
20.00	0.849	30.00	0.452	40.00	0.267	50.00	0.167
20.20	0.837	30.20	0.447	40.20	0.265	50.20	0.165
20.40	0.825	30.40	0.442	40.40	0.262	50.40	0.164
20.60	0.813	30.60	0.437	40.60	0.259	50.60	0.162
20.80	0.802	30.80	0.432	40.80	0.257	50.80	0.161

ml_s = ml standard CN solution added,
ml_d = ml original sample, and
S = Nernstian slope of electrode.

c. Use Table 413:I to find

$$\frac{1}{(\text{antilog } \dfrac{\Delta m V}{S}) - 1}$$

The appropriate expression is the one that corresponds to the observed change in millivolt reading.

d. Multiply C_Δ by the value from the table. The result is the sample's original CN concentration in mg/l.

7. Precision

The precision of the cyanide ion selective electrode method was determined from four levels of cyanide concentration by five laboratories and seven analysts. The precision of the method within its designated range may be expressed as follows:

$$S_T = 0.113X + 0.024$$

where S_T = overall precision and X = CN concentration, mg/l.

413 F. Cyanides Amenable to Chlorination after Distillation

1. General Discussion

This method is applicable to the determination of cyanides amenable to chlorination, to determine the dissociable cyanide content of the sample. Use a titration when it is known that the concentration of cyanides amenable to chlorination is more than 1 but less than 10 mg/l. With higher concentrations, use a smaller portion as described in 413B.3d and 413C.4b. Use a colorimetric determination when the cyanides amenable to chlorination are known to be 1 mg/l or less. The selective-ion electrode method is useful in the concentration range of 0.05 to 10 mg/l CN. When uncertain of the cyanides-amenable-to-chlorination concentration, use the Spot Test Procedure as given in Section 413I for estimation.

After part of the sample is chlorinated to decompose the cyanides, both the chlorinated and the raw sample are subjected to distillation as described in Section 413B. The difference between the cyanide concentrations found in the two samples is expressed as cyanides amenable to chlorination.

2. Apparatus

a. *Distillation apparatus:* See Section 413B.1.

b. *Apparatus for determining cyanide* by either the titrimetric method, Section 413C.2, the colorimetric method, Section 413D.2, or the electrode method, Section 413E.2, depending on concentration, range, and preference.

3. Reagents

a. *All reagents listed in Section 413B.3.*

b. *All reagents listed in Section 413C.3, 413D.3 or 413E.3,* depending on which method of estimation is to be used.

c. Calcium hypochlorite solution: Dissolve 5 g $Ca(OCl)_2$ in 100 ml distilled water. Store in an amber-colored glass bottle in the dark. Prepare monthly.

d. Potassium iodide-starch test paper.

4. Procedure

a. Divide the sample into two equal parts and chlorinate one portion as in ¶*b.* Analyze both portions for cyanide. The difference in determined concentrations will be the amount of cyanide amenable to chlorination.

b. Add $Ca(OCl)_2$ solution dropwise to the sample while agitating and maintaining the pH between 11 and 12 by the addition of NaOH solution. Test for chlorine by placing a drop of the treated sample on a strip of KI-starch paper. A distinct blue color indicates sufficient chlorine (approximately 50 to 100 mg/l Cl_2). Maintain the excess residual chlorine for 1 hr while agitating. If necessary, add more $Ca(OCl)_2$.

c. Add approximately 0.1 g/l ascorbic acid to reduce the residual chlorine. Test with KI-starch paper; there should

be no color change. Add approximately 0.05 g/l more ascorbic acid to ensure the presence of excess reducing agent.

d. Distill both the chlorinated and unchlorinated samples as in Section 413B. Use the magnesium chloride reagent whenever the presence of thiocyanate is suspected. Test according to Section 413C, 413D, or 413E.

5. Calculation

mg/l CN amenable to chlorination$=G-H$

where $G=$ mg/l CN found in the unchlorinated portion of the sample and $H=$ mg/l CN found in the chlorinated portion of the sample.

6. Precision

The precision, with the titrimetric finish, for cyanides amenable to chlorination was determined from a mixed cyanide solution containing sodium, zinc, copper, and silver cyanides and sodium ferrocyanide. The precision of the method within its designated range may be expressed as follows:

$$S_T = 0.049X + 0.162$$

where $S_T =$ overall precision and $X =$ CN concentration, mg/l.

413 G.   Cyanides Amenable to Chlorination without Distillation, Short-Cut Method

1. General Discussion

This method covers the determination of free CN and CN complexes that are amenable to chlorination. The procedure does not measure cyanates or iron cyanide complexes, but does determine cyanogen chloride. This test requires neither the lengthy distillation procedure nor the chlorination of one sample before distillation. The recovery of cyanide from metal cyanide complexes will be comparable to that in Method F.

The cyanides are converted to cyanogen chloride by chloramine-T after the sample has been heated. In the absence of nickel, copper, silver, and gold cyanide complexes, the cyanogen chloride complex may be developed at room temperature. The mixed reagent, pyridine-barbituric acid, produces a red-blue color in the sample. The color can be estimated visually against standards or photometrically at 578 nm. The limits of the determination are 0.2 μg to 6 μg CN, representing 0.01 to 0.30 mg/l in a 20-ml sample. Higher CN concentrations may be determined by suitable dilution.

The sensitivity of the test may be extended to the 5- to 150-μg/l level if a fresh, unstabilized sample is used. In these circumstances (pH < 9), add phosphate buffer dropwise to a pH of 6.5 (pH 6.0 to 6.6) and use a 40-ml sample, minimizing dilution before color development.

2. Interferences

Interfering agents may be removed as described in Section 413A. The thiocyanate ion, which also reacts with chloramine-T, will give a positive error equivalent to its concentration. When thiocyanates are present or other color- or turbidity-producing interferences are encountered, use Method F.

3. Apparatus

a. *Apparatus listed in 413D.2.*
b. *Hot water bath.*

4. Reagents

See Section 413A and D.3.

5. Procedure

a. Calibrate as directed in Section 413D.4a.

b. Pipet a 20-ml sample into a beaker. If more than 0.3 mg/l CN is known to be present, use a smaller sample diluted to 20 ml with water.

c. Add phosphate buffer dropwise, while stirring, to a pH of 6.5 (pH 6.0 to 6.6). Note the number of drops of buffer required.

d. Prepare a second portion as directed in ¶b and place in a 50-ml volumetric flask. Add the established number of drops of phosphate buffer required and swirl to mix. Add one drop 0.1 M EDTA solution. Heat in a water bath at 50 C (120 to 125 F) for 1 min while swirling.

e. While the sample is still hot, add 2 ml of chloramine-T solution and swirl to mix. After 1 min, add 5 ml of pyridine-barbituric acid solution and swirl in the water bath for 1 min.

f. Remove from water bath, dilute to the mark (50 ml), and allow 7 min more for color development. Cool to room temperature, if necessary, and read the absorbance at 578 nm in a 1.0-cm cell within a total of 15 min from the time the pyridine-barbituric acid solution was added.

6. Calculation

$$\text{mg/l CN amenable to chlorination} = \frac{A}{B}$$

where $A = \mu g$ CN read from calibration curve and $B =$ ml sample used.

7. Precision

The analysis of a mixed cyanide solution in tap water, containing sodium, zinc, copper, and silver cyanides, gave a precision within the designated range as follows:

$$S_T = 0.097X + 0.004$$

where S = overall precision and X = CN concentration, mg/l.

413 H.   Cyanogen Chloride

1. General Discussion

Cyanogen chloride is the first reaction product when cyanide compounds are chlorinated. It is a volatile gas, only slightly soluble in water, but highly toxic even in low concentrations (CAUTION: *Avoid inhalation or contact.*) Mixed pyridine-barbituric acid reagent produces a red-blue color with cyanogen chloride.

Because cyanogen chloride hydrolyzes to cyanate at a pH of 12 or more, a separate sample should be collected for cyanogen chloride analysis (See Section 413A.2) in a closed container without caustic soda. A quick test with a spot plate or comparator as soon as the sample is collected may be the only procedure for avoiding the hydrolysis of cyanogen chloride due to the lapse of time between sampling and analysis.

If the orthotolidine test (Section 413A.2) indicates that free chlorine is present, add ascorbic acid to the sample immediately until a negative test with the paper is obtained (see Section 413F.4c).

2. Apparatus

See Section 413D.2.

3. Reagents

See Section 413D.3.

4. Procedure

Calibrate as directed in Section 413D.4a. To a 50-ml volumetric flask, add a portion of unstabilized sample, diluted if necessary, to contain 0.2 to 6 μg of CN/40 ml. Add phosphate buffer to a pH of 6.5 (pH 6.0 to 6.6). (Unstabilized sample has to be used.) Add only 5 ml pyridine-barbituric acid solution. Dilute to the mark with distilled water and mix well by inversion. Allow 8 min for color development. Measure the absorbance at 578 nm in a 1.0-cm cell within 15 min. Using the calibration curve, determine the cyanogen chloride as CN.

5. Calculations

$$\text{mg/l CNCl, as CN} = \frac{A}{B}$$

where $A = \mu g$ CN read from calibration curve and $C = $ml original unstabilized sample.

6. Precision

The instability of cyanogen chloride precludes round-robin testing procedures and a precision statement is not possible.

413 I. Spot Test for Sample Screening

1. General Discussion

The spot test procedure allows a quick screening of the sample to establish if more than 50 $\mu g/l$ of cyanide amenable to chlorination are present. The test also establishes the presence or absence of cyanogen chloride. With practice or dilution, the test reveals the approximate concentration range of these compounds by the color development compared with similarly treated standards.

When chloramine-T is added to cyanides amenable to chlorination, cyanogen chloride is formed. Cyanogen chloride forms a red-blue color with the mixed reagent pyridine-barbituric acid. When testing for cyanogen chloride, omit the chloramine-T addition. (CAUTION: *Cyanogen chloride is a toxic gas; avoid inhalation.*)

Thiocyanate will give a positive interference. The presence of formaldehyde in excess of 0.5 mg/l interferes with the test. A spot test for the presence of aldehydes and method for removal of this interference are given in Section 413A.3.

2. Apparatus

a. Porcelain spot plate with 6 to 12 cavities.

b. Dropping pipets.

c. Glass stirring rods.

3. Reagents

a. Chloramine-T solution: See Section 413D.3*a*.

b. Stock cyanide solution: See Section 413D.3*b*.

c. Pyridine-barbituric acid reagent: See Section 413D.3*d*.

d. Hydrochloric acid, HCl, 1+9.

e. Phenolphthalein indicator solution.

f. Sodium carbonate, Na₂CO₃, anhydrous.

4. Procedure

If the solution to be tested has a pH value greater than 10, neutralize a 20- to 25-ml portion. Add about 250 mg Na₂CO₃ and swirl to dissolve. Add 1 drop phenolphthalein indicator. Add 1+9 HCl dropwise with constant swirling until the solution becomes colorless. Place 3 drops sample and 3 drops distilled water (for blanks) in separate cavities of a white spot plate. To each cavity, add 1 drop chloramine-T solution and mix with a clean stirring rod. Add 1 drop pyridine-barbituric acid solution to each cavity and again mix. After 1 min, the sample spot will turn pink to red if 50 $\mu g/l$ or more of CN are present. The blank spot will be faint yellow because of the color of the reagents. Until familiarity with the spot test is gained, use, in place of the water blank, a standard solution containing 50 $\mu g/l$ CN for color comparison. This standard can be made up by diluting the stock cyanide solution (¶3b).

413 J.   Cyanates

1. General Discussion

Cyanate (CNO^-) may be of interest in analysis of industrial waste samples because the alkaline chlorination process used for the oxidation of cyanide yields cyanate in the second reaction.

Cyanate is unstable at neutral or low pH; therefore, stabilize the sample as soon as collected by the addition of sodium hydroxide to pH >12. Remove residual chlorine by the addition of ascorbic acid (see Section 413A.2).

a. Principle: Cyanate hydrolyzes to ammonia when heated at low pH.

$$2NaCNO + H_2SO_4 + 4H_2O \rightarrow (NH_4)_2SO_4 + 2NaHCO_3$$

The ammonia concentration must be determined on one portion of the sample before acidification. The ammonia content before and after hydrolysis of cyanate may be measured by the direct nesslerization or phenate methods (see Sections 418B and 418C) or by the ammonia-selective electrodes using the standard addition technic. The test is applicable to cyanate compounds in natural waters and industrial waste.

b. Interferences:

1) Organic nitrogenous compounds may hydrolyze to ammonia upon acidification. To minimize this interference, control acidification and heating closely.

2) Metal compounds may precipitate or form colored complexes with the nessler's reagent. Addition of Rochelle salt or EDTA in the procedure for the determination of ammonia overcomes these interferences. Metal precipitates do not interfere with the ion-selective electrode method.

3) Oxidants that oxidize cyanate to carbon dioxide and nitrogen should be reduced with ascorbic acid (see Section 413F.4d).

4) Industrial waste containing organic material may contain unknown interferences.

c. Detection limit: 1 to 2 mg/l cyanate.

2. Apparatus

a. Expanded-scale pH meter or selective-ion meter.

b. Ammonia-selective electrode*.

---

* Orion Model 95-10 or equivalent.

c. Magnetic mixer, with TFE fluorocarbon-coated stirring bar.

3. Reagents

a. Stock ammonia solution: Dissolve 314.1 mg NH₄Cl in ammonia-free water, dilute to 1,000 ml, and mix thoroughly; 1.00 ml = 100 μg NH₃.

b. Standard ammonia solution: Dilute 10.0 ml stock ammonia solution to 100.0 ml with ammonia-free water; 1.00 ml = 10.0 μg NH₃.

c. Sodium hydroxide, 10N: Dissolve 400 g NaOH in water and dilute to 1 l.

d. Sulfuric acid solution, H_2SO_4, 1+1.

4. Procedure

a. Calibration: From the stock and standard ammonia solutions, prepare three standards containing 1.0, 10.0, and 100.0 mg/l ammonia. Pipet 100 ml of these solutions into 250-ml beakers and add 1 ml 10N NaOH to each. Immerse the ammonia electrode in the 1.0-mg/l solution first, and mix the solution on a magnetic stirrer. Maintain the same stirring rate throughout the calibration and testing procedure. When the electrode has reached a constant potential as indicated by the millivolt meter, record the reading. Repeat for the 10.0- and 100.0- mg/l ammonia solutions.

The electrode is functioning properly if 10-fold change of ammonia concentration produces a potential change of 59 mV.

b. Treatment of sample:

1) Dilute the sample if necessary so that the concentration of cyanate is 0 to 30 mg/l or ammonia 0 to 15 mg/l. Take or prepare at least 200 ml.

2) From these 200 ml, take 100 ml and follow steps 6) through 9) below.

3) Acidify 100 ml prepared sample by adding 0.5 ml 1+1 sulfuric acid to a pH of 2.0 to 2.5.

4) Heat the sample to 90 to 95 C and maintain temperature for 30 min.

5) Cool to room temperature and restore to original volume by adding ammonia-free water.

6) Pour into a 250-ml beaker, stir with a magnetic mixer stirrer, and add 1 ml 10 N NaOH.

7) Immerse the ammonia electrode and after equilibrium is reached (30 sec) record the millivolt reading (*A*).

8) Add 10.0 ml ammonia standard. The standard used depends on the expected amount of ammonia in the sample. If the ammonia is in the range of 1 to 25 mg/l, use the 100-mg/l ammonia standard. If the range is 0.1 to 2.5 mg/l ammonia, use the 10-mg/l ammonia standard. The purpose is to create a significant millivolt reading change by a known amount of ammonia added to the sample. Estimate the approximate ammonia content from the calibration chart.

9) After equilibrium is reached (30 sec), record the new millivolt reading (*B*).

5. Calculations:

a. Calculate ΔE:

$$\Delta E = A - B$$

where ΔE = millivolt change due to the ammonia addition, A = reading before addition, and B = reading after addition.

b. Use Table 413:II to determine Q corresponding to ΔE.

c. Multiply Q times the concentration (mg/l) of the ammonia standard used. The result is the ammonia concentration (mg/l) in the sample.

d. Compute cyanate concentration as:

$$mg/l\,CNO^- = 2.46 \times (BB{-}AA)$$

where AA = ammonia concentration in original sample, mg/l, and BB = ammonia concentration after CNO^- hydrolysis, mg/l.

6. Precision

No data on the precision of this method are available.

413 K.   Thiocyanate

1. General Discussion

When wastewater containing thiocyanate is chlorinated the highly toxic cyanogen chloride is formed. At an acidic pH, ferric ion forms an intense red color with thiocyanate, which is suitable for colorimetric determination.

a. Interference:

1) Hexavalent chromium interference is removed by adding ferrous sulfate after adjusting the pH value to 1 to 2 with HNO_3. Raising the pH to 9 with $1N$ sodium hydroxide precipitates Fe(III) and Cr(III), which are filtered off.

2) Reducing agents that reduce Fe(III) to Fe(II), thus preventing formation of the ferric thiocyanate complex, are destroyed by a few drops of H_2O_2.

3) Industrial wastes may be highly colored or contain various interfering organic compounds. Test the applicability of the method with samples to which SCN has been added.

b. Application: 1 to 10 mg/l SCN in natural waters. Colored samples may reduce the sensitivity.

2. Apparatus

Spectrophotometer or filter photometer, for use at 480 nm, providing a light path of 1 cm.

3. Reagents

a. Ferric nitrate solution: Dissolve 50 g $Fe(NO_3)_3$ in 500 ml distilled water. Add 25 ml conc HNO_3 and dilute to 1 l.

b. Nitric acid, HNO_3, 1+1.

c. Standard thiocyanate solution: Dissolve 1.673 g potassium thiocyanate in distilled water and dilute to 1,000 ml. 1.00 ml = 1.00 mg SCN.

4. Procedure

a. Preparation of calibration curve: From the standard thiocyanate solution, prepare a series of 50-ml standards containing 50 to 500 μg SCN. Develop the color in accordance with ¶*b* below. Plot percent transmittance on semilogarithmic paper against SCN concentration in μg/50 ml.

b. Color development: Use a filtered sample containing 50 to 500 μg SCN. Adjust the pH to 5 to 7 by adding 1+1

TABLE 413:II. VALUES OF FACTOR Q FOR VARIOUS CHANGES IN MILLIVOLT READING (ΔE) AT 25 C

ΔE	Q	ΔE	Q	ΔE	Q	ΔE	Q	ΔE	Q
		−3.0	0.423	−8.5	0.188	−18.0	0.0822	−29.0	0.0417
+2.4	52.6	3.1	0.415	8.6	0.186	18.2	0.0811	29.2	0.0412
+2.3	17.2	3.2	0.407	8.7	0.184	18.4	0.0799	29.4	0.0408
+2.2	10.3	3.3	0.399	8.8	0.182	18.6	0.0788	29.6	0.0403
+2.1	7.32	3.4	0.391	8.9	0.180	18.8	0.0777	29.8	0.0399
+2.0	5.68	3.5	0.384	9.0	0.178	19.0	0.0767	30.0	0.0394
+1.9	4.63	3.6	0.377	9.1	0.176	19.2	0.0756	30.2	0.0390
+1.8	3.91	3.7	0.370	9.2	0.174	19.4	0.0746	30.4	0.0386
+1.7	3.38	3.8	0.363	9.3	0.173	19.6	0.0736	30.6	0.0382
+1.6	2.98	3.9	0.357	9.4	0.171	19.8	0.0726	30.8	0.0378
+1.5	2.66	4.0	0.351	9.5	0.169	20.0	0.0716	31.0	0.0374
+1.4	2.40	4.1	0.345	9.6	0.167	20.2	0.0707	31.2	0.0370
+1.3	2.19	4.2	0.339	9.7	0.165	20.4	0.0698	31.4	0.0366
+1.2	2.01	4.3	0.333	9.8	0.164	20.6	0.0689	31.6	0.0362
+1.1	1.86	4.4	0.327	9.9	0.162	20.8	0.0680	31.8	0.0358
+1.0	1.72	4.5	0.322	10.0	0.160	21.0	0.0671	32.0	0.0354
+0.9	1.61	4.6	0.319	10.2	0.157	21.2	0.0662	32.2	0.0351
+0.8	1.51	4.7	0.312	10.4	0.154	21.4	0.0654	32.4	0.0347
+0.7	1.42	4.8	0.307	10.6	0.151	21.6	0.0645	32.6	0.0343
+0.6	1.34	4.9	0.302	10.8	0.148	21.8	0.0637	32.8	0.0340
+0.5	1.27	5.0	0.297	11.0	0.145	22.0	0.0629	33.0	0.0336
+0.4	1.21	5.1	0.293	11.2	0.143	22.2	0.0621	33.2	0.0333
+0.3	1.15	5.2	0.288	11.4	0.140	22.4	0.0613	33.4	0.0329
+0.2	1.09	5.3	0.284	11.6	0.137	22.6	0.0606	33.6	0.0326
+0.1	1.05	5.4	0.280	11.8	0.135	22.8	0.0598	33.8	0.0323
0.0	1.00	5.5	0.276	12.0	0.133	23.0	0.0591	34.0	0.0319
−0.1	0.959	5.6	0.272	12.2	0.130	23.2	0.0584	34.2	0.0316
0.2	0.921	5.7	0.268	12.4	0.128	23.4	0.0576	34.4	0.0313
0.3	0.886	5.8	0.264	12.6	0.126	23.6	0.0569	34.6	0.0310
0.4	0.853	5.9	0.260	12.8	0.123	23.8	0.0563	34.8	0.0307

TABLE 413:II. (Continued)

ΔE	Q	ΔE	Q	ΔE	Q	ΔE	Q	ΔE	Q
0.5	0.822	6.0	0.257	13.0	0.121	24.0	0.0556	35.0	0.0304
0.6	0.794	6.1	0.253	13.2	0.119	24.2	0.0549	36.0	0.0289
0.7	0.767	6.2	0.250	13.4	0.117	24.4	0.0543	37.0	0.0275
0.8	0.742	6.3	0.247	13.6	0.115	24.6	0.0536	38.0	0.0261
0.9	0.718	6.4	0.243	13.8	0.113	24.8	0.0530	39.0	0.0249
1.0	0.696	6.5	0.240	14.0	0.112	25.0	0.0523	40.0	0.0237
1.1	0.675	6.6	0.237	14.2	0.110	25.2	0.0517	41.0	0.0226
1.2	0.655	6.7	0.234	14.4	0.108	25.4	0.0511	42.0	0.0216
1.3	0.637	6.8	0.231	14.6	0.106	25.6	0.0505	43.0	0.0206
1.4	0.619	6.9	0.228	14.8	0.105	25.8	0.0499	44.0	0.0198
1.5	0.602	7.0	0.225	15.0	0.103	26.0	0.0494	45.0	0.0187
1.6	0.586	7.1	0.222	15.2	0.1013	26.2	0.0488	46.0	0.0179
1.7	0.571	7.2	0.219	15.4	0.0997	26.4	0.0482	47.0	0.0171
1.8	0.556	7.3	0.217	15.6	0.0982	26.6	0.0477	48.0	0.0163
1.9	0.542	7.4	0.214	15.8	0.0967	26.8	0.0471	49.0	0.0156
2.0	0.529	7.5	0.212	16.0	0.0952	27.0	0.0466	50.0	0.0149
2.1	0.516	7.6	0.209	16.2	0.0938	27.2	0.0461	51.0	0.0143
2.2	0.504	7.7	0.207	16.4	0.0924	27.4	0.0456	52.0	0.0137
2.3	0.493	7.8	0.204	16.6	0.0910	27.6	0.0450	53.0	0.0131
2.4	0.482	7.9	0.202	16.8	0.0897	27.8	0.0445	54.0	0.0125
2.5	0.471	8.0	0.199	17.0	0.0884	28.0	0.0440	55.0	0.0120
2.6	0.461	8.1	0.197	17.2	0.0871	28.2	0.0435	56.0	0.0115
2.7	0.451	8.2	0.195	17.4	0.0858	28.4	0.0431	57.0	0.0110
2.8	0.441	8.3	0.193	17.6	0.0846	28.6	0.0426	58.0	0.0105
2.9	0.432	8.4	0.190	17.8	0.0834	28.8	0.0421	59.0	0.0101

HNO₃ dropwise. Transfer the sample to a 50-ml volumetric flask and add 5 ml ferric nitrate solution. If the pH is not between 1 and 2, adjust with 1+1 nitric acid. Dilute to volume with distilled water and shake well. Measure the absorbance of the sample at 480 nm using distilled water as a blank.

5. Calculation

$$mg/l = \frac{\mu g \; SCN}{ml \; sample}$$

6. Precision

No data on the precision of this method are available.

413 L.   References

1. ELLIS, M.M. 1937. Detection and Measurement of Stream Pollution. U. S. Dep. Commerce, Bur. Fish., Bull. No. 22.

2. DOUDOROFF, P. & M. KATZ. 1950. Critical review of literature on the toxicity of industrial wastes and their components to fish. Sewage Ind. Wastes 22:1432.

3. DOUDOROFF, P. 1956. Some experiments on the toxicity of complex cyanides to fish. Sewage Ind. Wastes 28:1020.

4. DOUDOROFF, P., G. LEDUC & C. R. SCHNEIDER. 1966. Acute toxicity to fish of solutions containing complex metal cyanides, in relation to concentrations of molecular hydrocyanic acid. Trans. Amer. Fish. Soc. 95:116.

5. MILNE, D. 1950. Disposal of cyanides by complexation. Sewage Ind. Wastes 22:1192.

6. MILNE, D. 1950. Equilibria in dilute cyanide waste solutions. Sewage Ind. Wastes 23:904.

7. BURDICK, G.E. & M. LIPSCHUETZ. 1948. Toxicity of ferro and ferricyanide solutions to fish. Trans. Amer. Fish. Soc. 78:192.

8. SCHNEIDER, C.R. & H. FREUND. 1962. Determination of low level hydrocyanic acid. Anal. Chem. 34:69.

9. CLAEYS, R. & H. FREUND. 1968. Gas chromatographic separation of HCN. Environ. Sci. Technol. 2:458.

10. MONTGOMERY, H.A.C., et al. 1969. Determination of free hydrogen cyanide in river water. Analyst 94:284.

11. MONTGOMERY, H.A.C. 1972. Some analytical aspects of the behavior of certain pollu-tants in aqueous systems. Paper presented at 6th Int. Conf. Water Pollut. Res.

12. NELSON, K.H. & I. LYSYJ. 1971. Analysis of water for molecular hydrogen cyanide. J. Water Pollut. Control Fed. 43:799.

13. ZILLICH, J.A. 1972. Toxicity of combined chlorine residuals to freshwater fish. J. Water Pollut. Control Fed. 44:212.

14. RESNICK, J.D., et al. 1958. The behavior of cyanates in polluted water. Ind. Eng. Chem. 50:71.

15. PETTET, A.E.J. & G.C. WARE. 1955. Disposal of cyanide wastes. Chem. Ind. 1232.

16. LANCY, L. & W. ZABBAN. 1962. Analytical methods and instrumentation for determining cyanogen compounds. Amer. Soc. Testing & Materials STP No. 337.

17. LANCY, L. & W. ZABBAN. 1963. Die Beziehung Zwischen Analyse und Behandlung von Cyanidhaltigem Abwasser. Metalloberflache 13:65.

18. SERFASS, E.J., et al. 1952. Analytical method for the determination of cyanides in plating wastes and in effluents from treatment processes. Plating 39:267.

19. LESCHBER, R. & H. SCHLICHTING. 1969. Uber die Zersetzlichkeit Komplexer Metallcyanide bie der Cyanidbestimmung in Abwasser. Z. Anal. Chem. ZANCA 245:300.

20. BASSETT, H., JR. & A.S. CORBET. 1924. J. Chem. Soc. 125:1358.

21. DODGE, B.F. & W. ZABBAN. 1952. Analytical methods for the determination of cyanates in plating wastes. Plating 39:381.

22. GARDNER, D.C. 1956. The colorimetric de-

termination of cyanates in effluents. *Plating* 43:743.

23. Procedures for Analyzing Metal Finishing Wastes. 1954. Ohio River Valley Sanitation Commission, Cincinnati, Ohio.

24. KRUSE, J.M. & M.G. MELLON. 1951. Colorimetric determination of cyanides. *Sewage Ind. Wastes* 23:1402.

25. CASAPIERI, P., R. SCOTT & E.A. SIMPSON. 1970. *Anal. Chim. Acta* 49:188.

26. GOULDEN, P.D., B.K. AFGHAM & P. BROOKSBANK. 1972. *Anal. Chem.* 44:1845.

27. RYAN, J.A. & G.W. CULSHAW. 1944. The use of p-dimethylaminobenzylidene rhodanine as an indicator for the volumetric determination of cyanides. *Analyst* 69:370.

28. ASMUS, E. & H. GARSCHAGEN. 1953. Z. *Anal. Chem. ZANCA* 138:414.

414   FLUORIDE

A fluoride concentration of approximately 1.0 mg/l effectively prevents dental caries without harmful effects on health. Fluoride may occur naturally in water or may be added in controlled amounts. Some fluorosis may occur when the fluoride level exceeds the recommended limits. In rare instances the fluoride concentration naturally occurring may approach 10 mg/l. Such waters should be defluoridated.

The accurate determination of fluoride has increased in importance with the growth of the practice of fluoridation of supplies as a public health measure. The maintenance of an optimum fluoride concentration is essential in maintaining the effectiveness and safety of the fluoridation procedure.

Among the many methods suggested for the determination of fluoride ion in water, the electrode and colorimetric methods are the most satisfactory at the present time. The colorimetric methods are based on the reaction between fluoride and a zirconium-dye lake. The fluoride reacts with the dye lake, dissociating a portion of it into a colorless complex anion (ZrF_6^{2-}) and the dye. As the amount of fluoride is increased, the color produced becomes progressively lighter or different in hue, depending on the reagent used.

Because all of the colorimetric methods are subject to errors due to interfering ions, it may be necessary to distill the sample as directed in Section 414A before making the fluoride determination. When interfering ions are not present in excess of the tolerances of the method, the fluoride determination may be made directly without distillation. The analysis is completed by using one of the two colorimetric methods (C and D).

1. Selection of Method

The addition of the prescribed buffer frees the electrode method from the interference caused by such relatively common ions as aluminum, hexametaphosphate, iron, and orthophosphate, which adversely affect the colorimetric methods and necessitate preliminary distillation. However, samples containing fluoroborate ion (BF_4) must be subjected to the preliminary distillation step to convert the fluoroborate to free fluoride before measurement by the electrode or colorimetric methods. Although a special electrode selective for fluoroborate is available commercially for the estimation of fluoroborate ion, the preferred approach is distillation followed by electrode measurement of the released fluoride. Both colorimetric methods are directly applicable to samples in the fluoride range 0.05 to 1.4 mg/l, while the electrode method can be applied to fluoride concentrations beginning at 0.1 mg/l and extending beyond 5 mg/l. The SPADNS and electrode methods allow measurements to be made at any time after reagent addition. Although the alizarin visual method does not require accurate time control because sample and standards are treated simultaneously under the same conditions, a waiting period of 1 hr after reagent addition is suggested as satisfactory for color development. The visual colorimetric method requires inexpensive laboratory glassware, while Methods B and C are instrumental.

Permanent colored standards, commercially or otherwise prepared, may be used if appropriate precautions are taken. These include strict adherence to the manufacturer's directions and care-

ful calibration of the permanent standards against standards prepared by the analyst. (See General Introduction, Section 102.7, for further discussion of their use.)

Fluoride also may be determined by the automated complexone method described in Section 603.

2. Interference in Colorimetric Methods

In general, the colorimetric methods are susceptible to the same interfering substances, but to different degrees. Table 414:I lists the substances that commonly cause interference with the methods. Because these interferences are neither linear in effect nor algebraically additive, mathematical compensation is unsatisfactory. Whenever any one substance is present in sufficient quantity to produce an error of 0.1 mg/l, or whenever the total interfering effect is in doubt, distill the sample. (Also distill colored or turbid samples.) In some instances, sample dilution or addition of the appropriate amounts of interfering

TABLE 414:I. CONCENTRATION OF INTERFERING SUBSTANCES CAUSING 0.1-MG/L ERROR AT 1.0 MG/L F* IN COLORIMETRIC METHODS

Substance	Method C (SPADNS)		Method D (Alizarin Visual)	
	Conc mg/l	Type of Error	Conc mg/l	Type of Error
Alkalinity ($CaCO_3$)	5,000	−	400	−
Aluminum (Al^{3+})	0.1†	−	0.25	−
Chloride (Cl^-)	7,000	+	2,000	−
Iron (Fe^{3+})	10	−	2	+
Hexametaphosphate ($[NaPO_3]_6$)	1.0	+	1.0	+
Phosphate (PO_4^{3-})	16	+	5	+
Sulfate (SO_4^{2-})	200	+	300	+

* Residual chlorine must be completely removed with arsenite reagent. Color and turbidity must be removed or compensated for.

† On immediate reading. Tolerance increases with time: after 2 hr, 3.0; after 4 hr, 30.

substances to the standards may be used to eliminate the interference effect. If alkalinity is the only significant interference, it may be neutralized with either hydrochloric or nitric acid.

Chlorine interferes in all colorimetric methods and provision for its removal is made.

The volume measurement of water sample, and particularly, the volume measurement of reagent are extremely important to the accuracy of the determination. Samples and standards must be at the same temperature, at least within 2 C, with constant temperature being maintained throughout the color development period. In the case of the SPADNS method, different calibration curves may be prepared for different temperatures.

3. Sampling and Storage

Polyethylene bottles are preferred for collecting and storing samples for fluoride analysis. Glass bottles are satisfactory provided that they have not previously contained high-fluoride solutions. Always rinse the bottle with a portion of the sample.

Never use an excess of dechlorinating agent in the sample. Sodium thiosulfate in excess of 100 mg/l will interfere by producing a precipitate.

414 A.   Preliminary Distillation Step

1. Discussion

Fluoride can be separated from other constituents in water by distillation of fluosilicic (or hydrofluoric) acid from a solution of the sample in an acid with a higher boiling point. Quantitative fluoride recovery is approached by using a relatively large sample volume, and sulfate carryover is minimized by conducting the distillation over a broad temperature range.

2. Apparatus

Distillation apparatus consisting of a 1-l round-bottom long-neck pyrex boiling flask, a connecting tube, an efficient condenser, a thermometer adapter, and a thermometer reading to 200 C is illustrated in Figure 414:1. Use any comparable apparatus with the essential design features. Figure 318:1 shows the general type of distillation apparatus* that is satisfactory for the fluoride, ammonia, phenol, and selenium distillations. The critical points to observe are those that could affect complete fluoride recovery—such as obstruction in the vapor path and trapping of liquid in the adapter and condenser—and conditions that might enhance sulfate carryover. Use an asbestos shield or similar device to protect the upper part of the distilling flask from the burner flame. If desired, this apparatus can be modified so that the heat is automatically shut off when distillation is completed.

3. Reagents

a. Sulfuric acid, H_2SO_4, conc.
b. Silver sulfate, Ag_2SO_4, crystals.

---

*Corning No. 3360 or equivalent.

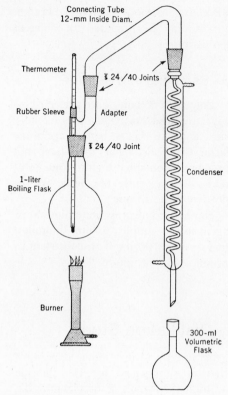

Figure 414:1. Direct distillation apparatus for fluoride.

4. Procedure

a. Place 400 ml distilled water in the distilling flask and carefully add 200 ml conc H_2SO_4. Swirl until the flask contents are homogeneous. Add 25 to 35 glass beads and connect the apparatus as shown in Figure 414:1, making sure all joints are tight. Begin heating slowly at first, then as rapidly as the efficiency of the condenser will permit (the distillate must be cool) until the temperature of the flask contents reaches exactly 180 C. Discard the distillate. This process removes fluoride contamination and adjusts the acid-water ratio for subsequent distillations.

b. After cooling the acid mixture remaining after the steps outlined in ¶4*a*, or previous distillations, to 120 C or below, add 300 ml of sample, mix thoroughly, and distill as before until the temperature reaches 180 C. To prevent sulfate carryover, do not heat above 180 C.

c. Add Ag_2SO_4 to the distilling flask at the rate of 5 mg/mg Cl when high-chloride samples are distilled.

d. Use the sulfuric acid solution in the flask repeatedly until the contaminants from the samples accumulate to such an extent that recovery is affected or interferences appear in the distillate. Check suitability of the acid periodically by distilling standard fluoride samples. After the distillation of high-fluoride samples, flush the still with 300 ml distilled water and combine the two fluoride distillates. If necessary, repeat the flushing operation until the fluoride content of the distillates is at a minimum. Include the additional fluoride recovered with that of the first distillation. After periods of inactivity, similarly flush the still and discard the distillate.

5. Interpretation of Results

The recovery of fluoride is quantitative within the accuracy of the methods used for its measurement.

414 B. Electrode Method

1. General Discussion

a. Principle: The fluoride electrode is a selective ion sensor. The electrode, commonly called a probe, is designed to be used with a standard calomel reference electrode and any modern pH meter having an expanded millivolt scale. The key element in the fluoride ion-activity electrode is the laser-type doped single lanthanum fluoride crystal across which a potential is established by the presence of fluoride ions. The crystal contacts the sample solution at one face and an internal reference solution at the other. The cell may be represented by:

Ag| AgCl, Cl$^-$ (0.3M), F$^-$ (0.001 M)| LaF₃| test solution| reference electrode

The fluoride ion-selective electrode can be used to measure the activity or the concentration of fluoride in aqueous samples by use of an appropriate calibration curve. However, the fluoride activity depends on the total ionic strength of the sample. The electrode does not respond to bound or complexed fluoride. These difficulties are largely overcome by the addition of a buffer solution of high total ionic strength to swamp variations in sample ionic strength and containing a chelate to complex aluminum preferentially.

b. Interference: Polyvalent cations such as Al(III), Fe(III), and Si(IV) will complex fluoride ion. The extent to which complexation takes place depends on the solution pH and the relative levels of the fluoride and the complexing species. However, the addition of CDTA (cyclohexylene diamine tetraacetic acid) preferentially will complex concentrations of aluminum up to 5.0 mg/l and release the fluoride as the free ion. Likewise, in acid solution, hydrogen ion forms complexes with fluoride ion but the complexing is negligible if the pH is adjusted to above pH 5. In alkaline solution the hydroxide ion also interferes with the electrode response to fluoride ion whenever the level of hydroxide ion is greater than one-tenth the level of fluoride ion present. At pH ≤ 8, the hydroxide concentration is ≤ 10^{-6} molar and no interference occurs with any measurable fluoride concentration.

A new class of compounds, the fluoroborates, is being used by the electroplating industry with increasing frequency. The fluoride probe does not respond to the fluoroborate ion (BF₄). If a sample is suspected of containing fluoroborates, distill it to achieve hydrolysis of the fluoroborate to free fluoride. Then use either the colorimetric or probe procedure. Fluoroborates also may be measured with an electrode selective for fluoroborate ions. However, distillation followed by fluoride measurement is preferred.

2. Apparatus

a. Expanded-scale or digital pH meter or ion-selective meter.

b. Sleeve-type reference electrode*: Do not use fiber-tip reference electrodes; they exhibit erratic behavior in very dilute solutions.

c. Fluoride electrode†.

---

*Orion #90-01-00, Beckman #40463 or Corning #476012.

†Orion #94-09.

d. Magnetic stirrer, with Teflon-coated stirring bar.

e. Stop watch or timer.

3. Reagents

a. Stock fluoride solution: Dissolve 221.0 mg anhydrous sodium fluoride, NaF, in distilled water and dilute to 1,000 ml; 1.00 ml = 100 μg F.

b. Standard fluoride solution: Dilute 100 ml stock fluoride solution to 1,000 ml with distilled water; 1.00 ml = 10.0 μg F.

c. Total ionic strength adjustment buffer (TISAB): Place approximately 500 ml distilled water in a 1-l beaker and add 57 ml glacial acetic acid, 58 g NaCl, and 4.0 g 1,2 cyclohexylene diamine tetraacetic acid‡ (CDTA). Stir to dissolve. Place beaker in a cool water bath and add slowly 6 N NaOH (about 125 ml) with stirring, until pH is between 5.0 and 5.5. Transfer to a 1-l volumetric flask and add distilled water to the mark.

4. Procedure

a. Instrument calibration: No major adjustment of any of the instruments is normally required to use the electrodes in the fluoride range of 0.2 to 2.0 mg/l. For those instruments with zero at center scale (e.g., most Beckman or Leeds and Northup meters), adjust the calibration control so that the 1.0 mg/l F standard reads at the center zero (100 mV) when the meter is in the expanded-scale position. This cannot be done on some meters, such as the Corning Model

‡Listed by Matheson, Coleman and Bell as 1,2 cyclohexylene dinitrilo tetraacetic acid; Catalogue #CX 2390.

12, which do not have a millivolt calibration control. To use a selective-ion meter follow instructions of the manufacturer for calibration.

b. Preparation of fluoride standards: Prepare a series of standards by adding, respectively, 2.5, 5.0, and 10.0 ml standard fluoride solution (1.00 ml = 10.0 μg F) to each of three 100-ml volumetric flasks. To each flask, add by pipet 50 ml of pH 5.0 to 5.5 TISAB solution and dilute to 100 ml with distilled water; mix well. These standards are equivalent to 0.5, 1.0, and 2.0 mg/l F. (Because the concentration of the sample is reduced by half by the addition of TISAB solution, doubling the standards' true concentration enables the analyst to read the samples' original concentration directly.)

c. Treatment of sample: To a 100-ml volumetric flask, add by pipet 50 ml sample, dilute to the mark with TISAB, and mix well. Bring the standards and the sample to the same temperature, preferably room temperature.

d. Measurement with electrode: Transfer each standard and sample to a series of 150-ml beakers. Immerse the electrodes and measure the developed potential while stirring the test solution on a magnetic stirrer. Avoid stirring the solution before immersing the electrodes because entrapped air around the crystal can produce erroneous readings or needle fluctuations. Let the electrodes remain in the solution 3 min before taking a final positive millivolt reading. Rinse the electrodes with distilled water and blot dry between readings.

When using an expanded-scale pH meter or selective-ion meter, recalibrate the electrode frequently by checking the potential reading of the 1.00-mg/l F standard and adjust the calibration control, if necessary, until the meter reads as before. Confirm the calibration after each unknown and also after reading each standard when preparing the standard curve.

Plot the potential measurement of the fluoride standards against concentration on two-cycle semilogarithmic graph paper. Plot milligrams per liter F on the logarithmic axis, with the lowest concentration at the bottom of the page. Using the potential measurement for each unknown sample, read the corresponding fluoride concentration from the standard curve.

414 C.　SPADNS Method

1. Discussion

The reaction rate between fluoride and zirconium ions is influenced greatly by the acidity of the reaction mixture. By increasing the proportion of acid in the reagent, the reaction can be made practically instantaneous. Under such conditions, however, the effect of various ions differs from that in the conventional alizarin methods. The selection of dye for this rapid fluoride method is governed largely by the resulting tolerance to these ions.

2. Apparatus

Colorimetric equipment: One of the following is required:

a. Spectrophotometer, for use at 570 nm, providing a light path of at least 1 cm.

b. Filter photometer, providing a light path of at least 1 cm and equipped with a greenish yellow filter having maximum transmittance at 550 to 580 nm.

3. Reagents

a. Standard fluoride solution: Prepare as directed in the electrode method, Section 414B.*3b.*

b. SPADNS solution: Dissolve 958 mg SPADNS, sodium 2-(para-sulfophenylazo)-1,8-dihydroxy-3,6-naphthalene disulfonate, also called 4,5-dihydroxy-3-(parasulfophenylazo)-2,7-naphthalenedisulfonic acid trisodium salt, in distilled water and dilute to 500 ml. This solution is stable indefinitely if protected from direct sunlight.

c. Zirconyl-acid reagent: Dissolve 133 mg zirconyl chloride octahydrate, $ZrOCl_2 \cdot 8H_2O$, in about 25 ml distilled water. Add 350 ml conc HCl and dilute to 500 ml with distilled water.

d. Acid zirconyl-SPADNS reagent: Mix equal volumes of SPADNS solution and zirconyl-acid reagent. The combined reagent is stable for at least 2 yr.

e. Reference solution: Add 10 ml SPADNS solution to 100 ml distilled water. Dilute 7 ml conc HCl to 10 ml and add to the diluted SPADNS solution. The resulting solution, used for setting the reference point (zero) of the spectrophotometer or photometer, is stable and may be reused indefinitely. Alternatively, use one of the prepared standards as a reference.

f. Sodium arsenite solution: Dissolve 5.0 g $NaAsO_2$ and dilute to 1 l with distilled water. (CAUTION: *Toxic—take care to avoid ingestion.*)

4. Procedure

a. Preparation of standard curve: Prepare fluoride standards in the range of 0 to 1.40 mg/l by diluting appropriate quantities of the standard fluoride solution to 50 ml with distilled water. Pipet 5.00 ml each of SPADNS solution and zirconyl-acid reagent, or 10.00 ml of the mixed acid-zirconyl-SPADNS reagent, to each standard and mix well. Avoid contamination during the process. Set the photometer to zero absorbance with the reference solution and obtain the absorbance readings of the standards immediately. Plot a curve of the fluoride-absorbance relationship. Prepare a new standard curve whenever a fresh reagent is made or a different standard temperature is desired. If no reference solution is used, set the photometer at some convenient point established with a prepared fluoride standard.

b. Sample pretreatment: If the sample contains residual chlorine, remove it by adding 1 drop (0.05 ml) $NaAsO_2$ solution/0.1 mg Cl and mix. (Sodium arsenite concentrations of 1,300 mg/l produce an error of 0.1 mg/l at 1.0 mg/l F.)

c. Color development: Use a 50.0-ml sample or a portion diluted to 50 ml. Adjust the temperature of the sample to that used for the standard curve. Add 5.00 ml each of the SPADNS solution and zirconyl-acid reagent, or 10.00 ml of the acid-zirconyl-SPADNS reagent; mix well and read the absorbance immediately or at any subsequent time, first setting the reference point of the photometer as above. If the absorbance falls beyond the range of the standard curve, repeat the procedure, using a smaller sample.

5. Calculation

$$mg/l\,F = \frac{A}{ml\,sample} \times \frac{B}{C}$$

where $A = \mu g$ F determined photometrically. The ratio B/C applies only when a sample is diluted to a volume B, and a portion C taken from it for color development.

6. Precision and Accuracy

A synthetic sample containing 830 $\mu g/l$ F and no interference in distilled water was analyzed in 53 laboratories by the SPADNS method, with a relative standard deviation of 8.0% and a relative error of 1.2%. After direct distillation of the sample, the relative standard deviation was 11.0% and the relative error 2.4%.

A synthetic sample containing 570 $\mu g/l$ F, 10 mg/l Al, 200 mg/l sulfate, and 300 mg/l total alkalinity was analyzed in 53 laboratories by the SPADNS method without distillation, with a relative standard deviation of 16.2% and a relative error of 7.0%. After direct distillation of the sample, the relative standard deviation was 17.2% and the relative error 5.3%.

A synthetic unknown sample containing 680 $\mu g/l$ F, 2 mg/l Al, 2.5 mg/l sodium hexametaphosphate, 200 mg/l sulfate, and 300 mg/l total alkalinity was analyzed in 53 laboratories by direct distillation and SPADNS methods with a relative standard deviation of 2.8% and a relative error of 5.9%.

414 D.   Alizarin Visual Method

1. Apparatus

Color comparison equipment: One of the following is required:
  a. Nessler tubes, matched, 100 ml tall form.
  b. Comparator, visual.

2. Reagents

  a. Standard fluoride solution: Prepare as directed in Section 414B.3*b*; 1.00 ml = 10.0 μg F.

  b. Zirconyl-alizarin reagent: Dissolve 300 mg zirconyl chloride octahydrate, $ZrOCl_2 \cdot 8H_2O$, in 50 ml distilled water contained in a 1-l glass-stoppered volumetric flask. Dissolve 70 mg of 3-alizarinsulfonic acid sodium salt (also called alizarin red S) in 50 ml distilled water and pour slowly into the zirconyl solution while stirring. The resulting solution clears on standing for a few minutes.

  c. Mixed acid solution: Dilute 101 ml conc HCl to approximately 400 ml with distilled water. Add carefully 33.3 ml conc H_2SO_4 to approximately 400 ml distilled water. After cooling, mix the two acids.

  d. Acid-zirconyl-alizarin reagent: To the clear zirconyl-alizarin reagent in the 1-l volumetric flask, add the mixed acid solution, add distilled water to the mark, and mix. The reagent changes in color from red to yellow within an hour and is then ready for use. Store away from direct sunlight to extend the reagent stability to 6 months.

  e. Sodium arsenite solution: Prepare as directed in Section 414C.3*f.*

3. Procedure

  a. Sample pretreatment: If the sample contains residual chlorine, remove by adding 1 drop (0.05 ml) of arsenite/0.1 mg Cl and mix.

  b. Preparation of standards: Prepare a series of standards by diluting various volumes of standard fluoride solution (1.00 ml = 10.0 μg F) to 100 ml in nessler tubes. Choose the standards so that there is at least one with lower and one with higher fluoride concentration than that of the unknown sample. The interval between standards determines the accuracy of the determination. An interval of 50 μg/l usually is sufficient.

  c. Color development: Adjust the temperature of samples and standards so that the deviation between them is no more than 2 C. A temperature near that of the room is satisfactory. To 100 ml of the clear sample, or a portion diluted to 100 ml, and to the standards in nessler tubes, add 5.00 ml of the acid-zirconyl-alizarin reagent from a volumetric pipet. Mix thoroughly, avoiding contamination, and compare the samples and standards after 1 hr.

4. Calculation

$$\text{mg/l F} = \frac{A}{\text{ml sample}} \times \frac{B}{C}$$

where $A = \mu$g F determined visually. The ratio B/C applies only when a sample is diluted to a volume B, and a portion C is taken from it for color development.

5. Precision and Accuracy

A synthetic sample containing 830 $\mu g/l$ F and no interference in distilled water was analyzed in 20 laboratories by the alizarin visual method, with a relative standard deviation of 4.9% and a relative error of 3.6%. After direct distillation of the sample, the relative standard deviation was 6.4% and the relative error 2.4%.

A synthetic sample containing 570 $\mu g/l$ F, 10 mg/l Al, 200 mg/l sulfate, and 300 mg/l total alkalinity was analyzed in 20 laboratories by the alizarin

visual method without distillation, with a relative standard deviation of 51.8% and a relative error of 29.8%. After direct distillation of the sample, the relative standard deviation was 11.1% and the relative error 0%.

A synthetic sample containing 680 $\mu g/l$ F, 2 mg/l Al, 2.5 mg/l sodium hexametaphosphate, 200 mg/l sulfate, and 300 mg/l total alkalinity was analyzed in 20 laboratories by the direct distillation and alizarin visual methods, with a relative standard deviation of 10.6% and a relative error of 1.5%.

414 E. Bibliography

Direct Distillation Step

BELLACK, E. 1958. Simplified fluoride distillation method. *J. Amer. Water Works Ass.* 50:530,

BELLACK, E. 1961. Automatic fluoride distillation. *J. Amer. Water Works Ass.* 53:98.

Electrode Method

FRANT, M.S. & J.W. Ross, JR. 1968. Use of total ionic strength adjustment buffer for electrode determination of fluoride in water supplies. *Anal. Chem.* 40:1169.

HARWOOD, J.E. 1969. The use of an ion-selective electrode for routine analysis of water samples. *Water Res.* 3:273.

SPADNS Method

BELLACK, E. & P.J. SCHOUBOF. 1968. Rapid photometric determination of fluoride with SPADNS-zirconium lake. *Anal. Chem.* 30:2032.

Alizarin Visual Method

SANCHIS, J.M. 1934. Determination of fluorides in natural waters. *Ind. Eng. Chem.*, Anal. Ed. 6:134.

SCOTT, R.D. 1941. Modification of fluoride determination. *J. Amer. Water Works Ass.* 33:2018.

TARAS, M.J., H.D. CISCO & M. GARNELL. 1950. Interferences in alizarin method of fluoride determination. *J. Amer. Water Works Ass.* 42:583.

415   IODIDE

Only trace quantities of iodide are normally present in a natural water. Higher concentrations are found in natural brines, certain industrial wastes, and in waters treated with iodine as the disinfectant (see Iodine, Section 416).

Selection of method: The catalytic reduction photometric method is applicable to waters containing iodide concentrations of 80 $\mu g/l$ or less. The leuco crystal violet method is better suited for determining iodide concentrations of 50

μg/l or greater. The leuco crystal violet method is also capable of determining iodide in the presence of iodine.

For natural and treated waters, both methods give acceptable results. For wastewaters or industrial wastes, high chloride concentrations may interfere with color development in the leuco crystal violet procedure. Normally, the choice of method for any water depends primarily on the concentration range to be determined.

415 A. Leuco Crystal Violet Method (TENTATIVE)

1. General Discussion

a. Principle: Iodide is selectively oxidized to iodine by the addition of potassium peroxymonosulfate, $KHSO_5$. The iodine produced reacts instantaneously with the colorless indicator reagent containing 4,4'4''-methylidynetris (N,N-dimethylaniline), also known by the common name of leuco crystal violet, to produce the highly colored leuco crystal violet dye. The developed color is sufficiently stable for the determination of an absorbance value and adheres to Beer's law over a wide range of iodide concentrations.

b. Interference: Chloride concentrations greater than 200 mg/l may interfere with color development. This interference may be eliminated by dilution of the sample to contain less than 200 mg/l of Cl. The only other serious interference is that caused by oxidized forms of manganese. Determine whether these compounds are absent before making the iodide test. For a more complete discussion of interfering substances, see Iodine, Section 416.

2. Apparatus

a. Colorimetric equipment: One of the following is required:

1) *Filter photometer,* providing a light path of 1 cm or longer, equipped with an orange filter having maximum transmittance near 592 nm.

2) *Spectrophotometer,* for use at 592 nm, providing a light path of 1 cm or longer.

b. Volumetric flasks: 100-ml, with plastic caps or ground-glass stoppers.

c. Glassware: Completely remove any reducing substances from all glassware or plastic containers, including containers for storage of reagent solutions, using either the chlorination or the chromic acid method (Section 409G.2c).

3. Reagents

a. Iodine-demand-free water: Prepare iodine-demand-free water by the ion-exchange method presented in Section 409G.3a2). Ordinary distilled water may be used if reducing substances are known to be absent. Do not chlorinate as in the preparation of chlorine-demand-free water, because excess chloride ion concentrations interfere in iodide determinations.

Prepare all stock iodide and reagent solutions with iodine-demand-free water.

b. Stock iodide solution: Dissolve 1.3081 g KI in iodine-demand-free water and dilute to 1,000 ml; 1 ml = 1 mg I.

c. Citric buffer solution, pH 3.8:

1) *Citric acid, 1M:* Dissolve 192.2 g $C_6H_8O_7$ or 210.2 g $C_6H_8O_7 \cdot H_2O$ and dilute to 1 l with iodine-demand-free water.

2) *Ammonium hydroxide, 2M:* Add 131 ml conc NH_4OH to about 700 ml iodine-demand-free water and dilute to 1 l. Store in a polyethylene bottle.

3) *Final buffer solution:* Slowly add, with mixing, 350 ml $2M$ NH_4OH solution to 670 ml of $1M$ citric acid. To the solution add 80 g $NH_4H_2PO_4$ and stir to dissolve.

d. Leuco crystal violet indicator: Measure 200 ml iodine-demand-free water and 3.2 ml conc H_2SO_4 into a brown glass container of at least 1-l capacity. Introduce a magnetic stirring bar and mix at moderate speed. Add 1.5 g of 4,4',4''-methylidynetris (N,N-dimethylaniline)* and with a small amount of water wash down any reagent adhering to the neck or sides of the container. Mix until dissolution is complete.

To 800 ml iodine-demand-free water, add 2.5 g of $HgCl_2$ and stir to dissolve. With mixing, add the $HgCl_2$ solution to the leuco crystal violet solution. For maximum stability, the pH of the final solution should be 1.5 or less. If necessary, add conc H_2SO_4 dropwise to adjust the pH to 1.5 or less. Store in a brown glass bottle away from direct sunlight. Discard after 6 months. Do not use a rubber stopper.

e. Potassium peroxymonosulfate solu-

tion: Obtain $KHSO_5$ as the commercial product Oxone†, which is a stable powdered mixture containing 42.8% $KHSO_5$ by weight and a mixture of $KHSO_4$ and K_2SO_4. Dissolve 1.5 g Oxone in iodine-demand-free water and dilute to 1 l.

f. Sodium thiosulfate solution: Dissolve 5.0 g of $Na_2S_2O_3 \cdot H_2O$ in distilled water and dilute to 1 l.

4. Procedure

a. Preparation of temporary iodine standards: Add suitable portions of stock iodide solution, or of dilutions of the stock iodide solution, to iodine-demand-free water to prepare an iodide series of 0.1 to 6.0 mg/l in increments of 0.1 mg/l or larger.

Measure 50.0 ml prepared iodide solution into a 100-ml glass-stoppered volumetric flask. By means of Mohr pipets, add 1.0 ml citric buffer and 0.5 ml of potassium peroxymonosulfate solution. Swirl to mix and let stand approximately 1 min. Add 1.0 ml leuco crystal violet indicator, mix, and dilute to 100 ml. For best results, read the absorbance as described below within 5 min after adding leuco crystal violet indicator solution.

b. Photometric calibration: Transfer the colored temporary standards of known iodide concentrations to cells of 1-cm light path and read the absorbance in a photometer or spectrophotometer at a wavelength of 592 nm against a distilled water reference. Plot the absorbance values against iodide concentrations to construct a curve that follows Beer's law.

---

*Eastman chemical No. 3651 or equivalent.

†A product of E. I. du Pont de Nemours and Co., Inc., Wilmington, Del.

c. Color development of iodide sample: Measure a 50.0-ml sample into a 100-ml volumetric flask and treat as described for preparation of temporary iodide standards, ¶4a. Read the absorbance photometrically and refer to the standard calibration curve for the iodide equivalent.

d. Samples containing >6.0 mg/l iodide: Place approximately 25 ml iodine-demand-free water in a 100-ml volumetric flask. Add 1.0 ml citric buffer and a measured volume of 25 ml or less of sample. Add 0.5 ml of potassium peroxymonosulfate solution. Swirl to mix and let stand for approximately 1 min. Add 1.0 ml leuco crystal violet indicator, mix, and dilute to 100 ml.

Read the absorbance photometrically and compare with the calibration curve from which the initial iodide is obtained by applying the dilution factor. Select one of the following sample volumes in order to remain within the optimum iodide range.

Iodide *mg/l*	Sample Volume Required *ml*
6.0-12	25.0
12-30	10.0
30-60	5.0

e. Determination of iodide in the presence of iodine: Determine the iodine concentration as described in Iodine, Leuco Crystal Violet Method, Section 416A. On a separate sample, measure the iodide and from the absorbance determine the total iodine plus iodide equivalent. Refer to either the calibration curve for iodine or the calibration curve for iodide. Determine the iodide concentration from the difference between the iodine determined on the first sample and the total iodine-iodide obtained on the second sample. (NOTE: Iodine also may be determined by not adding potassium peroxymonosulfate solution in the iodide method and by comparing the absorbance value to the calibration curve developed for iodide.)

f. Compensation for turbidity and color: Compensate for the presence of natural color or turbidity by adding 5 ml of thiosulfate solution to a 50-ml sample. Add reagents to sample as described previously and use as the blank to set zero absorbance on the photometer. Measure all samples in relation to this blank and, from the calibration curve, determine the concentrations of iodide or the total iodine-iodide present in the samples.

415 B. Photometric Method

1. General Discussion

a. Principle: Iodide can be determined in water by using its ability to catalyze the reduction of ceric ions by arsenious acid. The effect is proportional nonlinearly to the amount of iodide present. Photometric determination of the loss of ceric ion color directly is difficult without a recording device because the color fades rapidly while it is being read in the photometer. If the reaction is stopped after a specific time interval by the addition of ferrous ammonium sulfate, the resulting ferric ions, which are directly proportional to the remaining ceric ions, develop a color complex with potassium thiocyanate that is relatively stable. This method has the advantages of requiring only small water samples, eliminating distillation procedures, minimizing certain interferences, and giving stable colors for spectrophotometric determinations.

Digestion with chromic acid and distillation must be undertaken where an estimate is desired of the organically bound and other nonsusceptible forms of iodine in addition to the usual iodide ion. The pertinent procedures for these special applications may be found in the 10th Edition of this work.

b. Interference: An excess of sodium chloride is added to the sample to eliminate the interference of chloride already present in the water by attaining a stable maximum chloride concentration that sensitizes the reaction. The formation of noncatalytic forms of iodine and the inhibitory effects of silver and mercury are reduced by this addition.

2. Apparatus

a. Water bath, capable of temperature control to 30 ± 0.5 C.

b. Colorimetric equipment—One of the following is required:

1) *Spectrophotometer*, for use at wavelengths of 510 or 525 nm and providing a light path of 1 cm.

2) *Filter photometer*, providing a light path of 1 cm and equipped with a green filter having maximum transmittance near 525 nm.

c. Test tubes, 2×15 cm.

d. Stopwatch.

3. Reagents

Store all of the following stock solutions in tightly stoppered containers in a dark place.

a. Distilled water, containing less than 0.3 μg/l iodine.

b. Sodium chloride solution: Dissolve 200.0 g NaCl in distilled water and dilute to 1 l. Recrystallize the NaCl if an interfering amount of iodine is present, using a water-ethanol mixture.

c. Arsenious acid, 0.1N: Dissolve 4.946 g As_2O_3 in distilled water, add 0.20 ml conc H_2SO_4, and dilute to 1,000 ml.

d. Sulfuric acid, H_2SO_4, conc.

e. Ceric ammonium sulfate, 0.02N: Dissolve 13.38 g $Ce(NH_4)_4(SO_4)_4 \cdot 4H_2O$ in distilled water, add 44 ml conc H_2SO_4, and make up to 1 l.

f. Ferrous ammonium sulfate reagent: Dissolve 1.50 g $Fe(NH_4)_2(SO_4)_2 \cdot 6H_2O$ in 100 ml distilled water containing 0.6 ml conc H_2SO_4. Prepare daily.

g. Potassium thiocyanate solution: Dissolve 4.00 g KSCN in 100 ml distilled water.

h. Stock iodide solution: Dissolve 261.6 mg anhydrous KI in distilled water and dilute to 1,000 ml; 1.00 ml = 200 μg I.

i. Intermediate iodide solution: Dilute 20.00 ml stock iodide solution to 1,000 ml with distilled water; 1.00 ml = 4.00 μg I.

j. Standard iodide solution: Dilute 25.00 ml intermediate iodide solution to 1,000 ml with distilled water; 1.00 ml = 0.100 μg I.

4. Procedure

a. Sample size: Add 10.00 ml water

sample, or a portion made up to 10.00 ml with iodine-free distilled water, to a 2×15 cm test tube. If possible, keep the iodide content of the diluted sample in the range 0.2 to 0.6 μg. Use thoroughly clean glassware and apparatus.

b. Color measurement: Add reagents to the sample in the following order: 1.00 ml NaCl solution, 0.50 ml arsenious acid solution, and 0.50 ml conc H_2SO_4.   .

Place the reaction mixture and the ceric ammonium sulfate solution in the 30 C water bath and allow to come to temperature equilibrium. Add 1.0 ml ceric ammonium sulfate solution, mix the contents of the test tube by inversion, and start the stopwatch to time the reaction. Use an inert clean test tube stopper when mixing. After 15 ± 0.1 min remove the sample from the water bath and add immediately 1.00 ml ferrous ammonium sulfate reagent with mixing, whereupon the yellow ceric ion color should disappear. Then add, with mixing, 1.00 ml potassium thiocyanate solution. Replace the sample in the water bath. Within 1 hr after the thiocyanate addition, read the red color as percent transmittance in a photometric instrument. Maintain the temperature of

the solution and the cell compartment at 30 ± 0.5 C until the transmittance is determined. If several samples are run, start the reactions at 1-min intervals to allow time for additions of ferrous ammonium sulfate and thiocyanate. (If temperature control of the cell compartment is not possible, allow the final solution to come to room temperature and measure the transmittance with the cell compartment at room temperature.)

c. Calibration standards: Treat standards containing 0, 0.2, 0.4, 0.6, and 0.8 μg I/10.00 ml of solution as in ¶4*b* above. Run with each set of samples to establish a calibration curve.

5. Calculation

$$mg/l\,I = \frac{\mu g\ I}{ml\ sample}$$

6. Precision and Accuracy

Results obtained by this tentative method are reproducible on samples of Los Angeles source waters, and have been reported to be accurate to ±0.3 μg/l I on samples of Yugoslavian water containing from 0 to 14.0 μg/l I.

415 C.   Bibliography

Leuco Crystal Violet Method
BLACK, A.P. & G.P. WHITTLE. 1967. New methods for the colorimetric determination of halogen residuals. Part I. Iodine, Iodide, and Iodate. *J. Amer. Water Works Ass.* 59:471.

Photometric Method
ROGINA, B. & M. DUBRAVCIC. 1953. Microdetermination of iodides by arresting the ca-

talytic reduction of ceric ions. *Analyst* 78:594.
Standard Methods for the Examination of Water, Sewage and Industrial Wastes, 10th ed. 1955. APHA, AWWA & FSIWA, New York, pp. 120-124
DUBRAVCIC, M. 1955. Determination of iodine in natural waters (sodium chloride as a reagent in the catalytic reduction of ceric ions). *Analyst* 80:295.

416   IODINE

Iodine is used to disinfect certain potable and swimming pool waters. For wastewaters, iodine has had limited application. Application of iodine is generally restricted to personal or remote water supplies where ease of application, storage stability, and an inertness toward organic matter are important considerations. Some swimming pool waters are treated with iodine to lessen eye burn among swimmers and to provide a stable disinfectant residual less affected by adverse environmental conditions.

Iodine is applied in the elemental form or produced in situ by the simultaneous addition of an iodide salt and a suitable oxidant. In the latter case, an excess of iodide may be maintained to serve as a reservoir for iodine production; the determination of iodide is desirable for disinfectant control (see Iodide, Section 415).

Because of hydrolysis, active iodine exists in the forms of elemental I_2, hypoiodous acid (HOI) or a form thereof, hypoiodite ion (OI^-), and, in the presence of excess iodide, the triiodide ion (I_3^-). Most analytical methods use the oxidizing power of all forms of active iodine for its determination and the results are generally expressed as an equivalent concentration of elemental iodine.

Selection of method: For potable and swimming pool waters treated with elemental iodine, both the amperometric titration and leuco crystal violet colorimetric methods give acceptable results. However, oxidized forms of manganese interfere with the leuco crystal violet method. Where the iodide and chloride ion concentrations are above 50 mg/l and 200 mg/l, respectively, interference in color production may occur in the leuco crystal violet method and the amperometric method is preferred. However, because of the extreme sensitivity of the leuco crystal violet method, this interference may be eliminated by sample dilution to obtain halogen ion concentrations less than 50 mg/l.

For wastewaters or highly polluted waters, organic constituents normally do not interfere with either the amperometric or leuco crystal violet procedures. Determine which of the methods yields the more acceptable results, because specific substances present in these waters may interfere in one method but not in the other. Certain metallic cations such as copper and silver interfere in the amperometric titration procedure. The leuco crystal violet method is relatively free of interference from these and other cations and anions with the exceptions noted previously.

For waters containing iodine coexisting with free chlorine, combined chlorine, or other excess oxidants, only the leuco crystal violet method can determine iodine specifically. This condition occurs in the in-situ production of iodine by the reaction of iodide and excess oxidant. Under these conditions, the amperometric method would continue to titrate the iodine produced in a cyclic reaction until exhaustion of the oxidant.

416 A.   Leuco Crystal Violet Method (TENTATIVE)

1. General Discussion

The leuco crystal violet method measures aqueous iodine present as elemental iodine and hypoiodous acid in the absence or presence of excess common oxidants. While the method utilizes the sum of the oxidative power of all forms of active iodine residuals, the results are expressed as the equivalent concentration of I_2. The method also is capable of determining the sum of iodine and free iodide concentrations; the free iodide concentration can be determined by difference (see Iodide, Section 415).

a. Principle: Mercuric chloride added to aqueous elemental iodine solutions causes essentially complete hydrolysis of iodine and the stoichiometric production of hypoiodous acid. The compound 4,4',4"-methylidynetris (N,N-dimethylaniline), also known by the common name of leuco crystal violet, reacts instantaneously with the hypoiodous acid to form crystal violet dye. The maximum absorbance of the developed crystal violet dye solution is produced in the pH range of 3.5 to 4.0 at a wavelength of 592 nm. The absorbance follows Beer's law over a wide range of iodine concentrations and the developed color is stable for several hours.

In the presence of certain excess oxidants such as free chlorine or chloramines, the iodine residual will exist exclusively in the form of hypoiodous acid. The leuco crystal violet is relatively insensitive to the combined forms of chlorine while any free chlorine is converted to chloramine by reaction with an ammonium salt incorporated in the test reagents. All of the hypoiodous acid is determined and, when expressed as an equivalent elemental I_2 concentration, will yield a weight concentration value twice that found in an elemental I_2 solution of the same weight concentration.

b. Interference: Oxidized forms of manganese interfere by oxidizing the indicator to crystal violet dye and yield apparent high iodine concentration results.

Iodide concentrations and chloride ion concentrations above 50 mg/l and 200 mg/l, respectively, interfere by inhibiting full color production. Dilution of the sample to obtain lesser concentrations of these ions will eliminate this interference.

Combined chlorine residuals do not normally interfere provided that the test is completed within 5 min after addition of the indicator solution. Interference from free chlorine is eliminated by the addition of an ammonium salt buffer and the subsequent formation of combined chlorine.

c. Minimum detectable concentration: 10 μg/l iodine.

2. Apparatus

a. Colorimetric equipment: One of the following is required:

1) *Filter photometer,* providing a light path of 1 cm or longer, equipped with an orange filter having maximum transmittance near 592 nm.

2) *Spectrophotometer,* for use at 592 nm, providing a light path of 1 cm or longer.

b. Volumetric flasks, 100-ml, with plastic caps or ground-glass stoppers.

c. Glassware: Completely remove any reducing substances from all glassware or plastic containers, including containers for storage of reagent solutions, by using either the chlorination or the chromic acid method (Section 409G.2c).

3. Reagents

a. Iodine-demand-free water: See Section 415A.3a.

Prepare all stock iodine and reagent solutions with the iodine-demand-free water.

b. Stock iodine solution: Prepare a saturated iodine solution by adding approximately 20 g elemental iodine to 300 ml iodine-demand-free water. Let stand for several hours. Decant the iodine solution and adjust the concentration to approximately 100 $\mu g/ml$. Standardize the adjusted iodine solution by titrating with standard sodium thiosulfate titrant as described in the iodometric method, Section 409A.3b and c, or by the amperometric titration method, Section 409C.3a2.

c. Citric buffer solution, pH 3.8: See Section 415A.3c.

d. Leuco crystal violet indicator: See Section 415A.3d.

e. Sodium thiosulfate solution: See Section 415A.3f.

4. Procedure

a. Preparation of temporary iodine standards: Add suitable portions of the standardized stock iodine solution to iodine-demand-free water to prepare an iodine series in the range of 0.1 to 6.0 mg/l in increments of 0.1 mg/l or larger. For greater accuracy, standardize the dilute iodine solutions immediately before use by the amperometric titration method, Section 416B.

Measure 50.0 ml dilute iodine solution into a 100-ml glass-stoppered volumetric flask. By means of a Mohr pipet, add 1.0 ml citric buffer, gently swirl the flask to mix, and let stand for at least 30 sec. With another measuring pipet, add 1.0 ml leuco crystal violet indicator and swirl to develop color. Dilute to 100 ml and mix.

b. Photometric calibration: Transfer the colored temporary standards of known iodine concentrations to cells of 1-cm light path and read the absorbance in a photometer or spectrophotometer at a wavelength of 592 nm against a distilled water reference. Plot the absorbance values against iodine concentrations to construct a curve that follows Beer's law.

c. Color development of iodine sample: Measure a 50.0-ml sample into a 100-ml volumetric flask and treat as described for preparation of temporary iodine standards, ¶4a. Match the test sample visually with the temporary standards or read the absorbance photometrically and refer to the standard calibration curve for the iodine equivalent.

d. Samples containing >6.0 mg/l iodine: Place approximately 25 ml iodine-free water in a 100-ml volumetric flask. Add 1.0 ml citric buffer and a measured volume of 25 ml or less of sample. Mix and let stand for at least 30 sec. Add 1.0 ml leuco crystal violet indicator, mix, and dilute to mark. Match visually with standards or read the absorbance photometrically and compare with the calibration curve from which the initial iodine is obtained by applying the dilution factor. Select one of the following sample volumes in order to remain within the optimum iodine range:

Iodine *mg/l*	Sample Volume Required *ml*
6.0-12.0	25.0
12.0-30	10.0
30-60	5.0

e. Samples containing both chlorine and iodine: For samples containing free or combined chlorine and iodine, follow the same procedure given in ¶4c or d above but read the absorbance within 5 min after addition of the leuco crystal violet indicator.

f. Compensation for turbidity and color: Compensate for the presence of natural color or turbidity by adding 5 ml thiosulfate solution to a 50-ml sample. Add reagents to sample as described previously and use as the blank to set zero absorbance on the photometer. Measure all samples in relation to this blank and, from the calibration curve, determine the concentrations of iodine present in the samples.

416 B. Amperometric Titration Method

1. General Discussion

The amperometric titration method for iodine is a modification of the amperometric method for residual chlorine (see Section 409C). Iodine residuals over 7 mg/l are best measured with smaller samples or by dilution. The titration results in most cases represent free available iodine since combined iodine is rarely encountered.

a. Principle: The principle of the amperometric method as described for the determination of total available residual chlorine is applicable to the determination of residual iodine. Iodine is determined on the titrator using buffer solution, pH 4.0, and potassium iodide solution. The pH is maintained at 4.0 because at pH values less than 3.5 substances such as oxidized forms of manganese interfere, while at pH values greater than 4.5, the reaction is not quantitative. The potassium iodide is used in the determination of iodide to improve the sharpness of the endpoint.

b. Interference: The interferences described in Section 409C.1*b* also apply in the case of iodine.

2. Apparatus

See Section 409C.2*a* through *d*.

3. Reagents

With the exception of phosphate buffer solution, pH 7.0, all reagents listed for the determination of residual chlorine in Section 409C.3 are required. Standardized phenylarsine oxide solution (1 ml = 1 mg/l chlorine for a 200-ml sample) is equivalent to 3.58 mg/l I_2/ml for a 200-ml sample.

4. Procedure

a. Sample volume: Select a sample volume that will require no more than 2 ml phenylarsine oxide titrant. For iodine concentrations of 7 mg/l or less, take a 200-ml volume; for iodine levels in excess of 7 mg/l, use 100 ml or proportionately less diluted to 200 ml with iodine-demand-free water.

b. Free available iodine: To the sample add 1 ml KI solution and 1 ml acetate buffer, pH 4.0 solution. Titrate with phenylarsine oxide titrant to the end point as described in Section 409C.4.

5. Calculation

Calculate the iodine concentration by the following equation:

$$mg/l \text{ iodine} = \frac{A \times 3.58 \times 200}{ml \text{ sample}}$$

where A = ml phenylarsine oxide titration to the end point.

416 C. Bibliography

Leuco Crystal Violet Method
BLACK, A.P. & G.P. WHITTLE. 1967. New methods for the colorimetric determination of halogen residuals. Part I. Iodine, iodide, and iodate. *J. Amer. Water Works Ass.* 59:471.

Amperometric Titration Method
MARKS, H.C. & J.R. GLASS. 1942. A new method of determining residual chlorine. *J. Amer. Water Works Ass.* 34:1227.

417   NITROGEN

In waters and wastewaters the forms of nitrogen of greatest interest are, in order of decreasing oxidation state, *nitrate, nitrite, ammonia,* and *organic nitrogen.* Organic nitrogen is defined functionally as organically bound nitrogen in the oxidation trinegative state. It does not include all organic nitrogen compounds. Analytically, organic nitrogen and ammonia can be determined together and have been referred to as "total nitrogen" or more correctly, "kjeldahl nitrogen", a term that reflects the technic used in their determination.

All the above-named forms of nitrogen, as well as nitrogen gas, are biochemically interconvertible and thus are components of the nitrogen cycle. They are of interest for many reasons. Nitrate generally occurs in trace quantities in surface water but may attain high levels in some groundwater. In excessive amounts, it contributes to the illness known as infant methemoglobinemia. A limit of 10 mg/l nitrate (as N) has been imposed on drinking water to prevent this disorder.

Nitrate is found only in small amounts in fresh domestic wastewater but in the effluent of nitrifying biological treatment plants nitrate may be found in concentrations of up to 50 mg/l nitrate nitrogen. It is an essential nutrient for many photosynthetic autotrophs and in some cases has been identified as the growth-limiting nutrient. Nitrite is an intermediate state of nitrogen, both in the oxidation of ammonia to nitrate and in the reduction of nitrate. Such oxidation and reduction may occur in wastewater treatment plants, water distribution systems, and natural waters. Nitrite can enter a water supply system through its use as a corrosion inhibitor in industrial process water.

Ammonia is naturally present in surface and groundwater and in wastewater. It is produced largely by the deamination of organic nitrogen-containing compounds and by the hydrolysis of urea. It also may be produced naturally by the reduction of nitrate under anaerobic conditions. At some water treatment plants ammonia is added in the combined residual chlorination of water.

In the chlorination of wastewater effluents containing ammonia, virtually no free residual chlorine is obtained until the ammonia has been oxidized. Ammonia concentrations encountered in water and wastewater vary from less than 10 μg N/l in the former to greater than 50 mg N/l in the latter.

Organic nitrogen includes such natural materials as proteins and peptides, nucleic acids and urea, and numerous synthetic organic materials. The organic nitrogen concentrations of water and wastewater vary from values of less than 10 μg/l for the former to more than 10 mg/l for the latter.

"Kjeldahl nitrogen" is the sum of organic nitrogen and ammonia nitrogen. Total oxidized nitrogen is the sum of nitrate and nitrite nitrogen.

418   NITROGEN (AMMONIA)

1. Selection of Method

The two major factors that influence the selection of the method to determine ammonia are the concentration and the presence of interferences. In general, direct determination of low concentrations of ammonia is confined to drinking waters, clean surface water, and good-quality wastewater effluent. In other instances and where greater precision is necessary a preliminary distillation step is required. For high ammonia concentrations a distillation and titration technic is preferred. The data presented in ¶4 below and Table 418:I should be helpful in selecting the appropriate method of analysis.

Two colorimetric technics are presented—the nesslerization and phenate methods—and one titration method. While the stated maximum concentration ranges are not rigorous limits, titration is preferred at concentrations higher than these stated maximum levels.

The nessler method is sensitive to 20 μg/l ammonia nitrogen under optimum conditions and may be used for up to 5 mg/l ammonia nitrogen. Turbidity and color and substances precipitated by hydroxyl ion, such as magnesium and calcium, interfere and may be removed by preliminary distillation or, less satisfactorily, by precipitation with zinc sulfate and alkali.

The phenate method has a sensitivity of 10 μg/l ammonia nitrogen and is useful for up to 500 μg/l ammonia nitrogen. Preliminary distillation is required if the alkalinity exceeds 500 mg/l or if color or turbidity is present. This step is also necessary before the phenate technic if the sample has been preserved with acid. An automated phenate method is given in Section 604.

The distillation and titration procedure especially is used for ammonia nitrogen concentrations greater than 5 mg/l.

Distillation into sulfuric acid absorbent is mandatory for the phenate method when interferences are present. Boric acid must be the absorbent following distillation if the distillate is to be nesslerized or titrated.

Ammonia may also be determined by the electrode method described in Section 413J.

2. Interferences

Glycine, urea, glutamic acid, cyanates, and acetamide hydrolyze very slowly in solution on standing, but, of these, only urea and cyanates will hydrolyze on distillation at a pH of 9.5. Hydrolysis amounts to about 7% at this pH for urea, and about 5% for cyanates. Glycine, hydrazine, and some amines will react with nessler reagent to give the characteristic yellow color in the time required for the test. Similarly, volatile alkaline compounds such as hydrazine and the amines will influence titrimetric results. Some organic compounds such as ketones, aldehydes, alcohols, and some amines may cause a yellowish or greenish off-color or a turbidity on nesslerization following distillation. Some of these, such as formaldehyde, may be eliminated by boiling off at a low pH before nesslerization. Residual chlorine must be removed before the ammonia determination by pretreatment of the sample.

3. Storage of Sample

The most reliable results are obtained on fresh samples. Destroy residual chlorine immediately after the sample is collected to prevent its reaction with ammonia. In the event that a prompt analysis is impossible, add 0.8 ml conc H_2SO_4/l sample and store at 4 C to preserve the ammonia concentration. If acid preservation is used, neutralize sample acidity with NaOH or KOH immediately before making the determination.

4. Precision and Accuracy

Six synthetic unknown samples containing ammonia and other constituents dissolved in distilled water were analyzed by five procedures. The first three samples were subjected to direct nesslerization alone, distillation followed by a nessler finish, and distillation coupled with a titrimetric finish. Samples 4 through 6 were analyzed by direct nesslerization, by distillation followed by a nessler finish, by the phenate method alone, and by distillation followed by a phenate finish. The results obtained by the participating laboratories are summarized in Table 418:I.

Sample 1 contained the following additional constituents: 10 mg/l chloride, 1.0 mg/l nitrate nitrogen, 1.5 mg/l organic nitrogen, 10.0 mg/l phosphate, and 5.0 mg/l silica.

Sample 2 contained the following additional constituents: 200 mg/l chloride, 1.0 mg/l nitrate nitrogen, 0.8 mg/l organic nitrogen, 5.0 mg/l phosphate, and 15.0 mg/l silica.

Sample 3 contained the following additional constituents: 400 mg/l chloride,

TABLE 418:1. PRECISION AND ACCURACY DATA FOR AMMONIA METHODS

Number of Laboratories	Ammonia Nitrogen Concentration μg/l	Relative Standard Deviation					Relative Error				
		Direct Nessleri-zation %	Direct Phenate Method %	Distillation Plus			Direct Nessleri-zation %	Direct Phenate Method %	Distillation Plus		
				Nessler Finish %	Phenate Finish %	Titri-metric Finish %			Nessler Finish %	Phenate Finish %	Titri-metric Finish %
20 44 21	200	38.1		46.3		69.8	0		10.0		20.0
20 42 20	800	11.2		21.2		28.6	0		8.7		5.0
21 42 21	1,500	11.6		18.0		21.6	0.6		4.0		2.6
70 3 9 5	200	22.0	39.2	15.7	15.1		8.3	2.4	2.0	16.7	
66 3 9 6	800	16.1	15.8	16.3	16.6		0.3	1.5	3.1	1.7	
71 3 8 6	1,500	5.3	26.0	7.5	7.3		1.2	10.0	3.6	0.4	

1.0 mg/l nitrate nitrogen, 0.2 mg/l organic nitrogen, 0.5 mg/l phosphate, and 30.0 mg/l silica.

Sample 4 contained the following additional constituents: 400 mg/l chloride, 0.05 mg/l nitrate nitrogen, 0.23 mg/l organic phosphorus added in the form of adenylic acid, 7.00 mg/l orthophosphate phosphorus, and 3.00 mg/l polyphosphate phosphorus added as sodium hexametaphosphate.

Sample 5 contained the following additional constituents: 400 mg/l chloride,

5.00 mg/l nitrate nitrogen, 0.09 mg/l organic phosphorus added in the form of adenylic acid, 0.6 mg/l orthophosphate phosphorus, and 0.3 mg/l polyphosphate phosphorus added as sodium hexametaphosphate.

Sample 6 contained the following additional constituents: 400 mg/l chloride, 0.5 mg/l nitrate nitrogen, 0.03 mg/l organic phosphorus added in the form of adenylic acid, 0.1 mg/l orthophosphate phosphorus, and 0.08 mg/l polyphosphate phosphorus added as sodium hexametaphosphate.

418 A.   Preliminary Distillation Step

1. General Discussion

The sample is buffered at pH 9.5 with a borate buffer to decrease hydrolysis of cyanates and organic nitrogen compounds and distilled into a solution of boric acid when nesslerization or titration is to be used or into sulfuric acid when the phenate method is used. The ammonia in the distillate can be determined either colorimetrically by nesslerization or the phenate method or titrimetrically with standard sulfuric acid and a mixed indicator or a pH meter. The choice between the colorimetric or acidimetric finish depends on the concentration of ammonia.

2. Apparatus

a. *Distillation apparatus:* Arrange a pyrex flask of 800- to 2,000-ml capacity attached to a vertical condenser so that the outlet tip may be submerged in the receiving boric acid solution. Use an all-pyrex apparatus or one with condensing units constructed of block tin or aluminum tubes.

b. *pH meter.*

3. Reagents

a. *Ammonia-free water:* Prepare by ion-exchange or distillation methods.

1) Ion exchange—Prepare ammonia-free water by passing distilled water through an ion-exchange column containing a strongly acidic cation-exchange resin mixed with a strongly basic anion-exchange resin. Select resins that will remove organic compounds that subsequently interfere with the ammonia determination. Regenerate the column according to the instructions of the manufacturer.

2) Distillation—Eliminate traces of ammonia in distilled water by adding 0.1 ml conc H_2SO_4 to 1 l distilled water and redistilling. Alternatively, treat dis-

tilled water with sufficient bromine or chlorine water to produce a free halogen residual of 2 to 5 mg/l and redistill after standing at least 1 hr. Discard the first 100 ml distillate. Check the redistilled water for the possibility of a high blank.

Since it is virtually impossible to store ammonia-free water in the laboratory without contamination from ammonia fumes, prepare fresh for each batch of samples.

Prepare all reagents with ammonia-free water.

b. Borate buffer solution: Add 88 ml 0.1 N NaOH solution to 500 ml 0.025 M sodium tetraborate ($Na_2B_4O_7$) solution (5.0 g $Na_2B_4O_7$ or 9.5 g $Na_2B_4O_7 \cdot 10H_2O/l$) and dilute to 1 l.

c. Sodium hydroxide, 6N: Dissolve 240 g NaOH in 1 l ammonia-free distilled water.

d. Dechlorinating agent, N/70: Use 1 ml of any of the following reagents to remove 1 mg/l of residual chlorine in 500 ml sample. Prepare the unstable thiosulfate and sulfite solutions fresh.

1) *Phenylarsine oxide*—Dissolve 1.2 g C_6H_5AsO in 200 ml 0.3N NaOH solution, filter if necessary, and dilute to 1 l with ammonia-free water. (CAUTION: *Toxic—take care to avoid ingestion.*)

2) *Sodium arsenite*—Dissolve 1.0 g $NaAsO_2$ in ammonia-free water and dilute to 1 l. (CAUTION: *Toxic—take care to avoid ingestion.*)

3) *Sodium sulfite*—Dissolve 0.9 g Na_2SO_3 in ammonia-free water and dilute to 1 l.

4) *Sodium thiosulfate*—Dissolve 3.5 g $Na_2S_2O_3 \cdot 5H_2O$ in ammonia-free water and dilute to 1 l.

e. Neutralization agent: Prepare with ammonia-free water.

1) *Sodium hydroxide,* NaOH, 1N.

2) *Sulfuric acid,* H_2SO_4, 1N.

f. Absorbent solution: Dissolve 20 g H_3BO_3 in ammonia-free water and dilute to 1 l.

4. Procedure

a. Preparation of equipment: Add 500 ml ammonia-free water, 20 ml borate buffer, and adjust pH to 9.5 with 6N NaOH solution. Add a few glass beads or boiling chips and use this mixture to steam out the distillation apparatus until the distillate shows no traces of ammonia.

b. Sample preparation: Use a 500-ml sample or a portion diluted to 500-ml with ammonia-free water. When the ammonia nitrogen content is less than 100 $\mu g/l$, use a sample volume of 1,000 ml. Remove the residual chlorine in the sample by adding dechlorinating agent equivalent to the chlorine residual. If necessary, neutralize the sample to approximately pH 7 with the dilute acid or base, using a pH meter.

c. Add 25 ml borate buffer and adjust pH to 9.5 with 6N NaOH using a pH meter or short-range pH paper.

d. Distillation: To minimize contamination, leave the entire distillation apparatus assembled after the steaming-out process until just before starting the sample distillation. Disconnect the steaming-out flask and immediately transfer the sample flask to the distillation apparatus. Distill at a rate of 6 to 10 ml/min with the tip of the delivery tube submerged. Collect the distillate in a 500-ml erlenmeyer flask containing 50 ml boric acid. Collect at least 300 ml distillate. Lower the collected distillate free of contact with the delivery tube and continue distillation during the last minute or two to cleanse the condenser and delivery tube. Dilute to 500 ml with ammonia-free water.

e. Ammonia determination: Determine the ammonia by the nesslerization method (Section 418B), the phenate method (Section 418C), or acidimetric method (Section 418D).

418 B.   Nesslerization Method (Direct and Following Distillation)

1. General Discussion

Use direct nesslerization only for purified drinking waters, natural water, and highly purified wastewater effluents, all of which should be low in color and have ammonia nitrogen concentrations exceeding 20 μg/l. Apply the direct nesslerization method to domestic wastewaters only when errors of 1 to 2 mg/l are acceptable. Pretreatment before direct nesslerization with zinc sulfate and alkali precipitates calcium, iron, magnesium, and sulfide, which form turbidity when treated with nessler reagent. The floc also removes suspended matter and sometimes colored matter. The addition of EDTA or Rochelle salt solution inhibits the precipitation of residual calcium and magnesium ions in the presence of the alkaline nessler reagent. However, the use of EDTA demands an extra amount of nessler reagent to insure a sufficient nessler excess for reaction with the ammonia.

The graduated yellow to brown colors produced by the nessler-ammonia reaction absorb strongly over a wide wavelength range. The yellow color characteristic of low ammonia nitrogen (20 to 250 μg/50 ml) can be measured with acceptable sensitivity in the wavelength region from 400 to 425 nm when a 1-cm light path is available. A light path of 5 cm extends measurements into the nitrogen range of 5 to 60 μg. The reddish brown hues typical of ammonia nitrogen levels approaching 500 μg may be measured in the wavelength region of 450 to 500 nm. A judicious selection of light path and wavelength thus enables the photometric determination of ammonia nitrogen concentrations over a considerable range.

Departures from Beer's law may be evident when photometers equipped with broad-band color filters are used. For this reason, the calibration curve should be prepared under conditions identical with those adopted for the samples.

A carefully prepared nessler reagent may respond under optimum conditions to as little as 1 μg ammonia nitrogen. In direct nesslerization, this represents 20 μg/l. However, reproducibility below 5 μg may be erratic.

2. Apparatus

a. Colorimetric equipment: One of the following is required:

1) *Spectrophotometer,* for use at 400

to 500 nm and providing a light path of 1 cm or longer.

2) *Filter photometer,* providing a light path of 1 cm or longer and equipped with a violet filter having maximum transmittance at 400 to 425 nm. A blue filter can be used for higher ammonia nitrogen concentrations.

3) *Nessler tubes,* matched, 50-ml, tall form.

b. pH meter, equipped with a high pH electrode.

3. Reagents

All the reagents listed in the Preliminary Distillation, Section 418A, except the borate buffer and absorbent solution, are required, plus the following. (Prepare all reagents with ammonia-free water.)

a. Zinc sulfate solution: Dissolve 100 g $ZnSO_4 \cdot 7H_2O$ and dilute to 1 l.

b. Stabilizer reagent: Use either EDTA or Rochelle salt to prevent calcium or magnesium precipitation in undistilled samples following the addition of the alkaline nessler reagent.

1) *EDTA reagent:* Dissolve 50 g disodium ethylenediamine tetraacetate dihydrate, also called (ethylenedinitrilo) tetraacetic acid disodium salt, in 60 ml water containing 10 g NaOH. If necessary, apply gentle heat to complete dissolution. Cool to room temperature and dilute to 100 ml.

2) *Rochelle salt solution:* Dissolve 50 g potassium sodium tartrate tetrahydrate, $KNaC_4H_4O_6 \cdot 4H_2O$, in 100 ml water. Remove ammonia usually present in the salt by boiling off 30 ml of solution. After cooling, dilute to 100 ml.

c. Nessler reagent: Dissolve 100 g HgI_2 and 70 g KI in a small quantity of

water and add this mixture slowly, with stirring, to a cool solution of 160 g NaOH in 500 ml water. Dilute to 1 l. Store in rubber-stoppered pyrex glassware and out of sunlight to maintain reagent stability for periods up to a year under normal laboratory conditions. Check the reagent to make sure that it yields the characteristic color with 100 $\mu g/l$ ammonia nitrogen within 10 min after addition and does not produce a precipitate with small amounts of ammonia within 2 hr. (CAUTION: *Toxic— take care to avoid ingestion.*)

d. Stock ammonium solution: Dissolve 3.819 g anhydrous NH_4Cl, dried at 100 C, in water, and dilute to 1,000 ml; 1.00 ml = 1.00 mg N = 1.22 mg NH_3.

e. Standard ammonium solution: Dilute 10.00 ml stock ammonium solution to 1,000 ml with water; 1.00 ml = 10.0 μg N = 12.2 μg NH_3.

f. Permanent color solutions:

1) *Potassium chloroplatinate solution:* Dissolve 2.0 g K_2PtCl_6 in 300 to 400 ml distilled water; add 100 ml conc HCl and dilute to 1 l.

2) *Cobaltous chloride solution:* Dissolve 12.0 g $CoCl_2 \cdot 6H_2O$ in 200 ml distilled water. Add 100 ml conc HCl and dilute to 1 l.

4. Procedure

a. Treatment of undistilled samples: If necessary, remove the residual chlorine of the sample with an equivalent amount of $N/70$ dechlorinating agent. Add 1 ml $ZnSO_4$ solution to 100 ml sample and mix thoroughly. Add 0.4 to 0.5 ml NaOH solution to obtain a pH of 10.5, as determined with a pH meter and a high-pH glass electrode and mix thoroughly. Let the treated sample stand for a few minutes, whereupon a heavy flocculent precipitate should fall, leaving a clear and colorless supernate. Clarify by centrifuging or filtering. Pretest any filter paper used to be sure no ammonia is present as a contaminant. Do this by running ammonia-free water through and testing the filtrate by nesslerization. Filter the sample, discarding the first 25 ml filtrate.

b. Color development:

1) Undistilled samples—Use 50.0 ml sample or a portion diluted to 50.0 ml with ammonia-free water. If the undistilled portion contains sufficient concentrations of calcium, magnesium, or other ions that produce a turbidity or precipitate with nessler reagent, add 1 drop (0.05 ml) EDTA reagent or 1 to 2 drops (0.05 to 0.1 ml) Rochelle salt solution. Mix well. Add 2.0 ml nessler reagent if EDTA reagent is used, or 1.0 ml nessler reagent if Rochelle salt is used.

2) Distilled samples—Neutralize the boric acid used for absorbing the ammonia distillate in one of two ways. Add 2 ml nessler reagent, an excess that raises the alkalinity to the desired high level. Alternatively, neutralize the boric acid with NaOH before adding 1 ml nessler reagent.

3) Mix the samples by capping the nessler tubes with clean rubber stoppers (which have been washed thoroughly with ammonia-free water) and then inverting the tubes at least six times. Keep such experimental conditions as temperature and reaction time the same in the blank, samples, and standards. Let the reaction proceed for at least 10 min after addition of the nessler reagent. Read the color in the sample and in the standards.

If the ammonia nitrogen is very low use a 30-min contact time for sample, blank, and standards. Measure the color either photometrically or visually as directed in ¶ *c* or *d* below:

c. Photometric measurement: Measure the absorbance or transmittance in a spectrophotometer or a filter photometer. Prepare the calibration curve at the same temperature and reaction time used for the samples. Make the transmittance readings against a reagent blank and run parallel checks frequently against standards in the nitrogen range of the samples. Redetermine the complete calibration curve for each new batch of nessler reagent.

For distilled samples, prepare the standard curve under the same conditions as the samples. Distill the reagent blank and appropriate standards—each diluted to 500 ml—in the same manner as the samples. Bring the 300 ml distillate and 50 ml boric acid absorbent to 500 ml and take a 50-ml portion for nesslerization.

d. Visual comparison: Compare the colors produced in the sample against those of the ammonia standards. Prepare temporary or permanent standards as directed below:

1) Temporary standards—Prepare a series of visual standards in nessler tubes by adding the following volumes of standard NH_4Cl solution and diluting to 50 ml with ammonia-free water: 0, 0.2, 0.4, 0.7, 1.0, 1.4, 1.7, 2.0, 2.5, 3.0, 3.5, 4.0, 4.5, 5.0, and 6.0 ml. Nesslerize the standards and the portions of distillate by adding 1.0 ml nessler reagent to each tube and mixing well.

2) Permanent standards—Measure into 50-ml nessler tubes the volumes of potassium chloroplatinate and cobaltous

TABLE 418:II. PREPARATION OF PERMANENT
COLOR STANDARDS FOR VISUAL DETERMINATION
OF AMMONIA NITROGEN

Value in Ammonia Nitrogen μg	Approximate Volume of Platinum Solution ml	Approximate Volume of Cobalt Solution ml
0	1.2	0.0
2	2.8	0.0
4	4.7	0.1
7	5.9	0.2
10	7.7	0.5
14	9.9	1.1
17	11.4	1.7
20	12.7	2.2
25	15.0	3.3
30	17.3	4.5
35	19.0	5.7
40	19.7	7.1
45	19.9	8.7
50	20.0	10.4
60	20.0	15.0

chloride solutions indicated in Table 418:II, dilute to the mark, and mix thoroughly. The values given in the table are *approximate;* actual equivalents of the ammonium standards will differ with the quality of the nessler reagent, the kind of illumination used, and the color sensitiveness of the analyst's eye. Therefore, compare the color standards with the nesslerized temporary ammonia standards and modify the tints as necessary. Make such comparisons for each newly prepared nessler reagent and satisfy each analyst as to the aptness of the color match. Protect the standards from dust to extend their usefulness for several months. Compare either 10 or 30 min after nesslerization, depending on the reaction time used in the preparation of the nesslerized ammonium standards against which they were matched.

5. Calculation

a. Deduct the amount of nitrogen in the ammonia-free water used for diluting the original sample before computing the final nitrogen value.

b. Deduct also the reagent blank for the volume of borate buffer and $6N$ NaOH solutions used with the sample.

c. Compute the total ammonia nitrogen by the following equation:

$$\text{mg/l ammonia N} = \frac{A}{\text{ml sample}} \times \frac{B}{C}$$

where $A = \mu g$ N found colorimetrically, $B =$ total distillate collected, including the acid absorbent, and $C =$ ml distillate taken for nesslerization. The ratio B/C applies only to the distilled samples and should be ignored in direct nesslerization.

6. Precision and Accuracy

See Section 418A and Table 418:I.

418 C.   Phenate Method

1. General Discussion

a. Principle: An intensely blue compound, indophenol, is formed by the reaction of ammonia, hypochlorite, and phenol catalyzed by a manganous salt.

b. Interference: Over 500 mg/l alkalinity, over 100 mg/l acidity, color, and turbidity interfere. These interferences may be removed by preliminary distillation.

2. Apparatus

a. Colorimetric equipment: One of the following is required:

1) *Spectrophotometer*, for use at 630 nm with a light path of approximately 1 cm.

2) *Filter photometer*, equipped with a red-orange filter having a maximum transmittance near 630 nm and providing a light path of approximately 1 cm.

b. Magnetic stirrer.

3. Reagents

a. Ammonia-free water: Prepare as directed in Preliminary Distillation Step, Section 418A.

b. Hypochlorous acid reagent: To 40 ml distilled water add 10 ml 5% commercial bleach. Adjust pH to 6.5 to 7.0 with HCl. Prepare this unstable reagent weekly.

c. Manganous sulfate solution, 0.003 M: Dissolve 50 mg $MnSO_4 \cdot H_2O$ in 100 ml distilled water.

d. Phenate reagent: Dissolve 2.5 g NaOH and 10 g phenol, C_6H_5OH, in 100 ml ammonia-free water. Because this reagent darkens on standing, prepare weekly.

e. Stock ammonium solution: Dissolve 381.9 mg anhydrous NH_4Cl, dried at 100 C, in ammonia-free water, and dilute to 1,000 ml; 1.00 ml = 100 μg N = 122 μg NH_3.

f. Standard ammonium solution: Dilute 5.00 ml stock ammonium solution to 1,000 ml with ammonia-free water; 1.00 ml = 0.500 μg N = 0.610 μg NH_3.

4. Procedure

To a 10.0-ml sample in a 50-ml beaker, add 1 drop (0.05 ml) $MnSO_4$ solution. Place on a magnetic stirrer and add 0.5 ml hypochlorous acid solution. Immediately add, a drop at a time, 0.6 ml phenate reagent. Add the reagent without delay using a bulb pipet for convenient delivery. Mark the pipet for hypochlorous acid at the 0.5-ml level and deliver the phenate reagent from a pipet that has been calibrated by counting the number of drops previously found to be equivalent to 0.6 ml. Stir vigorously during addition of the reagents. Because the color intensity is affected somewhat by the age of the reagents, carry a blank and a standard through the procedure along with each batch of unknowns. Measure absorbance using the reagent blank to zero the spectrophotometer. Color formation is complete in 10 min and is stable for at least 24 hr. Although the blue color has a maximum absorbance at 630 nm, satisfactory measurements can be made in the 600- to 660-nm region. Prepare a calibration curve in the ammonia nitrogen range of 0.1 to 5 μg, treating the standards exactly as the sample throughout the procedure.

5. Calculation

Beer's law governs. Calculate the ammonia concentration as follows:

$$\text{mg/l ammonia N} = \frac{A \times B}{C \times S} \times \frac{D}{E}$$

where:

A = absorbance of sample,
B = μg ammonia nitrogen in standard taken,
C = absorbance of standard,

S = ml unknown water sample used,
D = total distillate collected, including the acid absorbent, and
E = ml distillate used for color development.

The ratio D/E applies only to the distilled samples.

6. Precision and Accuracy

See Section 418A.4 and Table 418:I.

418 D.   Acidimetric Method

1. General Discussion

The acidimetric method is used only on samples that have been carried through the preliminary distillation step described in Section 418A. The following table is useful in selecting sample volume for the distillation and titration method.

Ammonia Nitrogen in Sample *mg/l*	Sample Volume *ml*
5-10	250
10-20	100
20-50	50.0
50-100	25.0

2. Apparatus

Distillation apparatus: See Section 418A.2a.

3. Reagents

a. Mixed indicator solution: Dissolve 200 mg methyl red indicator in 100 ml 95% ethyl or isopropyl alcohol. Dissolve 100 mg methylene blue in 50 ml 95% ethyl or isopropyl alcohol. Combine the two solutions. Prepare monthly.

b. Indicating boric acid solution: Dissolve 20 g H_3BO_3 in ammonia-free distilled water, add 10 ml mixed indicator solution, and dilute to 1 l. Prepare monthly.

c. Standard sulfuric acid titrant, 0.02N: Prepare and standardize as directed in Alkalinity, Section 403.3c. For greatest accuracy, standardize the titrant against an amount of sodium carbonate that has been incorporated in the indicating boric acid solution to reproduce the actual conditions of the sample titration. If the acid is 0.0200N, 1.00 ml= 280 μg/l.

4. Procedure

a. Proceed as described in the preliminary distillation step (Section 418A), using indicating boric acid solution as an absorbent for the distillate.

b. Sludge or sediment samples: Rapidly weigh to within ±1% a wet sample, containing approximately 1 g dry solids, in a weighing bottle or crucible. Wash the sample into a 500-ml kjeldahl flask with ammonia-free distilled water and dilute to 250 ml. Proceed as in ¶4a but add a piece of paraffin wax to the distillation flask and collect only 100 ml distillate.

c. Titrate the ammonia in the distillate with standard 0.02N H₂SO₄ titrant until the indicator turns a pale lavender.

d. *Blank:* Carry a blank through all the steps of the procedure and apply the necessary correction to the results.

5. Calculation

$$\text{mg/l ammonia N} = \frac{(A-B) \times 280}{\text{ml sample}}$$

where A = ml H_2SO_4 titration for sample and B = ml H_2SO_4 titration for blank.

6. Precision and Accuracy

See Section 418A.4 and Table 418:I.

418 E.   Bibliography

Distillation & Nesslerization Methods

Jackson, D.D. 1900. Permanent standards for use in the analysis of water. *Mass. Inst. Technol. Quart.* 13:314.

Nichols, M.S. & M.E. Foote. 1931. Distillation of free ammonia from buffered solutions. *Ind. Eng. Chem.*, Anal. Ed. 3:311.

Griffin, A.E. & N.S. Chamberlin. 1941. Relation of ammonia nitrogen to breakpoint chlorination. *Amer. J. Pub. Health* 31:803.

Palin, A.T. 1950. Symposium on the sterilization of water: Chemical aspects of chlorination. *J. Inst. Water Eng.* 4:565.

Sawyer, C.N. 1953. pH adjustment for determination of ammonia nitrogen. *Anal. Chem.* 25:816.

Taras, M.J. 1953. Effect of free residual chlorination of nitrogen compounds in water. *J. Amer. Water Works Ass.* 45:47.

Boltz, D.F., ed. 1958. Colorimetric Determination of Nonmetals. Interscience Publishers, New York, N.Y. pp. 75-97.

Jenkins, D. 1967. The differentiation, analysis and preservation of nitrogen and phosphorous forms in natural waters. In: Trace Inorganics in Water. American Chemical Society, Washington, D.C.

Phenate Method

Rossum, J.R. & P.A. Villarruz. 1963. Determination of ammonia by the indophenol method. *J. Amer. Water Works Ass.* 55:657.

Weatherburn, M.W. 1967. Phenolhypochlorite reaction for determination of ammonia. *Anal. Chem.* 39:971.

Distillation and Titration Methods

Meeker, E.W. & E.C. Wagner. 1933. Titration of ammonia in the presence of boric acid. *Ind. Eng. Chem.*, Anal. Ed. 5:396.

Wagner, E.C. 1940. Titration of ammonia in the presence of boric acid. *Ind. Eng. Chem.*, Anal. Ed. 12:711.

419   NITROGEN (NITRATE)

1. Selection of Method

Nitrate is a difficult determination because of the relatively complex procedures required, the high probability that interfering constituents will be present,

and the limited concentration ranges of the various technics. This section includes two screening technics for determining the approximate range of nitrate in the sample. A choice of technics, depending on concentration range and/or the presence of interferences, is then presented.

The screening methods are: (a) an ultraviolet technic that measures the absorbance of NO_3^- at 220 nm and is suitable for relatively unpolluted waters and (b) a nitrate electrode method that may be used in both unpolluted water and wastewater.

Once a sample has been screened, a method suitable for its concentration range may be selected. If the concentration range is already known, screening may be omitted. For the concentration range below 0.1 mg NO_3-N/l, use the cadmium reduction method. An automated version of this method is also available (Section 605). For the concentration range from 0.1 to 2 mg NO_3-N/l, use the brucine method; for the concentration range 0.1 to 5 mg NO_3-N/l, use the chromotropic acid method. For higher nitrate concentrations, dilute into the range of the brucine or chromotropic acid technic or use the Devarda's alloy reduction method for "total oxidized nitrogen."

2. Precision and Accuracy

Five synthetic unknown samples containing nitrate and other constituents dissolved in distilled water were analyzed by the brucine method. Three of the samples also were analyzed by the cadmium reduction method. The results obtained by the participating laboratories are summarized in Table 419:I.

Sample 1 contained the following additional constituents: 400 mg/l chloride, 0.2 mg/l ammonia nitrogen, 0.23 mg/l organic phosphorus added in the form of adenylic acid, 7.00 mg/l orthophosphate phosphorus, and 3.00 mg/l polyphosphate phosphorus added as sodium hexametaphosphate.

Sample 2 contained the following additional components: 400 mg/l chloride, 1.50 mg/l ammonia nitrogen, 0.03 mg/l organic phosphorus added in the form of adenylic acid, 0.10 mg/l orthophosphate phosphorus, and 0.08 mg/l polyphosphate phosphorus added as sodium hexametaphosphate.

TABLE 419: I. PRECISION AND ACCURACY DATA FOR NITRATE METHODS

Method	Nitrate-Nitrogen Concentration $\mu g/l$	No. of Laboratories	Relative Standard Deviation %	Relative Error %
C. Cadmium reduction	50	11	96.4	47.3
	500	11	25.6	6.4
	5,000	10	9.2	1.0
D. Brucine	50	50	66.7	7.6
	500	50	14.4	0.6
	1,000*	17	5.5	6.0
	1,000†	17	7.9	0
	5,000	50	15.4	4.5

* Synthetic sample 4.
† Synthetic sample 5.

Sample 3 contained the following additional constituents: 400 mg/l chloride, 0.8 mg/l ammonia nitrogen, 0.09 mg/l organic phosphorus added in the form of adenylic acid, 0.6 mg/l orthophosphate phosphorus, and 0.3 mg/l polyphosphate phosphorus added as sodium hexametaphosphate.

Sample 4 contained the following additional constituents: 10 mg/l chloride, 0.2 mg/l ammonia nitrogen, 1.5 mg/l organic nitrogen, 10.0 mg/l phosphate, and 5.0 mg/l silica.

Sample 5 contained the following additional constituents: 200 mg/l chloride,

0.8 mg/l ammonia nitrogen, 0.8 mg/l organic nitrogen, 5.0 mg/l phosphate, and 15.0 mg/l silica.

3. Storage of Samples

Start nitrate determinations promptly after sampling. If storage is necessary, preserve samples at a temperature just above the freezing point with or without H_2SO_4 (0.8 ml conc H_2SO_4/l). Neutralize the sample to pH 7 before screening and analysis.

419 A. Ultraviolet Spectrophotometric Method (TENTATIVE)

1. General Discussion

a. Principle: Use this technic for screening only those samples that have low organic matter contents, that is, unpolluted natural waters and potable water supplies.

Measurement of the ultraviolet absorption at 220 nm enables rapid determination of nitrate. The nitrate calibration curve follows Beer's law up to 11 mg/l N. Because dissolved organic matter may also absorb at 220 nm and nitrate does not absorb at 275 nm, a second measurement can be made at 275 nm to correct the nitrate value. The extent of this empirical correction is related to the nature and concentration of the organic matter and may vary from one water to another. Filtration of the sample is intended to remove possible

interference from suspended particles. Acidification with $1N$ hydrochloric acid is designed to prevent interference from hydroxide or carbonate concentrations up to 1,000 mg/l as $CaCO_3$. Chloride has no effect on the determination.

b. Interference: Dissolved organic matter, nitrite, hexavalent chromium, and surfactants interfere. The latter three substances may be compensated for by the preparation of individual correction curves.

Organic matter can cause a positive but variable interference, the degree depending on the nature and concentration of the organic material.

Clean all glassware thoroughly and rinse to reduce the error that might result from streaks or particles on the outside of the cuvets, as well as traces of surfactants or dichromate cleaning solution that might adhere on the interior glass surfaces.

Treat colored samples with aluminum hydroxide suspension or dilute to minimize color interference.

c. Minimum detectable concentration: 40 μg/l nitrate N.

2. Apparatus

a. Spectrophotometer, for use at 220 nm and 275 nm with matched silica cells of 1-cm or longer light path. A Beckman Model DU spectrophotometer with a photomultiplier attachment and hydrogen lamp source, or equivalent, is satisfactory.

b. Filter: One of the following is required:

1) *Membrane filter:* 0.45 μm membrane filter, and appropriate filter assembly.

2) *Paper:* Acid-washed, ashless hard-finish filter paper sufficiently retentive for fine precipitates.

c. Nessler tubes, 50-ml, short form.

3. Reagents

a. Redistilled water: Use redistilled water for the preparation of all solutions and dilutions.

b. Stock nitrate solution: Prepare as described in Section 419B; 1.00 ml= 100 μg N=443 μg NO_3.

c. Standard nitrate solution: Dilute 100.0 ml stock nitrate solution to 1,000 ml with distilled water; 1.00 ml=10.0 μg N=44.3 μg NO_3.

d. Hydrochloric acid solution, HCl, 1N: 1+11.

e. Aluminum hydroxide suspension: Dissolve 125 g $AlK(SO_4)_2 \cdot 12H_2O$ or $AlNH_4(SO_4)_2 \cdot 12H_2O$ in 1 l distilled water. Warm to 60 C and add 55 ml conc NH_4OH slowly, with stirring. Let the mixture stand about 1 hr, transfer to a large bottle, and wash the precipitate by successive additions (with thorough mixing) and decantations of distilled water, until free from ammonia, chloride, nitrate, and nitrite. Finally, after settling, decant off as much clear liquid as possible, leaving only the concentrated suspension.

4. Procedure

a. Color removal: If the sample has a high color or is known to contain organic interference, add 4 ml $Al(OH)_3$ suspension/100 ml sample in an erlenmeyer flask. Swirl to mix and let settle for 5 min. Filter through a 0.45 μm membrane filter previously washed with about 200 ml distilled water.

b. Treatment of sample: To 50 ml clear sample, filtered if necessary, or to 50 ml sample filtered after color removal, add 1 ml 1N HCl and mix thoroughly.

c. Preparation of standard curve: Prepare nitrate calibration standards in the range 0 to 350 μg N by diluting to 50 ml the following volumes of the standard nitrate solution: 0, 1.00, 2.00, 4.00, 7.00 ... 35.0 ml. Treat the nitrate standards in the same manner as the samples.

d. Spectrophotometric measurement: Read the absorbance or transmittance against redistilled water set at zero absorbance or 100% transmittance. Use a wavelength of 220 nm to obtain the nitrate reading and, if necessary, a wavelength of 275 nm to obtain the interference due to dissolved organic matter.

5. Calculation

a. Correction for dissolved organic matter: Subtract 2 times the reading at 275 nm from the reading at 220 nm to obtain the absorbance due to nitrate. Convert this absorbance value into equivalent nitrate by reading the nitrate value from a standard calibration curve obtained at 220 nm.

b. Calculate as follows:

$$\text{Approx. mg/l nitrate N} = \frac{\text{net } \mu g \text{ nitrate N}}{\text{ml sample}}$$

$$\text{Approx. mg/l NO}_3 = \text{Approx. mg/l nitrate N} \times 4.43$$

419 B.   Nitrate Electrode Method (TENTATIVE)

1. General Discussion

a. Principle: The nitrate ion electrode is a selective sensor that develops a potential across a thin, porous, inert membrane that holds in place a water-immiscible liquid ion exchanger. The electrode responds only to ionized nitrate ion activity between about 10^{-1} and $10^{-5}M$ (0.2 to 1,400 mg/l NO_3-N). The lower limit of detection is determined by the small but finite solubility of the liquid ion exchanger.

b. Inteferences: Chloride ion and bicarbonate ion interfere when their ratios to nitrate are >10 or >5, respectively. These interferences can be removed in the procedures outlined below.

Ions that are potential interferences but do not normally occur at significant levels in potable waters are NO_2^-, S^{2-}, Br^-, ClO_3^-, I^-, and ClO_4^-. The procedure outlined for the removal of chloride interferences, Ag_2SO_4 addition, will also remove CN^-, S^{2-}, Br^-, and I^- ions.

c. The procedure presented here is for screening fresh water samples with similar ionic strengths. This screening procedure can be used for both water and wastewater samples.

2. Apparatus

a. Expanded-scale or digital pH meter.

b. Double-junction reference electrode: (This is necessary only if chloride ion is removed by Ag_2SO_4 addition.) Use inner chamber filling solution supplied. Fill outer chamber with either 0.1M KCl or 0.25M Na$_2$SO$_4$.

*c. Nitrate ion electrode.**

d. Magnetic stirrer: Teflon-coated stirring bar.

3. Reagents

a. Stock nitrate solution: Dissolve 721.8 mg anhydrous potassium nitrate, KNO_3, and dilute to 1,000 ml with distilled water; 1 ml=0.1 mg N.

b. Standard nitrate solutions: Dilute 1, 10, and 50 ml stock nitrate solution to 100 ml with distilled water to obtain standard solutions of 1, 10, and 50 mg/l, respectively.

c. Reagent-grade silver sulfate powder.

---

* Orion Model 92-07, Corning Model 476134, or equivalent.

d. Sulfuric acid: Add 5 ml conc H_2SO_4 to 95 ml distilled water.

4. Procedure

a. No major adjustment of any instrument normally is required to use the electrodes in the concentration range of 1.0 to 50 mg NO_3-N/l.

b. Chloride removal: If the chloride to nitrate ratio is >10, remove chloride by adding a spatula-full of solid Ag_2SO_4, and stirring for 1 to 2 min.

c. Bicarbonate removal: If the bicarbonate to nitrate ratio is >5, remove bicarbonate by adjusting the pH to 4 to 4.5 with H_2SO_4.

d. Preparation of calibration curve: Transfer about 100 ml of 1 mg/l NO_3-N standard to a 150-ml beaker, add Ag_2SO_4 and H_2SO_4 if these have been added to the samples, and stir for a constant time (2 or 3 min) with a magnetic stirrer. Immerse the tips of the electrodes and record the millivolt reading after 1 min. Remove the electrodes from the solution, rinse, and blot dry. Repeat for 10 mg/l and 50 mg/l NO_3-N standards. Plot the potential measurements of the standards against the nitrate concentration on two-cycle semilogarithmic graph paper, plotting NO_3-N activity on the logarithmic axis, with the lowest activity to the left of the page, and millivolts on the linear axis. A straight line with a slope of 59 (58+ to 59+ for solutions at 24 to 26 C) mV/decade should result. Recalibrate the electrodes several times daily by checking the potential reading of the 10 mg/l NO_3-N standard and adjusting the calibration control on the meter until the reading plotted on the calibration curve is displayed again.

e. Measurement of samples: After any necessary pretreatment, transfer about 100 ml sample to a 150-ml beaker and stir with a magnetic stirrer. Adjust the pH, if necessary, to 3 to 9. Immerse the electrode tips in the sample and record the potential reading after 1 min. Read the concentration from the calibration curve.

419 C.   Cadmium Reduction Method (TENTATIVE)

1. General Discussion

Nitrate is reduced almost quantitatively to nitrite when a sample is run through a column containing amalgamated cadmium filings. The nitrite thus produced is determined by diazotizing with sulfanilamide and coupling with N-(1-naphthyl)-ethylenediamine to form a highly colored azo dye that is measured colorimetrically. A correction may be made for any nitrite initially present in the sample. The method is recommended for the concentration range below 0.1 mg NO_3-N/l.

2. Apparatus

a. Reduction columns (see Figure 419:1) constructed from three pieces of glass tubing joined end to end: 10 cm of 5-cm-ID tubing is joined to 30 cm of 10-mm-ID tubing, which in turn is joined to 35 cm of 2-mm-ID tubing.

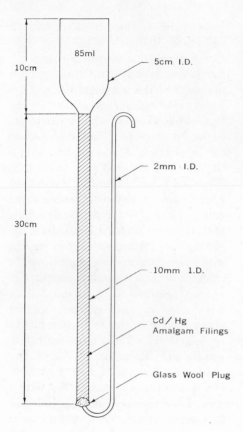

Figure 419:1. Reduction column.

The last tube is bent just below the joint into a U, so that it runs up parallel to the 10-mm-diam tube; its upper end is bent over to form an inverted U-siphon. This last bend should be just level with the top of the 10-mm-diam tube. With this arrangement, liquid placed in the top reservoir should flow out of the system and stop when the level of the liquid just covers the metal filings (see below). Place a mark on the upper wide portion of the column to indicate the height of an additional 80 ml of liquid.

b. Colorimetric equipment: One of the following is required:

1) *Spectrophotometer*, for use at 543 nm, providing a light path of 1 cm or longer.

2) *Filter photometer*, providing a light path of 1 cm or longer and equipped with a yellow-green filter having maximum transmittance near 543 nm.

3. Reagents

a. Distilled water: Use distilled water of the highest purity, preferably prepared by mixed-bed ion-exchange deionization of ordinary distilled water.

b. Ammonium chloride solution, conc: Dissolve 100 g NH_4Cl in 500 ml distilled water and store in a glass or plastic bottle.

c. Dilute ammonium chloride solution: Dilute 50 ml conc ammonium chloride solution to 2,000 ml with distilled water. Store in a glass or plastic bottle.

d. Amalgamated cadmium filings: File sticks of pure cadmium metal (reagent grade) with a coarse metal hand file (about second cut) and collect the fraction that passes a sieve with 2-mm openings and is retained on a sieve with 0.5-mm openings. Stir about 300 g filings with 300 ml $HgCl_2$ solution (1 g $HgCl_2/100$ ml) for 3 min. (This amount suffices for six reduction columns.) Let the metal particles settle and decant the liquid. Wash the amalgamated filings several times with distilled water, then several times with $1+99$ HCl. Wash copiously with distilled water until no nitrite can be detected in the supernatant fluid. Store the filings in the dark under dilute NH_4Cl solution.

e. Sulfanilamide reagent: Dissolve 5 g sulfanilamide in a mixture of 50 ml conc HCl and about 300 ml distilled water. Dilute to 500 ml with distilled water. The solution is stable for many months.

f. N - (1-naphthyl) - ethylenedia-mine dihydrochloride solution: Dissolve 500 mg dihydrochloride in 500 ml distilled water. Store the solution in a dark bottle. Renew the solution once a month, or immediately when it develops a strong brown coloration.

g. Hydrochloric acid, HCl, 1 + 19

h. Stock nitrate solution: Dissolve 721.8 mg anhydrous KNO_3 in distilled water and dilute to 1,000 ml. This solution contains 100 mg/l NO_3-N.

i. Standard nitrate solution. Dilute 4.00 ml stock standard nitrate to 2,000 ml with distilled water and use immediately; 1.0 ml = 0.20 μg NO_3-N.

4. Procedure

a. Preparation of reduction column: Pack a plug of glass wool in the bottom of a reduction column and fill the column with distilled water. Pour in sufficient amalgamated cadmium filings to produce a column 30 cm long. Use the column size specified because columns of lesser diameter and length give erratic results and show rapid deterioration. Wash the column thoroughly with dilute NH_4Cl solution. Use a flow rate no greater than 8 ml/min. If the rate is too fast, slow it by constricting the end of the outlet siphon, packing more glass wool at the base of the column, or attaching a piece of tubing to the column outlet and using a pinch clamp to control the flow rate. Flow rates of less than 5 ml/min unnecessarily increase the time for an analysis and may give low results. When apparatus is not in use, cover the metal in the column with dilute NH_4Cl solution.

b. Treatment of sample:

1) Turbidity removal—If turbidity or suspended solids are present, clarify the sample by membrane filtration.

2) pH adjustment—If the pH of the sample is above 9, adjust to between 8 and 9, using a pH meter and dilute HCl.

3) Reduction of nitrate—Place 80 to 90 ml sample in a 125-ml erlenmeyer flask and add 2.0 ml conc NH_4Cl solution. Mix, and pour the sample from the flask onto the column until the marked level in the top part of the column is reached. Place a 50-ml graduated cylinder under the outlet to collect the effluent and discard any sample left in the erlenmeyer flask. Shake the flask as dry as possible and retain it for collecting the main portion of the effluent.

Collect between 25 and 30 ml effluent in the cylinder and then replace it with the original erlenmeyer flask that contained the sample. Discard the contents of the cylinder. (Passing 25 to 30 ml removes the NH_4Cl solution or a previous sample from the voids in the reduction column. The volume flushed through is not critical provided that it exceeds 25 ml. Leave sufficient sample in the column so that 50 ml more can be reduced; thus, do not use more than about 30 ml. A maximum of about eight columns can be handled conveniently at one time. Determine a suitable short delay between adding the samples to successive columns so that there will be time to reject the flushing liquid from one column and replace the cylinder with the erlenmeyer flask before too much flushing liquid has escaped from the next column in line. In the case where a sample having a very low concentration of nitrate is followed by a sample with a high nitrate concentration, or vice versa, use a full 30-ml volume to flush the column.)

Let the remainder of the sample collect in the flask. When the flow of sample from the column has ceased, pour exactly 50 ml from the flask into the 50-ml measuring cylinder. Drain and discard the remaining effluent from the erlenmeyer flask. Shake the flask as dry as possible and then pour back into it the 50 ml of reduced sample from the measuring cylinder.

There is no need to wash columns between samples, but if columns are not to be reused for several hours or longer, pour 50 ml dilute NH_4Cl solution onto the top and let it pass through the system. Store the cadmium filings in this NH_4Cl solution and never allow them to go dry. If there are indications that the columns are becoming inactivated, as shown by a significant decrease in the color intensity produced per microgram NO_3-N in the standards, empty the columns, wash the cadmium filings briefly with $1+19$ HCl and copiously with distilled water, air-dry at about 60 C, resieve, and reamalgamate. Well-prepared columns of the correct size should be stable for many weeks before such reactivation becomes necessary.

4) Color development and measurement—As soon as possible, and not more than 15 min after reduction, add to the sample 1.0 ml sulfanilamide solution from an automatic pipet. Let the reagent react for a period longer than 2 min but not exceeding 8 min. Add 1.0 ml 1-naphthyl-ethylenediamine solution and mix immediately. Between 10 min and 2 hr afterward, measure the absorb-

ance of the solution against a distilled-water reagent blank, using a wavelength of 543 cm. As a guide, use the following recommended light paths for the indicated NO_3-N concentration ranges:

Light Path Length cm	NO_3-N Concentration $\mu g/l$
1	2-20
5	2-6
10	<2

c. Standards: Use the standards both to obtain a calibration curve and to check the efficiency of the reduction columns.

Add about 110 ml dilute standard nitrate solution to clean, dry, 125-ml erlenmeyer flasks and carry out the determination exactly as described for the samples, but collect 50 ml flushing liquid from each column. Measure the absorbance in a cell that provides a suitable light path. Perform the determination initially in triplicate for each column and correct the mean of the three absorbances thus obtained by the absorbance of a distilled water reagent blank. Subsequently check each column once a day.

Determine the factor F relating absorbance in a 1-cm cell to NO_3-N concentration in milligrams per liter from the following equation:

$$F = \frac{0.2}{A}$$

where A is the absorbance of the standard nitrate solution (0.2 mg/l) at 543 nm.

Reactivate the column when the value of F consistently increases beyond 0.33.

5. Calculation

$$mg\ NO_3\text{-}N/l = (A_s - A_b) \times \frac{F}{L} - C$$

$$mg\ NO_3/l = mg\ NO_3\text{-}N/l \times 4.43$$

where:

A_s = absorbance of sample,
A_b = absorbance of reagent blank,

F = factor defined in ¶4c above,
L = light path length, cm, and
C = concentration of NO_2-N (separately determined).

6. Precision and Accuracy

See Section 419.2.

419 D. Brucine Method (TENTATIVE)

1. General Discussion

The reaction between nitrate and brucine produces a yellow color that can be used for the colorimetric estimation of nitrate. The intensity of the color is measured at 410 nm. The reaction rate between brucine and nitrate ion is affected significantly by the amount of heat generated during the test. Heat control in the procedure is achieved by reagent addition sequence and incubation of the reaction mixture for a precise interval of time at a known temperature. Acid concentration and reaction time have been selected to yield optimum development and stability of color. The method works well in waters of salinities varying from that of fresh water to that of seawater. The method is recommended only for the concentration range of 0.1 to 2 mg NO_3-N/l, because above this range anomalous results occur while below this range the sensitivity of the method is poor. The ideal range for the method is from 0.1 to 1 mg NO_3-N/l.

Interferences: All strong oxidizing or reducing agents interfere. The presence of oxidizing agents may be determined by the addition of orthotolidine reagent, as in the measurement of residual chlorine. The interference by residual chlorine may be eliminated by the addition of sodium arsenite, provided that the residual chlorine does not exceed 5 mg/l. A slight excess of sodium arsenite will not affect the determination. Ferrous and ferric iron and quadrivalent manganese give slight positive interferences, but in concentrations less than 1 mg/l these are negligible. The interference due to nitrite up to 0.5 mg NO_2-N/l is eliminated by the use of sulfanilic acid. Chloride interference is masked by the addition of excess NaCl.

High concentrations of organic matter such as in undiluted raw wastewater usually will interfere.

2. Apparatus

a. Colorimetric equipment: One of the following is required:

1) *Spectrophotometer,* for use at 410 nm providing a light path of 2.5 cm (1 in.)

2) *Filter photometer,* providing a light path of 2.5 cm (1 in.) and equipped with a violet filter having maximum transmittance between 400 and 425 nm.

b. Safety pipet.

c. *Wire racks*, to hold tubes in which samples are to be incubated.*

d. *Stirred boiling water bath*, with heating facility sufficient to maintain a temperature of at least 95 C when cooled samples are introduced.

e. *Reaction tubes:* Borosilicate glass test tubes, of approximate dimensions 2.5×15 cm, in which reaction is performed. [The 2.5-cm (1-in.) colorimeter tubes† used in conjunction with the Bausch & Lomb Spectronic 20 are convenient because their use avoids the necessity for a transfer, following reaction, to determine transmittance.]

f. *Cool water bath.*

3. Reagents

a. *Stock nitrate solution:* See Section 419B.3a.

b. *Standard nitrate solution:* Dilute 10.00 ml stock nitrate solution to 1,000 ml with distilled water; 1.00 ml = 1.00 μg N. Prepare immediately before using.

c. *Sodium arsenite solution:* Dissolve 5.0 g NaAsO₂ and dilute to 1 l with distilled water. (CAUTION: *Toxic—take care to avoid ingestion.*).

d. *Brucine-sulfanilic acid solution:* Dissolve 1 g brucine sulfate and 0.1 g sulfanilic acid in approximately 70 ml hot distilled water. Add 3 ml conc HCl, cool, and make up to 100 ml. This solution is stable for several months. The pink color that develops slowly does not affect its usefulness. (CAUTION: *Brucine is toxic—take care to avoid ingestion.*).

e. *Sulfuric acid solution:* Carefully add 500 ml conc H₂SO₄ to 125 ml distilled water. Cool to room temperature

---

* Van Waters and Rogers No. 60935 or equivalent.

† Van Waters and Rogers No. 22366, or equivalent.

before using and keep tightly stoppered to prevent absorption of atmospheric moisture.

f. *Sodium chloride solution:* Dissolve 300 g NaCl and dilute to 1,000 ml with distilled water.

4. Procedure

a. *Preparation of nitrate standards:* Prepare nitrate standards in the range 0.1 to 1 mg/l N by diluting 1.00, 2.00, 4.00, 7.00, and 10.0 ml standard nitrate solution to 10.0 ml with distilled water.

b. *Pretreatment of sample:* If the sample contains residual chlorine, remove by adding 1 drop (0.05 ml) sodium arsenite solution for each 0.10 mg Cl and mix. Add 1 drop in excess to a 50-ml portion.

c. *Color development:* Set up the required number of reaction tubes in the wire rack, spacing them so that each tube is surrounded by empty spaces. Include a reaction tube for a reagent blank and reaction tubes for as many standards as desired. To each tube add 10.0 ml sample or a portion diluted to 10 ml so that the sample volume taken for analysis contains between 0.1 and 8 μg NO₃-N. Place the rack in a cool water bath and add 2 ml NaCl solution. Mix thoroughly by hand and add 10 ml H₂SO₄ solution. In no case use a "Vortex" mixer, since this type of mixing produces inconsistent results in the analysis. Mix again thoroughly by swirling and allow to cool. At this point, if any turbidity or color is present or if optically unmatched colorimeter tubes are being used as reaction tubes, dry the tubes and read a "sample blank" value against the reagent blank tube at 410 nm. Replace the rack of tubes in the cool water bath and add 0.5 ml brucine-sulfanilic acid reagent. Swirl the tubes to mix thoroughly and then place the rack of tubes in a well-stirred boiling water bath that maintains a temperature of not less than 95 C. After exactly 20 min, remove the samples and immerse in a cold water bath. When thermal equilibrium is reached (at approximately room temperature), dry the tubes with tissue and read the standards and samples against the reagent blank at 410 nm in the spectrophotometer. Check the technic and the constancy of reaction conditions by running at least two standards with each batch of samples.

Prepare a standard curve from the absorbance values of the standards (minus the blank) run together with the samples. Correct the absorbance readings of the samples by subtracting their "sample blank" values from their final absorbance values. Read the concentrations of NO_3-N directly from the standard curve.

5. Calculation

$$\text{mg/l nitrate N} = \frac{\mu g\ NO_3\text{-}N}{\text{ml sample}}$$

$$\text{mg/l } NO_3 = \text{mg/l nitrate N} \times 4.43$$

6. Precision and Accuracy

See Section 419.2.

419 E.   Chromotropic Acid Method (TENTATIVE)

1. General Discussion

a. Principle: Two moles of nitrate react with one mole of chromotropic acid to form a yellow reaction product exhibiting maximum absorbance at 410 nm. The maximum color develops within 10 min and is stable for 24 hr. The cooling bath dissipates sufficient heat to prevent boiling of the solutions; for this reason, the temperature of the cooling bath may vary from 10 to 20 C without critically affecting the results. Residual chlorine, certain oxidants, and nitrite also yield yellow colors with chromotropic acid. However, the addition of sulfite completely eliminates the interference from residual chlorine and oxidizing agents, while urea converts nitrite to nitrogen gas. Antimony effectively masks up to 2,000 mg/l chloride, a tolerance level that can be raised to 4,000 mg/l by doubling the strength of the specified antimony reagent. The method is recommended for the concentration range 0.1 to 5 mg NO_3-N/l.

b. Interferences: The yellow color of the chloroferrate (III) complex in amounts up to 40 mg/l ferric ion is completely discharged by the addition of antimony. Barium, lead, strontium, iodide, iodate, selenite, and selenate ions are incompatible with the system and form precipitates. However, their occurrence in significant amounts is unlikely in most samples. Concentrations of chromic ion exceeding 20 mg/l contribute interfering color.

c. *Minimum detectable concentration:* 50 μg/l NO$_3$-N.

2. Apparatus

Colorimetric equipment: One of the following is required:

a. *Spectrophotometer,* for use at 410 nm, providing a light path of 1 cm or longer.

b. *Filter photometer,* providing a light path of 1 cm or longer and equipped with a violet filter having maximum transmittance near 410 nm.

3. Reagents

a. *Redistilled water:* Redistill single-distilled water from a borosilicate glass still. Prepare all aqueous solutions from this double-distilled water.

b. *Stock nitrate solution:* See Section 419B.3a.

c. *Standard nitrate solution:* Dilute 50 ml stock nitrate solution to 500 ml with distilled water; 1.00 ml = 10 μg NO$_3$-N/l.

d. *Sulfite-urea reagent:* Dissolve 5 g urea and 4 g anhydrous sodium sulfite, Na$_2$SO$_3$, in redistilled water and dilute to 100 ml.

e. *Antimony reagent:* Heat 500 mg antimony metal in 80 ml conc H$_2$SO$_4$ until all the metal has dissolved. Cool and cautiously add to 20 ml iced redistilled water. If crystals separate upon standing overnight, redissolve them by heating.

f. *Chromotropic acid reagent:* Purify the chromotropic acid (4,5-dihydroxy-2,7-naphthalene disulfonic acid)

in the following manner. Boil 125 ml distilled water in a beaker and gradually add 15 g 4,5-dihydroxy-2,7-naphthalene disulfonic acid disodium salt, with constant stirring. To the solution add 5 g activated decolorizing charcoal. Boil the mixture for about 10 min. Add distilled water to make up the loss due to evaporation. Filter the hot solution through cotton wool. Add 5 g activated charcoal to the filtrate and boil for 10 more min. Filter, first through cotton wool and then through a filter paper to remove the charcoal completely. Cool the solution and slowly add 10 ml nitrate-free conc H$_2$SO$_4$. Boil the solution until about 100 ml are left in the beaker. Allow the solution to stand overnight. Transfer the crystals of chromotropic acid to a Buchner funnel and wash thoroughly with 95% alcohol until the crystals are white. Dry the crystals at 80 C.

Dissolve 100 mg purified chromotropic acid in 100 ml conc H$_2$SO$_4$ and store in a brown bottle. Prepare every 2 wk. A colorless reagent solution signifies the absence of nitrate contamination from the sulfuric acid.

g. *Sulfuric acid,* H$_2$SO$_4$, conc, nitrate-free.

4. Procedure

a. *Preparation of nitrate standards:* Prepare nitrate standards in the range 0.10 to 5 mg/l N by diluting 0, 1.0, 5.0, 15, 25, 35, and 50 ml standard nitrate solution to 100 ml with redistilled water.

b. *Color development:* If appreciable amounts of suspended matter are present in the sample, remove by centrifugation or filtration. Pipet 2.5-ml portions of the standards, clear samples, and a blank consisting of redistilled water into dry 10-ml volumetric flasks. Use dilutions of the standards and samples containing nitrate nitrogen concentrations in the range 0.1 to 5 mg/l (0.25 to 12.5 μg in 2.5 ml). To each flask add 1 drop (0.05 ml) sulfite-urea reagent. Place the flasks in a tray of cold water (10 to 20 C) and add 2 ml antimony reagent. Swirl flasks during the addition of each reagent. After the mixtures have stood in the bath for about 4 min, add 1 ml chromotropic acid reagent, swirl flasks again, and then allow to stand in the cooling bath for 3 min more. Add conc H_2SO_4 to bring the volume to the 10-ml mark. Stopper the flasks and mix the contents by inverting each flask four times. Allow the solutions to stand for 45 min at room temperature

and again adjust the volume to the 10-ml mark with conc H_2SO_4. Perform the final mixing very gently to avoid introducing gas bubbles. Read the absorbance at 410 nm 15 min or more after the last adjustment of volume. In the reference cell of the spectrophotometer use redistilled water. Rinse the sample cell with the sample solution and then fill carefully, to avoid trapping bubbles, by holding the cell in a slanting position and pouring the solution very slowly down the side of the cell.

5. Calculation

$$\text{mg/l nitrate N} = \frac{\mu\text{g nitrate N}}{\text{ml sample}}$$

$$\text{mg/l NO}_3 = \text{mg/l nitrate N} \times 4.43$$

6. Precision and Accuracy

See Section 419.2.

419 F. Devarda's Alloy Reduction Method (TENTATIVE)

1. General Discussion

a. Principle: This method is recommended for samples in which the nitrate-nitrogen concentration is greater than 2 mg/l. It is especially convenient to perform if an ammonia determination employing the preliminary distillation step (Section 418A) has been made. In this technic, nitrate and nitrite are reduced to ammonia under hot alkaline conditions in the presence of the reducing agent, Devarda's alloy (an alloy of 50% Cu, 45% Al, and 5% Zn). The reduction is carried out in a kjeldahl distillation apparatus. Under the hot alkaline conditions the ammonia formed distills and is trapped in a receiving flask containing boric acid (Section 418A).

The ammonia so formed can then be determined either by nesslerization (Section 418B.4*b*) or acidimetrically (Section 418D.4).

b. Interferences: The preliminary distillation technic described in Section 418A.4*b-d* is used for this procedure if ammonia is not being determined before the Devarda's alloy reduction method for nitrate. Nitrite is reduced to ammonia under the conditions of the reduction. A separate determination of nitrite (Section 420) can be made and the result subtracted. If this is not done the result should be reported as "total oxidized nitrogen". Ammonia must be removed from the sample before the determination. The method is not recommended for levels of nitrate below 2 mg/l and at this level, especially in the presence of high concentrations of amino- or albuminoid nitrogen, it is necessary to use at least 50-ml and preferably 100-ml samples because of the possibility of positive interference by the decomposition of this nitrogenous matter.

2. Apparatus

a. Distillation apparatus: Glass kjeldahl flask, 800 ml, with a condenser and adapter so arranged that the distillate can be collected in boric acid solution either for nesslerization or titration with standard sulfuric acid.

b. Measuring scoop: To contain 1 g Devarda's alloy.

c. Colorimetric equipment: See Section 418.2*a* 1), 2), and 3).

3. Reagents

a. Ammonia-free water: See Section 418A.3*a*.

b. Borate buffer solution: See Section 418A.3*b*.

c. Sodium hydroxide, 6N: See Section 418A.3*c*.

d. Devarda's alloy: 200 mesh or less containing less than 0.0005% N.

e. For acidimetric finish: All reagents listed in Section 418D.3*a, b,* and *c*.

f. For nesslerization finish:

1) *Nessler reagent:* See Section 418B.3*d*.

2) *Stock ammonium solution;* See Section 418B.3*e*.

3) *Standard ammonium solution:* See Section 418B.3*f*.

4. Procedure

a. If ammonia nitrogen has not been determined by a method involving preliminary distillation, add the sample to a distillation flask and make up to 500 ml with distilled water. Add 25 ml borate buffer and adjust pH to 9.5 with 6N NaOH using a pH meter or short-range pH paper. Distill 250 to 300 ml into a dry receiving flask and discard. Make sure that the last part of the distillation is conducted with the tip of the condenser out of the liquid in the receiving flask.

b. To the residue in the flask after removing ammonia as in ¶4*a* above, add 1 g Devarda's alloy and sufficient ammonia-free distilled water to bring the total liquid volume in the flask to about 350 ml.

Place in a receiver 50 ml boric acid absorbent for each milligram of nitrate nitrogen. Immerse the end of the condenser in the absorbent.

Heat the distillation flask until boiling or vigorous bubbling occurs. Reduce the heat and distill at a rate of 5 to 10 ml/min until at least 150 ml distillate has been collected. Lower the receiver so that the liquid is below the end of the condenser and continue distillation for 1 to 2 min to cleanse the condenser.

Proceed with the determination of ammonia nitrogen either by nesslerization (Section 418B) or titration with standard strong acid (Section 418D).

5. Calculation

Calculate the ammonia nitrogen as in Section 418B or 418D. The ammonia determined represents that produced from the reduction of both nitrite and nitrate nitrogen (total oxidized nitrogen). To obtain nitrate nitrogen, separately determine nitrite nitrogen (Section 420) and subtract.

6. Precision

The recovery of 200 to 400 μg nitrate nitrogen from partially treated wastewater effluents using a borate, NaOH buffer system that had a final pH range of 9.7 to 10.2 was found to average 96% with a coefficient of variation of 7.7%.

419 G. Bibliography

Ultraviolet Screening Method

HOATHER, R.C. 1953. Applications of spectrophotometry in the examination of waters. *Proc. Soc. Water Treat. Exam.* 2:9.

BASTIAN, R. et al. 1957. Ultraviolet spectrophotometric determination of nitrate. *Anal. Chem.* 29:1795.

HOATHER, R.C. & R.F. RACKMAN. 1959. Oxidized nitrogen and sewage effluents observed by ultraviolet spectrophotometry. *Analyst* 84:549.

GOLDMAN, E. & R. JACOBS. 1961. Determination of nitrates by ultraviolet absorption. *J. Amer. Water Works Ass.* 53:187.

ARMSTRONG, F.A.J. 1963. Determination of nitrate in water by ultraviolet spectrophotometry. *Anal. Chem.* 35:1292.

NAVONE, R. 1964. Proposed method for nitrate in potable waters. *J. Amer. Water Works Ass.* 56:781.

Nitrate Electrode Screening Method

LANGMUIR, D. & R.L. JACOBSON. 1970. Specific ion electrode determination of nitrate in some freshwaters and sewage effluents. *Environ. Sci. Technol.* 4:835.

KEENEY, D. R., B.H. BYRNES & J. J. GENSON. 1970. Determination of nitrate in waters with nitrate-selective ion electrode. *Analyst* 95:383.

SOMMERFELDT, T.C., R. A. MILNE & G.C. KOZUB. 1971. Use of the nitrate-specific ion electrode for the determination of nitrate nitrogen in surface and groundwater. *Commun. Soil Sci. Plant Anal.* 2:415.

Cadmium Reduction Method

STRICKLAND, J.D.H. & T.R. PARSONS. 1968. A Manual of Sea Water Analysis, 2nd ed. Fish. Res. Board Can., Ottawa, Bull. No. 168.

Brucine Method

GREENBERG, A.E., J.R. ROSSUM, N. MOSKOWITZ & P.A. VILLARRUZ. 1958. Study of methods for the determination of nitrates. *J. Amer. Water Works Ass.* 50:821.

JENKINS, D. & L.L. MEDSKER. 1964. A brucine method for the determination of nitrate in ocean, estuarine and fresh waters. *Anal. Chem.* 36:610.

HOLTY, G.H. & H.S. POTWOROWSKI. 1972. Brucine analysis for high nitrate concentrations. *Environ. Sci Technol.* 6:835.

Chromotropic Acid Method

WEST, P.W. & T.P. RAMACHANDRAN. 1966. Spectrophotometric determination of nitrate using chromotropic acid. *Anal. Chim. Acta* 35:317.

Devarda's Alloy Method

ALLERTON, F.W. 1947. The determination of nitrates in water. *Analyst* 72:349.

JENKINS, S.H. 1950. The determination of ammoniacal nitrogen in sewage, sewage effluents, and river water. *J. Proc. Inst. Sewage Purif.* 1950 (Part 2):144.

Ministry of Housing and Local Government. 1956. Methods of Chemical Analysis as Applied to Sewage and Sewage Effluents. 2nd ed. H.M. Stationery Office, London.

ASSOCIATION OF BRITISH CHEMICAL MANUFACTURERS & SOCIETY FOR ANALYTICAL CHEMISTRY. 1958. Recommended Methods for the Analysis of Trade Effluents. W. Heffer & Sons, Ltd., Cambridge, England.

BREMMER, J.M. & D.R. KEENEY. 1965. Steam distillation methods for determination of ammonium, nitrate and nitrite. *Anal. Chim. Acta* 32:485.

EVANS, W.H. & J.G. STEVENS. 1972. An investigation into the determination of nitrate in potable waters and effluents by the reduction method employing Devarda's alloy. *J. Inst. Water Pollut. Control* 71:98.

420   NITROGEN (NITRITE)

1. General Discussion

a. Principle: The nitrite concentration is determined through the formation of a reddish purple azo dye produced at pH 2.0 to 2.5 by the coupling of diazotized sulfanilic acid with N-(1-napththyl)-ethylenediamine dihydrochloride. The diazotization method is suitable for the determination of nitrite nitrogen in the range 1 to 25 μg/l N. Photometric measurements can be made in the range 5 to 50 μg/l if a 5-cm light path and a green color filter are available. The color system obeys Beer's law up to 180 μg/l N with a 1-cm light path at 543 nm.

b. Interference: Chemical incompatibility makes it unlikely that nitrite, free available chlorine, and nitrogen trichloride will coexist in a sample. Nitrogen trichloride imparts a false red color when the normal order of reagent addition is followed. Although this effect may be minimized somewhat by adding the N-(1-naphthyl)-ethylenediamine dihydrochloride reagent first and then the sulfanilic acid reagent, an orange color still may result when a substantial nitrogen trichloride concentration is present. A check for a free available chlorine and nitrogen trichloride residual is advisable under such circumstances. The following ions interfere because of precipitation under the conditions of the test and therefore should be absent: antimonous, auric, bismuth, ferric, lead, mercurous, silver, chloroplatinate, and metavanadate. Cupric ion may cause low results by catalyzing the decomposition of the diazonium salt. Colored ions that alter the color system also should be absent.

Remove suspended solids by filtration through a 0.45-μm membrane filter before color development.

c. Storage of sample: Make the determination promptly on fresh samples to prevent bacterial conversion of the nitrite to nitrate or ammonia.

Never use acid preservation for samples to be analyzed for nitrite. For short-term preservation for 1 to 2 days deep-freeze at –20 C or add 40 mg $HgCl_2$ sample and store at 4 C.

2. Apparatus

Colorimetric equipment: One of the following is required:

a. Spectrophotometer, for use at 543 nm, providing a light path of 1 cm or longer.

b. Filter photometer, providing a light path of 1 cm or longer and equipped with a green color filter having maximum transmittance near 540 nm.

c. Nessler tubes, matched, 50-ml, tall form.

3. Reagents

Prepare all reagents from chemicals that are white in color.

a. Nitrite-free water: If it is not known that the distilled or demineralized water is free from nitrite, use either of the following procedures to prepare nitrite-free water:

1) Add to 1 l distilled water one small crystal each of potassium permanganate and barium or calcium hydroxide. Redistill in an all-pyrex apparatus and discard the initial 50 ml of distillate. Collect the distillate fraction

that is free of permanganate. [A yellow color with the orthotolidine reagent, Section 411B.3a1), indicates the presence of permanganate.]

2) Add 1 ml conc H_2SO_4 and 0.2 ml managanous sulfate solution (36.4 g $MnSO_4 \cdot H_2O/100$ ml aqueous solution) to each 1 l distilled water, and make pink with 1 to 3 ml potassium permanganate solution (400 mg $KMnO_4/l$ aqueous solution).

b. *Sulfanilamide reagent:* Dissolve 5 g sulfanilamide in a mixture of 50 ml conc HCl and about 300 ml distilled water. Dilute to 500 ml with distilled water. The solution is stable for many months.

c. *N-(1-naphthyl)-ethylenediamine dihydrochloride solution:* Dissolve 500 mg dihydrochloride in 500 ml distilled water. Store in a dark bottle. Renew the solution monthly or immediately when it develops a strong brown coloration.

d. *Hydrochloric acid,* HCl, 1+3.

e. *Stock nitrite solution:* Commercial reagent-grade $NaNO_2$ assays at less than 99%. Because nitrite is readily oxidized in the presence of moisture, use a fresh bottle of reagent for preparing the stock solution. Determine $NaNO_2$ content immediately before preparing the stock solution and keep bottles tightly stoppered against the free access of air when not in use. To determine the sodium nitrite content, add an excess of standard potassium permanganate solution, discharge the permanganate color with a standard reductant such as sodium oxalate or ferrous ammonium sulfate solution, and finally back-titrate with standard permanganate solution.

1) Preparation of stock solution—Dissolve 1.232 g $NaNO_2$ in nitrite-free water and dilute to 1,000 ml; 1.00 ml =

250 μg N. Preserve with 1 ml chloroform.

2) Standardization of stock solution—Pipet, in order, 50.00 ml standard 0.05N $KMnO_4$ (prepared and standardized as described under Calcium, Section 306B), 5 ml conc H_2SO_4, and 50.00 ml stock nitrite solution into a glass-stoppered flask or bottle. Submerge the tip of the nitrite pipet well below the surface of the permanganate acid solution. Shake gently and warm to 70 to 80 C on a hot plate. Discharge the permanganate color by adding sufficient standard 0.05N sodium oxalate (3.350 g $Na_2C_2O_4$, primary standard grade, per 1,000 ml solution) in 10.00-ml portions. Titrate the excess sodium oxalate with standard 0.05N $KMnO_4$ to the faint pink end point. Carry a nitrite-free water blank through the entire procedure and make the necessary corrections in the final calculation.

If standard 0.05N ferrous ammonium sulfate solution is substituted for sodium oxalate, omit heating to 70 to 80 C and extend the reaction period between the permanganate and ferrous ions to 5 min before making the final $KMnO_4$ titration. This standard 0.05N ferrous solution contains 19.607 g $Fe(NH_4)_2(SO_4)_2 \cdot 6H_2O$ and 20 ml conc $H_2SO_4/1,000$ ml solution. Standardize as described in Section 508.3.

Calculate the nitrite nitrogen content of the stock solution by the following equation:

$$A = \frac{[(B \times C) - (D \times E)] \times 7}{F}$$

where:

A = mg/ml nitrite nitrogen in stock nitrite solution.

B = total ml standard $KMnO_4$ used,
C = normality of standard $KMnO_4$,
D = total ml standard reductant added,
E = normality of standard reductant, and
F = ml stock $NaNO_2$ solution taken for titration.

Each 1.00 ml 0.05N $KMnO_4$ consumed by the nitrite corresponds to 1,725 μg $NaNO_2$, or 350 μg N.

f. Intermediate nitrite solution: Calculate the volume, G, of stock nitrite solution required for the intermediate nitrite solution by means of the following equation: $G = 12.5/A$. Dilute to 250 ml the calculated volume, G (approximately 50 ml), of the stock nitrite solution with nitrite-free water; 1.00 ml = 50.0 μg N. Prepare daily.

g. Standard nitrite solution: Dilute 10.00 ml intermediate nitrite solution to 1,000 ml with nitrite-free water; 1.00 ml = 0.500 μg N. Prepare daily.

4. Procedure

a. Removal of turbidity: If the sample contains suspended solids filter through a 0.45-μm membrane filter.

b. Color development: To 50.0 ml clear sample neutralized to pH 7, or to a portion diluted to 50.0 ml, add 1 ml sulfanilamide solution from an automatic pipet. Allow the reagent to react for a period of more than 2 min but not longer than 8 min. Add 1.0 ml 1-naphthyl-ethylenediamine solution and mix immediately.

c. Photometric measurement: Between 10 min and 2 hr afterwards measure the absorbance of the solution at 543 nm. As a guide use the following light paths for the indicated NO_2-N concentrations:

Light Path Length cm	NO_2-N $\mu g/l$
1	2-20
5	2-6
10	<2

Run parallel checks frequently against known nitrite standards, preferably in the nitrogen range of the samples. Redetermine complete calibration curves after preparing new reagents.

d. Color standards for visual comparison: Prepare a suitable series of visual color standards in nessler tubes by adding the following volumes of standard sodium nitrite solution and diluting to 50 ml with nitrite-free water: 0, 0.1, 0.2, 0.4, 0.7, 1.0, 1.4, 1.7, 2.0, and 2.5 ml, corresponding, respectively, to 0, 1.0, 2.0, 4.0, 7.0, 10, 14, 17, 20, and 25 $\mu g/l$ NO_2-N.

5. Calculation

$$\text{mg/l nitrite N} = \frac{\mu g \text{ nitrite N}}{\text{ml sample}}$$

6. Bibliography

RIDER, B. F. & M. G. MELLON. 1946 Colorimetric determination of nitrates. *Ind. Eng. Chem.*, Anal. Ed. 18:96.

BARNES, H. & A. R. FOLKARD. 1951. The determination of nitrites. *Analyst* 76:599.

BOLTZ, D. F., ed. 1958. Colorimetric Determination of Nonmetals. Interscience Publishers, New York, N.Y.

421 NITROGEN (ORGANIC)

The kjeldahl method determines nitrogen in the trinegative state.

The method offered herein fails to account for nitrogen in the form of azide, azine, azo, hydrazone, nitrate, nitrite, nitrile, nitro, nitroso, oxime, and semicarbazone. If ammonia nitrogen is not removed as described in the initial phase (¶4b below) of the procedure, the term "total kjeldahl nitrogen" is applied to the result. Should the total kjeldahl nitrogen and ammonia nitrogen be determined individually, the "organic nitrogen" can be obtained by difference.

This is the preferred technic for sediment and sludge samples.

1. General Discussion

a. Principle: In the presence of sulfuric acid, potassium sulfate, and mercuric sulfate catalyst, the amino nitrogen of many organic materials is converted to ammonium sulfate. After the mercury ammonium complex in the digestate has been decomposed by sodium thiosulfate, the ammonia is distilled from an alkaline medium and absorbed in boric acid. The ammonia is determined colorimetrically or by titration with a standard mineral acid.

b. Selection of modification: The sensitivity of the colorimetric methods makes them useful for the determination of organic nitrogen levels below 5 mg/l. The titrimetric method of measuring the ammonia in the distillate is suitable for the determination of a wide range of organic nitrogen concentrations, depending on the volume of boric acid absorbent used and the concentration of the standard acid titrant.

c. Storage of sample: The most reliable results are obtained on fresh samples. If prompt analysis of a relatively unpolluted water is impossible, retard biological activity by storing the sample at a low temperature, preferably just above freezing. Where such a measure is impractical, and for wastewater and polluted water, add 0.8 ml conc H_2SO_4/l sample.

2. Apparatus

a. Digestion apparatus: Kjeldahl flasks with a total capacity of 800 ml yield the best results. Digest over a heating device adjusted so that 250 ml of distilled water at an initial temperature of 25 C can be heated to a rolling boil in approximately 5 min. A heating device meeting this specification usually will provide the temperature range of 344 to 371 C, which is desirable for effective digestion.

b. Distillation apparatus: See Section 418A.2a.

c. Colorimetric equipment: One of the following is required:

1) Spectrophotometer, for use at 400 to 425 nm, providing a light path of 1 cm or longer.

2) Filter photometer, providing a light path of 1 cm or longer and equipped with a violet filter having maximum transmittance at 400 to 425 nm.

3) Nessler tubes, matched, 50-ml, tall form.

3. Reagents

All of the reagents listed for the determination of Nitrogen (Ammonia), Sections 418B.3 or 418D.3, are required, plus the following:

a. Digestion reagent: Dissolve 134 g K$_2$SO$_4$ in 650 ml ammonia-free distilled water and 200 ml conc H$_2$SO$_4$. Add, with stirring, a solution prepared by dissolving 2 g red mercuric oxide, HgO, in 25 ml 6N H$_2$SO$_4$. Dilute the combined solution to 1 l. Keep at a temperature above 14 C to prevent crystallization.

b. Phenolphthalein indicator solution.

c. Sodium hydroxide-sodium thiosulfate reagent: Dissolve 500 g NaOH and 25 g Na$_2$S$_2$O$_3$•5H$_2$O in ammonia-free distilled water and dilute to 1 l.

d. Borate buffer solution: See Section 418A.3b.

e. Sodium hydroxide, 6N.

4. Procedure

a. Selection of sample volume: Place a measured sample into an 800-ml kjeldahl flask. Determine the sample size from the following tabulation:

Organic Nitrogen in Sample *mg/l*	Sample Size *ml*
0–1	500
1–10	250
10–20	100
20–50	50.0
50–100	25.0

If necessary, dilute the sample to 300 ml and neutralize to pH 7.

b. Ammonia removal: Add 25 ml borate buffer and 6N NaOH until pH 9.5 is reached. Add a few glass beads or boiling chips and boil off 300 ml. If desired, distill this fraction and determine the ammonia nitrogen. Alternatively, if ammonia has been determined by the distillation method, use the residue in the distilling flask for the organic nitrogen determination. For sludge and sediment samples weigh wet sample in a crucible or weighing bottle, transfer the contents to a kjeldahl flask, and determine total kjeldahl nitrogen. Follow a similar procedure for ammonia nitrogen determination and organic nitrogen determined by difference. Determinations of organic and total kjeldahl nitrogen on dried sludge and sediment samples are not accurate because drying results in loss of ammonium salts.

c. Digestion: Cool and add carefully 50 ml digestion reagent (or substitute 10 ml conc H$_2$SO$_4$, 6.7 g K$_2$SO$_4$, and 1.5 ml mercuric sulfate solution). If large quantities of nitrogen-free organic matter are present, add an additional 50 ml digestion reagent for each gram of solid matter in the sample. After mixing, heat under a hood or with suitable ejection equipment to fumes of SO$_3$ and continue to boil briskly until the solution clears (becomes colorless or a pale straw color). Then digest for an additional 30 min. Let flask and contents cool, dilute to 300 ml with ammonia-free water, and add 0.5 ml phenolphthalein indicator solution and mix. Tilt the flask and carefully add sufficient (approximately 50 ml/50 ml digestion reagent used) hydroxide-thiosulfate reagent to form an alkaline layer at the bottom of the flask.

Connect the flask to the steamed-out distillation apparatus and shake the flask to insure complete mixing. Add more hydroxide-thiosulfate reagent in the prescribed manner if a red phenolphthalein color fails to appear at this stage.

d. Distillation: Distill and collect 200 ml distillate below the surface of 50 ml boric acid solution. Use plain boric acid solution when the ammonia is to be determined by nesslerization and use indicating boric acid for a titrimetric finish. Extend the tip of the condenser well below the level of boric acid solution and do not allow the temperature in the condenser to rise above 29 C. Lower the collected distillate free of contact with the delivery tube and continue distillation during the last minute or two to cleanse the condenser.

e. *Final ammonia measurement:* Determine the ammonia by either nesslerization or titration.

1) Nesslerization—Mix the distillate thoroughly and measure a 50.0-ml portion or less. Complete the determination as described in Nitrogen (Ammonia), Section 418B.4*b-e*.

2) Titration—Titrate the ammonia in the distillate as described in Nitrogen (Ammonia), Section 418D.4*c*.

f. *Blank:* Carry a blank through all the steps of the procedure and apply the necessary correction to the results.

5. Calculation

a. *Nesslerization finish:*

$$\text{mg/l organic N} = \frac{A \times 1,000}{\text{ml sample}} \times \frac{B}{C}$$

where A = mg N found colorimetrically, B = ml total distillate collected including the H_3BO_3, and C = ml distillate taken for nesslerization.

b. *Titrimetric finish:*

$$\text{mg/l organic N} = \frac{(D-E) \times 280}{\text{ml sample}}$$

where D = ml H_2SO_4 titration for sample and E = ml H_2SO_4 titration for blank.

6. Precision and Accuracy

Three synthetic unknown samples containing varying organic nitrogen concentrations and other constituents

TABLE 421:I. PRECISION AND ACCURACY DATA FOR ORGANIC NITROGEN

Sample	No. of Laboratories	Organic Nitrogen Concentration µg/l	Relative Standard Deviation			Relative Error		
			Nessler Finish %	Titrimetric Finish %	Calculation of Total Kjeldahl N Minus Ammonia N %	Nessler Finish %	Titrimetric Finish %	Calculation of Total Kjeldahl N Minus Ammonia N %
1	26	200	94.8			55.0		
	29			104.4			70.0	
	15				68.8			70.0
2	26	800	52.1			12.5		
	31			44.8			3.7	
	16				52.6			8.7
3	26	1,500	43.1			9.3		
	30			54.7			22.6	
	16				45.9			4.0

were analyzed by three procedural modifications: kjeldahl-nessler finish, kjeldahl-titrimetric finish, and calculation of the difference between the total kjeldahl nitrogen and ammonia nitrogen, both determined by a nessler finish. The results obtained by laboratories are summarized in Table 421:I.

Sample 1 contained the following additional constituents: 400 mg/l chloride, 1.50 mg/l ammonia nitrogen, 1.0 mg/l nitrate nitrogen, 0.5 mg/l phosphate, and 30.0 mg/l silica.

Sample 2 contained the following additional constituents: 200 mg/l chloride, 0.8 mg/l ammonia nitrogen, 1.0 mg/l nitrate nitrogen, 5.0 mg/l phosphate, and 15.0 mg/l silica.

Sample 3 contained the following additional constituents: 10 mg/l chloride, 0.2 mg/l ammonia nitrogen, 1.0 mg/l nitrate nitrogen, 10.0 mg/l phosphate, and 5.0 mg/l silica.

7. Bibliography

KJELDAHL, J. 1883. A new method for the determination of nitrogen in organic matter. Z. Anal. Chem. 22:366.

PHELPS, E.B. 1905. The determination of organic nitrogen in sewage by the Kjeldahl process. J. Infect. Dis. (Suppl.) 1:225.

MEEKER, E.W. & E.C. WAGNER. 1933. Titration of ammonia in the presence of boric acid. Ind. Eng. Chem., Anal. Ed. 5:396.

WAGNER, E.C. 1940. Titration of ammonia in the presence of boric acid. Ind. Eng. Chem., Anal. Ed. 12:771.

McKENZIE, H.A. & H.S. WALLACE. 1954. The Kjeldahl determination of nitrogen: A critical study of digestion conditions. Aust. J. Chem. 7:55.

MORGAN, G.B., J.B. LACKEY & F.W. GILCREAS. 1957. Quantitative determination of organic nitrogen in water, sewage, and industrial wastes. Anal. Chem. 29:833.

BOLTZ, D.F., ed. 1958. Colorimetric Determination of Nonmetals. Interscience Publishers, New York, N.Y.

422 OXYGEN (DISSOLVED)

Dissolved oxygen (DO) levels in natural and wastewaters are dependent on the physical, chemical, and biochemical activities prevailing in the water body. The analysis for DO is a key test in water pollution control activities and waste treatment process control.

Two methods for DO analysis are described: the Winkler or iodometric method and its modifications and the electrometric method using membrane electrodes. The iodometric method[1] is a titrimetric procedure based on the oxidizing property of DO, while the membrane electrode procedure is based on the rate of diffusion of molecular oxygen across a membrane.[2] The choice of test procedure is dependent on the interferences present, the accuracy desired, and, in some cases, convenience or expedience.

422 A.   Iodometric Methods

1. Principle

Improved by variations in technic and equipment and aided by instrumentation, the iodometric test remains the most precise and reliable titrimetric procedure for DO analysis. The test is based on the addition of divalent manganese solution, followed by strong alkali, to the sample in a glass-stoppered bottle. DO present rapidly oxidizes an equivalent amount of the dispersed divalent manganous hydroxide precipitate to hydroxides of higher valency states. In the presence of iodide ions and acidification, the oxidized manganese reverts to the divalent state, with the liberation of iodine equivalent to the original DO content in the sample. The iodine is then titrated with a standard solution of thiosulfate.

The titration end point can be detected visually, with a starch indicator, or electrometrically, with potentiometric or dead-stop technics.[3] Experienced analysts can maintain a precision of ±50 $\mu g/l$ with visual end-point detection and a precision of ±5 $\mu g/l$ with electrometric end-point detection. [2, 3]

The liberated iodine also can be determined directly by simple absorption spectrophotometers.[4] This method can be used easily on a routine basis and can provide very accurate estimates for DO in the microgram-per-liter range provided that interfering particulate matter, color, and chemical interferences are not present.

2. Selection of Method

Before using the iodometric methods, the analyst should consider the effect of interferences, oxidizing or reducing materials that may be present in the sample. Certain oxidizing agents liberate iodine from iodides (positive interference) and some reducing agents reduce iodine to iodide (negative interference). Certain organic compounds interfere with the test by hindering the settling of the oxidized manganese precipitate and by partially obscuring the end point of the iodometric titration with starch indicator.

Several modifications of the iodometric method are given to minimize the effect of interfering materials.[2] Among the more commonly used procedures are the azide modification,[5] the permanganate modification,[6] the alum flocculation modification,[7] and the copper sulfate-sulfamic acid flocculation modification.[8, 9] The azide modification (B) effectively removes the interference caused by nitrite, which is the most common interference in biologically treated effluents and incubated BOD samples. Use the permanganate modification (C) in the presence of ferrous iron. When the sample contains 5 mg/l ferric iron salts or more, add potassium fluoride as the first reagent in the azide modification or after the permanganate treatment for ferrous iron. Alternately, eliminate Fe(III) interference by using 90% H_3PO_4 instead of H_2SO_4 for acidification. This procedure has not been tested for Fe(III) concentrations above 20 mg/l.

Use the alum flocculation modification (D) in the presence of suspended solids that cause interference and the copper sulfate-sulfamic acid flocculation modification (E) on activated-sludge mixed liquor.

3. Collection of Samples

Collect samples for the DO analysis very carefully. Methods of sampling are highly dependent on the source to be sampled and, to a certain extent, on the method of analysis. Do not let the sample remain in contact with air or be agitated, because either condition causes a change in its gaseous content. Samples from any depth in streams, lakes, or reservoirs, and samples of boiler waters, need special precautions to eliminate changes in pressure and temperature.

Procedures and equipment have been developed for sampling waters under pressure and unconfined waters (e.g., streams, rivers, and reservoirs). Sampling procedures and the equipment needed are described in American Society for Testing and Materials Special Technical Publication No. 148-1 and in U.S. Geological Survey Water Supply Paper No. 1454.

Collect surface water samples in narrow-mouth glass-stoppered BOD bot-

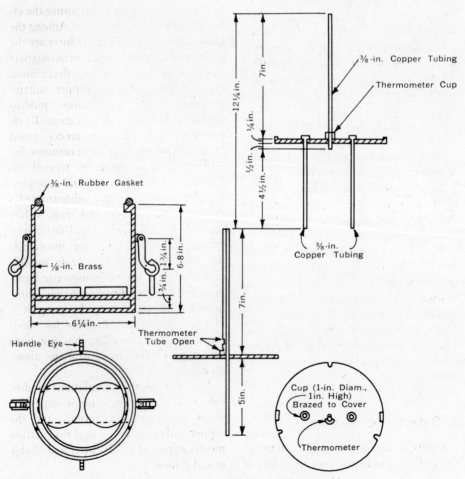

Figure 422:1. DO and BOD sampler assembly.

tles of 300-ml capacity with tapered ground-glass pointed stoppers and flared mouths. Avoid entraining or dissolving atmospheric oxygen. In sampling from a line under pressure, attach a glass or rubber tube to the tap and extend to the bottom of the bottle. Let the bottle overflow two or three times its volume and replace the stopper so that no air bubbles are entrained.

Suitable samplers for streams, ponds, or tanks of moderate depth are of the APHA type shown in Figure 422:1. Use a Kemmerer-type sampler for samples collected from depths greater than 2 m. In the latter case, bleed the sample from the bottom of the sampler through a tube extending to the bottom of a 250- to 300-ml BOD bottle. Fill the bottle to overflowing (overflow for approximately 10 sec), and prevent turbulence and the formation of bubbles while filling the bottle. Record the temperature of the sample to the nearest degree Celsius or more precisely.

4. Preservation of Samples

Determine DO immediately on all samples that contain an appreciable oxygen or iodine demand. Samples with no iodine demand may be stored for a few hours without change after the addition of manganese sulfate solution, alkali-iodide solution, and H_2SO_4, followed by shaking in the usual way. Protect samples stored at this point from strong sunlight and titrate as soon as possible.

For samples with an iodine demand, preserve for 4 to 8 hr by adding 0.7 ml conc H_2SO_4 and 1 ml sodium azide solution (2 g NaN_3/100 ml distilled water) to the DO bottle. This will arrest biological activity and maintain the DO if the bottle is stored at the temperature of collection or water-sealed and kept at a temperature of 10 to 20 C. As soon as possible, complete the procedure, using 2 ml manganese sulfate solution, 3 ml alkali-iodide solution, and 2 ml conc H_2SO_4.

422 B. Azide Modification

1. General Discussion

Use the azide modification for most sewage, effluent, and stream samples. It is recommended especially if samples contain more than 50 μg/l nitrite nitrogen and not more than 1 mg/l ferrous iron. Other reducing or oxidizing materials should be absent. If 1 ml fluoride solution is added before the sample is acidified and there is no delay in titration, the method is applicable in the presence of 100 to 200 mg/l ferric iron.

2. Reagents

a. *Manganese sulfate solution:* Dissolve 480 g $MnSO_4 \cdot 4H_2O$, 400 g $MnSO_4 \cdot 2H_2O$, or 364 g $MnSO_4 \cdot H_2O$ in distilled water, filter, and dilute to 1 l. The manganese sulfate solution should not give a color with starch when added to an acidified solution of KI.

b. *Alkali-iodide-azide reagent:* Prepare the reagent by one of the following procedures:

1) Dissolve 500 g NaOH (or 700 g

KOH), and 135 g NaI, (or 150 g KI) in distilled water and dilute to 1 l. Add 10 g sodium azide, NaN_3, dissolved in 40 ml distilled water. Potassium and sodium salts may be used interchangeably. This reagent should not give a color with starch solution when diluted and acidified.

2) Dissolve 400 g NaOH in 500 ml boiled and cooled distilled water, cool slightly, and then dissolve 900 g NaI in the caustic solution. Dissolve 10 g NaN_3 in 40 ml distilled water. Add the latter to the former and dilute, if necessary, to 1 l. The final volume may be slightly over 1 l because of the very high concentrations of dissolved salts. The amount of NaI is sufficient to measure up to 40 mg/l DO. With this reagent, use the following revised volumes in ¶3a of the procedure: 2.5 ml alkali-iodide-azide reagent and 2 ml conc H_2SO_4.

c. *Sulfuric acid,* H_2SO_4, conc: One milliliter is equivalent to about 3 ml alkali-iodide-azide reagent.

d. *Starch:* Use either the aqueous solution or soluble starch powder mixtures.

To prepare the aqueous solution, add a cold water suspension of 5 g arrowroot or soluble starch to approximately 800 ml of boiling water, with stirring. Dilute to 1 l, boil a few minutes, and let settle overnight. Use the clear supernate. Preserve with 1.25 g salicylic acid/l or by adding a few drops of toluene.

e. *Sodium thiosulfate stock solution,* 0.10N: Dissolve 24.82 g $Na_2S_2O_3 \cdot 5H_2O$ in boiled and cooled distilled water and dilute to 1 l. Preserve by adding 5 ml chloroform or 1 g NaOH/l.

f. *Standard sodium thiosulfate titrant,* 0.0250N: Prepare either by diluting

250.0 ml sodium thiosulfate stock solution to 1,000 ml or by dissolving 6.205 g $Na_2S_2O_3 \cdot 5H_2O$ in freshly boiled and cooled distilled water and diluting to 1,000 ml. Preserve by adding 5 ml chloroform or 0.4 g NaOH/l, or 4 g borax and 5 to 10 mg HgI_2/l. 1.00 ml = 200 μg DO.

Standardize with biniodate or dichromate:

1) *Standard potassium biniodate solution,* 0.0250N: A stock solution equivalent in strength to 0.100N thiosulfate solution contains 3.249 g/l $KH(IO_3)_2$. The biniodate solution equivalent to the 0.0250N thiosulfate contains 812.4 mg/l $KH(IO_3)_2$. Prepare by diluting 250 ml stock solution to 1 l.

Standardization: Dissolve approximately 2 g KI, free from iodate, in an erlenmeyer flask with 100 to 150 ml distilled water. Add 10 ml 1+9 H_2SO_4, then 20.00 ml standard biniodate solution. Dilute to 200 ml and titrate the liberated iodine with the thiosulfate titrant, adding starch toward the end of the titration, when a pale straw color is reached. When the solutions are of equal strength, 20.00 ml 0.0250N thiosulfate should be required. If not, adjust the thiosulfate solution to 0.0250N.

2) *Standard potassium dichromate solution,* 0.0250N: Potassium dichromate may be substituted for biniodate. A solution equivalent to 0.0250N sodium thiosulfate contains 1.226 g/l $K_2Cr_2O_7$. Dry the $K_2Cr_2O_7$ at 103 C for 2 hr before making solution. Prepare the solution in a volumetric flask.

Standardization: Same as with biniodate, but use 20.00 ml standard dichromate solution. Place in the dark for 5 min, dilute to approximately 400 ml, and titrate with 0.0250N thiosulfate solution.

g. *Special reagent—potassium fluoride solution:* Dissolve 40 g KF•2H$_2$O in distilled water and dilute to 100 ml.

3. Procedure

a. To the sample as collected in a 250- to 300-ml bottle, add 2 ml* manganese sulfate solution, followed by 2 ml* alkali-iodide-azide reagent, well below the surface of the liquid. Stopper carefully to exclude air bubbles and mix by inverting the bottle at least 15 times. When the precipitate settles, leaving a clear supernate above the manganese hydroxide floc, shake again. With seawater, allow at least a 2-min period of contact with the precipitate. After at least 2 min settling has produced at least 100 ml of clear supernate, carefully remove the stopper and immediately add 2.0 ml conc H$_2$SO$_4$ by allowing the acid to run down the neck of the bottle, restopper, and mix by gentle inversion until dissolution is complete. Distribute the iodine uniformly throughout the bottle before decantation of the amount needed for titration. Use a volume corresponding to 200 ml of the original sample after correction for the loss of sample by displacement with the reagents. Thus, for a total of 4 ml (2 ml each) of the manganese sulfate and alkali-iodide-azide reagents in a 300-ml bottle, titrate $200 \times 300/(300-4) = 203$ ml.

b. Titrate with 0.0250N thiosulfate solution to a pale straw color. Add 1 to 2 ml starch solution and continue the titration to the first disappearance of the blue color. If the end point is overrun, back-titrate with 0.0250N biniodate solution added dropwise, or by adding a measured volume of sample. Correct for the amount of biniodate solution or sample. Disregard subsequent recolorations due to the catalytic effect of nitrite or to traces of ferric salts that have not been complexed with fluoride.

4. Calculation

a. For 200 ml of original sample, 1 ml 0.0250N sodium thiosulfate = 1 mg/l DO.

b. To obtain the results in milliliters of oxygen gas per liter, corrected to 0 C and 760 mm pressure, multiply mg/l DO by 0.70.

c. To express the results as percent saturation at 760 mm atmospheric pressure, use the solubility data in Table 422:I. Equations for correcting the solubilities to barometric pressures other than mean sea level are given below the table.

d. Calculate the solubility of oxygen in distilled water at any barometric pressure, P (mm Hg), temperature, t C, and saturated vapor pressure, u (mm Hg), for the given t, between the temperature of 0 and 30 C, by:

$$mg/l \; DO = \frac{(P-u) \times 0.678}{35+t}$$

and between 30 and 50 C by:

$$mg/l \; DO = \frac{(P-u) \times 0.827}{49+t}$$

---

* Although 2-ml quantities of the reagents insure better contact with less agitation, it is permissible to use 1-ml reagent quantities with 250-ml bottles.

TABLE 422:I. SOLUBILITY OF OXYGEN IN WATER EXPOSED TO WATER-SATURATED AIR*

Temperature C	Chloride Concentration in Water mg/l					Difference /100 mg Chloride
	0	5,000	10,000	15,000	20,000	
	Dissolved Oxygen mg/l					
0	14.6	13.8	13.0	12.1	11.3	0.017
1	14.2	13.4	12.6	11.8	11.0	0.016
2	13.8	13.1	12.3	11.5	10.8	0.015
3	13.5	12.7	12.0	11.2	10.5	0.015
4	13.1	12.4	11.7	11.0	10.3	0.014
5	12.8	12.1	11.4	10.7	10.0	0.014
6	12.5	11.8	11.1	10.5	9.8	0.014
7	12.2	11.5	10.9	10.2	9.6	0.013
8	11.9	11.2	10.6	10.0	9.4	0.013
9	11.6	11.0	10.4	9.8	9.2	0.012
10	11.3	10.7	10.1	9.6	9.0	0.012
11	11.1	10.5	9.9	9.4	8.8	0.011
12	10.8	10.3	9.7	9.2	8.6	0.011
13	10.6	10.1	9.5	9.0	8.5	0.011
14	10.4	9.9	9.3	8.8	8.3	0.010
15	10.2	9.7	9.1	8.6	8.1	0.010
16	10.0	9.5	9.0	8.5	8.0	0.010
17	9.7	9.3	8.8	8.3	7.8	0.010
18	9.5	9.1	8.6	8.2	7.7	0.009
19	9.4	8.9	8.5	8.0	7.6	0.009
20	9.2	8.7	8.3	7.9	7.4	0.009
21	9.0	8.6	8.1	7.7	7.3	0.009
22	8.8	8.4	8.0	7.6	7.1	0.008
23	8.7	8.3	7.9	7.4	7.0	0.008
24	8.5	8.1	7.7	7.3	6.9	0.008
25	8.4	8.0	7.6	7.2	6.7	0.008

* At a total pressure of 760 mm Hg. Under any other barometric pressure, P, the solubility, S' (mg/l), can be obtained from the corresponding value in the table by the equation:

$$S' = S \frac{P-p}{760-p}$$

in which S is the solubility at 760 mm and p is the pressure (mm) of saturated water vapor at the temperature of the water. For elevations less than 1,000 m and temperatures below 25 C, p can be ignored. The equation then becomes:

$$S' = S \frac{P}{760} = S\frac{P'}{29.92}$$

Dry air is assumed to contain 20.90% oxygen. (Calculations made by Whipple and Whipple, 1911. J. Amer. Chem. Soc. 33:362.)

TABLE 422:I. *(Continued)*

Temperature C	Chloride Concentration in Water mg/l					Difference /100 mg Chloride
	0	5,000	10,000	15,000	20,000	
	Dissolved Oxygen mg/l					
26	8.2	7.8	7.4	7.0	6.6	0.008
27	8.1	7.7	7.3	6.9	6.5	0.008
28	7.9	7.5	7.1	6.8	6.4	0.008
29	7.8	7.4	7.0	6.6	6.3	0.008
30	7.6	7.3	6.9	6.5	6.1	0.008
31	7.5					
32	7.4					
33	7.3					
34	7.2					
35	7.1					
36	7.0					
37	6.9					
38	6.8					
39	6.7					
40	6.6					
41	6.5					
42	6.4					
43	6.3					
44	6.2					
45	6.1					
46	6.0					
47	5.9					
48	5.8					
49	5.7					
50	5.6					

5. Precision and Accuracy

The DO can be determined with a precision, expressed as a standard deviation, of about 20 μg/l in distilled water and about 60 μg/l in wastewater and secondary effluents. In the presence of appreciable interference, even with the proper modifications the standard deviation may be as high as 100 μg/l. Still greater errors may occur in the testing of waters having organic suspended solids or heavy pollution. Avoid errors due to carelessness in collecting samples, prolonging the completion of the test, or selection of an unsuitable modification.

422 C.   Permanganate Modification

1. General Discussion

Use the permanganate modification only on samples containing ferrous iron.

High concentrations of ferric iron (up to several hundred milligrams per liter), such as may be present in acid mine water, may be overcome by the addition of 1 ml potassium fluoride and azide, provided that the final titration is made immediately upon acidification.

This modification is ineffective for the oxidation of sulfite, thiosulfate, polythionate, or the organic matter in wastewater. The error with samples containing 0.25% by volume of digester waste from the manufacture of sulfite pulp may amount to 7 to 8 mg/l DO. With such samples, a crude accuracy may be secured through preliminary treatment with the alkali-hypochlorite modification.[10] At best, however, the latter procedure gives low results, the deviation amounting to 1 mg/l for samples containing 0.25% digester wastes.

2. Reagents

All the reagents required for Method B, and in addition:

a. Potassium permanganate solution: Dissolve 6.3 g $KMnO_4$ in distilled water and dilute to 1 l.

b. Potassium oxalate solution: Dissolve 2 g $K_2C_2O_4 \cdot H_2O$ in 100 ml distilled water; 1 ml of this solution is sufficient for the reduction of about 1.1 ml of the permanganate solution.

3. Procedure

a. To the sample collected in a 250-to 300-ml bottle add, below the surface, exactly 0.7 ml conc H_2SO_4 followed by 1 ml potassium permanganate solution and 1 ml potassium fluoride solution. Stopper and mix by inversion. Never add more than 0.7 ml conc H_2SO_4 as the first step of pretreatment. Add the acid with a 1-ml pipet graduated to 0.1 ml. The amount of permanganate added should be sufficient to obtain a violet tinge that persists for 5 min. If the permanganate color is destroyed in a shorter time, add additional potassium permanganate solution, but avoid large excesses.

b. Remove the permanganate color completely by adding 0.5 to 1.0 ml potassium oxalate solution. Mix well and let stand in the dark to facilitate the reaction. Excess oxalate causes low results; add only an amount of oxalate that completely decolorizes the potassium permanganate without having an excess of more than 0.5 ml. Decolorization should occur in 2 to 10 min. If it is impossible to decolorize the sample without adding a large excess of oxalate, the DO result will be inaccurate.

c. From this point the procedure closely parallels that in Section 422B.3. Add 2 ml manganese sulfate solution followed by 3 ml alkali-iodide-azide reagent. Stopper, mix, and let the precipitate settle. Remix for 20 sec and let the precipitate settle a second time; then acidify with 2 ml conc H_2SO_4. When 0.7 ml acid, 1 ml potassium permanganate solution, 1 ml potassium oxalate solution, 2 ml manganese sulfate solution, and 3 ml alkali-iodide-azide (or a total of 7.7 ml of reagents) are used in a 300-ml bottle, take $200 \times 300/(300-7.7) = 205$ ml for titration.

This correction is slightly in error because the potassium permanganate solution is near saturation in DO and 1 ml would add about 0.008 mg oxygen to the DO bottle. However, because the precision of the method (standard deviation, 0.06 ml of thiosulfate titration, or 0.012 mg oxygen) is 50% greater than the error, it is not necessary to correct for this small error. When substantially more potassium permanganate solution is used routinely, use a solution several times more concentrated so that 1 ml will generally satisfy the permanganate demand.

422 D.   Alum Flocculation Modification

1. General Discussion

Samples high in suspended solids may consume appreciable quantities of iodine in acid solution. This interference may be removed by alum flocculation.

2. Reagents

All the reagents required for the azide modification (Section 422B.2) and in addition:

a. *Alum solution:* Dissolve 10 g aluminum potassium sulfate, $AlK (SO_4)_2 \cdot 12H_2O$, in distilled water and dilute to 100 ml.

b. *Ammonium hydroxide*, NH_4OH, conc.

3. Procedure

Collect a sample in a glass-stoppered bottle of 500 to 1,000 ml capacity, using the same precautions as for regular DO samples. Add 10 ml alum solution and 1 to 2 ml conc NH_4OH. Stopper and invert gently for about 1 min. Let sample settle quiescently for about 10 min and then siphon the clear supernate into a 250- to 300-ml DO bottle until it overflows. Avoid aeration and keep the siphon submerged at all times. Continue the sample treatment as in Section 422B.3 or an appropriate modification.

422 E.   Copper Sulfate-Sulfamic Acid Flocculation Modification

1. General Discussion

This modification is used for biological flocs such as activated sludge mixtures, which have high oxygen utilization rates.

2. Reagents

All the reagents required for the azide modification (Section 422B.2) and, in addition:

Copper sulfate-sulfamic acid inhibitor

solution: Dissolve 32 g technical-grade sulfamic acid, NH_2SO_2OH, without heat in 475 ml distilled water. Dissolve 50 g copper sulfate, $CuSO_4 \cdot 5H_2O$, in 500 ml water. Mix the two solutions and add 25 ml conc acetic acid.

3. Procedure

Add 10 ml copper sulfate-sulfamic acid inhibitor to a 1-l glass-stoppered bottle. Insert the bottle in a special sampler designed so that the bottle fills from a tube near the bottom and overflows only 25 to 50% of bottle capacity. Collect the sample, stopper, and mix by inversion. Let the suspended solids settle quiescently and siphon the relatively clear supernatant liquor into a 250- to 300-ml DO bottle. Continue the sample treatment as rapidly as possible by the azide (Section 422B.3) or other appropriate modification.

422 F.   Membrane Electrode Method

1. General Discussion

Various modifications of the iodometric method have been developed to eliminate or minimize the effects of interferences; nevertheless, the method is still inapplicable to a variety of industrial and domestic wastewaters.[11] Moreover, the iodometric method is not ideally suited for field testing and cannot be adapted easily for continuous monitoring or for dissolved oxygen determinations in situ.

Polarographic methods using the dropping mercury electrode or the rotating platinum electrode have not always been reliable for the DO analysis in domestic and industrial wastewaters because impurities present in the test solution can cause electrode poisoning or other interferences.[12, 13] With the membrane-covered electrode systems these problems are minimized, because the sensing element is protected by an oxygen-permeable plastic membrane that serves as a diffusion barrier against impurities.[14-16] Under steady-state conditions the current is directly proportional to the DO concentration* in the test solution.

Membrane electrodes of the polarographic[14] as well as the galvanic[15] type have been used for DO measurements in lakes and reservoirs,[17] for stream survey and control of industrial effluents,[18, 19] for continuous monitoring of DO in activated sludge units,[20] and for estuarine and oceanographic studies.[21] Being completely submersible, membrane electrodes are well suited for analysis in situ. Their portability and ease of operation and maintenance make them particularly convenient for field applications. In laboratory investigations, membrane electrodes have been used for continuous DO analysis in bacterial cultures, including the BOD test. [15, 22]

Membrane electrodes provide an excellent method for DO analysis in polluted waters, highly colored waters, and

---

* Fundamentally the current is directly proportional to the activity of molecular oxygen.[2]

strong waste effluents. They are recommended for use especially under conditions that are unfavorable for use of the iodometric method, or when that test and its modifications are subject to serious errors caused by interferences.

a. Principle: Oxygen-sensitive membrane electrodes of the polarographic as well as the galvanic type are composed of two solid metal electrodes in contact with a certain volume of supporting electrolyte separated from the test solution by a selective membrane. The basic difference between the galvanic and the polarographic systems is that in the former the electrode reaction is spontaneous (similar to that in a fuel cell), while in the latter an external source of applied voltage is needed to polarize the indicator electrode. Polyethylene and teflon membranes are used commonly because they are permeable to molecular oxygen and possess a certain degree of ruggedness.

Membrane electrodes are commercially available in some variety. In all these instruments the "diffusion current" is linearly proportional to the concentration of molecular oxygen in the test solution. The current can be converted easily to concentration units (e.g., milligrams per liter) by a number of calibration procedures.

Membrane electrodes exhibit a relatively high temperature coefficient largely due to changes in the membrane permeability.[16] The effect of temperature on the electrode sensitivity, ϕ (μamp per mg/l), can be expressed by the following simplified relationship:[16]

$$\log \phi = 0.43\, mt + b$$

where t is the temperature in degrees Celsius, m is a constant that depends on the membrane material, and b is a constant that largely depends on the membrane thickness. If ϕ and m are determined for one temperature, it is possible to calculate the sensitivity at any desired temperature as follows:

$$\log \phi = \log \phi_0 + 0.43 m(t - t_0)$$

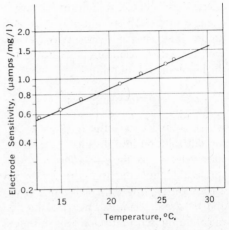

Figure 422:2. Effect of temperature on electrode sensitivity.

Nomographic charts for temperature correction can be constructed easily[2] and they are available from certain manufacturers. An example is shown in Figure 422:2, in which for simplicity the sensitivity is plotted versus the temperature Celsius on semilogarithmic coordinates. It is recommended that one or two points be checked frequently to confirm the original calibration. If calibration changes, the new calibration should be parallel to the original, provided that the same membrane material is used.

Temperature compensation also can be made automatically by using thermistors in the electrode circuit.[14] However, thermistors may not compensate fully over a wide temperature range.

For certain applications where high accuracy is required, use calibrated nomographic charts to correct for the temperature effect.

In order to use the DO membrane electrode in estuarine waters or in wastewaters with varying ionic strength, make a correction for the effect of salting-out on electrode sensitivity.[2, 16] This effect is particularly significant for large changes in the salt content of the test solution. The electrode sensitivity varies with the salt concentration according to the following relationship:

$$\log \phi_s = 0.43 m_s C_s + \log \phi_o$$

where ϕ_s and ϕ_o are the sensitivities in the salt solution and distilled water, respectively, C_s is the salt concentration (preferably the ionic strength), and m_s is a constant (salting-out coefficient). If ϕ_o and m_s are determined, it is possible to calculate the sensitivity for any value of C_s. It is possible to use specific conductance to approximate the salt content in the test solution (C_s). This is particularly applicable to estuarine waters. Figure 422:3 shows calibration curves for sensitivity of varying salt solutions at different temperatures.

b. *Interference:* Plastic films used with the membrane electrode systems are permeable to a variety of gases besides oxygen, none of which is easily depolarized at the indicator electrode. Prolonged use of membrane electrodes in waters containing such gases as H_2S tends to lower the cell sensitivity. The effect of this interference is eliminated by frequent changing and calibration of the membrane electrode.

c. *Sampling:* Membrane electrodes offer the advantage of analysis in situ

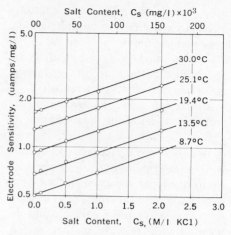

Figure 422:3. The salting-out effect at different temperatures.

and therefore eliminate errors caused by sample handling and storage. If sampling is required, use the same precautions suggested for the iodometric method.

2. Apparatus

Oxygen-sensitive membrane electrode, polarographic or galvanic, with appropriate meter.

3. Procedure

a. *Calibration:* Because the differences between makes and models of satisfactory electrodes and meters make it impossible to formulate detailed instructions applicable to every instrument, follow the manufacturer's calibration procedure exactly in order to obtain the guaranteed precision and accuracy. Generally, calibrate the membrane electrode by reading against air or a water sample of known DO concentration (determined by the iodometric method) as well as in a sample with zero DO. (Add excess sodium sulfite and a trace of CoCl₂ to bring the DO to zero.) Preferably calibrate with samples of the water under test. Avoid an iodometric calibration where interfering substances are suspected. The following illustrate the recommended procedures:

1) Fresh water—For river and lake samples where pollution is relatively light and interfering substances are absent, calibrate in the test solution or distilled water, whichever is more convenient.

2) Salt water—Use samples of seawater or waters having a constant salt concentration in excess of 1,000 mg/l, directly for calibration.

3) Fresh water containing pollution or interfering substances—Calibrate with distilled water because of the erroneous results that will occur with the test solution.

4) Salt water containing pollution or interfering substances—Calibrate with a sample of clean water containing the same salt content as the test solution. Add a strong potassium chloride solution (Conductivity, Section 205 and Table 205:I) to distilled water to produce the same specific conductance as that in the test sample. In the case of polluted ocean waters, calibrate with a sample of unpolluted seawater.

5) Estuary water containing varying quantities of salt—Calibrate with a sample of uncontaminated seawater or distilled or tap water. Determine the chloride or salt concentration of the test sample and revise the calibration to take into account the change of oxygen solubility in the estuary water.[2]

b. Sample measurement: Follow all precautions recommended by the manufacturer to insure acceptable results. Carefully change the electrode system to avoid contamination of the sensing element and also trapping minute air bubbles under the membrane, which can lead to lowered response and high residual current. Provide sufficient flow of the test solution across the membrane surface to overcome erratic response (see Figure 422:4 for a typical example of the effect of stirring).

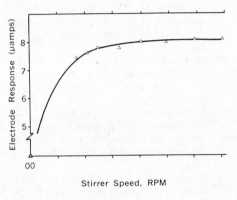

Figure 422:4. The effect of stirring on electrode response.

c. Validation of temperature effect: Check frequently one or two points to confirm the applicability of the temperature correction data.

4. Precision and Accuracy

With most commercially available membrane electrode systems the operator can obtain an accuracy of ±0.1 mg/l DO and a precision of ±0.05 mg/l DO.

422 G.   References

1. WINKLER, L.W. 1888. The determination of dissolved oxygen in water. *Berlin. Deut. Chem. Ges.* 21:2843.

2. MANCY, K.H. & T. JAFFE. 1966. Analysis of dissolved oxygen in natural and waste waters. USPHS Publ. No. 999-WP-37, Washington, D.C.

3. POTTER, E.C. & G.E. EVERITT. 1957. Advances in dissolved oxygen microanalysis. *J. Appl. Chem.* 9:642.

4. OULMAN, C.S. & E.R. BAUMANN. 1956. A colorimetric method for determining dissolved oxygen. *Sewage Ind. Wastes* 28:1461.

5. ALSTERBERG, G. 1925. Methods for the determination of elementary oxygen dissolved in water in the presence of nitrite. *Biochem. Z.* 159:36.

6. RIDEAL, S. & G.G. STEWART. 1901. The determination of dissolved oxygen in waters in the presence of nitrites and of organic matter. *Analyst* 26:141.

7. RUCHHOFT, C.C. & W.A. MOORE. 1940. The determination of biochemical oxygen demand and dissolved oxygen of river mud suspensions. *Ind. Eng. Chem.*, Anal. Ed. 12:711.

8. PLACAK, O.R. & C.C. RUCHHOFT. 1941. Comparative study of the azide and Rideal-Stewart modifications of the Winkler method in the determination of biochemical oxygen demand. *Ind. Eng. Chem.*, Anal. Ed. 13:12.

9. RUCHHOFT, C.C. & O.R. PLACAK. 1942. Determination of dissolved oxygen in activated-sludge sewage mixtures. *Sewage Works J.* 14:638.

10. THERIAULT, E.J. & P.D. McNAMEE. 1932. Dissolved oxygen in the presence of organic matter, hypochlorites, and sulfite wastes. *Ind. Eng. Chem.*, Anal. Ed. 4:59.

11. McKEOWN, J.J., L.C. BROWN & G.W. GOVE. 1967. Comparative studies of dissolved oxygen analysis methods. *J. Water Pollut. Control Fed.* 39:1323.

12. LYNN, W.R. & D.A. OKUN. 1955. Experience with solid platinum electrodes in the determination of dissolved oxygen. *Sewage Ind. Wastes* 27:4.

13. MANCY, K.H. & D.A. OKUN. 1960. Automatic recording of dissolved oxygen in aqueous systems containing surface active agents. *Anal. Chem.* 32:108.

14. CARRITT, D.E. & J.W. KANWISHER. 1959. An electrode system for measuring dissolved oxygen. *Anal. Chem.* 31:5.

15. MANCY, K.H. & W.C. WESTGARTH. 1962. A galvanic cell oxygen analyzer. *J. Water Pollut. Control Fed.* 34:1037.

16. MANCY, K.H., D.A. OKUN & C.N. REILLEY. 1962. A galvanic cell oxygen analyzer. *J. Electroanal. Chem.* 4:65.

17. WEISS, C.M. & R.T. OGLESBY. 1963. Instrumentation for monitoring water quality in reservoirs. Amer. Water Works Ass. 83rd Annual Conf., New York, N.Y.

18. CLEARY, E.J. 1962. Introducing the ORSANCO robot monitor. *Proc. Water Quality Meas. Instrum.* Publ. No. 108, USPHS, Washington, D.C.

19. MACKERETH, F.J.H. 1964. An improved galvanic cell for determination of oxygen concentrations in fluids. *J. Sci. Instrum.* 41:38.

20. SULZER, F. & W.M. WESTGARTH. 1962. Continuous D.O. recording in activated sludge. *Water Sewage Works* 109:376.

21. DUXBURY, A.C. 1963. Calibration and use of a galvanic type oxygen electrode in field work. *Limnol. Oceanogr.* 8:483.

22. LIPNER, H.J., L.R. WITHERSPOON & V.C. CHAMPEAUS. 1964. Adaptation of a galvanic cell for microanalysis of oxygen. *Anal. Chem.* 36:204.

422 H.   Bibliography

BRIGGS, R. & M. VINEY. 1964. The design and performance of temperature compensated electrodes for oxygen measurements. *J. Sci. Instrum.* 41:78.

423   OZONE (RESIDUAL)

Ozone, a potent germicide, also is used as an oxidizing agent for the destruction of organic compounds producing taste and odor in water, for the destruction of organic coloring matter, and for the oxidation of reduced iron or manganese salts to insoluble oxides, which can then be precipitated or filtered from the water. Waters containing such oxidizable minerals must be filtered after ozonation. The presence of ozone residuals of even less than 0.1 mg/l at the outlet of the ozonation chamber is generally effective for disinfection; therefore, the demonstration of an ozone residual in the water is usually sufficient. For other purposes, perhaps as much as 0.2 mg/l may be necessary.

ozone in air by absorption of the ozone in iodide solution.

The orthotolidine-manganese sulfate method (B), generally abbreviated OTM, is semiquantitative. It is subject to relatively slight interference from other common oxidants.

The orthotolidine-arsenite method (C), usually designated OTA, is largely qualitative because of its susceptibility to interference. However, it is useful for such control purposes as determination at the outlet of the ozonation chamber.

The ozone concentration in water or air also can be determined continuously by photometric instruments, which can measure the strong absorption ozone exerts at the wavelength of 253.7 nm.

2. Sampling and Storage

Determine ozone immediately; samples cannot be preserved or stored because of the instability of the residual. The stability of residual ozone is markedly improved at low temperatures and low pH. Collect samples in a manner that will minimize aeration.

1. Selection of Method

Three methods are described for the determination of ozone in water. The iodometric method (A) is quantitative, subject to the fewest interferences, and capable of good precision. The method also can be used for the determination of

423 A.   Iodometric Method

1. General Discussion

a. *Principle:* Ozone liberates free iodine from a potassium iodide solution. For accurate results the solution should be alkaline during the absorption of ozone. In practice, solutions of potassium iodide quickly become alkaline during the process. After acidification, the liberated iodine is titrated with

standard 0.005N sodium thiosulfate with starch indicator.

b. *Interference:* Because ozonated water may contain manganese dioxide, ferric ion, nitrite, possibly peroxide, and other oxidation products, avoid these interferences by passing the ozone through the gaseous phase into a potassium iodide solution for titration. The stability of ozone solutions decreases progressively at each increment in temperature above freezing and with each increment in pH above 3.0.

c. *Minimum detectable concentration:* Approximately 30 $\mu g/l$ ozone.

2. Apparatus

The following are required for sample collection:

a. *Standard gas-washing bottles and absorbers*, 1-l and 500-ml capacities, with medium-permeability porous-plate diffusers at bottom.

b. *Pure air or pure nitrogen gas supply*, 0.2- to 1.0-l/min capacity.

c. *Glass, stainless steel, or aluminum piping*, for carrying ozonized air. Good-quality Tygon* tubing also may be used for short runs, but not rubber.

3. Reagents

a. *Potassium iodide solution:* Dissolve 20 g KI, free from iodine, iodate, and reducing agents, in 1 l freshly boiled and cooled distilled water. Store in a brown bottle.

b. *Sulfuric acid*, H_2SO_4, 1N.

c. *Standard sodium thiosulfate*, 0.1N: Dissolve 25 g $Na_2S_2O_3 \cdot 5H_2O$ in 1 l freshly boiled distilled water. Standardize against potassium biniodate (also called potassium hydrogen iodate) or potassium dichromate according to the procedure described in Section 409A.2c.

d. *Standard sodium thiosulfate titrant*, 0.005N: Dilute the proper volume (approximately 50 ml) of 0.1N sodium thiosulfate to 1,000 ml. For accurate work, standardize this solution daily, using either 0.005N potassium biniodate or potassium dichromate solu-

---

*US Stoneware Company.

tion for the purpose. Perform the standardization exactly as described in ¶4c below. Standard sodium thiosulfate titrant, exactly 0.0050N, is equivalent to 120 μg ozone/1.00 ml.

e. *Starch indicator solution:* To 5 g potato, arrowroot, or soluble starch in a mortar, add a little cold distilled water and grind to a thin paste. Pour into 1 l boiling distilled water, stir, and allow to settle overnight. Use the clear supernate. Preserve with 1.25 g salicylic acid, 4 g zinc chloride, or a combination of 4 g sodium propionate and 2 g sodium azide added to 1 l starch solution.

f. *Standard iodine*, 0.1N: Dissolve 40 g KI in 25 ml distilled water. Add 13 g resublimed iodine and stir until dissolved. Dilute to 1 l and standardize against sodium arsenite, primary standard grade, as described in Section 409C.3a2).

g. *Standard iodine*, 0.005N: Dissolve 16 g KI in a little distilled water in a 1-l volumetric flask, add the proper volume (approximately 50 ml) of 0.1N iodine solution, and dilute to the mark. For accurate work, standardize daily. Store the solution in a brown bottle or in the dark. Protect from direct sunlight at all times and keep from all contact with rubber.

4. Procedure

a. *Sample collection:* Collect an 800-ml sample in a 1-l washing bottle with a porous diffuser at the bottom. (Some prefer to add 8 ml 1N H_2SO_4 before proceeding to ¶4b below; others think this may result in increased interference from the acid itself or from breakdown of substances in the sample.)

b. *Ozone absorption:* Pass a stream of pure air or nitrogen through the sample and then through an absorber containing 400 ml KI solution. Continue for not less than 5 min at a rate of 0.2 to 1.0 l/min to insure that all ozone is swept from the sample and absorbed in the KI solution.

c. *Titration:* Transfer the KI solution to a 1-l beaker, rinse the absorber, and add 20 ml H_2SO_4 to produce a pH below 2.0. Titrate with $0.005N$ sodium thiosulfate titrant until the yellow color of the liberated iodine is almost discharged. Add 4 ml starch indicator solution to impart a blue color and continue the titration carefully but rapidly to the end point at which the blue color just disappears. Long contact of iodine and starch develops a blue compound that is difficult to decolorize. (The end point may be determined amperometrically as described in Section 409C.4b, except that sodium thiosulfate can be used as the titrant.)

d. *Blank test:* Correct the result of the sample titration by determining the blank contributed by such reagent impurities as the free iodine or iodate in the KI, which liberates extra iodine, or the traces of reducing agents that might reduce some of the liberated iodine.

Take 400 ml KI solution, 20 ml H_2SO_4, and 4 ml starch indicator solu-

tion. Perform whichever one of the blank titrations below applies:

1) If a blue color occurs, titrate with $0.005N$ sodium thiosulfate to the disappearance of the blue and record the result.

2) If no blue color occurs, titrate with $0.005N$ iodine solution until a blue color appears. Back-titrate with $0.005N$ sodium thiosulfate and record the difference.

Before calculating the ozone, subtract the result of the blank titration in ¶4d1) from the sample titration, or add the result of ¶4d2) above.

5. Calculation

$$\text{mg/l } O_3 = \frac{(A \pm B) \times N \times 24,000}{\text{ml sample}}$$

where A = ml titration for sample, B = ml titration for blank (positive or negative), and N = normality of $Na_2S_2O_3$.

6. Interpretation of Results

The precision of the actual test is within ±1%. However, rapid deterioration of the residual occurs in the time elapsing between sampling and performance of the test. Temperature is also an important factor in the deterioration.

423 B.   Orthotolidine-Manganese Sulfate (OTM) Method

1. General Discussion

a. Principle: Residual ozone oxidizes manganous ion to the manganic state, which in turn reacts with the acidic orthotolidine reagent. The final yellow color can be measured visually with a comparator suitable for residual chlorine estimations or photometrically in the wavelength range of 400 to 450 nm.

b. Interference: This method may be affected by the presence of a high oxide of manganese in the sample but not by such slow-acting interfering agents as nitrite or oxidized iron. The correction for interferences can be determined by thoroughly aerating a second portion of the sample and then following the procedure described in ¶4 following.

c. Minimum detectable concentration: Approximately 20 μg/l ozone.

2. Apparatus

Color comparison equipment: One of the following is required:

a. Comparator, color- and turbidity-compensating, equipped with permanent glass standards suitable for the estimation of residual chlorine by the orthotolidine method.

b. Filter photometer, providing a light path of 1 cm or longer and equipped with a violet filter exhibiting maximum transmittance in the wavelength range of 400 to 450 nm.

c. Spectrophotometer, for use at 435 nm and providing a light path of 1 cm or longer.

3. Reagents

a. Manganese sulfate reagent: Dissolve 3.1 g $MnSO_4 \cdot H_2O$ in distilled water containing 3 ml conc H_2SO_4, and dilute to 1 l. This solution contains approximately 1 g/l Mn and may be used for many months.

b. Orthotolidine reagent: See Section 411B.3*a.*

4. Procedure

Place 5 ml manganese sulfate reagent in a 250-ml flask. Add 95 ml sample and mix quickly. Add 5 ml orthotolidine reagent and mix quickly. Measure the developed yellow color in a comparator fitted with a chlorine color disk, or photometrically in the wave-length range of 400 to 450 nm.

5. Calculation

$$\text{mg/l } O_3 = \frac{\text{mg/l apparent ``chlorine''}}{1.45}$$

6. Interpretation of Results

The yellow color developed by ozone in this method is theoretically equal to 1.45 times the amount produced by an equal quantity of chlorine. Interfering compounds and uncertainties in reading a color disk comparator may cause appreciable variations in this theoretical factor. Photometric measurement of the color density improves the test accuracy.

423 C. Orthotolidine-Arsenite (OTA) Method

1. General Discussion

a. Principle: Ozone produces an instantaneous yellow color with acid orthotolidine reagent. The addition of arsenite reagent minimizes interference from such slower-acting ions as nitrite or oxidized iron.

b. Interference: This method is affected by colloidal manganese dioxide, which rapidly reacts with the acid orthotolidine reagent.

c. Minimum detectable concentration: Approximately 20 μg/l ozone.

2. Apparatus

Color comparison equipment: One of the following is required:

a. Comparator, color- and turbidity-compensating, equipped with permanent glass standards for the estimation of residual chlorine by the orthotolidine method.

b. French square bottles, capacity 30 to 60 ml (1 to 2 oz).

3. Reagents

a. Orthotolidine reagent: See Section 411B.3*a*.

b. Sodium arsenite solution: Dissolve 5 g NaAsO$_2$ in distilled water and dilute to 1 liter. The solution may be used for several months. (CAUTION: *Toxic—take care to avoid ingestion.*)

4. Procedure

a. Sample and reagent volumes: Label two comparator cells or two French square bottles "A" and "B." Add 0.5 ml orthotolidine reagent to 10-ml cells, 0.75 ml to 15-ml cells, and the same ratio for other volumes of sample. Use the same volume of arsenite solution after color development in ¶4*b* and also for the determination of the interference correction in ¶4*c* below.

b. Color development: To Cell A, containing orthotolidine reagent, add a measured volume of sample. Mix quickly and thoroughly, and within 5 sec add the sodium arsenite solution. Mix quickly and compare with color standards in the comparator as rapidly as possible. Record the result as *A*.

c. Estimation of interference: To Cell B, containing arsenite solution, add a measured volume of sample. Mix quickly and thoroughly and add orthotolidine reagent. Again mix quickly and compare with color standards in the comparator as rapidly as possible. Record the result as *B*, which represents the interfering substances in the water.

5. Calculation

$$\text{mg/l O}_3 = A - B$$

6. Interpretation of Results

The color developed in this test by a given amount of ozone varies greatly in different waters. On the average it approximates the color produced by an equal quantity of chlorine. The method is qualitative only.

423 D. Bibliography

Foulk, C. W. & A. T. Bawden. 1926. A new type of endpoint in electrometric titration and its application of iodimetry. *J. Amer. Chem. Soc.* 48:2045.

Hann, V. A. & T. C. Manley. 1952. Ozone. pp. 735-753 *in* Encyclopedia of Chemical Technology. Vol. 9. Interscience Publishers, New York, N.Y.

Birdsall, C. M., A. C. Jenkins & E. Spadinger. 1952. The iodometric determination of ozone. *Anal. Chem.* 24:662.

Zehender, F. & W. Stumm. 1953. Determination of ozone in drinking water (in German). *Mitt. Gebiete Lebensm. Hyg.* 44:206.

Ingols, R. S. & R. H. Fetner. 1956. Ster-ilization of water by ozone under arctic conditions. Rept. PB 124786, Office of Technical Services, U. S. Dept. Commerce, Washington, D. C.

Ingols, R. S., R. H. Fetner & W. H. Eberhardt. 1956. Determination of ozone in solution. *Proc. Int. Ozone Conf.*, American Chemical Society, Advan. Chem. Ser. No. 21.

Hann, V. A. 1956. Disinfection of drinking water with ozone. *J. Amer. Water Works Ass.* 48:1316

Ingols, R. S. & R. H. Fetner. 1957. Some studies of ozone for use in water treatment. *Proc. Soc. Water Treat. Exam.* 6:8.

424 pH VALUE

The pH of most natural waters falls within the range of 4 to 9. The majority of waters are slightly basic because of the presence of carbonates and bicarbonates. A departure from a normal pH for a given water could be caused by the influx of acidic or alkaline industrial wastes. Neutralization of spent acids or bases is an important waste treatment practice, and measurement and control of pH in industrial effluents is often required for water pollution control. It is also relatively common to practice pH adjustment of water treatment plant effluents to control corrosion in distribution systems.

The pH of a solution refers to its hydrogen ion activity and is expressed as the logarithm of the reciprocal of the hydrogen ion activity in moles per liter at a given temperature. It is used in the calculation of carbonate, bicarbonate, and carbon dioxide, corrosion and stability index, and other acid-base equilibria of importance to water and wastewater analysis and treatment control. The practical pH scale extends from 0, very acidic, to 14, very alkaline, with 7 corresponding to exact neutrality at 25 C. Whereas "alkalinity" and "acidity" are measures of the total resistance to pH change or buffering capacity of a sample, pH represents the free hydrogen ion activity not bound by carbonate or other bases.

The pH can be measured either colorimetrically or electrometrically. The colorimetric method is less expensive but suffers from interferences due to color, turbidity, salinity, colloidal matter, and various oxidants and reductants. The indicators are subject to deterioration as are the color standards with which they are compared. Moreover, no single indicator encompasses the pH range of interest in waters and wastewaters. In poorly buffered liquids, the indicators themselves may alter the pH of the sample unless preadjusted to nearly the same pH as the sample. For these reasons, the colorimetric method is suitable only for rough estimation and is not described herein. (For details on the colorimetric method, see Clark,[1] Kolthoff,[2] and AWWA.[3]) The glass electrode method is the standard technic.

1. General Discussion

a. Principle: Although the hydrogen electrode is recognized as the primary standard, the glass electrode is less subject to interferences and is used in combination with a calomel reference electrode. The glass-reference electrode pair produces a change of 59.1 mV/pH unit at 25 C.

b. Interferences: The glass electrode is relatively free from interference from color, turbidity, colloidal matter, oxidants, reductants, or high salinity, except for a sodium error at high pH. This error at a pH above 10 may be reduced by using special "low sodium error" electrodes. When using ordinary glass electrodes, make approximate corrections for the sodium error in accordance with information supplied by the manufacturer. Temperature exerts two significant effects on pH measurement: the pH potential, i.e., the change in potential per pH unit, varies with temperature; and ionization in the sample also varies.* The first effect can be overcome by a temperature com-

pensation adjustment provided on the better commercial instruments. The second effect is inherent in the sample and is taken into consideration by recording both temperature and pH of each sample.

2. Apparatus

a. Electronic pH meter with temperature compensation adjustment.

b. Glass electrode: Glass electrodes are available for measurement over the entire pH range with minimum-sodium-ion-error types for high pH-high sodium samples.

c. Reference electrode: Use a calomel, silver-silver chloride, or other constant-potential electrode.

d. Magnetic stirrer, with teflon-coated stirring bar or a mechanical stirrer with inert plastic-coated or glass impeller.

e. Flow chamber for measurement of continuously flowing or unbuffered solutions.

3. Standard Solutions

a. General preparation: Calibrate the electrode system against standard buffer solutions of known pH. Because buffer solutions may deteriorate as a result of mold growth or contamination, prepare fresh as needed for accurate work by weighing the amounts of chemicals specified in Table 424:I, dissolving in dis-

---

* This ionization, dependent on values of the ionization constants for the various weak acids and bases in the sample at a particular temperature, is to a significant extent related to the alkalinity. Increasing alkalinity reduces the effect of temperature change on the pH. This effect of alkalinity is not a direct relationship but it can be quite pronounced even at very low concentrations of alkalinity.

The temperature dial on pH meters is designed only to correct for the temperature characteristics of the electrodes. Instruments without a temperature dial are often provided with data from which this correction for the characteristics of the electrodes may be calculated.

Data for calculating, by interpolation, the pH of natural waters at temperatures other than that of the measurement have been provided by Langelier.[4]

TABLE 424:I. PREPARATION OF pH STANDARD SOLUTIONS

Standard Solution (molality)	pH at 25 C	Weight of Chemicals Needed/1,000 ml Aqueous Solution at 25 C
Primary standards:		
Potassium hydrogen tartrate (saturated at 25 C)	3.557	6.4 g $KHC_4H_4O_6$*
0.05 potassium dihydrogen citrate	3.776	11.41 g $KH_2C_6H_5O_7$
0.05 potassium hydrogen phthalate	4.008	10.12 g $KHC_8H_4O_4$
0.025 potassium dihydrogen phosphate+0.025 disodium hydrogen phosphate	6.865	3.388 g KH_2PO_4†+3.533 g Na_2HPO_4†‡
0.008695 potassium dihydrogen phosphate+0.03043 disodium hydrogen phosphate	7.413	1.179 g KH_2PO_4†+4.302 g Na_2HPO_4†‡
0.01 sodium borate decahydrate (borax)	9.180	3.80 g $Na_2B_4O_7\cdot10H_2O$‡
0.025 sodium bicarbonate+0.025 sodium carbonate	10.012	2.092 g $NaHCO_3$+2.640 g Na_2CO_3
Secondary standards:		
0.05 potassium tetroxalate dihydrate	1.679	12.61 g $KH_3C_4O_8\cdot2H_2O$
Calcium hydroxide (saturated at 25 C)	12.454	1.5 g $Ca(OH)_2$*

* Approximate solubility.

† Dry chemical at 110 to 130 C for 2 hr.

‡ Prepare with freshly boiled and cooled distilled water (carbon-dioxide-free).

tilled water at 25 C, and diluting to 1,000 ml. This procedure is particularly important for the borate and carbonate buffers.

Use distilled water having a conductivity of less than 2 μsiemens at 25 C and a pH 5.6 to 6.0 for the preparation of all standard solutions. Freshly boil and cool this distilled water to expel the carbon dioxide to produce a pH of 6.7 to 7.3 for the preparation of the borate and phosphate solutions. Dry the potassium dihydrogen phosphate at 110 C to 130 C for 2 hr before weighing. Do not heat the unstable hydrated potassium tetroxalate above 60 C nor dry the other specified buffer salts.

Although ACS-grade chemicals are generally satisfactory for the preparation of buffer solutions, use certified materials available as NBS standard samples from the National Bureau of Standards where the greatest accuracy is required. For routine analysis, commercially available buffer tablets, powders, or solutions of tested quality also are permissible. In preparing buffer solutions from solid salts, dissolve all the material; otherwise, the pH calibration will be incorrect. Prepare and calibrate the electrode system with buffer solutions with pH approximating that of the sample to minimize error resulting from nonlinear response of the electrode.

As a rule, select and prepare the buffer solutions classed as primary standards in Table 424:I; reserve the secondary standards for extreme situations

TABLE 424:II. STANDARD pH VALUES ASSIGNED BY THE NATIONAL BUREAU OF STANDARDS

Temperature C	Primary Standards							Secondary Standards	
	Tartrate (Saturated)	Citrate (0.05 m)	Phthalate (0.05 m)	Phosphate (1:1)	Phosphate (1:3.5)	Borax (0.01 m)	Carbonate (0.025 m)	Tetroxalate (0.05 m)	Calcium Hydroxide (Saturated)
0		3.863	4.003	6.984	7.534	9.464	10.317	1.666	13.423
5		3.840	3.999	6.951	7.500	9.395	10.245	1.668	13.207
10		3.820	3.998	6.923	7.472	9.332	10.179	1.670	13.003
15		3.802	3.999	6.900	7.448	9.276	10.118	1.672	12.810
20		3.788	4.002	6.881	7.429	9.225	10.062	1.675	12.627
25	3.557	3.776	4.008	6.865	7.413	9.180	10.012	1.679	12.454
30	3.552	3.766	4.015	6.853	7.400	9.139	9.966	1.683	12.289
35	3.549	3.759	4.024	6.844	7.389	9.102	9.925	1.688	12.133
38	3.548		4.030	6.840	7.384	9.081		1.691	12.043
40	3.547	3.753	4.035	6.838	7.380	9.068	9.889	1.694	11.984
45	3.547	3.750	4.047	6.834	7.373	9.038	9.856	1.700	11.841
50	3.549	3.749	4.060	6.833	7.367	9.011	9.828	1.707	11.705
55	3.554		4.075	6.834		8.985		1.715	11.574
60	3.560		4.091	6.836		8.962		1.723	11.449
70	3.580		4.126	6.845		8.921		1.743	
80	3.609		4.164	6.859		8.885		1.766	
90	3.650		4.205	6.877		8.850		1.792	
95	3.674		4.227	6.886		8.833		1.806	

encountered in wastewater measurements. Consult Table 424:II for the accepted pH of the standard buffer solutions at temperatures other than 25 C. Where the intent is to apply them for routine control, store the buffer solutions and samples preferably in polyethylene bottles or, at least, pyrex glassware. Even in such circumstances, replace buffer solutions every 4 wk.

b. Saturated potassium hydrogen tartrate solution: Shake vigorously an excess (5 to 10 g) of finely crystalline $KHC_4H_4O_6$ with 100 to 300 ml distilled water at 25 C in a glass-stoppered bottle. Separate the clear solution from the undissolved material by decantation or filtration. If this solution is to be used for routine control, preserve for 2 months or more by adding a thymol crystal (8 mm diam) for each 200 ml solution.

c. Saturated calcium hydroxide solution: Place the well-washed, low-alkali-grade calcium carbonate, $CaCO_3$, in a platinum dish and ignite for 1 hr at 1,000 C. After cooling the calcium oxide, hydrate by slowly adding distilled water with stirring and heating to boiling. Cool and filter the suspension and collect the solid calcium hydroxide on a fritted glass filter of medium porosity. Dry the calcium hydroxide in an oven at 110 C, cool, and pulverize to uniformly fine granules. Vigorously shake an excess of fine granules with distilled water in a stoppered polyethylene bottle, allowing the temperature to come to 25 C after mixing. Filter the supernatant under suction through a sintered glass filter of medium porosity and use the filtrate as the buffer solution. Discard the buffer solution when atmospheric carbon dioxide causes turbidity to appear.

4. Procedure

Because of the differences between the many makes and models of commercially available pH meters, it is impossible to provide detailed instructions for the proper operation of every instrument. In each case, follow the manufacturer's instructions. Thoroughly wet the glass and reference electrodes by immersing the tips in water overnight or in accordance with instructions. Thereafter, when the meter is not in use for pH measurement, keep the tips of the electrodes immersed in water.

Before use, remove the electrodes from the water and rinse with distilled or demineralized water. Dry the electrodes by gentle wiping with a soft tissue. Standardize the instrument with the electrodes immersed in a buffer solution with a pH approaching that of the sample and note the temperature of the buffer and the pH at the measured temperature. Remove the electrodes from the buffer, rinse thoroughly, and dry. Immerse in a second buffer approximately 4 pH units different from the first and note the pH reading; the reading should be within 0.1 unit of the pH for the second buffer. Rinse electrodes thoroughly, dry, and immerse in the sample. Agitate the sample sufficiently to provide homogeneity and keep solids in suspension. If the sample temperature is different from that of the buffers, let the electrodes equilibrate with the sample. Measure the sample temperature and set the temperature compensator on the pH meter to the measured temperature. Note and record the pH and temperature. Rinse electrodes and immerse in water until the next measurement.

When only occasional pH measurements are made, standardize the instrument before each measurement. Where frequent measurements are made, less frequent standardization (every 1 or 2 hr) is satisfactory. However, if sample pH values vary widely, standardize more frequently with a buffer having a pH within 1 to 2 pH units of that of the sample. Measure with two or more buffers of different pH at least once daily and more frequently if samples contain abrasive solids or dissolved fluorides, in order to check the linearity of response. When electrode response to two buffers 4 pH units different shows differences greater than 0.1 pH unit, replace the glass electrode.

pH measurements in high-purity waters such as condensate or demineralizer effluents are subject to atmospheric contamination and require special procedures for accurate pH measurement.

5. Precision and Accuracy

The precision and accuracy attainable with a given pH meter will depend on the type and condition of the instrument and the care used in standardization and operation. Guard against possible erratic results arising from mechanical or electrical failures—weak batteries, damaged electrodes, plugged liquid junctions, and fouling of the electrodes with oily or precipitated materials. With the proper care, a precision of ±0.02 pH unit and an accuracy of ±0.05 pH unit can be achieved with many of the new models. However, ±0.1 pH unit represents the limit of accuracy under normal conditions. For this reason, report pH values to the nearest 0.1 pH unit. A synthetic sample consisting of a Clark and Lubs buffer solution of pH 7.3 was analyzed electrometrically by 30 laboratories, with a standard deviation of ±0.13 pH unit.

6. References

1. CLARK, W.M. 1928. The Determination of Hydrogen Ions, 3rd ed. Williams & Wilkins Co., Baltimore, Md.
2. KOLTHOFF, I.M. 1937. Acid-Base Indicators, 4th ed. Macmillan Co., New York, N.Y.
3. AMERICAN WATER WORKS ASSOCIATION. 1964. Simplified Procedures for Water Examination. Manual M12, AWWA, New York, N.Y.
4. LANGELIER, W.F. 1946. Effect of temperature on the pH of natural waters. *J. Amer. Water Works Ass.* 38:179.

7. Bibliography

DOLE, M. 1941. The Glass Electrode. John Wiley & Sons, New York, N.Y.

BATES, R.G. & S.F. ACREE. 1945. pH of aqueous mixtures of potassium dihydrogen phosphate and disodium hydrogen phosphate at 0 to 60 C. *J. Res. Nat. Bur. Standards* 34:373.

BATES, R.G. 1954. Electrometric pH Determinations. John Wiley & Sons, New York, N.Y.

FELDMAN, I. 1956. Use and abuse of pH measurements. *Anal. Chem.* 28:1859.

BRITTON, H.T.S., 1956. Hydrogen Ions, 4th ed. D. Van Nostrand Co., Princeton, N.J.

KOLTHOFF, I.M. & H.A. LAITINEN. 1958. pH and Electrotitrations. John Wiley & Sons, New York, N.Y.

KOLTHOFF, I.M. & P.J. ELVING. 1959. Treatise on Analytical Chemistry. Part 1, Vol. 1, Chapter 10, Wiley—Interscience, New York, N.Y.

BATES, R.G. 1962. Revised standard values for pH measurements from 0 to 95 C. *J. Res. Nat. Bur. Standards* 66A:179.

BATES, R.G. 1964. Determination of pH. John Wiley & Sons, New York, N.Y.

STAPLES, B.R. & R.G. BATES. 1969. Two new standards for the pH scale. *J. Res. Nat. Bur. Standards* 73A:37.

425   PHOSPHATE

Phosphorus occurs in natural waters and in wastewaters almost solely in the form of various types of phosphate. These forms are commonly classified into orthophosphates, condensed phosphates (pyro-, meta-, and polyphosphates), and organically bound phosphates. These may occur in the soluble form, in particles of detritus, or in the bodies of aquatic organisms.

The various forms of phosphate find their way into wastewater, effluents, and polluted water from a variety of sources. Small amounts of certain condensed phosphates are added to some water supplies in the course of treatment. Larger quantities of the same compounds may be added when the water is used for laundering or other cleaning, since these materials are major constituents of many commercial cleaning preparations. Phosphates are used extensively in the treatment of boiler waters. Orthophosphates applied to agricultural or residential cultivated land as fertilizers are carried into surface waters with storm runoff and to a lesser extent with melting snow. Organic phosphates are formed primarily by biological processes. They are contributed to sewage in body wastes and food residues. They also may be formed from orthophosphates in biological treatment processes or by the receiving water biota.

Phosphorus is essential to the growth of organisms and it can be the nutrient that limits the productivity of a body of water. In instances where phosphate is a growth-limiting nutrient, the discharge of raw or treated wastewater, agricultural drainage, or certain industrial wastes to a receiving water may stimulate the growth, in nuisance quantities, of photosynthetic aquatic micro- and macroorganisms.

Phosphates occur in bottom sediments and in biological sludges, both as precipitated inorganic forms and incorporated into organic compounds.

1. Definition of Terms

Phosphate analyses embody two general procedural steps: (a) conversion of the phosphorus form of interest to soluble orthophosphate, and (b) colorimetric determination of soluble orthophosphate. The separation of phosphorus into its various forms is largely analytically defined but the analytical differentiations have been selected so that they may be used for interpretive purposes.

Separation of "filtrable" (or "dissolved") from "particulate" forms of phosphate depends on filtration through a 0.45-μm membrane filter. The selection of membrane filtration over depth filtration is made because of the greater likelihood of obtaining a consistent separation of particle sizes by the membrane filtration technic. Prefiltration through a glass fiber filter may be used to hasten the filtration rate. No claim is made that filtration through 0.45-μm membrane filters is a true separation of suspended and soluble forms of phosphate; it is merely a convenient and replicable analytical technic designed to make a gross separation. This is reflected in the use of the term "filtrable" (rather than "soluble") to describe the phosphate forms determined in the filtrate that passes the 0.45-μm membrane.

The phosphates that respond to the colorimetric tests without preliminary hydrolysis or oxidative digestion of the sample are considered as "orthophosphate." Strictly speaking, a small fraction of any condensed phosphates present is usually hydrolyzed unavoidably in the procedure, and thus is reported as a part of the orthophosphate. Orthophosphates occur both in filtrable (dissolved) and in particulate form.

Acid hydrolysis at boiling-water temperature is designed to convert filtrable and particulate condensed phosphates to filtrable orthophosphate. The hydrolysis unavoidably releases some phosphate from organic compounds, but this factor has been reduced to a minimum (consistent with good condensed phosphate hydrolysis) by judicious selection of acid strength and hydrolysis time and temperature. Nevertheless, the term "acid-hydrolyzable phosphate" is preferred over "condensed phosphate" for this technic.

The phosphate fractions that are converted to orthophosphate only by oxidative destruction of the organic matter present are considered "organic" or "organically bound" phosphate. The severity of the oxidation required for this conversion depends on the form—and to some extent on the amount—of the organic phosphate present. Like the orthophosphates and acid-hydrolyzable phosphates, the organic phosphates occur both in the filtrable (dissolved) and in the particulate fractions.

In practice, the total phosphate contained in a sample may be separated analytically by filtration into filtrable and particulate fractions. With usually minor variations, these would correspond to soluble and suspended phosphates. These three total fractions (i.e., whole sample, dissolved, and particulate) may each be divided analytically into the three chemical types that have been described; ortho-, acid-hydrolyzable, and organic phosphates. This gives a total of twelve reportable phosphate fractions; these are summarized in Table 425:I.

TABLE 425:I. CLASSIFICATION OF PHOSPHATE FRACTIONS

Chemical Types	Physical States		
	Total	Filtrable (Dissolved)	Nonfiltrable (Particulate)
Total	*a.* Total filtrable and nonfiltrable phosphate	*e.* Total filtrable phosphate	*i.* Total nonfiltrable phosphate
Ortho	*b.* Total filtrable and nonfiltrable orthophosphate	*f.* Filtrable orthophosphate	*j.* Nonfiltrable orthophosphate
Acid-hydrolyzable	*c.* Total filtrable and nonfiltrable acid-hydrolyzable phosphate	*g.* Filtrable acid-hydrolyzable phosphate	*k.* Nonfiltrable acid-hydrolyzable phosphate
Organic	*d.* Total filtrable and nonfiltrable organic phosphate	*h.* Filtrable organic phosphate	*l.* Nonfiltrable organic phosphate

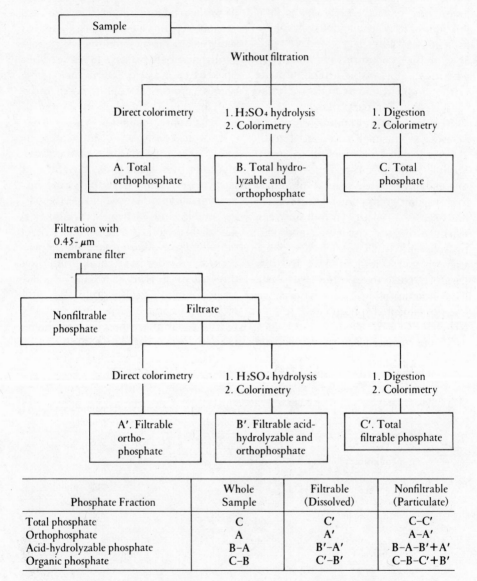

Figure 425:1. Flow chart for classification of phosphate fractions.

Figure 425:1 shows the six fractions that are determined by analysis. As described below the analytical flow chart, these fractions normally are used to calculate eight of the reportable fractions, with only four being determined directly.

2. Selection of Procedure

a. Total filtrable and nonfiltrable phosphate: Digestion of the whole sample is followed by orthophosphate determination. Difficulties may be encountered with highly saline samples when digestion technics that drastically reduce the volume of the sample are used, because of the precipitation of large quantities of salt. If it is necessary to carry out total phosphate analyses on such samples, directly determine total filtrable phosphate (*e*) and total nonfiltrable phosphate (*i*) and add the results.

b. Total filtrable and nonfiltrable orthophosphate: Use colorimetric method D, E, or F without preliminary filtration, hydrolysis, or digestion of the sample. Anomalous results may be obtained on samples containing large amounts of suspended sediments through a time-dependent desorption of orthophosphate from the suspended particles. Very often the result depends largely on the degree of agitation and mixing to which the sample is subjected during analysis.

c. Total filtrable and nonfiltrable acid-hydrolyzable phosphate: The unfiltered sample is treated by mild acid hydrolysis, followed by orthophosphate determination. The result includes filtrable and nonfiltrable orthophosphates and acid-hydrolyzable phosphates originally present in the sample. The concentration of filtrable and nonfiltrable acid-hydrolyzable phosphate is obtained by subtracting the filtrable and nonfiltrable orthophosphate (*b*).

d. Total filtrable and nonfiltrable organic phosphate: The concentration is calculated by subtracting from the total filtrable and nonfiltrable phosphate (*a*) the concentration of filtrable and nonfiltrable orthophosphate (*b*), and acid-hydrolyzable phosphate (*c*).

e. Total filtrable (dissolved) phosphate: Filtration of the sample through a 0.45-μm membrane filter is followed by digestion of the filtrate and orthophosphate determination. Persulfate digestion is usually suitable for filtered samples.

f. Filtrable (dissolved) orthophosphate: Filtration of the sample through a 0.45-μm membrane filter is followed by orthophosphate determination on the filtrate.

g. Filtrable (dissolved) acid-hydrolyzable phosphate: Filtration of the sample through a 0.45-μm membrane filter is followed by mild acid hydrolysis of the filtrate and orthophosphate determination. The result includes the filtrable orthophosphate and acid-hydrolyzable phosphate of the original sample. The concentration of filtrable acid-hydrolyzable phosphate is obtained by subtracting the filtrable orthophosphate (*f*).

h. Filtrable (dissolved) organic phosphate: The concentration is calculated by subtracting from the total filtrable phosphate (*e*) the concentration of filtrable orthophosphate (*f*) and acid-hydrolyzable phosphate (*g*).

i. Total nonfiltrable phosphate: The concentration may be obtained either by difference or by direct determination. To calculate total particulate phosphate by difference, the concentration of filtrable phosphate (*e*) is subtracted from the total filtrable and nonfiltrable phosphate (*a*). For a direct determination, the membrane filter containing the particulate matter collected from the sample is treated by digestion with nitric acid and then perchloric acid, followed by colorimetric determination. The latter technic is suggested for use with saline samples (see ¶*a*). It also makes possible the determination of small amounts of nonfiltrable phosphate with greater precision than that obtained in the calculation by difference, because the particles can be derived from a large sample volume.

j. Nonfiltrable orthophosphate: The concentration is usually calculated by subtracting the filtrable orthophosphate (*f*) from the total filtrable and nonfiltrable orthophosphate (*b*).

k. Nonfiltrable acid-hydrolyzable phosphate: The concentration usually is calculated by subtracting the filtrable acid-hydrolyzable phosphate (*g*) from the total filtrable and nonfiltrable acid-hydrolyzable phosphate (*c*).

l. Nonfiltrable organic phosphate: The concentration usually is calculated by subtracting the filtrable organic phosphate (*h*) from the total filtrable and nonfiltrable organic phosphate (*d*).

In many cases, it is unnecessary to determine or report all the various phosphate fractions given in Table 425:I and Figure 425:1. Select appropriate procedures to provide the information required.

3. Selection of Method

a. Digestion methods: Because phosphorus may occur in suspension and in combination with organic matter, a digestion method to determine total phosphate must be able to oxidize organic matter effectively, rupturing both C-P and C-O-P bonds, and to solubilize suspended material to release the phosphorus as soluble orthophosphate.

Three digestion methods are given. The perchloric acid method, the most drastic and time-consuming method, is recommended only for particularly difficult samples such as sediments. The nitric acid-sulfuric acid method is recommended for most samples. By far the simplest method is the persulfate oxidation technic. It is recommended that this method be checked against one or more of the more drastic digestion technics and be adopted if identical recoveries are obtained.

b. Colorimetric methods: Three methods of orthophosphate determination are described. Selection depends largely on the concentration range of orthophosphate. Thus, the vanadomolybdic acid method (D) is most useful for routine analyses in the range of 1 to 20 mg P/l. The stannous chloride method (E) or the ascorbic acid method (F) are more suited for the range of 0.01 to 6 mg P/l. An automated version of the ascorbic acid method also is available (Part 606). With the stannous chloride method, an extraction step is recommended for the lower levels of this range and when interferences need to be overcome.

TABLE 425:II. PRECISION AND ACCURACY DATA FOR PHOSPHORUS METHODS

Method	Phosphorus Concentration			No. of Laboratories	Relative Standard Deviation %	Relative Error %
	Ortho-phosphorus phosphate $\mu g/l$	Poly-phosphate $\mu g/l$	Total $\mu g/l$			
D. Vanadomolybdate	100			45	75.2	21.6
	600			43	19.6	10.8
	7,000			44	8.6	5.4
E. Stannous chloride	100			45	25.5	28.7
	600			44	14.2	8.0
	7,000			45	7.6	4.3
F. Ascorbic acid	100			3	9.1	10.0
	600			3	4.0	4.4
	7,000			3	5.2	4.9
Hydrolysis+ vanadomolybdate		80		37	106.8	7.4
		300		38	66.5	14.0
		3,000		37	36.1	23.5
Hydrolysis+stannous chloride		80		39	60.1	12.5
		300		36	47.6	21.7
		3,000		38	37.4	22.8
Persulfate+ vanadomolybdate			210	32	55.8	1.6
			990	32	23.9	2.3
			10,230	31	6.5	0.3
Sulfuric-nitric acids+ vanadomolybdate			210	23	65.6	20.9
			990	22	47.3	0.6
			10,230	20	7.0	0.4
Perchloric acid+ vanadomolybdate			210	4	33.5	45.2
			990	5	20.3	2.6
			10,230	6	11.7	2.2
Persulfate+stannous chloride			210	29	28.1	9.2
			990	30	14.9	12.3
			10,230	29	11.5	4.3
Sulfuric-nitric acids+ stannous chloride			210	20	20.8	1.2
			990	17	8.8	3.2
			10,230	19	7.5	0.4

4. Precision and Accuracy

To aid the analyst in method selection, Table 425:II presents the results of various combinations of digestion, hydrolysis, and colorimetric technics for three synthetic samples of the following compositions:

Sample 1 contained the following components: 100 $\mu g/l$ orthophosphate phosphorus, 80 $\mu g/l$ polyphosphate phosphorus added as sodium hexametaphosphate, 30 $\mu g/l$ organic phosphorus in the form of adenylic acid, 1,500 $\mu g/l$ ammonia nitrogen, 500

$\mu g/l$ nitrate nitrogen, and 400,000 $\mu g/l$ chloride.

Sample 2 contained 600 $\mu g/l$ orthophosphate phosphorus, 300 $\mu g/l$ polyphosphate phosphorus added as sodium hexametaphosphate, 90 $\mu g/l$ organic phosphorus in the form of adenylic acid, 800 $\mu g/l$ ammonia nitrogen, 5,000 $\mu g/l$ nitrate nitrogen, and 400,000 $\mu g/l$ chloride.

Sample 3 contained 7.00 mg/l orthophosphate phosphorus, 3.00 mg/l polyphosphate phosphorus added as sodium hexametaphosphate, 0.230 mg/l organic phosphorus in the form of adenylic acid, 0.20 mg/l ammonia nitrogen, 0.05 mg/l nitrate nitrogen, and 400 mg/l chloride.

5. Sampling and Storage

If differentiation of phosphorus forms is to be made, filter immediately after sample collection and preserve by freezing (at or below −10 C) either in the presence or absence of 40 mg $HgCl_2/l$. Add the mercury preservative especially when samples are to be stored for long periods. *Avoid preservation with acid or chloroform.* If total phosphorus alone is to be determined, do not preserve. Do not store samples containing low concentrations of phosphorus in plastic bottles because phosphate may be adsorbed onto the walls of the bottles. Rinse all glass containers with hot dilute HCl, then rinse several times in distilled water. Never use commercial detergents containing phosphate for cleansing of glassware used in phosphate analyses.

425 A.   Preliminary Filtration Step

Filter samples for the determination of filtrable orthophosphate, filtrable acid-hydrolyzable phosphate, and total filtrable phosphate through membrane filters of 0.45-μm pore size. If the specified pore size is unavailable, use any size from 0.4 to 0.6. However, for reproducible separations, consistent use of a given pore size is important. Unless the standard 0.45-μm filters are used, report the pore size with the results of the analyses. A glass fiber prefilter may be used to speed filtration of hard-to-filter samples.

Wash membrane filters by soaking in distilled water before using, because they may contribute significant amounts of phosphate to samples containing low concentrations of phosphate. Use one of two washing technics: (*a*) Soak filters (50/2 l) in distilled water for 24 hr; (*b*) soak filters (50/2 l) in distilled water for 1 hr, change the distilled water, and soak the filters an additional 3 hr.

After the membrane filters have been washed properly, insert in a suitable filter holder connected to a suction flask and vacuum source and collect a sufficient volume of filtrate for the required determinations.

425 B.   Preliminary Acid Hydrolysis Step for Condensed Phosphates

1. Discussion

The acid-hydrolyzable phosphate content of the sample is defined operationally as the difference between the orthophosphate as measured in the untreated sample and the phosphate found after mild acid hydrolysis. Generally, it includes the condensed phosphates such as pyro-, tripoly-, and higher-molecular-weight species like hexametaphosphate. In addition, some natural waters contain organic phosphate compounds that are hydrolyzed to orthophosphate under the conditions of this test. Polyphosphates generally do not respond to the orthophosphate tests but can be hydrolyzed to orthophosphate by boiling with acid.

After hydrolysis, determine orthophosphate by colorimetric method D, E, or F. The degree of interference, precision, accuracy, and sensitivity will depend on the colorimetric method used.

2. Apparatus

Autoclave or pressure cooker, capable of operating at 1.0 to 1.4 kg/cm^2 (15 to 20 psig) (optional).

3. Reagents

a. Phenolphthalein indicator solution.

b. Strong acid solution: Slowly add 300 ml conc H_2SO_4 to about 600 ml distilled water. When cool, add 4.0 ml conc HNO_3 and dilute to 1 l.

c. Sodium hydroxide, NaOH, 6N.

4. Procedure

a. To 100-ml sample or a portion diluted to 100 ml, add 1 drop (0.05 ml) phenolphthalein indicator solution. If a red color develops, add strong acid solution dropwise, to just discharge the color. Then add 1 ml in excess.

b. Boil gently for at least 90 min, adding distilled water to keep the volume between 25 and 50 ml. Alternatively, heat for 30 min in an autoclave or pressure cooker at 1.0 to 1.4 kg/cm^2 (15 to 20 psig). Cool, neutralize to a faint pink color with NaOH solution, and restore to the original 100-ml volume with distilled water.

c. Prepare a calibration curve by carrying a series of standards containing orthophosphate (see Colorimetric Method D, E, or F) through the hydrolysis step. Do not use orthophosphate standards without hydrolysis, because the salts added in hydrolysis cause an increase in the color intensity in some methods.

d. Determine the orthophosphate content of the treated portions, using Colorimetric Method D, E, or F. This gives the sum of polyphosphate and orthophosphate in the sample. To calculate its content of acid-hydrolyzable phosphate, determine orthophosphate in a portion of the sample that has not been hydrolyzed, using the same colorimetric method as that for the treated sample, and subtract.

425 C.   Preliminary Digestion Steps for Total Phosphorus

The total phosphate content of the sample includes all of the ortho-phosphates and condensed phosphates, both soluble and insoluble, and organic and inorganic species. To release phosphate from combination with organic matter, digest or oxidize. The rigor of the digestion required depends on the type of sample. The three digestion technics presented, in order of decreasing rigor, are perchloric acid digestion, sulfuric acid-nitric acid digestion, and persulfate digestion. It is recommended that the phosphate recovery by each digestion technic be compared for the specific type of samples being tested. If it is found that the less tedious persulfate method gives good phosphate recovery, use this method.

After digestion, determine the liberated orthophosphate by Colorimetric Method D, E, or F. The colorimetric method used, rather than the digestion procedure, governs in matters of interference and minimum detectable concentration.

I—PERCHLORIC ACID DIGESTION

1. Apparatus

   a. Hot plate: A 30- × 50-cm heating surface is adequate.
   b. Safety shield.
   c. Safety goggles.
   d. Conical flasks, 125-ml, acid-washed and rinsed with distilled water.
   e. Porcelain evaporating dishes, acid-washed and rinsed in distilled water.

2. Reagents

   a. Nitric acid, HNO_3, conc.
   b. Perchloric acid, $HClO_4 \cdot 2H_2O$, purchased as 70 to 72% $HClO_4$, reagent grade.
   c. Sodium hydroxide, NaOH, 6N.
   d. Methyl orange indicator solution.

3. Procedure

   a. CAUTION—Heated mixtures of $HClO_4$ and organic matter may explode violently. Avoid this hazard by taking the following precautions: (*a*) Do not add $HClO_4$ to a hot solution that may contain organic matter. (*b*) Always pretreat samples containing organic matter with HNO_3 before addition of $HClO_4$. (*c*) Use a mixture of HNO_3 and $HClO_4$ in starting the digestion step. (*d*) Avoid repeated fumings with perchloric acid in ordinary hoods. For routine operations, use hoods of all-stone or asbestos-cement. For occasional work with $HClO_4$, connect a water pump to a glass fume eradicator.* (*e*) Never let samples being digested with $HClO_4$ evaporate to dryness.

   b. Measure out a sample containing the desired amount of phosphate (this will be determined by whether Method D, E, or F is to be used for the colorimetric finish). Acidify to methyl orange with conc HNO_3, add another 5 ml conc HNO_3, and evaporate on a steam bath or hot plate to 15 to 20 ml, cov-

---

* Such as those obtainable from G. F. Smith Chemical Company, Columbus, Ohio.

ering the vessel with a watch glass when necessary to avoid loss of material by spattering. Place an infrared lamp over the sample to hasten evaporation if desired.

c. Transfer the evaporated sample to a 125-ml conical flask using 5 ml conc HNO_3 to rinse the evaporating dish, cool, and add 5 ml HNO_3 and 10 ml 70 to 72% $HClO_4$. After adding a few boiling chips, heat on a hot plate and evaporate gently until dense white fumes of $HClO_4$ just appear. If the solution is not clear at this point, cover the neck of the flask with a watch glass and keep the solution just barely boiling until it clears. If necessary, add 10 ml more HNO_3 to aid the oxidation.

d. Cool the digested solution and add 1 drop aqueous phenolphthalein solution. Neutralize with $6N$ NaOH solution. If necessary, filter the neutralized solution, washing the filter liberally with distilled water. Make up to 100 ml with distilled water.

e. Determine the orthophosphate of the treated sample by Method D, E, or F.

f. Prepare a calibration curve by carrying a series of standards containing orthophosphate (see Method D, E, or F) through the digestion step. Do not use orthophosphate standards without treatment, because the salts added in digestion cause an increase in the color intensity in some methods.

II—SULFURIC ACID-NITRIC ACID DIGESTION

1. Apparatus

a. *Digestion rack:* An electrically or gas-heated digestion rack with a provision for withdrawal of fumes is recommended. Digestion racks typical of those used for microkjeldahl digestions are suitable.

b. *Microkjeldahl flasks.*

2. Reagents

a. *Sulfuric acid*, H_2SO_4, conc.
b. *Nitric acid*, HNO_3, conc.
c. *Phenolphthalein indicator solution.*
d. *Sodium hydroxide*, NaOH, $1N$.

3. Procedure

a. Into a microkjeldahl flask, measure a sample containing the desired amount of phosphate (this is determined by the method used for the colorimetric finish). Add 1 ml conc H_2SO_4 and 5 ml conc HNO_3.

b. Digest the sample to a volume of 1 ml and then continue the digestion until the solution becomes colorless in order to remove HNO_3.

c. Cool and add approximately 20 ml distilled water, 1 drop phenolphthalein indicator, and as much $1N$ NaOH solution as required to produce a faint pink tinge in the solution. Transfer the neutralized solution, filtering if necessary to remove particulate material or turbidity, into a 100-ml volumetric flask. Add the filter washings to the flask and adjust the sample volume to 100 ml with distilled water.

d. Determine the phosphorus present by Method D, E, or F, for which a separate calibration curve has been constructed by carrying standards through the acid digestion procedure described above.

III—PERSULFATE DIGESTION

1. Apparatus

a. Hot plate: A 30- × 50-cm heating surface is adequate.

b. Autoclave: An autoclave or pressure cooker capable of developing 1 to 1.4 kg/cm² (15 to 20 psig) may be used in place of a hot plate.

c. Glass scoop: To hold approximately 0.4 g ammonium persulfate.

2. Reagents

a. Phenolphthalein indicator solution.

b. Sulfuric acid soltuion: Carefully add 300 ml conc H_2SO_4 to approximately 600 ml distilled water and then dilute to 1 l with distilled water.

c. Ammonium persulfate, solid.

d. Sodium hydroxide, NaOH, 1N.

3. Procedure

a. Use 50 ml or a suitable portion of thoroughly mixed sample. Add 1 drop (0.05 ml) phenolphthalein indicator solution. If a red color develops, add H_2SO_4 solution dropwise to just discharge the color. Then add 1 ml H_2SO_4 solution and 0.4 g solid ammonium persulfate.

b. Boil gently on a preheated hot plate for 30 to 40 min or until a final volume of 10 ml is reached. Cool, dilute to 30 ml with distilled water, add 1 drop (0.05 ml) phenolphthalein indicator solution, and neutralize to a faint pink color with NaOH solution. Alternatively, heat for 30 min in an autoclave or pressure cooker at 1.0 to 1.4 kg/cm² (15 to 20 psig). Cool, add 1 drop (0.05 ml) phenolphthalein indicator solution, and neutralize to a faint pink color with NaOH solution. Make up to 100 ml with distilled water. In some samples a precipitate may form at this stage. Do not filter. For any subdividing of the sample after this stage, shake the sample well. The precipitate (which is possibly a calcium phosphate) will redissolve under the acid conditions of the color-imetric phosphate test. Determine the phosphate present by means of Method D, E, or F, for which a separate calibration curve has been constructed by carrying the standards through the persulfate digestion procedure.

425 D.   Vanadomolybdophosphoric Acid Colorimetric Method

1. General Discussion

a. Principle: In a dilute orthophosphate solution, ammonium molybdate reacts under acid conditions to form a heteropoly acid, molybdophosphoric acid. In the presence of vanadium the vanadomolybdophosphoric yellow color is formed. The intensity of the yellow color is proportional to the phosphate concentration in the solution.

b. Interference: Positive interference is caused by silica and arsenic only if the sample is heated. Negative interferences are caused by arsenate, fluoride, thorium, bismuth, sulfide, thiosulfate, thiocyanate, or excess molybdate. Blue color is caused by ferrous iron but this does not affect results if the Fe(II) is less than 100 mg/l. Sulfide interference may be removed by oxidation with bromine water. Ions that do not interfere in concentrations up to 1,000 mg/l are Al, Fe(III), Mg, Ca, Ba, Sr, Li, Na, K, NH_4^+, Cd, Mn, Pb, Hg(I), Hg(II), Sn(II), Cu, Ni, Ag, U, Zr, AsO_3^-, Br^-, CO_3^{2-}, ClO_4^-, CN^-, IO_3^-, SiO_4, NO_3^-, NO_2^-, SO_4^{2-}, SO_3^{2-}, pyrophosphate, molybdate, tetraborate, selenate, benzoate, citrate, oxalate, lactate, tartrate, formate, and salicylate. If nitric acid is used in the test, chloride interferes at 75 mg/l.

c. Minimum detectable concentration: The minimum detectable concentration is 0.2 mg/l P in 1-cm spectrophotometer cells.

2. Apparatus

a. Colorimetric equipment: Visual comparison in nessler tubes is not recommended because the sensitivity of the method is dependent on the wavelength used. One of the following is required:

1) *Spectrophotometer,* for use at approximately 400 to 490 nm.

2) *Filter photometer,* provided with a blue or violet filter exhibiting maximum transmittance between 400 and 470 nm.

The wavelength at which color intensity is measured depends on the sensitivity desired, because the sensitivity varies tenfold with wavelengths from 400 to 490 nm. Ferric iron causes interference at low wavelengths, particularly at 400 nm. A wavelength of 470 nm is usually used. Concentration ranges for different wavelengths are:

Range mg/l P	Wavelength nm
1.0–5.0	400
2.0–10	420
4.0–18	470

b. Acid-washed glassware: Use acid-washed glassware for determining low concentrations of phosphate. Phosphate contamination is common because of its adsorption on glass surfaces. *Avoid using commercial detergents containing phosphate.* Clean all glassware with hot dilute HCl and rinse well with distilled water. Alternatively, fill the glassware with conc H_2SO_4, let stand overnight, and then rinse thoroughly. Preferably, reserve the glassware only for the determination of phosphate, and after use wash it and keep it filled with water until needed. If this is done, the acid treatment is required only occasionally.

3. Reagents

a. Phenolphthalein indicator solution.

b. Hydrochloric acid, HCl, conc.

c. Activated carbon.

d. Vanadate-molybdate reagent:

1) *Solution A:* Dissolve 25 g ammonium molybdate, $(NH_4)_6Mo_7O_{24} \cdot 4H_2O$, in 400 ml distilled water.

2) *Solution B:* Dissolve 1.25 g ammonium metavanadate, NH_4VO_3, by heating to boiling in 300 ml distilled water. Cool and add 330 ml conc HCl (see note).

Cool Solution B to room temperature, pour Solution A into Solution B, and dilute to 1 l.

NOTE: H_2SO_4, $HClO_4$, or HNO_3 may be substituted for HCl. The acid concentration in the determination is not critical but a final sample concentration of $0.5N$ is recommended.

e. Standard phosphate solution: Dissolve in distilled water 219.5 mg anhydrous potassium dihydrogen phosphate, KH_2PO_4, and dilute to 1,000 ml; 1.00 ml = 50.0 μg PO_4–P.

4. Procedure

a. Sample pH adjustment: If the pH of the sample is between 4 and 10, no adjustment is necessary. If the pH is less than 4, dilute 50 ml to 100 ml in a volumetric flask with distilled water and mix thoroughly. Use this diluted sample in the following steps. If the pH is greater than 10, add 1 drop phenolphthalein indicator to 50.0 ml sample and discharge the red color with conc HCl before diluting to 100 ml. [Dilution also is useful when concentrations greater than 15 mg PO_4–P/l are present. When dilutions are made, correctly interpret "ml sample" in the calculation as the volume of original (undiluted) sample contained in the portion taken for the color development step, ¶*c* below.]

b. Color removal from sample: Remove any excessive color present in the sample by shaking about 50 ml sample with 200 mg activated carbon* in an erlenmeyer flask for 5 min, then filtering the sample through filter paper† to re-

---

* Darco G60 or equivalent.
† Whatman No. 42 or equivalent.

move the carbon. Check each batch of carbon for phosphate, because some batches produce high reagent blanks.

c. Color development in sample: Place 35 ml or less of the sample, containing 50 to 1,000 μg P, in a 50-ml volumetric flask. Add 10 ml vanadate-molybdate reagent and dilute to the mark with distilled water. Prepare a blank in which 35 ml distilled water is substituted for the sample. Ten minutes or more after adding the vanadate-molybdate reagent, measure the transmittance of the sample versus the blank at a wavelength of 400 to 490 nm, depending on the sensitivity desired (see ¶2*a* above). The color is stable for days and its intensity is unaffected by variations in room temperature.

d. Preparation of calibration graph: Prepare a calibration curve by using suitable volumes of standard phosphate solution and proceeding as in ¶4*c*. When ferric ion is low enough not to interfere, plot a family of calibration curves of one series of standard solutions for various wavelengths. This permits a wide latitude of concentrations in one series of determinations. Analyze at least one standard with each set of samples.

5. Calculation

$$mg/l\ P = \frac{mg\ P \times 1,000}{ml\ sample}$$

6. Precision and Accuracy

See Table 425:II.

425 E.   Stannous Chloride Method

1. General Discussion

a. Principle: Molybdophosphoric acid is formed and reduced to the intensely colored complex, molybdenum blue, by stannous chloride. This method is much more sensitive than Method D, and makes feasible an extraction step that increases reliability of the method at concentrations below 0.1 mg P/l and lessens interference.

b. Interference: See Section 425D. 1*b*.

c. Minimum detectable concentration: The minimum detectable concentration is about 3 μg/l P. The sensitivity at 50% transmittance is about 10 μg/l for 1% change in transmittance.

2. Apparatus

The same apparatus is required as for Method D, except when the extraction step is used, in which case a safety aspirator also is required. Set the spectrophotometer at 625 nm in the measurement of benzene-isobutanol extracts, and at 690 nm for aqueous solutions. Use a wavelength of 650 nm for the aqueous solutions, with somewhat reduced sensitivity and precision, if the instrument is not equipped to read at 690 nm.

3. Reagents

a. Phenolphthalein indicator solution.

b. Strong-acid solution: Prepare as directed in Method B, ¶3*b* above.

c. Ammonium molybdate reagent I: Dissolve 25 g $(NH_4)_6Mo_7O_{24}\cdot4H_2O$ in 175 ml distilled water. Cautiously add 280 ml conc H_2SO_4 to 400 ml distilled water. Cool, add the molybdate solution, and dilute to 1 l.

d. Stannous chloride reagent I: Dissolve 2.5 g of fresh $SnCl_2\cdot2H_2O$ in 100 ml glycerol. Heat in a water bath and stir with a glass rod to hasten dissolution. This reagent is stable and requires neither preservatives nor special storage.

e. Standard phosphate solution: Prepare as directed in Method D, ¶3*e*.

f. Reagents for extraction:

1) *Benzene-isobutanol solvent:* Mix equal volumes of benzene and isobutyl alcohol. (CAUTION—*This solvent is highly flammable.*)

2) *Ammonium molybdate reagent II:* Dissolve 40.1 g $(NH_4)_6Mo_7O_{24}\cdot4H_2O$ in approximately 500 ml distilled water. Slowly add 396 ml molybdate reagent I. Cool and dilute to 1 l.

3) *Alcoholic sulfuric acid solution:* Cautiously add 20 ml conc H_2SO_4 to 980 ml methyl alcohol with continuous mixing.

4) *Dilute stannous chloride reagent II:* Mix 8 ml stannous chloride reagent I with 50 ml glycerol. This reagent is stable for at least 6 months.

4. Procedure

a. Preliminary sample treatment: To a 100-ml sample containing not more than 0.2 mg P and free from color and turbidity, add 0.05 ml (1 drop) phenolphthalein indicator. If the sample turns pink, add strong acid solution dropwise to discharge the color. If more than 0.25 ml (5 drops) is required, take a smaller sample and dilute to 100 ml with distilled water after first discharging the pink color with acid.

b. Color development: Add, with thorough mixing after each addition, 4.0 ml molybdate reagent I and 0.5 ml (10 drops) stannous chloride reagent I. The rate of color development and the intensity of color depend on the temperature of the final solution, each 1 C increase producing about 1% increase in color. Hence, samples, standards, and reagents should be within 2 C of one another and in the temperature range between 20 and 30 C.

c. Color measurement: After 10 min, but before 12 min, using the same specific interval for all determinations, measure the color photometrically at 690 nm and compare with a calibration curve, using a distilled water blank. Light path lengths suitable for various concentration ranges are as follows:

Approximate P Range $\mu g/l$	Light Path cm
0.3–2	0.5
0.1–1	2
0.007–0.2	10

Always run a blank on the reagents and distilled water. Inasmuch as the color at first develops progressively and later fades, maintain equal timing conditions for samples as for standards. Prepare at least one standard with each set of samples or once each day that tests are made. The calibration curve may deviate from a straight line at the upper concentrations of the 300- to 2,000-$\mu g/l$ range.

d. Extraction: When increased sensitivity is desired or interferences must be overcome, extract the phosphate as follows: Pipet a suitable portion into a 100-ml graduated extraction cylinder and dilute, if necessary, to 40 ml with distilled water. Add 50.0 ml benzene-isobutanol solvent and 15.0 ml molybdate reagent II. Close container at once and shake vigorously for exactly 15 sec. If polyphosphate is present, any delay will increase the amount of it that will be included in the orthophosphate value. Remove the stopper and withdraw 25.0 ml of separated organic layer, using a pipet and a safety aspirator. Transfer to a 50-ml volumetric flask, add 15 to 16 ml alcoholic sulfuric acid solution, swirl, add 0.50 ml (10 drops) dilute stannous chloride reagent II, swirl, and dilute to the mark with alcoholic sulfuric acid. Mix thoroughly. After 10 min, but before 30 min, read against the blank at 625 nm. Prepare the blank by carrying 40 ml distilled water through the same procedure used for the sample. Read the PO$_4$ concentration from a calibration curve prepared by taking known phosphate standards through the same procedural steps used for the samples.

5. Calculation

Calculate the results from the direct and the extraction procedures by the following equation:

$$mg/l\ P = \frac{mg\ P \times 1,000}{ml\ sample}$$

6. Precision and Accuracy

See Table 425:II.

425 F.   Ascorbic Acid Method

1. General Discussion

a. *Principle:* Ammonium molybdate and potassium antimonyl tartrate react in an acid medium with dilute solutions of orthophosphate to form a heteropoly acid—phosphomolybdic acid—that is reduced to the intensely colored molybdenum blue by ascorbic acid.

b. *Interference:* Arsenates react with the molybdate reagent to produce a blue color similar to that formed with phosphate. Concentrations as low as 0.10 mg/l arsenic interfere with the phosphate determination. Hexavalent chromium and nitrite interfere to give results about 3% low at concentrations of 1.0 mg/l and 10 to 15% low at concentrations of 10 mg/l chromium and nitrite. Sulfide (Na_2S) and silicate do not interfere in concentrations of 1.0 and 10.0 mg/l.

c. *Minimum detectable concentration:* Approximately 10 μg P/l. P ranges are as follows:

Approximate P Range	Light Path Length
mg/l	*cm*
0.30-2.0	0.5
0.15-1.30	1.0
0.01-0.25	5.0

2. Apparatus

a. *Colorimetric equipment:* One of the following is required:

1) *Spectrophotometer,* with infrared phototube for use at 880 nm, providing a light path of 2.5 cm (1 in.) or longer.

2) *Filter photometer,* equipped with a red color filter and a light path of 0.5 cm or longer.

b. *Acid-washed glassware:* See Method D, ¶ 2b above.

3. Reagents

a. *Sulfuric acid solution, 5N:* Dilute 70 ml conc H_2SO_4 with distilled water to 500 ml.

b. *Potassium antimonyl tartrate solution:* Dissolve 1.3715 g $K(SbO)C_4H_4O_6 \cdot 1/2 H_2O$ in 400 ml distilled water in a 500-ml volumetric flask and dilute to volume. Store in a glass-stoppered bottle.

c. *Ammonium molybdate solution:* Dissolve 20 g $(NH_4)_6Mo_7O_{24} \cdot 4H_2O$ in 500 ml distilled water. Store in a plastic bottle at 4 C.

d. *Ascorbic acid, 0.1M:* Dissolve 1.76 g ascorbic acid in 100 ml distilled water. The solution is stable for about 1 wk at 4 C.

e. *Combined reagent:* Mix the above reagents in the following proportions for 100 ml of the combined reagent: 50 ml 5N H_2SO_4, 5 ml potassium antimonyl tartrate solution, 15 ml ammonium molybdate solution, and 30 ml ascorbic acid solution. *Mix after addition of each reagent.* All reagents must reach room temperature before they are mixed and must be mixed in the order given. If turbidity forms in the combined reagent, shake and let it stand for a few minutes until the turbidity disappears before proceeding. The reagent is stable for 4 hr.

f. *Stock phosphate solution:* See Method D, ¶ 3e.

g. *Standard phosphate solution:* Dilute 50.0 ml stock phosphate solution to 1,000 ml with distilled water; 1.00 ml = 2.50 μg P.

4. Procedure

a. Treatment of sample: Pipet 50.0 ml sample into a clean dry test tube or 125-ml erlenmeyer flask. Add 1 drop phenolphthalein indicator. If a red color develops add $5N$ H_2SO_4 solution dropwise to just discharge the color. Add 8.0 ml combined reagent and mix thoroughly. After at least 10 min but no longer than 30 min, measure the color absorbance of each sample at 880 nm, using the reagent blank as the reference solution.

b. Correction for turbidity or interfering color: Natural color of water generally does not interfere at the high wavelength used. In the case of highly colored or turbid waters, prepare a blank by adding all the reagents except ascorbic acid and antimonyl potassium tartrate to the sample. Subtract the absorbance of the blank from the absorbance of each of the unknown samples.

c. Preparation of calibration curve: Prepare individual calibration graphs from a series of six standards within the phosphate ranges indicated in Section 425F.1c. Use a distilled water blank with the combined reagent to make the photometric readings for the calibration curve. Plot absorbance vs. phosphate concentration to give a straight line passing through the origin. Test at least one phosphate standard with each set of samples.

5. Calculation

$$\text{mg/l P} = \frac{\text{mg P} \times 1,000}{\text{ml sample}}$$

6. Precision and Accuracy

The precision and accuracy values given in Table 425:II are for a single solution procedure given in the previous edition. The technic presented differs in reagent-to-sample ratios, no addition of solvent, and acidity conditions. It is superior in precision and accuracy to the 13th edition technic in the analysis of both distilled water and river water at the 228 μg P/l level (Table 425:III).

TABLE 425:III. COMPARISON OF PRECISION AND ACCURACY OF ASCORBIC ACID METHODS

Ascorbic Acid Method	Phosphorus Concentration, Filtrable Orthophosphate mg/l	No. of Laboratories	Relative Standard Deviation %		Relative Error %	
			Distilled Water	River Water	Distilled Water	River Water
13th Edition (Edwards, Molof, and Schneeman)	0.228	8	3.87	2.17	4.01	2.08
Current method (Murphy and Riley)	0.228	8	3.03	1.75	2.38	1.39

425 G.   Bibliography

BOLTZ, D.F. & M.G. MELLON. 1947. Determination of phosphorus, germanium, silicon, and arsenic by the heteropoly blue method. *Ind. Eng. Chem.*, Anal. Ed. 19: 873.

GREENBERG, A.E., L.W. WEINBERGER & C.N. SAWYER. 1950. Control of nitrite interference in colorimetric determination of phosphorus. *Anal. Chem.* 22:499.

YOUNG, R.S. & A. GOLLEDGE. 1950. Determination of hexametaphosphate in water after threshold treatment. *Ind. Chem.* 26:13.

GRISWOLD, B.L., F.L. HUMOLLER & A.R. MCINTYRE. 1951. Inorganic phosphates and phosphate esters in tissue extracts. *Anal. Chem.* 23:192.

BOLTZ, D.F., ed. 1958. Colorimetric Determination of Nonmetals. Interscience Publishers, New York, N.Y.

AMERICAN WATER WORKS ASSOCIATION. 1958. Committee report. Determination of orthophosphate, hydrolyzable phosphate, and total phosphate in surface waters. *J. Amer. Water Works Ass.* 50:1563.

JACKSON, M.L. 1958. Soil Chemical Analysis. Prentice-Hall, Englewood Cliffs, N.J.

SLETTEN, O. & C.M. BACH. 1961. Modified stannous chloride reagent for orthophosphate determination. *J. Amer. Water Works Ass.* 53:1031.

STRICKLAND, J.D.H. & T.R. PARSONS. 1965. A Manual of Sea Water Analysis, 2nd ed. Fish. Res. Board, Ottawa, Canada.

BLACK, C.A., D.D. EVANS, J.L. WHITE, L.E. ENSMINGER & F.E. CLARK, eds. 1965. Methods of Soil Analysis, Part 2. Chemical and Microbiological Properties. American Society for Agronomy, Madison, Wisc.

EDWARDS, G.P., A.H. MOLOF & R.W. SCHNEEMAN. 1965. Determination of orthophosphate in fresh and saline waters. *J. Amer. Water Works Ass.* 57:917.

LEE, G.F., N.L. CLESCERI & G.P. FITZGERALD. 1965. Studies on the analysis of phosphates in algal cultures. *J. Air Water Poll.* 9:715.

JENKINS, D. 1965. A study of methods suitable for the analysis and preservation of phosphorus forms in an estuarine environment. SERL Report No. 65-18, Sanitary Engineering Research Laboratory, Univ. of California, Berkeley.

SHANNON, J.E. & G.F. LEE. 1966. Hydrolysis of condensed phosphates in natural waters. *J. Air Water Poll.* 10:735.

GALES, M.E., JR., E.C. JULIAN & R.C. KRONER. 1966. Method for quantitative determination of total phosphorus in water. *J. Amer. Water Works Ass.* 58:1363.

LEE, G. F. 1967. Analytical chemistry of plant nutrients. *In* Proc. Int. Conf. Eutrophication, Madison, Wisc.

FITZGERALD, G.P. & S.L. FAUST. 1967. Effect of water sample preservation methods on the release of phosphorus from algae. *Limnol. Oceanogr.* 12:332.

MURPHY, J. & J. RILEY. 1962. A modified single solution method for the determination of phosphate in natural waters. *Anal. Chem. Acta.* 27:31.

ABBOT, D.C., G.E. EMSDEN & J.R. HARRIS. 1963. A method for determining orthophosphate in water. *Analyst* 88:814.

GOTTFRIED, P. 1964. Determination of total phosphorus in water and wastewater as molybdovanadophosphoric acid. *Limnologica* 2:407.

HENRIKSEN, A. 1966. An automatic method for determining orthophosphate in sewage and highly polluted waters. *Analyst* 91:652.

KITSON, R.E. & M.G. MELLON. 1944. Colorimetric determination of phosphorus as molybdovanadophosphoric acid. *Ind. Eng. Chem.*, Anal. Ed. 16:379.

426   SILICA

Silica ranks next to oxygen in abundance in the earth's crust, appearing as the oxide in many rocks and combined with metals in the form of many silicate minerals, particularly the igneous and metamorphic rocks. Degradation of these silica-containing rocks results in the presence of silica in natural waters as suspended particles, in a colloidal or polymeric state, and as the silicate ion. A more complete discussion of the occurrence and chemistry of silica in natural waters in given by Hem.[1]

The silica content of natural water is most commonly in the 1- to 30-mg/l range, although concentrations as high as 100 mg/l are not unusual and concentrations exceeding 1,000 mg/l are found in some brackish waters and brines.

Silica in water is undesirable for a number of industrial uses because it forms difficult-to-remove silica and silicate scales in various equipment and particularly because of the formation of a pure silica deposit on high-pressure steam-turbine blades. Silica removal is accomplished most often by the use of strongly basic anion-exchange resins in the deionization process or by distillation. Some older plants use precipitation with magnesium oxide in either the hot or cold lime softening process.

1. Selection of Method

Use Method A to standardize the sodium silicate solutions used as standards for Methods B and C. It is the preferred method for water samples that contain at least 20 mg/l silica, but is not recommended for determining lower concentrations. Method B is recommended for relatively pure waters containing from 0.4 to 25 mg/l silica. As with most colorimetric methods, the range can be extended, if necessary, by taking smaller portions, by concentrating, or by varying the light path. The interferences due to tannin, color, and turbidity are more severe with this method than with Method C. Moreover, the yellow color produced by Method B has a limited stability and some attention to timing is necessary. When applicable, however, it offers greater speed and simplicity than Method C because one less reagent is used; one timing step is eliminated; and many natural waters can be analyzed without dilution, which is not often the case with Method C. Method C is recommended for the low range, from 0.04 to 2 mg/l silica. This range also can be extended if necessary. Such extension may be desirable if interference is expected from tannin, color, or turbidity. A combination of factors renders Method C less susceptible than Method B to those interferences; also, the blue color of Method C is more stable than the yellow color of Method B. However, many samples will require dilution because of the high sensitivity. Permanent artificial color standards are not available for the blue color developed in Method C.

2. Sampling and Storage

Collect samples in bottles of polyethylene, other plastic, or hard rubber, especially if there will be a delay between collection and analysis. Pyrex glass is a less desirable choice.

426 A.   Gravimetric Method

1. General Discussion

a. Principle: Hydrochloric acid decomposes silicates and dissolved silica, forming silicic acids that are precipitated as partially dehydrated silica during evaporation and baking. Ignition completes dehydration of the silica, which is weighed and then volatilized as silicon tetrafluoride, leaving any impurities behind as nonvolatile residue. The residue is weighed and silica is determined as loss on volatilization. Perchloric instead of hydrochloric acid may be used to dehydrate the silica. A single fuming with perchloric acid will recover more silica than one with hydrochloric acid, although for complete silica recovery two dehydrations with either acid are necessary. The use of perchloric acid lessens the tendency to spatter, yields a silica precipitate that is easier to filter, and shortens the time required for the determination. Because perchloric acid is explosive, a shield must be used.

b. Interference: Because glassware may contribute silica, avoid its use as much as possible. Use agents and distilled water low in silica. Carry out a blank determination to correct for silica introduced by the reagents and apparatus.

2. Apparatus

a. Platinum crucibles, with covers.

b. Platinum evaporating dishes, 200-ml. In the dehydration steps, acid-leached glazed porcelain evaporating dishes free from etching may be substituted for platinum.

3. Reagents

For maximum accuracy, set aside batches of chemicals low in silica for this method. Store all reagents in plastic containers and run blanks.

a. Hydrochloric acid, HCl, 1+1 and 1+50.

b. Sulfuric acid, H_2SO_4, 1+1.

c. Hydrofluoric acid, HF, 48%.

d. Perchloric acid, $KClO_4$, 72%.

4. Procedure

Before performing silica determinations, test the H_2SO_4 and HF for interfering nonvolatile matter by carrying out the procedure of ¶a5) below. Use a clean empty platinum crucible. If any increase in weight is observed, make a correction in the silica determinations.

a. Hydrochloric acid dehydration:

1) Sample evaporation—To a clear sample containing at least 10 mg silica, add 5 ml 1+1 HCl. Evaporate the mixture to dryness in a 200-ml platinum evaporating dish, in several portions if necessary, on a water bath or suspended on an asbestos ring over a hot plate. Protect against contamination by atmospheric dust. During the evaporation, add a total of 15 ml 1+1 HCl in several portions. After the dish is dry, place it in a 110 C oven or over a hot plate to bake for 1/2 hr.

2) First filtration—To the residue in the dish, add 5 ml 1+1 HCl, warm, and add 50 ml hot distilled water. While hot, filter the suspension through an ashless medium-texture filter paper, decanting as much of the liquid as pos-

sible. Wash the dish and the residue with hot 1+50 HCl and then with a minimum volume of distilled water until the washings are chloride-free. Save all washings. Set aside the filter paper with its residue.

3) Second filtration—Evaporate the filtrate and washings from the above operation to dryness in the original platinum dish and bake the residue in a 110 C oven or over a hot plate for 1/2 hr. Repeat the steps in ¶2) above. Use a separate filter paper and a rubber policeman to aid in transferring all the residue from the dish to the filter.

4) Ignition—Transfer the two filter papers and residues to a covered platinum crucible, dry at 110 C, and ignite at 1,200 C to constant weight. Avoid mechanical loss of residue when first charring and burning off the paper. Cool the crucible in a desiccator, weigh, and repeat the ignition and weighing until constant weight is attained. Record the weight of the crucible and the contents.

5) Volatilization with hydrofluoric acid—Thoroughly moisten the weighed residue in the crucible with distilled water. Add 4 drops 1+1 H_2SO_4, followed by 10 ml HF, measuring the latter in a plastic graduated cylinder or pouring an estimated 10 ml directly from the reagent bottle. Slowly evaporate the mixture to dryness over an air bath or hot plate in a hood and avoid loss by splattering. Ignite the crucible to constant weight at 1,200 C. Record the weight of the crucible and contents.

b. Perchloric acid dehydration: Review ¶1a, preceding. Follow the procedure in ¶4a1) above until all but 50 ml

of the sample has been evaporated. Add 5 ml perchloric acid and evaporate until dense white fumes appear. (CAUTION: Explosive—place a shield between personnel and the fuming dish.)

Continue dehydration for 10 min. Cool, add 5 ml 1+1 HCl and then 50 ml hot distilled water. Bring to a boil and filter through an ashless quantitative filter paper. Wash thoroughly ten times with hot distilled water and proceed as directed in ¶s 4a4) and 5) preceding. For routine work, the silica precipitate is often sufficiently pure for the purpose intended and may be weighed directly, omitting the HF volatilization. Make an initial check against the longer procedure, however, to be sure that the result is within the limits of accuracy required.

5. Calculation

Subtract the weight of crucible and contents after the HF treatment from the corresponding weight before HF treatment. The difference, A, in milligrams is "loss on volatilization" and represents silica:

$$mg/l\ SiO_2 = \frac{A \times 1,000}{ml\ sample}$$

6. Precision and Accuracy

The accuracy is limited both by the finite solubility of silica in water under the conditions of the analysis and by the sensitivity of the analytical balance. Under optimum conditions, the precision is approximately ±0.2 mg SiO_2. If a 1-l sample is taken for analysis, this represents a precision of ±0.2 mg/l.

426 B. Molybdosilicate Method

1. General Discussion

a. *Principle:* Ammonium molybdate at pH approximately 1.2 reacts with silica and any phosphate present to produce heteropoly acids. Oxalic acid is added to destroy the molybdophosphoric acid but not the molybdosilicic acid. Even if phosphate is known to be absent, the addition of oxalic acid is highly desirable and is a mandatory step in both this method and Method C. The intensity of the yellow color is proportional to the concentration of "molybdate-reactive" silica. In at least one of its forms, silica does not react with molybdate even though it is capable of passing through filter paper and is not noticeably turbid. It is not known to what extent such "unreactive" silica occurs in waters, and the literature on the subject is contradictory. In the past, terms such as "colloidal," "crystalloidal" and "ionic" have been used to distinguish between various forms of silica in waters. Such terminology cannot be substantiated. An optional step is included in the procedure to convert any "molybdate-unreactive" silica into the "molybdate-reactive" form. These terms do not imply reactivity, or lack of it, toward *other* reagents or processes.

b. *Interference:* Because both apparatus and reagents may contribute silica, avoid the use of glassware as much as possible and use reagents low in silica. Also, carry out a blank determination to correct for silica so introduced. In both this method and Method C, tannin, large amounts of iron, color, turbidity, sulfide, and phosphate are potential sources of interference. The treatment with oxalic acid eliminates interference from phosphate and decreases interference from tannin. If necessary, photometric compensation may be used to cancel interference from color or turbidity in the sample.

c. *Minimum detectable concentration:* Approximately 1 mg/l SiO_2 can be detected in 50-ml nessler tubes.

2. Apparatus

a. *Platinum dishes,* 100-ml.

b. *Colorimetric equipment:* One of the following is required:

1) *Spectrophotometer,* for use at 410 nm, providing a light path of 1 cm or longer.

2) *Filter photometer,* providing a light path of 1 cm or longer and equipped with a violet filter having maximum transmittance near 410 nm.

3) *Nessler tubes,* matched, 50-ml, tall form.

3. Reagents

For best results, set aside and use batches of chemicals low in silica. Store all reagents in plastic containers to guard against high blanks.

a. *Sodium bicarbonate* (also called sodium hydrogen carbonate), $NaHCO_3$, powder.

b. *Sulfuric acid,* H_2SO_4, 1 N.

c. *Hydrochloric acid,* HCl, 1+1.

d. *Ammonium molybdate reagent:* Dissolve 10 g $(NH_4)_6Mo_7O_{24} \cdot 4H_2O$ in distilled water, with stirring and gentle warming, and dilute to 100 ml. Filter if necessary. Adjust to pH 7 to 8 with silica-free NH_4OH or NaOH and store in a polyethylene bottle to stabilize the reagent. (If the pH is not adjusted, a precipitate gradually forms. If the solution is stored in glass, silica may leach out and cause high blanks.) If necessary, prepare silica-free NH_4OH by passing gaseous NH_3 into distilled water contained in a plastic bottle.

e. Oxalic acid solution: Dissolve 10 g $H_2C_2O_4 \cdot 2H_2O$ in distilled water and dilute to 100 ml.

f. Stock silica solution: Dissolve 4.73 g sodium metasilicate nonahydrate, $Na_2SiO_3 \cdot 9H_2O$, in recently boiled and cooled distilled water and dilute to approximately 900 ml. Analyze 100.0-ml portions by Method A and adjust the remainder of the solution to contain 1.000 mg/l SiO_2. Store in a tightly stoppered plastic bottle.

g. Standard silica solution: Dilute 10.00 ml stock solution to 1,000 ml with recently boiled and cooled distilled water; this solution contains 10.0 mg/l SiO_2 or 1.00 ml = 10.0 μg SiO_2. Store in a tightly stoppered plastic bottle.

h. Permanent color solutions:

1) *Potassium chromate solution:* Dissolve 630 mg K_2CrO_4 in distilled water and dilute to 1 l.

2) *Borax solution:* Dissolve 10 g sodium borate decahydrate, $Na_2B_4O_7 \cdot 10H_2O$, in distilled water and dilute to 1 l.

4. Procedure

Convert any molybdate-unreactive silica to the reactive form or state by digesting the sample with sodium bicarbonate. Omit the digestion if all the silica in the sample is known to react with molybdate.

a. Digestion with sodium bicarbonate: Prepare a clear sample by filtration if necessary. Place 50.0 ml, or a smaller portion diluted to 50 ml, in a 100-ml platinum dish. Add 200 mg silica-free $NaHCO_3$ and digest on a steam bath for 1 hr. Cool and add slowly, with stirring, 2.4 ml H_2SO_4. Do not interrupt the analysis but proceed *at once* with the remaining steps. Transfer quantitatively to a 50-ml nessler tube and make up to the mark with distilled water. (Tall-form 50-ml nessler tubes are convenient for mixing even if the solution is subsequently transferred to an absorption cell for photometric measurement.)

b. Color development: To the prepared sample, or to 50.0 ml of an untreated sample if the conversion step is omitted, add in rapid succession 1.0 ml 1+1 HCl and 2.0 ml ammonium molybdate reagent. Mix by inverting at least six times and let the solution stand for 5 to 10 min. Add 1.5 ml oxalic acid solution and mix thoroughly. Read the color after 2 min but before 15 min, measuring time from the addition of oxalic acid. Since the yellow color obeys Beer's law, measure photometrically or visually.

c. Preparation of standards: If $NaHCO_3$ pretreatment is used for the samples, add to the standards 200 mg $NaHCO_3$ and 2.4 ml H_2SO_4, to compensate both for the slight amount of silica that may be introduced by the reagents and for the effect of the salt on the intensity of the color.

d. Photometric measurement: Prepare a calibration curve from a series of approximately six standards to cover the optimum ranges cited in Table 426:I. Carry out the steps of ¶4b above on suitable portions of standard silica solution

TABLE 426:I. SELECTION OF LIGHT PATH LENGTH FOR VARIOUS SILICA CONCENTRATIONS

Light Path cm	Method B	Method C	
	Silica in 54.5-ml Final Volume μg	Silica in 56.5-ml Final Volume μg	
		650 nm Wave-length	815 nm Wave-length
1	200–1,300	40–300	20–100
2	100–700	20–150	10–50
5	40–250	7–50	4–20
10	20–130	4–30	2–10

diluted to 50.0 ml in nessler tubes. Set the photometer at 100% transmittance (zero absorbance) with distilled water and read all standards, including a reagent blank against the distilled water. Plot micrograms of silica in the final (54.5 ml) developed solution against photometer readings. Run a reagent blank and at least one standard with each group of samples to confirm that the calibration curve previously established has not shifted.

e. Visual comparison: Make up a set of permanent artificial color standards, using potassium chromate and borax solutions. Mix the volumes of liquids specified in Table 426:II and place them in well-stoppered, appropriately labeled 50-ml nessler tubes. Verify the correctness of these permanent artificial standards by comparing them visually against standards prepared by analyzing portions of the standard silica solution. Use the permanent artificial color standards only for visual comparison, never to calibrate a photometer.

f. Correction for color or turbidity: Prepare a special blank for every sample that needs such correction. Carry two identical portions of each such sample through the procedure, including NaHCO₃ treatment if this is elected. To one portion add all reagents as directed in ¶4*b* preceding. To the other portion add HCl and oxalic acid but no molybdate. Null the photometer with the blank containing no molybdate before reading the absorbance or transmittance of the molybdate-treated sample.

TABLE 426:II. PREPARATION OF PERMANENT COLOR STANDARDS FOR VISUAL DETERMINATION OF SILICA

Value in Silica mg	Potassium Chromate Solution ml	Borax Solution ml	Water ml
0.00	0.0	25	30
0.10	1.0	25	29
0.20	2.0	25	28
0.40	4.0	25	26
0.50	5.0	25	25
0.75	7.5	25	22
1.0	10.0	25	20

5. Calculation

$$\text{mg/l SiO}_2 = \frac{\mu\text{g SiO}_2}{\text{ml sample}}$$

Report whether NaHCO₃ digestion was involved in the colorimetric determination.

6. Precision and Accuracy

A synthetic unknown sample containing 5.0 mg/l SiO₂, 10 mg/l chloride, 0.200 mg/l ammonia N, 1.0 mg/l nitrate N, 1.5 mg/l organic N, and 10.0 mg/l phosphate in distilled water was analyzed in 19 laboratories by the molybdosilicate method, with a relative standard deviation of 14.3% and a relative error of 7.8%.

Another synthetic unknown sample containing 15.0 mg/l SiO_2, 200 mg/l chloride, 0.800 mg/l ammonia N, 1.0 mg/l nitrate N, 0.800 mg/l organic N, and 5.0 mg/l phosphate in distilled water was analyzed in 19 laboratories by the molybdosilicate method, with a relative standard deviation of 8.4% and a relative error of 4.2%.

A third synthetic unknown sample containing 30.0 mg/l SiO_2, 400 mg/l chloride, 1.50 mg/l ammonia N, 1.0 mg/l nitrate N, 0.200 mg/l organic N, and 0.500 mg/l phosphate in distilled water was analyzed in 20 laboratories by the molybdosilicate method, with a relative standard deviation of 7.7% and a relative error of 9.8%.

All results were obtained after sample digestion with $NaHCO_3$.

426 C. Heteropoly Blue Method

1. General Discussion

a. Principle: The principles outlined under Method B, Section 1*a*, also apply to this method. The yellow molybdosilicic acid is reduced by means of aminonaphtholsulfonic acid to heteropoly blue. The blue color is more intense than the yellow color of Method B and provides increased sensitivity.

b. Interference: See Section 426B.1*b*.

c. Minimum detectable concentration: Approximately 20 $\mu g/l$ SiO_2 can be detected in 50-ml nessler tubes.

2. Apparatus

a. Platinum dishes, 100-ml.

b. Colorimetric equipment: One of the following is required:

1) *Spectrophotometer,* for use at approximately 815 nm. The color system also obeys Beer's law at 650 nm, with appreciably reduced sensitivity. A light path of 1 cm or longer yields satisfactory results.

2) *Filter photometer,* provided with a red filter exhibiting maximum transmittance in the wavelength range of 600 to 815 nm. Sensitivity improves with increasing wavelength. A light path of 1 cm or longer yields satisfactory results.

3) *Nessler tubes,* matched, 50 ml, tall form.

3. Reagents

For best results, set aside and use batches of chemicals low in silica. Store all reagents in plastic containers to guard against high blanks. Use distilled water that does not contain detectable silica after storage in glass.

All of the reagents listed in Section 426B.3 are required, and in addition:

Reducing agent: Dissolve 500 mg 1-amino-2-naphthol-4-sulfonic acid and 1 g Na_2SO_3 in 50 ml distilled water, with gentle warming if necessary; add this to a solution of 30 g $NaHSO_3$ in 150 ml distilled water. Filter into a plastic bottle. Discard the solution when it becomes dark. Prolong reagent life by storing in a refrigerator and away from light. Avoid aminonaphtholsulfonic acid that is incompletely soluble or that produces reagents that are dark even when freshly prepared; such material is not suitable for silica determinations.*

4. Procedure

a. Color development: Proceed as in Section 426B.4*a* and *b* up to and including the words, "Add 1.5 ml oxalic acid solution and mix thoroughly." Measuring time from the moment of addition of oxalic acid, wait for at least 2 min but not more than 15 min, add 2.0 ml reducing agent, and mix thoroughly After 5 min, measure the blue color photometrically or visually. If NaHCO₃ pretreatment is used, follow Section 426B.4*c*.

b. Photometric measurement: Prepare a calibration curve from a series òf approximately six standards to cover the optimum range indicated in Table 426:I. Carry out the steps described above on suitable portions of standard silica solution diluted to 50.0 ml in nessler tubes. Null the photometer with distilled water and read all the standards, including a reagent blank, against the distilled water. If it is necessary to correct for color or turbidity in a sample, consult Section 426B.4*f*. To the special blank add HCl and oxalic acid, but no molybdate or reducing agent. Plot micrograms of silica in the final 56.5-ml developed solution against photometer readings. Run a reagent blank and at least one standard with each group of samples to check the calibration curve.

c. Visual comparison: Prepare a series of not less than twelve standards, covering the range 0 to 120 μg SiO₂, by placing the calculated volumes of standard silica solution in 50-ml nessler tubes,

diluting to the mark with distilled water, and developing the color as described in ¶*a* preceding.

5. Calculation

$$\text{mg/l SiO}_2 = \frac{\mu\text{g SiO}_2}{\text{ml sample}}$$

Report whether NaHCO₃ digestion was involved in the colorimetric determination.

6. Precision and Accuracy

A synthetic unknown sample containing 5.0 mg/l SiO₂, 10 mg/l chloride, 0.200 mg/l ammonia N, 1.0 mg/l nitrate N, 1.5 mg/l organic N, and 10.0 mg/l phosphate in distilled water was analyzed in 11 laboratories by the heteropoly blue method, with a relative standard deviation of 27.2% and a relative error of 3.0%.

A second synthetic unknown sample containing 15.0 mg/l SiO₂, 200 mg/l chloride, 0.800 mg/l ammonia N, 1.0 mg/l nitrate N, 0.800 mg/l organic N, and 5.0 mg/l phosphate in distilled water was analyzed in 11 laboratories by the heteropoly blue method, with a relative standard deviation of 18.0% and a relative error of 2.9%.

A third synthetic unknown sample containing 30.0 mg/l SiO₂, 400 mg/l chloride, 1.50 mg/l ammonia N, 1.0 mg/l nitrate N, 0.200 mg/l organic N, and 0.500 mg/l phosphate in distilled water was analyzed in 10 laboratories by the heteropoly blue method, with a relative standard deviation of 4.9% and a relative error of 5.1%.

All results were obtained after digestion of the sample with NaHCO₃.

---

* Eastman No. 360 has been found satisfactory.

426 D. Reference

1. HEM, J.D. 1959. Study and interpretation of the chemical characteristics of natural wa-

ter. U.S. Geol. Surv. Water Supply Pap. No. 1473.

426 E. Bibliography

General

ROY, C.J. 1945. Silica in natural waters. *Amer. J. Sci.* 243:393.

VAIL, J.G. 1952. The Soluble Silicates, Their Properties and Uses. Reinhold Publishing Corp., New York, N.Y. Vol. 1, pp. 95–97, 100–161.

Gravimetric Method

HILLEBRAND, W.F. et al. 1953. Applied Inorganic Analysis, 2nd ed. John Wiley & Sons, New York, N.Y. Chapter 43.

KOLTHOFF, I.M., E.J. MEEHAN, E.B. SANDELL & S. BRUCKENSTEIN. 1969. Quantitative Chemical Analysis, 4th ed. Macmillan Co., New York, N.Y.

Colorimetric Methods

DIENERT, F. & F. WANDENBULCKE. 1923. On the determination of silica in waters. *Bull. Soc. Chim. France* 33:1131, *Compt. Rend.* 176:1478.

DIENERT, F. & F. WANDENBULCKE. 1924. A study of colloidal silica. *Compt. Rend.* 178:564.

SWANK, H.W. & M.G. MELLON, 1934. Colorimetric standards for silica. *Ind. Eng. Chem.,* Anal. Ed. 6:348.

TOURKY, A.R. & D.H. BANGHAM. 1936. Colloidal silica in natural waters and the "silicomolybdate" colour test. *Nature* 138:587.

BIRNBAUM, N. & G.H. WALDEN. 1938. Coprecipitation of ammonium silicomolybdate and ammonium phosphomolybdate. *J. Amer. Chem. Soc.* 60:66.

KAHLER, H.L. 1941. Determination of soluble silica in water: A photometric method. *Ind. Eng. Chem.,* Anal. Ed. 13:536.

NOLL, C.A. & J.J. MAGUIRE. 1942. Effect of container on soluble silica content of water samples. *Ind. Eng. Chem.,* Anal. Ed. 14:569.

SCHWARTZ, M.C. 1942. Photometric determination of silica in the presence of phosphates. *Ind. Eng. Chem.,* Anal. Ed. 14:893.

BUNTING, W.E. 1944. Determination of soluble silica in very low concentrations. *Ind. Eng. Chem.,* Anal. Ed. 16:612.

STRAUB, F.G. & H. GRABOWSKI. 1944. Photometric determination of silica in condensed steam in the presence of phosphates. *Ind. Eng. Chem.,* Anal. Ed. 16:574.

GUITER, H. 1945. Influence of pH on the composition and physical aspects of the ammonium molybdates. *Compt. Rend.* 220:146.

BOLTZ, D.F. & M.G. MELLON. 1947. Determination of phosphorus, germanium, silicon, and arsenic by the heteropoly blue method. *Ind. Eng. Chem.,* Anal. Ed. 19:873.

MILTON, R.F. 1951. Formation of silicomolybdate. *Analyst* 76:431.

MILTON, R.F. 1951. Estimation of silica in water. *J. Appl. Chem.* (London) 1: (Supplement No. 2) 126.

CARLSON, A.B. & C.V. BANKS. 1952. Spectrophotometric determination of silicon. *Anal. Chem.* 24:472.

KILLEFFER, D.H. & A. LINZ. 1952. Molybdenum Compunds, Their Chemistry and Technology. Interscience Publishers, New York, N.Y. pp. 1–2. 42–45, 67–82, 87–92.

STRICKLAND, J.D.H. 1952. The preparation and properties of silicomolybdic acid. *J. Amer. Chem. Soc.* 74:862, 868, 872.

CHOW, D.T.W. & R.J. ROBINSON. 1953. The forms of silicate available for colorimetric determination. *Anal. Chem.* 25:646.

427   SULFATE

Sulfate is widely distributed in nature and may be present in natural waters in concentrations ranging from a few to several thousand milligrams per liter. Mine drainage wastes may contribute high sulfate by virtue of pyrite oxidation. Sodium and magnesium sulfate exert a cathartic action and should not be present in excess in drinking water.

1. Selection of Method

The choice of method will depend on the concentration range of sulfate and the degree of accuracy required. Dilution or concentration of the sample will bring most waters into the desired range for any of the methods. Method A is the preferred standard method and is the most accurate for sulfate concentrations above 10 mg/l. It should be used for obtaining theoretical ion balances and whenever results of the greatest accuracy are required. Method B is similar but substitutes drying of the filter and residue for the more rigorous heat treatment by ignition at 800 C that is re-quired to expel occluded water. This method is acceptable in routine work where the greatest attainable accuracy is not required. Method C is more rapid and may be either more or less accurate than Methods A or B for sulfate concentrations less than 10 mg/l, depending on a number of factors, including the skill of the analyst. Although usually less accurate than Methods A or B above 10 mg/l, Method C may be applied to concentrations up to 60 mg/l. Sulfate also may be determined by the automated method described in Section 607.

2. Sampling and Storage

In the presence of organic matter certain bacteria may reduce sulfate to sulfide. To avoid this, store heavily polluted or contaminated samples at low temperatures or treat with formaldehyde. Sulfite may be oxidized to sulfate by dissolved oxygen above pH 8.0. If samples contain sulfite, adjust the pH below this level.

427 A.   Gravimetric Method With Ignition of Residue

1. General Discussion

a. Principle: Sulfate is precipitated in a hydrochloric acid medium as barium sulfate by the addition of barium chloride. The precipitation is carried out near the boiling temperature, and after a period of digestion the precipitate is filtered, washed with water until free of chlorides, ignited or dried, and weighed as $BaSO_4$.

b. Interference: The gravimetric determination of sulfate is subject to many errors, both positive and negative. In potable waters where the mineral concentration is low, these may be of minor importance.

1) Interferences leading to high results—Suspended matter, silica, barium chloride precipitant, nitrate, sulfite, and water are the principal factors in posi-

tive errors. Suspended matter may be present in both the sample and the precipitating solution; soluble silicate may be rendered insoluble and sulfite may be oxidized to sulfate during processing of the sample. Barium nitrate, barium chloride, and water are occluded to some extent with the barium sulfate, although water is driven off if the temperature of ignition is sufficiently high.

2) Interferences leading to low results—Alkali metal sulfates frequently yield low results. This is especially true of alkali hydrogen sulfates. Occlusion of alkali sulfate with barium sulfate causes the substitution of an element of lower atomic weight than barium in the precipitate. Hydrogen sulfates of alkali metals act similarly and, in addition, decompose on being heated. Heavy metals, such as chromium and iron, cause low results by interfering with the complete precipitation of sulfate and by formation of heavy metal sulfates. Barium sulfate has small but significant solubility, which is increased in the presence of acid. Although an acid medium is necessary to prevent precipitation of barium carbonate and phosphate, it is important to limit its concentration to minimize the solution effect.

2. Apparatus

a. Steam bath.

b. Drying oven, equipped with thermostatic control.

c. Muffle furnace, with heat indicator.

d. Desiccator.

e. Analytical balance, capable of weighing to 0.1 mg.

f. Filter: Acid-washed, ashless hard-finish filter paper sufficiently retentive for fine precipitates.

3. Reagents

a. Methyl red indicator solution: Dissolve 100 mg methyl red sodium salt in distilled water and dilute to 100 ml.

b. Hydrochloric acid, HCl, 1+1.

c. Barium chloride solution: Dissolve 100 g $BaCl_2 \cdot 2H_2O$ in 1 l distilled water. Filter through a membrane filter or hard-finish filter paper before use; 1 ml of this reagent is capable of precipitating approximately 40 mg SO_4.

d. Silver nitrate-nitric acid reagent: Dissolve 8.5 g $AgNO_3$ and 0.5 ml conc HNO_3 in 500 ml distilled water.

4. Procedure

a. Removal of silica: If the silica concentration exceeds 25 mg/l, evaporate the sample nearly to dryness in a platinum dish on a steam bath. Add 1 ml HCl, tilt the dish, and rotate it until the acid comes in contact with the residue on the sides; continue the evaporation to dryness. Complete the drying in an oven at 180 C and if organic matter is present, char over the flame of a burner. Moisten the residue with 2 ml distilled water and 1 ml HCl, and evaporate to dryness on a steam bath. Add 2 ml HCl, take up the soluble residue in hot water, and filter. Wash the insoluble silica with several small portions of hot distilled water. Combine the filtrate and washings.

b. Precipitation of barium sulfate: Adjust the clarified sample—treated if necessary to remove interfering agents— to contain approximately 50 mg sulfate ion in a 250-ml volume. Adjust the acidity with HCl to pH 4.5 to 5.0, using a pH meter or the orange color of methyl red indicator. Then add an additional 1 to 2 ml HCl. Lower concentrations of sulfate ion may be tolerated if it is impracticable to concentrate the sample to the optimum level, but in such cases fix the total volume at 150 ml. Heat the solution to boiling and, while stirring gently, add warm BaCl$_2$ solution slowly until precipitation appears to be complete; then add about 2 ml in excess. If the amount of precipitate is small, add a total of 5 ml BaCl$_2$ solution. Digest the precipitate at 80 to 90 C, preferably overnight but for not less than 2 hr.

c. Filtration and weighing: Mix a small amount of ashless filter paper pulp with the BaSO$_4$ and filter at room temperature. The pulp aids filtration and reduces the tendency of the precipitate to creep. Wash the precipitate with small portions of warm distilled water until the washings are free of chloride, as in-

dicated by testing with silver nitrate-nitric acid reagent. Dry the filter and precipitate and ignite at 800 C for 1 hr. *Do not let the filter paper flame.* Cool in a desiccator and weigh.

5. Calculation

$$mg/l\ SO_4 = \frac{mg\ BaSO_4 \times 411.5}{ml\ sample}$$

6. Precision and Accuracy

A synthetic unknown sample containing 259 mg/l sulfate, 108 mg/l Ca, 82 mg/l Mg, 3.1 mg/l K, 19.9 mg/l Na, 241 mg/l chloride, 0.250 mg/l nitrite N, 1.1 mg/l nitrate N, and 42.5 mg/l total alkalinity (contributed by NaHCO$_3$) was analyzed in 32 laboratories by the gravimetric method, with a relative standard deviation of 4.7% and a relative error of 1.9%.

427 B. Gravimetric Method with Drying of Residue

1. General Discussion

See Method A, preceding.

2. Apparatus

With the exception of the filter paper, all of the apparatus cited in Section 427A.2 is required, plus the following:

a. Filters: Use one of the following:

1) *Fritted-glass filter,* fine ("F") porosity, with a maximum pore size of 5 μm.

2) *Membrane filter,* with a pore size of about 0.45 μm.

b. Filtering apparatus, appropriate to the type of filter selected. (Coat the holder used for the membrane filter with silicone fluid to prevent the precipitate from adhering to it.)

c. Vacuum oven.

3. Reagents

All the reagents listed in Section 427A.3 are required, and in addition:

*a. Silicone fluid.**

_____

* "Desicote" (Beckman) or similar.

b. Anticreep fluid: Commercial non-ionic wetting agents are satisfactory.

4. Procedure

a. Removal of interference: See Section 427A.4*a*.

b. Precipitation of barium sulfate: See Section 427A.4*b*.

c. Preparation of filters:

1) Fritted glass filter—Dry to constant weight in an oven maintained at 105 C or higher, cool in a desiccator, and weigh.

2) Membrane filter—Place the filter on a piece of filter paper or a watch glass and dry to constant weight† in a vacuum oven at 80 C, while maintaining a vacuum of at least 640 mm (25 in.) of

---

† Constant weight is defined as a change of not more than 0.5 mg in two successive operations consisting of heating, cooling in a desiccator, and weighing.

mercury, or in a conventional oven at a temperature of 103 to 105 C. Cool in a desiccator and weigh the membrane only.

d. Filtration and weighing: Filter the $BaSO_4$ at room temperature. Wash the precipitate with several small portions of warm distilled water until the washings are free of chloride, as indicated by testing with silver nitrate-nitric acid reagent. If the membrane filter is used add a few drops of anticreep solution to the suspension before filtering, to prevent adherence of the precipitate to the holder. Dry the filter with precipitate by the same procedure used in the preparation of the filter. Cool in a desiccator and weigh.

5. Calculation

$$\text{mg/l } SO_4 = \frac{\text{mg } BaSO_4 \times 411.5}{\text{ml sample}}$$

427 C.   Turbidimetric Method

1. General Discussion

a. Principle: Sulfate ion is precipitated in a hydrochloric acid medium with barium chloride in such a manner as to form barium sulfate crystals of uniform size. The absorbance of the barium sulfate suspension is measured by a nephelometer or transmission photometer and the sulfate ion concentration is determined by comparison of the reading with a standard curve.

b. Interference: Color or suspended matter in large amounts will interfere with this method. Some suspended mat-

ter may be removed by filtration. If both are small in comparison with the sulfate ion concentration, interference is corrected for as indicated in ¶4*d* below. Silica in excess of 500 mg/l will interfere, and in waters containing large quantities of organic material it may not be possible to precipitate barium sulfate satisfactorily.

There are no ions other than sulfate in normal waters that will form insoluble compounds with barium under strongly acid conditions. Make determinations at room temperature, which may vary over a range of 10 C without causing appreciable error.

c. Minimum detectable concentration: Approximately 1 mg/l sulfate.

2. Apparatus

a. Magnetic stirrer: It is convenient to incorporate a timing device to permit the magnetic stirrer to operate for exactly 1 min. Use a constant stirring speed. It is also convenient to incorporate a fixed resistance in series with the motor operating the magnetic stirrer to regulate the speed of stirring. Use magnets of identical shape and size. The exact speed of stirring is not critical, but it should be constant for each run of samples and standards and should be adjusted to about the maximum at which no splashing occurs.

b. Photometer: One of the following is required, with preference in the order given:

1) *Nephelometer.*

2) *Spectrophotometer,* for use at 420 nm, providing a light path of 4 to 5 cm.

3) *Filter photometer,* equipped with a violet filter having maximum transmittance near 420 nm and providing a light path of 4 to 5 cm.

c. Stopwatch, if the magnetic stirrer is not equipped with an accurate timer.

d. Measuring spoon, capacity 0.2 to 0.3 ml.

3. Reagents

a. Conditioning reagent: Mix 50 ml glycerol with a solution containing 30 ml conc HCl, 300 ml distilled water, 100 ml 95% ethyl or isopropyl alcohol, and 75 g NaCl.

b. Barium chloride, $BaCl_2$, crystals, 20 to 30 mesh.

c. Standard sulfate solution: Prepare a standard sulfate solution as described in 1) or 2); 1.00 ml = 100 μg SO_4.

1) Dilute 10.41 ml standard 0.0200N H_2SO_4 titrant specified in Alkalinity, Section 403.3c, to 100 ml with distilled water.

2) Dissolve 147.9 mg anhydrous Na_2SO_4 in distilled water and dilute to 1,000 ml.

4. Procedure

a. Formation of barium sulfate turbidity: Measure 100 ml sample, or a suitable portion made up to 100 ml, into a 250-ml erlenmeyer flask. Add exactly 5.00 ml conditioning reagent and mix in the stirring apparatus. While the solution is being stirred, add a spoonful of $BaCl_2$ crystals and begin timing immediately. Stir for exactly 1 min at a constant speed.

b. Measurement of barium sulfate turbidity: Immediately after the stirring period has ended, pour some of the solution into the absorption cell of the photometer and measure the turbidity at 30-sec intervals for 4 min. Because maximum turbidity usually occurs within 2 min and the readings remain constant thereafter for 3 to 10 min, consider the turbidity to be the maximum reading obtained in the 4-min interval.

c. Preparation of calibration curve: Estimate the sulfate concentration in the sample by comparing the turbidity reading with a calibration curve prepared by carrying sulfate standards through the entire procedure. Space the standards at 5 mg/l increments in the 0- to 40-mg/l sulfate range. Above 40 mg/l the accuracy of the method decreases and the suspensions of barium sulfate lose stability. Check reliability of the calibration curve by running a standard with every three or four unknown samples.

d. Correction for sample color and turbidity: Correct for the color and turbidity present in the original sample by running blanks from which the $BaCl_2$ is withheld.

5. Calculation

$$mg/l\ SO_4\ =\ \frac{mg\ SO_4 \times 1,000}{ml\ sample}$$

6. Precision and Accuracy

A synthetic unknown sample containing 259 mg/l sulfate, 108 mg/l Ca, 82 mg/l Mg, 3.1 mg/l K, 19.9 mg/l Na, 241 mg/l chloride, 0.250 mg/l nitrite N, 1.1 mg/l nitrate N, and 42.5 mg/l total alkalinity (contributed by $NaHCO_3$) was analyzed in 19 laboratories by the turbidimetric method, with a relative standard deviation of 9.1% and a relative error of 1.2%.

427 D.   Bibliography

Gravimetric Methods

HILLDBRAND, W.F. et al. 1953. Applied Inorganic Analysis, 2nd ed. John Wiley & Sons, New York, N.Y.

KOLTHOFF, I.M., E.J. MEEHAN, E.B. SANDELL & S. BRUCKENSTEIN. 1969. Quantitative Chemical Analysis, 4th ed. Macmillan Co., New York, N.Y.

Turbidimetric Method

SHEEN, R.T., H.L. KAHLER & E.M. ROSS. 1935. Turbidimetric determination of sulfate in water. *Ind. Eng. Chem.*, Anal. Ed. 7:262.

THOMAS, J.F. & J.E. COTTON. 1954. A turbidimetric sulfate determination. *Water Sewage Works* 101:462.

ROSSUM, J.R. & P. VILLARRUZ. 1961. Suggested methods for turbidimetric determination of sulfate in water. *J. Amer. Water Works Ass.* 53:873.

FRITZ, J.S. & S.S. YAMAMURA. 1955. Rapid microdetermination of sulfate. *Anal. Chem.* 27:1461.

FRITZ, J.S., S.S. YAMAMURA & M.J. RICHARD. 1957. Titration of sulfate following separation with alumina. *Anal. Chem.* 29:158.

BERTOLACINI, R.J. & J.E. BARNEY. 1958. Ultraviolet spectrophotometric determination of sulfate, chloride, and fluoride with chloranilic acid. *Anal. Chem.* 30:202.

428   SULFIDE

1. General Discussion

Sulfide is often present in groundwater, especially in hot springs, and it is common in wastewaters, coming in part from the decomposition of organic matter, sometimes from industrial wastes, but mostly from the bacterial reduction of sulfate. Hydrogen sulfide escaping into the air from sulfide-containing wastewater causes odor nuisances. The threshold odor concentration of H_2S in clean water is between 0.01 and 0.1 $\mu g/l$. H_2S is very toxic and has claimed the lives of numerous workmen in sewers. It attacks metals directly, and indirectly has caused serious corrosion of concrete sewers, because it is oxidized biologically to sulfuric acid on the pipe wall.

From an analytical standpoint, three categories of sulfide in water and wastewater are distinguished:

a. *Total sulfide* includes dissolved H_2S and HS^-, as well as *acid-soluble* metallic sulfides present in the suspended matter. The S^{2-} is negligible, amounting to less than 0.5% of the dissolved sulfide at pH 12, less than 0.05% at pH 11, etc. Copper and silver sulfides are so insoluble that they do not respond in the ordinary sulfide determinations; they can be ignored for practical purposes.

b. *Dissolved sulfide* is that remaining after the suspended solids have been removed by flocculation and settling.

c. *Un-ionized hydrogen sulfide* may be calculated from the concentration of dissolved sulfide, the pH of the sample, and the practical ionization constant of hydrogen sulfide.

2. Sampling and Storage

Take samples with a minimum of aeration. Preserve a sample for a total sulfide determination by putting 4 drops of $2N$ zinc acetate into a 100-ml bottle, filling completely with the sample, and stoppering.

3. Qualitative Tests

A qualitative test for sulfide is often useful and is advisable in the examination of certain industrial wastes containing interfering substances that may give a false negative result in the methylene blue procedure.

a. *Antimony test:* Add 0.5 ml saturated solution of potassium antimony tartrate to about 200 ml sample in a bottle, and follow with 0.5 ml $6N$ HCl in excess of phenolphthalein alkalinity. The yellow Sb_2S_3 is discernible at a sulfide concentration of 0.5 mg/l. Comparisons with samples of known sulfide concentrations make the technic roughly quantitative. The only known interferences are metallic ions such as lead, which hold the sulfide so firmly that it does not produce antimony sulfide, and dithonite, which decomposes in acid solution to produce sulfide.

b. *Silver sulfide-silver electrode test:* The potential of a silver sulfide-silver electrode assembly relative to a reference electrode varies with the activity of the sulfide ion in solution. By correcting for the ion activity coefficient and pH, this potential allows an estimate of the sulfide concentration. Standardize the electrode frequently against a sulfide solution of known strength. An electrode of

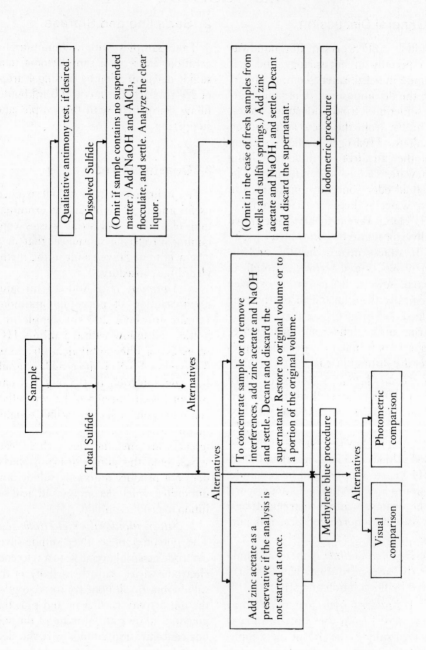

Figure 428:1. Analytical flow paths for sulfide determinations.

this type can be used as an endpoint indicator for titration of dissolved sulfide with a standard solution of a silver or lead salt, but slow response is always a problem.

c. Lead acetate paper and silver foil tests: Confirm odors attributed to H_2S with lead acetate paper. On exposure to the vapor of a slightly acidified sample, the paper becomes blackened by the formation of PbS. A strip of silver foil is more sensitive than lead acetate paper. Clean the silver by dipping in a sodium cyanide solution, and rinse. Silver is particularly suitable for long-time exposure in the vicinity of possible H_2S sources because the black Ag_2S is permanent, whereas PbS slowly oxidizes.

4. Selection of Quantitative Methods

Iodine reacts with sulfide in acid solution, oxidizing it to sulfur. A titration based on this reaction is an accurate method for determining sulfide at concentrations above 1 mg/l if interferences are absent and if loss of H_2S is avoided. The unmodified iodine method (D) is useful for standardizing the colorimetric method and is suitable for analyzing samples freshly taken from wells or springs. The method can be used for wastewater and partly oxidized water from sulfur springs if interfering substances are separated first.

The colorimetric method (C) is based on the reaction of sulfide, ferric chloride, and dimethyl-p-phenylenediamine (p-aminodimethylaniline) under conditions that produce methylene blue. Ammonium phosphate is added after color development to remove the ferric chloride color. The procedure is applicable at sulfide concentrations only up to 20 mg/l.

Figure 428:1 shows analytical flow paths for sulfide determinations under various conditions and options.

428 A.   Separation of Soluble and Insoluble Sulfides

Unless the sample is entirely free from suspended solids (dissolved sulfide equals total sulfide), to measure dissolved sulfide first remove insoluble matter. Accomplish the separation by producing an aluminum hydroxide floc that is settled, leaving a clear supernatant for analysis.

1. Apparatus

Glass bottles with stoppers. Use 100 ml if sulfide will be determined by the methylene method, and 500 to 1,000 ml if by the titrimetric method.

2. Reagents

a. Sodium hydroxide solution, NaOH, 6N.

b. Aluminum chloride solution, 6N: Because of the hygroscopic and caking tendencies of this chemical, purchase 100-g (or 1/4-lb) bottles of the hexahydrate, $AlCl_3 \cdot 6H_2O$. Dissolve the contents of a previously unopened 100-g bottle in 144 ml distilled water (or the contents of a 1/4-lb bottle in 164 ml water).

3. Procedure

a. To a 100-ml glass bottle add 0.2 ml (4 drops) 6N NaOH. Fill the bottle with sample and add 0.2 ml (4 drops) 6N AlCl$_3$. Stopper the bottle with no air under the stopper. Rotate back and forth about a transverse axis vigorously for 1 min or longer to flocculate the contents. Vary the volumes of these chemicals to get good clarification without using excessively large amounts and to produce a pH of 6 to 9. If a 500- or 1,000-ml bottle is used, add proportionally larger amounts of reagents.

b. Let settle until reasonably clear supernatant can be drawn off. With proper flocculation, this may take 5 to 15 min. Do not wait longer than necessary.

428 B. Sample Pretreatment to Remove Interfering Substances or to Concentrate the Sulfide

The iodine titration method suffers interference by any reducing substances that react with iodine, including thiosulfate, sulfite, and various organic compounds, both solid and dissolved.

Strong reducing agents also interfere in the colorimetric test by preventing the formation of the blue color. Thiosulfate at concentrations above 10 mg/l may retard color formation or completely prevent it. Sulfide itself prevents the reaction if its concentration is very high, in the range of several hundred milligrams per liter. Test qualitatively industrial wastes likely to contain these substances but showing no color by the antimony method to avoid the possibility of a falsely negative report. Iodide, which is likely to be present in oil-field wastewaters, may diminish color formation if its concentration exceeds 2 mg/l. Ferrocyanide produces a blue color.

Eliminate interferences due to sulfite, thiosulfate, iodide, and many other soluble substances, but not ferrocyanide, by first precipitating the sulfide as ZnS, then removing all or most of the solution and replacing with distilled water. Use the same procedure, even when not needed for removal of interferences, to concentrate the sulfide content into a smaller volume for greater analytical sensitivity.

1. Apparatus

Glass bottles with stoppers (see Section 428A).

2. Reagents

a. Zinc acetate, 2N: Dissolve 220 g Zn(C$_2$H$_3$O$_2$)$_2$•2H$_2$O in 870 ml water; this makes 1 l solution.

b. Sodium hydroxide solution, NaOH, 6N.

3. Procedure

a. Put 0.15 ml (3 drops) 2N zinc acetate solution into a 100-ml glass bottle, fill the bottle with sample, and add 0.10 ml (2 drops) 6N NaOH solution. Stopper with no air bubbles under the stopper and mix by rotating back and forth about a transverse axis. For the titrimetric procedure, use a 500-ml bottle or other convenient size, with proportionally larger volumes of reagents. The volume of reagents added may be varied, depending on the nature of the sample, since the objective is to obtain a precipitate that is not excessively bulky but that settles readily. Add enough NaOH to produce a pH above 9. Let the precipitate settle for 30 min. The treated sample is relatively stable and can be held for several hours. However, if much iron is present, oxidation may be fairly rapid.

b. If the titrimetric method is to be used, filter the precipitate through glass fiber filter paper and continue at once with titration. If the methylene blue method is used, let the precipitate settle for 30 min and decant off as much water as possible without loss of precipitate. Refill the bottle with distilled water, resuspend the precipitate, and withdraw a sample. If interfering substances are present in high concentration, settle, decant, and refill a second time. If the sulfide concentration is known to be low, add only enough water to bring the volume to one-half or one-fifth of the original volume. Use this technic for analyzing samples of very low sulfide concentrations. After determining the sulfide concentration colorimetrically, multiply the result by the ratio of the final to the initial volume.

428 C.   Methylene Blue Method

1. Apparatus

a. Matched test tubes, approximately 125 mm long and 15 mm OD.

b. Droppers, delivering 20 drops/ml methylene blue solution. To obtain uniform drops it is essential to hold the dropper in a vertical position and to allow the drops to form slowly.

c. If photometric rather than visual color determination will be used, either:

1) *Spectrophotometer,* for use at a wavelength of 625 nm with cells providing light paths of 1 cm and 1 mm, or

2) *Filter photometer,* with a filter providing maximum transmittance near 600 nm.

2. Reagents

a. Amine-sulfuric acid stock solution: Dissolve 27 g N,N-dimethyl-*p*-phenylenediamine oxalate* (also called *p*-aminodimethylaniline oxalate) in a cold mixture of 50 ml conc H_2SO_4 and 20 ml distilled water. Cool and dilute to 100 ml with distilled water. The amine oxalate should be fresh; an old supply may be oxidized and discolored to a degree that results in interfering colors in the test. Store in a dark glass bottle. When this stock is diluted and used in

---

* Eastman catalog No. 5672 has been found satisfactory for this purpose.

the procedure with a sulfide-free sample, it must yield a colorless solution.

b. *Amine-sulfuric acid reagent:* Dilute 25 ml amine-sulfuric acid stock solution with 975 ml 1+1 H_2SO_4. Store in a dark glass bottle.

c. *Ferric chloride solution:* Dissolve 100 g $FeCl_3 \cdot 6H_2O$ in 40 ml water.

d. *Sulfuric acid solution,* H_2SO_4, 1+1.

e. *Diammonium hydrogen phosphate solution:* Dissolve 400 g $(NH_4)_2HPO_4$ in 800 ml distilled water.

f. *Methylene blue solution I:* Use USP grade dye or one certified by the Biological Stain Commission. The dye content should be reported on the label and should be 84% or more. Dissolve 1.0 g in distilled water and make up to 1 l. This solution will be approximately the correct strength, but because of variation between different lots of dye, standardize against sulfide solutions of known strength and adjust its concentration so that 0.05 ml (1 drop)=1.0 mg/l sulfide.

Standardization—Put several grams of clean, washed crystals of sodium sulfide, $Na_2S \cdot 9H_2O$, into a small beaker. Add somewhat less than enough water to cover the crystals. Stir occasionally for a few minutes, then pour the solution into another vessel. This solution reacts slowly with oxygen, but the change is unimportant in a period of a few hours. Make the solution daily. To 1 l distilled water add 1 drop of solution and mix. Immediately determine the sulfide concentration by the methylene blue procedure and by the titrimetric procedure. Repeat the procedures, using more than 1 drop of Na_2S solution or smaller volumes of water, until at least five tests have been made, with a range of sulfide concentrations between 1 and 8 mg/l. Calculate the average percent error of the methylene blue result as compared to the titrimetric result. If the average error is negative, that is, the methylene blue results are lower than the titrimetric results, dilute the methylene blue solution by the same percentage, so that a greater volume will be used in matching colors. If the methylene blue results are high, increase the strength of the solution by adding more dye.

g. *Methylene blue solution II:* Dilute 10.00 ml of the adjusted methylene blue solution I to 100 ml.

3. Procedure

a. *Color development:* Transfer 7.5 ml sample to each of two matched test tubes, using a special wide-tip pipet or filling to the marks on the test tubes. Add to Tube A 0.5 ml amine-sulfuric acid reagent and 0.15 ml (3 drops) $FeCl_3$ solution. Mix immediately by inverting the tube slowly, only once. To Tube B add 0.5 ml 1+1 H_2SO_4 and 0.15 ml (3 drops) $FeCl_3$ solution and mix. The presence of sulfide ion will be indicated by the appearance of blue color in Tube A. Color development is usually complete in about 1 min, but a longer time is often required for the fading out of the initial pink color. Wait 3 to 5 min, then add 1.6 ml $(NH_4)_2HPO_4$ solution to each tube. Wait 3 to 15 min and make color comparisons. If zinc acetate was used wait at least 10 min before making a visual color comparison.

b. *Color determination:*

1) Visual color estimation—Add methylene blue solution I or II, depending on the sulfide concentration and the

desired accuracy of the test, dropwise, to the second tube, until the color matches that developed in the first tube. If the concentration exceeds 20 mg/l, repeat the test with a portion of the sample diluted to one tenth.

With methylene blue solution I, adjusted so that 0.05 ml (1 drop)=1.0 mg/l sulfide when 7.5 ml of sample are used:

mg/l sulfide
=No. drops solution I+0.1 (No. drops solution II)

2) Photometric color measurement— A cell with a light path of 1 cm is suitable for measuring sulfide concentrations from 0.1 to 2.0 mg/l. Use shorter or longer light paths for higher or lower concentrations. The upper limit of the method is 20 mg/l. Zero the instrument with a portion of the treated sample from Tube B. Prepare calibration curves on the basis of the colorimetric tests made on Na_2S solutions simultaneously analyzed by the titrimetric method, plotting concentration vs. absorbance. A straight-line relationship between concentration and absorbance can be assumed from 0 to 1.0 mg/l.

Read the sulfide concentration from the calibration curve

4. Precision and Accuracy

The accuracy is about ±10%. The standard deviation has not been determined.

428 D.   Titrimetric (Iodine) Method

1. Reagents

a. Hydrochloric acid, HCl, 6N.

b. Standard iodine solution, 0.0250N: Dissolve 20 to 25 g potassium iodide, KI, in a little water and add 3.2 g iodine. After the iodine has dissolved, dilute to 1,000 ml and standardize against 0.02050N sodium thiosulfate, using starch solution as indicator.

c. Standard sodium thiosulfate solution, 0.0250N: See Section 422B.3f.

d. Starch solution: See Section 422B.3d.

2. Procedure

a. If the sulfide was precipitated with zinc and water was decanted, make the titration in the original bottle. If the precipitate was dewatered on a glass filter paper, return the filter with precipitate to the original bottle.

b. Measure from a buret into a 500-ml flask an amount of iodine solution estimated to be an excess over the amount of sulfide present. Add distilled water, if necessary, to bring the volume to about 20 ml. Add 2 ml 6N HCl. Pipet 200 ml sample into the flask, discharging the sample under the surface of the solution. If the iodine color disappears, add more iodine so that the color remains. Back-titrate with sodium thiosulfate solution, adding a few drops of starch solution as the end point is approached, and continuing until the blue color disappears.

3. Calculation

One ml of $0.025N$ iodine solution reacts with 0.4 mg of sulfide:

$$mg/l\ S\ =\ \frac{400\,(a-b)}{ml\ sample}$$

where a = ml $0.025N$ iodine and b = ml $0.025N$ thiosulfate solution.

4. Precision

The precision of the end point varies with the nature of the sample. In clean waters, it should be determinable within 1 drop, which is equivalent to 0.1 mg/l in a 200-ml sample.

428 E.   Calculation of Un-ionized Hydrogen Sulfide

Hydrogen sulfide and HS^-, which together constitute dissolved sulfide, are in equilibrium with hydrogen ions:

$$H_2S \rightleftharpoons H^+ + HS^-$$

The ionization constant of H_2S is used to calculate the distribution of dissolved sulfide between the two forms. The practical constant written in the logarithmic form, pK', is used. The constant varies with temperature and ionic strength of the solution. The ionic strength effect can be estimated most easily from the conductivity. Because the effect of ionic strength is not large, values that are sufficiently dependable generally can be assumed if the nature of the sample is known. Table 428:I gives values of pK' for various temperatures and ionic strengths. The temperature effect is practically linear over the range from 15 C to 35 C; interpolations or extrapolations can be used.

The last line of Table 428:I corresponds approximately to seawater.

From the pH of the sample and the appropriate value of pK', calculate pH-pK'. From Figure 428:2 read the proportions of dissolved sulfide present as

TABLE 428:I. VALUES OF pK', LOGARITHMIC PRACTICAL IONIZATION CONSTANTS FOR HYDROGEN SULFIDE

Conductivity at 25 C, $\mu siemens$ /cm	pK' at Given Temperature		
	20 C	25 C	30 C
0	—	7.03*	—
100	7.08	7.01	6.94
200	7.07	4.00	6.93
400	7.06	6.99	6.92
700	7.05	6.98	6.91
1,200	7.04	6.97	6.90
2,000	7.03	6.96	6.89
3,000	7.02	6.95	6.88
4,000	7.01	6.94	6.87
5,200	7.00	6.93	6.86
7,200	6.99	6.92	6.85
10,000	6.98	6.91	6.84
14,000	6.97	6.90	6.83
22,000	6.96	6.89	6.82
50,000	6.95	6.88	6.81

* Theoretical.

H_2S (left-side scale of Figure 428:2). Let this proportion equal J,

$$J \times (\text{dissolved sulfide})$$
$$= \text{un-ionized } H_2S \text{ expressed as S}$$

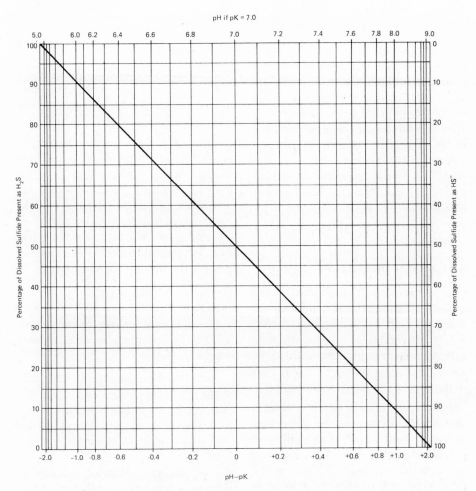

pH if pK = 7.0

Percentage of Dissolved Sulfide Present as H_2S

Percentage of Dissolved Sulfide Present as HS^-

pH—pK

Figure 428:2. Proportions of H₂S and HS⁻ in dissolved sulfide.

428 F. Bibliography

Pomeroy, R.D. 1936. The determination of sulfides in sewage. *Sewage Works J.* 8:572.

Pomeroy, R.D. 1941. Hydrogen sulfides in sewage. *Sewage Works J.* 13:498.

Nusbaum, I. 1953. Determination of phenols by the *p*-nitrosodimethylaniline method—A discussion. *Sewage Ind. Wastes* 25:312.

Camp, T.R. 1963. Water and Its Impurities. Reinhold Publishing Corp., New York, N.Y. p. 63.

Nusbaum, I. 1965. Determining sulfides in water and waste water. *Water Sewage Works* 112:113.

Platford, R.F. 1965. The activity coefficient of sodium chloride in seawater. *J. Mar. Res.* 23:55.

Lawrence, A.W., P.L. McCarty & F.J.A.Guerin. 1966. The effects of sulfides on anaerobic treatment. *Int. J. Air Water Pollut.* 10:207.

429 SULFITE

Although sulfite may occur in certain industrial wastes and polluted waters, it is most commonly found in boiler and boiler feedwater to which sodium sulfite has been applied to reduce dissolved oxygen to a minimum and to prevent corrosion. The development of catalyzed sodium sulfite has extended its field of usefulness to the treatment of cooling, process, and distribution water systems at cold water temperatures.

1. General Discussion

a. Principle: An acidified water sample containing sulfite is titrated with a standardized potassium iodide-iodate titrant. Free iodine is released when the sulfite has been completely oxidized, resulting in the formation of a blue color in the presence of starch indicator.

b. Interference: The presence of other oxidizable substances in the water, such as organic matter and sulfide, will result in higher titration values for sulfite than are actually present. Nitrite, on the other hand, will combine with sulfite in the acid medium to destroy both, leading to low results. No interference occurs with the dual-purpose dry starch indicator powder because the sulfamic acid in this proprietary compound destroys the nitrite. Copper ion rapidly accelerates the oxidation of sulfite solution. Certain heavy metals also may react in a manner similar to copper. Proper sampling and immediate fixing by acid addition should minimize those difficulties.

c. Minimum detectable concentration: 2 mg/l SO₃.

2. Reagents

a. Sulfuric acid, H_2SO_4, 1+1.

b. Starch indicator: Either the aqueous solution or the dry powders may be used.

1) To 5 g starch (potato, arrowroot, or soluble) in a mortar, add a little cold distilled water and grind to a paste. Pour into 1 l boiling distilled water, stir, and allow to settle overnight. Use the clear supernate. Preserve by adding either 1.3 g salicylic acid, 4 g zinc chloride, or a combination of 4 g sodium propionate and 2 g sodium azide to 1 l starch solution.

2) Soluble starch powder* provides a sharp end-point change to blue when 0.1 g of the powder is used in the presence of free iodine.

3) A dual-purpose sulfite indicator powder † composed of cold-water-soluble starch in a sulfamic acid medium is used extensively in control work. When this proprietary formulation is used, omit the H_2SO_4 and add 3 to 4 drops phenolphthalein indicator solution to the sample followed by sufficient dipperfuls (1 g) of indicator powder to discharge the alkaline red color. After a final dipperful in excess is added, titrate the sample with standard potassium io-

---

* The product known as Thyodene is imported by the Magnus Chemical Co. of Garwood, N.J., and is available from the Fisher Scientific Co. of Pittsburgh, Pa., and others.

† The use of this product, known as Dual-Purpose Sulfite Indicator Powder, is covered by U.S. Patent No. 2,963,443 issued to E.T. Erickson.

dide-iodate titrant to the appearance of a permanent blue color in the sample.

c. *Standard potassium iodide-iodate titrant*, 0.0125N: Dissolve 445.8 mg anhydrous potassium iodate, KIO_3 (primary standard grade dried for several hours at 120 C), 4.35 g KI, and 310 mg $NaHCO_3$ in distilled water and dilute to 1,000 ml. This titrant is equivalent to 500 μg SO_3/1.00 ml.

3. Procedure

a. *Sample collection:* Collect a fresh water sample, allowing as little contact with air as possible. Cool hot samples to 50 C or below in the cooling apparatus depicted in Figure 107:1. Do not filter.

b. *Titration:* Add 1 ml H_2SO_4 (or 1 g dual-purpose sulfite indicator) [¶2b3)

above] to a 250-ml erlenmeyer flask or other titrating vessel, then measure 50 ml water sample in a graduated cylinder and transfer to the flask. Add 1 ml starch indicator solution or 0.1 g starch powder [¶2b2) above], omitting this step if dual-purpose sulfite indicator powder [¶2b3)] is used. Titrate with potassium iodide-iodate titrant until a faint permanent blue color develops in the sample. View the color change against a white background.

4. Calculation

$$mg/l\ SO_3 = \frac{A \times N \times 40,000}{ml\ sample}$$

$$mg/l\ Na_2SO_3 = mg/l\ SO_3 \times 1.57$$

where A = ml titration for sample and N = normality of KI-KIO_3.

PART 500

DETERMINATION OF

ORGANIC CONSTITUENTS

501 INTRODUCTION

The analysis of organic matter in water and wastewater can be classified into two general types of measurements: those that seek to express either the total amount of organic matter or some fraction of the total in general terms and those that are specific for individual organic compounds. Both types of analyses are presented below.

Methods for total carbon, chemical oxygen demand, and carbon chloroform extract are used to assess the total amount of organics present. Gross fractions of the organic matter can be identified analytically, as in the measurement of BOD, which is an index of the biodegradable organics present, or oil and grease, which represents material extractable from a sample by a nonpolar solvent. Examples of specific tests for individual organic compounds or groups of compounds are measurements of pesticides, phenols, and synthetic detergents.

Analyses of organics are made to evaluate possible effects on health of water consumers, measure the efficiency of waste treatment processes, and assess the quality of receiving waters.

The sampling, field treatment, preservation, and storage of samples taken for analysis of organic matter analysis are covered in detail in the individual introductions to the methods. Generally, immediate analysis is preferred because preservatives often interfere with the tests. Storage at a low temperature (4 C) is the best way known to preserve most samples until the day following collection. Use chemical preservatives only when they are shown not to interfere with the examinations to be made. For example, never use preservatives for samples to be analyzed for BOD. When preservatives are used, add them to the sample bottle initially so that all portions are preserved as soon as collected. No single method of preservation is entirely satisfactory; choose the preservative with due regard to the determinations that are to be made. All methods of preservation may be inadequate when applied to samples containing significant amounts of suspended matter.

502 GREASE AND OIL

1. Limitations

In the determination of grease and oil, an absolute quantity of a specific substance is not measured. Rather, groups of substances with similar physical characteristics are determined quantitatively on the basis of their common solubility in freon. Grease and oil may therefore be said to include hydrocarbons, fatty acids, soaps, fats, waxes, oils, and any other material that is extracted by the solvent from an acidified sample and that is not volatilized during the manipulations of the test. It is important that this limitation be clearly understood. Unlike some constituents—which represent distinct chemical elements, ions, compounds, or groups of compounds—greases and oils are defined by the method used for their determination.

The methods presented here are suitable for biological lipids and mineral hydrocarbons in natural waters or domestic wastewaters. They also are suitable for most industrial wastewaters, although certain wastes may yield low results because of the presence of either excessive concentrations of natural greases or synthetic or modified compounds that are not well recovered by the standard procedures.

Modern industry uses a number of long-chain carbon compounds as lubricants and emulsifiers, as well as for other purposes. Often the composition of these materials differs from that of natural greases and oils, and may render them more soluble in water or more easily emulsified than the natural products. As a result, they behave as greases and oils in treatment processes and the receiving water, but the problems they cause may be accentuated by their special properties. The procedures described here may fail to give complete recovery of such products.[1,2]

Low-boiling fractions are lost in the solvent-removal steps of the gravimetric procedures. Even lubricating oil fractions evaporate at a significant rate at the temperature necessary for removal of the last traces of the extraction solvent. Kerosene is still more volatile and gasoline cannot be determined with any reliability by any of the organic solvent extraction methods.

2. Significance

Greases and oils are particularly resistant to anaerobic digestion, and when present in sludge they cause excessive scum accumulation in digesters, clog the pores of filters, and deter the use of the sludge as fertilizer.

When these substances are discharged in wastewater or treated effluents, they often cause surface films and shoreline deposits.

A knowledge of the quantity of grease and oil present in a waste is helpful in overcoming difficulties in plant operation, in determining plant efficiencies, and in controlling the subsequent discharge of these materials to receiving streams. A knowledge of the amount of grease present in sludge can aid in the diagnosis of digestion and dewatering problems and indicate the suitability of a particular sludge for use as a fertilizer.

3. Selection of Method

For liquid samples, three methods are presented: the partition-gravimetric method (A); the partition-infrared method (B); and the Soxhlet method (C). Method B is designed for samples that might contain volatile hydrocarbons that otherwise would be lost in the solvent removal operations of the gravimetric procedure. Method C is the method of choice when relatively polar, heavy petroleum fractions are present, or when the levels of nonvolatile greases may challenge the solubility limit of the freon solvent. For low levels of grease and oil (<10 mg/l), Method B is the method of choice because the gravimetric methods do not provide the needed precision for accurate work.

Method D is a modification of the Soxhlet method and is suitable for sludges and similar materials. Method E resolves the hydrocarbons from the total grease and oil on the basis of the polar or nonpolar nature of the compounds present and determines the hydrocarbons separately.

4. Sampling and Storage

In sampling water, wastewater, and effluents, collect a representative sample in a wide-mouth glass bottle and acidify in the sample bottle. Collect a separate sample for a grease and oil determination and avoid subdividing the sample in the laboratory. When information is required about the average grease concentration of a waste over an extended period, examine individual portions collected at prescribed time intervals to eliminate losses of grease on sampling equipment during collection of a composite sample.

In sampling sludges, take every possible precaution to obtain a representative sample. When analysis cannot be made immediately, preserve samples with 1 ml conc H_2SO_4/80 g sample. Never preserve samples with chloroform or sodium benzoate when grease is to be determined.

502 A.   Partition-Gravimetric Method

1. General Discussion

a. Principle: Dissolved or emulsified grease or oil is extracted from water by intimate contact with freon. Some extractables, especially unsaturated fats and fatty acids, oxidize readily; hence, special precautions regarding temperature and solvent vapor displacement are included to minimize this effect.

b. Interference: Freon has the ability to dissolve not only grease and oil, but also other organic substances. No solvent is known that will selectively dissolve only grease and oil. Solvent removal results in the loss of short-chain hydrocarbons and simple aromatics by volatilization. Significant portions of the petroleum distillates from gasoline through No. 2 fuel oil are lost in this process. In addition, heavier residuals of petroleum may contain a significant portion of materials insoluble in freon.

2. Apparatus

a. Separatory funnel, with Teflon stopcock.
b. Distilling flask, 125 ml.
c. Water bath.

3. Reagents

a. Hydrochloric acid, HCl, 1 +1.
b. Freon (1,1,2-trichloro-1,2,2-trifluoroethane), boiling point 47 C. The solvent should leave no measurable residue on evaporation; distill if necessary.
c. Filter paper, Whatman No. 40, 11 cm.
d. Sodium sulfate, Na_2SO_4, anhydrous crystal.

4. Procedure

Collect about 1 l of sample and mark the sample level in the bottle for later determination of sample volume. Acidify to pH 2 or lower; generally, 5 ml HCl is sufficient. Transfer the sample to a separatory funnel. Carefully rinse the sample bottle with 30 ml freon and add the solvent washings to the separatory funnel. Shake vigorously for 2 min. Allow the layers to separate. Drain the freon layer through a funnel containing solvent-moistened filter paper into a clean, tared distilling flask. If a clear solvent layer cannot be obtained, add 1 g Na_2SO_4 to the filter paper cone and slowly drain the emulsified solvent onto the crystals. Add more Na_2SO_4 if necessary. Extract twice more with 30 ml freon each but first rinse the sample container with each solvent portion. Combine the extracts in the tared distilling flask and wash the filter paper with an additional 10 to 20 ml freon. Distill the freon from the extraction flask in a water bath at 70 C. Place the flask on a warm steam bath for 15 min and draw air through the flask by means of an applied vaccum for the final 1 min. Cool in a desiccator for exactly 30 min and weigh.

5. Calculation

If the organic solvent used is known to be free of residue, the gain in weight of the tared distilling flask is mainly due to grease and oil. The total gain in weight, A, of the tared flask less the calculated residue, B, from a freon blank is the amount of grease or oil in the water sample:

$$mg/l \text{ grease or oil} = \frac{(A-B)\times 1,000}{ml \text{ sample}}$$

6. Precision and Accuracy

Methods A, B, and C were tested by a single laboratory on a sewage sample. By this method the grease and oil concentration was 12.6 mg/l. When 1-l portions of the sewage were dosed with 14.0 mg of a mixture of No. 2 fuel oil and Wesson oil, the recovery was 93% with a standard deviation of ±0.9 mg.

502 B.   Partition-Infrared Method (TENTATIVE)

1. General Discussion

a. *Principle:* Although the extraction procedure for this method is identical to that of Method A, infrared detection permits the measurement of many relatively volatile hydrocarbons. Thus, the lighter petroleum distillates, with the exception of gasoline, may be measured accurately. Adequate instrumentation allows for the measurement of as little as 0.2 mg/l grease and oil.

b. *Interference:* Some degree of selectivity is offered by this method to overcome some of the coextracted interferences discussed in Method A. Heavier residuals of petroleum may contain a significant portion of materials that are not soluble in freon.

c. *Definitions:* A "known oil" is defined as a sample of grease and/or oil that represents the only material of that type used or manufactured in the processes represented by a wastewater. An "unknown oil" is defined as one for which a representative sample of the grease or oil is not available for preparation of a standard.

2. Apparatus

a. *Separatory funnel,* with Teflon stopcock.

b. *Infrared spectrophotometer,* double beam, recording.

c. *Cells,* quartz.

3. Reagents

a. *Hydrochloric acid,* HCl, 1 + 1.

b. *Freon* (1,1,2-trichloro-1,2,2,-trifluoroethane).

c. *Filter paper,* Whatman No. 41, 11 cm.

d. *Sodium sulfate,* Na_2SO_4, anhydrous crystal.

e. *Reference oil:* Prepare a mixture of 37.5% isoctane, 37.5% hexadecane, and 25% benzene. Store in sealed container to prevent evaporation.

4. Procedure

Refer to Method A for sample collection, acidification, and extraction. Collect the combined extracts in a 100-ml volumetric flask and adjust final volume to 100 ml.

Prepare a stock solution of known oil by rapidly transferring about 1 ml (0.5 to 1.0 g) of the grease or oil to a tared 100-ml volumetric flask. Stopper the flask and weigh to nearest milligram. Add freon to dissolve and dilute to mark. If the oil identity is unknown (¶1c) use the reference oil (¶3e) for the standard. Using volumetric technics prepare a series of standards over the range of interest. Select a pair of matched quartz cells. A 1-cm-path-length cell is appropriate for a working range of about 4 to 40 mg. Scan standards and samples from 3,200/cm to 2,700/cm with freon in the reference beam and record the results on absorbance paper. Measure the absorbances of samples and standards by constructing a straight baseline over the range of the scan and measuring the absorbance of the peak maximum at 2,930/cm and subtracting the baseline absorbance at that point. If the absorbance exceeds 0.8 for a sample, select a shorter pathlength or dilute as required. Use the scans of the standards to prepare a calibration curve.

5. Calculation

$$mg/l \text{ grease or oil} = \frac{A \times 1,000}{ml \text{ sample}}$$

where A = mg of grease or oil in freon extract as determined from the calibration curve.

6. Precision and Accuracy

See 502A.6. By this method the oil and grease concentration was 17.5 mg/l. When 1-l portions of the sewage were dosed with 14.0 mg of a mixture of No. 2 fuel oil and Wesson oil, the recovery was 99% with a standard deviation of ±1.4 mg.

502 C. Soxhlet Extraction Method

1. General Discussion

a. Principle: Soluble metallic soaps are hydrolyzed by acidification. The solid or viscous grease and any oils present are separated from the liquid sample by filtration. After extraction in a Soxhlet apparatus with freon, the residue remaining after evaporation of the solvent is weighed to determine the grease and oil content of the sample. Compounds volatilized at or below 103 C will be lost when the filter is dried.

b. Interference: The method is entirely empirical, and duplicate results can be obtained only by strict adherence to all details. By definition, any material recovered is called grease and oil and any filtrable freon-soluble substances, such as elemental sulfur and certain organic dyes, will be extracted as grease and oil. The rate and time of extraction in the Soxhlet apparatus must be exactly as directed because of varying solubilities of different greases. In addition, the length of time required for drying and cooling the extracted material cannot be varied. There may be a gradual increase in weight, presumably due to the absorption of oxygen, or a gradual loss of weight due to volatilization.

2. Apparatus

a. Extraction apparatus, Soxhlet.
b. Vacuum pump or other source of vacuum.
c. Buchner funnel, 12-cm.
d. Electric heating mantle.
e. Extraction thimble, paper.

3. Reagents

a. Hydrochloric acid, HCl, 1+1.

b. Freon (1,1,2-trichloro-1,2,2,-trifluoroethane), boiling point 47 C. The solvent should leave no measurable residue on evaporation; distill if necessary.

c. Filter paper, Whatman No. 40, 11 cm.

d. Muslin cloth disks, 11 cm.

*e. Diatomaceous-silica filter aid suspension,** 10 g/l distilled water.

4. Procedure

Collect about 1 l of sample in a wide-mouth glass bottle and mark the sample level in the bottle for later determination of sample volume. Acidify to pH 2 or lower; generally, 5 ml HCl is sufficient. Prepare a filter consisting of a muslin cloth disk overlaid with filter paper. Wet the paper and muslin and press down the edges of the paper. Using a vacuum, pass 100 ml filter aid suspension through the prepared filter and wash with 1 l distilled water. Apply vacuum until no more water passes the filter. Filter the acidified sample through the prepared filter. Apply vacuum until no more water passes through the filter. Using forceps, transfer the filter paper to a watch glass. Add the material adhering to the edges of the muslin cloth disk. Wipe the sides and bottom of the collecting vessel and the Buchner funnel with bits of filter paper soaked in freon, taking care to remove all films caused by grease and to collect all solid material. Add the bits of filter paper to the filter paper on the watch glass. Roll all the filter paper containing sample and fit into a paper extraction thimble. Add any bits

---

*Hyflo Super-Cel (Johns-Manville Corp.) or equivalent.

of material remaining on the watch glass. Wipe the watch glass with a bit of filter paper soaked in freon and place in the paper extraction thimble. Dry the filled thimble in a hot-air oven at 103 C for 30 min. Fill the thimble with glass wool or small glass beads. Weigh the extraction flask. Extract the grease and oil in a Soxhlet apparatus, using freon, at a rate of 20 cycles/hr for 4 hr. Time from the first cycle. Distill the freon from the extraction flask in a water bath at 70 C. Place the flask on a warm steam bath for 15 min and draw air through the flask by means of an applied vacuum for the final 1 min. Cool in a desiccator for exactly 30 min and weigh.

5. Calculation

See Section 502A.5.

6. Precision and Accuracy

See Section 502A.6. By this method the grease and oil concentration was 14.8 mg/l. When 1-l portions of the sewage were dosed with 14.0 mg of a mixture of No. 2 fuel oil and Wesson oil, the recovery was 88% with a standard deviation of ±1.1 mg.

502 D.   Extraction Method for Sludge Samples

1. General Discussion

a. Principle: Drying acidified sludge by heating leads to low results. Magnesium sulfate monohydrate is capable of combining with 75% of its own weight in water in forming the heptahydrate and is used to dry sludge. After drying, the oil and grease can be extracted with freon.

b. Interference: Sec 502C.1*b*.

2. Apparatus

a. Extraction apparatus, Soxhlet.

b. Vacuum pump or other source of vacuum.

c. Extraction thimble, paper.

3. Reagents

a. Hydrochloric acid, HCl, conc.

b. Magnesium sulfate monohydrate: Prepare $MgSO_4 \cdot H_2O$ by overnight drying of a thin layer of $MgSO_4 \cdot 7H_2O$ in an oven at 103 C.

c. Freon (1,1,2-trichloro- 1,2,2,-trifluoroethane), boiling point 47 C. The solvent should leave no measurable residue on evaporation; distill if necessary.

d. Grease-free cotton: Extract nonabsorbent cotton with freon.

4. Procedure

In a 150-ml beaker weigh a sample of wet sludge, 20±0.5 g, of which the dry-solids content is known. Acidify to pH 2.0 (generally, 0.3 ml conc HCl is sufficient). Add 25 g $MgSO_4 \cdot H_2O$. Stir to a smooth paste and spread on the sides of the beaker to facilitate subsequent removal. Allow to stand until solidified, 15 to 30 min. Remove the solids and grind in a porcelain mortar. Add the powder to a paper extraction thimble. Wipe the beaker and mortar with small pieces of filter paper moistened with freon and add to the thimble. Fill the thimble with glass wool or small glass beads. Extract in a Soxhlet apparatus, using freon, at a rate of 20 cycles/ hr for 4 hr. If any turbidity or suspended matter is present in the extraction flask, remove by filtering through grease-free cotton into another weighed flask. Rinse flask and cotton with freon. Distill the solvent from the extraction flask in water at 70 C. Place the flask on a warm steam bath for 15 min and draw air through the flask by means of an applied vacuum for the final 1 min. Cool in a desiccator for exactly 30 min and weigh.

5. Calculation

Grease and oil as % dry solids

$$= \frac{\text{gain in weight of flask, g} \times 100}{\text{weight of wet solids, g} \times \% \text{ dry solids}}$$

6. Precision

The examination of six replicate samples of sludge yielded a standard deviation of 4.6%.

502 E.   Hydrocarbons

In the absence of specially modified industrial products, grease and oil is composed primarily of fatty matter from animal and vegetable sources and hydrocarbons of petroleum origin. A knowledge of the percentage of each of these constituents in the total grease and oil minimizes the difficulty in determining the major source of the material and simplifies the correction of grease and oil problems in wastewater treatment plant operation and stream pollution abatement.

The method described can be used in conjunction with Methods A, B, C, or D to obtain a hydrocarbon measurement in addition to, or instead of, the grease and oil.

1. General Discussion

a. Principle: Silica gel has the ability to adsorb polar materials. If a solution of hydrocarbons and fatty materials is mixed in freon with silica gel the fatty acids are selectively removed from solution. The materials not eliminated by silica gel adsorption are designated hydrocarbons by this test.

b. Interference: The more polar hydrocarbons, such as the complex aromatic compounds and the hydrocarbon derivatives of chlorine, sulfur, and nitrogen, may be adsorbed by the silica gel. Any compounds other than hydrocarbons and fatty matter recovered by the procedures for the determination of grease and oil also interfere.

2. Reagents

a.   Freon (1,1,2-trichloro- 1,2,2-trifluoroethane), boiling point 47 C.

b.   Silica gel, 60 to 200 mesh.*

3. Procedure

Use the oil and grease extracted by Method A, B, C, or D for this test. When only hydrocarbons are of interest

---

*Davidson Grade 950 or equivalent.

introduce this procedure in any of the previous methods before final measurement. When hydrocarbons are to be determined after the total grease and oil has been measured, redissolve, if necessary, the extracted grease and oil in freon. To 100 ml freon containing less than 100 mg fatty material, add 3.0 g silica gel. Stopper container and stir on a magnetic stirrer for 5 min. For infrared measurement of hydrocarbons no further treatment is required before measurement as described in Method B. For gravimetric determinations filter the solution through paper before performing the solvent stripping steps outlined in Methods A, C, or D.

4. Calculation

Calculate hydrocarbon concentration, in milligrams per liter, in the same manner as grease and oil (Method A, B, C, or D).

5. Precision and Accuracy

The accuracy of this determination cannot be determined directly in wastewaters. The following data, obtained on synthetic samples, may be considered indicative for natural animal, vegetable, and mineral products, but cannot be applied to the specialized industrial products previously discussed.

For hydrocarbon determination on 10 synthetic freon extracts containing known amounts of a wide variety of petroleum products, average recovery was 97.2%. Similar synthetic extracts of Wesson oil, olive oil, Crisco, and butter gave 0.0% recovery as hydrocarbons measured by infrared analysis.

502 F.   References

1. CHANIN, G., E.H. CHOW, R.B. ALEXANDER & J.F. POWERS. 1968. Scum analysis: A new solution to a difficult problem. *Water Works Wastes Eng.* 5, 6:49.

2. TARAS, M.J. & K.A. BLUM. 1968. Determination of emulsifying oil in industrial wastewater. *J. Water Pollut. Control. Fed.* 40:R404.

502 G.   Bibliography

HATFIELD, W.D. & G.E. SYMONS. 1945. The determination of grease in sewage. *Sewage Works J.* 17:16.

KIRSCHMAN, H.D. & R. POMEROY. 1949. Determination of oil in oil field waste waters. *Anal. Chem.* 21:793.

GILCREAS, F.W., W.W. SANDERSON & R.P. ELMER. 1953. Two new methods for the determination of grease in sewage. *Sewage Ind. Wastes* 25:1379.

ULLMANN, W.W. & W.W. SANDERSON. 1959. A further study of methods for the determination of grease in sewage. *Sewage Ind. Wastes* 31:8.

CHANIN, G., E.H. SHOW, R.B. ALEXANDER & J.F. POWERS. 1967. A safe solvent for oil and grease analyses. *J. Water Pollut. Control Fed.* 39:1892.

GRUENFELD, M. 1973. Extraction of dispersed oils from water for quantitative analysis by infrared spectrophotometry. *Environ. Sci. Technol.* 7:636.

503   METHANE

Methane is a colorless, odorless, tasteless combustible gas occasionally found in groundwaters. The escape of this gas from water may cause an explosive atmosphere not only in the utility's facilities, such as tanks and pumphouses, but also on the consumer's property, particularly where water is sprayed through poorly ventilated spaces such as public showers.

The explosive limits of methane in air are 5 to 15% by volume. At sea level, a 5% methane concentration in air theoretically could be reached in a poorly ventilated space sprayed with hot (68 C) water having a methane concentration of only 0.7 mg/l. At higher water temperatures, the vapor pressure of water is so great that no explosive mixture can form. At lower barometric pressures, the theoretical hazardous concentration of methane in water will be reduced proportionately. In an atmosphere of nitrogen or other inert gas, at least 12.8% oxygen must be present.

A qualitative test for high methane concentration can be made as follows: Invert a 1-l bottle of water and immerse the neck in a pan or trough of water. Insert a tube or hose from a tap upward through the mouth of the bottle and allow the tap water to flow into the bottle, displacing the original water and permitting "gas" to accumulate at the top of the inverted bottle. After approximately 1/8 to 1/4 of the bottle is filled with "gas," remove the hose, place a hand over the mouth of the bottle, and again invert to an upright position, holding the hand in place. Bring a lighted match to the mouth of the bottle immediately on removing the hand and observe a brief wisp of blue flame in the neck of the bottle if the "gas" is methane in high concentration. Observe the blue flame in a darkened room. This is not a quantitative test but may indicate as little as 5.35 mg/l methane ($1 ft^3/1,000$ gal). A positive result warrants precautionary measures. A negative result requires a quantitative analysis. Use great care in the qualitative test; take every safeguard against bodily injury that might result from shattering the glass container during the flaming operation. Adequately shield the container and wear goggles or a face shield.

Selection of method: The combustible-gas indicator method (A) offers the advantages of simplicity, speed, and great sensitivity. The volumetric method (B) can be made more accurate for concentrations of 4 to 5 mg/l and higher, but will not be satisfactory for very low concentrations. The volumetric method also is applicable to differentiate between methane and other gases, as when a water supply is contaminated by a liquid petroleum gas or other volatile combustible materials.

Methane also may be determined with the gas chromatograph as described in Sludge Digester Gas, Section 511. The gas chromatograph permits differentiation between hydrogen, methane, and/or the higher homologs.

503 A.   Combustible-Gas Indicator Method

1. General Discussion

a. Principle: An equilibrium according to Henry's law is established between methane (CH_4) in solution and the partial pressure of methane in the gas phase above the solution. The partial pressure of methane can be determined with a combustible-gas indicator. The operation of the instrument is based on the catalytic oxidation of a combustible gas on a heated platinum filament that is made a part of a Wheatstone bridge. The heat generated by the oxidation of the gas increases the electrical resistance of the filament. The resulting imbalance of the electrical circuit causes deflection of a milliammeter. The milliammeter may be calibrated in terms of the percentage of methane or the percentage of the lower explosive limit of the gas sampled.

b. Interference: Small amounts of ethane are usually associated with methane in natural gas and presumably would be present in water that contains methane. Hydrogen gas has been observed in well waters and would behave similarly to methane in this procedure. Hydrogen sulfide may interfere if the pH of the water is low enough for an appreciable fraction of the total sulfide to exist in the un-ionized form. The vapors of combustible oils also may interfere. In general, these interferences are of no practical importance because primary interest is in calculating the explosion hazard to which all combustible gases and vapors contribute.

Interference due to hydrogen sulfide can be reduced by the addition of solid sodium hydroxide to the container before sampling.

c. Minimum detectable concentration: The limit of sensitivity of the test is approximately 0.2 mg/l.

d. Sampling: If the water is supersaturated with methane, a representative sample cannot be obtained unless the water is under sufficient pressure to keep all of the gas dissolved. Operate wells for a period sufficient to insure that water coming directly from the aquifer is being sampled. Representative samples can be expected only when the well is equipped with a pump operating at sufficient submergence to assure that no gas escapes from the water.

2. Apparatus

*a. Combustible-gas indicator:** Connect a three-way stopcock to the inlet so that the instrument may be zeroed on atmospheric air immediately before obtaining the sample reading. For laboratory use, replace the suction bulb with a filter pump throttled to draw gas through the instrument at a rate of approximately 600 ml/min. A diagrammatic view of the apparatus is shown in Figure 503:1.

---

*Marketed under the following trade names: "Explosimeter," "Methane Gas Detector," and "Methane Tester," all manufactured by Mine Safety Appliance Company, Pittsburgh, Pa.; "J-W Combustible Gas Indicator," manufactured by Johnson-Williams, Inc., Palo Alto, Calif.; and "Vapotester" manufactured by Davis Emergency Equipment Company, Newark, N.J.

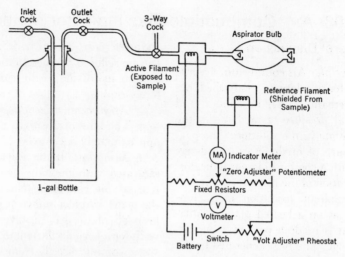

Figure 503:1. Combustible-gas indicator circuit and flow diagram.

b. Laboratory filter pump.

c. Glass bottle, 4-l (1-gal), fitted with a two-hole rubber stopper. Extend the inlet tube to within 1 cm of the bottom. End outlet tube approximately 1 cm from the stopper. Use metal or glass tubes, each fitted with stopcocks or with short (approximately 5-cm) lengths of rubber tubing and pinchcocks. The entire assembly should be capable of holding a low vacuum for several hours. Determine the volume of the assembly by filling with water and measuring the volume, or weight, of the water contained.

3. Reagents

Sodium hydroxide, NaOH, pellets.

4. Procedure

a. Rough estimation of methane concentration: Fill the bottle about half full of water, using a rubber tube connecting the sampling tap and the inlet tube,

with the outlet tube open. With both the inlet and outlet tubes closed, shake the bottle vigorously for approximately 15 sec and let the water stand for approximately 1 min. Sample the gas phase by withdrawing gas from the outlet, leaving the inlet open to admit air. If the needle swings rapidly to a high level on the meter and then drops to zero, the methane-air mixture is too rich to burn; take a smaller volume of water for the final test. If the needle deflection is too small to be read accurately, take a larger volume of water.

b. Accurate determination: If the water contains H_2S, add approximately 0.5 g NaOH pellets to the empty bottle to suppress interference from this gas. Evacuate the bottle, using the filter pump. Fill the bottle not more than three-quarters full by connecting the inlet tube to the sampling cock, with the outlet tube closed. After collecting the desired volume of water, let the bottle fill with air through the inlet tube. Close the inlet cock, shake the bottle vigorously for 60 sec, and let stand for at least 2 hr. Sample the gas phase through the outlet tube with the inlet cock open. Take the reading as rapidly as possible before the entering air has diluted the sample appreciably. Measure the volume of water sampled.

5. Calculation

The weight of methane (w), in mg, in the sample is given by the equation:

$$w = P\left(\frac{0.257V_g}{T} + \frac{890V_l}{H}\right)$$

where P=partial pressure of methane, mm mercury; T=temperature, K; V_g=volume of the gas phase, ml; V_l=volume of the liquid phase, ml; and H= the Henry's law constant, mm mercury/mole CH_4 per mole of water. The values for Henry's constant are as follows:

Temperature C	Henry's Constant $10^6 H$	Temperature C	Henry's Constant $10^6 H$
0	16.99	40	39.46
5	19.69	45	41.83
10	22.58	50	43.85
15	25.60	60	47.57
20	28.53	70	50.62
25	31.36	80	51.84
30	34.08	90	52.60
35	36.95	100	53.30

For most determinations, it may be assumed that atmospheric pressure is 760 mm and that the temperature is 20 C.

The concentration of methane in the sample is then given by:

$$\text{mg/l } CH_4 = Rf\left(6.7\ \frac{V_0 - V_1}{V_1} + 0.24\right)$$

where R=scale reading, V_0=total volume of the sample bottle, V_1=volume of water sampled, and f=factor depending on the instrument used. If the instrument reads directly in percentage of methane, f=1.00. If the instrument reads in percentage of the lower explosive limit of methane, the factor is 0.05. For instruments that require additional factors, consult the manufacturer. For example, one commercial instrument with a scale that reads in percentage of the lower explosive limit of combustible gases requires an additional factor of 0.77 for methane. Hence, the value of f in the above equation would be 0.77×0.05, or 0.0385.

For more accurate work, or in locations where the normal barometric pressure is significantly lower than 760 mm, use the equation:

$$\text{mg/l } CH_4 = RBf\left(2.57\frac{V_0 - V_1}{TV_1} + \frac{8,900}{H}\right)$$

where B=barometric pressure, mm mercury, and other symbols are as above.

6. Accuracy

The accuracy of the determination is limited by the accuracy of the instrument used. Errors of approximately 10% may be expected. Calibration of the instrument on known methane-air mixtures will improve accuracy.

503 B.   Volumetric Method

1. General Discussion

a. Principle: If methane is slowly mixed with an excess of oxygen in the presence of a platinum coil heated to yellow incandescence, most of the methane will be converted to carbon dioxide and water in a smooth reaction. Several subsequent passes of the mixed gases over the hot coil will serve to burn substantially all of the methane present in the sample. Oxygen and carbon dioxide must be removed from the original sample before the slow combustion is started. The concentration of methane in the sample should not exceed 20%, the remainder being an inert gas such as nitrogen.

Methane also may be converted to carbon dioxide and water in a catalytic oxidation assembly. If this procedure is followed, an excess of oxygen is mixed with the sample before passage through the assembly.

b. Interference: Low-boiling hydrocarbons other than ethane, and vapors from combustible oils, could interfere. These substances, however, are not likely to be present in water in sufficiently high concentration to affect the results significantly.

c. Minimum detectable concentration: This method is not satisfactory for determining methane in water where the concentration is less than 2 mg/l.

d. Sampling: Collect the sample as directed in Method A and observe the same precautions to obtain representative samples (Section 503A.1*d*). Omit NaOH pellets and fill the sample bottle with water up to 90% of capacity.

Consult Section 511A for a description of the apparatus, reagents, procedure, calculation, and precision and accuracy pertaining to the volumetric method.

Use the percentage of CH_4 found by this method with Henry's law to obtain the CH_4 concentration in the original water sample. Substitute the CH_4 percentage for R (scale reading) and $f = 1$ in the calculation given under the Combustible-Gas Indicator Method, Section 503A.5 preceding.

503 C.   Bibliography

Combustible-Gas Indicator Method

ROSSUM, J.R., P.A. VILLARRUZ & J.A. WADE. 1950. A new method for determining methane in water. *J. Amer. Water Works Ass.* 42:413.

Volumetric Method

DENNIS, L.M. & M.L. NICHOLS. 1929. Gas Analysis. Macmillan Co., New York, N.Y.
HALDANE, J.S. & J.I. GRAHAM. 1935. Methods of Air Analysis. Charles Griffin & Co., London.
BUSWELL, A.M. & T.E. LARSON. 1937. Methane in ground waters. *J. Amer. Water Works Ass.* 29:1978.
BERGER, L.B. & H.H. SCHRENK. 1938. Bureau of Mines Haldane gas analysis apparatus. U.S. Bur. Mines Information Circ. No. 7017.
LARSON, T.E. 1938. Properties and determination of methane in ground waters. *J. Amer. Water Works Ass.* 30:1828.

504   ORGANIC ACIDS AND VOLATILE ACIDS

The measurement of organic acids either by adsorption and elution from a chromatographic column or by distillation (with or without steam) can be used as a control test for anaerobic digestion. The method using chromatographic separation is presented for organic acids (Section 504A), while methods using distillation are presented for volatile acids.

Volatile fatty acids are classified as water-soluble fatty acids that can be distilled at atmospheric pressure. These volatile acids can be removed from aqueous solution by steam distillation, in spite of the high boiling points, because of their high vapor tension. This group includes water-soluble fatty acids with up to six carbon atoms.

Selection of method: The methods are by straight distillation or steam distillation. The straight distillation method is empirical and results in incomplete and somewhat variable recovery. It is suitable for routine control purposes. The steam distillation method is more tedious, taking some 4 hr to complete, but results in recovery of 92 to 98% of the volatile acids from sewage sludge. The steam distillation is conducted on a $MgSO_4$-saturated, acidified, sludge-free liquor produced by chemical treatment with $FeCl_3$ and filter aid followed by vacuum filtration. By this technic, the effects of varying concentrations of dissolved solids and mineral acid during distillation are avoided. The separation of sludge before distillation also reduces the possibility of hydrolysis of complex materials to volatile acids.

504 A.   Chromatographic Separation Method for Organic Acids

1. General Discussion

a. Principle: An acidified aqueous sample containing organic acids is adsorbed on a column of silicic acid and the acids are eluted with *n*-butanol in chloroform. The eluate is collected and titrated with standard base. All short-chain (1- to 6-carbon) organic acids are eluted with the solvent system used in the method and are reported collectively as total organic acids.

b. Interference: The chloroform-butanol solvent system is capable of eluting organic acids other than the volatile acids and also some synthetic detergents. Besides the so-called volatile acids, crotonic, adipic, pyruvic, phthalic, fumaric, lactic, succinic, malonic, gallic, aconitic, and oxalic acids; alkyl sulfates; and alkyl-aryl sulfonates are adsorbed by silicic acid and eluted.

c. Precautions: The normalities of basic alcohol solutions decrease with time, particularly when subjected to repeated exposure to the atmosphere. These decreases usually are accompanied by the appearance of a white precipitate. The magnitudes of such changes are not normally significant in ordinary process control if the tests are made within a few days of standardization. To minimize this effect, store the standard NaOH titrant in a tightly stoppered pyrex glass bottle and protect from atmospheric CO_2 by attaching a tube of carbon dioxide-absorbing material, as described in the inside front cover. For more precise analyses, standardize the titrant or prepare it before each analysis.

Although the procedure is adequate for routine analysis of most sludge samples, volatile-acids concentrations above 5,000 mg/l may require an increased amount of organic solvent for quantitative recovery. Elute with a second portion of solvent and titrate to reveal possible incomplete recoveries.

2. Apparatus

a. *Centrifuge or filtering assembly.*

b. *Crucibles,* Gooch or fritted-glass, with filtering flask and vacuum source.

c. *Separatory funnel,* 1,000 ml.

3. Reagents

a. *Silicic acid,* specially prepared for chromatography, 50 to 200 mesh: Remove fines by slurrying the acid in distilled water and decanting the supernatant after settling for 15 min. Repeat several times. Dry the washed acid in an oven at 103 C until *absolutely dry,* then store in a desiccator.

b. *Chloroform-butanol reagent:* Mix 300 ml reagent-grade chloroform, 100 ml *n*-butanol, and 80 ml 0.5 N H_2SO_4 in a separatory funnel. Let the water and organic layers separate. Drain off the lower organic layer through a fluted filter paper into a dry bottle.

c. *Thymol blue indicator solution:* Dissolve 80 mg thymol blue in 100 ml absolute methanol.

d. *Phenolphthalein indicator solution:* Dissolve 80 mg phenolphthalein in 100 ml absolute methanol.

e. *Sulfuric acid,* H_2SO_4, conc.

f. *Standard sodium hydroxide,* NaOH, 0.02 N: Dilute 20 ml 1.0N NaOH stock solution to 1 l with absolute methanol. Prepare the stock in water and standardize in accordance with the methods outlined in Section 402.3d.

4. Procedure

a. *Pretreatment of sample:* Centrifuge or vacuum-filter enough sludge to obtain 10 to 15 ml clear sample in a small test tube or beaker. Add a few drops of thymol blue indicator solution, then conc H_2SO_4 dropwise, until definitely red to thymol blue (pH=1.0 to 1.2).

b. *Column chromatography:* Place 12 g silicic acid in a Gooch or fritted-glass crucible and apply suction to pack the column. With a pipet, distribute 5.0 ml of the acidified sample as uniformly as possible over the surface of the column. Apply suction momentarily to draw the sample into the silicic acid. Release the vacuum as soon as the last portion of the sample has entered the column. Quickly add 65 ml chloroform-butanol reagent and apply suction. Discontinue the suction just before the last of the reagent enters the column. Use a new column for each sample.

c. Titration: Remove the filter flask and purge the eluted sample with nitrogen gas or CO_2-free air immediately before titrating. (Obtain CO_2-free air by passing air through Ascarite or equivalent.)

Titrate the sample with standard $0.02N$ NaOH to the phenolphthalein end point, taking care to avoid aeration of the sample. Use nitrogen gas or CO_2-free air delivered through a small glass tube to purge and mix the sample and to prevent contact with atmospheric CO_2 during titration.

d. Blank: Prepare a blank composed of 5.0 ml acidified (H_2SO_4) distilled water, place on column, extract with 65 ml of chloroform-butanol reagent, and titrate in a similar manner.

5. Calculation

Total organic acids (mg/l as acetic acid)

$$= \frac{(a-b) \times N \times 60,000}{\text{ml sample}}$$

where $a =$ ml NaOH used for sample, $b =$ ml NaOH used for blank, and $N =$ normality of NaOH.

6. Precision

Average recoveries of about 95% are obtained for organic acid concentrations above 200 mg/l as acetic acid. Individual tests generally vary from the average by approximately 3%. A greater variation results when lower concentrations of organic acids are present. Titration precision expressed as the standard deviation is about ±0.1 ml, or approximately 24 mg/l as acetic acid.

504 B.   Steam Distillation Method for Volatile Acids

1. Apparatus

The required apparatus listed below is shown in Figure 504:1.

a. Steam generator: 1-l capacity, with a safety tube and a steam bypass valve.

b. Distillation flask, 1-l.

c. Condenser, at least 76 cm (30 in.) long.

d. Receiving flask, provided with a soda-lime tube to protect the distillate from air.

e. Buchner funnel, 14 cm (5.5 in.), with suction.

2. Reagents

a. Sulfuric acid, H_2SO_4, 1+1,

b. Ferric chloride solution: Dissolve 82.5 g $FeCL_3 \cdot 6H_2O$ in 1 l distilled water.

*c. Diatomaceous-silica filter aid.**

d. Magnesium sulfate: $MgSO_4 \cdot 7H_2O$.

e. Standard sodium hydroxide titrant, $0.1N$: See Section 402.3c.

f. Phenolphthalein indicator solution.

------

*Hyflo Super-Cell (Johns-Manville Corp.).

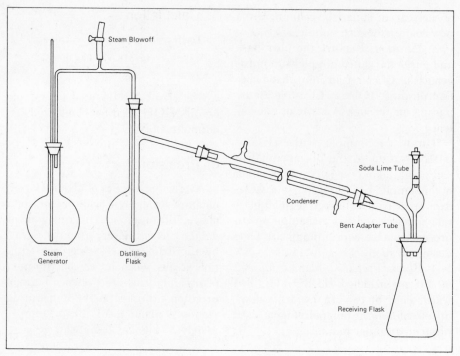

Figure 504:1. Volatile-acid distillation apparatus.

3. Procedure

Adjust a sludge sample, 200 to 1,000 ml, to pH 3.5 with 1+1 H_2SO_4. Add 6 ml $FeCl_3$ solution/l sample (equivalent to 500 mg/l); add 50 g filter aid/l. Mix well. Filter by suction, using a Buchner funnel containing a filter paper freshly coated with a thin layer of filter aid. Wash the residue thoroughly 3 or 4 times with water and adjust the filtrate to pH 11 with NaOH solution. Concentrate by evaporation to 150 ml and cool in a refrigerator.

Adjust the cooled filtrate to pH 4 with 1+1 H_2SO_4 and add it quantitatively and quickly to the distilling flask. Add $MgSO_4$ to slight excess of saturation. Apply heat with a small flame to the flask until rapid evolution of volatile acids commences. This will prevent excessive increase in the volume of the mixture. Steam distill slowly so that about 200 ml of distillate will be collected in 25 min. Increase the rate of distillation and continue until a total of 600 ml is collected. By careful control of the steam rate, excessive foaming can be prevented readily.

Titrate the distillate with 0.1N NaOH, using phenolphthalein indicator.

4. Calculation

$$\text{mg/l volatile acids as acetic acid} = \frac{\text{ml NaOH} \times 6{,}000}{\text{ml sample}}$$

504 C. Distillation Method (TENTATIVE)

1. General Discussion

The following short method often is applicable for control purposes. Because the method is empirical it should be carried out exactly as described. It is assumed that 70% of the volatile acids will be found in the distillate. This is corrected for in the computations. However, this factor has been found to vary from 68 to 85%, depending on the nature of the acids and the rate of distillation.

2. Apparatus

a. Centrifuge, with head to carry four 50-ml tubes or 250-ml bottles.

b. Distillation flask, 500-ml capacity.

c. Condenser, about 76 cm (30 in.) in length.

d. Adapter tube.

3. Reagents

a. Sulfuric acid, H_2SO_4, 1+1.

b. Standard sodium hydroxide titrant, 0.1N, See Section 402.3c.

c. Phenolphthalein indicator solution.

4. Procedure

Centrifuge 200 ml sample for 5 min. Pour off and combine the supernatant liquors. Place 100 ml supernatant liquor in a 500-ml distillation flask. Add 100 ml distilled water, 4 to 5 clay chips or similar material to prevent bumping, and 5 ml H_2SO_4. Mix so that the acid does not remain on the bottom of the flask. Connect the flask to a condenser and adapter tube and distill at the rate of about 5 ml/min. Collect 150 ml distillate in a 250-ml conical flask and titrate with 0.1N NaOH, using phenol-phthalein as an indicator. The endpoint is the first pink coloration that persists on standing a short time. Titration at 95 C produces a stable endpoint.

5. Calculation

$$\frac{\text{mg/l volatile acids as acetic acid}}{} = \frac{\text{ml NaOH} \times 6,000}{\text{ml sample} \times 0.7}$$

6. Bibliography

OLMSTEAD, W.H., W.M. WHITAKER & C.W. DUDEN. 1929-1930. Steam distillation of the lower volatile fatty acids from a saturated salt solution. *J. Biol. Chem.* 85:109.

OLMSTEAD, W.H. et al. 1929-1930. A method for the rapid distillation of the lower volatile fatty acids from stools. *J. Biol. Chem.* 85:115.

Illinois State Water Surv. Bull. 1930. 30:76.

HEUKELEKIAN, H. & KAPLOVSKY, A.J. 1949. Improved method of volatile-acid recovery from sewage sludges. *Sewage Works J.* 21:974.

KAPLOVSKY, A.J. 1951. Volatile-acid production during the digestion of seeded, unseeded, and limed fresh solids. *Sewage Ind. Wastes* 23:713.

MUELLER, H.F., A.M. BUSWELL & T.E. LARSON. 1956. Chromatographic determination of volatile acids. *Sewage Ind. Wastes* 28:255.

MUELLER, H.F., T.E. LARSON & M. FERRETTI. 1960. Chromatographic separation and identification of organic acids. *Anal. Chem.* 32:687.

WESTERHOLD, A.F. 1963. Organic acids in digester liquor by chromatography. *J. Water Pollut. Control Fed.* 35:1431.

HATTINGH, W.H.J. & F.V. HAYWARD. 1964. An improved chromatographic method for the determination of total volatile fatty acid content in anaerobic digester liquors. *Int. J. Air Water Pollut.* 8:411.

POHLAND, F.G. & B.H. DICKSON, JR. 1964. Organic acids by column chromatography. *Water Works Wastes Eng.* 1:54.

505   ORGANIC CARBON (TOTAL)
Combustion-Infrared Method*

The total organic carbon concentration generally falls below the true value of organic contaminants because other constituent elements are excluded. After an empirical relationship has been established between the total organic carbon, and the biochemical oxygen demand or the chemical oxygen demand, the total organic carbon (TOC) provides a speedy and convenient way of estimating the other parameters that express the degree of organic contamination.

Furthermore, total organic carbon is a more direct expression of the organic chemical content of water than either of the two other analyses. As such, TOC can be used to monitor processes for the treatment or removal of organic contaminants without undue dependence on the oxidation states, and can do so at low concentrations.

1. General Discussion

The carbon analyzer offers a means of measuring total organic carbon in the range of 1 to 150 mg/l in water and wastewater. Appropriate dilution of the sample enables the determination of greater carbon concentrations as well as the analysis of water samples bearing a high salt, acid, or base content. Smaller carbon concentrations can be estimated by suitable concentration of the sample or through the use of larger portions. The procedure yields the best results with homogeneous samples that are reproducibly (± 1.0 mg/l carbon) in-

jectable into the apparatus by a microliter-type syringe. The needle opening of the syringe restricts the maximum size of particles that may be included in the samples.

a. Principle: The water sample is homogenized or diluted as necessary and a microportion is injected into a heated, packed tube in a stream of oxygen or purified air. The water is vaporized and the organic matter is oxidized to carbon dioxide, which is measured by means of a nondispersive type of infrared analyzer. Because the carbon analyzer measures all of the carbon in a sample after injection into the combustion tube, procedural modifications are needed to limit the determination to organic carbon. Inorganic carbonates may be decomposed with acid and volatilized in the form of carbon dioxide before the organic carbon is determined. Alternatively, the total organic and inorganic carbon determination can be followed by a separate determination for the inorganic carbon. The difference between the total and the inorganic carbon then yields the organic carbon.

b. Interference: Removal of carbonate and bicarbonate by means of acidification and purging with nitrogen gas can result in the loss of very volatile organic substances. Another important loss can occur if large carbon-containing particles in the sample fail to enter the hypodermic needle used for injection. Filtration, although desirable to limit the insoluble inorganic matter, can result in loss or gain of TOC, depending on the physical properties of the carbon-

---

*This method is identical in substance to ASTM D2579-69.

containing compounds and the adsorption or desorption of carbonaceous matter from the filter. Any sample treatment may alter the measurable carbon. Record such treatment and consider it in any interpretation of results.

c. Minimum detectable concentration: 1 mg/l carbon. This concentration may be lowered by concentrating the sample or by increasing the portion taken for analysis.

d. Sampling and storage: Collect and store samples in bottles made of glass, preferably brown. Plastic containers are acceptable after tests have demonstrated the absence of extractable carbonaceous substances. Use a Kemmerer or similar type sampler for collection of samples from a depth exceeding 2m (5 ft). Protect samples that cannot be examined promptly from decomposition or oxidation by preservation at ice temperatures, minimal exposure to light and atmosphere, or acidification with hydrochloric acid to a pH not over 2. Under any conditions, minimize storage time.

2. Apparatus

a. Sample blender or homogenizer, Waring type or ultrasonic.

b. Magnetic stirrer.

c. Hypodermic syringe, 0 to 50 or 0 to 500 μl capacity.†

d. Total organic carbon analyzer.‡

3. Reagents

a. Redistilled water: Prepare the blank and standard solutions with redistilled water.

---

†Hamilton No. 705 N or 750 N; CR-700-20 or CR 700-200 with needle point style No. 3.

‡Beckman Instruments, Inc., or equivalent.

b. Hydrochloric acid, HCl, conc.

c. Standard carbon solution: Dissolve 5.571 g anhydrous sodium oxalate, $Na_2C_2O_4$, in redistilled water and dilute to 1,000 ml; 1.00 ml = 1.00 mg carbon. Alternatively, use any other carbon-containing compound of adequate purity, stability, and water solubility.

d. Packing for oxidation tube: Follow the directions supplied with the total organic carbon analyzer.

e. Oxygen gas, carbon-dioxide-free.

f. Nitrogen gas, carbon-dioxide-free.

4. Procedure

a. Instrument operation: The differences between satisfactory analyzers make it impossible to give detailed instructions applicable to every instrument. Therefore, follow the manufacturer's instructions for assembly, testing, calibration, and operation of the analyzer on hand. Vary the injected sample size from that normally recommended according to manufacturer's instructions or if an enlarged combustion tube is available.

b. Sample treatment: If the sample contains gross solid or insoluble liquid matter, homogenize sample with a blender or ultrasonics, until satisfactory repeatability is obtained.

If inorganic carbon must be removed before analysis, transfer a representative portion of 10 to 15 ml to a 30-ml beaker, add 2 drops (0.1 ml) conc HCl to reduce the pH to 2 or less, and purge with carbon-dioxide-free nitrogen gas for 10 min. Do not use plastic tubing. While stirring on a magnetic stirrer, withdraw the sample from the beaker by means of a hypodermic needle with a 150-μm opening. Inject the sample into the analyzer and obtain the peak-height reading. Repeat the injection twice or until three consecutive peaks are obtained that are reproducible to within ±3%.

If the available instrument provides for a separate determination of the carbonate-plus-bicarbonate carbon, omit the decarbonation step with conc HCl and proceed according to the manufacturer's directions.

c. *Preparation of standard curve:* Prepare a standard carbon series of 10, 20, 30, 40, 50, 60, 80, and 100 mg/l with redistilled water by diluting 10, 20, 30, 40, and 50 ml standard carbon solution to 1,000 ml, and 30, 40, and 50 ml standard carbon solution to 500 ml. Inject and record the peak heights of these standards and dilution water blank. Correct peak height for blank.

Plot the carbon concentrations of the standards in milligrams per liter versus the corrected peak height in millimeters on rectangular coordinate paper.

Inject samples and reagent blanks § and ascertain the sample concentrations from the corrected peak heights of the samples by reference to this calibration curve.

5. Calculation

a. Calculate the corrected peak height in millimeters by deducting the blank correction in the standards and samples as follows:

---

§Redistilled dilution water and HCl may be contaminated with organic carbon so results must be corrected if blank TOC results are significant.

Corrected peak height, mm $= A - B$

where $A =$ peak height in mm of the standards or sample and $B =$ peak height in mm of the blank.

b. Apply the appropriate dilution factor when necessary.

6. Precision

The difficulty of sampling particulate matter on unfiltered samples limits the precision of the method to approximately 5 to 10%. On clear samples or on those that have been filtered before analysis, the precision approaches 1 to 2% or 1 to 2 mg/l carbon, whichever is greater.

7. Bibliography

Van Hall, C.E., J. Safranko & V.A. Stenger. 1963. Rapid combustion method for the determination of organic substances in aqueous solutions. *Anal. Chem.* 35:315.

Van Hall, C.E., D. Barth & V.A. Stenger. 1965. Elimination of carbonates from aqueous solutions prior to organic carbon determinations. *Anal. Chem.* 37:769.

Schaffer, R.B. et al. 1965. Application of a carbon analyzer in waste treatment. *J. Water Pollut. Control Fed.* 37:1545.

Busch, A.W. 1966. Energy, total carbon, and oxygen demand. *Water Resour. Res.* 2:59.

Williams, R.T. 1967. Water-pollution instrumentation—Analyzer looks for organic carbon. *Instrum. Technol.* 14:63.

Blackmore, R.H. & D. Voshel. 1967. Rapid determination of total organic carbon (TOC) in sewage. *Water Sewage Works* 114:398.

Van Hall, C.E. & V.A. Stenger. 1967. An instrumental method for rapid determination of carbonate and total carbon in solutions. *Anal. Chem.* 39:503.

506 ORGANIC CONTAMINANTS
Organics-Carbon Adsorbable

Organic contaminants—natural substances, insecticides, herbicides, and other agricultural chemicals—enter water in precipitation runoff. Domestic and industrial wastewaters, depending on their degree of treatment, also contribute contaminants in various amounts. As a result of accidental spills and leaks, industrial organic wastes may enter streams. Some of the contaminants, extremely persistent and only partially removed by treatment, reach the consumer in drinking water.

Both natural and man-made contaminants can have undesirable effects on health.[1,2] Some of these materials interfere with water quality by causing tastes and odors and killing fish. The isolation and recovery of insecticides, nitriles, ortho-nitrochlorobenzene, aromatic ethers, waste hydrocarbons, and many other synthetic chemicals suggest that a method for assessing these materials in water is desirable.

The first group of methods for total organic contaminants includes direct determination of contaminating components by OC-A or TOC analysis. In principle, the Organics-Carbon Adsorbable Method (O-CA) is most appropriate because it is based on the direct recovery and weighing of the organics. However, the method is time-consuming. The Total Organic Carbon (TOC) Method can be carried out in a few minutes and gives a quantitative measure of the carbon (see Section 505). The results are related to the weight of organic contaminants. However, special effort is needed to make this method useful for drinking water analysis.

The second group of methods for measuring organic contaminants depends on determining the equivalence of oxidizing agents reacting with the organic substances. The two common procedures are Oxygen Demand (Biochemical) (BOD) (Section 507) and Oxygen Demand (Chemical) (COD) (Section 508). These methods, while not directly measuring organic contaminants, are widely used, and a rationale for interpretation of the data has been developed extensively. Both of these methods have the disadvantage of relatively low sensitivity.

Organics-Carbon Adsorbable (O-CA), also called carbon-chloroform extract (CCE-m), has an operational definition. CCE-m is a mixture of organic compounds that can be adsorbed on activated carbon under prescribed conditions and then desorbed with the solvent chloroform. The lower-case letter "m" denotes that this parameter is determined by using a miniaturized sampler and extraction technic and distinguishes it from the high-flow (hf) and low-flow (lf) carbon adsorption method (CAM) technic recommended in the 13th edition of this manual.[3-6]

1. General Discussion

In this gravimetric adsorption-extraction method organic materials are adsorbed on activated carbon and removed by extraction with an organic solvent. The extract is processed by volume reduction through distillation and drying. The quantity of organic materials is determined gravimetrically.

a. Inadequacies: Some organic compounds may not be adsorbed on activated carbon or recovered from the activated carbon by the solvent used, causing a negative error. Inorganic substances may contribute to the weight of extract obtained, causing a positive error.

b. Application: This method is useful for sampling water that contains organic matter mostly in the dissolved form, for example, drinking water, surface water, and groundwater. Because the adsorption capacity of the activated carbon is limited, this technic is not suited to waste waters containing high concentrations of organics.

The method is used primarily for monitoring the general organic concentration and not as a collector of organics for further identification, although with certain precautions, the resulting extract can be reprocessed.* Although all adsorption-desorption technics have inherent limitations, this method does not require expensive instrumentation and should be within the capabilities of most water treatment plant laboratories as well as central laboratories. Toxicological studies on the components of CCE-m are not complete but control of the concentration of CCE-m in drinking water will protect the consumer.

Typical values are shown in Table 506:I.

c. Sampling and storage: In addition to the normal precautions to obtain a representative sample, use the special

TABLE 506:I. CONCENTRATIONS OF CCE-m IN VARIOUS CLASSES OF WATER

Class of Sample	CCE-m mg/l	Number of Samples Averaged
Well water	0.1	2
Spring water stored in small pond	0.1	3
Finished water from lightly polluted surface water:		
Autumn	0.3	10
Finished water from moderately polluted surface water:		
Summer	0.4	11
Winter	0.5	5
Finished water from heavily polluted surface water:		
Summer and autumn	0.9	9
Winter	1.2	9

sampler to give about 60 l. If necessary, store the dried, exposed activated carbon in a sealed glass container at about 4 C. Dry as soon as possible to prevent biodegradation of the adsorbed organics.

2. Apparatus

a. Boiling flask: 300-ml, round or flat bottom, borosilicate glass, Standard Taper (ST) 24/40 joint (two required).

b. Condenser: Graham, outer ST 24/40 joint.

c. Distilling column packing: berl saddles, porcelain, 6 mm.

d. Drying tray: stainless steel, 22 cm (8-7/8 in.) long, 13 cm (5 in.) wide, and 5 cm (2 in.) deep. Do not use aluminum or galvanized metals for trays, because they react with wet activated carbon.†

---

*Reference 7 contains details of a technic for re-extracting the activated carbon with 95% ethyl alcohol. Although the resulting extract is too heavily contaminated with inorganic salts to produce useful gravimetric data, it can be used as a source of additional organics from the original water sample that can be reprocessed for identification.

†Matheson Scientific No. 63127-10 trays, instrument, stainless steel, round corners, 1-l (1-qt) capacity have been found satisfactory for this purpose.

e. Extraction apparatus Soxhlet, with Allihn condenser, borosilicate glass, 50-mm-ID extractor, ST 55/50 top joint, ST 24/40 bottom joint.

f. Extraction thimbles: paper, seamless, fat-free, single thickness, 43 mm ID, 123 mm length.

g. Filtering screen: 40-mesh, stainless steel.

h. Forceps: aquarium, metal‡.

i. Forceps: small, metal, to handle berl saddles and vials.

j. Heating mantle for distillation step. §

k. Heating mantle for distillation step. ||

l. Mechanical convection oven regulated to a temperature of 40±1 C.#

*m. Miniature CAM sampler:*** See Figure 506:1.

n. Miniature CAM sample columns:[8] See Figure 506:2.

---

‡Turtox No. 205A40, or any forceps with a large-tip surface area to avoid tearing the thimbles, is satisfactory.

§Glas-Col No. STM-800, or equivalent. When purchasing this item, specify if it is to be used for 300-ml round- or flat-bottom flasks according to the choice made for the boiling flask. Do not use flat-bottom flasks in mantles designed for round-bottom flasks.

||Glas-Col No. M-104, or equivalent. See note for extraction-heating mantle.

#The Blue M, Model OV-490 A-C, is satisfactory. If a gravity convection incubator operating at 35±0.5 C (as used for incubation of total coliform tubes or plates) is available, it can be used for activated carbon drying, but determine the minimum acceptable drying time for the activated carbon, because excess residual moisture will interfere with extraction.

**C.F.H. Research Laboratories, Box 269, Springfield, Mass. 01101, and Belcan Corp., 9546 Montgomery Rd., Cincinnati, Ohio 45242, or equivalent. A parts list, construction drawings, and a manual on the installation, operation, and maintenance of the miniaturized CAM sampler[8] are available from the Director, Water Supply Research Lab., National Environmental Research Center, USEPA, 4676 Columbia Pkwy., Cincinnati, Ohio 45268.

o. Stopper: Polyethylene, hollow, ST 24/40 cone size.

p. Stopwatch.

q. Transformer, variable output, 10 A, 120 V.

r. Tube, connecting, distilling, borosilicate glass, ST 24/40 joints.

s. Vial: 5 dram (18.5 ml), flint glass, with polyethylene stopper.

3. Reagents

a. Activated carbon: granular, coal base, 14×40 mesh grain size, Filtrasorb 200.††

b. Chloroform, Spectroanalyzed.‡‡

c. Compressed air, dry, oil-free.§§

4. Procedure

a. A schematic drawing of the miniature CAM sampler apparatus is shown in Figure 506:1. The sampler operates with a low constant head of water of less than 1 m (3 ft). The water to be sampled is supplied by gravity from a very low constant-head tank (less than 13 cm or 5 in.) and flows upward through 70.0 g activated carbon at a rate of about 20 ml/min (4.5-min contact time) for a 48-hr period, thereby sam-

---

††Filtrasorb 200, manufactured by the Calgon Corp., Pittsburgh, Pa., is a satisfactory adsorbant. Calgon manufactures a special sampling activated carbon with the CCE-m blank value per 70.0 g activated carbon predetermined.

‡‡Chloroform distilled during reduction of solvent volume may be reused. Gas chromatographic (GC) analysis of this distillate shows that some impurities are present, but less than 1%. Prevent buildup of impurities to significant concentrations in the reused chloroform by diluting with fresh chloroform (required to offset solvent losses that are up to 60%).

§§If a central source of compressed air is not available, use a small air pump such as Fisher Scientific Co. No. 1-092-5, Dyna-Pump, or a small tank of compressed air.

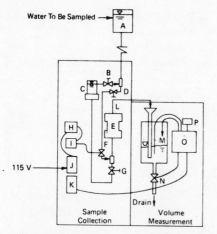

Figure 506:1. Schematic of miniature CAM sampler, Model A. Model B does not have parts M–P and replaces them with a calibrated collection vessel. A—constant head main tank, B—sample column feed-tank valve, C—sample column feed tank, D—flushing valve, E—sample column, F—flushing solenoid valve, G—sample column flow-regulating valve, H—30-min timer, I—delay timer set for 7-8 s, J—power on-off switch, K—duplex outlet, L—sample column outlet tube, M—volume-measuring tank, N—volume-measuring solenoid valve, O—volume-measurement control, P—digital-counter volume recorder. SOURCE: BUELOW, R.W., J.K. CARSWELL & J.M. SYMONS.[7]

pling about 60 l of water. Once each 30 min the activated carbon is flushed automatically for 7 to 8 sec (in the same direction as sample flow) at a flow rate of about 400 ml/min. This increased upward flow rate (flushing) expands the carbon in the column slightly and washes out air and fine particles that would impede flow.

The sampler can be operated on high- or low-pressure water supplies and requires 115 V to operate the flushing-cycle timers, the solenoid valves, and the volume-measuring apparatus if Model A is used. If sufficient water pressure is not available or cannot be created by use of a siphon, use a small pump constructed of materials that will not introduce organics into the water or allow lubricants to contaminate the sample. Do not use rubber or plastic tubing to connect the sampler to the sampling point because the plasticizers in the tubing will contaminate the sample.

b. Preparation of sample column: Place 70.0 g activated carbon in the miniature CAM sample column (Figure 506:2). Apply a double layer of trifluorethylene tape on the column threads for the first use and a single layer for repeat uses. When the tape builds up on the threads so that it interferes with assembling the column, strip it off completely and retape as for the first use. Assemble the column and prevent leakage by hand-tightening the PVC end cap. Disassembly by hand is possible but a vise and strap wrench may be used. Care in wrapping of the trifluorethylene tape on the threads is the best leak preventative. Avoid excessive tightening because it shortens the effective length of the sample column, reduces the volume for the activated carbon, and restricts cleansing of the activated carbon during flushing.

c. Start of sampling: Attach sample column to column inlet connection, clamp column to board, and connect sample column outlet tube. Turn power switch on and open sample column flow-regulating valve fully until a stream of water flows from the sample column outlet tube. This should take less

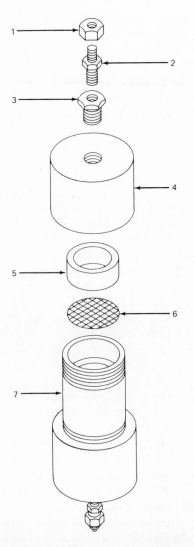

Figure 506:2. **Miniature CAM sample column assembly.** 1—fitting cap; 2—adapter, ¼-in. pipe to ¼-in. OD tubing; 3—bushing, pipe, brass, ½ × ¼-in.; 4—PVC end cap, pipe thread, PVC schedule 80; 5—spacer-screen support, 1½ in., PVC schedule 80, ⅝-in. high; 6—screen, 2¼-in. diameter stainless steel wire cloth 40 × 40 mesh, wire 0.012-in. diameter; 7—nipple, pipe, PVC schedule 80, 2-in. pipe threaded, 3-in. long (note: both ends are identical). SOURCE: BUELOW, R.W., J.K. CARSWELL & J.M. SYMONS.[7]

timer so that one flush occurs at any fixed minute during an hour.

Recheck sampling flow with graduated cylinder about 1 to 2 hr after start-up. Readjust if necessary.

d. Daily, during sampling: Once the flushing volume has been set, make a daily visual check of the flushing flow. A decrease in flushing volume can result in column blocking. Check the sample flow rate once a day. If it is outside the range 18 to 22 ml/min, adjust flow rate to about 20 ml/min with the column flow-regulating valve. The sample flow rate usually does not require adjustment in the sampling period.

Record the volume counter reading and the date and time of reading if Model A is used. If Model B is used, mark expected daily levels on the collection container and check. About 31 l should pass through the sampler each 24 hr.

e. End of sampling: Shut off sample column flow-regulating valve and power switch. Record final volume counter reading (Model A) or final volume in collection container (Model B). Remove

than 1 min. Close sample column regulating valve, then reopen 2.5 turns. Measure sampling flow in graduated cylinder and adjust to about 20 ml/min.

If flushing valve was not previously set, open about three-fourths of a turn. Activate flushing timer and check flushing volume—50 to 55 ml during the 7 to 8 sec flushing. Adjust flushing valve as necessary. If desired, set the 30-min sample column outlet tubing from top of column. Remove column clamp and tilt column forward slightly. Place fitting cap on top fitting of column. Loosen sample column inlet connection and remove column. Drain water from column by removing fitting cap from top fitting. Place fitting caps on fittings at both ends of column. If the screen in the main tank is coated with floc or particulates, clean it. If main tank or sample column feed tank shows a buildup of sediment, clean by brushing and flushing. Between runs store the sampler full of water with the sample column flow-regulating valve and power switch off.

f. Emptying sample column: Remove activated carbon sample from the column as soon as possible after collection. Loosen one of the PVC end caps and remove fitting caps to permit air to enter the sample column. Remove loosened PVC end cap while holding column over and close to the drying tray. Remove the bulk of the activated carbon from the column and PVC end cap by tapping together and catching the activated carbon in the drying tray. Do not spill activated carbon outside of tray. Rinse the activated carbon adhering to the column surfaces directly into the drying tray by a stream of distilled water from a squeeze bottle. Ignore the few granules of activated carbon remaining after thorough rinsing but take care to keep activated carbon loss to a minimum.

Shake the drying tray lightly to distribute the activated carbon evenly. In the recommended tray the activated carbon layer will be about 0.5 cm (3/16 in.) deep. Without shifting the carbon distribution, remove excess water by slowly pouring from a corner of the tray. Drain this excess water through a screening device‖ ‖ that will retain any activated carbon particles that flow off with the water. Return to the tray any particles retained by the screening device.

g. Drying of activated carbon: Dry wet activated carbon sample in a mechanical convection drying oven regulated to a temperature of 40 ± 1 C for at least 24 hr but not more than 72 hr. Alternatively, use a gravity convection drying oven or incubator. Locate the drying oven in a dust- and organic-vapor-free area.

If an alternate drying device is used, check its drying capabilities as follows: Weigh 70.0 g unexposed activated carbon and soak in distilled water in a covered glass container for at least 24 hr, drain in the standard manner, and place the sample in the drying device. Weigh at 24-hr intervals until the weight of the dried activated carbon returns to 70.0 g. The time required to reach this weight will be the minimum allowable drying time for the device.

h. Storage of dried activated carbon samples: If extraction is delayed, store the dried activated carbon samples at about 4 C in clean 500-ml (1 pint) glass container with screw-on lid.

i. Extraction: Add 250 ml chloroform to the 300-ml boiling flask. Add 10 berl saddles, prerinsed in chloroform, as boiling stones. Stopper the flask to prevent solvent evaporation and place in the extraction-type heating mantle. Place a sample of dried activated carbon in the extraction thimble and with aquarium

---

‖ ‖A 40-mesh circular stainless steel screen pressed into an 80-mm polypropylene powder funnel has been found satisfactory for this purpose.

forceps transfer the thimble to the Soxhlet extractor. Put the extractor on the boiling flask and connect the condenser.

Extract the sample for 44 hr after adjusting the transformer to attain an initial extraction cycle time of 6 min $\pm$ 15 sec/cycle. As a minimum, check cycle times after about 2 hr operation and three or four times during the second day of extraction. Readjust the transformer setting if the time is less than 5.5 min/cycle or more than 6.5 min/cycle.

Some loss of solvent through the glass joints and condenser will occur during the course of the extraction. Periodically observe the level of the solvent remaining in the boiling flask when the extractor is ready to siphon. Never allow this solvent level to fall below the aluminum top surface of the mantle. If the extractor is to run unattended overnight, adjust this carefully. Add chloroform as necessary by slowly pouring small quantities (approximately 25 ml) down the top opening of the condenser.

The weight of extract obtained is directly influenced by the total number of extraction cycles to which the activated carbon sample is subjected. To insure that a total number of cycles within the desired range is obtained, check cycle times throughout the extraction period and compute an average cycle time. The specified cycle time will produce 405 to 480 total cycles in 44 hr and is easily obtainable. Monitor the air temperature in the immediate vicinity of the extraction equipment continuously as a useful check on the regularity of operation.

After completing extraction, turn off the heating mantle and let the apparatus cool 15 min before removing the condenser. Transfer the remaining extraction solvent in the extractor to the 300-ml flask by draining and removing the thimble with the aquarium forceps. Tip the extractor-flask assembly to start the siphon. Remove the flask from the heating mantle. Drain additional solvent from the thimble into a beaker and add to the 300-ml flask. Stopper the flask to prevent evaporation.

j. Reduction of solvent volume: Before beginning the solvent-volume reduction step, inspect the contents of the 300-ml flask for carbon particles. If some are evident, remove by filtration through Whatman No. 1 (or equivalent) filter paper. In a hood, using the distillation-type heating mantle, connecting tube, and Graham condenser, distill off excess $CHCl_3$ until the volume remaining is less than 20 ml. Use the same transformer as in the extraction step at a setting of about 60. Occasionally swirl the contents during distillation to dissolve extract from the sidewalls. Until boiling is well established, swirl the contents of the boiling flask continuously and vigorously for 3 to 5 min. This will avoid abrupt, massive boil-over of the flask contents, which will terminate the determination. If the solvent is not to be collected, boil off the excess in a hood without condensing. The time required to reach the desired final volume may be longer.

Remove the boiling flask from the still while hot, using a towel or gloves. Swirl contents vigorously to dissolve extract from the sidewalls and let cool. Transfer the residue to a clean, tared 5-dram (18.5-ml) vial. Avoid tipping the berl saddles into the vial. Rinse the flask and berl saddles with 2 ml $CHCl_3$ and add to the vial. Repeat with 1 ml solvent and add to the vial.

k. Drying of extract: Evaporate the contents of the tared vial to dryness using a gentle stream of dry, oil-free air di-

TABLE 506:II. REPLICATE CCE-m ANALYSES FROM DIFFERENTLY EXPOSED ACTIVATED CARBON SAMPLES

Type of Carbon Sample	Analyst No.	No. of Replicates	Mean Weight of Extract /70.0 g Adsorbant mg	Standard Deviation mg	Coefficient Variation, Mean %
Unexposed activated carbon (from shipping container)	1	5	2.2*	0.1	4.5
	1	5	3.6*	1.0	28
Activated carbon exposed in large container, dried, mixed, and divided in 70.0-g portions.	1	6	87.0†	1.7	2.0
	1	6	86.6†	2.8	3.2
	2	6	66.3†	5.2	7.8
	2	4	63.8†	2.0	3.1
Activated carbon exposed to same water in separate minisamplers (collected by Analyst No. 3)	1	4	0.330‡	0.010	3.0
	2	6	0.503‡	0.013	2.6

* Extract weighed daily until Δ weight/day ≤ 0.1 mg.
† Extract weighed daily until Δ weight/day ≤ 1% previous day's weight.
‡ Extracts weighed daily until dry to constant concentration. See Procedure (drying of extract).

rected into the vial with a tube or in an unheated mechanical convection oven in which no other samples are being processed. After about 24 hr of drying, tilt the vial, using small forceps, to determine if the contents will still "flow." If "flow" is evident, continue drying and re-examine at 24-hr intervals.

If "flow" is not evident, weigh vial and calculate the CCE-m concentration. Place vial in a desiccator with $CaSO_4$ dessicant for 24 hr, reweigh, and recalculate the concentration. If it is unchanged report the calculated concentration. If the concentration has decreased, continue desiccator drying and daily reweighing until the concentration is the same on two successive days. If it is necessary to delay the start of extract drying cover the vial with aluminum foil and store at room temperature for 2 or 3 days.

If the extract is to be reprocessed for identification of components, test also an extract from blank activated carbon to insure that any compound identified did not originate from the activated carbon, the solvent, or the thimble.

5. Calculation

$$\text{mg/l CCE-m} = \frac{[(A-B) \times 1000] - C}{D}$$

where A = weight of vial plus extract, B = tare weight of vial, C = weight of CCE-m average blank, ## mg, and D = volume of water sampled. Express result to nearest 0.1 mg/l.

CCE-m blanks are dried by the standard procedure of air followed by desiccator drying until their weight changes at successive 24-hr intervals are ≤ 0.1 mg.

6. Precision and Accuracy

Insufficient data are available to calculate precision, but some information on reproducibility is available. See Table 506:II. The concentrations in these data were calculated to three decimals and analyzed statistically.

Although percentage-recovery determinations with known compounds have not been made, the increase in extract yield[7] over that obtained by previous methods[5] indicates improved accuracy.

7. References

1. HEUPER, W.C. & W.W. PAYNE. 1963. Carcinogenic effects of raw and finished water supplies. *Amer. J. Clin. Pathol.* 39:475.
2. McCABE, L.J. 1964. Life table analysis of Heuper's data. Interoffice memo, Robert A. Taft Sanitary Engineering Center, Cincinnati, Ohio (unpublished).
3. Standard Methods for the Examination of Water and Wastewater, 13th ed. 1971. American Public Health Ass., New York, N.Y.
4. BOOTH, R.L., J.N. ENGLISH & G.N. McDERMOTT. 1965. Evaluation of sampling conditions in the carbon adsorption methods. *J. Amer. Water Works Ass.* 57:215.
5. REID, B.H., H. STIERLI, C. HENKE & A.W. BREIDENBACH. 1965. Field Evaluation of Low-Flow-Rate Carbon Adsorption Equipment and Methods for Organics Sampling of Surface Waters. PHS Water Pollution Surveillance System Applications and Development Rep. No. 14, Div. Water Supply and Pollution Control, U.S. Dep. HEW, Cincinnati, Ohio (mimeo).
6. Installation, Operation, and Maintenance of Models No. LF-1 and LF-2, Organics Samplers for Water. 1967. Div. Pollution Surveillance, FWPCA. U.S. Dep. Interior, Cincinnati, Ohio.
7. BUELOW, R.W., J.K. CARSWELL & J.M. SYMONS. 1973. An improved method for determining organics in water by activated carbon adsorption and solvent extraction. *J. Amer. Water Works Ass.* 65:57 and 65:195.
8. CARSWELL, J.K., R.W. BUELOW & J.M. SYMONS. 1973. The Determination of Organics—Carbon Adsorbable in Water. Water Supply Research Lab., National Environmental Research Center, USEPA, Cincinnati, Ohio (mimeo).

507   OXYGEN DEMAND (BIOCHEMICAL)*

1. Discussion

The biochemical oxygen demand (BOD) determination described herein is an empirical test in which standardized laboratory procedures are used to determine the relative oxygen requirements of wastewaters, effluents, and polluted waters. The test has its widest application in measuring waste loadings to treatment plants and in evaluating the efficiency (BOD removal) of such treatment systems. BOD values cannot be compared unless the results have been obtained under identical test conditions.

The test is of limited value in measuring the actual oxygen demand of surface waters. The extrapolation of test results to actual stream oxygen demands is highly questionable because the laboratory environment does not reproduce stream conditions such as temperature, sunlight, biological population, water movement, and oxygen concentration.

Samples for BOD analysis may undergo significant degradation during

---

*BOD, biochemical oxygen demand.

handling and storage. Some of the demand may be satisfied if the sample is held for several days before the test is initiated; this results in a low estimation of the true BOD. The extent of change appears to be a function of the amount of organic matter (food supply) and the number and types of organisms (biological population). To reduce the change in oxygen demand that occurs between sampling and testing, keep all samples at or below 4 C and begin incubation not more than 24 hr after the sample is collected.

The amount of oxygen demand in the sample will govern the need for and the degree of dilution.

Aerate samples with low DO values to increase the initial DO content above that required by the BOD. Let air bubble through a diffusion tube into the sample for 5 min, or until the DO is at least 7 mg/l. Determine DO on one portion of the aerated sample; seed another portion only if necessary, and incubate it for the BOD determination.

Complete stabilization of a given waste may require a period of incubation too long for practical purposes. For this reason, the 5-day period has been accepted as standard. However, for certain industrial wastes it may be advisable to determine the oxidation curve obtained. Conversion of data from one incubation period to another can be made only if such special studies are carried out. Studies in recent years have shown that the exponential rate of carbonaceous oxidation, k, at 20 C rarely has a value of 0.1, although it may vary from less than one-half to more than twice this value. This fact usually makes it impossible to calculate the ultimate carbonaceous demand, L, of a sample from 5-day BOD values unless the k value has been determined on the sample. The exponential interpretation of BOD rate curves is a gross oversimplification; a good exponential fit is not obtained always.

The test measures the oxygen demand produced by carbonaceous and nitrogenous compounds, and immediate oxidation. All of these have a bearing on the oxygen balance of the receiving water and must be considered in the discharge of a waste to such water. Differentiation of the immediate dissolved oxygen demand is described in ¶4j below. Appropriate technics for the suppression of nitrification in tests for carbonaceous demand only are given elsewhere.[1-5] If nitrification suppression is used, state this clearly when reporting results. Bear in mind that some suppressors may also inhibit carbonaceous oxidation.

2. Apparatus

a. *Incubation bottles*, 250- to 300-ml capacity, with ground-glass stoppers. Clean bottles with a good detergent, rinse thoroughly, and drain before use. As a precaution against drawing air into the dilution bottle during incubation, use a water seal. Satisfactory water seals are obtained by inverting the bottles in a water bath or adding water to the flared mouth of special BOD bottles.

b. *Air incubator or water bath*, thermostatically controlled at 20 C±1 C: Exclude all light to prevent formation of DO by algae in the sample.

3. Reagents

a. *Distilled water:* Use only high-quality water distilled from a block tin or all-glass still. Alternatively, use deionized water. The water must contain less than 0.01 mg/l copper, and be free of chlorine, chloramines, caustic alkalinity, organic material, or acids.

b. Phosphate buffer solution: Dissolve 8.5 g potassium dihydrogen phosphate, KH_2PO_4; 21.75 g dipotassium hydrogen phosphate, K_2HPO_4; 33.4 g disodium hydrogen phosphate heptahydrate, $Na_2HPO_4 \cdot 7H_2O$; and 1.7 g ammonium chloride, NH_4Cl, in about 500 ml distilled water and dilute to 1 l. The pH of this buffer should be 7.2 without further adjustment. Discard the reagent (or any of the following reagents) if there is any sign of biological growth in the stock bottle.

c. Magnesium sulfate solution: Dissolve 22.5 g $MgSO_4 \cdot 7H_2O$ in distilled water and dilute to 1 l.

d. Calcium chloride solution: Dissolve 27.5 g anhydrous $CaCl_2$ in distilled water and dilute to 1 l.

e. Ferric chloride solution: Dissolve 0.25 g $FeCl_3 \cdot 6H_2O$ in distilled water and dilute to 1 l.

f. Acid and alkali solutions, 1N: For neutralization of caustic or acidic waste samples.

g. Sodium sulfite solution, 0.025N: Dissolve 1.575 g anhydrous Na_2SO_3 in 1,000 ml distilled water. This solution is not stable; prepare daily.

b. Seeding: The purpose of seeding is to introduce into the sample a biological population capable of oxidizing the organic matter in the wastewater. Where such microorganisms are already present, as in domestic wastewater or unchlorinated effluents and surface waters, seeding is unnecessary and should not be used.

When the sample contains very few microorganisms—as a result, for example, of chlorination, high temperature, or extreme pH—seed the dilution water. The standard seed material is settled domestic wastewater that has been stored at 20 C for 24 to 36 hr. Use sufficient seed to produce a seed correction (¶4g) of at least 0.6 mg/l.

Some samples—for example, certain industrial wastes—may require seeding because of low microbial population, but they contain organic compounds that are not readily oxidized by domestic wastewater seed. For evaluating the effect of such a waste in a treatment system, it is better to use specialized seed material containing organisms adapted to the use of the organic compounds present. Obtain such adapted seed from the effluent of a biological treatment process receiving the waste in question, or from the receiving water below the point of discharge [preferably 3 to 8 km (2 to 5 miles) below] if the waste is not being treated. When these sources are not available, develop adapted seed in the laboratory by continuously aerating a large sample of water and feeding it with small daily increments of the particular waste, together with soil or domestic sewage, until a satisfactory microbial population has developed. The special circumstances that call for the use of adapted seed also may require a seed concentration higher than the standard 1 to 2 ml/l. Decide on the kind and amount of seed required for such special-purpose studies on the basis of prior experience with the particular waste and the purpose for which the determination is being made.

Adapted seed also has been used in attempts to estimate the effect of a waste on the receiving water. (See Section 507.1).

4. Procedure

a. Preparation of dilution water: Before use, store the distilled water in cotton-plugged bottles long enough for it to become saturated with DO; or, if such storage is not practical, saturate the water by shaking the partially filled bottle or by aerating with a supply of clean compressed air. Use distilled water at 20±1 C.

Place the desired volume of distilled water in a suitable bottle and add 1 ml each of phosphate buffer, $MgSO_4$, $CaCl_2$, and $FeCl_3$ solutions/l of water. If dilution water is to be stored in the incubator, add the phosphate buffer just before using the dilution water.

b. Seeding: See ¶ 3*b* et seq, preceding. If the dilution water is seeded, use it the same day it is prepared.

c. Pretreatment:

1) Samples containing caustic alkalinity or acidity—Neutralize to about pH 7.0 with 1N H_2SO_4 or NaOH, using a pH meter or bromthymol blue as an outside indicator. The pH of the seeded dilution water should not be changed by the preparation of the lowest dilution of sample.

2) Samples containing residual chlorine compounds—If the samples stand for 1 to 2 hr, the residual chlorine often will be dissipated. Prepare BOD dilutions with properly seeded standard dilution water. Destroy higher chlorine residuals in neutralized samples by adding Na_2SO_3. Determine the appropriate quantity of sodium sulfite solution on a 100- to 1,000-ml portion of the sample by adding 10 ml of 1+1 acetic acid or 1+50 H_2SO_4, followed by 10 ml KI solution (10 g/100 ml) and titrating with 0.025N Na_2SO_3 solution to the starch-iodide end point. Add to a volume of sample the quantity of Na_2SO_3 solution determined by the above test, mix, and after 10 to 20 min test a sample for residual chlorine to check the treatment. Prepare BOD dilutions with seeded standard dilution water.

3) Samples containing other toxic substances—Samples such as those from industrial wastes—for example, toxic metals derived from plating wastes—frequently require special study and treatment.

4) Samples supersaturated with DO—Samples containing more than 9 mg/l DO at 20 C may be encountered during winter months or in localities where algae are growing actively. To prevent loss of oxygen during incubation of these samples, reduce the DO to saturation by bringing the sample to about 20 C in a partly filled bottle and agitating it by vigorous shaking or by aerating with compressed air.

d. Dilution technic: Make several dilutions of the prepared sample to obtain the required depletions. The following dilutions are suggested: 0.1 to 1.0% for strong trade wastes, 1 to 5% for raw and settled sewage, 5 to 25% for oxidized effluents, and 25 to 100% for polluted river waters.

1) Carefully siphon standard dilution water, seeded if necessary, into a graduated cylinder of 1,000 to 2,000 ml capacity, filling the cylinder half full without entrainment of air. Add the quantity of carefully mixed sample to make the desired dilution and dilute to the appropriate level with dilution water. Mix well with a plunger-type mixing rod, avoiding entrainment of air. Siphon the mixed dilution into two BOD bottles, one for incubation and the other for de-

termination of the initial DO in the mixture; stopper tightly and incubate for 5 days at 20 C. Water-seal the BOD bottles by inverting in a tray of water in the incubator or by using a special water-seal bottle. Prepare succeeding dilutions of lower concentration in the same manner or by adding dilution water to the unused portion of the preceding dilution.

2) The dilution technic may be greatly simplified when suitable amounts of sample are measured directly into bottles of known capacity with a large-tip volumetric pipet and the bottles are filled with sufficient dilution water to permit insertion of the stopper without leaving air bubbles. Make dilutions greater than 1:100 by diluting the waste in a volumetric flask before adding it to the incubation bottles for final dilution.

e. *Determination of DO:* If the sample represents 1% or more of the lowest BOD dilution, determine DO on the undiluted sample. This determination is usually omitted on sewage and settled effluents known to have a DO content of practically zero. *With samples having an immediate oxygen demand, use a calculated initial DO, inasmuch as such a demand represents a load on the receiving water.*

f. *Incubation:* Incubate the blank dilution water and the diluted samples for 5 days in the dark at 20 C. Then determine the DO in the incubated samples and the blank using the azide modification of the iodometric method or a membrane electrode. Unless the membrane electrode is used, use the alum flocculation method for incubated samples of muds and the copper sulfate-sulfamic acid method for activated sludges. In special cases, other modifications may be necessary. Those dilutions showing a residual DO of at least 1 mg/l and a depletion of at least 2 mg/l are most reliable.

g. *Seed correction:* If the dilution water is seeded, determine the oxygen depletion of the seed by setting up a separate series of seed dilutions and selecting those resulting in 40 to 70% oxygen depletions in 5 days. Use one of these depletions to calculate the correction due to the small amount of seed in the dilution water. Do not use the seeded blank for seed correction because the 5-day seeded dilution water blank is subject to erratic oxidation due to the very high dilution of seed, which is not characteristic of the seeded sample.

h. *Dilution water control:* Fill two BOD bottles with unseeded dilution water. Stopper and water-seal one of these for incubation. Determine the DO before incubation in the other bottle. Use the DO results on these two bottles as a rough check on the quality of the unseeded dilution water. Do not use the depletion obtained as a blank correction; it should not be more than 0.2 mg/l and preferably not more than 0.1 mg/l.

i. *Glucose-glutamic acid check:* The BOD test is a bioassay procedure; consequently, the results obtained are influenced greatly by the presence of toxic substances or the use of a poor seeding material. Distilled waters frequently are contaminated with toxic substances—most often copper—and some sewage seeds are relatively inactive. The results obtained with such waters are always low.

The quality of the dilution water, the effectiveness of the seed, and the technic of the analyst should be checked periodically by using pure organic compounds having known or determinable BOD. If a particular organic compound is known to be present in a given waste, it may well serve as a control on the seed used. For general BOD work, a mixture of glucose and glutamic acid (150 mg/l of each) has certain advantages. Glucose has an exceptionally high and variable oxidation rate with relatively simple seeds. When it is used with glutamic acid, the oxidation rate is stabilized and is similar to that obtained with many municipal wastes (0.16 to 0.19 exponential rate). In exceptional cases, a given component of a particular waste may be the best choice to test the efficacy of a particular seed.

To check the dilution water, the seed material, and the technic of the analyst, prepare a standard solution containing 150 mg/l each of reagent-grade glucose and glutamic acid that have been dried at 103 C for 1 hr. Pipet 5.0 ml of this solution into calibrated incubation bottles, fill with seeded dilution water, and incubate with seed control at 20 C for 5 days. On the basis of a mixed primary standard containing 150 mg/l each of glucose and glutamic acid, the 5-day BOD varies in magnitude according to the type of seed, and precision varies

with the quality of seed, as shown in Table 507:I.

Except with the oxidized river water and effluents, a low seed correction resulted in an appreciably higher value for the standard deviation. Check each seed source to determine the amount required to obtain optimum precision. If results differ appreciably from those given in Table 507:I after the seed source has been considered, the technic is questionable.

j. Immediate dissolved oxygen demand: Substances oxidizable by molecular oxygen, such as ferrous iron, sulfite, sulfide, and aldehyde, impose a load on the receiving water and must be taken into consideration. The total oxygen demand of such a substrate may be determined by using a calculated initial DO or by using the sum of the immediate dissolved oxygen demand (IDOD) and the 5-day BOD. Where a differentiation of the two components is desired, determine the IDOD. The IDOD does not necessarily represent the immediate oxidation by molecular DO but may represent an oxidation by the iodine liberated in the acidification step of the iodometric method.

TABLE 507:I. EFFECT OF SEED TYPE AND QUALITY ON BOD RESULTS

Type of Seed	5-day Seed Correction mg/l	Mean 5-day BOD mg/l	Standard Deviation mg/l
Settled fresh sewage	>0.6	218	±11
Settled stale sewage	>0.6	207	± 8
River water (4 sources)	0.05-0.22	224-242	±7-13
Activated sludge effluent	0.07-0.68	221	±13
Trickling filter effluent	0.2-0.4	225	± 8

The depletion of DO in a standard water dilution of the sample in 15 min has been arbitrarily selected as the IDOD. To determine the IDOD, separately measure the DO of the sample (which in most cases is zero) and the DO of the dilution water. Prepare an appropriate dilution of the sample and dilution water and determine the DO after 15 min. The calculated DO of the sample dilution minus the observed DO after 15 min is the IDOD, in milligrams per liter, of the sample dilution.

5. Calculation

a. Definitions:

D_0 = DO of original dilution water
D_1 = DO of diluted sample 15 min after preparation
D_2 = DO of diluted sample after incubation
S = DO of original undiluted sample
D_c = DO available in dilution at zero time
  = $D_0p + SP$
p = decimal fraction of dilution water used
P = decimal fraction of sample used
B_1 = DO of dilution of seed control before incubation
B_2 = DO of dilution of seed control after incubation
f = ratio of seed in sample to seed in control
  = $\dfrac{\% \text{ seed in } D_1}{\% \text{ seed in } B_1}$

Seed correction = $(B_1 - B_2)f$.

b. Biochemical oxygen demand:

When seeding is not required,

$$\text{mg/l BOD} = \frac{D_1 - D_2}{P}$$

When using seeded dilution water,

$$\text{mg/l BOD} = \frac{(D_1 - D_2) - (B_1 - B_2)f}{P}$$

Including IDOD if small or not determined,

$$\text{mg/l BOD} = \frac{D_c - D_2}{P}$$

c. Immediate dissolved oxygen demand:

$$\text{mg/l IDOD} = \frac{D_c - D_1}{P}$$

The DO determined on the unseeded dilution water after incubation is not used in the BOD calculations because this practice would overcorrect for the dilution water. In all the above calculations, corrections are not made for small losses of DO in the dilution water during incubation. If the dilution water is unsatisfactory, proper corrections are difficult and the results are questionable.

6. Precision and Accuracy

At present there is no standard against which the accuracy of the BOD test can be measured. To obtain interlaboratory precision data, a glucose-glutamic acid mixture (¶4i preceding) with a theoretical oxygen demand value of 194 mg/l was analyzed by 73 participants, with each laboratory using its own seed material. The arithmetic mean of all results was 175 mg/l and the standard deviation of that mean was ±26 mg/l (15%).

7. References

1. RUCHHOFT, C.C., O.R. PLACAK & M.B. ETTINGER. 1946. Correction of BOD velocity constants for nitrification. *Sewage Works J.* 20:832.
2. HURWITZ, E. et al. 1947. Nitrification and BOD. *Sewage Works J.* 19:995.
3. BUSWELL, A.M., I. VAN METER & J.R. GERKE. 1950. Study of the nitrification phase of the BOD test. *Sewage Ind. Wastes* 22:508.

4. Montgomery, H.A.C. & B.J. Borne. 1966. The inhibition of nitrification in the BOD test. *J. Proc Inst. Sewage Purif.* Part 4.

5. Young, J.C. 1973. Chemical methods for nitrification control. *J. Water Pollut. Control Fed.* 45:637.

8. Bibliography

Theriault, E.J. 1927. The oxygen demand of polluted waters. Pub. Health Bull. No. 173.

Theriault, E.J. 1931. Detailed instructions for the performance of the dissolved oxygen and biochemical oxygen demand tests. *Pub. Health Rep.* Suppl. 90.

Theriault, E.J., P.D. McNamee & C.T. Butterfield. 1931. Selection of dilution water for use in oxygen demand tests. *Pub. Health Rep.* 48:1084.

Lea, W.L. & M.S. Nichols. 1937. Influence of phosphorus and nitrogen on biochemical oxygen demand. *Sewage Works J.* 9:34.

Ruchhoft, C.C. 1941. Report on the cooperative study of dilution waters made for the Standard Methods Committee of the Federation of Sewage Works Associations. *Sewage Works J.* 13:669.

Sawyer, C.N. & L. Bradney. 1946. Modernization of the BOD test for determining the efficiency of the sewage treatment process. *Sewage Works J.* 18:1113.

Ruchhoft, C.C. et al. 1948. Variations in BOD velocity constants of sewage dilutions. *Ind. Eng. Chem.* 40:1290.

Abbott, W.E. 1948. The bacteriostatic effects of methylene blue on the BOD test. *Water Sewage Works* 95:424.

Mohlman, F.W. et al. 1950. Experience with modified methods for BOD. *Sewage Ind. Wastes* 22:31.

Sawyer, C.N. et al. 1950. Primary standards for BOD work. *Sewage Ind. Wastes* 22:26.

508 OXYGEN DEMAND (CHEMICAL)

The chemical oxygen demand (COD) determination is a measure of the oxygen equivalent of that portion of the organic matter in a sample that is susceptible to oxidation by a strong chemical oxidant. It is an important, rapidly measured parameter for stream and industrial waste studies and control of waste treatment plants. However, in the absence of a catalyst the method fails to include some organic compounds (such as acetic acid) that are biologically available to the stream organisms, while including some biological compounds (such as cellulose) that are not a part of the immediate biochemical load on the oxygen assets of the receiving water. The carbonaceous portion of nitrogenous compounds can be determined, but there is no reduction of the dichromate by ammonia in a waste or by ammonia liberated from the proteinaceous matter. With certain wastes containing toxic substances, this test or a total organic carbon determination may be the only method for determining the organic load. Where wastes contain only readily available organic bacterial food and no toxic matter, the results can be used to approximate the ultimate carbonaceous BOD values.

The use of exactly the same technic each time is important because only a part of the organic matter is included, the proportion depending on the chemical oxidant used, the structure of the organic compounds, and the manipulative procedure.

The dichromate reflux method has been selected for the COD determination because it has advantages over other oxidants in oxidizability, applicability to a wide variety of samples, and ease of manipulation. The test will find its major usefulness for waste control purposes after many values have been obtained and correlated with some other important parameter or parameters.

1. General Discussion

a. Principle: Most types of organic matter are destroyed by a boiling mixture of chromic and sulfuric acids. A sample is refluxed with known amounts of potassium dichromate and sulfuric acid and the excess dichromate is titrated with ferrous ammonium sulfate. The amount of oxidizable organic matter, measured as oxygen equivalent, is proportional to the potassium dichromate consumed.

b. Interference and inadequacies: Straight-chain aliphatic compounds, aromatic hydrocarbons, and pyridine are not oxidized to any appreciable extent, although this method gives more nearly complete oxidation than the permanganate method. The straight-chain compounds are oxidized more effectively when silver sulfate is added as a catalyst; however, silver sulfate reacts with chloride, bromide, or iodide to produce precipitates that are oxidized only partially by the procedure. There is no advantage in using the catalyst in the oxidation of aromatic hydrocarbons, but it is essential to the oxidation of straight-chain alcohols and acids.

The oxidation and other difficulties caused by the presence of chloride may be overcome by using a complexing technic for the elimination of chloride. This is accomplished by adding mercuric sulfate to the samples before refluxing. This ties up the chloride ion as a soluble mercuric chloride complex and greatly reduces its ability to react further.

Nitrite exerts a COD of 1.1 mg/mg N. Since concentrations of nitrite in polluted waters rarely exceed 1 or 2 mg/l the interference is considered insignificant and usually is ignored. To eliminate a significant interference due to nitrite, add 10 mg sulfamic acid/mg nitrite N in the refluxing flask. Add the sulfamic acid to the standard dichromate solution, since it must be included in the distilled water blank.

c. Application: The method can be used to determine COD values of 50 mg/l or more with the concentrated dichromate. With the dilute dichromate, values below 10 mg/l are less accurate but indicate the order of magnitude.

d. Sampling and storage: Test unstable samples without delay. Homogenize samples containing settleable solids in a blender to permit representative sampling. If there is to be a delay before analysis, preserve the sample by acidification with sulfuric acid. Make initial dilutions in volumetric flasks for wastes containing a high COD in order to reduce the error inherent in measuring small volumes.

2. Apparatus

a. Reflux apparatus, consisting of 500-ml or 250-ml erlenmeyer flasks with ground-glass 24/40 neck* and 300-mm jacket Liebig, West, or equivalent condensers† with 24/40 ground-glass joint, and a hot plate having suf-

---

*Corning 5000 or equivalent.
†Corning 2360, 91548, or equivalent.

ficient power to produce at least 1.4 W/ cm^2 (9 W/in.^{2}) of heating surface, or equivalent, to insure adequate boiling of the contents of the refluxing flask.

3. Reagents

a. Standard potassium dichromate solution, 0.250N: Dissolve 12.259 g K$_2$Cr$_2$O$_7$, primary standard grade, previously dried at 103 C for 2 hr, in distilled water and dilute to 1,000 ml.

b. Sulfuric acid reagent: conc H$_2$SO$_4$ containing 22 g silver sulfate, Ag$_2$SO$_4$, per 4 kg (9-lb) bottle (1 to 2 days required for dissolution).

c. Standard ferrous ammonium sulfate titrant, 0.1N: Dissolve 39 g Fe(NH$_4$)$_2$(SO$_4$)$_2$•6H$_2$O in distilled water. Add 20 ml conc H$_2$SO$_4$, cool, and dilute to 1,000 ml. Standardize this solution daily against the standard K$_2$Cr$_2$O$_7$ solution.

Standardization—Dilute 10.0 ml standard K$_2$Cr$_2$O$_7$ solution to about 100 ml. Add 30 ml conc H$_2$SO$_4$ and cool. Titrate with the ferrous ammonium sulfate titrant, using 2 to 3 drops (0.10 to 0.15 ml) ferroin indicator.

$$\text{Normality} = \frac{\text{ml K}_2\text{Cr}_2\text{O}_7 \times 0.25}{\text{ml Fe(NH}_4)_2(\text{SO}_4)_2}$$

d. Ferroin indicator solution: Dissolve 1.485 g 1,10-phenanthroline monohydrate, together with 695 mg FeSO$_4$•7H$_2$O in water and dilute to 100 ml. This indicator solution may be purchased already prepared.[‡]

e. Mercuric sulfate, HgSO$_4$, crystals.

f. Sulfamic acid: Required only if the interference of nitrites is to be eliminated (see ¶ 1*b* above).

[‡]G.F. Smith Chemical Company, Columbus, Ohio.

4. Procedure

a. Treatment of samples with COD values over 50 mg/l:

Place 50.0 ml sample or a smaller sample portion diluted to 50.0 ml in the 500-ml refluxing flask. Add 1 g HgSO$_4$,[§] several boiling chips, and 5.0 ml H$_2$SO$_4$. Add the H$_2$SO$_4$ very slowly, with mixing to dissolve the HgSO$_4$. Cool while mixing to avoid possible loss of volatile materials in the sample. Add 25.0 ml 0.250 N K$_2$Cr$_2$O$_7$ solution and again mix. Attach the flask to the condenser and start the cooling water. Add the remaining acid reagent (70 ml) through the open end of the condenser. Continue swirling and mixing while the acid is being added. Mix the reflux mixture thoroughly before heat is applied; if this is not done, local heating occurs in the bottom of the flask and the mixture may be blown out of the condenser.

Alternatively, use sample volumes from 10.0 ml to 50.0 ml and adjust volumes, weights, and normalities accordingly. Consult Table 508:I below for examples of applicable ratios. Maintain these ratios and follow the complete procedure as outlined above.

Use 1 g HgSO$_4$ with a 50.0-ml sample to complex 100 mg chloride (2,000 mg/l). For smaller volume samples use less HgSO$_4$, according to the chloride concentration; maintain a 10:1 ratio of HgSO$_4$:Cl. A slight precipitate does not affect the determination adversely. As a general rule, COD cannot be measured accurately in samples containing more than 2,000 mg/l chloride.

[§]HgSO$_4$ may be measured conveniently by volume, using a reagent spoon (e.g., Hach Company No. 638 or equivalent).

TABLE 508:I. REAGENT QUANTITIES AND NORMALITIES FOR VARIOUS SAMPLE SIZES

Sample Size ml	0.25N Standard Dichromate ml	Conc H₂SO₄ with Ag₂SO₄ ml	HgSO₄ g	Normality of Fe(NH₄)₂- (SO₄)₂	Final Volume Before Titration ml
10.0	5.0	15	0.2	0.05	70
20.0	10.0	30	0.4	0.10	140
30.0	15.0	45	0.6	0.15	210
40.0	20.0	60	0.8	0.20	280
50.0	25.0	75	1.0	0.25	350

Reflux the mixture for 2 hr or use a shorter period for particular wastes if it has been found to give maximum COD. Cover the open end of the condenser with a small beaker to prevent foreign material from entering the refluxing mixture. Cool and wash down the condenser with distilled water.

Dilute the mixture to about twice its volume with distilled water, cool to room temperature, and titrate the excess dichromate with standard ferrous ammonium sulfate, using ferroin indicator. Generally, use 2 to 3 drops (0.10 to 0.15 ml) indicator. Although the quantity of ferroin is not critical, use a constant volume. Take as the end point the sharp color change from blue-green to reddish brown, even though the blue-green may reappear within minutes.

Reflux in the same manner a blank consisting of distilled water, equal in volume to that of the sample, together with the reagents.

b. *Alternate procedure for low-COD samples:*

Follow the standard procedure, ¶ 4a, with two exceptions: (i) Use 0.025N standard K₂Cr₂O₇, and (ii) back-titrate with 0.10N ferrous ammonium sulfate. Exercise extreme care with this procedure because even a trace of organic matter in the glassware or the atmosphere may cause a gross error. If a further increase in sensitivity is required, reduce a larger sample to 20 ml (final total volume 60 ml) by boiling in the refluxing flask on a hot plate in the presence of all reagents. Carry a blank through the same procedure. This technic has the advantage of concentrating the sample without significant loss of easily digested volatile materials. Hard-to-digest volatile materials such as volatile acids are lost, but an improvement is gained over ordinary evaporative concentration methods. As sample volume increases, chloride concentration also increases and more HgSO₄ is required.

c. *Determination of standard solution:* Evaluate the technic and quality of reagents with a standard solution of either glucose or potassium acid phthalate. See Precision and Accuracy, below, for reference to phthalate. Because glucose has a theoretical COD of 1.067 g/ g, dissolve 468.6 mg glucose in distilled water and dilute to 1,000 ml for a 500-mg/l COD solution. Potassium acid phthalate has a theoretical COD of 1.176 g/g; therefore, dissolve 425.1 mg potassium acid phthalate in distilled water and dilute to 1,000 ml for a 500-mg/l COD solution. A 98 to 100% recovery of the theoretical oxygen demand can be expected with potassium acid phthalate. This reagent has an advantage over glucose in that it can be standardized chemically. It is also stable over a period of time, whereas glucose may be decomposed biologically quite rapidly.

5. Calculation

$$\text{mg/l COD} = \frac{(a-b)N\times8,000}{\text{ml sample}}$$

where COD=chemical oxygen demand from dichromate, a=ml Fe(NH$_4$)$_2$(SO$_4$)$_2$ used for blank, b=ml Fe(NH$_4$)$_2$(SO$_4$)$_2$ used for sample, and N=normality of Fe(NH$_4$)$_2$(SO$_4$)$_2$.

6. Precision and Accuracy

A set of synthetic unknown samples containing potassium acid phthalate and sodium chloride was tested by 74 laboratories. At 200 mg/l COD in the absence of chloride, the standard deviation was ±13 mg/l (coefficient of variation, 6.5%). At 160 mg/l COD and 100 mg/l chloride, the standard deviation was ±14 mg/l (10.8%).

The accuracy of this method has been determined by Moore and associates. For most organic compounds the oxidation is 95 to 100% of the theoretical value. Benzene, toluene, and pyridine are not oxidized.

7. Bibliography

Muers, M.M. 1936. Biological purification of whey solutions. *J. Soc. Chem. Ind.* (London) 55:711.

Moore, W.A., R. C. Kroner, & C.C. Ruchhoft. 1949. Dichromate reflux method for determination of oxygen consumed. *Anal. Chem.* 21:953.

Moore, W.A., F.J. Ludzack & C. C. Ruchhoft. 1951. Determination of oxygen-consumed values of organic wastes. *Anal. Chem.* 23:1297.

Medalia, A.I. 1951. Test for traces of organic matter in water. *Anal. Chem.* 23:1318.

Subrahmanyan, P., C. Sastry & S. Pallai. 1959. Determination of the permanganate value for waters and sewage effluent containing nitrite. *Analyst* 84:731.

Symons, J.M., R.E. McKinney & H.H. Hassis. 1960. A procedure for determination of the biological treatability of industrial wastes. *J. Water Pollut. Control Fed.* 32:841.

Dobbs, R.A. & R.T. Williams. 1963. Elimination of chloride interference in the chemical oxygen demand test. *Anal. Chem.* 35:1064.

509 PESTICIDES (ORGANIC)

Large-scale application of pesticides in agricultural and forest areas can contribute to the presence of these toxic materials in surface and groundwaters and ultimately in water supplies. Contamination can occur through drainage from the surrounding terrain, precipitation from the atmosphere, accidental spills of pesticides in the watershed area, or a cross-connection on a distribution system.

Gas chromatographic methods for the determination of the organochlorine pesticides and chlorinated phenoxy acid herbicides in water are presented here.

A cholinesterase inhibition method is presented as a means of screening samples for organophosphorus and carbamate pesticides. The methods are applicable to both finished and natural surface waters.

509 A.   Organochlorine Pesticides (TENTATIVE)

1. General Discussion

a. Principle: This gas chromatographic procedure is suitable for the quantitative determination of the following specific compounds: BHC, lindane, heptachlor, aldrin, heptachlor epoxide, dieldrin, endrin, Captan, DDE, DDD, DDT, methoxychlor, endosulfan, dichloran, mirex, and pentachloronitrobenzene. Under favorable circumstances, Strobane, toxaphene, chlordane (tech.), and others also may be determined. Certain organophosphorus pesticides, such as parathion, methylparathion, and malathion, which respond to the electron capture detector, also may be determined. However, the analyst must demonstrate the usefulness of the method for the organophosphorus or other specific pesticides before applying it to sample analysis.

In gas chromatography a mobile phase (a carrier gas) and a stationary phase (column packing) are used to separate individual compounds. The carrier gas is N_2, Ar, He, or H_2. The stationary phase is a liquid that has been coated on an inert granular solid, called the column packing, that is held in borosilicate glass tubing. The column is installed in an oven so that the inlet is attached to a heated injector block and the outlet is attached to a detector. Precise and constant temperature control of the injector block, the oven, and the detector is maintained. Stationary phase material and concentration, column length and diameter, oven temperature, carrier gas flow, and detector type are the controlled variables.

The sample solution is injected through a silicone rubber septum onto the column with a microsyringe. The pesticides are vaporized and moved through the column by the carrier gas. They travel through the column at different rates, depending on differences in the partition coefficients between the mobile and the stationary phase. As each component passes through the detector a quantitatively proportional change in electrical signal is measured on a strip-chart recorder. Each component is observed as a peak on the recorder chart. The retention time is indicative of the particular pesticide and the peak height is proportional to its quantity.

Variables may be manipulated to obtain important confirmatory identification data. For example, the detector system may be selected on the basis of the specificity and sensitivity needed. The detector used in this method is an electron-capture detector that is very sensitive to chlorinated compounds. Additional confirmatory identification can be made from retention data on two or more columns where the stationary phases are of different polarities. A two-column procedure that has been found particularly useful is specified.

b. Interference: Some substances other than chlorinated compounds respond to the electron capture detector. Among these are oxygenated and unsaturated compounds. Sometimes plant or animal extractives essentially obscure the pesticide peaks. These interfering substances often can be removed by ancillary cleanup technics. A Florisil column cleanup and separation procedure is used for this purpose. Such cleanup usually is not required for potable waters.

1) Polychlorinated biphenyls (PCB's) —Industrial plasticizers and hydraulic fluids such as the PCB's are a potential source of interference in pesticide analysis. The presence of PCB's is indicated by a large number of partially resolved or unresolved peaks that may occur throughout the entire chromatogram. Particularly severe PCB interference will require special separation procedures.[1]

2) Phthalate esters—These compounds, widely used as plasticizers, respond to the electron capture detector and are a source of interference in the determination of organochlorine pesticides. Water leaches these materials from plastics, such as polyethylene bottles and tygon tubing. The phthalates can be separated from many of the important pesticides by the Florisil column cleanup. They do not respond to halogen-specific detectors such as the microcoulometric or electrolytic conductivity detectors.

c. Detection limits: The ultimate detection limit of a substance is affected by many factors, for example, the detector sensitivity, the extraction and cleanup efficiency, the concentrations, and detector signal-to-noise level. Lindane usually can be determined at 10 ng/l in a sample of relatively unpolluted water; the DDT detection limit is somewhat higher, 20 to 25 ng/l.

Increased sensitivity is likely to increase the interference. The greater the number of pesticides investigated, the longer will be the time required for analysis.

2. Apparatus

Clean thoroughly all glassware used in sample collection and pesticide residue analyses. Clean the glassware as soon as possible after use. Rinse with water or the solvent that was last used in it, wash with soapy water, rinse with tap water, distilled water, redistilled acetone, and finally with pesticide-quality hexane. Ignite heavily contaminated glassware at 400 C for 15 to 30 min. High boiling materials such as the polychlorinated biphenyls (PCB's) may not be eliminated completely by heat treatment. Do not ignite volumetric ware. After drying, store the glassware to prevent accumulation of dust or other contaminants. Store inverted or cover mouth with foil.

a. Sample bottles: 1-l (1 qt) capacity, glass, with teflon-lined screw cap.

b. Evaporative concentrator, Kuderna Danish, 500 ml flask and 10 ml graduated lower tube, or equivalent.

c. Separatory funnels, 2-l capacity, with Teflon stopcock.

d. Graduated cylinders, 1-l capacity.

e. Funnels, 125 ml (4 oz).

f. Glass wool, filter grade.

g. Chromatographic column, 20 mm diameter by 400 mm long, with coarse fritted disk at bottom.

h. Microsyringes, 10 and 25 μl capacity.

i. Steam bath.

j. Morton flasks, 300 ml.

k. Rotary evaporator.

l. Gas chromatograph, equipped with:

1) *Glass-lined injection port.*

2) *Electron capture detector,* tritium or nickel-63.

3) *Recorder:* potentiometric strip chart, 25 cm (10 in.). compatible with detector and associated electronics.

4) *Pyrex glass column,* 180 cm long ×4 mm ID.

The many variations in gas chromatographic instrumentation available necessitate different operating procedures for each. Therefore, the chromatographer should be familiar with the manufacturer's operating manuals, gas chromatography catalogs, and other references (see Bibliography). In general, use equipment with the following features:

1) Carrier gas line with a molecular sieve drying cartridge. Use only dry carrier gas and insure that there are no gas leaks in the system.

2) Oven temperature stable to ±0.5 C or better at the desired setting.

3) Chromatographic columns—A well-prepared column is essential to an acceptable gas chromatographic analysis. Obtain the column packings and pre-packed columns from commercial sources or prepare column packing in the laboratory.

It is inappropriate to give rigid specifications on the size or compositions to be used because some instruments perform better with different columns than do others. Adequate separations have been obtained using 5% OV-210 on 100/120 mesh Gas-Chrom Q in a 2-m (6-ft) column. The 1.5% OV-17 and 1.95% QF-1 column is recommended for confirmatory analysis. A column is suitable when it effects adequate and reproducible resolution.

3. Reagents

Use solvents, reagents, and other materials for pesticide analysis that are free from interferences under the condition of the analysis. Specific selection of reagents and distillation of solvents in an all-glass system may be required. "Pesticide quality" solvents usually do not require redistillation; however, determine a blank before use.

a. Hexane.

b. Petroleum ether, boiling range 30 to 60 C.

c. Diethyl ether.

d. Ethyl acetate.

e. Florisil, PR (60 to 100 mesh). Purchase activated at 676 C and store in the dark in glass container with glass stopper or foil-lined screw cap. Before use, activate each batch overnight at 130 C in foil-covered glass container.

f. Sodium sulfate, anhydrous, granular.

g. Silanized glass wool.

h. Column packing:

1) Solid support—Gas-Chrom Q (100 to 120 mesh)

2) Liquid phases—OV-210, OV-17, and QF-1.

i. Carrier gas: One of the following is required:

1) Nitrogen gas—purified grade, moisture- and oxygen-free.

2) Argon-methane (95+5%) for use in pulse mode.

j. Pesticide reference standards: Obtain purest standards available from gas chromatographic and chemical supply houses.

k. Stock pesticide solutions: Dissolve 100 mg of each of the pesticides of interest in ethyl acetate and dilute to 100 ml in a volumetric flask; 1.00 ml = 1.00 mg.

l. Intermediate pesticide solutions: Dilute 1.0 ml stock solution to 100 ml with ethyl acetate; 1.0 ml = 10 µg.

m. Working standard solutions for gas chromatography: Prepare the final concentration of standards in hexane solution as required by the detector sensitivity and linearity.

4. Procedure

a. Preparation of chromatograph:

1) Preparation of column packings— One acceptable method of preparing column packings is the rotary vacuum technic. On the basis of a 20-g total batch size, compute the amount of liquid phases to weigh in 30-ml beakers on an analytical balance. Weigh out the liquid phases to two-place accuracy. If making mixed-phase packing, weigh each liquid phase in separate beaker since each may require a different solvent. The liquid phases mentioned above can be dissolved in acetone.

With a 25-ml graduate, transfer 15 ml of the appropriate solvent into each beaker. Stir with a glass rod until solution is complete. Transfer each liquid phase solution through a glass funnel into a 300-ml Morton flask. From this point on, *measure* all solvent used for rinsing beakers and funnels so that the final solvent volume in the flask will be just sufficient to produce a slurry of about heavy cream consistency when the support is added. (This is somewhat critical because too little solvent prevents adequate mixing for uniform support coating, and too much solvent requires excessive evaporation time. A total of 90 ml solvent is required for a 20-g batch of Gas-Chrom Q.) Use a 10-ml Mohr pipet for adding and measuring the applied solvent. Rinse the beakers with four consecutive applications of 7 to 9 ml solvent.

After the liquid phase is transferred, place a powder funnel in the flask and add the support. For a 20-g batch of column packing, weigh out an amount of support that is the difference, in grams, between the total amount of liquid phase weighed and 20 g. For example, when preparing a 20-g batch of packing of 1.5% OV-17/1.95% QF-1 take:

OV-17	0.015	× 20	=	0.30 g
QF-1	0.0195	× 20	=	0.39 g
Total liquid phase				0.69 g
Solid support		20 − 0.69	=	19.31 g

Attach the flask to the rotary evaporator. *Mix slowly* for 10 min at room temperature with just enough vacuum applied to hold flask in place. Rotate the flask *very slowly* to avoid crushing the solid support. (This is a *very critical point*. Because it is not possible to slow a Powerstat or Variac sufficiently, the operator must brake further by hand. This requires *continuous* attention throughout.)

Advance hot plate control sufficiently to raise temperature of water in the beaker to 45 C in about 20 min. Increase vacuum slightly at the start of heating and continue increasing, a little at a time. When the temperature reaches 45 C, the vacuum should be such that the slurry is at a near-boil. Maintain this condition until all visible solvent is removed.

Advance heat gradually to 55 C, applying as much vacuum as possible just short of flushing liquid solvent out of the flask. Remove all visible solvent at this temperature. Advance heat to produce 65 C, apply all vacuum available, and rotate *very slowly* and intermittently. When all evident solvent is removed, release vacuum slowly and shut down the assembly. Transfer the flask of packing to an oven and hold at 130 C at least 2 hrs, or overnight.

2) Packing the column—Use a column constructed of borosilicate glass be-cause other tubing materials may catalyze sample component decomposition. Pack the column to a uniform density not so compact as to cause unnecessary back pressure and not so loose as to create voids during use. Do not crush the packing. Rinse and dry the column tubing with solvent, e.g., chloroform, before packing. Fill the column through a funnel connected by flexible tubing to one end. Plug the other end of the column with about 1.3 cm (0.5 in.) silanized glass wool and fill with the aid of *gentle* vibration or tapping. Optionally, apply a vacuum to the plugged end. Plug the open end with silanized glass wool. In a similar manner, fill one-half of a "U"-shaped column and then the other, and plug the ends with silanized glass wool.

3) Conditioning—Proper thermal and pesticide conditioning are essential to eliminate column bleed and to provide acceptable gas chromatographic analysis. The following procedure provides excellent results: Install the packed column in the oven. *Do not* connect the column to the detector. However, maintain gas flow through the detector by using the purge gas line, or in dual column ovens, by connecting an unpacked column to the detector. Adjust the carrier gas flow to about 50 ml/min and slowly (over a 1-hr period) raise the oven temperature to 230 C. After 48 hr at this temperature the column is ready for pesticide conditioning.

Adjust the oven temperature and carrier gas flow rate to the approximate operating levels. Make six consecutive 10-μl injections of a concentrated pesticide mixture through the column at about 15-min intervals. Prepare this injection mixture from lindane, heptachlor, aldrin, heptachlor epoxide, dieldrin, endrin, and p,p'-DDT, each compound at a concentration of 200 ng/μl. After pesticide conditioning, connect the column to the detector and let equilibrate for at least 1 hr, preferably overnight. The column is then ready for use.

4) Injection technic—

a) One acceptable technic of loading the syringe and measuring volume injected is as follows: Wet the syringe needle and barrel with solvent solution of the standard or sample to be injected and expel all air bubbles. Draw the entire quantity of solution into the calibrated barrel and note volume. Inject into the chromatograph rapidly and withdraw syringe immediately. Then partially withdraw plunger and note volume remaining in the syringe. Determine volume injected by subtracting the remaining volume from the original volume. Clean the syringe thoroughly after each injection with several solvent rinses.

b) Inject standard solutions of such concentration that the injection volume and peak height of the standard are approximately the same as those of the sample.

b. Treatment of samples:

1) Sample collection—Fill sample bottle to the neck. Collect samples in duplicate.

2) Extraction of samples—Shake the sample well and accurately measure in a 1-l graduated cylinder. Pour the sample into a 2-l separatory funnel. Rinse the sample bottle and the cylinder with 60 ml 15% ethyl ether in hexane, pour this solvent into the separatory funnel, and shake vigorously for 2 min. Let the phases separate for at least 10 min.

Place a small piece of filter grade glass wool in the bottom of a 125-ml (4-oz) funnel, fill the funnel three-quarters full of sodium sulfate, and wash with several portions of 15% ethyl ether in hexane.

Drain the water phase from the separatory funnel into the sample bottle and pour the organic phase through the Na_2SO_4-filled funnel into a Kuderna-Danish apparatus fitted with a 10-ml concentrator tube.

Rinse the sample bottle with 60 ml mixed solvent, use the solvent to repeat extraction of the sample, and pass the organic phase through the Na_2SO_4. Complete a third extraction with 60 ml hexane (not ethyl ether-hexane) that has been used to rinse the sample bottle again, and pass the organic phase through the Na_2SO_4. Wash the Na_2SO_4 with several portions of hexane and drain well. Fit the Kuderna-Danish apparatus with a three-ball Snyder column and reduce the volume to about 7 ml on the steam bath. Remove the concentrator tube from the Kuderna-Danish apparatus, immerse the apparatus in a water bath at 50 C, and evaporate to below 5 ml with a gentle stream of dry nitrogen. Dilute the sample to 5 ml with hexane.

3) Gas chromatography—Inject 5 μl of the extract solution into one of the columns of the gas chromatograph. Always inject the same volume. Inspect the resulting chromatogram for peaks corresponding to the pesticides of concern and for the presence of interferences.

a) If there are presumptive pesticide peaks and no significant interference, then rechromatograph 5.0 μl of the extract solution on the alternate column.

b) Inject standards frequently to insure optimum operating conditions. If necessary, concentrate or dilute the extract so the peak height of the sample is very close to the height of corresponding peaks in the standard. (See dilution factor, ¶5a).

c) If significant interference is present, separate the interfering substances from the pesticide materials by using the cleanup procedure described in the following paragraph.

4) Florisil cleanup—Adjust the sample extract volume to 10 ml with hexane. Place a charge of activated Florisil (weight determined by lauric-acid value, see Appendix) in a chromatographic column. After settling the Florisil by tapping the column, add about 1.3 cm (0.5 in.) of anhydrous granular Na2SO4 to the top. Pre-elute the column, after cooling, with 50 to 60 ml petroleum ether. Discard the eluate and just before exposing the sulfate layer to air, quantitatively transfer the sample extract into the column by decantation and with subsequent petroleum ether washings. Adjust the elution rate to about 5 ml/min and, separately, collect up to four eluates in 500-ml Kuderna-Danish flasks equipped with 10-ml ampuls.

Make the first elution with 200 ml 6% ethyl ether, and the second with 200 ml 15% ethyl ether in petroleum ether. Make the third elution with 200 ml 50% ethyl ether-petroleum ether and the fourth with 200 ml of 100% ethyl ether.

Concentrate the eluates in the Kuderna-Danish evaporator in a hot water bath as in ¶4b2) preceding, dilute to appropriate volume, and analyze by gas chromatography.

Eluate composition—By use of an equivalent quantity of any bath of Florisil as determined by its lauric acid value, the pesticides will be separated into the eluates indicated below:

6% Ethyl Ether Eluate

Aldrin	Heptachlor	Pentachloro-
BHC	Heptachlor	nitrobenzene
Chlordane	epoxide	Strobane
DDD	Lindane	Toxaphene
DDE	Methoxychlor	Trifluralin
DDT	Mirex	PCB's

15% Ethyl Ether Eluate	*50% Ethyl Ether Eluate*
Endosulfan I	Endosulfan II
Endrin	Captan
Dieldrin	
Dichloran	
Phthalate esters	

Certain thiophosphate pesticides will occur in each of the above fractions as well as the 100% ethyl ether fraction. For additional information regarding eluate composition and the procedure for determining the lauric acid value, refer to the FDA Pesticide Analytical Manual (see Bibliography).

5) Determination of extraction efficiency—Add known amounts of pesticides in ethyl acetate solution to 1 l water sample and carry through the same procedure as the samples. Dilute an equal amount of the intermediate pesticide solution (¶3l above) to the same final volume. Call the peak height from the standard "*a*" and the peak height from the sample to which pesticide was added "*b*", whereupon the extraction efficiency, *E*, equals *b/a*. Periodically determine extraction efficiency and a control blank to test the procedure. Also analyze one set of duplicates with each series of samples as a quality control check.

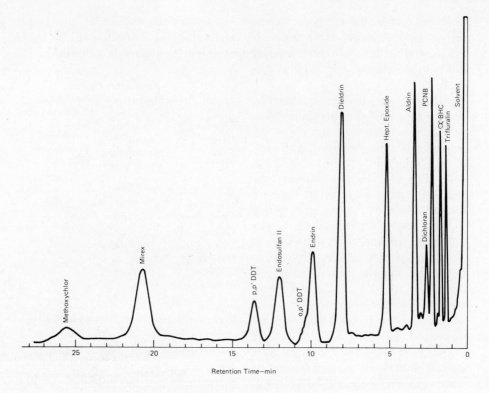

Figure 509:1. Results of gas chromatographic procedure for organochlorine pesticides. Column packing: 1.5% OV-17+1.95% QF-1; carrier gas: argon/methane at 60 ml/min; column temperature: 200 C; detector: electron capture.

5. Calculation

a. Dilution factor: If a portion of the extract solution was concentrated, the dilution factor, *D*, is a decimal; if it was diluted, the dilution factor exceeds 1.

b. Determine pesticide concentrations by direct comparison to a single stand-ard when the injection volume and re-sponse are close to that of the sample (Table 509:I, Figures 509:1 and 2). Calculate the concentration of pesticide

$$\mu g/l = \frac{A \times B \times C \times D}{E \times F \times G}$$

TABLE 509:1. RETENTION TIMES OF VARIOUS
ORGANOCHLORINE PESTICIDES RELATIVE TO
ALDRIN

Pesticide	Relative Retention Time under Given Conditions*	
	Liquid phase: 1.5% OV-17 +1.95% QF-1 Column Temp.: 200 C Argon/ Methane Carrier Flow: 60 ml/min	Liquid phase: 5% OV-210 Column Temp.: 180 C Argon/ Methane Carrier Flow: 70 ml/min
∝-BHC	0.54	0.64
PCNB	0.68	0.85
Lindane	0.69	0.81
Dichloran	0.77	1.29
Heptachlor	0.82	0.87
Aldrin	1.00	1.00
Heptachlor epoxide	1.54	1.93
Endosulfan I	1.95	2.48
p,p'-DDE	2.23	2.10
Dieldrin	2.40	3.00
Captan	2.59	4.09
Endrin	2.93	3.56
o,p'-DDT	3.16	2.70
p,p'-DDD	3.48	3.75
Endosulfan II	3.59	4.59
p,p'-DDT	4.18	4.07
Mirex	6.1	3.78
Methoxychlor	7.6	6.5
Aldrin (min absolute)	3.5	2.6

* All columns glass, 180 cm×4 mm ID, solid
support Gas-Chrom Q (100/120 mesh).

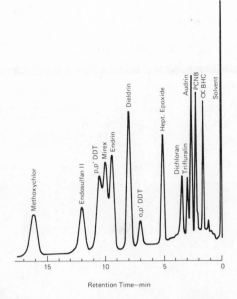

Figure 509:2. Results of gas chromatographic procedure for organochlorine pesticides. Column packing: 5% OV-210; carrier gas: argon/methane at 70 ml/min; column temperature: 180 C; detector: electron capture.

where A =ng standard pesticide, B = peak height of sample, mm, C =extract volume, μl, D =dilution factor, E = peak height of standard, mm, F =volume of extract injected, μl, and G =volume of sample extracted, ml.

Report results in micrograms per liter without correction for efficiency.

6. Precision and Accuracy

Precision and accuracy data are given in Table 509:II.

7. Reference

1. LEONI, V. 1971. The separation of fifty pesticides and related compounds and polychlorinated biphenyls into four groups by silica gel microcolumn chromatography. *J. Chromatog.* 62:63.

TABLE 509:II. PRECISION AND ACCURACY DATA FOR SELECTED ORGANOCHLORINE PESTICIDES

Pesticide	Level Added ng/l	Pre-treatment	Mean Recovery ng/l	Recovery %	Precision* ng/l	
					S_T	S_O
Aldrin	15	No cleanup	10.42	69	4.86	2.59
	110		79.00	72	32.06	20.19
	25	Cleanup†	17.00	68	9.13	3.48‡
	100		64.54	65	27.16	8.02‡
Lindane	10	No cleanup	9.67	97	5.28	3.47
	100		72.91	73	26.23	11.49‡
	15	Cleanup†	14.04	94	8.73	5.20
	85		59.08	70	27.49	7.75‡
Dieldrin	20	No cleanup	21.54	108	18.16	17.92
	125		105.83	85	30.41	21.84
	25	Cleanup	17.52	70	10.44	5.10‡
	130		84.29	65	34.45	16.79‡
DDT	40	No cleanup	40.30	101	15.96	13.42
	200		154.87	77	38.80	24.02
	30	Cleanup†	35.54	118	22.62	22.50
	185		132.08	71	49.83	25.31

* S_T=overall precision and S_O=single operator precision.
† Use of Florisil column cleanup before analysis.
‡ $S_O < S_T/2$

Appendix—Standardization of Florisil Column by Weight Adjustment Based on Adsorption of Lauric Acid

A rapid method for determining adsorptive capacity of Florisil is based on adsorption of lauric acid from hexane solution. An excess of lauric acid is used and the amount not adsorbed is measured by alkali titration. The weight of lauric acid adsorbed is used to calculate, by simple proportion, equivalent quantities of Florisil for batches having different adsorptive capacities.

1. Reagents

a. Ethyl alcohol, USP or absolute, neutralized to phenophthalein.

b. Hexane, distilled from all-glass apparatus.

c. Lauric acid solution: Transfer 10.000 g lauric acid to a 500-ml volumetric flask, dissolve in hexane, and dilute to 500 ml (1.00 ml = 20 mg).

d. Phenolphthalein indicator: Dissolve 1 g in alcohol and dilute to 100 ml.

e. Sodium hydroxide, 0.05N: Dilute 25 ml 1N NaOH to 500 ml with distilled water. Standardize as follows: Weigh 100 to 200 mg lauric acid into 125-ml erlenmeyer flask; add 50 ml neutralized ethyl alcohol and 3 drops phenolphthalein indicator; titrate to permanent end point; and calculate milligrams lauric acid per milliliter NaOH (about 10 mg/ml).

2. Procedure

Transfer 2.000 g Florisil to a 25-ml glass-stoppered erlenmeyer flask. Cover loosely with aluminum foil and heat overnight at 130 C. Stopper, cool to room temperature, add 20.0 ml lauric acid solution (400 mg), stopper, and shake occasionally during 15 min. Let adsorbent settle and pipet 10.0 ml supernatant into a 125-ml erlenmeyer flask. Avoid including any Florisil. Add 50 ml neutral alcohol and 3 drops phenolphthalein indicator solution; titrate with 0.05N NaOH to a permanent end point.

3. Calculation of Lauric Acid Value and Adjustment of Column Weight

Calculate amount of lauric acid adsorbed on Florisil as follows:

Lauric acid value = mg lauric acid/g Florisil =
200−(ml required for titration×mg lauric acid/ml 0.05N NaOH).

To obtain an equivalent quantity of any batch of Florisil, divide 110 by lauric acid value for that batch and multiply by 20 g. Verify proper elution of pesticides by the procedure given below.

4. Test for Proper Elution Pattern and Recovery of Pesticides

Prepare a test mixture containing aldrin, heptachlor epoxide, p,p'-DDE, dieldrin, parathion, and malathion. Dieldrin and parathion should elute in the 15% eluate; all but a trace of malathion in the 50% eluate, and the others in the 6% eluate.

509 B.   Chlorinated Phenoxy Acid Herbicides (TENTATIVE)

Phenoxy acid herbicides are used extensively for weed control. Esters and salts of 2,4-D and silvex have been used as aquatic herbicides in lakes, streams, and irrigation canals. Phenoxy acid herbicides are very potent even at low concentrations.

1. General Discussion

a. Principle: Chlorinated phenoxy acid herbicides such as 2,4-D [2,4-dichlorophenoxyacetic acid], silvex [2-(2,4,5 - trichlorophenoxy) propionic acid], 2,4,5-T [2,4,5-trichlorophenoxy-acetic acid], and similar chemicals may be determined by a gas chromatographic procedure.

Because these compounds may occur in water in various forms (e.g., acid, salt, ester) a hydrolysis step is included to permit determination of the active part of the herbicide.

Chlorinated phenoxy acids and their esters are extracted from the acidified water sample with ethyl ether. The extracts are hydrolyzed and extraneous material is removed by a solvent wash. The acids are converted to methyl esters and are further "cleaned up" on a microadsorption column. The methyl esters are determined by gas chromatography.

b. Interference: See Section 509A.1*b*. Clean glassware with detergent in the usual manner, rinse in dilute HCl, and finally rinse in distilled water. To assure removal of organic matter, follow the procedure given in Section 509A.2.

Organic acids, especially chlorinated acids, cause the most direct interference with the determination. Phenols, including chlorophenols, also may interfere. Alkaline hydrolysis and subsequent extraction eliminates many of the predominant chlorinated insecticides. Because the herbicides react readily with alkaline substances loss may occur if there is alkaline contact at any time except in the controlled alkaline hydrolysis step. Acid-rinse glassware and glass wool and acidify sodium sulfate to avoid this possibility.

c. Detection limits: The practical lower limits for measurement of the phenoxy acid herbicides depend primarily on the size of the sample and the instrumentation used. If the extract from a 1-l sample is concentrated to 2.00 ml

and 5.0 μl of the concentrate is injected into the electron-capture gas chromatograph, reliable measurement of 50 ng/l 2,4-D, 10 ng/l silvex, and 10 ng/l 2,4,5-T is feasible. Concentrating the extract to 0.50 ml permits detection of approximately 10 ng/l 2,4-D and 2 ng/l silvex, and 2 ng/l 2,4,5-T. The sensitivity of the electron-capture detector often is affected adversely by extraneous material in the sample or reagents. Concentrating the extract progressively amplifies this complication. Thus, the practical lower limits of measurement are difficult to define.

2. Apparatus

a. Sample bottles: 1-l (1-qt) capacity, glass, with teflon-lined screw cap.

b. Evaporative concentrator, Kuderna-Danish, 250-ml flask and 5-ml volumetric receiver, Kontes, or equivalent.

c. Snyder columns, three-ball macro, one-ball micro.

d. Separatory funnels, 2-l and 60-ml sizes with TFE-fluorocarbon stopcocks and taper ground glass stoppers, Kontes or equivalent.

e. Pipets, Pasteur, disposable, 140 mm long and 5 mm ID, glass.

f. Microsyringes, 10 μl.

g. Sand bath, fluidized (TeCam or equivalent) or water bath.

h. Erlenmeyer flask, 250-ml, with ground glass mouth to fit Snyder columns.

i. Gas chromatographic system: See Section 509A.2*l*. Operating parameters that produce satisfactory chromatograms for herbicide analyses are: injector temperature, 215 C; oven temperature, 185 C; and carrier gas flow

70 ml/min in a 6.4-mm-(1/4-in.-) OD column.

3. Reagents

Check all reagents for purity by the gas chromatographic procedure. Much time and effort is saved by selecting high-quality reagents that do not require further preparation. Some purification of reagents may be necessary as outlined below. If more rigorous treatment is indicated, obtain the reagent from an alternate source.

a. Ethyl ether, reagent grade. Redistill in glass after refluxing over granulated sodium-lead alloy for 4 hr.

b. Benzene, pesticide quality, distilled in glass.

c. Sodium sulfate, anhydrous, granular. Store at 130 C.

d. Sodium sulfate solution: Dissolve 50 ml anhydrous Na_2SO_4 in distilled water and dilute to 1 l.

e. Sodium sulfate, acidified: Add 0.1 ml conc H_2SO_4 to 100 g Na_2SO_4 slurried with enough ethyl ether to just cover the solid. Remove the ether by vacuum drying. Mix 1 g of the resulting solid with 5 ml distilled water and confirm that the mixture has a pH value below 4. Store at 130 C.

f. Sulfuric acid, H_2SO_4, conc.

g. Sulfuric acid, H_2SO_4, 1+3. Store in refrigerator.

h. Potassium hydroxide solution: Dissolve 37 g KOH pellets in distilled water and dilute to 100 ml.

i. Boron trifluoride-methanol, 14% boron trifluoride by weight.

j. Florisil, PR grade (60 to 100 mesh). Purchase activated at 676 C and store at 130 C.

k. Glass wool, filtering grade, acid-washed.

l. Herbicide standards, acids, and methyl esters, analytical reference grade or highest purity available.

m. Stock herbicide solutions: Dissolve 100 mg herbicide or methyl ester in 60 ml ethyl ether; dilute to 100 ml in a volumetric flask with hexane; 1.00 ml = 1.00 mg.

n. Intermediate herbicide solution: Dilute 1.0 ml stock solution to 100 ml in a volumetric flask with a mixture of equal volumes of ethyl ether and benzene; 1.00 ml = 10.0 μg.

o. Standard solution for chromatography: Prepare final concentration of methyl ester standards in benzene solution according to the detector sensitivity and linearity.

4. Procedure

a. Sample extraction: Accurately measure in a 1-l graduated cylinder. Acidify to pH 2 with conc H_2SO_4 and pour into a 2-l separatory funnel. Add 150 ml ethyl ether to the separatory funnel and shake vigorously for 1 min. Let phases separate for at least 10 min. Occasionally, emulsions prevent adequate separation. If emulsions form, drain off the separated aqueous layer, invert the separatory funnel, and shake rapidly. CAUTION: Vent the funnel frequently to prevent excessive pressure buildup. Collect the extract in a 250-ml ground-glass-stoppered erlenmeyer flask containing 2 ml KOH solution. Extract the sample twice more, using 50 ml of ethyl ether each time, and combine the extracts in the erlenmeyer flask.

b. Hydrolysis: Add 15 ml distilled water and a small boiling stone and fit the flask with a three-ball Snyder column. Remove the ether on a steam bath and continue heating for a total of 60 min. Transfer the concentrate to a 60-ml separatory funnel. Extract twice, with 20 ml ethyl ether each time, and discard the ether layers. The herbicides remain in the aqueous phase.

Acidify by adding 2 ml cold (4 C) 1+3 H_2SO_4. Extract once with 20 ml and twice with 10 ml ethyl ether each. Collect the extracts in a 125-ml erlenmeyer flask containing about 0.5 g acidified anhydrous Na_2SO_4. Let the extract remain in contact with the Na_2SO_4 for at least 2 hr.

c. Esterfication: Fit a Kuderna-Danish apparatus with a 5-ml volumetric receiver. Transfer the ether extract to the Kuderna-Danish apparatus through a funnel plugged with glass wool. Use liberal washing of ether. Crush any hardened Na_2SO_4 with a glass rod. Before concentrating, add 0.5 ml benzene.

Table 509:III. Retention Times for Methyl Esters of Some Chlorinated Phenoxy Acid Herbicides Relative to 2, 4-D Methyl Ester

Herbicide	Relative Retention Time for Given Liquid Phase*	
	1.5% OV-17 + 1.95% QF-1	5% OV-210
2,4-D	1.00	1.00
Silvex	1.34	1.22
2,4,5-T	1.72	1.51
2,4-D (min. absolute)	2.00	1.62

* All columns glass, 180 cm×4 mm ID, solid support Gas Chrom Q (100/120 mesh); column temperature 185 C; argon/methane carrier flow, operated in pulse mode, 70 ml/min.

Reduce the volume to less than 1 ml on a sand bath or on a steam bath heated to 60 to 70 C. Attach a Snyder microcolumn to the Kuderna-Danish receiver and concentrate to less than 0.5 ml.

Cool and add 0.5 ml boron trifluoride-methanol reagent. Use the small one-ball Snyder column as an air-cooled condenser and hold the contents of the receiver at 50 C for 30 min in the sand bath. Cool and add enough Na_2SO_4 solution (¶3d above) so that the benzene-water interface is in the neck of the Kuderna-Danish volumetric receiver flask (about 4.5 ml). Stopper the flask with a ground-glass stopper and shake vigorously for about 1 min. Let stand for 3 min for phase separation.

Pipet the solvent layer from the receiver to the top of a small column prepared by plugging a disposable Pasteur pipet with glass wool and packing with 2.0 cm Na_2SO_4 over 1.5 cm Florisil adsorbent. Collect the eluate in a 2.5-ml graduated centrifuge tube. Complete the transfer by repeatedly rinsing the volumetric receiver with small quantities of benzene until a final volume of 2.0 ml of eluate is obtained. Check calibration of centrifuge tubes to insure that the graduations are correct.

d. Gas chromatography: Analyze a suitable portion, 5 to 10 μl, by gas chromatography, using at least two columns for identification and quantification. Inject standard herbicide methyl esters frequently to insure optimum operating conditions. Always inject the same volume. Adjust the volume of sample extract with benzene, if necessary, so that the heights of the peaks obtained are close to those of the standards. (See Dilution factor, ¶5a below).

e. Determination of recovery efficiency: Add known amounts of herbicides to 1 l water sample, carry through the same procedure as the samples, and determine recovery efficiency. Periodically determine recovery efficiency and a control blank to test the procedure. Analyze one set of duplicates with each series of samples as a quality control check.

5. Calculation

a. Dilution factor: If a portion of the extract solution was concentrated, the dilution factor, D, is less than 1; if it was diluted, the dilution factor exceeds 1.

Compare the peak height of a standard to the peak height of the sample to determine the amount of the herbicide injected.

Calculate the concentration of herbicide:

$$\mu g/l = \frac{A \times B \times C \times D}{E \times F \times G}$$

where A = weight of herbicide standard injected, ng, B = peak height of sample, mm, C = extract volume, μl, D = dilution factor, E = peak height of standard, mm, F = volume injected, μl, and G = volume of sample extracted, ml.

b. Molecular weight of herbicides: Molecular weights of herbicides are as follows:

Compound	Molecular Weight
2,4-D	222.0
2,4-D methyl ester	236.0
Silvex	269.5
Silvex methyl ester	283.5
2,4,5-T	255.5
2,4,5-T methyl ester	269.5

Report results in micrograms per liter without correction for recovery efficiency.

7. Precision and Accuracy

No collaborative study has been conducted.

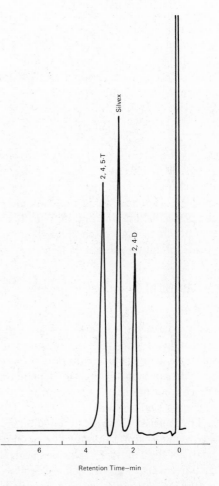

Figure 509:3. Results of gas chromatographic procedure for chlorinated phenoxy acid herbicides. Column: 1.5% OV-17; +1.95% QF-1; carrier gas: argon (5%)/ methane at 70 ml/min; column temperature: 185 C; detector: electron capture.

509 C.   Organophosphate and Carbamate Pesticides (TENTATIVE)

Restricting the use of chlorinated hydrocarbon pesticides has caused an increase in the use of other types of pesticides, many of which are either organophosphates or carbamates. These compounds degrade more rapidly than the chlorinated hydrocarbons, but are more acutely toxic because they inhibit the enzyme cholinesterase, an essential component of the animal nervous system.

Because these pesticides possess the same mode of biological activity it is not necessary to determine the exact amount of each pesticide; rather, determine the total cholinesterase inhibition caused by the pesticide. The method described is a nonspecific in-vitro method for cholinesterase-inhibiting substances in water.

1. General Discussion

a. Principle: The rate of an enzyme-catalyzed reaction depends on the concentration of enzyme, concentration of substrate, temperature, and pH. If these are held constant the rate will depend on the concentration of enzyme-inhibitors in the reaction mixture.

The normal substrate of cholinesterase in vivo is acetylcholine. The enzyme catalyzes the following reaction: acetylcholine + water → acetic acid + choline. In this in vitro method 3,3-dimethylbutyl acetate (DMBA) is used as a substrate and the enzyme catalyzes the hydrolysis of the ester to 3,3-dimethylbutanol (DMB) and acetic acid. The rate is followed by determining the concentration of 3,3-dimethylbutanol produced in a specific reaction time.

There are several reasons for using 3,3-dimethylbutyl acetate rather than acetyl choline: (*a*) decreased non-enzymatic hydrolysis, (*b*) solubility in carbon disulfide, a solvent of low hydrogen flame response, (*c*) increased response of 3,3-dimethylbutanol with respect to choline or acetic acid, (*d*) satisfactory chromatographic characteristics of both 3,3-dimethylbutyl acetate and 3,3-dimethylbutanol, and (*e*) equal substrate to enzyme affinity.

Many of the organophosphates are latent cholinesterase-inhibitors and exhibit no inhibition in vitro. In vivo these compounds are oxidized enzymatically to potent inhibitors. These compounds may be oxidized (activated) with bromine water in vitro. Other pesticides, e.g., phosdrin and carbaryl, require no activation and treatment with an oxidizing agent such as bromine water will destroy their inhibitory property. Since the total cholinesterase inhibition in a sample may be due to the presence of a mixture of pesticides, it is necessary to choose a method that will activate pesticides requiring it while not affecting the others. In this procedure the pesticides are extracted into methylene chloride before activation, thus allowing activation of the latent inhibitors while preserving the activity of the others.

After the pesticides have been extracted and activated a portion of the extract is evaporated to dryness and the residue is incubated with a solution of cholinesterase to allow reaction between the enzyme and any inhibitors present. The activity of the residue-treated enzyme is determined by measuring its capacity to hydrolyze the ester 3,3-dimethylbutyl acetate (DMBA). After a reaction period the hydrolysis is stopped with formic acid and the reaction mixture extracted with carbon disulfide. The determination of 3,3-dimethylbutanol (DMB) in the CS₂ is made by gas chromatography using a hydrogen flame ionization detector. See Figure 509:4.

b. *Interference:* Constituents of certain plants, i.e., tea, potatoes, tobacco, contain enzyme-inhibiting impurities. Bromine may convert some plant constituents into antiesterase compounds.

2. Apparatus

a. *Water bath* set at 37 C.

b. *Oxford pipettors*; 10 μl, 100 μl, 200 μl, and 1 ml.

c. *Centrifuge tubes*, 15-ml, glass-stoppered.

d. *Vortex action test tube mixer.*

e. *Gas chromatograph*, with hydrogen flame ionization detector. Operational parameters are as follows:

1) Column—a glass U-tube, 6 mm (1/4 in.) by 2 m (6 ft), packed with Johns-Manville Chromosorb 101, mesh size 80–100, and conditioned overnight at 250 C.

2) Instrument conditions: column oven, 215 C; detector, 265 C; inlet, 245 C; air, 300 ml/min; hydrogen, 20 ml/min; nitrogen, 40 ml/min.

3. Reagents

a. *Stock buffer solution:* Dissolve 44.73 g KCl, 4.12 g sodium barbital, and 0.55 g K₂HPO₄ dissolved in 200 ml water.

b. *Working buffer:* Add 20 ml stock buffer to 75 ml distilled water, adjust the pH to 8.0 with 0.1N HCl, and dilute to 100 ml with distilled water.

c. *Tween 20® emulsifier.*

d. *3,3-dimethylbutyl acetate:* To remove butanol impurities from DMBA, mix 5 parts DMBA with 1 part acetic anhydride. Keep the mixture at 37 C for 24 hr and wash once with water to remove the acetic anhydride and impurities. Prepare a 0.2M emulsion containing 0.2% emulsifier by diluting 0.72 g DMBA with 20 ml working buffer and adding 50 mg Tween 20.® Adjust the emulsion to pH 8 with NaOH and dilute to 25 ml with working buffer. Shake well before using. Store in refrigerator.

e. *True cholinesterase*, Type I.* Keep refrigerated. Add 3 ml working buffer to 50 μm units of enzyme.

f. *Formic acid solution:* Dilute conc (88%) HCHO with an equal volume of distilled water.

g. *Bromine water:* Dilute 0.2 ml bromine with 100 ml distilled water.

h. *Acetone*, pesticide quality. Redistill from glass.

i. *Methylene chloride*, pesticide quality. Wash with water, dry over androus CaCl₂, and redistill from glass.

j. *Carbon disulfide.†*

k. *Stock parathion solution:* Dissolve 100 mg parathion in acetone and dilute to 100 ml; 1.00 ml=1.00 mg. Store in refrigerator.

l. *Standard parathion solutions:* Dilute the stock parathion solution with distilled water to prepare standards containing 25, 50, and 100 μg/ml. Store in refrigerator.

---

*Sigma Chemical Company. Activity in μm units per milligram solids is indicated by the manufacturer on each bottle.

†Spectro AR grade, Mallinckrodt Chemical Works, or equivalent.

4. Procedure

a. Sample analysis: Place 1.00 ml sample in a 15-ml centrifuge tube and add 1 ml methylene chloride. Shake the tube for 5 sec in the tube mixer, add 0.1 ml bromine water, and shake the tube for another 5 sec. Remove the upper aqueous layer with a pipet and discard. Transfer 10 μl of the organic layer to another centrifuge tube. Make the transfer with a 10-μl Oxford pipettor as follows: Place the tip of the pipettor below the liquid surface, depress the plunger to the first stop, and release 6 to 8 times to

allow equalization of the partial pressures in the tip so that the liquid will remain until expelled by fully depressing the plunger. Evaporate to dryness at 37 C (about 2 min). Evaporate the methylene chloride completely to permit the pesticides to dissolve in the enzyme solution.

Add 100 μl enzyme solution. Swirl the tube by hand and hold in the 37 C water bath for 1 hr. Transfer 10 μl of the residue-treated enzyme to another centrifuge tube containing 1 ml pH 8 working buffer. Warm the tube to 37 C and add 0.2 ml DMBA emulsion. In-

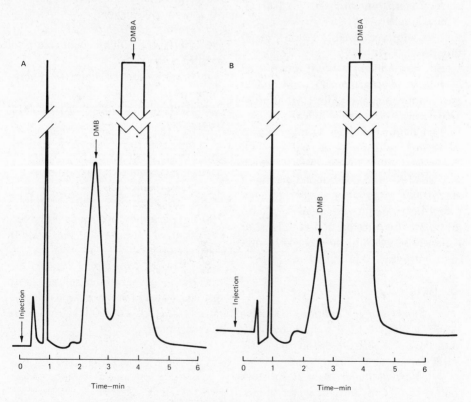

Figure 509:4. Typical gas chromatogram of (A) control sample containing no inhibitor and (B) sample containing 0.05 ppm parathion.

cubate the tube at 37 C for 30 min to allow enzymatic hydrolysis of the DMBA.

Stop the reaction by adding 0.1 ml formic acid solution and 2 ml carbon disulfide, stopper the tube, and shake it from end to end in a horizontal position for 10 sec. Let the layers separate, remove the top aqueous layer by pipet, and discard.

Inject 5 μl of the carbon disulfide layer into the gas chromatograph for DMB determination. See Figure 509:4.

b. Preparation of standard curve: Because sample inhibition is related to the concentration of parathion causing an equal amount of inhibition, prepare a standard curve of parathion concentration versus percent inhibition. Also analyze controls with distilled water as the sample and a blank that contains all reagents except enzyme. The blank should yield only a very small amount of DMB; because no enzyme is contained in the blank, it is a measure of non-enzymatic hydrolysis of the DMBA substrate.

The relative enzyme-inhibiting powers of the most commonly used organophosphates are shown in Table 509:IV. The I_{50} value is defined as the concentration of pesticide, in milligrams per lit-

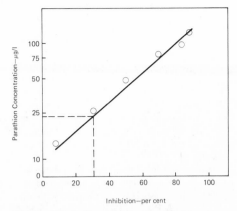

Figure 509:5. Standard curve of percent enzyme inhibition related to parathion concentration.

er, required to cause 50% inhibition of the enzyme.

5. Calculation

Measure the height of the DMB peaks obtained with controls, blank, standards, and samples. Calculate the percent inhibition caused by each standard and sample from the following equation:

$$\% \text{ Inhibition} = \frac{(a-c)-(b-c)}{(a-c)}$$

where a = height of control DMB peak, b = height of sample or standard DMB peak, and c = height of blank DMB peak.

Prepare a standard curve of parathion concentration versus percent inhibition on semilog paper as shown in Figure 509:5.

Relate the inhibition caused by a sample to a parathion concentration by using this standard curve. For example, if a sample produced 30% inhibition, this corresponds to a parathion equivalent of 23 μg/l from the standard curve.

TABLE 509:IV. I_{50} VALUES FOR EIGHT COMMON ORGANOPHOSPHATE PESTICIDES

Pesticide	I_{50} Concentration
Parathion	0.04
Guthion	0.90
Diazinon	0.93
Methyl parathion	1.2
DDVP	1.4
Malathion	1.7
Dipterex	4.4
Disyston	17.

509 D. Bibliography

Organochlorine Pesticides

TEASLEY, J.I. & W.J. Cox. 1963. Determination of pesticides in water by microcoulometric gas chromatography after liquid-liquid extraction. *J. Amer. Water Works Ass.* 55:1093.

BURCHFIELD, H.P., D.C. JOHNSON & E.F. STORRS. 1965. Guide to the Analysis of Pesticide Residues. PHS Office of Pesticides, Washington, D.C.

BREIDENBACH, A.W. et al. 1966. Identification and Measurement of Chlorinated Hydrocarbon Pesticides in Surface Waters. FWPCA Publ. WP-22, 2nd ed. FWPCA, Washington, D.C.

Pesticide Analytical Manual. 1968. U.S. Department of Health, Education and Welfare, Food and Drug Administration, 2nd ed., revised June, 1973. Washington, D.C.

THOMPSON, J.F., A.C. WALKER & R.F. MOSEMAN. 1969. Study of the performance of gas chromatographic columns under severe injection loading. *J. Offic. Anal. Chem.* 52:1251.

Methodology for Aroclors—Analysis of Environmental Materials for Biphenyls. 1970. Analytical Chemistry Method 71-35, Monsanto Co., St. Louis, Mo.

Methods for Organic Pesticides in Water and Wastewater. 1971. U.S. Environmental Protection Agency, National Research Center, Cincinnati, Ohio.

GOERLITZ, D.F. & E. BROWN. 1972. Methods for analysis of organic substances in water. In: Techniques of Water Resources Investigations of the United States Geological Survey. Book 5, p. 24.

Chlorinated Phenoxy Acid Herbicides

METCALF, L.D. & A.A. SCHMITZ. 1961. The rapid preparation of fatty acid esters for gas chromatographic analysis. *Anal. Chem.* 33:363.

GOERLITZ, D.F. & W.L. LAMAR. 1967. Determination of phenoxy acid herbicides in water by electron-capture and microcoulometric gas chromatography. U.S. Geol. Surv. Water-Supply Paper 1817-C.

Organophosphate and Carbamate Pesticides

CRANMER, M. & A. PEOPLES. 1971. Application of a cholinesterase microassay to the determination of trace quantities of anticholinesterase pesticides in air and water. Paper presented at 162nd National Meeting American Chemical Society.

CRANMER, M.F. & A. PEOPLES. 1971. A sensitive gas chromatographic method for human cholinesterase determination. *J. Chromatogr.* 57:365.

510 PHENOLS

Phenols, defined as hydroxy derivatives of benzene and its condensed nuclei, may occur in domestic and industrial wastewaters and in drinking water supplies. Chlorination of such waters may produce odoriferous and objectionable-tasting chlorophenols, which may include *o*-chlorophenol, *p*-chlorophenol, 2,6-dichlorophenol, and 2,4-dichlorophenol. Phenol removal processes in water treatment include super-chlorination, chlorine dioxide or chlorine ammonia treatment, ozonation, and activated carbon adsorption.

Of the four analytical procedures offered here, three use the 4-aminoantipyrine colorimetric method that determines phenol, the ortho- and meta-substituted phenols, and, under proper pH conditions, those parasubstituted phenols in which the substitution is a carboxyl, halogen, methoxyl, or sulfonic acid group. Presumably, the 4-aminoantipyrine method does not determine those para-substituted phenols in which the substitution is an alkyl, aryl, nitro, benzoyl, nitroso, or aldehyde group. A typical example of these latter groups is paracresol, which may be present in certain industrial wastewaters and in polluted surface waters. The fourth procedure is a gas-liquid chromatographic technic.

1. Selection of Method

The 4-aminoantipyrine method is given in three forms: Method B, for extreme sensitivity, is adaptable for use in water samples containing less than 1 mg/l phenol and concentrates the color in a nonaqueous solution; Method C, used for phenol concentrations greater than 1 mg/l in which a high degree of sensitivity is not required, retains the color in the unconcentrated aqueous solution. Because the percentage of various phenolic compounds in a given sample is unpredictable, it is not possible to provide a standard containing a mixture of phenols applicable to all samples. For this reason, phenol itself has been selected as a standard for colorimetric procedures, and any color produced by the reaction of other phenolic compounds is reported as phenol. Because substitution generally reduces response, this value represents the minimum concentration of phenolic compounds present. Method D, a tentative procedure, is used where an estimation of para-substituted phenols, especially the halogenated types, is required; 2,4 dichlorophenol is used as a standard for this technic. Method E, a tentative gas-liquid chromatographic procedure, may be applied to samples or concentrates that contain more than 1 mg/l of phenolic compounds.

2. Interferences

a. Domestic and industrial wastewaters may contain such interferences as phenol-decomposing bacteria, oxidizing and reducing substances, and alkaline pH values. Biological degradation is inhibited by the addition of $CuSO_4$ to the sample. Acidification with H_3PO_4 assures the presence of the copper ion and eliminates any chemical changes resulting from the presence of strong alkaline conditions.

b. Some of the treatment procedures used for the removal of interferences before analysis may result in an unavoidable loss of certain types of phenols. Consequently, some highly contaminated wastewaters may require specialized screening technics for elimination of interferences and for quantitative recovery of the phenolic compounds.

c. Eliminate major interferences as follows (see Section 510A for the required reagents):

1) Oxidizing agents, such as chlorine and those detected by the liberation of iodine upon acidification in the presence of KI—Remove immediately after sampling by adding an excess of $FeSO_4$ or $NaAsO_2$. If oxidizing agents are not removed, the phenolic compounds will be partially oxidized and the results will be low.

2) Sulfur compounds—Remove by acidifying the sample to a pH of less than 4.0 with H_3PO_4 and aerating briefly by stirring before adding $CuSO_4$.

This eliminates the interferences of H_2S and SO_2.

3) Oils and tars—These contain phenols. Perform an alkaline extraction before adding $CuSO_4$. Adjust sample pH to 12 to 12.5 by adding NaOH pellets. Extract oil and tar from the aqueous solution by CCl_4. Discard the oil- or tar-containing layer. Remove any excess of CCl_4 in the aqueous layer by warming on a water bath before proceeding with the distillation step.

3. Sampling

Sample domestic and industrial wastewaters in accordance with the instructions of Section 105.

4. Preservation and Storage of Samples

a. Phenols in concentrations usually encountered in wastewaters are subject to biological and chemical oxidation. Preserve and store samples unless they will be analyzed within 4 hr after collection.

b. Acidify to a pH of approximately 4.0 with H_3PO_4, using methyl orange or a pH meter. If H_2S or SO_2 is known to be present, briefly aerate or stir the sample with caution.

c. Add 1.0 g $CuSO_4•5H_2O/l$ sample to inhibit biodegradation of phenols.

d. Keep the sample cold (5 to 10 C). Analyze the preserved and stored samples within 24 hr after collection.

510 A.   Distillation Step for Methods B and C

1. Principle

The phenols are distilled at a more or less constant rate from the nonvolatile impurities. The rate of volatilization of the phenols is gradual, so that the volume of the distillate must equal that of the sample being distilled. The use of $CuSO_4$ during distillation of an acidic sample permits the formation of cupric sulfide without subsequent decomposition to H_2S. The acidic solution also prevents the precipitation of cupric hydroxide, which acts as an oxidizing agent toward phenols.

2. Apparatus

a. Distillation apparatus, all-glass, consisting of a 1-l pyrex distilling appa-

ratus with Graham condenser* (see Figure 318:1.)

b. pH meter.

3. Reagents

Prepare all reagents with distilled water free of phenols and chlorine.

a. Copper sulfate solution: Dissolve 100 g $CuSO_4•5H_2O$ in distilled water and dilute to 1 l.

b. Phosphoric acid solution, 1+9: Dilute 10 ml 85% H_3PO_4 to 100 ml with distilled water.

c. Methyl orange indicator: Dissolve 0.5 g methyl orange in 1 l distilled water.

d. Special reagents for turbid distillates:

---

*Corning No. 3360 or equivalent.

1) *Sulfuric acid, 1N.*

2) *Sodium chloride.*

3) *Chloroform or ethyl ether.*

4) *Sodium hydroxide, 2.5N*: Dilute 41.7 ml 6N NaOH to 100 ml or dissolve 10 g NaOH in 100 ml distilled water.

4. Procedure

a. Measure 500 ml sample into a beaker, lower the pH to approximately 4.0 with the 1+9 H₃PO₄ solution using the methyl orange indicator or a pH meter, add 5 ml CuSO₄ solution, and transfer to the distillation apparatus. Use a 500-ml graduated cylinder as a receiver. Omit adding H₃PO₄ and CuSO₄ if the sample was preserved as described in 510.4.

b. Distill 450 ml sample, stop the distillation, and when boiling ceases add 50 ml phenol-free distilled water to the distilling flask. Continue distillation until a total of 500 ml has been collected.

c. One distillation should purify the sample adequately. Occasionally, however, the distillate is turbid. In this case, acidify the distillate with 1+9 H₃PO₄, add 5 ml CuSO₄ solution, and distill as described in ¶4*b* above. If the second distillate is still turbid, use the extraction process described in ¶4*d* following *before* distilling the sample.

d. Treatment when second distillate is turbid: Extract a 500-ml portion of the original sample as follows: Add 4 drops methyl orange indicator and sufficient 1N H₂SO₄ to make the solution acidic. Transfer to a separatory funnel and add 150 g NaCl. Shake with five increments of chloroform, using 40 ml in the first increment and 25 ml in each of the increments following. Transfer the chloroform layer to a second separatory funnel and shake with three successive increments of 2.5N NaOH solution, using 4.0 ml in the first increment and 3.0 ml in each of the next two increments. Combine the alkaline extracts, heat on a water bath until the chloroform has been removed, cool, and dilute to 500 ml with distilled water. Proceed with distillation as described in ¶s 4*a* and *b* above.

NOTE: Diethyl ether may be used instead of chloroform, especially if an emulsion forms when the chloroform solution is extracted with NaOH. When ether is used, a better distribution coefficient is obtained for phenol between the ether and water phases and it is not necessary to use NaCl. Chloroform is preferred because of the hazards in handling ether.

510 B.   Chloroform Extraction Method*

1. General Discussion

a. Principle: The steam-distillable phenols react with 4-aminoantipyrine at

*Similar in principle to, but different in detail from, ASTM D-1783-62 (Standard). Both methods were adapted from E. EISENSTAEDT. 1938. *J. Organic Chem.* 3:153.

a pH of 10.0±0.2 in the presence of potassium ferricyanide to form a colored antipyrine dye. This dye is extracted from aqueous solution with chloroform and the absorbance is measured at 460 nm. The concentration of phenolic compounds is expressed as μg/l of phenol (C₆H₅OH). This method covers the phenol concentration range of 0.0 to 1,000 $\mu g/l$ with a sensitivity of 1 $\mu g/l$.

b. *Interference*: All interferences are eliminated or reduced to a minimum if the sample has been preserved, stored, and distilled in accordance with the foregoing instructions.

c. *Minimum detectable concentration*: The minimum detectable quantity is 0.5 μg phenol when a 25-ml $CHCl_3$ extraction with a 5-cm cell, or a 50-ml $CHCl_3$ extraction with a 10-cm cell, is used in the photometric measurement. The minimum detectable quantity is 1 $\mu g/l$ phenol in a 500-ml distillate.

2. Apparatus

a. *Photometric equipment*: Use one of the following, equipped with absorption cells providing light paths of 1 to 10 cm (depending on the absorbances of the colored solutions and the individual characteristics of the photometer; in general, if the absorbance readings are greater than 1.0 in a given cell size, use the next smaller size cell):

1) *Spectrophotometer*, for use at 460 nm.

2) *Filter photometer*, equipped with a filter exhibiting maximum light transmission near 460 nm.

b. *Funnels*: Buchner type with fritted disk (such as 15-ml Corning No. 36060 or equivalent).

c. *Filter paper*: An appropriate 11-cm filter paper may be used for filtration of the chloroform extracts in place of the Buchner-type funnels and anhydrous Na_2SO_4.

d. *pH meter*.

e. *Separatory funnels*, 1,000-ml, Squibb form, with ground-glass stoppers and teflon stopcocks. At least eight are required.

f. *Nessler tubes*, matched, 50-ml, tall form.

3. Reagents

Prepare all reagents with distilled water free of phenols and chlorine.

a. *Stock phenol solution*: Dissolve 1.00 g phenol in freshly boiled and cooled distilled water and dilute to 1,000 ml. Ordinarily this direct weighing of the phenol yields a standard solution. However, if extreme accuracy is required, standardize as follows:

1) To 100 ml distilled water in a 500-ml glass-stoppered conical flask, add 50.0 ml stock phenol solution and 10.0 ml 0.1N bromate-bromide solution. Immediately add 5 ml conc HCl and swirl the stoppered flask gently. If the brown color of free bromine does not persist, add 10.0-ml portions of bromate-bromide solution until the color does persist. Keep the flask stoppered and let stand for 10 min; then add approximately 1 g KI. Usually four 10-ml portions of bromate-bromide solution are required if the stock phenol solution contains 1,000 mg/l phenol.

2) Prepare a blank in exactly the same manner, using distilled water and 10.0 ml 0.1N bromate-bromide solution. Titrate the blank and sample with the 0.025N sodium thiosulfate titrant, using starch solution as the indicator.

3) Calculate the concentration of the phenol solution as follows:

$$mg/l\ phenol = 7.842\ (AB-C)$$

where A = ml thiosulfate for blank; B = ml bromate-bromide solution used for sample divided by 10, and C = ml thiosulfate used for sample.

b. *Intermediate phenol solution*: Dilute 10.0 ml stock phenol solution to

1,000 ml in freshly distilled water; 1 ml = 10.0 μg phenol. Prepare a fresh solution on each day of use.

c. *Standard phenol solution:* Dilute 50.0 ml intermediate phenol solution to 500 ml with freshly boiled and cooled distilled water; 1 ml = 1.0 μg phenol. Prepare this solution within 2 hr of use.

d. *Bromate-bromide solution*, 0.10N: Dissolve 2.784 g anhydrous $KBrO_3$, in distilled water, add 10 g KBr crystals, dissolve, and dilute to 1,000 ml.

e. *Hydrochloric acid*, HCl, conc.

f. *Standard sodium thiosulfate titrant*, 0.025 N: See Section 422B.2f.

g. *Starch solution:* See Section 422B.2d.

h. *Ammonium chloride solution:* Dissolve 50 g NH_4Cl in distilled water and dilute to 1,000 ml.

i. *Ammonium hydroxide*, NH_4OH, conc.

j. *Aminoantipyrine solution:* Dissolve 2.0 g 4-aminoantipyrine in distilled water and dilute to 100 ml. Prepare a fresh solution on each day of use.

k. *Potassium ferricyanide solution:* Dissolve 8.0 g $K_3Fe(CN)_6$ in distilled water and dilute to 100 ml. Filter if necessary. Prepare fresh each week of use.

l. *Chloroform*, $CHCl_3$.

m. *Sodium sulfate*, anhydrous Na_2SO_4, granular.

n. *Potassium iodide*, KI, crystals.

4. Procedure

a. *Treatment of sample:*

1) Place 500 ml of the distillate, or a suitable portion containing not more than 50 μg phenol, diluted to 500 ml, in a 1-l beaker.

2) If the approximate phenol concentration of the original sample is not known, determine by a preliminary check the proper volume of distillate and of $CHCl_3$ to use for the final determination. Make the check without $CHCl_3$ extraction by carrying out the reaction in 50-ml nessler tubes and comparing suitable phenol standards.

3) Prepare a 500-ml distilled water blank and a series of 500-ml phenol standards containing 5, 10, 20, 30, 40, and 50 μg phenol.

4) Treat sample, blank, and standards as follows: Add 10 ml NH_4Cl solution and adjust with conc NH_4OH to pH 10.0±0.2. Transfer to a 1-l separatory funnel, add 3.0 ml aminoantipyrine solution, mix well, add 3.0 ml potassium ferricyanide solution, again mix well, and let the color develop for 3 min. The solution should be clear and light yellow.

5) Extract immediately with $CHCl_3$, using 25 ml for 1- to 5-cm cells and 50 ml for a 10-cm cell. Shake the separatory funnel at least 10 times, let the $CHCl_3$ settle, shake again 10 times, and let the $CHCl_3$ settle again.

6) Filter each of the chloroform extracts through filter paper or fritted-glass funnels containing 5-g layer of anhydrous Na_2SO_4. Collect the dried extracts in clean cells for the absorbance measurements; do not add more $CHCl_3$.

7) Read the absorbance of the sample and standards against the blank at a wavelength of 460 nm. Plot absorbance against micrograms phenol for the calibration curve. Estimate the phenol concentration of the sample from the calibration curve. Construct a separate

calibration curve for each photometer and check each curve periodically to insure reproducibility.

b. Alternative procedure:

1) If infrequent analyses for phenol are made, prepare only one standard phenol solution instead of a series of solutions and a calibration curve.

2) In this case, prepare 500 ml standard phenol solution approximately equal to the phenolic content of that portion of the original sample used for final analysis. Also prepare a 500-ml distilled water blank.

3) Proceed as described in ¶s 4*a* through 7), but measure the absorbances of sample and standard phenol solution against the blank at 460 nm.

5. Calculation

a. Use of calibration curve:

$$\mu\text{g/l phenol} = \frac{A}{B} \times 1,000$$

where $A = \mu$g phenol in sample, from calibration curve, and $B =$ ml original sample.

b. Use of alternative procedure:

$$\mu\text{g/l phenol} = \frac{CD}{E} \times \frac{1,000}{B}$$

where $C = \mu$g standard phenol solution, $D =$ absorbance reading of sample, $E =$ absorbance of standard phenol solution, and $B =$ ml original sample.

6. Precision and Accuracy

The precision of this method depends on the skill of the analyst and on the interferences present after the distillation procedure. Because the "phenol" value is based on C_6H_5OH, this method can be regarded only as an approximation and as representing the minimum amount of phenols present. This is true because the phenolic value varies with the types of phenols within a given sample. Therefore, it is impossible to express the accuracy of the method.

510 C.   Direct Photometric Method*

1. General Discussion

a. Principle: The steam-distillable phenols react with 4-aminoantipyrine at a pH of 10.0±0.2 in the presence of potassium ferricyanide to form a colored antipyrine dye. This dye is kept in an aqueous solution and the absorbance is measured at 510 nm. Because extreme

sensitivity is not required in this method, smaller distillate volumes may be used for analysis. For example, this permits determination of 0.5 mg phenol, expressed as C_6H_5OH, in a 100-ml volume of distillate. Practically, the smallest distillate volume would be 10 ml. Consequently, this method covers the phenol concentration range of 0.0 to 50 mg/l, with a sensitivity of 1 mg/l.

b. Interference: All interferences are eliminated or reduced to a minimum by

---

*Adapted ASTM D-1783-Standard, as published in ASTM *Book of Standards*, Part 23 (1968).

using only the distillate from the preliminary distillation procedure.

c. Minimum detectable concentration: This method has considerably less sensitivity than Method B. The minimum detectable quantity is 0.1 mg phenol when a 5-cm cell is used in the photometric measurement and 100 ml distillate are used in the determination.

2. Apparatus

a. Photometric equipment: One of the following, equipped with absorption cells providing light paths of 1 to 5 cm, is required:

1) *Spectrophotometer,* for use at 510 nm.

2) *Filter photometer,* equipped with a green filter exhibiting maximum light transmittance near 510 nm.

b. pH meter.

3. Reagents

See Section 510B.3.

4. Procedure

Place 100 ml of the distillate, or a suitable portion containing not more than 0.5 mg phenol diluted to 100 ml, in a 250-ml beaker.

Prepare a 100-ml distilled water blank and a series of 100-ml phenol standards containing 0.1, 0.2, 0.3, 0.4, and 0.5 mg phenol.

Treat sample, blank, and standards as follows: Add 2.0 ml NH$_4$Cl solution and adjust with conc NH$_4$OH to pH 10.0±0.2. Add 2.0 ml aminoantipyrine solution, mix well, add 2.0 ml potassium ferricyanide solution, and again mix well.

After 15 min, transfer to cells and read the absorbance of the sample and standard against the blank at 510 nm.

5. Calculation

a. Use of calibration curve: Estimate the phenol content of the sample from the photometric readings by using a calibration curve as directed in Section 510B.4a7).

$$\text{mg/l phenol} = \frac{A}{B} \times 1{,}000$$

where A=mg phenol in sample, from calibration curve, and B=ml original sample.

b. Use of single phenol standard:

$$\text{mg/l phenol} = \frac{CD}{E} \times \frac{1{,}000}{B}$$

where C=mg standard phenol solution, D=absorbance of sample, E=absorbance of standard phenol solution, and B=ml original sample.

5. Precision and Accuracy

Refer to Section 510B.5.

510 D. Aminoantipyrine Method for Halogenated Phenols* (TENTATIVE)

1. General Discussion

a. Principle: This procedure involves a petroleum ether extraction of the phenols (especially the para-substituted halogenated types) from an acidified aqueous sample, an alkaline aqueous extraction of the phenols from the petroleum ether, and color development with 4-aminoantipyrine and potassium ferricyanide at pH 7.9 ± 0.1. This procedure uses 2,4-dichlorophenol for the calibration curve. Thus, any other phenol that reacts with 4-aminoantipyrine at pH 7.9 will be reported in equivalents of 2,4-dichlorophenol. This method eliminates the distillation screening procedure required for Method B.

b. Interference: Most of the organic and inorganic compounds known to interfere with 4-aminoantipyrine are eliminated by acid extraction of the aqueous sample with petroleum ether.

c. Minimum detectable concentration: The analytical sensitivity depends on the size of the sample extracted and the path length of the absorbance cell. With a path length of 2.54 cm and a 100-ml sample, the sensitivity is 70 μg/l; if 1,000 ml are extracted, the sensitivity is 7 μg/l. If a path length greater than 2.54 cm is used, then a greater sensitivity is obtained.

d. Absorptivity values: Table 510:I presents absorptivity and molar absorptivity values for a number of phenols.

---

*And other phenols, as indicated in introductory paragraph.

2. Apparatus

a. Spectrophotometer: Any suitable spectrophotometer providing a light path of at least 2.54 cm for use at 500 nm.

b. Separatory funnels, Squibb form, 250-, 500-, or 1,000-ml, glass-stoppered, with teflon stopcock.

TABLE 510:I. ABSORPTIVITY AND MOLAR ABSORPTIVITY VALUES OF PHENOLS

Phenol	Absorptivity $1\ cm^{-1}g^{-1}$	Molar Absorptivity
4-Cl	39.0 ± 2.7	5020 ± 350
3-Cl	102.7 ± 4.5	13200 ± 580
2-Cl	135.9 ± 2.9	17470 ± 370
2,4-Cl	86.9 ± 4.5	14170 ± 730
3,4-Cl	27.4 ± 3.1	4470 ± 505
2,5-Cl	99.0 ± 3.6	16140 ± 590
2,3-Cl	103.6 ± 4.0	16885 ± 644
2,6-Cl	104.9 ± 3.2	17100 ± 513
2,4,6-Cl	36.8 ± 2.7	7270 ± 530
2,4,5-Cl	45.3 ± 2.7	8950 ± 530
2,3,4,5,6-Cl	No reaction	No reaction
4-Br	31.0 ± 2.7	5360 ± 470
3-Br	77.0 ± 2.7	13320 ± 470
2-Br	98.0 ± 3.6	16960 ± 620
2,4-Br	55.0 ± 2.9	13860 ± 730
2,6-Br	71.0 ± 2.6	17880 ± 680
2,4,6-Br	27.4 ± 2.2	9065 ± 730
2,3,4,5,6-Br	No reaction	No reaction

3. Reagents

a. Hydrochloric acid, HCl, conc.

b. Petroleum ether, 30 to 60 C: Purify this solvent by extracting with the $0.5N$ NH₄OH before use.

c. Ammonium hydroxide, NH₄OH, $0.5N$: Dilute 35 ml *fresh*, conc NH₄OH to 1 l with distilled water.

d. Phosphate buffer solution: Dissolve 104.5 g K_2HPO_4 and 72.3 g KH_2PO_4 in distilled water and dilute to 1 l. The pH of this buffer solution should be 6.8.

e. Aminoantipyrine solution: See Section 510B3*j*.

f. Potassium ferricyanide solution: See Section 510B3*k*.

g. 2,4-dichlorophenol, analytical reference grade.†

h. Ethyl alcohol, 95%.

i. Stock 2,4-dichlorophenol (Solution A): Dissolve 0.100 g 2,4-dichlorophenol in 100 ml of 95% ethyl alcohol; 1 ml=1,000 μg.

j. Intermediate 2,4-dichlorophenol (Solution B): Dilute 10.0 ml stock 2,4-dichlorophenol (Solution A) to 100.0 ml with phenol-free distilled water; 1 ml=100 μg.

k. Standard 2,4-dichlorophenol (Solution C): Dilute 25.0 ml intermediate solution (B) to 250 ml with phenol-free distilled water; 1 ml=10 μg.

4. Procedure

a. Extraction: Place an appropriate volume of sample and an equal volume of a distilled water blank in separatory funnels. Add 5.0 ml conc HCl and mix.

Extract the phenols from the acidified sample with three 50-ml portions petroleum ether. Shake each extraction for 3 min. Combine the extracts in a 250-ml separatory funnel. Wash the extracts with two 50-ml portions distilled water to remove any emulsified HCl.

Extract the phenols from the washed petroleum ether with one 10.0-ml and two 5.0-ml portions 0.5N NH_4OH. Shake each extraction for 3 min.

†Eastman White Label #1933 or equivalent.

Transfer the ammoniacal extracts to 50-ml volumetric flasks. Add 20.0 ml phosphate buffer solution and mix well. The pH of this solution should be 7.9±0.1; adjust pH if necessary.

b. Color development and measurement: Add 0.50 ml 4-aminoantipyrine solution and mix well. Add 0.50 ml potasium ferricyanide solution and mix well. Bring the solution to the 50.0-ml mark with distilled water and mix well. Allow 15 min for maximum color to develop. Read the absorbance at 500 nm against a reagent blank. Estimate the phenol concentration of the sample from the calibration curve.

c. Preparation of calibration curve: Add the appropriate volumes of standard 2,4-dichlorophenol (Solution C) to a 500-ml separatory funnel so that quantities of 0, 10, 30, 50, 70, and 100 μg are obtained. Adjust these volumes to approximately 250 ml with phenol-free distilled water. Follow the steps outlined in ¶s 4*a* and 4*b* to develop and measure the color.

Construct the calibration curve by plotting absorbance against micrograms 2,4-dichlorophenol. Prepare a calibration curve for each photometer and check periodically.

5. Calculation

$$\mu g/l\ 2,4\text{-dichlorophenol} = \frac{A}{B} \times 1,000$$

where A = μg 2,4-dichlorophenol in sample from calibration curve and B = ml original sample.

6. Precision and Accuracy

a. This method gives only an approximation representing the minimum amount of phenols present because 2,4-dichlorophenol is used as the standard. Therefore, no statement of accuracy can be given.

b. The precision of this method depends on interferences present and on the skill of the analyst. Precision varies with concentration of the phenolic compounds. Round-robin tests by four laboratories and five operators on standard 2,4-dichlorophenol solutions yielded the following standard deviations:

2,4-Dichlorophenol µg	Standard Deviation ± µg
9.67	0.92
50.23	2.61
103.47	3.40

510 E.   Gas-Liquid Chromatographic Method*

1. General Discussion

This method covers a direct aqueous-injection procedure for the gas-liquid chromatographic determination of phenols, cresols, and mono- and dichlorophenols in water.[2] The method may be applied to wastewater or to concentrates containing more than 1 mg/l phenolic compounds.

a. Principle: This method specifies a single gas-liquid chromatographic column for the separation of phenolic compounds and a flame-ionization detector for their measurement. The peak area of each component is measured and compared with that of a known standard to obtain quantitative results. Elution of characteristic phenols occurs in the following order: (1) *o*-chlorophenol, (2) phenol and *o*-cresol, (3) *m*- and *p*-cresol, (4) 2,3- 2,4- 2,5-and 2,6-dichlorophenols, (5) *m*- and *p*-chlorophenols, and (6) 3,4-dichlorophenol.

b. Interference: Particulate or suspended matter, unless very finely subdivided, may plug the needle of the microsyringe used for sample injection. Remove particulates by centrifugation or filtration, provided that compounds of interest are not removed also. Use a colloid mill, if necessary, to prepare a colloidal solution or suspension suitable for injection. Particulate matter may serve as condensation nuclei for samples; acid treatment may often dissolve such interfering solids.

Nonphenolic organic compounds that have the same retention time as the phenolic compounds interfere with the test. Eliminate such compounds by the distillation step (Section 510A).

Under strong alkaline conditions, some chlorophenols may form salts that reduce their volatility. Also, some nonphenolic organics—for example, tar bases—may be more volatile in basic solutions. Simple pH adjustment to near neutral or slightly acid will eliminate these interferences.

A "ghost" is an interference, showing as a peak, that appears at the same elution time as an organic component of a previous analysis. To minimize or eliminate this effect, inject 3 µl water be-

*Adapted from ASTM D-2580-68-Standard, as published in ASTM *Book of Standards*, Part 23 (1968).

tween samples. The water wash usually clears the injection port, column, and detector of artifacts; however, repeated wash injections may be necessary to clear the system. Set the electrometer at maximum sensitivity during the wash injections to facilitate detection of ghosts. Use glass injector inserts that are easy to clean or replace because they minimize cleanup difficulties.

2. Apparatus

a. Gas chromatograph, equipped with a hydrogen flame-ionization detector: A commercial or custom-designed gas chromatograph with a column oven capable of isothermal temperature control to at least 210 ± 0.2 C. A unit for temperature programming will facilitate elution of a mixture of phenolics of wide boiling-point range. Temperature programming is optional.

b. Recorder, to measure chromatographic output at a full-scale range of 1 mV with a response time of 1 sec.

c. Chromatographic columns: Purchase columns or prepare in the laboratory. Variations in column loading, length, diameter, support size, treatment, etc., are possible. Three columns are cited in this procedure. Modifications may alter elution time and sensitivity.

1) Carbowax 20M: A 3.2-mm (1/8 in.) by 3-m (10-ft) stainless steel column packed with 60/80 mesh Chromosorb W (acid-washed and hexamethyldisilazane-treated) coated with 20% by weight of Carbowax 20M-TPA (terephthalic acid).

2) Free Fatty Acid Phase, 1.5 m (5 ft): A 3.2-mm (1/8 in.) by 1.5-m (5-ft) stainless steel column packed with 70/

80 mesh Chromosorb W (acid-washed) coated with 5% by weight Free Fatty Acid Phase (FFAP). †

3) Free Fatty Acid Phase, 3m (10 ft): A 3.2-mm (1/8 in.) by 3-m (10-ft) stainless steel column packed with 60/80 mesh Chromosorb T coated with 10% Free Fatty Acid Phase. Chromosorb T is a TFE fluorocarbon-6 product; it melts at 327 C and may begin to fuse above 250 C. It is available from suppliers of gas-chromatographic materials.

d. Syringe, 10 μl.

3. Reagents

a. Carrier gases: Research-grade nitrogen or helium of highest purity.

b. Hydrogen, for use with the flame-ionization detector; obtain by using a hydrogen generator, or from a high-purity tank supply.

c. Water, redistilled deionized: If only ordinary distilled water is available, treat it by *both* redistillation and deionization as described in Section 418A.3a. Test the treated water in the chromatograph to assure freedom from false peaks.

d. Phenolic compounds: Use research grades of high purity. Prepare highest-purity compounds by redistillation or recrystallization, or by using a preparatory gas-chromatographic instrument. The following phenolic compounds are suggested: *o*-chlorophenol, *m*-chlorophenol, *p*-chlorophenol, *o*-cresol, *m*-cresol, *p*-cresol, 2,3-dichlorophenol, 2,4-dichlorophenol, 2,5-dichlorophenol, 2,6-dichlorophenol, 3,4-dichlorophenol,

---

†Available from Varian Aerograph, Walnut Creek, Calif.

and phenol. Prepare 100 mg/l solutions in redistilled deionized water.

4. Procedure

a. Preparation of chromatograph: Install the packed column in the chromatograph, using suitable fittings. Use antigalling thread lubricant.

b. Check for leaks: Test for leaks at approximately 1 kg/cm² (15 psig) above the operating pressure by shutting off the downstream end of the system and pressurizing from the carrier gas supply. Shut off the cylinder valve and observe the pressure gage. If no drop occurs in 10 to 15 min, consider the system to be tight. Locate minor leaks with aqueous soap solution but do so with caution, because soap solution entering the system may cause extraneous peaks or affect the stability of the system. Do not use the soap method for leak-testing near the ionization detector.

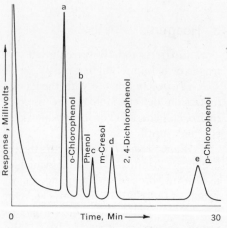

Figure 510:1. Analyses were made with 3 m by 3.2 mm stainless steel column coated with 20% Carbowax-terephthalic acid on 60/80-mesh diatomite, HMDS treated. Column temperature was 210 C, and injection temperature, 250 C. Hydrogen and helium flow rates were each 20 ml/min at electrometer range 1 and attenuation 1, with chart speed at 30 cm/hr, 1-mV full-scale response, and 1-μl sample of approximately 100-mg/l solutions of each phenolic. Peak A is for *o*-chlorophenol; B, phenol; C, *m*-cresol; D, 2,4-dichlorophenol; E, *p*-chlorophenol.

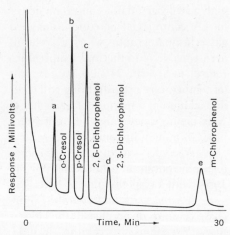

Figure 510:2. Analyses were made with 3 m by 3.2 mm stainless steel column coated with 20% Carbowax-terephthalic acid on 60/80-mesh diatomite, HMDS treated. Column temperature was 210 C, and injection temperature 250 C. Hydrogen and helium flow rates were each 20 ml/min, at electrometer range 1 and attenuation 1, with chart speed at 30 cm/hr, 1-mV full scale response, and 1-μl sample of approximately 100 ml/l solutions of each phenolic. Peak A is for *o*-cresol; B, *p*-cresol; C, 2-6-dichlorophenol; D, 2,3-dichlorophenol; E, *m*-chlorophenol.

c. Column conditioning: Before use, condition columns for at least 24 hr at temperatures 30 to 50 C above the expected operating temperature. Do not exceed the maximum allowable temperature for both the packing and the substrate. Disconnect the column at the end near the detector base to avoid deposition of volatiles on the detector during conditioning. Adjust carrier gas flow to 20 to 40 ml/min for a 3.2-mm (1/8-in.-) diam column. Occasionally inject 3 to 5 μl water during conditioning to facilitate elution of impurities.

After conditioning, connect the column to the flame-ionization detector. Adjust the hydrogen flow to the detector to about 25 ml/min for a 3.2-mm-(1/8-in.-) diam column. Adjust the air-flow as specified for the instrument being used and ignite the hydrogen flame at the detector. Adjust the column temperature to the desired level and the carrier gas flow rate to 20 to 40 ml/

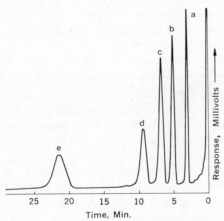

Figure 510:3. Analyses were made with 3 m by 3.2 cm stainless steel column coated with 10% polyester on 60/80-mesh fluorocarbon resin medium. Column temperature was 188 C, and injection temperature, 250 C. Flow rates for nitrogen were 60 ml/min, for hydrogen, 30 ml/min, at electrometer range 1 and attenuation 1, with chart speed at 30 cm/hr., 1-mV full-scale response, and 1-μl sample of approximately 100-mg/l solutions of each phenolic. Peak A is for *o*-chlorophenol; B, phenol; C, *m*-cresol; D, 2,4-dichlorophenol; E, *p*-chlorophenol.

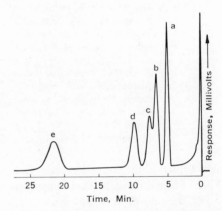

Figure 510:4. Analyses were made with 3 m by 3.2 cm stainless steel column coated with 10% polyster on 60/80-mesh fluorocarbon resin medium. Column temperature was 188 C, and injection temperature, 250 C. Flow rates for nitrogen were 60 ml/min, for hydrogen, 30 ml/min, at electrometer range 1 and attenuation 1, with chart speed at 30 cm/hr., 1-mV full-scale response, and 1-μl sample of approximately 100-mg/l solutions of each phenolic. Peak A is for *o*-cresol; B, *p*-cresol, C, 2,6-dichlorophenol; D, 2,3-dichlorophenol; E, *m*-chlorophenol.

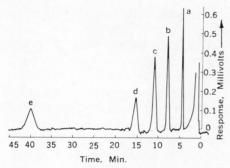

Figure 510:5. Analyses were made with 1.5 m by 3.2 cm stainless steel column coated with 5% polyester on acid-washed 70/80-mesh diatomite. Column temperature was 147 C. Flow rates for helium were 35 ml/min, for hydrogen, 25 ml/min, at electrometer range 0.1 and attenuation 1, with chart speed 30 cm/hr, 1-mV full-scale response; for 1-μl sample. Peak A is for o-chlorophenol, 10.4 mg/l; B, phenol, 9.3 mg/l; C, m-cresol, 10.7 mg/l; D, 2,4-dichlorophenol, 10.7 mg/l; E, p-chlorophenol, 11.2 mg/l.

min. Observe the recorder base line. When a base-line drift is no longer apparent, the column is ready for use.

When the series of analyses is completed and the column is to be removed and stored, seal or cap the ends.

d. Operating conditions for analysis: Typical operating conditions are summarized in Table 510:II. If these operating parameters are varied, reconcile analytical and calibration test variations in calculating results. For example, either nitrogen or helium may be used as the carrier gas; recorder chart speeds of approximately 76 cm (30 in.)/hr are commonly used; sample sizes of 3 to 5 μl usually are injected.

e. Method of compound identification: Compound identification is based on the retention time—the time that elapses from the introduction of the sample until the peak maximum is reached. Compare retention times of sample peaks with those of known standards obtained under the same operating conditions. When several related materials are eluted at the same time, reanalyze the sample with a column of a different type that effects a better separation, or supplement the chromatographic procedure with spectrographic analyses.[3] If necessary, trap the various sample components as they emerge from the system, then analyze them by other appropriate methods.

To determine the retention time of phenol, cresols, and mono- and dichlorophenols, take the following steps:

With the column at operating conditions, inject in turn a 1-μl sample of a 100 mg/l aqueous solution of each phenolic compound. Use a 10-μl syringe. Adjust the instrument attenuation so that the peak height is on scale, preferably near 50% of full scale. Mark the injection point on the recorder chart. Measure the retention time in minutes to at least two significant figures.

To eliminate errors induced by ghosting, inject distilled water after each phenolic sample. Set the electrometer range and attenuation at maximum sensitivity during water washing. Inject the same volume of water as that used for the sample. Repeat water injections until a steady base line free of ghosts has been attained, then make the next sample injection.

Make triplicate determinations for each phenolic compound and record the

TABLE 510:II. TYPICAL OPERATING CONDITIONS FOR CHROMATOGRAPHIC COLUMN

Column and Packing	Column No. (Chromatographic Columns)		
	1 ¶2c1)	2 ¶2c2)	3 ¶2c3)
Carrier gas	Helium	Helium	Nitrogen
Carrier gas flow, ml/min	25	35	60
Temperature, degrees Celsius:			
Injection port	250	205	250
Column	210	147	188
Hydrogen for detector, ml/min	25	25	30
Chart speed, cm/hr	30	30	30
Sensitivity, mV	1	1	1
Electrometer range	1	0.1	1
Attenuation	1	1	1
Sample volume, µl	1	1	1
Results	*	†	‡

   * See Figures 510:1 and 510:2.
   † See Figure 510:5.
   ‡ See Figures 510:3 and 510:4.

average retention value. (Mixtures of phenols having different retention intervals may be injected simultaneously to expedite the standardizations.)

CAUTION—Flush the injection syringe used for calibration with each new sample at least three times before injecting into the chromatograph.

Calculate the retention of all compounds relative to phenol. The relative retention times with approximate chromatograph calibration factors are shown

TABLE 510:III. CHROMATOGRAPHIC RETENTION TIMES

Phenolic Compound	Boiling Point	Relative Retention	Calibration Factor*† $ng/in.^2$	Relative Retention	Calibration Factor†‡ $ng/in.^2$
Phenol	182 C	1.0	45.2	1.0	28.8
o-Cresol	192 C	1.0	51.0	1.0	27.0
m-Cresol	203 C	1.3	51.9	1.3	30.5
p-Cresol	202 C	1.3	51.3	1.3	31.3
o-Chlorophenol	176 C	0.8	86.7	0.6	44.8
m-Chlorophenol	214 C	3.6	106	3.6	45.4*
p-Chlorophenol	217 C	3.6	125	3.6	46.5*
2,3-Dichlorophenol	—	1.8	76.5	1.9	46.8
2,4-Dichlorophenol	210 C	1.8	117	1.9	55.3
2,5-Dichlorophenol	210 C	1.8	113	1.9	50.4
2,6-Dichlorophenol	220 C	1.6	71.5	1.5	50.0
3,4-Dichlorophenol	254 C	—	—	11.5	43.0*

   * Column at 210 C.
   † Calibration in ng $(10^{-9}g)/in.^2$ at chart speed of 90 in./hr, 1-mV response, range 1, attenuation 1.
   ‡ Column at 188 C.

in Table 510:III for two columns. These calibration values are presented for information only. Determine and regularly recheck calibration values for each column and phenolic material used.

f. Calibration and standardization: The area under the peak of the chromatogram is a quantitative measure of the amount of the corresponding compound. To calibrate, select the phenolic concentration range desired (for example, 1 mg/l or 10 mg/l) and prepare fresh solutions of each compound in redistilled deionized water.

With the column at equilibrium operating conditions, inject measured volumes (e.g., 3 μl) of the standard solutions, using the previously described procedure and observing all precautions. Continue until at least three peaks are obtained that deviate by no more than ±1% in area at the same attenuation. Adjust the attenuation in all cases to keep the peak on scale and preferably with a height of 50% of full-scale recorder range.

Measure the peak area for each standard by triangulation, mechanical or electronic integration, or weighing the peak cutouts.

If overlapping of peaks or other interaction between the components of the sample to be analyzed is anticipated, inject into the column prepared mixtures of standards representing the phenolic compounds expected in the sample. Measure the peak areas as for the pure compounds. Express the results as nanograms per unit area.

Typical calibration factors are shown in Table 510:III. Do not use these in quantitative analysis but only as a guide.

g. Sample treatment: With the column at operating conditions, inject 1 to 3 μl sample into the injection port. Determine the retention times of the phenols in the sample. If necessary, adjust the attenuation to keep the highest peak on scale for the major phenolic component in the sample. Make triplicate determinations at identical column and instrument conditions; flush as required to eliminate artifacts. Characterize and measure the peak areas obtained. Average the results of the triplicate determinations.

5. Calculation

a. Characterize each peak by a retention time. Report supplementary tests, such as infrared and ultraviolet used in the characterization of trapped fractions.

b. For those peak areas representing two or more phenolic compounds, use an average value of the calibration obtained with the standards in the calculation or measure the area as a given material, with the notation in the results that other components have comparable elution intervals and may be represented.

c. Calculate the concentration of each component by the equation:

$$\text{Phenolic compound(s), mg/l} = \frac{A \times B}{C}$$

where A = area of sample peak, cm^2; B = calibration factor, ng/cm^2; and C = sample volume, ml.

6. Precision

The precision of this method has been tested with four master solutions, each containing four phenolic compounds. The compositions of the master solutions were as follows:

	Master Solution mg/l			
Phenolic Compounds	1	2	3	4
Phenol	20	80	40	10
m-Cresol	40	10	20	80
o-Chlorophenol	10	20	80	40
2,4-Dichlorophenol	80	40	10	20

The respective precisions may be expressed as follows:

$$\text{Phenol}: S_T = 0.048X + 0.6$$
$$S_O = 0.017X + 0.3$$
$$m\text{-Cresol}: S_T = 0.029X + 2.2$$
$$S_O = 0.014X + 0.7$$
$$o\text{-Chlorophenol}: S_T = 0.083X + 1.2$$
$$S_O = 0.031X + 0.2$$
$$2,4\text{-Dichlorophenol}: S_T = 0.172X + 0.1$$
$$S_O = 0.036X + 1.2$$

where S_T = overall precision, mg/l; S_O = single-operator precision, mg/l; and X = concentration of phenolic determined, mg/l.

7. Additional Information

The information in Tables 510:IV and 510:V is presented to aid the analyst.

TABLE 510:IV. COMPARISON OF PHENOLIC ANALYTICAL PROCEDURES

Phenolic Compound	Concentration mg/l		
	By Weight	4-Amino-anti-pyrine*	GLC
Phenol	1.06	0.97	0.97
o-Cresol	1.04	0.64	1.03
m-Cresol	1.02	0.38	1.03
p-Cresol	1.00	0.00	1.00
			3.94†
Composite	4.12‡	2.40	4.11§

* Reported as phenol; ASTM Method D 1783, Test for Phenolic Compounds in *Industrial Water and Industrial Wastewater*; average of two analyses.

† Based on m- and p-cresol of 2.01, plus o-cresol and phenol as phenol of 1.93; average of four analyses.

‡ Composite of the four phenolics.

§ Based on m- and p-cresols of 2.01, plus o-cresol and phenol, equal concentrations, with calibration factors averaged.

TABLE 510:V. EFFECT OF pH IN GLC ANALYSES OF 2,4-DICHLOROPHENOL*

pH	4.5	7.7	9.7	10.8	11.7
Peak area, in.²	2.88	2.90	2.90	2.93	1.08

* Column and operating conditions: column, 5 ft by 1/8 in., stainless steel; 5% FFAP, 60/80 Chromosorb W. Flow rates and temperature: hydrogen, 25 ml/min; nitrogen, 25 ml/min. Tc=176 C; Ti=205 C; R=0.1, x, 1; 3 samples in distilled water; chart, 90 in./hr; pH adjusted by NaOH; 1 mV full scale. Initial dichlorophenolic concentration, 5 mg/l.

510 F.   References

1. BURTSCHELL, R.H. et al. 1959. Chlorine derivatives of phenol causing taste and odor. *J. Amer. Water Works Ass.* 51:205.

2. BAKER, R.A. 1966. Phenolic analyses by direct aqueous injection gas chromatography. *J. Amer. Water Works Ass.* 58:751.

3. BAKER, R.A. 1966. Trace organic analyses by aqueous gas-liquid chromatography. *J. Air Water Pollut.* 10:591.

510 G.   Bibliography

SCOTT, R.D. 1931. Application of a bromine method in the determination of phenols and cresols. *Ind. Eng. Chem.*, Anal. Ed. 3:67.

EMERSON, E., H.H BEACHAM & L.C. BEEGLE. 1943. The condensation of aminoantipyrine. II. A new color test for phenolic compounds. *J. Org. Chem.* 8:417.

ETTINGER, M.B., S. SCHOTT & C.C. RUCHHOFT. 1943. Preservation of phenol content in polluted river water samples previous to analysis. *J. Amer. Water Works Ass.* 35:299.

ETTINGER, M.B. & R.C. KRONER. 1949. The determination of phenolic materials in industrial wastes. *Proc. 5th Ind. Waste Conf.* (Purdue Univ.), p. 345.

ETTINGER, M.B., C.C. RUCHHOFT & R.J. LISHKA. 1951. Sensitive 4-aminoantipyrine method for phenolic compounds. *Anal. Chem.* 23:1783.

DANNIS, M. 1951. Determination of phenols by the aminoantypyrine method. *Sewage Ind. Wastes* 23:1516.

MOHLER, E.F., JR. & L.N. JACOB. 1957. Determination of phenolic-type compounds in water and industrial waste waters: Comparison of analytical methods. *Anal. Chem.* 29:1369.

GORDON, G.E. 1960. Colorimetric determination of phenolic materials in refinery waste waters. *Anal. Chem.* 32:1325.

OCHYNSKI, F.W. 1960. The absorptiometric determination of phenol. *Analyst* 85:278.

FAUST, S.D. & O.M. ALY. 1962. The determination of 2,4-dichlorophenol in water. *J. Amer. Water Works Ass.* 54:235.

FAUST, S.D. & E. W. MIKULEWICZ. 1967. Factors influencing the condensation of 4-aminoantipyrine with derivatives of hydroxybenzene. II. Influence of hydronium ion concentration on absorptivity. *Water Res.* 1:509.

BAKER, R.A. & B.A. MALO. 1967. Phenolics by aqueous injection gas chromatography. *Environ. Sci. Technol.* 1:997.

511   SLUDGE DIGESTER GAS

Gas produced during the anaerobic decomposition of wastes contains methane and carbon dioxide as the major components with varying quantities of hydrogen, hydrogen sulfide, nitrogen, and oxygen. It is saturated with water vapor. Common practice is to analyze the gases produced to estimate their fuel value and to check on the treatment process. The relative proportions of carbon dioxide, methane, and nitrogen are normally of most concern and the easiest to determine because of the relatively high percentages of these gases.

1. Selection of Method

Two different procedures are described for gas analysis, the Volumetric Method (A), and the Gas Chromatographic Method (B). The volumetric analysis is suitable for the determination of carbon dioxide, hydrogen, methane, and oxygen. Nitrogen is estimated indirectly by difference. Although the method is time-consuming, the equipment is relatively simple. Because no calibration is needed before use, the procedure is particularly appropriate when analyses are conducted on an infrequent basis.

The principal advantage of gas chromatography is speed. Commercial equipment is specifically designed for ambient-temperature gas analysis and permits the routine separation and measurement of carbon dioxide, nitrogen, oxygen, and methane in less than 5 min. The requirement for a recorder, pressure-regulated bottles of carrier gas, and certified standard gas mixtures for calibration raise costs to the point where infrequent analyses by this method may be uneconomical. The advantages of this system are freedom from the cumulative errors found in sequential volumetric measurements, adaptability to other gas component analyses, adaptability to intermittent on-line sampling and analysis, and the use of samples of 1 ml or less.[1]

2. Sample Collection

When the source of gas is some distance from the apparatus used for analysis, collect samples in sealed containers and bring to the instrument. Displacement collectors are the most suitable containers. Long glass tubes with

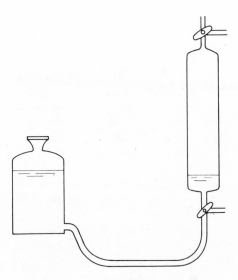

Figure 511:1. Gas collection apparatus.

three-way glass stopcocks at each end, as indicated in Figure 511:1, are particularly useful. These also are available with centrally located ports provided with septa for syringe transfer of samples. Connect one end of the collector to the gas source and vent the three-way stopcock to the atmosphere. Clear the line of air by passing 10 to 15 volumes of gas through the vent and open the stopcock to admit the sample. If large quantities of gas are available, sweep the air away by passing 10 to 15 volumes of gas through the tube. If the gas supply is limited, fill the tube with a liquid that is displaced with gas. Use either mercury or an acidified salt solution. The latter solution is easier and the less expensive to use, but dissolves gases to some extent. Therefore, fill the collection tube completely with the gas and seal off from any contact with the displacement fluid during temporary storage. When transferring gas to the gas-analyzing apparatus, do not transfer any fluid.

511 A.   Volumetric Method

1. General Discussion

a. Principle: This method may be used for the analysis either of digester gas or of methane in water (see Section 503, Methane). A measured volume of gas is passed first through a solution of potassium hydroxide to remove carbon dioxide, next through a solution of alkaline pyrogallol to remove oxygen, and then over heated cupric oxide, which removes hydrogen by oxidation to water. After each of the above steps, the volume of gas remaining is measured; the decrease that results is a measure of the relative percentage by volume of each component in the mixture. Finally, methane is determined by conversion to carbon dioxide and water in a slow-combustion pipet (for methane in water) or a catalytic oxidation assembly (for digester gas). The volume of carbon dioxide formed during the combustion is measured to determine the fraction of methane originally present. Nitrogen is estimated by assuming that it represents the only gas remaining and equals the difference between 100% and the sum of the measured percentages of the other components.

When only carbon dioxide is measured, report only carbon dioxide. No valid assumptions may be made about the remaining gases present without making a complete analysis.

Follow the equipment manufacturers' recommendations with respect to oxidation procedures. CAUTION: DO NOT attempt any slow combustion procedure on digester gas because of the high probability of exceeding the explosive 5% by volume concentration of methane.

2. Apparatus

Orsat-type gas-analysis apparatus, consisting of at least: (1) a water-jacketed gas buret with leveling bulb; (2) a carbon dioxide-absorption pipet; (3) an oxygen-absorption pipet; (4) a cupric oxide-hydrogen oxidation assembly; (5) a shielded catalytic methane-oxidation assembly or slow-combustion pipet assembly; and (6) a leveling bulb. If the slow-combustion pipet is used, use a controlled source of current to heat the platinum filament electrically. Mercury is recommended as the displacement fluid; Aqueous sodium Na_2SO_4-H_2SO_4 solution for sample collection also has been used successfully. Use any commercially available gas analyzer having these units.

3. Reagents

a. Potassium hydroxide solution: Dissolve 500 g KOH in distilled water and dilute to 1 l.

b. Alkaline pyrogallol reagent: Dissolve 30 g pyrogallol (also called pyrogallic acid) in distilled water and make up to 100 ml. Add 500 ml KOH solution.

c. Oxygen gas: Use approximately 100 ml for each gas sample analyzed.

d. Displacement liquid: Mercury, or 200 g Na_2SO_4 plus 30 ml conc H_2SO_4/ 800 ml water.

4. Procedure

a. Sample introduction: Transfer 5 to 10 ml gas sample into the gas buret through a capillary-tube connection to the collector. Expel this sample to the atmosphere to purge the system. Transfer up to 100 ml gas sample to the buret. Bring the sample in the buret to atmospheric or reference pressure by adjusting the leveling bulb. Measure the volume accurately and record as V_1.

b. *Carbon dioxide absorption:* Remove CO_2 from the sample by passing it through the CO_2-absorption pipet charged with the KOH solution. Pass the gas back and forth until the sample volume remains constant. Before opening the stopcocks between the buret and any absorption pipet make sure that the gas in the buret is under a slight positive pressure to prevent reagent in the pipet from contaminating the stopcock or manifold. After absorption of CO_2, transfer the sample to the buret and measure its volume. Record as V_2.

c. *Oxygen absorption:* Remove the O_2 by passing the sample through the O_2-absorption pipet charged with alkaline pyrogallol reagent until the volume of the sample remains constant. Measure the volume accurately and record as V_3. In the case of a digester gas sample, continue as directed in 4d. For methane in water, store the gas in the CO_2 pipet and proceed to ¶4e below.

d. *Hydrogen oxidation:* Remove the H_2 by passing the sample through the CuO assembly maintained at a temperature in the range of 290 to 300 C. When a constant volume has been obtained, transfer the sample back to the buret, cool, and measure its volume accurately. Record as V_4.

Waste to the atmosphere all but 20 to 25 ml of the remaining gas. Measure the volume accurately and record as V_5. Store temporarily in the CO_2-absorption pipet.

e. *Methane oxidation:* Purge the inlet connections to the buret with oxygen by drawing 5 to 10 ml into the buret and expelling to the atmosphere. Oxidize the methane by either the catalytic oxidation process for digester gas and the gas phase of water samples or the slow-combustion process for the gas phase of water samples.

1) Catalytic oxidation process—For catalytic oxidation of digester gas and the gas phase of water samples, transfer 65 to 70 ml O_2 to the buret and measure accurately. Record this volume as V_6. Pass the O_2 into the CO_2-absorption pipet so that it will mix with the sample stored there. Bring this mixture back to the buret and measure its volume accurately. Record as V_7. This volume should closely equal V_5 plus V_6. Pass the O_2-sample mixture through the catalytic oxidation assembly, which should be heated in accordance with directions from the manufacturer. Keep rate of passage less than 30 ml/min. After the first pass, transfer the mixture back and forth through the assembly between the buret and the reservoir at a rate not faster than 60 ml/min until a constant volume is obtained. Record as V_8.

2) Slow-combustion process—For slow combustion of the gas phase of the water samples, transfer 35 to 40 ml O_2 to the buret and measure accurately. Record this volume as V_6. Transfer the O_2 to the slow-combustion pipet and then transfer the sample from the CO_2-absorption pipet to the buret. Heat the platinum coil in the combustion pipet to yellow heat while controlling the temperature by adjusting the current. Reduce the pressure of O_2 in the pipet to somewhat less than atmospheric pres-

sure by means of the leveling bulb attached to the pipet. Pass the sample into the slow-combustion pipet at the rate of approximately 10 ml/min. After the first pass, transfer the sample and oxygen mixture back and forth between the pipet and buret several times at a faster rate, allowing the mercury in the pipet to rise to a point just below the heated coil. Collect the sample in the combustion pipet, turn off the coil, and cool pipet and sample to room temperature with a jet of compressed air. Transfer the sample to the buret and measure its volume. Record as V_8.

f. Measurement of carbon dioxide produced: Determine the amount of CO_2 formed in the reaction by passing the sample through the CO_2-absorption pipet until the volume remains constant. Record the volume as V_9.

Check the accuracy of the determination by absorbing the residual oxygen from the sample. After this absorption, record the final volume as V_{10}.

5. Calculation

a. Methane and hydrogen are usually the only combustible gases present in sludge digester gas. When this is the case, determine the percentage by volume of each gas as follows:

$$\% \, CO_2 = \frac{(V_1 - V_2) \times 100}{V_1}$$

$$\% \, O_2 = \frac{(V_2 - V_3) \times 100}{V_1}$$

$$\% \, H_2 = \frac{(V_3 - V_4) \times 100}{V_1}$$

$$\% \, CH_4 = \frac{V_4 \times (V_8 - V_9) \times 100}{V_1 \times V_5}$$

$$\% N_2 = 100 - (\% CO_2 + \% O_2 + \% H_2 + \% CH_4)$$

b. Alternatively, calculate methane by either of the two following equations:

$$\% \, CH_4 = \frac{V_4 \times (V_6 + V_{10} - V_9) \times 100}{2 \times V_1 \times V_5}$$

$$\% \, CH_4 = \frac{V_4 \times (V_7 - V_8) \times 100}{2 \times V_1 \times V_5}$$

Results from the calculations for methane by the three equations should be in reasonable agreement. If not, repeat the analysis after checking the apparatus for sources of error, such as leaking stopcocks or connections. Other combustible gases, such as ethane, butane, or pentane, will cause a lack of agreement among the calculations; however, the possibility that digester gas contains a significant amount of any of these is remote.

6. Precision and Accuracy

A gas buret measures gas volume with a precision of 0.05 ml and a probable accuracy of 0.1 ml. With the large fractions of carbon dioxide and methane normally present in digester gas, the overall error for their determination can be made less than $\pm 1\%$. The error in the determination of oxygen and hydrogen, however, can be considerable because of the small concentrations normally present. For a concentration as low as 1%, an error as large as $\pm 20\%$ can be expected. When nitrogen is present in a similar low-volume percentage, the error in its determination would be even greater, since errors in each of the other determinations would be reflected in the calculation for nitrogen.

511 B.   Gas Chromatographic Method

1. General Discussion

a. *Principle:* See Section 509A for a discussion of gas chromatography.

b. *Equipment selection:* Many columns have been proposed for gas mixture analyses. Any that is capable of the desired separation is acceptable, provided that all of the exact conditions of analysis are reported along with the calibration standards. The following directions are necessarily general; follow the manufacturer's recommendations for the specific instrumentation.

2. Apparatus

a. *Gas chromatograph:* Use any commercially available instrument equipped with a thermal conductivity detector. With some column packings, ovens and temperature controls are necessary. A unit with a gas sampling valve is desirable.

b. *Recorder:* Use a 10-mV full-span strip chart recorder for the gas chromatograph. When minor components such as hydrogen and hydrogen sulfide are to be detected, a 1-mV full-span recorder is preferable.

c. *Column packing:* Some commercially available column packings useful for separating sludge gas components are listed below along with the routine separations possible at room temperature[2,3]:

1) Silica gel at room temperature: H_2, air (O_2+N_2), CH_4, (CO_2-slow)

2) Molecular Sieve 13×: H_2, O_2, N_2, CH_4

3) HMPA (hexamethylphosphoramide) 30% on Chromosorb P: CO_2 from (O_2, N_2, H_2, CH_4)

4) DEHS (di-2-ethylhexylsefacate) 30% on Chromosorb P: CO_2 from (O_2, N_2, H_2, CH_4)

Combinations of Columns 1 and 2, 3 and 2, or 4 and 2 when properly sized and used in the sequence: 1st column, detector, 2nd column, detector, will readily separate H_2, O_2, N_2, CH_4, and CO_2. Commercial equipment specifically designed for such operations is available[3].

d. *Sample introduction apparatus:* Preferably use an instrument equipped with gas-sampling valves designed to permit automatic injection of a specific sample volume into the chromatograph. If such an instrument is not available, introduce samples with a 2-ml syringe fitted with a 27-gauge hypodermic needle. Reduce escape of gas by greasing the plunger lightly with mineral oil or by using a special gas-tight syringe.

3. Reagents

a. *Carrier gas:* Use helium for separating digester gases. If hydrogen is to be determined, use argon as a carrier gas to increase the sensitivity greatly.

b. *Calibration gases:* Use pure samples of methane, carbon dioxide, and nitrogen, or mixtures of known composition, for calibration. Also use samples of oxygen, hydrogen, and hydrogen sulfide if these gases are to be measured.

4. Procedure

a. *Preparation of gas chromatograph:* Adjust the carrier gas flow rate to 60 to 80 ml/min. Turn on the oven heaters, if used, and the detector current and adjust to the desired values. The instrument is ready for use when the recorder yields a stable base line. Silica gel and molecular sieve columns gradually will lose activity because of adsorbed moisture or materials permanently adsorbed at room temperature. If insufficient separations occur, reactivate by heating or repacking.

b. Calibration: For accurate results, prepare a calibration curve for each gas to be measured because different gas components do not give equivalent detector responses on either a weight or a molar basis. Calibrate with synthetic mixtures or with pure gases.

1) Synthetic mixtures—Use purchased gas mixtures of known composition or prepare in the laboratory. Inject a standard volume of each mixture into the gas chromatograph and note the response for each gas. Compute the detector response, either as the area under a peak or as the height of the peak, after correcting for attenuation. Read peak heights accurately and correlate with concentration of the component in the sample. Reproduce operating parameters exactly from one analysis to the next. If sufficient reproducibility cannot be obtained by this procedure, use peak areas for calibration. Prepare the calibration curve by plotting either peak area or peak height against volume percent for each component.

2) Pure gases—Introduce pure gases into the chromatograph individually with a syringe. Inject sample volumes of 0.25, 0.5, 1.0 ml, etc., and plot the detector response, corrected for attenuation, against the gas volume.

When the analysis system yields a linear detector response with increasing gas component concentration from zero to the range of interest, run standard mixtures along with samples. If the same sample size is used, calculate gas concentration by direct proportions.

c. Sample analysis: If samples are to be injected with a syringe, equip the sample collection container with a port closed by a rubber or silicone septum. To take a sample for analysis, expel air from the barrel of the syringe by depressing the plunger and force the needle through the septum. Withdraw the plunger to take the gas volume desired, pull the needle from the collection container, and inject the sample rapidly into the chromatograph.

When samples are to be injected through a gas-sampling valve, connect the sample collection container to the inlet tube. Permit gas to flow from the collection tube through the valve to purge the dead air space and fill the sample tube. About 15 ml are normally sufficient to clear the lines and to provide a sample of 1 to 2 ml. Transfer the sample from the loop into the carrier gas stream by following the manufacturer's directions. Bring samples to atmospheric pressure before injection.

When calibration curves have been prepared with synthetic mixtures, use the same sample volume as that used during calibration. When calibration curves are prepared by the procedure using varying volumes of pure gases, inject any convenient gas sample volume up to about 2 ml.

5. Calculation

a. When calibration curves have been prepared with synthetic mixtures and the volume of the sample analyzed is the same as that used in calibration, read the volume percent of each component directly from the calibration curve after the detector response for that component is computed.

b. When calibration curves are prepared with varying volumes of pure gases, calculate the percentage of each gas in the mixture as follows:

$$\text{Volume \%} = \frac{A}{B} \times 100$$

where A = partial volume of component (read from calibration curve) and B = volume sample injected.

c. Where standard mixtures are run with the samples and instrument response is linear from zero to the concentration range of interest:

$$\text{Volume \%} = \text{Vol \% (std)} \times \frac{C}{D}$$

where C = recorder value of sample and D = recorder value of standard.

6. Precision and Accuracy

The precision and accuracy will depend on the instrument used and the technics of operation. With proper care, a precision of 2% generally can be achieved. With digester gas the sum of the percent methane, carbon dioxide, and nitrogen should approximate 100%. If it does not, suspect errors in collection, handling, storage, and injection of gas, or in instrumental operation or calibration.

511 C. References

1. ANDREWS, J.F. 1968. Chromatographic analysis of gaseous products and reactants for biological processes. *Water Sewage Works* 115:54.

2. Column Systems for the Fisher Gas Partitioner. Tech. Bull. TB-154, Fisher Scientific Co., Atlanta, Ga.

3. Catalogue 70, Fisher Scientific Co., 523.

511 D. Bibliography

Volumetric Method

YANT, W.F. & L.B. BERGER. 1936. Sampling of Mine Gases and the Use of the Bureau of Mines Portable Orsat Apparatus in Their Analysis. Miner's Circ. No. 34, U.S. Bur. Mines, Washington, D.C.

MULLEN, P.W. 1955. Modern Gas Analysis. Interscience Publishers, New York, N.Y.

Chromatographic Method

GRUNE, W.N. & C.F. CHUEH. 1962-63. Sludge gas analysis using gas chromatograph. *Water Sewage Works* 109:468; 110:43, 77, 102, 127, 171, 220, and 254.

SHEA, T.G., W.A. PRETORIUS & E.A. PEARSON. 1967. Notes on Chromatographic Analysis of Digester Gases. Sanitary Engineering Research Laboratory, Univ. of California, Richmond Field Station, Richmond, Calif.

512   SURFACTANTS (ANIONIC)

The popularity of synthetic detergents (containing surface-active agents, or "surfactants") for general cleaning purposes has on occasion resulted in the frothing of some natural waters. This was especially true when alkyl benzene sulfonate (ABS) was in common use. In mid-1965, the detergent industry completed its full-scale conversion from ABS to the more biodegradable linear alkylate sulfonate (LAS). LAS is an alkyl aryl sulfonate having a structure made up of a straight-chain alkyl group (ABS has a branched-chain alkyl group), a benzene ring, and a sulfonate. The straight-chain alkyl group is condensed with benzene to yield linear alkylate and the alkylate is then sulfonated to yield LAS.

Since the changeover, the number of detergent-caused foaming incidents has dropped sharply. Because the single most widely used surfactant now is LAS, it is the most likely to be present in raw water. For this reason, LAS has been selected as the standard compound in the following two analytical methods.

Selection of method: First analyze the sample by the methylene blue method (A). If the concentration of methylene-blue-active substances is low (500 μg/l or so) make no further analysis because the sum of the interferences (usually positive) plus true LAS is such that LAS is not a significant factor in the water. The methylene blue procedure suffices when no problems are observed in a water supply. Should the concentration of methylene-blue-active substances be high, however, it becomes important to know how much represents true LAS and how much interferences. In such a case, make an infrared determination (B) or, if infrared equipment is not available, carry the analysis by Method B through to the recovery of the purified LAS and then complete colorimetrically by the methylene blue procedure. This alternative eliminates the need for expensive infrared equipment, which few laboratories have. The big drawback to the infrared method is that, compared to the methylene blue colorimetric process, it is fairly complicated and time-consuming.

512 A.   Methylene Blue Method for Methylene-Blue-Active Substances

1. General Discussion

a. Principle: This method depends on the formation of a blue salt when methylene blue reacts with anionic surfactants, including LAS, alkyl sulfates, and alkyl polyethoxyl sulfates. The materials determined are designated methylene-blue-active substances. The salt is soluble in chloroform and the intensity of color is proportional to the concentration. The intensity is measured by making spectrophotometric readings in this solvent at a wavelength of 652 nm. The method is applicable in the 0.025- to 100-mg/l LAS range.

b. Interference: Both organic and inorganic compounds interfere with the determination of LAS. Some of the proven interferences can be predicted on the basis of chemical properties. Organic sulfates, sulfonates, carboxylates, phosphates, and phenols—which complex methylene blue—and inorganic cyanates, chlorides, nitrates, and thiocyanates—which form ion pairs with methylene blue—are among the positive interferences. Organic materials, especially amines, which compete with the methylene blue in the reaction, can cause low results. Positive errors are much more common than negative ones.

c. Minimum detectable quantity: 10 μg LAS.

d. Application: The methylene blue method has been successfuly applied to the examination of the anionic surfactant content in drinking water supplies. Unfortunately, the numerous materials normally present in wastewater, industrial wastes, and sludge can seriously interfere with the determination and lead to incorrect results and conclusions.

2. Apparatus

a. Colorimetric equipment—One of the following is required:

1) *Spectrophotometer*, for use at 652 nm, providing a light path of 1 cm or longer.

2) *Filter photometer*, providing a light path of 1 cm or longer and equipped with a red color filter exhibiting maximum transmittance near 625 nm.

b. Separatory funnels, 500-ml, preferably with inert teflon stopcocks.

3. Reagents

a. Stock linear alkylate sulfonate (LAS) solution: Weigh an amount of the reference material* equal to 1.000 g LAS on a 100% active basis. Dissolve in distilled water and dilute to 1,000 ml; 1.00 ml = 1.00 mg LAS. Store in a refrigerator to minimize biodegradation. If necessary, prepare weekly.

b. Standard linear alkylate sulfonate (LAS) solution: Dilute 10.00 ml stock LAS solution to 1,000 ml with distilled water; 1.00 ml = 10.0 μg LAS. Prepare daily.

c. Phenolphthalein indicator solution.

d. Sodium hydroxide, NaOH, 1N.

e. Sulfuric acid, H_2SO_4, 1N.

f. Chloroform.

g. Methylene blue reagent: Dissolve 100 mg methylene blue† in 100 ml distilled water. Transfer 30 ml to a 1,000-ml flask. Add 500 ml distilled water, 6.8 ml conc H_2SO_4, and 50 g monosodium dihydrogen phosphate monohydrate, $NaH_2PO_4 \cdot H_2O$. Shake until dissolution is complete. Dilute to the 1,000-ml mark.

h. Wash solution: Add 6.8 ml conc H_2SO_4 to 500 ml distilled water in a 1,000-ml flask. Then add 50 g $NaH_2PO_4 \cdot H_2O$ and shake until dissolution is complete. Dilute to the 1,000-ml mark.

4. Procedure

a. Preparation of calibration curve: Prepare a series of 10 separatory funnels

---

*Obtain from U.S. Environmental Protection Agency, Environmental Monitoring and Support Laboratory, Cincinnati, Ohio 45268.

†Eastman No. P573 or equivalent.

with 0, 1.00, 3.00, 5.00, 7.00, 9.00, 11.00, 13.00, 15.00, and 20.00 ml of the standard LAS solution. Add sufficient water to make the total volume 100 ml in each separatory funnel. Treat each standard as described in ¶s 4c and 4d following, and plot a calibration curve of micrograms LAS versus absorbance.

b. Volume of sample: Select the volume of the water sample to be tested on the expected LAS concentration:

Expected LAS Concentration mg/l	Sample Taken ml
0.025– 0.080	400
0.08 – 0.40	250
0.4 – 2.0	100
2 – 10	20.0
10 –100	2.00

If a sample of less than 100 ml is indicated, dilute to 100 ml with distilled water; if 100 ml or more are used, extract the entire sample.

c. Extraction and color development:

1) Add the sample solution to a separatory funnel. Make the solution alkaline by dropwise addition of $1N$ NaOH, using phenolphthalein indicator. Discharge the pink color by dropwise addition of $1N$ H_2SO_4.

2) Add 10 ml chloroform and 25 ml methylene blue reagent. Rock funnel vigorously for 30 sec and let the phases separate. Excessive agitation may cause emulsion trouble. Some samples require a longer period of phase separation than others. Before draining the chloroform layer, swirl the sample gently, then let it settle.

3) Draw off the chloroform layer into a second separatory funnel. Rinse the delivery tube of the first separatory funnel with a small amount of chloroform. Repeat the extraction three times, using 10 ml chloroform each time. If the blue color in the water phase becomes faint and disappears, discard the sample and repeat the determination, using a smaller sample size.

4) Combine all chloroform extracts in the second separatory funnel. Add 50 ml wash solution and shake vigorously for 30 sec. Emulsions do not form at this stage. Let settle, swirl the contents and then draw off the chloroform layer through glass wool that has been pre-extracted with chloroform into a 100-ml volumetric flask. Extract wash solution twice with 10 ml chloroform, adding these to the volumetric flask. Rinse the glass wool and the funnel with chloroform. Collect the washing in the volumetric flask, dilute to the mark with chloroform, and mix well.

d. Measurement: Determine the absorbance of the solution at 652 nm against a blank of chloroform.

5. Calculation

$$\text{mg/l total apparent LAS} = \frac{\mu g \text{ LAS}}{\text{ml sample}}$$

Report as methylene-blue-active substances (MBAS).

6. Precision and Accuracy

A synthetic unknown sample containing 270 μg/l LAS in distilled water was analyzed in 110 laboratories with a relative standard deviation of 14.8% and a relative error of 10.6%.

A tap water unknown sample to which were added 480 μg/l LAS was analyzed in 110 laboratories with a relative standard deviation of 9.9% and a relative error of 1.3%.

A river water unknown sample to which were added 2.94 mg/l LAS was analyzed in 110 laboratories with a relative standard deviation of 9.1% and a relative error of 1.4%.

512 B.   Carbon Adsorption Method* (TENTATIVE)

1. General Discussion

a. Principle: This method involves the collection and isolation of a few milligrams of LAS and its quantitative determination based on infrared absorption of an amine complex of LAS. Though lengthy, this method is specific and accurate for low LAS concentrations in water and it eliminates alkyl sulfates. When an infrared spectrophotometer is not available, a colorimetric determination can be substituted by recovering the purified LAS and applying the methylene blue method (A).

b. Application: This method is applicable to raw-water samples only, not to domestic or industrial wastes.

c. Precaution: Most samples contain both solid and liquid phases, and LAS is highly concentrated in the solid phase. For accurate analyses, it is essential that the solids be representatively sampled or excluded.

2. Apparatus

a. Carbon adsorption tube: Charge the glass column, about 5×60 cm, with 100 g carbon. Screens of stainless steel

*This method is identical in source and substance to that developed by the Subcommittee on Analytical Methods, Technical Advisory Committee, The Soap and Detergent Association.

or brass, about 30-mesh, divide the carbon into sections of 20, 30, 40, and 10 g (see Figure 512:1)

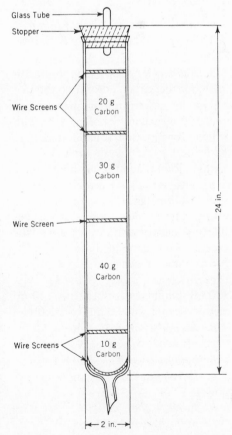

Figure 512:1. Carbon adsorption tube.

b. Buchner funnel, 500-ml, medium-porosity, sintered-glass.

c. pH meter.

d. Volumetric flasks, either 2 or 5 ml.

e. Separatory funnels, 500 ml.

f. Infrared spectrophotometer, for use at 2 to 15 μm.

g. Acid-washed glassware: Keep all glassware used in the infrared method free of contamination. Rinse thoroughly with a solution composed of equal volumes of water and HCl to remove adsorbed LAS.

3. Reagents

a. Standard linear alkylate sulfonate (LAS), for calibration. (See Section 512A.3a.)

b. Activated carbon, unground, 30-mesh, for the carbon adsorption tube.†

Test for impurities in carbon—Extract 100 g carbon by boiling 1 hr with 1 l benzene-alcohol solution (see ¶3*c* following). Filter, wash with 100 ml methyl alcohol, add the washings to the remainder of the solvent mixture, evaporate to dryness on a steam bath, and weigh. The residue consists of extractable organic impurities and should be less than 10 mg, not including any residue from the solvent.

c. Benzene-alcohol solution: Mix 500 ml thiophene-free benzene, 420 ml methyl alcohol, and 80 ml 0.5N KOH.

d. Methyl alcohol, absolute.

e. Hydrochloric acid, HCl, conc.

f. Sodium hydroxide, NaOH, 1N.

g. Petroleum ether, boiling range 35 to 60 C.

h. Ethyl alcohol, 95%.

i. Sulfuric acid, H₂SO₄, 1N.

j. Buffer solution: Dissolve 6.8 g monopotassium dihydrogen phosphate, KH₂PO₄, in 1 l distilled water. Adjust to pH 6.8 to 6.9 with 6N NaOH.

k. l-methylheptylamine. ‡

l. Solution for extracting LAS: Dissolve 400 mg (20 drops) 1-methylheptylamine in 400 ml chloroform. Prepare daily.

m. Chloroform, CHCl₃.

n. Carbon disulfide, CS₂.

4. Procedure

a. Preparation of calibration curve: Place 25 mg standard LAS in a 20-l (5-gal) glass vessel and dilute with about 15 l (4 gal) distilled water. Mix thoroughly and, using synthetic rubberlike tubing, siphon the entire solution through the carbon column. Treat as described in (¶4*c*1) through 7) below. Repeat with 20, 15, 10, 5, and 0 mg LAS. Make two calibration curves by plotting the LAS added as the abscissa and the absorbances of the maxima at 9.6 and 9.9 μm as the ordinate. The baseline technic is best used in determining the absorbance of the maxima.

b. Volume of sample: Estimate the concentration of LAS in the sample. Calculate the volume of sample required to supply 10 to 25 mg LAS. If 2 l or less, measure about 10 g granular activated carbon into a 2-l glass-stoppered graduated cylinder, add the sample, and shake well for 2 min. Filter on a medium-porosity, sintered-glass Buchner funnel. If more than 2 l sample are required, pass through the carbon column at the rate of 630 ml/min or less.

c. Extraction and measurement of LAS:

---

†Nuchar C190 (Westvaco), or equivalent.

‡Eastman No. 2439 or equivalent.

1) Transfer the carbon from the Buchner funnel or column, treating the sections separately, to porcelain evaporating dishes and dry at 105 to 110 C. Brush the dried carbon from each dish into separate 2-l bottles or flasks with standard-taper necks and add 1 l benzene-alcohol solution. Add boiling chips and reflux under an air condenser for 1 hr. Filter with vacuum through a Buchner funnel, draw off all liquid, release the vacuum, and add 100 ml methyl alcohol. Stir with a glass rod and draw off the wash with vacuum. Wash a second time with another 100-ml portion of methyl alcohol. Return the carbon to the flask, add solvent as before, and reflux for 1 hr. While making this second extraction, evaporate the solvent from the first extract and washes. Carry out this evaporation in a 2-l beaker on a steam bath. (A gentle stream of nitrogen or air on the surface will hasten evaporation.)

2) Filter off the second extract and wash the carbon as before. Add the extract and washes to the beaker containing the first extract. Discard the carbon. Evaporate sufficiently to combine in one beaker the extracts from the 20-, 30-, and 40-g sections of the column. Treat the extracts of the 10-g section separately throughout the entire procedure. After the solvent has been removed, take up the residue in 50 ml warm distilled water. Transfer to a 250-ml standard-taper erlenmeyer flask. Rinse the beaker with 30 ml conc HCl and add slowly to the flask. Carbon dioxide is evolved. Rinse the beaker with 50 ml distilled water and combine with the other washings in the flask. Reflux under an air condenser for 1 hr.

3) Remove the condenser and continue boiling until the volume is reduced to 20 to 30 ml, transfer to a steam bath, and evaporate to near dryness. (A jet of air directed on the surface of the liquid will greatly aid evaporation.) Take the solids up in 100 ml distilled water and neutralize with NaOH solution to a pH of 8 to 9. Extract once with 50 ml petroleum ether. Add up to 70% ethyl alcohol, if necessary, to break emulsions. Wash the petroleum ether twice with 25-ml portions of distilled water, discard the petroleum ether layer, and add the washes to the aqueous solution. Boil off any alcohol that was added.

4) Cool and transfer quantitatively to a 500-ml separatory funnel. Neutralize by adding H_2SO_4 until just acidic to litmus. Add 50 ml buffer solution (¶3j) and 2 drops methylheptylamine (¶3k), and shake vigorously. Add 50 ml LAS extracting solution and 25 ml chloroform. Shake for 3 min and let the phases separate. If an emulsion forms, draw off the lower (chloroform) phase, including any emulsion, and filter through a plug of glass wool wet with chloroform, using suction if necessary, into a 500-ml separatory funnel. Draw off the chloroform phase into a 400-ml beaker and return any aqueous solution to the first separatory funnel. Wash the glass wool plug with 10 ml chloroform and add to the chloroform extract.

5) Make an additional extraction with 50 ml LAS extracting solution and 25 ml chloroform. Shake 2 min and separate the phases as in ¶4c4) preceding if necessary. Extract a third time with 5 ml amine solution and 45 ml chloroform. Evaporate the combined chloroform extracts on a steam bath. With 10 ml chloroform, quantitatively transfer the residue to a 50-ml beaker, using three 5-ml portions of chloroform

as rinses. Evaporate to dryness and continue heating on the steam bath for 30 min to remove excess amine. Take up the residue in about 1 ml carbon disulfide and filter through a plug of glass wool in a funnel stem (2-mm bore) into a 2- or 5-ml volumetric flask. Dilute to volume through the filter with several rinsings from the beaker.

6) Transfer a portion of the sample to an infrared cell without further dilution. Run the infrared absorption curve from 9.0 to 10.5 μm against a solvent blank. Measure the absorbance of the 9.6- and 9.9-μm peaks, using baselines from 9.5 to 9.8 and from 9.8 to 10.1 μm. From appropriate calibration curves calculate the LAS in the original sample. Report the values based on each wavelength separately (if infrared equipment is unavailable, use a colorimetric finish). Break the sulfonate-amine complex by boiling with aqueous alkali. After the amine has been boiled off (as indicated by a lack of amine odor) and suitable dilutions are made, colorimetric results should check well with infrared values.

7) Evaporate a 0.5 to 1.0-ml portion of the LAS solution on a sodium chloride flat. Record the absorption spectrum from 2 to 15 μm for positive qualitative identification of LAS.

PRECAUTION—Use carbon adsorption on all samples. It separates the LAS from many of the other substances present and reduces emulsion difficulties.

NOTE: From 10 to 50 ml of water may be lost through a 60×1-cm air condenser during acid hydrolysis. This loss, while not affecting the hydrolysis, reduces the amount of water that needs to be boiled off after removal of the condenser.

512 C.   Bibliography

General and Colorimetric Methods

BARR, T., J. OLIVER & W.V. STUBBINGS. 1948. The determination of surface-active agents in solution. *J. Soc. Chem. Ind.* (London) 67:45.

EPTON, S.R. 1948. New method for the rapid titrimetric analysis of sodium alkyl sulfates and related compounds. *Trans. Faraday Soc.* 44:226.

EVANS, H C. 1950. Determination of anionic synthetic detergents in sewage. *J. Soc. Chem. Ind.* (London) 69:Suppl. 2:576.

DEGENS, P.N., JR. et al. 1953. Determination of sulfate and sulfonate anion-active detergents in sewage. *J. Appl. Chem.* (London) 3:54.

AMERICAN WATER WORKS ASSOCIATION. 1954. Task Group Report. Characteristics and effects of synthetic detergents. *J. Amer. Water Works Ass.* 46:751.

EDWARDS, G.P. & M.E. GINN. 1954. Determination of synthetic detergents in sewage. *Sewage Ind. Wastes* 26:945.

LONGWELL, J. & W.D. MANIECE. 1955. Determination of anionic detergents in sewage, sewage effluents, and river water. *Analyst* 80:167.

MOORE, W.A. & R.A. KOLBESON. 1956. Determination of anionic detergents in surface waters and sewage with methyl green. *Anal. Chem.* 28:161.

AMERICAN WATER WORKS ASSOCIATION. 1958. Task Group Report. Determination of synthetic detergent content of raw water supplies. *J. Amer. Water Works Ass.* 50:1343.

OGDEN, C.P. et al. 1961. Determination of biologically soft and hard alkylbenzenesulfonate in detergents and sewage. *Analyst* 86:22.

MAGUIRE, O.E. et al. 1962. Field test for analysis of anionic detergents in well waters. *J. Amer. Water Works Ass.* 54:665.

ABBOTT, D.C. 1962. The determination of traces of anionic surface-active materials in water. *Analyst* 87:286.

ABBOTT, D.C. 1963. A rapid test for anionic detergents in drinking water. *Analyst* 88:240.

REID, V.W. et al. 1967. Determination of anionic-active detergents by two-phase titration. *Tenside* 4:292.

Carbon Adsorption Method

SALLEE, E.M. et al. 1956. Determination of trace amounts of alkyl benzenesulfonates in water. *Anal. Chem.* 28:1822.

513   TANNIN AND LIGNIN

Lignin is a plant constituent that often is discharged as a waste during the manufacture of paper pulp. Another plant constituent, tannin, may enter the water supply through the process of vegetative degradation or through the wastes of the tanning industry. Tannin also is applied in the so-called internal treatment of boiler waters, where it reduces scale formation by causing the production of a more easily handled sludge.

Both lignin and tannin contain aromatic hydroxyl groups that react with tungstophosphoric and molybdophosphoric acids to form a blue color. However, the reaction is not specific for lignin or tannin, inasmuch as other reducing materials respond similarly.

The nature of the substance suspected in the water sample will dictate the choice of tannic acid or lignin for use in the preparation of the standard solution. This course is necessary because it is impossible to distinguish among hydroxylated aromatic compounds. Unless tannin or lignin is definitely known to be present in the sample, the results of this determination logically may be reported in the more general terms of "tannin-like," "lignin-like," or simply as "hydroxylated aromatic" compounds.

1. General Discussion

a. Principle: Tannins and lignins reduce tungstophosphoric and molybdophosphoric acids to produce a blue color suitable for the estimation of concentrations up to at least 9 mg/l for tannic acid as well as lignin.

b. Interference: Such reducing substances as 2 mg/l ferrous iron and 125 mg/l sodium sulfite individually produce a color equivalent to 1 mg/l tannic acid.

c. Minimum detectable concentration: Approximately 0.1 mg/l for tannic acid and 0.3 mg/l for lignin.

2. Apparatus

Colorimetric equipment: One of the following is required:

a. Spectrophotometer, for use at 700 nm. A light path of 1 cm or longer yields satisfactory results.

b. Filter photometer, provided with a red filter exhibiting maximum transmittance in the wavelength range of 600 to 700 nm. Sensitivity improves with increasing wavelength. A light path of 1 cm or longer yields satisfactory results.

c. Nessler tubes, matched, 100-ml, tall form, marked at 50-ml volume.

3. Reagents

a. Tannin-lignin reagent: Transfer 100 g sodium tungstate, $Na_2WO_4 \cdot 2H_2O$, and 25 g sodium molybdate, $Na_2MoO_4 \cdot 2H_2O$, together with 700 ml distilled water, to a 1,500-ml florence flask. Add 50 ml 85% phosphoric acid, H_3PO_4, and 100 ml conc HCl. Connect to a reflux condenser and boil gently for 10 hr. Add 150 g lithium sulfate, Li_2SO_4, 50 ml distilled water, and a few drops of liquid bromine. Boil the mixture without the condenser for 15 min to remove the excess bromine. Cool to 25 C, dilute to 1 l, and filter. Store the finished reagent, which should have no greenish tint, in a tightly stoppered bottle to protect against reduction by dust and organic materials.

b. Carbonate-tartrate reagent: Dissolve 200 g Na_2CO_3 and 12 g sodium tartrate, $Na_2C_4H_4O_6 \cdot 2H_2O$, in 750 ml hot distilled water, cool to 25 C, and dilute to 1 l.

c. Stock solution: Weigh 1.000 g tannic acid or tannin, or lignin compound being used for boiler water treatment or known to be a contaminant of the water sample. Dissolve in distilled water and dilute to 1,000 ml.

d. Standard solution: Dilute 10.00 ml or 50.00 ml stock solution to 1,000 ml with distilled water; 1.00 ml = 10.0 or 50.0 μg active ingredient.

4. Procedure

Bring 50 ml of the clear sample and standards to a temperature above 20 C and maintain within a ± 2 C range. Add in rapid succession 1 ml tannin-lignin reagent and 10 ml carbonate-tartrate reagent. Allow 30 min for color development. Compare visually against simultaneously prepared standards, or make photometric readings against a reagent blank prepared at the same time. Because different tannin and lignin compounds react with variable sensitivity, use the appropriate tannin or lignin material for the preparation of the calibration curve and visual standards. Use the following guide for the instrumental meaurements in the wavelength region of 600 to 700 nm:

Tannic Acid in 62-ml Final Volume μg	Lignin in 62-ml Final Volume μg	Light Path cm
50-600	100-1,500	1
10-150	30- 400	5

5. Bibliography

BERK, A.A. & W.C. SCHROEDER. 1942. Determination of tannin substances in boiler water. *Ind. Eng. Chem.*, Anal. Ed. 14:456.

KLOSTER, M.B. 1973. Determination of tannin and lignin. *J. Amer. Water Works Ass.* 66:44.

PART 600
AUTOMATED
LABORATORY ANALYSES

601 INTRODUCTION

Automated analytical instruments are available and in use to analyze individual samples at rates of 10 to 60 samples/hr. The same instruments can be modified to make analyses for multiple constituents simultaneously from one sample. The instruments consist of a group of interchangeable modules joined together in series by a tubing system. Each module performs an individual operation such as filtering, heating, digesting, time delay, color sensing, etc., that the procedure requires.

The read-out system includes sensing elements with indicators, alarms, and/or recorders. For monitoring applications, automatic standardization-compensation, electrical and chemical, is done by a self-adjusting recorder when known chemical standards are sent periodically through the same analytical train.

Appropriate methodology is supplied by the manufacturer for many of the common constituents of water and wastewater. Some methods are based on procedures described in this manual, while others originate from the manufacturer's adaptation of published research. Since a number of methods of varying reliability may be available for a single constituent of water and wastewater, a critical appraisal of the method adopted is mandatory.

Automated methodology is susceptible to the same interferences as the original method from which it derives. For this reason, new methods developed for automated analysis must be subjected to exacting tests for accuracy and freedom from adverse response already met by the accepted standard methods.

Off color and turbidity produced during an analysis will be visible to an analyst manually performing a given determination and the result properly will be discarded. Such abnormal effects caused by unsuspected interferences may escape notice in an automated analysis. Calibration of the instrument system at least daily with standards containing interferences of known concentration could help to expose such difficulties. Good practice is to check instrument action routinely and to guard against questionable results by the insertion of standards and blanks at regular intervals— perhaps after every 10 samples in the train. Proper sample identification by arrangement into convenient groups is essential.

In brief, a fair degree of operator skill and knowledge, together with adequately detailed instructions, is required for successful automated analysis.

Although products of Technicon Instruments Corporation are specified in these methods, automated systems of other manufacture that perform equivalent functions with satisfactory overall results also are acceptable.

In the opinion of the inventors a patent monopoly will not result in an exorbitant price to users. "Standard Methods" does not undertake to insure against liability of infringement nor does it assume such liability.

1. Apparatus

The Technicon ™ AutoAnalyzer ™ continuous-flow analytical instrument* consists of the following interchangeable components, which are assembled in the number and manner indicated in the figures appearing with each method:

a. Sampler.

b. Manifold for the AutoAnalyzer I system or *analytical cartridge* for the AutoAnalyzer II system.

c. Proportioning pump.

d. Heating bath, operable at the proper temperature.

e. Colorimeter equipped with tubular flow cell of specified length.

f. Filters of specified transmittance.

g. Recorder.

h. Digital printer for AutoAnalyzer II system (optional).

2. General Procedure

The following general procedure applies to each of the described automated methods:

a. Depending on the model available,

_____
* Technicon and AutoAnalyzer are trademarks of Technicon Instruments Corporation, Tarrytown, N.Y.

set up the manifold and complete system as shown in the figure(s) for each method.

b. Allow both the colorimeter and recorder to warm up for 30 min.

c. Run a baseline with all reagents, feeding the proper type of distilled water through the sample line.

d. Adjust the colorimeter to obtain a stable baseline.

e. Sample at the rate indicated under each method.

f. Arrange the standards in the sampler in order of decreasing concentration.

g. Load the sampler tray with the unknown samples.

h. Switch the sample line from water to the sampler and begin the analysis.

3. Calculation

Prepare the standard curve or curves by plotting peak heights of the standards processed through the manifold against known concentrations of the constituent under examination.

Compute the concentrations of the samples by comparing the sample peak heights with the standard curve.

602   CHLORIDE
Ferricyanide Method (TENTATIVE)

1. General Discussion

a. Principle: Thiocyanate ion is liberated from mercuric thiocyanate by the formation of soluble mercuric chloride. In the presence of the ferric ion, the free

c. Application: This automated method is applicable to potable, surface, and saline waters as well as domestic and industrial wastewaters. The range of concentrations can be varied by using the colorimeter controls.

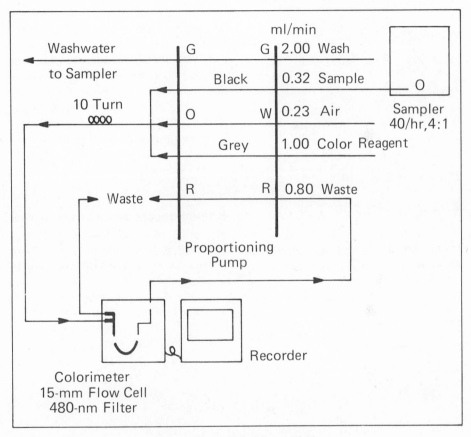

Figure 602:1. Chloride manifold.

thiocyanate ion forms a highly colored ferric thiocyanate, which is proportional to the chloride concentration.

b. Interferences: None of significance. However, use a continuous filter on samples containing turbidity.

2. Apparatus

*Automated analytical equipment,** consisting of the components (except the

* Technicon™ AutoAnalyzer™ II or equivalent.

heating bath) listed in Section 601 and the addition of 480-nm filters.

3. Reagents

a. Stock mercuric thiocyanate solution: In a 1-l volumetric flask, dissolve 4.17 g $Hg(SCN)_2$ in about 500 ml methanol. Dilute to volume with methanol, mix, and then filter through filter paper.

b. Stock ferric nitrate solution: Place about 500 ml distilled water in a 1-l volumetric flask and add 202 g $Fe(NO_3)_3 \cdot 9H_2O$. After dissolution, carefully add 21 ml conc HNO_3. Dilute to volume with distilled water and mix. Filter through filter paper and store in an amber bottle.

c. Color reagent: Add 150 ml stock mercuric thiocyanate solution to 150 ml stock ferric nitrate solution. Mix and dilute to 1,000 ml with distilled water. Add 0.5 ml Brij-35†.

---

† Polyoxyethylene 23 lauryl ether, available from ICI United States, Chicago, Ill., or Technicon Instruments Corporation, Tarrytown, N.Y.

d. Stock chloride solution: Dissolve 1.6482 g NaCl, dried at 140 C, in distilled water and dilute to 1,000 ml; 1.00 ml = 1.00 mg Cl.

e. Standard chloride solutions: Prepare chloride standards in the desired concentration range, such as 1 to 200 mg/l, using the stock chloride solution.

4. Procedure

Set up the manifold as shown in Figure 602:1 and follow the general procedure described in Section 601.

5. Calculation

See Section 601.3.

6. Bibliography

ZALL, D.M., D. FISHER & M.D. GARNER. 1956. *Anal. Chem.* 28:1665.
O'BRIEN, J.E. 1962. Automatic analysis of chlorides in sewage. *Wastes Eng.* 33:670.

603   FLUORIDE
Complexone Method (TENTATIVE)

1. General Discussion

a. Principle: The sample is distilled and the distillate is reacted with alizarin fluorine blue-lanthanum reagent to form a blue complex that is measured colorimetrically at 620 nm.

b. Interferences: Interferences normally associated with the determination of fluoride are removed by distillation.

c. Application: This method is applicable to potable, surface, and saline waters as well as domestic and industrial wastewaters. The range of the method, which can be modified by using the adjustable colorimeter, is 0.1 to 2.0 mg/l F.

2. Apparatus

Automated analytical equipment,[*] consisting of the components listed in Section 601 with the following additions: heating bath with distillation head, 15-mm tubular flow cell, and 620-nm filters.

3. Reagents

a. Stock fluoride solution: Dissolve 2.210 g anhydrous NaF in about 600 ml distilled water and dilute to 1,000 ml; 1.00 ml = 1.00 mg F.

b. Standard fluoride solution: Prepare fluoride standards in concentrations of 0.1 to 2.0 mg/l, using the stock fluoride solution.

c. Distillation reagent: Add 50 ml conc H_2SO_4 to about 600 ml distilled water. Add 1.00 ml stock fluoride solution and dilute to 1,000 ml.

d. Acetate buffer solution: Dissolve 60 g anhydrous sodium acetate, $NaC_2H_3O_2$, in about 600 ml distilled water. Add 100 ml conc (glacial) acetic acid and dilute to 1 l.

e. Alizarin fluorine blue stock solution: Add 960 mg alizarin fluorine[†], $C_{14}H_7O_4 \cdot CH_2N(CH_2 \cdot COOH)_2$, to 100 ml distilled water. Add 2 ml conc

NH_4OH and mix until the dye is dissolved. Add 2 ml conc (glacial) acetic acid, dilute to 250 ml, and store in an amber bottle in the refrigerator.

f. Lanthanum nitrate stock solution: Dissolve 1.08 g $La(NO_3)_3$ in about 100 ml distilled water, dilute to 250 ml, and store in refrigerator.

g. Working color reagent: Mix in the following order: 300 ml acetate buffer solution, 150 ml acetone, 50 ml tertiary butanol, 36 ml alizarin fluorine blue stock solution, 40 ml lanthanum nitrate stock solution, and 2 ml Brij-35[‡]. Dilute to 1 l with distilled water. This reagent is stable for 2 to 4 days.

4. Procedure

No special handling and preparation of sample are required.

Set up the manifold as shown in Figure 603:1 and follow the general procedure described in Section 601.

5. Calculation

See Section 601 for pertinent details.

6. Bibliography

WEINSTEIN, L.H., R.H. MANDL, D.C. MCCUNE, J.S. JACOBSON & A.E. HITCHCOCK. 1963. A semi-automated method for the determination of fluorine in air and plant tissues. *Boyce Thompson Inst.* 22:207.

---

[*] Technicon™ AutoAnalyzer™ II or equivalent.

[†] J.T. Baker Catalog number J-112 or equivalent.

[‡] Polyoxyethylene 23 lauryl ether available from ICI United States, Chicago, Ill., or Technicon Instruments Corporation, Tarrytown, N.Y.

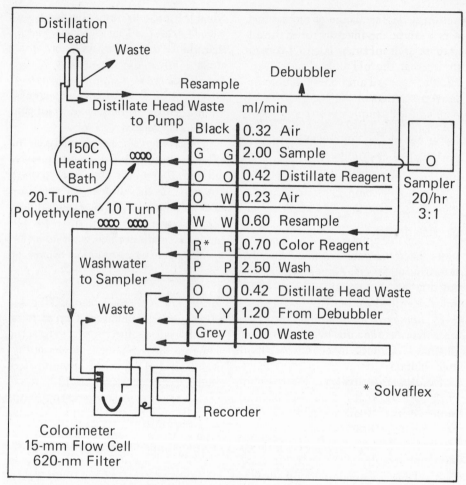

Figure 603:1. Fluoride manifold.

604   NITROGEN (AMMONIA)
Phenate Method (TENTATIVE)

1. General Discussion

a. Principle: Alkaline phenol and hypochlorite react with ammonia to form indophenol blue that is proportional to the ammonia concentration. The blue color formed is intensified with sodium nitroprusside.

b. Interferences: Seawater contains calcium and magnesium ions in sufficient concentrations to cause precipitation problems during analysis. The addition of EDTA and sodium potassium tartrate is intended to solve this problem. Eliminate any marked variation in acidity or alkalinity among samples because the intensity of the measured color is pH-dependent. Likewise, insure that the pH of the wash water and the standard ammonia solutions approximates that of the sample. For example, if the sample has been preserved with 1 ml conc H_2SO_4/l, the wash water and standards should also contain 1 ml conc H_2SO_4/l. Mercuric chloride used as a preservative gives a negative interference by complexing with the ammonia, an effect that can be overcome by adding a comparable amount of $HgCl_2$ to the ammonia standards. Remove interfering turbidity by filtration before analysis. Sample color that absorbs in the photometric range used for analysis will also interfere. See Section 418C.1b.

c. *Application:* Ammonia nitrogen can be determined in potable, surface, and saline waters as well as domestic and industrial wastewaters over a range of 0.01 to 2.0 mg/l when photometric measurement is made at 630 to 660 nm in a 15- or 50-mm tubular flow cell. Determine higher concentrations by diluting the sample.

2. Apparatus

*Automated analytical equipment,** consisting of the components listed in Section 601 with the following additions: heating bath with double delay coil, 15- or 50-mm tubular flow cell, and 630- or 650-nm filters.

3. Reagents

a. *Ammonia-free distilled water:* See

---

* Technicon™ AutoAnalyzer™ I or II, or equivalent.

Section 418A.3a. Use ammonia-free water for preparing all reagents and dilutions.

b. *Sulfuric acid,* H_2SO_4, 5 N: Air scrubber solution. Carefully add 139 ml conc H_2SO_4 to approximately 500 ml ammonia-free water, cool to room temperature, and dilute to 1 l.

c. *Sodium phenate solution:* In a 1-l erlenmeyer flask, dissolve 83 g phenol in 500 ml ammonia-free water. In small increments and with agitation, cautiously add 32 g NaOH. Cool flask under running water and dilute to 1 l.

d. *Sodium hypochlorite solution:* Dilute 250 ml bleach solution containing 5.25% NaOCl† to 500 ml with ammonia-free water.

e. *EDTA reagent:* Dissolve 50 g disodium ethylenediamine tetraacetate, also called (ethylenedinitrilo)-tetraacetic acid disodium salt, and approximately six pellets NaOH in 1 l ammonia-free water. For salt-water samples where EDTA reagent does not prevent precipitation of cations, use sodium potassium tartrate solution prepared as follows:

Sodium potassium tartrate solution: To 900 ml ammonia-free water add 100 g $NaKC_4H_4O_6 \cdot 4H_2O$, two pellets NaOH, and a few boiling chips, and boil gently for 45 min. Cover, cool, and dilute to 1 l. Adjust pH to 5.2 ± 0.05 with H_2SO_4. Let settle overnight in a cool place and filter to remove precipitate. Add 0.5 ml Brij-35‡ solution and store in stoppered bottle.

f. *Sodium nitroprusside solution:* Dis-

---

† Chlorox or equivalent.
‡ Polyoxyethylene 23 lauryl ether available from ICI United States, Chicago, Ill., or Technicon Instrument Corporation, Tarrytown, N.Y.

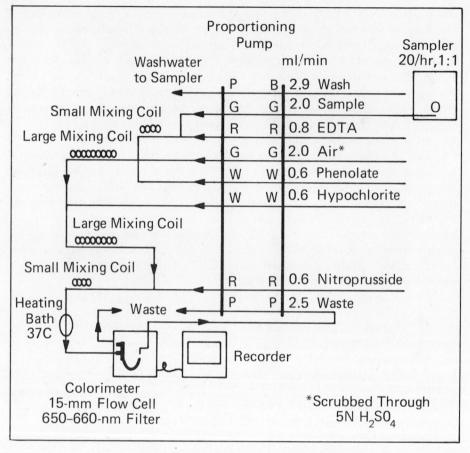

Figure 604:1. Ammonia manifold for AutoAnalyzer I.

solve 0.5 g sodium nitroprusside, $Na_2(NO)Fe(CN)_5 \cdot 2H_2O$, also called sodium nitroferricyanide, in 1 l ammonia-free water.

g. *Ammonia standard solutions:* See Sections 418C.3e and f. Use the standard ammonia solution and ammonia-free water to prepare the calibration curve in the appropriate ammonia concentration range. For the examination of saline waters use substitute ocean water

of the following composition to prepare the calibration standards:

NaCl	24.53 g/l	Na_2SO_4	4.09 g/l
$MgCl_2$	5.20	$NaHCO_3$	0.20
$CaCl_2$	1.16	KBr	0.10
KCl	0.70	H_3BO_3	0.03
$SrCl_2$	0.03	NaF	0.003

Subtract the blank background response of the substitute seawater from the standards before preparing the standard curve.

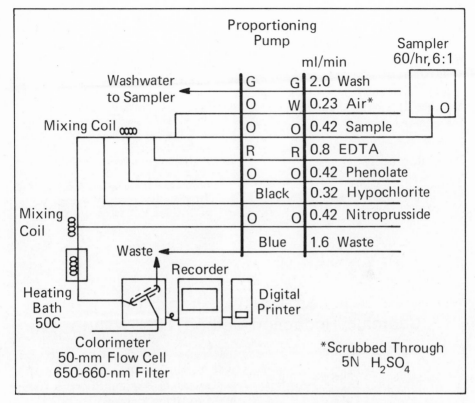

Figure 604:2. Ammonia manifold for AutoAnalyzer II.

4. Procedure

a. Eliminate any marked variation in acidity or alkalinity among samples because the intensity of the color is pH-dependent. Likewise, adjust the pH of the wash water and standard ammonia solutions to approximately that of the sample.

b. Depending on the model available, set up manifold and complete system as shown in Figure 604:1 (AutoAnalyzer I) or Figure 604:2 (AutoAnalyzer II).

c. Obtain a stable baseline with all reagents, feeding ammonia-free water through sample line.

d. For the AutoAnalyzer I system, sample at a rate of 20/hr, 1:1; for the AutoAnalyzer II system, use a 60/hr, 6:1 cam with a common wash.

e. Follow the general procedure described in Section 601.

5. Calculation

See Section 601.3.

6. Precision and Accuracy

Results with AutoAnalyzer I system have been as follows: In a single laboratory using surface water samples at concentrations of 1.41, 0.77, 0.59, and

0.43 mg/l NH₃-N, the standard deviation was ±0.005, and at concentrations of 0.16 and 1.44 mg/l NH_3-N, recoveries were 107 and 99 percent, respectively.

Single-laboratory data on the AutoAnalyzer II system show comparable precision and accuracy.

7. Bibliography

HILLER, A. & D. VAN SLYKE. 1933. Determination of ammonia in blood. *J. Biol. Chem.* 102:499.

FIORE, J. & J.E. O'BRIEN. 1962. Ammonia determination by automatic analysis. *Wastes Eng.* 33:352.

AMERICAN SOCIETY FOR TESTING AND MATERIALS. 1966. Manual on Industrial Water and Industrial Waste Water. 2nd ed. ASTM, Philadelphia, Pa., p. 418.

O'CONNOR, B., R. DOBBS, B. VILLIERS, & R. DEAN. 1967. Laboratory distillation of municipal waste effluents. *J. Water Pollut. Control Fed.* 39:25.

BOOTH, R.L. & L.B. LOBRING. 1973. Evaluation of the AutoAnalyzer II: A progress report. *In* Advances in Automated Analysis: 1972 Technicon International Congress. Vol. 8, p. 7, Mediad Inc., Tarrytown, N.Y.

605   NITROGEN (NITRATE)
Cadmium Reduction Method (TENTATIVE)

1. General Discussion

a. Principle: A filtered sample is passed through a column containing granulated copper-cadmium to reduce nitrate to nitrite. The nitrite originally present plus reduced nitrate is determined by diazotizing with sulfanilamide and coupling with N-(1-naphthyl) ethylenediamine dihydrochloride to form a red color suitable for photometric measurement. Separate as well as combined nitrate-nitrite values can be obtained by carrying out the procedure with, and then without, Cu-Cd reduction.

b. Interferences: Sample turbidity may interfere with this method. Remove by filtration before analysis. Sample color that absorbs in the photometric range used for analysis also will interfere.

c. Application: Nitrate and nitrite, singly or combined, that are present in potable, surface, and saline waters, as well as domestic and industrial wastewaters, can be determined over a range of 0.5 to 10 mg/l nitrogen.

2. Apparatus

*Automated analytical equipment,** consisting of the components (except a heating bath) listed in Section 601 with the following additions: 15- or 50-mm tubular flow cell and 540-nm filters.

3. Reagents

a. Deionized distilled water: Because of possible contamination, prepare by passing distilled water through an ion exchange column containing a mixture of both strongly acidic cation and

---

*Technicon ™ AutoAnalyzer™ I or II, or equivalent.

strongly basic anion exchange resins. Regenerate the ion exchange column according to the manufacturer's instructions. Use deionized distilled water for the preparation of all reagents and dilutions.

b. Copper sulfate solution: Dissolve 20 g $CuSO_4 \cdot 5H_2O$ in 500 ml deionized distilled water and dilute to 1 l.

c. Wash solution: Use deionized distilled water for unpreserved samples. For samples preserved with H_2SO_4, add 2 ml conc H_2SO_4/l wash water.

d. Copper-cadmium granules: Clean the cadmium granules†, new or used, with $1+1$ HCl and treat with copper sulfate solution in the following manner: Wash the cadmium with $1+1$ HCl and rinse with deionized distilled water. Swirl 10 g cadmium in 100-ml portions of $CuSO_4$ solution for 5 min or until the blue color partially fades, decant, and repeat with fresh $CuSO_4$ solution until a brown colloidal precipitate forms. Wash the cadmium-copper with wash solution at least 10 times to remove all precipitated copper.

e. Hydrochloric acid, HCl, conc.

f. Ammonium hydroxide, NH_4OH, conc.

g. Color reagent: To approximately 800 ml deionized distilled water, add, while stirring, 100 ml conc phosphoric acid, 40 g sulfanilamide, and 2 g N-(1-naphthyl) ethylenediamine dihydrochloride. Stir until dissolved and dilute to 1 l. Store in brown bottle and keep in the dark when not in use. This solution is stable for several months.

h. Ammonium chloride solution: Dissolve 85 g NH_4Cl in deionized distilled water and dilute to 1 l. Add 0.5 ml Brij-35‡.

i. Stock nitrate solution: Dissolve 7.218 g anhydrous KNO_3 and dilute to the mark of a 1-l volumetric flask with deionized distilled water; 1.00 ml = 1.00 mg N. Preserve with 2 ml chloroform/l. Solution is stable for 6 months.

j. Stock nitrite solution: Dissolve 6.072 g anhydrous KNO_2 in 500 ml deionized distilled water and dilute to the mark of a 1-l volumetric flask; 1.00 ml = 1.00 mg N. Preserve with 2 ml chloroform and refrigerate.

k. Intermediate nitrate solution: Dilute 10.0 ml stock nitrate solution to 1,000 ml with deionized distilled water; 1.00 ml = 10.0 μg N. Preserve with 2 ml chloroform/l. Solution is stable for 6 months.

l. Intermediate nitrite solution: Dilute 10.0 ml stock nitrite solution to 1,000 ml with deionized distilled water; 1.00 ml = 10.0 μg N. Prepare as needed because solution is unstable.

m. Standard nitrate solutions: Using the intermediate nitrate solution and deionized distilled water, prepare standards for the calibration curve in the appropriate nitrate range. Compare at least one nitrite standard to a nitrate standard at the same concentration to verify the column reduction efficiency. To examine saline waters prepare the standard solutions with the substitute ocean water described in Section 604.3g.

4. Procedure

a. Preparation of reduction column:

---

† E.M. Laboratories, Inc., 500 Exec. Blvd., Elmsford, N.Y. 10523. Cat. No. 2001, Cadmium, Coarse Powder, 40-60 mesh.

‡ Polyoxyethylene 23 lauryl ether available from ICI United States, Chicago, Ill., or Technicon Instruments Corporation, Tarrytown, N.Y.

For Technicon Autoanalyzer I system—The reduction column is an 8- by 50-mm glass tube with the ends reduced in diameter to permit insertion into the system. Place the copper-cadmium granules in the column between glass wool plugs. Set the packed reduction column in an upflow 20-degree incline to minimize channeling.

For Autoanalyzer II systems—The reduction column is glass tubing, U-shaped, 35 cm long, of 2 mm ID. Fill the reduction column with distilled water to prevent entrapment of air bubbles during the filling operation. Transfer copper-cadmium granules to reduction column and place a glass wool plug in each end. To prevent entrapment of air

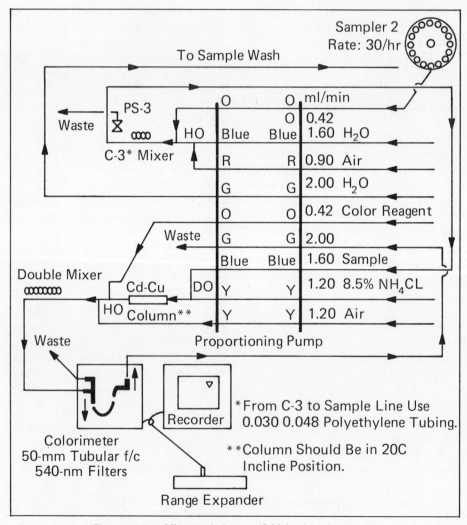

Figure 605:1. Nitrate-nitrite manifold for AutoAnalyzer I.

bubbles in reduction column be sure that all pump tubes are filled with reagents before putting the column into the analytical system. A 0.081-in.-ID pump tube may be used in place of the 2-mm glass tube.

b. If the pH of the sample is below 5 or above 9, adjust to between 5 and 9 with either conc HCl or conc NH₄OH.

d. For the AutoAnalyzer I system, sample at a rate of 30/hr, 1:1; for the AutoAnalyzer II system, use a 40/hr, 4:1 cam and a common wash.

e. Follow the general procedure in Section 601.

5. Calculation

See Section 601 for pertinent details.

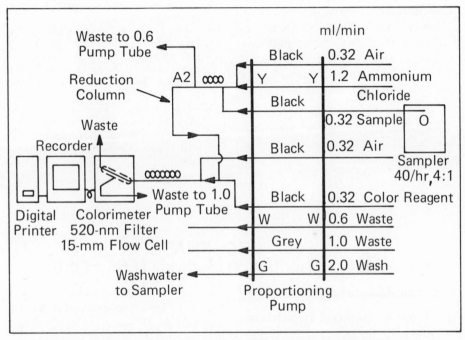

Figure 605:2. Nitrate-nitrite manifold for AutoAnalyzer II.

c. Set up the manifold as shown in Figure 605:1 (AutoAnalyzer I) or Figure 605:2 (AutoAnalyzer II). Note that the reductant column should be in a 20-degree inclined position (AutoAnalyzer I). Take care not to introduce air into the reduction column on the Auto-Analyzer II.

6. Precision and Accuracy

Results with AutoAnalyzer I system have been as follows:

Three laboratories analyzed four natural water samples containing exact increments of inorganic nitrate with the following results:

Increment as Nitrate Nitrogen ($\mu g/l$)	Precision as Standard Deviation ($\mu g/l\,N$)	Accuracy as	
		Bias %	Bias $\mu g/l\,N$
290	12	+5.75	+17
350	92	+18.10	+63
2,310	318	+4.47	+103
2,480	176	-2.69	-67

In a single laboratory using surface water samples at concentrations of 100, 200, 800, and 2,100 $\mu g/l$ N, the standard deviations were 0, ±40, ±50, and ±50 $\mu g/l$, respectively, and at concentrations of 200 and 2,200 $\mu g/l$ N, recoveries were 100 and 96%, respectively.

Single-laboratory data on the Auto-Analyzer II system show comparable precision and accuracy.

7. Bibliography

FIORE, J. & J.E. O'BRIEN. 1962. Automation in sanitary chemistry—Parts 1 and 2. Determination of nitrates and nitrites. *Wastes Eng.* 33:128 & 238.

FEDERAL WATER POLLUTION CONTROL ADMINISTRATION. 1966. Chemical Analyses for Water, Quality Manual. Dep. Interior, R.A. Taft Sanitary Engineering Center Training Program, Cincinnati, Ohio.

AMERICAN SOCIETY FOR TESTING AND MATERIALS. 1966. Manual of Industrial Water and Industrial Waste Water. ASTM, Philadelphia, Pa., pp. 418 & 465.

ARMSTRONG, F.A., C.R. STEARNS & J.D. STRICKLAND. 1967. The measurement of upwelling and subsequent biological processes by means of the Technicon AutoAnalyzer and associated equipment. *Deep Sea Res.* 14:381.

U.S. ENVIRONMENTAL PROTECTION AGENCY. FWQA Method Study 4, Automated Methods. National Environmental Research Center, Cincinnati, Ohio (in preparation).

606 PHOSPHATE
Ascorbic Acid Reduction Method (TENTATIVE)

1. General Discussion

a. Principle: Ammonium molybdate and antimony potassium tartrate react with orthophosphate in an acid medium to form an antimony-phosphomolybdate complex, which, on reduction with ascorbic acid, yields an intense blue color suitable for photometric measurement.

b. Interferences: As much as 50 mg/l ferric iron, 10 mg/l copper, and 10 mg/l silica can be tolerated in the test. Higher silica concentrations cause positive interference over the range of the test. In terms of phosphorus, the results are high by 0.005, 0.015, and 0.025 mg/l for silica concentrations of 20, 50, and 100 mg/l, respectively. Salt concentrations up to 20% cause an error of less than 1%. Because arsenic is determined similarly to phosphorus, it should be considered when present in concentrations higher than those of phosphorus. Eliminate interference from nitrite or sulfide by adding an excess of bromine water or a saturated potassium permanganate solution. Remove interfering turbidity by filtration before analysis. Filter samples for total or total hydrolyzable phosphorus only after digestion. Sample color that absorbs in the photometric range used for analysis will also interfere. See also Section 425F.1*b*.

c. Application: Orthophosphate can be determined in potable, surface, and saline waters as well as domestic and industrial wastewaters over a range of 0.001 to 10.0 mg/l P when photometric measurements are made at 650 to 660 or 880 nm in a 15-mm or 50-mm tubular flow cell. Determine higher concentrations by diluting the sample. Although the automated test is designed for orthophosphate only, other phosphorus compounds can be converted to this reactive form by various sample pretreatments described in Methods 425A, 425B, and 425C.III.

2. Apparatus

a. Automated analytical equipment,[*] consisting of the components listed in Section 601 with the following additions: heating bath adjusted at 50 C for the AutoAnalyzer I system or 37 C for the AutoAnalyzer II system, 15- or 50-mm tubular flow cell, and 650- to 660- or 880-nm filters.

b. Hot plate or autoclave.

c. Acid-washed glassware: Wash all glassware with hot 1+1 HCl and rinse with distilled water. Fill the acid-washed glassware with distilled water and treat with all the reagents to remove the last traces of phosphate that might be adsorbed on the glassware. Preferably, reserve this glassware for the determination of phosphate. After use, rinse it with distilled water and keep it covered until it is needed again. If this is

---

[*] Technicon™ AutoAnalyzer™ I or II, or equivalent.

done, treatment with 1+1 HCl and reagents is required only occasionally. *Never use commercial detergents.*

3. Reagents

a. Antimony potassium tartrate solution: Dissolve 0.3 g $K(SbO)C_2H_4O_6 \cdot \frac{1}{2}H_2O$ in approximately 50 ml distilled water and dilute to 100 ml. Store at 4 C in a dark, glass-stoppered bottle.

b. Ammonium molybdate solution: Dissolve 4 g $(NH_4)_6Mo_7O_{24} \cdot 4H_2O$ in 100 ml distilled water. Store in a plastic bottle at 4 C.

c. Ascorbic acid solution: Dissolve 1.8 g ascorbic acid in 100 ml distilled water. The solution is stable for a week if prepared with water containing no more than a trace amount of heavy metals and if stored at 4 C.

d. Combined reagent: To prepare 100 ml of the mixed reagent, mix in the following proportions: 50 ml H_2SO_4 (3 *f*), 5.00 ml antimony potassium tartrate solution, 15 ml ammonium molybdate solution, and 30 ml ascorbic acid solution. *Mix after addition of each reagent.* Let all reagents reach room temperature before mixing. Mix in the order given. If turbidity forms in the combined reagent, shake it and let it stand for several minutes until the turbidity disappears, then continue. This 100 ml of reagent is enough for 4 hr operation. Because the stability of this solution is limited, prepare fresh for each run. To prepare a stable solution, exclude ascorbic acid from the combined reagent. If this reagent is used, pump the mixed reagent (molybdate, tartrate, and acid) through the distilled water line and the ascorbic acid solution (30 ml of 3*c* diluted to 100 ml with distilled water) through the original mixed reagent line.

e. Sulfuric acid solution: Slowly add 310 ml conc H_2SO_4 to 600 ml distilled water. When cool, dilute to 1 l.

f. Sulfuric acid solution: Slowly add 140 ml conc H_2SO_4 to 600 ml distilled water. When cool, dilute to 1 l.

g. Ammonium persulfate, crystalline.

h. Phenolphthalein indicator solution.

i. Stock phosphate solution: Dissolve 439.3 mg anhydrous KH_2PO_4, dried for 1 hr in an oven at 105 C, in distilled water and dilute to 1,000 ml; 1.00 ml = 100 μg P.

j. Intermediate phosphate solution: Dilute 100.0 ml stock phosphate solution to 1,000 ml with distilled water; 1.00 ml = 10.0 μg P.

k. Standard phosphate solutions: Prepare a suitable series of standards by diluting appropriate volumes of the intermediate phosphate solution.

4. Procedure

a. Set up manifold and complete system as shown in Figure 606:1 or Figure 606:2.

b. For the AutoAnalyzer I system, sample at a rate of 20/hr, 1 min sample, 2 min wash; for the AutoAn-

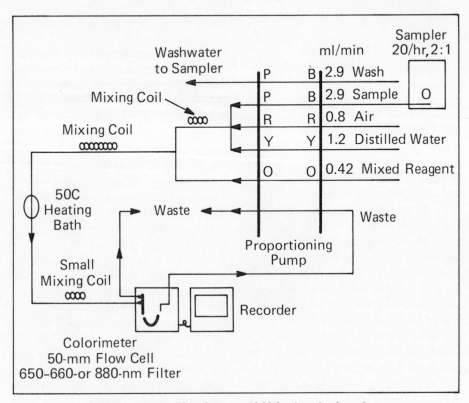

Figure 606:1. Phosphate manifold for AutoAnalyzer I.

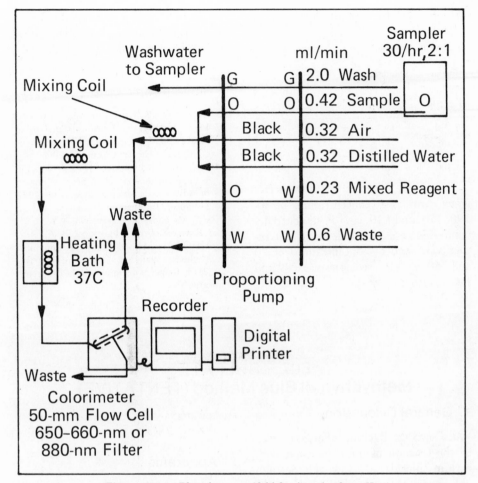

Figure 606:2. Phosphate manifold for AutoAnalyzer II.

alyzer II system, use a 30/hr, 2 : 1 cam, and a common wash.

c. Add 1 drop phenolphthalein indicator solution to approximately 50 ml sample. If a red color develops, add H_2SO_4 (*3e*) dropwise to just discharge the color.

d. Follow the general procedure in Section 601.

5. Calculation

See Section 601.3.

6. Precision and Accuracy

Results with Technicon AutoAnalyzer I system are as follows: Six laboratories analyzed four natural water samples containing exact increments of orthophosphate, with the following results:

Increment as Ortho-phosphate ($\mu g/l\,P$)	Precision as Standard Deviation ($\mu g/l\,P$)	Accuracy as	
		Bias %	Bias $\mu g/l\,P$
40	19	+16.7	+7
40	14	-8.3	-3
290	87	-15.5	-50
300	66	-12.8	-40

In a single laboratory, using surface water samples at concentrations of 40, 190, 350, and 840 $\mu g/l\,P$, standard deviations were ±5, ±0, ±3, and ±0, respectively, and at concentrations of 70 and 760 $\mu g/l\,P$, recoveries were 99 and 100%, respectively.

Single-laboratory data on the Technicon AutoAnalyzer II system show comparable precision and accuracy.

7. Bibliography

U.S. ENVIRONMENTAL PROTECTION AGENCY. 1971. Methods for Chemical Analysis of Water and Wastes. National Environmental Research Center, Cincinnati, Ohio.

LOBRING, L.B. & R.L. BOOTH. 1973. Evaluation of the AutoAnalyzer II; A progress report. *In* Advances in Automated Analysis: 1972 Technicon International Congress. Vol. 8, p. 7, Mediad, Inc., Tarrytown, N.Y.

U.S. ENVIRONMENTAL PROTECTION AGENCY. MDQARL Method Study 4, Automated Methods. National Environmental Research Center, Cincinnati, Ohio (in preparation).

607 SULFATE
Methylthymol Blue Method (TENTATIVE)

1. General Discussion

a. Principle: Barium sulfate is formed by the reaction of the sulfate ion with barium chloride at a low pH. At high pH excess barium reacts with methylthymol blue to produce a blue-colored chelate. The uncomplexed methylthymol blue is gray. The amount of gray, uncomplexed methylthymol blue indicates the concentration of sulfate ion.

b. Interferences: Because many cations, such as aluminum and calcium, interfere with sulfate analysis, use the ion exchange column to remove the interferences.

c. Application: This method is applicable to potable, surface, and saline waters as well as domestic and industrial wastewaters over a range from about 10 to 300 mg/l SO_4.

2. Apparatus

a. Automated analytical equipment, consisting of the components listed in Section 601 and 460-nm filters.

b. Ion exchange column: Fill a piece of 2-mm-ID glass tubing about 20 cm (8 in.) long with the ion exchange resint. To simplify filling the column put the resin in distilled water and aspirate it into the tubing, which con-

---

* Technicon™ AutoAnalyzer™ II or equivalent.

† Ion exchange resin Bio-Rex 70, 20-50 mesh, sodium form, available from Bio-Rad Laboratories, Richmond, Calif.

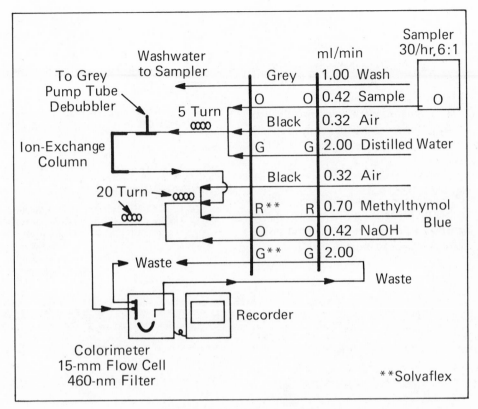

Figure 607:1. Sulfate manifold.

tains a glass wool plug. After filling, plug the other end of the tube with glass wool. Avoid trapped air in the column.

3. Reagents

a. Barium chloride solution: Dissolve 1.526 g $BaCl_2 \cdot 2H_2O$ in 500 ml distilled water and dilute to 1 l. Store in a polyethylene bottle.

b. Methylthymol blue reagent: In 25 ml $BaCl_2$ solution dissolve 118.2 mg methylthymol blue‡. Add 4 ml 1 N

‡ Eastman Organic Chemicals, Rochester, N.Y. No. 8068. 3′,3″-Bis\|[N,N-bis(carboxymethyl)-amino]-methyl\|thymolsulfonphthalein pentasodium salt.

HCl and 71 ml distilled water and dilute to 500 ml with ethanol. Store in a brown glass bottle. Prepare fresh daily.

c. Buffer solution, pH 10.1: Dissolve 6.75 g NH_4Cl in 500 ml distilled water. Add 57 ml conc NH_4OH and dilute to 1 l with distilled water. Adjust pH to 10.1 and store in a polyethylene bottle.

d. EDTA reagent: Dissolve 40 g tetrasodium ethylenediamine tetraacetate, also called (ethylenedinitrilo)-tetraacetic acid tetrasodium salt, in 500 ml pH 10.1 buffer solution. Dilute to 1 l with pH 10.1 buffer solution and store in a polyethylene bottle.

e. Sodium hydroxide solution: Dissolve 7.2 g NaOH in 500 ml distilled water. Cool and make up to 1 l with distilled water.

f. Stock sulfate solution: Dissolve 1.479 g anhydrous Na_2SO_4 in 500 ml distilled water and dilute to 1,000 ml; 1.00 ml = 1.00 mg SO_4.

g. Standard sulfate solutions: Prepare in appropriate concentrations from 10 to 300 mg/l SO_4, using the stock sulfate solution.

4. Procedure

Set up the manifold as shown in Figure 607:1 and follow the general procedure described in Section 601.2.

After use, rinse the methylthymol blue and NaOH reagent lines in water for a few minutes, then rinse them in the EDTA solution for 10 min and then in water.

5. Calculation

See Section 601.3.

6. Bibliography

Lazrus, A.L., K.C. Hill & J.P. Lodge. 1965. A new colorimetric microdetermination of sulfate ion. *Automation Anal. Chem.* p. 291.

PART 700
EXAMINATION OF WATER AND WASTEWATER FOR RADIOACTIVITY

701 INTRODUCTION

The radioactivity in water and wastewater originates from natural and artificial or man-made sources. The natural or background radioactivity generally contributes less than picocurie quantities of alpha activity and tens of picocuries of beta activity in each liter of surface water. Gamma activity is also associated with alpha and beta emissions. Artificial sources of radioactivity include fission, fusion, or particle acceleration, giving rise largely to alpha, beta, and gamma radioactivity. The development of nuclear science and its application to power development, industrial operations, and industrial uses require that attention be given to the formulation of technics to assess the resulting degree of environmental radioactive contamination. It is important to provide adequate warning of unsafe conditions so that proper precautions can be taken. It is of nearly equal importance to assure that conditions are indeed safe when they are, in fact, safe.

In either event it is necessary to establish base lines for the kinds and amount of radionuclides that are present naturally and to measure manmade additions to this background. In this way, measurements may be made to provide information for sound judgments regarding the hazardous or non-hazardous nature of increased concentrations.

Measurement technics are not difficult to devise because radiation counting equipment of high sensitivity, selectivity, and stability is fairly commonplace. Furthermore, the guides provided by the Federal Radiation Council[1] on the permissible daily intake of some radionuclides, the recommendations on radionuclide concentrations in water made by the National Council on Radiation Protection and Measurements (NCRP),[2] those made by the International Commission on Radiation Protection (ICRP),[3] and the Public Health Service Drinking Water Standards[4] are, with few exceptions, at concentrations that are readily measured by current methods and instruments.

Meaningful measurements do require the careful application of good scientific technics. Gross alpha and gross beta measurements are relatively inexpensive and serve a useful purpose for screening samples. Samples sufficiently low in radioactivity do not require further analyses. Samples at intermediate concentrations may be composited for the more complete and expensive analysis of specific radionuclides. To be effective, a gross screening technic must be based on knowledge of the relationship between the gross measurements and the radionuclides of greatest concern.

Both natural and artificial sources of radiation from samples emitting alpha, beta, or gamma activity are included in the examination (to the exclusion of radiation external to the sample—i.e., cosmic, gamma, X-ray, and hard beta radiation in the environment). Because the rate of decay and the energy of radiation are unique characteristics of each radioelement, strict adherence to a standard procedure is essential to the proper interpretation of a radioactivity examination. Frequently the procedure may

633

have rigid timing requirements to discriminate between radioelements. For example, the rapid alpha analysis of airborne particulates usually consists of the measurement of radon daughter products (largely ^{218}Po and ^{214}Po) from which the equilibrium parent radon concentration and each of its descendent products may be estimated. Subsequent alpha-counting of the same sample could be designed to measure thoron daughter activity or long-lived alpha emitters. The beta activity of fresh rain a few minutes to several hours after collection includes significant contamination by radon daughter products. If the analysis is postponed for 6 hr, the radon daughters will disappear, along with some short-lived artificial radionuclides. The loss of activity resulting from delayed counting can be estimated by the extrapolation of decay data. During the concentration of water samples by evaporation, radionuclides such as elemental iodine or hydrogen iodide (in acid solution) may be lost by volatilization at temperatures below 105 C. If the sample is ignited, the chance of volatilization is even greater. Radioactive substances such as carbon 14 and tritium may be present as volatile chemicals for the procedure of sample preparation used. Groundwater generally contains nuclides of the uranium and thorium series. Special care in sampling and analyses is necessary because members of these series are often not in secular equilibrium. This is particularly true of gaseous radon, thoron, and their daughter products, which may be present far in excess of the equilibrium concentration from radium in solution.

701 A.   Collection of Samples

The principles of representative sampling of water and wastewater apply to sampling for radioactivity examinations.

Because a radioactive element is often present in submicrogram quantities, a significant fraction of it may be readily lost by adsorption on the surface of containers or glassware used in the examination. Similarly, a radionuclide may be largely or wholly adsorbed on the surface of suspended particles.

1. Sample Containers

When radioactive industrial wastes or comparable materials are sampled, consideration should be given to the deposition of radioactivity on the walls and surfaces of glassware, plastic containers, and equipment. This may cause a loss of radioactivity and the possible contamination of subsequent samples due to reuse of inadequately cleansed containers.

2. Preservation of Samples

The comments in Part 100 are particularly appropriate for all types of samples collected for tests described in Part 700. Inasmuch as preservatives may alter the distribution of radioactivity in a sample, they should not be used until after the sample is separated into suspended and dissolved fractions. Formaldehyde or ethyl alcohol is suggested as a preservative for highly perishable samples such as food or foodlike samples. Preservatives and reagents should be tested for their radioactive content.

701 B. Counting Room

The design and construction of the counting room may vary widely, according to the work to be accomplished. The room should be free of dust and fumes that may affect the electrical stability of instruments. The background can be stabilized and lowered considerably by making the walls, floor, and ceiling out of several inches of concrete. Some shales, granites, and sands may contain sufficient natural activity to affect instrument background if used in the construction of a counting room.

A modern chemical laboratory can be used for processing routine environmental samples. It is generally better to segregate monitoring work from other laboratory operations when possible.

The need for air-conditioning and humidity control depends on the number of instruments to be used and the prevailing climatic conditions. Generally, electronic instruments perform best when the temperature remains constant within 3 C and does not exceed 30 C. The temperature inside the chassis of the instrument should be kept below that specified by the manufacturer.

Humidity affects instrument performance to an even greater extent than extremes of temperature because of moisture buildup on critical components. This causes leakage and arcing, and shortens the life of these components. A humidity between 30 and 80% is usually satisfactory.

Most scalers are supplied with constant-voltage regulators suitable for controlling the usual minor fluctuations in line voltage. For unusual fluctuations an auxiliary voltage regulation transformer should be used. A manually reset voltage-sensitive device in series with a voltage regulator placed in the main power line to instruments is suggested to protect them in case of power failure or a fluctuating line voltage.

Samples containing appreciable activity should be stored at a distance so as not to affect instrument background counting rate.

Floors and desk tops should be covered with a material that can be cleaned easily or replaced if necessary.

701 C.   Counting Instruments

The operating principle of Geiger-Mueller and proportional counters is that the expenditure of energy by a radiation event causes ionization of counter gas and electron collection at the anode of the counting chamber. Through gas or electronic amplification, or both, the ion-collection event triggers an electronic scaler recorder.

The principle of scintillation counters is similar in that quanta of light caused by the interaction of a radiation event and the detection phosphor are seen by a photomultiplier tube. The tube converts the light pulse into an amplified electrical pulse that is recorded by an electronic scaler. Thallium-activated sodium iodide crystals and silver-activated zinc sulfide screens form useful scintillation detectors for counting gamma and alpha radioactivity, respectively.

Characteristic of most counters is a background or instrument counting rate usually due to cosmic radiation, to radioactive contaminants of instrument parts and counting room construction material, and to the nearness of radioactive sources such as samples, fallout dust, and X-ray machines. In general, the background is roughly proportional to the size or mass of the counting chamber or detector, but it can be reduced by metal shielding, such as several inches of lead.

Instrument "noise", or the false recording of radiation events, may be caused by faulty circuitry, too sensitive a gain setting, effects of high humidity, and variable line voltage or transients. This problem is controlled by constant-voltage transformers with transient filters, proper adjustment of gain setting as specified by the manufacturer, and air-conditioning of the counting room.

The internal proportional counter accepts counting pans within the counting chamber and thus, at the beta operating voltage, records all alpha, all beta, and a little gamma radiation emitted into the counting gas. Theoretically, half of the radiation is emitted in the direction of the counting pan. Some of the beta radiation, but only 1 to 2% of the alpha radiation, is backscattered into the counting gas by sample solids, the counting pan, or the walls of the counting chamber, so that, for substantially weightless samples, considerably more than 50% of the beta radiation and slightly more than 50% of the alpha radiation is counted. However, considerable care must be taken in sample preparation to prevent the sample or counting pan from distorting the electrical field of the counter and thus depressing the counting rate. Nonconducting surfaces, airborne dusts, and vapor from moisture or solvents in particular interfere with counting.

The end-window Geiger-Mueller counting tubes are rugged and stable counting detectors. Usually the samples are mounted 5 to 15 mm from the window. Under these conditions, most alpha and weak beta radiations are completely stopped by the air gap and mica window and are not counted. Counting efficiencies for mixed fission products are frequently less than 10% for substantially weightless samples having an area less than that of the window. Because most Geiger-Mueller tubes have diameters of about 2.5 cm, the pan size—and, as a consequence, the water sample volume—must be restricted. Under these conditions, the detectability is low and uncertain, particularly for unknown sources of radiation. On the other hand, the Geiger-Mueller tubes are excellent for counting samples of tracers or purified radionuclides. Usually, standard sample mounts can be prepared that yield reproducible counting efficiencies, and counting is not affected by the electrical conductance of sample pans.

Thin-window (Mylar less than 250 μg/cm^2) tubes approximately 5 cm in diameter provide counting efficiencies intermediate between conventional Geiger-Mueller tubes and internal counters. The counting of alpha activity in these thin-window counters is satisfactory.

The chamber diameter may be greater than 60 mm and sample mount diameters may be greater than 50 mm. The counting chambers have operational stability and less interference from nonconducting surfaces and moisture vapors than internal proportional counters. These counters are superior to the more conventional small-diameter mica window counters.

1. Internal Proportional Counters

a. Uses: Internal proportional counters are suitable for determining alpha activity at the alpha operating plateau and alpha-plus-beta activity at the beta operating plateau. The alpha or beta activity, or both, can refer to a single or to several radionuclides.

The instruments usually consist of a counting chamber, a preamplifier, and a scaler with high-voltage power supply, timer, and register. Each instrument requires the use of a specified type of counting gas and accessories, the making of adjustments for sensitivity, and the carrying out of prescribed operating instructions.

b. Plateau (alpha or beta): It is necessary to find the operating voltage where the counting rate is constant—i.e., varies less than 5% over a 150-V change in anode voltage.

1) With the instrument in operating order, place the alpha or beta standard (see Section 701D.3) in the chamber, close, and flush the chamber with counter gas for 2 to 5 min.

2) Using the manufacturer's recommended operating voltage, count for a convenient time giving an acceptable coefficient of variation, preferably 2%. Repeat the test at voltages higher and lower than the suggested operating voltage in increments of 50 V. (CAUTION: *Instrument damage will result from prolonged continuous discharge at too high a voltage.*)

3) Plot the relative counting rate (ordinate) against anode voltage (abscissa). A plateau of at least 150 V in length, with a slope of 5% or less, should result (see Figure 701:1). Select an anode voltage near the center of this plateau for the operating voltage.

c. Counter stability: Check instrument stability at the operating voltage by counting the plateau source daily (see Section 701D.3 below). If the instrument reproduces the source count within two standard deviations of the count rate, proceed as in the paragraph following. If the source count is not so reproduced, repeat the test. If stability is not attained, service the instrument.

d. Background: Determine the background (with an empty counting pan in

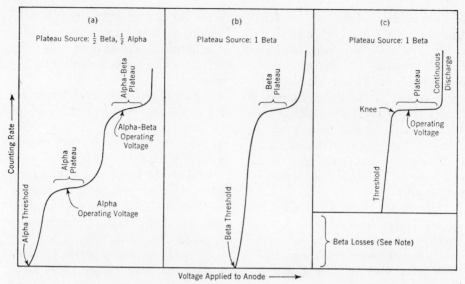

Figure 701:1. Shape of counting rate—anode voltage curves. Key: (a) and (b) are for internal proportional counter with P-10 gas; (c) is for end-window Geiger-Mueller counter with Geiger gas (Note: Beta losses are dependent on energy of radiation and thickness of window and air path.).

the counting chamber). The background counting time should be as long as the longest sample-counting time. Control charts are useful for stability testing.

e. Sample counting: Place the sample in the counting chamber. Be sure it is dry and adequately grounded to the chamber piston. (Thin aluminum metal pans can be grounded by impaling the pan wall on a pin mounted in the piston; heavier pans are self-grounded.) Flush with counter gas and count for a preset time, or preset count, to give the desired counting precision (see Section 701F).

f. Calibration of overall counter efficiency: It is necessary to correct the observed counting rate for the factors affecting efficiency: geometry, backscatter, and self-absorption (sample absorption).

Although it is useful to know the variation in these factors, the overall efficiency can be determined by preparing standard sample sources and unknowns.

1) For measuring mixed fission products or beta radioactivity of unknown composition, use a standard solution of cesium 137 * for calibration of overall counter efficiency.

Prepare a standard (known disintegration rate) in an aqueous solution of sample solids similar in composition to that present in the unknown samples. Dispense increasing increments of solution in tared pans and evaporate. Make a series of samples having a solids thickness of 1 to 10 mg/cm^2 of bottom area in the counting pan. Use care in evapo-

---

*For calibration standards and certification see The Isotope Index, J.S. Sommerville, ed. Scientific Equipment Co., P.O. Box 19086, Indianapolis, Ind.

ration to obtain uniform solids deposition. Dry (103 to 105 C), weigh, and count. Calculate the ratio of counts per minute to disintegrations per minute (efficiency) for different weights of sample solids. Plot the efficiency as a function of sample thickness and use the resulting calibration curve to convert counts per minute (cpm) to disintegrations per minute (dpm).

2) If other radionuclides are to be tested, repeat the above procedure, using certified solutions of each radionuclide. Unequal distribution of sample solids, particularly in the 0- to 3- mg/cm^2 range, should be avoided in both calibration and unknown sample preparation; otherwise, inconsistent results will occasionally be obtained.

3) For alpha calibration, proceed as above, using a standard solution of natural uranium salt (avoid the use of depleted uranium).

2. End-Window Counters

End-window counters may be used for beta-gamma and absorption examinations. Most alpha and soft beta radiations are stopped by the air gap and window. The sample pan should have a diameter less than that of the window and, for maximum efficiency, should be placed as close to the window as possible. Housing the detector inside a 5-cm-thick lead shield will improve sensitivity of counting by decreasing the background by about 50%. Associated equipment generally consists of a scaler having a timer, a register, and a high-voltage power supply.

The operation and calibration of these counters are performed as described in Section 701C.1a-f, with

modifications as applicable to the specific instrument.

COINCIDENCE CORRECTION: Geiger-Mueller counters commonly have resolving times of 100 to 400 μsec; therefore, data on samples of high counting rate must be corrected for loss in counts.

3. Thin-Window Proportional Counter

The thin-window proportional counter has application for counting moderate to high levels and for counting residues that adhere poorly to the counting pan. The counters detect alpha and low-energy beta emitters. They are about one-half as sensitive as internal counters because the geometry of counting is not as favorable and absorption losses (air path and window) are greater. However, because the sample is on the outside, this counter is less affected than the internal counter by conditions such as contamination from loose residues and losses due to residue moisture and poor electrical conductance. The operation and calibration of these counters are as described in Section 701C.1a-f, with modifications applicable to the specific instrument.

4. Low-Background Beta Counter

The low-background beta counter is useful primarily for measurements as low as 0.1 and as high as 50 pCi per sample. Higher activity levels, to about 1,000 pCi, can be counted if other beta detectors are not available. The counters are designed primarily for beta emitters having a maximum beta energy above 0.3 MeV.

Usually the detector window thickness is less than 1.0 mg/cm^2, so that the attenuation of high-energy beta rays is relatively minor. The diameter of sample pans should be less than that of the window. The counting efficiencies for weightless samples vary from 30 to 55% for beta radiation of moderate energy.

The detectors of instruments with a background counting rate of 1 cpm or less normally have a lead or steel shield and an anticoincidence device of one or more guard detectors with the electronics needed to prevent counting in the sample detectors when a count is recorded in the guard. Some instruments have automatic sample changers. Most counters of this type use helium-isobutane or similar gases that operate in the Geiger region. Instruments using proportional counting gas are available. Geiger-Mueller counters commonly have resolving times of 100 to 400 μsec; therefore, data on samples of high counting rate must be corrected for loss of counts.

5. Multichannel Gamma Spectrum Analysis

An attractive feature of gamma spectrum analysis is that an analysis is made with minimum sample preparation. Unless a complex spectrum with overlapping primary photopeaks is obtained, chemical separation followed by gamma analysis for quantitative measurements on each fraction of the sample is unnecessary. An important limitation of the method is that nongamma-emitting radionuclides are excluded from consideration and those having photon energies of less than 0.1 MeV are usually measured with considerable uncertainty.

Details on the operation and calibration of multichannel gamma spectrum analysis may be found in the literature.[5-8]

a. Principle: The principle of a gamma spectrometer is that gamma photons from a sample enter a sensitive detector and interact with the detector atoms. The interaction gives rise to pulses of light. The light pulses are proportional in intensity to the gamma photon energy transferred to the detector. The light pulses enter a photomultiplier tube and are converted to electrical voltage pulses proportional to the light intensity. The pulses are stored in sequence into finite energy increments (such as 0.02 MeV) over the entire spectrum range (such as 0.1 to 2.0 MeV), depending on instrument capabilities and operator's choice.

After the sample is counted, the accumulated counts in each energy increment of the entire spectrum are analyzed for the number and energy of photopeaks (a qualitative test) or the number of pulses associated with each photopeak, with correction for background counts and interference from other gamma emitters (a quantitative test). Since each gamma-emitting radionuclide usually has several photopeaks, one of which yields the greatest abundance of pulses, the number of radionuclides in the sample to be analyzed is limited by the probability that overlapping photopeaks will cause errors in a quantitative estimation. Analysis of four to eight components is practical. For more complex mixtures, chemical separations followed by a gamma spectrum analysis of each fraction are necessary.

b. Components: A gamma spectrometer consists of a scintillation detector system, a pulse-height analyzer system, and a data readout system. The scintillation detector system is a detector enclosed in a shield and connected to a preamplifier and a high-voltage power supply. A common detector for gamma spectrometric analysis of environmental samples is a 10-cm (4-in.) diam by 10-cm (4-in.) thick sodium iodide crystal (thallium-activated) enclosed in a hermetically sealed can coupled to a photomultiplier tube. The crystal and sample are placed in a metal shield (10 to 20 cm of steel or equivalent) to reduce external gamma radiation.

The pulse-height analyzer system consists of a linear amplifier, a pulse-height analyzer, a memory storage, and a logic control mechanism. The logic control capability permits storage of data in various modes and the displaying or recalling of data for visual display or use.

The data readout system contains one or more of the following devices: an oscilloscope for visual display, a readout indicator, an electric typewriter, a digital printer, a paper-tape perforator, a magnetic tape recorder, a strip chart recorder, and an x-y recorder. The oscilloscope is useful in aligning the instrument with standards such as ^{60}Co, ^{137}Cs, and ^{207}Bi.

The digital printer records the number of pulses accumulated in each pulse-height range covering the spectrum range set by the mode of operation.

6. Single-Channel Gamma Spectrum Analysis

A single-channel gamma spectrum analyzer is similar to a multichannel analyzer but is limited to the examination of a single energy range at a time. The instrument is best used for situations such as the continuous monitoring of waste having fixed radionuclide composition, making gross gamma measurements, or measuring a single gamma-emitting radionuclide in a sample. The single-channel gamma analyzer is similar to the multichannel analyzer, except that the design is inexpensive compared with that of a multichannel analyzer.

The instrument consists of a sodium iodide (thallium-activated) crystal detector; a high-voltage supply; a photomultiplier tube; an amplifier; a pulse-height discriminator that can be set to obtain anything within a narrow to a broad energy range of the gamma spectrum; a scaler; and a shield to reduce external gamma background.

Operations of the single-channel analyzer are detailed in the literature.[5-8]

7. Alpha Scintillation Counter

When an alpha particle bombards an impure crystal of zinc sulfide, a portion of the kinetic energy is transformed into visible light. The sulfide scintillates more efficiently when it contains silver impurities and when the duration of the light pulse is shortened by the presence of nickel ions.

The alpha scintillation counter consists of a phosphor detector coupled to a photomultiplier, a high-voltage supply, an amplifier-discriminator, and a scaler. Generally the photomultiplier tube should have a window diameter greater than the diameter of the sample unless the phosphor is coupled to a light-focusing optical system.

The silver-activated and nickel-quenched zinc sulfide phosphor is placed near, or in contact with, the alpha-emitting sample and is so arranged that a photomultiplier tube observes the light pulses, which are amplified and recorded on the scaler.

a. Solid samples should be mounted in a thin layer (less than 3 mg/cm^2) on a planchet. The phosphor is located between the sample and the photomultiplier tube. The sample and detector are enclosed in a light-tight chamber 3 to 5 mm from the phototube window. Under these conditions the counting efficiency is from 35 to 40%.

b. Gaseous samples contained in a dome-shaped cell coated with zinc sulfide "paint" are observed more efficiently than solid samples. Details of one such system are described under the determinations of radium 226 by radon (Section 706).

8. Liquid Beta Scintillation Counter

The principle of liquid scintillation counters is that the sample having radionuclides is mixed with an organic liquid scintillator, resulting in the production of light. The flashes of light are detected and amplified by one or more photomultiplier tubes.

Liquid scintillation counters are particularly well suited for counting low-energy beta emitters such as tritium or carbon 14 because self-absorption losses are eliminated. Counting efficiencies can approach 100% for high-energy betas, but for tritium the efficiency is much lower because the low beta pulses are not detected. These weak pulses are at the level of the "dark current" pulses from the photomultiplier tube and are discriminated against to reduce background. Some liquid scintillation instruments use two photomultipliers in coincidence as a means of reducing the background from "dark current." Most liquid scintillation counter systems incorporate at least a two-channel analyzer, which enables more than one beta emitter to be counted at the same time if their respective E's (maximum beta energies) differ by a factor of at least three.

Usually in a liquid scintillation counter the samples are dissolved or suspended in a scintillator solvent such as toluene, xylene, or 1-4-dioxane. The samples are placed in a transparent bottle to enable the light flashes to be transmitted to the phototube. As in any other counter, the calibration standard must contain the same radionuclide prepared in the same medium. Background is determined by putting a bottle containing both solvent and scintillator into the counter because this mixture is the sensor and a slight amount of activity may be present in the material itself. Background should be taken at least once daily.

701 D.   Laboratory Reagents and Apparatus

See Section 102 for basic standards applying to laboratory reagents and apparatus. The following special instructions are pertinent.

1. Reagents and Distilled Water

Make periodic checks on the background radioactivity of all solutions and reagents used in an examination. Discard those having a radioactivity that significantly interferes with the test.

2. Apparatus

Before reuse, thoroughly decontaminate apparatus and glassware with detergents and complexing agents, followed, if necessary, by acid and distilled-water rinses. Segregate equipment and glassware for storage and reuse on samples of comparable activity—i.e., keep apparatus for background and low-level studies separate from that for higher-level studies by the use of distinctive markings and different storage cabinets or laboratories. It is wise to adopt single-use counting pans, planchets, and auxiliary supplies. Slightly radio-contaminated glassware may be entirely satisfactory for use in chemical tests but is unsatisfactory for radioanalysis.

3. Radioactivity Sources

a. Solutions: Use standard solutions having calibrations traceable to sources of radioactivity certified by the National Bureau of Standards.

b. Plateau sources:

1) ALPHA—Uranium oxide (U_3O_8) plated, not less than 45 mm in diameter, having an alpha activity of about 10,000 cpm. Plutonium may also be plated as a weightless alpha standard source.

2) BETA—Uranium oxide (U_3O_8), plated as described above, is covered with 8 to 10 mg/cm^2 of aluminum foil. Cesium 137 will also provide an excellent beta standard source.

701 E.   Expression of Results

Results of radioactivity analyses are reported, preferably in terms of picocuries per liter (pCi/l) at 20 C or, for samples of specific gravity significantly different from 1.00, picocuries per gram, where 1 picocurie = 10^{-12} curies = 2.22 dpm. For samples normally containing 1,000 to 1,000,000 pCi per unit volume or weight, the nanocurie (nCi) unit is preferred (1 nCi = 10^{-9} Ci = 1,000 pCi). If the values are higher than 1,000 nCi, the microcurie (μCi) unit is preferred. Ordinarily, the liter, kilogram, and square meter are preferred units of volume, weight, and area, respectively.

It is important to report results in such a way that they will not imply greater or less accuracy than can be obtained by the method used. This matter is discussed in Part 100.

"Gross alpha" implies unknown alpha sources in which natural uranium salts have been used to determine self-absorption and efficiency factors.

"Gross beta" implies unknown sources of beta, including some gamma radiation, and calibration with ^{137}Cs as in Section 701.C1*f* above.

701 F.   Statistics

Section 104 of this manual discusses the statistics of analytical problems as applied to chemical parameters. These remarks are also generally applicable to radioactivity examinations.

The variability of any measurement is measured by the standard deviation, which can be obtained from replicate determinations by well-known methods. There is an inherent variability in radioactivity measurements because the disintegrations occur in a random manner described by the Poisson distribution. This distribution is characterized by the property that the standard deviation of a large number of events, N, is equal to its square root, or:

$$\sigma(N) = N^{1/2}$$

For ease in mathematical application, the normal (Gaussian) approximation to the Poisson distribution is ordinarily used. This approximation, which is generally valid at $N \geq 20$, is the particular normal distribution with a mean of N and standard deviation of $N^{1/2}$.

Generally, the concern is not with the standard deviation of the number of counts but rather with the deviation in the rate (number of counts per unit time):

$$R' = \frac{N}{t}$$

where t is the time of observation, which is assumed to be known with such high precision that its error may be neglected. The standard deviation in the counting rate, $\sigma(R')$, can be calculated by the usual methods for propagation of error:

$$\sigma(R') = \frac{N^{1/2}}{t} = \left(\frac{R'}{t}\right)^{1/2}$$

In practice, all counting instruments have a background counting rate, B, when no sample is present. When a sample is present, the counting rate increases to R_0. The counting rate R due to the sample then is:

$$R = R_0 - B$$

By propagation-of-error methods, the standard deviation of R can be calculated as follows:

$$\sigma(R) = \left(\frac{R_0}{t_1} + \frac{B}{t_2}\right)^{1/2}$$

where t_1 and t_2 are the times at which the gross sample and background counting rates were measured, respectively. Practical counting times are often 30 min, or 2,500 total counts above background, whichever takes less time. It is desirable to divide the counting time into two equal periods, so as to check constancy of the observed counting rate. For low-level counting, t_2 should be about the same as t_1. *The error thus calculated includes only the error caused by inherent variability of the radioactive disintegration process and should be reported as the "counting error."*

A confidence level of 95%, or 1.96 standard deviations, preferably should be selected and reported as the counting error.

701 G. References

1. FEDERAL RADIATION COUNCIL. 1961. Background Material for the Development of Radiation Protection Standards. Rep. No. 2 (Sept.). U.S. Govt. Printing Off., Washington, D.C.

2. NATIONAL COMMITTEE ON RADIATION PROTECTION AND MEASUREMENTS. 1959. Maximum Permissible Body Burdens and Maximum Permissible Concentrations of Radionuclides in Air and Water for Occupational Exposure. NBS Handbook No. 69, pp. 1, 17, 37, 38, and 93.

3. Recommendation of the International Commission on Radiological Protection (rev. Dec. 1, 1954). 1960. *Health Phys.* 3:1.

4. U.S. PUBLIC HEALTH SERVICE. 1962. Public Health Service Drinking Water Standards, 1962. PHS Publ. No. 956. U.S. Govt. Printing Off., Washington, D.C.

5. HEATH, R.L. 1964. Scintillation Spectrometry, Gamma Ray Spectrum. IDO-16880. Technical Information Div., U.S. Atomic Energy Comm., Washington, D.C., Vols. 1 and 2.

6. CROUTHAMEL, C.E., ed. 1960. Applied Gamma-Ray Spectrometry. Pergamon Press, New York, N.Y. Vol. II.

7. NATIONAL CENTER FOR RADIOLOGICAL HEALTH. 1967. Radioassay Procedures for Environmental Samples. PHS Publ. No. 999-RH-27. U.S. Dep. Health, Education & Welfare, Washington, D.C.

8. INTERLABORATORY TECHNICAL ADVISORY COMMITTEE. 1968. Report No. 2: Common Laboratory Instruments for Measurement of Radioactivity. PHS Publ. No. 999-RH-32. National Center for Radiological Health, U.S. Dep. Health, Education & Welfare, Washington, D.C.

701 H. Bibliography

JARRETT, A.A. 1946. Statistical Methods Used in the Measurement of Radioactivity (Some Useful Graphs). U.S. Atomic Energy Comm. Document No. AECU-262 (June 17). AEC, Washington, D.C.

CORYELL, C.D. & N. SUGARMAN, eds. 1951. Radiochemical Studies: The Fission Products. McGraw-Hill Book Co., New York, N.Y.

NADER, J.S., G.R. HAGEE & L.R. SETTER. 1954. Evaluating the performance of the internal counter. *Nucleonics* 12:6, 29.

COMAR, C.I. 1955. Radioisotopes in Biology and Agriculture. McGraw-Hill Book Co., New York, N.Y.

JOHNSON, N.F., E. EICHLER & G.O. O'KELLEY. 1963. Nuclear Chemistry. Vol. II of Technique of Inorganic Chemistry. Interscience Publishers, New York, N.Y.

FRIEDLANDER, G., J.W. KENNEDY & J.M. MILLER. 1964. Nuclear and Radiochemistry, 2nd ed. John Wiley & Sons, New York, N.Y.

LEDERER, C.M. J.M. HOLLANDER & I. PERLMANN. 1967. Table of Isotopes, 6th ed. John Wiley & Sons, New York, N.Y.

LOS ALAMOS SCIENTIFIC LABORATORY, Radiochemistry Group J-11. 1967. Collected Radiochemical Procedures. U.S. Atomic Energy Comm. Rep. No. LA-1721 (3rd ed.). AEC, Washington, D.C.

HARLEY, J.R., ed. 172. Health and Safety Laboratory Procedures Manual. HASL-300. U.S. Atomic Energy Comm., New York, N.Y.

702   RADIOACTIVITY IN WASTEWATER

1. Discussion

Factors considered in sampling and sample preservation and the behavior of radioactive species are of great significance in the analysis of wastewater. Usually wastewater contains larger amounts of nonradioactive suspended and dissolved solids than does water, and often a preponderance of the radioactivity is in the solid phase. Generally, the use of carriers in the analysis is ineffective without prior conversion of the solid phase to the soluble phase; even then the high fixed solids may interfere with radioanalytical procedures. Table 702:I shows the usual solubility characteristics of common radioelements in wastewater.

TABLE 702:I. THE USUAL DISTRIBUTION OF COMMON RADIOELEMENTS BETWEEN THE SOLID AND LIQUID PHASES OF WASTEWATER

In Solution	In Suspension
HCO₃	Ce
Co	Cs
Cr	Mn
Cs	Nb
H	P
I	Pm
K	Pu
Ra	Ra
Rn	Sc
Ru	Th
Sb	U
Sr	Y
	Zn
	Zr

Moreover, the radioelements may exhibit unusual chemical characteristics because of the presence of complexing agents or the method of waste production. For example, tritium may be combined in an organic compound when used in the manufacture of luminous articles; radioiodine from hospitals may occur as complex organic compounds, compared to elemental and iodide forms found in fission products from the processing of spent nuclear fuels; uranium and thorium daughter products often exist as inorganic complexes other than oxides after processing in uranium mills; and strontium 90 titanate waste from a radioisotope heat source would be quite insoluble compared to most other strontium wastes.

Valuable information on the chemical composition of wastes, the behavior of radioelements, and the quantity of radioisotopes in use appears in the literature.[1,2] Radionuclides having or likely to have a public health significance are here emphasized. Methods are provided for radionuclides of high radiotoxicity. Some of these are beta emitters. The levels of most gamma emitters that have public health significance can be measured by gamma spectrometry without chemical separation. This is usually true for ^{106}Ru, ^{137}Cs, ^{131}I, and ^{60}Co.

Information on the determination of radioactivity in wastes, as well as other environmental samples, may be found, for example, in manuals on Radioassay Procedures of the Public Health Service,[3,4] the AEC manual,[5] and the American Society for Testing and Materials' Book of Standards.[6] General information on the behavior of the radioelements and on analytical methods are found in the monographs of the National Research Council.[7]

Radionuclide standards for elements commonly encountered in wastewater are available from one or more of the following: The National Bureau of Standards and Amersham/Searle Corporation in the United States; the Radiochemical Centre, Amersham, England; the International Atomic Energy Agency, Vienna, Austria; and CEA-Saclay, France. General information on radionuclide standards is available in publications issued in the United States.[8,9]

For data on half-lives and decay schemes, the most authoritative sources are the publications of the Oak Ridge,[10] California,[11] and Savannah River[12] groups. The Environmental Protection Agency, through its Office of Quality Assurance—Radiation, National Environmental Research Center* assists laboratories in achieving radioanalytical proficiency.

It is not generally feasible to perform collaborative (interlaboratory) analyses of wastewater samples because of the variable composition of elements and solids from one facility to the next, but the methods that follow have been evaluated by use of homogeneous samples and could be useful for nonhomogeneous samples after sample preparation (wet or dry oxidation and/or fusion and solution) resulting in homogeneity. A potential problem or characteristic of reference samples used for collaborative testing is that they may be deficient in radioelements exhibiting interferences due to decay during shipment of short-half-life radionuclides. Generally, however, analytical steps have been incorporated into the methods to eliminate these

---

*Office of Quality Assurance—Radiation, National Environmental Research Center, P.O. Box 15027, Las Vegas, Nev. 89114.

interferences, even though they may not be necessary for the reference samples under study.

2. References

1. INTERNATIONAL ATOMIC ENERGY AGENCY. 1960. Disposal of Radioactive Wastes. IAEA, Vienna, Austria.

2. NEMEROW, N.L. 1963. Industrial Waste Treatment. Addison-Wesley, Reading, Mass.

3. DOUGLAS, G.S., ed. 1967. Radioassay Procedures for Environmental Samples. PHS Publ. No. 999-RH-27. U.S. Dep. Health, Education & Welfare. Washington, D.C.

4. INTERLABORATORY TECHNICAL ADVISORY COMMITTEE. 1968. Common Laboratory Instruments for Measurement of Radioactivity. PHS Publ. No. 999-RH-32. National Center for Radiological Health, U.S. Dep. Health, Education & Welfare, Washington, D.C.

5. HARLEY, J.H., ed. 1972. Health and Safety Laboratory Procedures Manual. HASL-300. U.S. Atomic Energy Comm., New York, N.Y.

6. AMERICAN SOCIETY FOR TESTING AND MATERIALS. 1974 Book of ASTM Standards. ASTM. Philadelphia, Pa.

7. NAS-NRC. 1960 to date. Radiochemistry of the Elements. Rep. Nos. NAS-NS-3001 et seq., and Radiochemical Techniques. Rep. Nos. 3101 et seq. Clearinghouse, Springfield, Va.

8. MANN, W.B. & H.H. SELIGER. 1958. Preparation, Maintenance, and Application of Standards of Radioactivity. NBS Circ. No. 594. U.S. Dep. Commerce, Washington, D.C.

9. BEEGHLY, H.F., J.P. CALI & W.W. MEINKE, eds. 1968. Nuclear Standards for Chemistry and Technology. NBS Spec. Publ. 310 (Dec.). U.S. Dep. Commerce, Washington, D.C.

10. WAY, K., ed. 1966. Nuclear Data Sheets; and Journal Nuclear Data, Part B. Academic Press, New York.

11. LEDERER, C.M., J.M. HOLLANDER & I. PERL-
    MAN. 1967. Table of Isotopes. John Wiley &
    Sons, New York, N.Y.
12. WAKAF, M.A. 1971. Catalogue of γ-rays
    Emitted by Radionuclides Nuclear Data Ta-
    bles. Vol. 8, No. 5-6. Academic Press, New
    York, N.Y.

3. Bibliography

GARFINKEL, S.B., A.P. BAERG & P.E. ZIGMAN.
    1966. Certificates of Radioactivity Stan-
    dards. Nat. Acad. Sci., Washington, D.C.
KAHN, B., C.R. CHOPPIN & J.G.V., TAYLOR.
    1967. Users Guide for Radioactivity Stan-
    dards. Nat. Acad. Sci., Washington, D.C.

703   GROSS ALPHA AND GROSS BETA RADIOACTIVITY IN WATER (TOTAL, SUSPENDED, AND DISSOLVED)

1. General Discussion

a. Natural radioactivity: Uranium, thorium, and radium are naturally occurring radioactive elements that have a long series of radioactive daughters that emit alpha or beta and gamma radiations until a stable end-element is produced. These naturally occurring elements, through their radioactive daughter gases, radon and thoron, cause an appreciable airborne particulate activity and contribute to the radioactivity of rain and groundwaters. Additional naturally radioactive elements include potassium 40, rubidium 87, samarium 147, lutetium 176, and rhenium 187.

b. Artificial radioactivity: With the development and operation of nuclear reactors and other atom-smashing machines, large quantities of radioactive elements are being produced. These include almost all the elements in the periodic table.

c. Significance of gross alpha and gross beta concentrations in water: The 1962 Public Health Service Drinking Water Standards recommended limits for the concentration of radium 226 (3 pCi/l) and strontium 90 (10 pCi/l) in water. Furthermore, if alpha-emitters

and strontium 90 were known to be a negligible fraction of the above-specified limits, the water supply would usually be regarded as radiologically acceptable, provided that the gross beta concentration did not exceed 1,000 pCi/l.

By using the simpler technics for routine measurement of gross beta activity, the presence of contamination may be determined in a matter of minutes, whereas hours or even days may be required to conduct the radiochemical analyses necessary to identify the particular radionuclides present in the sample.

Regular measurements of gross alpha and gross beta activity in water may be invaluable for early detection of radioactive contamination and indicate the need for supplemental data on the concentrations of the more hazardous radionuclides.

d. Preferred counting instrument and calibration standard: The internal proportional counter is the recommended instrument for counting gross beta radioactivity because of its superior operating characteristics. These include a high sensitivity to detect and count a wide range of low- to high-energy beta radiation and a high geometry (2π) due to the introduction of the sample into the counting chamber. In this case the system of assay is calibrated by adding standard nuclide portions to media comparable to the samples and preparing, mounting, and counting the standards exactly as one does for the samples.

Thin-window proportional or Geiger counters may be used for this determination although they have lower counting efficiencies than the internal proportional counter. When a Geiger counter is used, the alpha activity cannot be determined separately. Alpha counting efficiency in end-window counters may be very low because of absorption in the air and the window.

When gross beta activity is assayed in samples containing mixtures of naturally radioactive elements and fission products, the choice of a calibration standard may significantly influence the beta results because self-absorption factors and counting chamber characteristics are beta-energy-dependent.

A standard solution of cesium 137, which is certified by the National Bureau of Standards or is traceable to a certified source, is recommended for calibration of counter efficiency and self-absorption for gross beta determinations. The half-life of cesium 137 is about 30 yr. The daughter products after beta decay of cesium 137 are stable barium 137 and metastable barium 137, which in turn disintegrates by gamma emission. For this reason, the standardization of cesium 137 solutions may be stated in terms of the gamma emission rate per milliliter or per gram. To convert gamma rate to equivalent beta disintegration rate, multiply the calibrated gamma emission rate by 1.33.

e. Radiation lost by self-absorption: The radiation from alpha emitters hav-

ing an energy of 8 MeV and from beta emitters having an energy of 60 KeV will not escape from the sample if the emitters are covered by a sample thickness of 5.5 mg/cm^2. The radiation from a weak alpha emitter will be stopped if covered by only 4 mg/cm^2 of sample solids. Consequently, for low-level counting it is imperative to evaporate all moisture and preferable to destroy organic matter before depositing a thin film of sample solids from which radiation may readily enter the counter. In counting water samples for gross beta radioactivity, a solids thickness of 10 mg/cm^2 or less on the bottom area of the counting pan is recommended. For the most accurate results, the self-absorption factor should be determined as outlined in Section 701C.1*f*.

2. Apparatus

a. Counting pans, of metal resistant to corrosion from sample solids or reagents, about 50 mm in diameter, 6 to 10 mm in height, and thick enough to be serviceable for one-time use. Stainless steel or aluminum pans are satisfactory, depending on the kind of sample and reagents added.

b. Internal proportional counting chambers, capable of receiving and maintaining good electrical contact with counting pans, complete with preamplifier, scaler, timer, register, constant-voltage supply, counting gas equipment, and counting gas.

c. Alternate counters: Other beta counters are thin end-window proportional and Geiger counters.

d. Membrane filter,† 0.45-µm pore size.

---

† Type HA (Millipore Filter Corp., Bedford, Mass.) or equivalent.

e. Gooch crucibles.

3. Reagents

a. Methyl orange indicator solution: Dissolve 0.5 g methyl orange in 1 l distilled water.

b. Hydrochloric acid, 1N (1 + 11).

c. Nitric acid, 1N: Dilute 64 ml conc HNO_3 to 1 l with distilled water.

d. Lucite solution: Dissolve 50 mg Lucite in 100 ml acetone.

e. Ethyl alcohol, 95%.

f. Conducting fluid: Anstac 2M‡ or equivalent; prepare according to manufacturer's directions.

g. Standard certified cesium 137 solution.

h. Reagents for wet-combustion procedure:

1) *Nitric acid, 6N:* Dilute 380 ml conc HNO_3 to 1 l with distilled water.

2) *Hydrogen peroxide solution:* Dilute 30% H_2O_2 with an equal volume of water.

4. Procedure for Gross Alpha and Gross Beta Activity

a. Total sample activity:

1) For each 20 cm^2 of counting pan area, take a volume of sample containing not more than 200 mg of residue for beta examination and not more than 100 mg of residue for alpha examination. The specific conductance test helps to select the appropriate sample volume.

2) Evaporate by either of the following technics:

a) Add the sample directly to a tared counting pan in small increments, with evaporation just below boiling temperature.

b) Place the sample in a pyrex beaker

---

‡Chemical Development Corporation, Danvers, Mass.

---

or evaporating dish, add a few drops of methyl orange indicator solution, add 1N HCl or 1N HNO_3 dropwise to pH 4 to 6, and evaporate on a hot plate or steam bath to near dryness. Avoid baking solids on the evaporation vessel. Transfer the residue to a tared counting pan with the aid of a rubber policeman and distilled water from a wash bottle. Thoroughly wet the walls of the evaporating vessel with a few drops of acid by means of a rubber policeman and transfer the acid washings to the counting pan. (Excess alkalinity or mineral acidity is corrosive to aluminum counting pans.)

3) Complete the drying in an oven at 103 to 105 C, cool in a desiccator, weigh, and keep the sample dry until counted.

4) Sample residues having particles that tend to be airborne, which are to be counted in internal counters, should be treated with a few drops of Lucite solution, then air- and oven-dried and weighed. The Lucite acts as a binder to prevent counter contamination by such particles.

5) For an internal counter, count the alpha activity at the alpha plateau and count the beta-gamma activity at the beta plateau.

6) Store sample in a desiccator and count for decay if necessary. Avoid heat treatment if ingrowth of gaseous daughter products is suspected.

b. Activity of dissolved matter:

1) Proceed as in ¶ 4a 1) above, with a sample volume containing the requisite maximum weight of dissolved matter.

2) Filter through a Gooch crucible or a 0.45-μm-pore diameter membrane filter.

3) Process the filtrate as described in ¶s 4a2)-6) above, and report the dis-

solved alpha activity and dissolved beta activity by Gooch or by membrane filtration, as the case may be.

c. Activity of suspended matter:

1) For each 10 cm² of membrane filter area, take a volume of sample not to exceed 50 mg of suspended matter for alpha assay and not to exceed 100 mg for beta assay.

2) Filter sample through the membrane filter with suction; then wash sides of filter funnel with a few milliliters of distilled water.

3) Transfer filter to a tared counting pan and oven-dry.

4) If the sample is to be counted in an internal counter, saturate the membrane with alcohol and ignite. (When beta or alpha activity is counted with another counter, ignition is not necessary provided that the sample is dry and flat.) When burning has stopped, direct the flame of a Meker burner down on the partially ignited sample to fix the sample to the pan and obtain more complete ignition.

5) Cool, weigh, and count at the alpha and the beta plateaus.

6) If sample particles tend to be airborne, treat the sample with a few drops of Lucite solution, air-dry, and count.

7) An alternate method of preparing membrane filters for counting in internal counters consists of wetting the filters with conducting fluid, drying, weighing, and counting. (The weight of the membrane filter is then included in the tare.)

d. Activity of suspended matter (alternate):

It is impractical to filter some sewage, highly polluted waters, and industrial wastes through membrane filters. In such cases it is necessary to proceed as follows:

1) Determine the total and dissolved activity by the procedures given in ¶s 4*a* and 4*b* and estimate the suspended activity by difference.

2) Filter the sample through an ashless mat or filter paper of stated porosity. Dry, ignite, and weigh the suspended fixed residue. Transfer and fix a thin uniform layer of sample residue to a tared counting pan with a few drops of Lucite solution. Dry, weigh, and count in an internal counter for alpha and beta, or count the beta with a thin endwindow counter and the alpha with an alpha scintillation counter.

e. Activity of nonfatty semisolid samples:

The following procedure is applicable to samples of sludge, vegetation, soil, and the like:

1) Determine the total residue and fixed residue of representative samples according to Sections 208A and B.

2) Reduce fixed residue of a granular nature to a fine powder with pestle and mortar.

3) Transfer a maximum of 100 mg fixed residue for alpha assay and 200 mg fixed residue for beta assay for each 20 cm² of counting pan area (see Note below).

4) Distribute the residue to uniform thickness in a tared counting pan by (*a*) spreading a thick aqueous cream of residue that is weighed after oven-drying, or (*b*) dispensing dry residue of known weight that is spread with acetone and a few drops of Lucite solution.

5) Oven-dry at 103 to 105 C, weigh, and count.

NOTE: The fixed residue of vegetation and similar samples is usually corrosive to aluminum counting pans. To avoid difficulty, use stainless steel pans or treat a weighed amount of fixed residue with HCl or HNO₃ in the presence of methyl orange indicator to pH 4 to 6, transfer to an aluminum counting pan, dry at 103 to 105 C, reweigh, and count.

f. Alternate wet-combustion procedure for biological samples: Some samples, such as fatty animal tissues, are difficult to process according to Section 4e above. An alternate procedure consists of acid digestion. Because the procedure creates a highly acid and oxidizing state, volatile radionuclides would be lost under these conditions.

1) To a 2- to 10-g sample in a tared silica dish or equivalent, add 20 to 50 ml $6N$ HNO_3 and 1 ml 15% H_2O_2 and digest at room temperature for a few hours or overnight. Heat gently and, when frothing subsides, heat more vigorously but without spattering, until nearly dry. Add two more $6N$ HNO_3 portions of 10 to 20 ml each, heat to near boiling, and continue gentle treatment until the sample is dry.

2) Ignite the sample in a muffle furnace for 30 min at 600 C, cool in a desiccator, and weigh.

3) Continue the test as described in ¶s 4e3)-5) above.

5. Calculation and Reporting

a. Counting error: Determine the counting error, E (in picocuries per sample), at the 95% confidence level from:

$$E = \frac{1.96\sigma(R)}{2.22e}$$

where $\sigma(R)$ is calculated as shown in Section 701F, using $t_1 = t_2$ (in minutes); and e, the counter efficiency, is defined and calculated as in Section 701C.1f preceding.

b. Alpha activity of water, biological

samples, or silts: Report the alpha activity of water, in pCi/l, by the equation

$$\text{Alpha} = \frac{\text{net cpm} \times 1,000}{2.22e\,v}$$

where:

e = calibrated overall counter efficiency (see Section 701C.1f), and

v = volume of sample counted, ml.

The counting error must also be expressed in terms of picocuries per liter by dividing the picocuries per sample by the sample volume in liters. Similarly, calculate and report the alpha activity in picocuries or nanocuries per kilogram of moist biological material or per kilogram of moist and per kilogram of dry silt.

c. Gross beta activity when alpha activity is insignificant: For samples having an alpha activity less than one-half the beta counting error, calculate and report the gross beta activity and counting error in picocuries or nanocuries per liter of water or fluid, per kilogram of moist (live weight) biological material, or per kilogram of moist and per kilogram of dry silt, according to ¶s *a* and *b* above, disregarding the slight amount of alpha activity.

For calculation of the picocuries per liter of beta activity, the value of e in the above equation is determined as described in Section 701C.1f preceding.

d. Beta activity when alpha activity is significant: For samples containing an alpha activity (in cpm) that exceeds one-half the beta error (in cpm), deduct the net alpha cpm from the net beta cpm to give the net corrected beta cpm. Proceed as in ¶c above to calculate and report the beta radioactivity in picocuries or nanocuries per liter of water, per kilogram of moist and per kilogram of dry silt. When the count of alpha activity at the beta plateau represents a small fraction of the activity, a rough approximation of the beta counting error consists of the gross beta counting error. Where greater precision is desired—for example, when the count of alpha activity at the beta plateau is a substantial fraction of the net cpm of gross beta activity—the beta counting error equals $(E_a^2 + E_b^2)^{1/2}$, where E_a is the alpha counting error and E_b the gross beta counting error.

e. Miscellaneous information to be reported: In reporting radioactivity data, it is important to identify adequately the sample, sampling station, date of collection, volume of sample, type of test, type of activity, type of counting equipment, standard calibration solutions used (particularly when standards other than natural uranium for alpha or cesium 137 for beta were used), time of counting (particularly if short-lived isotopes are involved), weight of sample solids, and kind and amount of radioactivity. So far as possible, the data should be tabulated for ease of interpretation and repetitious items should be incorporated in the table heading or in footnotes. Unless especially inconvenient, quantity units should not change within a given table. For low-level assays, where the counting error represents a significant fraction of the measurement, it should be reported to assist in the interpretation of results.

6. Precision and Accuracy

In a collaborative study of two sets of paired water samples containing known additions of radionuclides, 15 laboratories determined the gross alpha activity and 16 analyzed the gross beta activity. The water samples contained simulated water minerals of approximately 350 mg fixed solids per liter. The alpha results of one laboratory were rejected as outliers.

The average recoveries of added gross alpha activity were 86, 87, 84, and 82%. The precision (random error) at the 95% confidence level was 20 and 24% for the two sets of paired samples. The method was biased low, but not seriously.

The average recoveries of added gross beta activity were 99, 100, 100, and 100%. The precision (random error) at the 95% confidence level was 12 and 18% for the two sets of paired samples. The method showed no bias.

7. Bibliography

BURTT, B.P. 1949. Absolute beta counting. *Nucleonics* 5:8, 28.

GOLDIN, A.S., J.S. NADLER & L.R. SETTER, 1953. The detectability of low-level radioactivity in water. *J. Amer. Water Works Ass.* 45:73.

SETTER, L.R., A.S. GOLDIN & J.S. NADER. 1954. Radioactivity assay of water and industrial wastes with internal proportional counter. *Anal. Chem.* 26:1304.

SETTER, L.R. 1964. Reliability of measurements of gross beta radioactivity in water. *J. Amer. Water Works Ass.* 56:228.

NATIONAL CENTER FOR RADIOLOGICAL HEALTH. 1967. Radioassay Procedures for Environmental Samples. PHS Publ. No. 999-RH-27 (Jan.). U.S. Dep. Health, Education & Welfare, Washington, D.C.

704   TOTAL RADIOACTIVE STRONTIUM AND STRONTIUM 90 IN WATER

The important radioactive nuclides of strontium produced in nuclear fission are ^{89}Sr and ^{90}Sr. Strontium 90 is one of the most hazardous of all fission products. It decays slowly, with a half-life of 28 yr. Upon ingestion, the strontium is concentrated in the bone; 10% of the occupational maximum permissible concentration for ^{90}Sr in water is 100 pCi/l, as compared to 10,000 pCi/l for ^{89}Sr, which has a half-life of only 50.5 days. The Federal Radiation Council intake guides for ^{90}Sr in Ranges I, II, and III are 0 to 20, 20 to 200, and 200 to 2,000 pCi/day/person, respectively, and for ^{89}Sr in Ranges I, II, and III the intake guides are 0 to 200, 200 to 2,000, and 2,000 to 20,000 pCi/day/person, respectively. The 1962 Public Health Service Drinking Water Standards limited the concentration of ^{90}Sr in water to 10 pCi/l when other sources of intake were not considered.

1. General Discussion

a. Principle: The following method is designed to measure total radioactive strontium (^{89}Sr and ^{90}Sr) or ^{90}Sr alone in drinking water or in filtered raw water. It is applicable to sewage and industrial wastes provided that steps are taken to destroy organic matter and eliminate other interfering ions. In this analysis, a known amount of inactive strontium ions, in the form of strontium nitrate, is added as a "carrier." The carrier, alkaline earths, and rare earths are precipitated as the carbonate to concentrate the radiostrontium. The carrier, along with the radionuclides of strontium, is sepa-

rated from other radioactive elements and inactive sample solids by precipitation as strontium nitrate from fuming nitric acid solution. The strontium carrier, together with the radionuclides of strontium, is finally precipitated as strontium carbonate, which is dried, weighed to determine recovery of carrier, and then measured for radioactivity. The activity in the final precipitate is due to radioactive strontium only, because all other radioactive elements have been removed. A correction is applied to compensate for losses of carrier and activity during the various purification steps. A delay in the count will give an increased counting rate due to the ingrowth of ^{90}Y.

b. Concentration technics: Because of the very low amount of radioactivity, a large sample must be taken and the activity concentrated by precipitation. Strontium nitrate and barium nitrate carriers are added to the sample. Sodium carbonate is then added to concentrate radiostrontium by precipitation of alkaline earth carbonates along with other radioactive elements. The supernate is discarded. The precipitate is dissolved and reprecipitated to remove interfering radionuclides.

c. Interference: Radioactive barium (^{140}Ba, ^{140}La) interferes in the determination of radioactive strontium inasmuch as it precipitates along with the radioactive strontium. This interference is eliminated by adding inactive barium nitrate carrier and separating this from the strontium by precipitating barium chromate in acetate buffer solution. Radium isotopes are also eliminated by this treatment.

In hard water, some calcium nitrate may be coprecipitated with strontium nitrate and can cause errors in measuring activity and recovery in the final precipitate. This interference is eliminated by repeated precipitations of strontium as the nitrate followed by leaching the $Sr(NO_3)_2$ with acetone (CAUTION).

For total radiostrontium, the precipitate should be counted within 3 to 4 hr after the final separation and before ingrowth of ^{90}Y.

d. Determination of ^{90}Sr: Because it is impossible to separate the isotopes ^{89}Sr and ^{90}Sr by any chemical procedure, the amount of ^{90}Sr is determined by separating and measuring the activity of ^{90}Y, its daughter. After equilibrium is reached, the activity of ^{90}Y is exactly equal to the activity of ^{90}Sr. Two alternate procedures are given for the separation of ^{90}Y. In the first method, ^{90}Y is separated by extraction into tributyl phosphate from concentrated nitric acid solution. It is back-extracted into dilute nitric acid and evaporated to dryness for beta counting. The second method consists of adding yttrium carrier, separating by precipitation as yttrium hydroxide, and finally precipitating yttrium oxalate for counting.

2. Apparatus

a. Counting instruments: Use either an internal proportional counter, gasflow, with scaler, timer, and register; or a thin end-window (Mylar) proportional or G-M counting chamber with scaler, timer, register amplifier, and preferably having an anticoincident system (low background).

b. Filter paper, Whatman No. 42, 2.4 cm in diameter; or glass fiber filters, 2.4 cm in diameter.

c. Two-piece filtering apparatus for 2.4-cm filters such as teflon filter holder*; stainless steel filter holder; or equivalent.

d. Stainless steel pans, about 50 mm in diameter and 7 mm deep, for counting solids deposited on pan bottom. For counting precipitates on 2.4-cm filters, use nylon disk with ring † on which the filter samples are mounted and covered by 0.25 mil Mylar film. ‡

3. Reagents

a. Strontium carrier (10 mg Sr^{2+}/ ml) standardized: Carefully add 24.16 g $Sr(NO_3)_2$ to a 1-l volumetric flask and dilute with distilled water to the mark. For standardization, pipet three 10.0-ml portions of strontium carrier solution into 40-ml centrifuge tubes and add 15 ml of $2N$ Na_2CO_3 solution. Stir, heat in a boiling water bath for 15 min, and cool. Filter the $SrCO_3$ precipitate through a tared fine-porosity sintered-glass crucible of 15-ml size. Wash the precipitate with three 5-ml portions of water and then with three 5-ml portions of absolute ethanol (or acetone). Wipe the crucible with absorbent tissue and dry to constant weight in an oven at 110 C (20 min). Cool in a desiccator and weigh.

$$Sr, mg/ml = \frac{(mg\ SrCO_3)\ (0.5935)}{10}$$

---

*Flurolon Laboratory, Box 305, Caldwell, N.J.
†Control Molding Corp., Staten Island, N.Y.
‡E.I. du Pont de Nemours, Wilmington, Del.

b. Barium carrier (10 mg Ba^{2+} / ml): Dissolve 19.0 g $Ba(NO_3)_2$ in distilled water and dilute to 1 l.

c. Rare earth carrier, mixed: Dissolve 12.8 g cerous nitrate hexahydrate, $Ce(NO_3)_3 \cdot 6H_2O$, 14 g zirconyl chloride octahydrate, $ZrOCl_2 \cdot 8H_2O$, and 25 g ferric chloride hexahydrate, $FeCl_3 \cdot 6H_2O$, in 600 ml distilled water containing 10 ml conc HCl, and dilute to 1 l.

d. Yttrium carrier: Dissolve 12.7 g yttrium oxide,§ Y_2O_3, in 30 ml conc HNO_3 by stirring and warming. Add an additional 20 ml of conc HNO_3 and dilute to 1 l with distilled water; 1 ml is equivalent to 10 mg Y, or approximately 34 mg $Y_2(C_2O_4)_3 \cdot 9H_2O$. Determine the exact equivalence by precipitating yttrium carrier in acid solution according to Section 704.4*c*2)–8) or by extracting yttrium carrier in acid solution according to Section 704.4*b*3)–11), following.

e. Acetate buffer solution: Dissolve 154 g ammonium acetate, $NH_4C_2H_3O_2$, in 700 ml distilled water, add 57 ml conc acetic acid, adjust pH to 5.5 by dropwise addition of conc acetic acid or 6N NH_4OH as necessary, and dilute to 1 l.

f. Acetic acid, 6N.

g. Acetone, anhydrous.

h. Ammonium hydroxide, 6N.

i. Hydrochloric acid, 6N.

j. Methyl red indicator, 0.1%: Dissolve 0.1 g methyl red in 100 ml distilled water.

§Yttrium oxide, Code 1118, American Potash and Chemical Corp., West Chicago, Ill., or equivalent. Yttrium oxide of purity less than Code 1118 may require purification because of radioactivity contamination.

k. Nitric acid, fuming (90%), conc, 14N, 6N, and 0.1N.

l. Oxalic acid, saturated solution: Approximately 11 g $H_2C_2O_4 \cdot 2H_2O$ in 100 ml distilled water.

m. Sodium carbonate solution, 2N: Dissolve 124 g sodium carbonate monohydrate, $Na_2CO_3 \cdot H_2O$, in distilled water and dilute to 1 l.

n. Sodium chromate solution, 0.5M: Dissolve 117 g sodium chromate tetrahydrate, $Na_2CrO_4 \cdot 4H_2O$, in distilled water and dilute to 1 l.

o. Sodium hydroxide, 6N: Dissolve 240 g NaOH in distilled water and dilute to 1 l.

p. Tributyl phosphate, reagent grade: Shake with an equal volume of 14N nitric acid to equilibrate. Separate and discard the nitric acid washings.

4. Procedure

a. Total radiostrontium:

1) To 1 l of drinking water, or a filtered sample of raw water in a beaker, add 2.0 ml of conc HNO_3 and mix. Add 2.0 ml each of strontium and barium carriers and mix well. (A precipitate of $BaSO_4$ may form if the water is high in sulfate ion, but this will cause no difficulties.) A smaller sample may be used if it contains at least 25 pCi of strontium. The suspended matter that has been filtered off may be digested [see Gross Alpha and Gross Beta Radioactivity, 703.4*f*1)], diluted, and analyzed separately.

2) Heat the solution to boiling, then add 20 ml 6N NaOH and 20 ml 2N sodium carbonate. Stir and allow to simmer at 90 to 95 C for about 1 hr.

3) Set beaker aside until the precipitate has settled (about 1 to 3 hr).

4) Decant and discard the clear supernate. Transfer the precipitate to a 40-ml centrifuge tube and centrifuge. Discard the supernate.

5) Add, dropwise (CAUTION—effervescence), 4 ml conc HNO_3 to the precipitate. Heat to boiling, stir, then cool under running water.

6) Add 20 ml fuming HNO_3, cool 5 to 10 min in ice bath, stir, and centrifuge. Discard the supernate.

7) Add 4 ml of water to the residue, stir, and heat to boiling to dissolve the strontium. Centrifuge while hot to remove remaining insolubles and decant supernate to a clean centrifuge tube. Add 2 ml $6N$ nitric acid to the residue, heat to boiling, centrifuge while hot, and combine the supernate with the aqueous supernate. Discard the insoluble residue of SiO_2, $BaSO_4$, and so on.

8) Cool combined supernates, then add 20 ml fuming HNO_3, cool 5 to 10 min in ice bath, stir, centrifuge, and discard the supernate.

9) Add 4 ml water to the precipitate and dissolve by heating. Repeat Step 8) preceding.

10) Repeat Step 9) preceding if more than 200 mg Ca were present in the water sample.

11) After the last HNO_3 precipitation, invert tube in a beaker for about 10 min to drain off most of the excess HNO_3 and then add 20 ml anhydrous acetone to the precipitate. Stir thoroughly, cool, and centrifuge. Discard the supernate (CAUTION).

12) Dissolve the precipitate of $Sr(NO_3)_2 + Ba(NO_3)_2$ in 10 ml distilled water and boil for 30 sec to remove any remaining acetone.

13) Add 0.25 ml (5 drops) mixed rare earth carrier and precipitate rare earth hydroxides by making the solution basic with $6N$ NH_4OH. Digest in a boiling water bath for 10 min. Cool, centrifuge, and decant the supernate to a clean tube. Discard the precipitate.

14) Repeat Step 13) preceding.

Note the time of rare earth precipitation, which marks the beginning of the ^{90}Y ingrowth period. Do not delay the procedure more than a few hours after the separation; otherwise, false results will be obtained because of the ingrowth of ^{90}Y.

15) Add 2 drops methyl red indicator and then add $6N$ acetic acid dropwise with stirring until the indicator changes from yellow to red.

16) Add 5 ml acetate buffer solution, heat to boiling, and add dropwise, with stirring, 2 ml sodium chromate solution. Digest in a boiling water bath for 5 min. Cool, centrifuge, and decant the supernate to a clean tube. Discard the residue.

17) Add 2 ml $6N$ NaOH to the supernate and then add 5 ml $2N$ sodium carbonate solution and heat to boiling. Cool in an ice bath (about 5 min) and centrifuge. Discard supernate.

18) Add 15 ml distilled water to the precipitate, stir, centrifuge, and discard the wash water.

19) Repeat Step 18), and proceed either as in Step 20a) or 20b), below. *Be sure to save this precipitate* if a determination of ^{90}Sr is required.

20a) Slurry the precipitate with a small volume of distilled H_2O and transfer to a tared stainless steel pan.

Dry under an infrared lamp, cool, weigh and count‖ the precipitate of $SrCO_3$.#

20b) Transfer the precipitate to a tared paper or glass filter mounted in a two-piece funnel. Allow gravity settling for uniform deposition and then apply suction. Wash precipitate with three 5-ml portions of water, three 5-ml portions of 95% alcohol, and three 5-ml portions of ethyl ether or acetone. Dry in an oven at 110 to 125 C for 15 to 30 min, cool, weigh,# mount on a nylon disk and ring with Mylar cover, and count.

21) Calculation:

$$\text{Total Sr activity in pCi/l} = \frac{b}{adf \times 2.22}$$

‖Strontium 90 in thick samples is counted with low efficiency; hence, a first count within hours favors ^{89}Sr counting, and a recount after 3 to 6 days that exceeds the first count provides a rough estimate of the ^{90}Y ingrowth—see Figure 704:1 and R.J. Velten (1966) below.

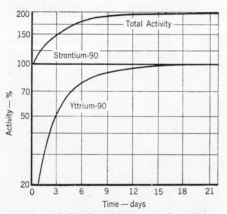

Figure 704:1. Yttrium 90 vs. strontium 90 activity as a function of time.

#When a determination of total strontium is not required, weigh the precipitate [Step 20a) or 20b)] for carrier recovery but do not count. Then proceed with ^{90}Sr determination according to Section 704.4b following.

where:

a = beta counter efficiency [see Step 22) below]

$d = \dfrac{\text{mg final SrCO}_3 \text{ precipitate}}{\text{mg SrCO}_3 \text{ in 2 ml of carrier}}$

= Correction for carrier recovery [see Step 23) below],

f = sample volume, liters,

b = beta activity, net cpm = $(i/t) - k$,

i = total counts accumulated,

t = time of counting, min, and

k = background, cpm.

22) Counting efficiency: As a first estimate, when mounting sample according to Step 20a), convert counts per minute to disintegrations per minute, based on the beta activity of cesium 137 standard solutions having a sample thickness equivalent to that of the $SrCO_3$ precipitate. More precise measurements may follow a second count after substantial ingrowth of ^{90}Y from ^{90}Sr, but this precision is not warranted for the usual total radiostrontium determination. When mounting samples according to Step 20b), determine self-absorption curves by separately precipitating standard solutions of ^{89}Sr and ^{90}Sr as the carbonate (see gross beta in Section 703).

23) Correction for carrier recovery: 20 mg Sr are equivalent to 33.7 mg $SrCO_3$. Should more than traces of stable strontium be present in the water sample, it would act as carrier; hence its determination, as by flame photometry, would be required.

*b. Strontium 90** by extraction of yttrium 90:*

Store the strontium carbonate precipitate, as in ¶ 4a 20), for at least 2 wk to

---

**See footnote to Step 20a) when a determination for only ^{90}Sr is required.

allow ingrowth of ^{90}Y and then proceed as given in this section or in an alternate procedure in Section 704.4c following.

1a) Place a small funnel upright into the mouth of a 60-ml separatory funnel; then place pan with precipitate, as in Step 20a), in funnel and add, dropwise, 1 ml 6N HNO₃. (CAUTION—effervescence.) Tilt pan to empty into funnel and rinse pan twice with 2-ml portions of 6N HNO₃.

1b) Uncover precipitate from filter, as in Step 20b), and transfer filter with forceps to upright funnel in mouth of 60-ml separatory funnel as in ¶ 1a above. Dislodge bulk of precipitate into funnel stem. Dropwise, add with caution 1 ml 6N HNO₃ to filter, which removes residual precipitate and dissolves bulk precipitate. Rinse filter and funnel twice with 2-ml portions of 6N HNO₃.

2) Remove filter or pan and add 10 ml fuming HNO₃ to separatory funnel through the upright funnel.

3) Remove upright funnel and add 1 ml yttrium carrier to solution in a separatory funnel.

4) Add 5.0 ml tributyl phosphate reagent, shake thoroughly for 3 to 5 min, allow the phases to separate, and transfer the aqueous layer to a second 60-ml separatory funnel.

5) Add 5.0 ml tributyl phosphate reagent, shake 5 min, allow the phases to separate, and transfer the aqueous layer to a third 60-ml separatory funnel.

6) Combine the organic extractants in the first and second funnels into one funnel and wash the organic phase twice with 5-ml portions of 14N HNO₃. Record the time as the beginning of ^{90}Y decay (combine acid washings with aqueous phase in the third funnel if a second ingrowth of ^{90}Y is desired).

7) Back-extract ^{90}Y from the combined organic phases with 10 ml of 0.1N HNO₃ for 5 min.

8) Continue as given in Section 704.4c, Steps 6)-8) below or transfer the aqueous phase from Step 7) immediately above into a 50-ml beaker and evaporate on a hotplate to 5 to 10 ml.

9) Repeat Step 7) above and transfer the aqueous phase to the beaker in Step 8) preceding; evaporate to 5 to 10 ml.

10) Transfer residual solution in beaker to a tared stainless steel counting pan and evaporate.

11) Rinse beaker twice with 2-ml portions of 0.1N HNO₃; add rinsings to counting pan, evaporate to dryness, and weigh.

12) Count in an internal proportional or end-window counter and calculate ^{90}Sr as given in Section 4c9) following.

c. Strontium 90 by oxalate precipitation of yttrium 90:**

1) Quantitatively transfer the SrCO₃ precipitate to a 40-ml centrifuge tube with 2 ml of 6N HNO₃. Add acid dropwise during dissolution. (CAUTION—effervescence.) Use 0.1N HNO₃ for rinsing.

2) Add 1 ml yttrium carrier, 2 drops methyl red indicator and, dropwise, add conc NH₄OH to the methyl red end point.

3) Add an additional 5 ml conc NH₄OH and record the time, which is the end of ^{90}Y ingrowth and the beginning of decay; centrifuge, and decant supernate to a beaker (save supernate and washings for a second ingrowth if desired).

***

**See footnote to Step 20a) when a determination for only ^{90}Sr is required.

4) Wash the precipitate twice with 20-ml portions of hot distilled water.

5) Add 5 to 10 drops of $6N$ HNO_3, stir to dissolve precipitate, add 25 ml distilled water, and heat in a water bath at 90 C.

6) Gradually add 15 to 20 drops of saturated oxalic acid reagent with stirring and adjust the pH to 1.5 to 2.0 (pH meter or indicator paper) by adding conc NH_4OH dropwise. Digest the precipitate for 5 min and then cool in an ice bath with occasional stirring.

7) Transfer the precipitate to a tared glass fiber filter in a two-piece funnel. Allow the precipitate to settle by gravity (for uniform deposition) and then apply suction. Wash precipitate in sequence with 10 to 15 ml hot distilled water and then three times with 95% ethyl alcohol and three times with diethyl ether.

8) Air-dry the precipitate with suction for 2 min, weigh, mount on a nylon disk and ring with Mylar cover, count, and calculate ^{90}Sr as follows.

9) Calculation:

$$^{90}Sr \ pCi/l = \frac{net \ cpm}{a \ b \ c \ d \ f \ g \times 2.22}$$

where:

a = counting efficiency for ^{90}Y,
b = chemical yield of extracting or precipitating ^{90}Y,
c = ingrowth correction factor if not in secular equilibrium,
d = chemical yield of strontium determined gravimetrically or by flame photometry,
f = volume, in liters, of original sample,
g = ^{90}Y decay factor, $e^{-\lambda t}$, and
e = base of natural logarithms,
λ = $0.693/T_{1/2}$, where $T_{1/2}$ for ^{90}Y is 64.2 hr, and
t = time between separation and counting, hr.

5. Precision and Accuracy

In a collaborative study of two sets of paired, moderately hard water samples containing known additions of radionuclides, 12 laboratories determined the total radiostrontium and 10 laboratories determined ^{90}Sr. The results of one sample from one laboratory were rejected as an outlier.

The average recoveries of added total radiostrontium from the four samples were 99, 99, 96, and 93%. The precision (random error) at the 95% confidence level was 10 and 12% for the two sets of paired samples. The method was biased on the low side, but not seriously biased.

The average recoveries of added ^{90}Sr from the four samples were 90, 96, 80, and 94%. The precision (random error) at the 95% confidence level was 14 and 28% for the two sets of paired samples. The method was biased toward the low side, but not seriously biased.

6. Bibliography

HAHN, R.B. & C.P. STRAUB. 1955. Determination of radioactive strontium and barium in water. *J. Amer. Water Works Ass.* 47:335.

GOLDIN, A.S., R.J. VELTEN & G.W. FRISHKORN. 1959. Determination of radioactive strontium. *Anal. Chem.* 31:1490.

GOLDIN, A.S. & R.J. VELTEN. 1961. Application of tributyl phosphate extraction to the determination of strontium 90. *Anal. Chem.* 33:149.

VELTEN, R.J. 1966. Resolution of Sr-89 and Sr-90 in environmental media by an instrumental technique. *Nucl. Instrum. Methods* 42:169.

705 RADIUM IN WATER BY PRECIPITATION

The determination of radium by precipitation is a screening technic applicable in particular to drinking water. As long as the concentration of radium is less than the ^{226}Ra drinking water standard, the need for examination by a more specific method is minimal.

There are four naturally occurring radium isotopes—11.6-day radium 223, 3.6-day radium 224, 1,600-yr radium 226, and 5.75-yr radium 228. Radium 223 is a member of the uranium 235 series, radium 224 and radium 228 are members of the thorium series, and radium 226 is a member of the uranium 238 series. The contribution of radium 228 (a beta emitter) to the total radium alpha activity is negligible because of the 1.9-yr half-life of its first alpha-emitting daughter product, thorium 228. The other three radium isotopes are alpha emitters; each gives rise to a series of relatively short-lived daughter products, including three more alpha emitters. Because of the difference in half-lives of the nuclides in these series, the isotopes of radium can be identified by the rate of ingrowth and decay of their daughters in a barium sulfate precipitate.[1-3] The ingrowth of alpha activity from radium 226 increases at a rate governed primarily by the 3.8-day half-life radon 222. The ingrowth of alpha activity in radium 223 is complete by the time a radium-barium precipitate can be prepared for counting. The ingrowths of the first two alpha-emitting daughters of radium 224 are complete within a few minutes and the third alpha daughter activity increases at a rate governed by the 10.6-hr half-life of lead 212. The activity of the radium 224 itself, with a 3.6-day half-life, is also decreasing, leading to a rather complicated ingrowth and decay curve.

The Federal Radiation Council has provided guidance for federal agencies conducting activities designed to limit exposure of people to radiation from radionuclides deposited in the body as a result of their occurrence in the environment. The recommended radiation protection guides (RPG) for radium 226 transient rates of intake are 0 to 2, 2 to 20, and 20 to 200 pCi/person/day for the Ranges I, II, and III, respectively. Range III calls for the application of control measures to reduce the intake to within Range II or below.

Inasmuch as these guides apply to total intake (from air, food, and water), the Public Health Service Advisory Committee on the 1962 Drinking Water Standards recommended a limit of 3 pCi/l for radium 226. The standard specified radium 226 in particular, because other radium isotopes are much less important in causing internal radiation exposure.

The principles of the two common methods for measuring radium are (a) the alpha-counting of a barium-radium sulfate precipitate that has been isolated from the sample and purified, and (b) the measurement of the radon 222 produced from the radium 226 in a sample or in a soluble concentrate isolated from the sample. The former technic includes all alpha-emitting radium isotopes present in the sample, whereas the latter (emanation) technic is quite, but not absolutely, specific for radium 226. At higher concentrations of total radium (above the former drinking water standard), the total alpha activity isolated by the precipitation technics requires further examination, such as a measurement of its rate of decay, to determine the radium 226 content. Preferably, the radium 226 content should be determined by the emanation technic, using either a new portion of the original sample or a solution of the barium-radium sulfate precipitate.

1. General Discussion

a. Principle: The following method is designed to measure radium in clear water. It is applicable to sewage and industrial wastes, provided that steps are taken to destroy organic matter and eliminate other interfering ions. (See Gross Alpha and Gross Beta Radioactivity, 703 4*f*) However, ignition of sample ash should be avoided or a fusion will be necessary. Radium carried by barium sulfate is determined by alpha-counting. Lead and barium carriers are added to the sample containing alkaline citrate, then sulfuric acid is added to precipitate radium, barium, and lead as sulfates. The precipitate is purified by washing with nitric acid, dissolving in alkaline EDTA, and reprecipitating as radium-barium sulfate after adjustment of the pH to 4.5. This slightly acidic EDTA keeps other naturally occurring alpha emitters and the lead carrier in solution.

2. Apparatus

a. Counting instruments: One of the following is required:

1) *Internal proportional counter*, gas-flow, with scaler and register.

2) *Alpha scintillation counter*, silver-activated zinc sulfide phosphor deposited on thin plastic (Mylar), with photo-multiplier tube, scaler, timer, and register; or

3) *Proportional counter*, thin end-window, gas-flow, with scaler and register.

b. Membrane filter holder, or stainless steel (or teflon) filter funnels (Tracerlab), with Fisher filtrator or an equivalent vacuum source.

c. Membrane filters (Millipore, type HAWP), or glass fiber filters.*

3. Reagents

a. Citric acid, 1*M:* Dissolve 210 g citric acid, $H_3C_6H_5O_7 \cdot H_2O$, in distilled water and dilute to 1 l.

b. Ammonium hydroxide, conc and 5*N:* The strength of old 5*N* ammonium hydroxide solution must be verified before use.

c. Lead nitrate carrier: Dissolve 160 g lead nitrate, $Pb(NO_3)_2$, in distilled water and dilute to 1 l; 1 ml = 100 mg Pb.

d. Stock barium chloride solution: Dissolve 17.79 g barium chloride, $BaCl_2 \cdot 2H_2O$, in distilled water and dilute to 1 l in a volumetric flask; 1 ml = 10 mg Ba.

e. Barium chloride carrier: To a 100-ml volumetric flask, add 20.00 ml of stock barium chloride solution using a transfer pipet, add distilled water to the mark, and mix; 1 ml = 2.00 mg Ba.

f. Methyl orange indicator solution: Dissolve 0.5 g methyl orange in 1 l distilled water.

g. Phenolphthalein indicator solution: Dissolve 0.5 g phenolphthalein in

---

* No. 934-AH, diameter 2.4 cm, H. Reeve Angel and Co.

50 ml 95% ethyl alcohol, add 50 ml distilled water, and mix.

b. Bromcresol green indicator solution: Dissolve 0.1 g bromcresol green sodium salt in 100 ml distilled water.

i. Sulfuric acid, 18N.

j. Nitric acid, conc.

k. EDTA reagent, 0.25M: Add 93 g disodium ethylenediaminetetraacetate dihydrate to distilled water, dilute to 1 l, and mix.

l. Acetic acid, conc.

m. Ethyl alcohol, 95%.

n. Acetone.

o. Lucite solution: Dissolve 50 mg Lucite in 100 ml acetone.

p. Standard radium 226 solution: Prepare as directed in method for radium 226 by radon 222, Section 706. 3d-f below, except that in ¶ f (standard radium 226 solution), add 0.50 ml of barium chloride stock solution (Section 706.3d, method for total radium) before adding the ^{226}Ra solution; 1 ml final standard radium solution so prepared contains 2.00 mg Ba/ml and approximately 3 pCi ^{226}Ra/ml after the necessary correcting factors are applied.

4. Procedure for Radium in Drinking Water and for Dissolved Radium

a. To 1 l drinking water or filtered raw water in a 1,500-ml beaker, add 5 ml 1M citric acid, 2.5 ml conc NH₄OH, 2 ml lead nitrate carrier, and 3.00 ml barium chloride carrier. In each batch of samples include a blank consisting of distilled water.

b. Heat to boiling and add 10 drops methyl orange indicator.

c. While stirring, slowly add 18N

H₂SO₄ to obtain a permanent pink color; then add 0.25 ml acid in excess.

d. Boil gently 5 to 10 min.

e. Set the beaker aside and let stand until the precipitate has settled (3 to 5 hr or more).†

f. Decant and discard the clear supernate. Transfer the precipitate to a 40-ml or larger centrifuge tube, centrifuge, decant, and discard the supernate.

g. Rinse the wall of the centrifuge tube with a 10-ml portion of conc HNO₃, stir precipitate with a glass rod, centrifuge, and discard supernate. Repeat the rinsing and washing two more times.

h. To the precipitate in the centrifuge tube, add 10 ml water and 1 to 2 drops phenolphthalein indicator solution. Stir and loosen precipitate from bottom of tube (using a glass rod if necessary) and add 5N NH₄OH, dropwise, until the solution is definitely alkaline (red). Add 10 ml EDTA reagent and 3 ml 5N NH₄OH. Stir occasionally for 2 min. Most of the precipitate should dissolve, but a slight turbidity may remain.

i. Warm in a steam bath to clear solution (about 10 min), but do not heat for an unnecessarily long period.‡ Add conc acetic acid, dropwise, until the red

---

† If original concentrations of isotopes of radium other than ^{226}Ra are of interest, the date and time of this original precipitation should be noted as the separation of the isotopes from their parents; the settling time should be minimal; and the procedure should be completed through ¶ j without delay. Assuming the presence of and separation of parents, decay of ^{223}Ra and ^{224}Ra begins at the time of the first precipitation, but ingrowth of decay products is timed from the second precipitation (¶ i). The time of the first precipitation is not needed if the objective is to check the final precipitate for its ^{226}Ra content only.

‡ If solution does not clear in 10 min, cool, add another ml of 5N NH₄OH, let stand 2 min, and heat for another 10-min period.

color disappears; add 2 or 3 drops bromcresol green indicator solution and continue to add conc acetic acid dropwise, while stirring with a glass rod, until the indicator turns green (aqua).§ Barium sulfate will precipitate. Note date and time of precipitation as zero time for ingrowth of alpha activity. Digest in a steam bath for 5 to 10 min, cool, and centrifuge. Discard supernate. The final pH should be about 4.5, which is sufficiently low to destroy the Ba-EDTA complex, but not the Pb-EDTA. A pH much below 4.5 will cause the precipitation of $PbSO_4$.

j. Wash the Ba-Ra sulfate precipitate with distilled water and mount in a manner suitable for counting as given in ¶s *k, l,* or *m* following.

k. Transfer the Ba-Ra sulfate precipitate to a tared stainless steel planchet with a minimum of 95% ethyl alcohol and evaporate under an infrared lamp. Add 2 ml acetone, 2 drops Lucite solution, disperse the precipitate evenly, and evaporate under an infrared lamp. Dry in oven at 110 C, weigh, and determine the alpha activity, preferably with an internal proportional counter. Calculate the net counts per minute and the weight of precipitate.

l. Weigh a membrane filter, a counting dish, and a weight (glass ring) as a unit. Transfer precipitate to the tared membrane filter in a holder and wash with 15 to 25 ml distilled water. Place membrane filter in the dish, add the glass ring, and dry at 110 C. Weigh and count in one of the counters mentioned under ¶ *2a* above. Calculate net counts

per minute and weight of the precipitate.

m. Add 20 ml distilled water to the Ba-Ra sulfate precipitate, allow to settle in a steam bath, cool, and filter through a special funnel with a tared glass fiber filter. Dry the precipitate in the oven at 110 C to constant weight, cool, and weigh. Mount the precipitate on a nylon disk and ring with an alpha phosphor on Mylar,[4] and count in an alpha scintillation counter without a ZnS phosphor. Calculate net counts per minute and weight of the precipitate.

n. If the isotopic composition of the precipitate is to be estimated, additional counting will be required, as mentioned in the calculation below.

o. Determination of combined efficiency and self-absorption factor: Prepare standards from 1 l distilled water and the standard radium 226 solution (¶ *3p* preceding). At least one blank should be included. The barium content will impose an upper limit of 3.0 ml on the volume of the standard radium 226 solution that can be used. If *x* is the volume of standard radium 226 solution added, then add (3.00 − *x*) ml of barium chloride carrier (¶ *3e* above). Analysis of standards is like that for samples, beginning with ¶ *4a,* but omitting the 3.00-ml barium chloride carrier.

From the observed net count rate, calculate the combined factor, *bc,* from the formula:

$$bc = \frac{\text{net cpm}}{ad \times 2.22 \times \text{pCi radium 226}} \, \|$$

where:

ad = ingrowth factor (see below) multiplied by chemical yield.

---

§ The end point is most easily determined by comparison with a solution of similar composition that has been adjusted to pH 4.5 using a pH meter.

‖ See calculation that follows.

If all chemical yields on samples and standards are not essentially equal, the factor bc will not be a constant. In this event, it will be necessary to construct a curve relating the factor bc to varying weights of recovered barium sulfate.

5. Calculation

$$\text{Radium, pCi/1} = \frac{\text{net cpm}}{a\,b\,c\,d\,e \times 2.22}$$

where:

a = ingrowth factor (as shown in the following tabulation):

Ingrowth (hr)	Alpha Activity from [226]Ra
0	1.000
1	1.016
2	1.036
3	1.058
4	1.080
5	1.102
6	1.124
24	1.489
48	1.905
72	2.253

b = efficiency factor for alpha counting,
c = self-absorption factor,
d = chemical yield, and
e = sample volume, liters.

The calculations are based on the assumption that the radium is radium 226. If the observed concentration approaches 3 pCi/l, it may be desirable to follow the rate of ingrowth and estimate the isotopic content[2,3] or, preferably, to determine radium 226 by radon 222.

The optimum ingrowth periods can be selected only if the ratios and identities of the radium isotopes are known. The number of observed count rates at different ages must be equal to or greater than the number of radium isotopes present in a mixture. In the general case, suitable ages for counting are 3 to 18 hr for the first count; for isotopic analysis, additional counting at 7, 14, or 28 days is suggested, depending on the number of isotopes in mixture. The amounts of the various radium isotopes can be determined by solving a set of simultaneous equations.[4] This approach is most satisfactory when radium 226 is the predominant isotope; in other situations, the approach suffers on the basis of statistical counting errors.

6. Precision and Accuracy

In a collaborative study, 20 laboratories analyzed four water samples for total (dissolved) radium. The radionuclide composition of these reference samples is shown in Table 705:I. It should be noted that Samples C and D had a [224]Ra concentration equal to that of [226]Ra.

The four results from each of two laboratories and two results from a third laboratory were rejected as outliers. The average recoveries of radium 226 from the remaining A, B, C, and D samples were 97.5, 98.7, 94.9, and 99.4%, respectively. At the 95% confidence level, the precision (random error) was 28% and 30% for the two sets of paired samples. The method is biased low for radium 226, but not seriously. The method appears satisfactory for radium 226 alone or in the presence of an equal activity of radium 224 when correction for radium 224 interference is made from a second count.

For the determination of [224]Ra in Samples C and D, the results of two laboratories were excluded. Hence the average recoveries were 51 and 45% for Samples C and D, respectively. At the 95% confidence level, the precision was 46% for this pair of samples. The results

TABLE 705:I. CHEMICAL AND RADIOCHEMICAL COMPOSITION OF SAMPLES USED TO DETERMINE ACCURACY AND PRECISION OF RADIUM 226 METHOD

Radionuclide Composition	Samples			
	Pair 1		Pair 2	
	A	B	C	D
Radium 226,* pCi/l	12.12	8.96	25.53	18.84
Thorium 228,* pCi/l	none	none	25.90	19.12
Uranium, natural, pCi/l	105	77.9	27.7	20.5
Lead 210,* pCi/l	11.5	8.5	23.7	17.5
Strontium 90,* pCi/l	49.1	36.3	13.9	10.2
Cesium 137, pCi/l	50.3	37.2	12.7	9.5
NaCl, mg/l	60	60	300	300
CaSO$_4$, mg/l	30	30	150	150
MgCl$_2$•6H$_2$O, mg/l	30	30	150	150
KCl, mg/l	5	5	10	10

*Daughter products were in substantial secular equilibrium.

indicated that the method for ^{224}Ra is seriously biased low. When the recoveries for radium 224 did not agree with those for radium 226, a search revealed that this may have been due, in part, to incomplete instructions given in the method to account for the transitory nature of ^{224}Ra activity. The method now contains footnotes calling attention to the importance of the time of counting. Still uncertain is the degree of separation of radium 224 from its parent, thorium 228, in ¶s 4a through g above.

Radium 223 and ^{224}Ra analysis by this method may be satisfactory, but special refinements and further investigations are required.

7. References

1. KIRBY, H.W. 1954. Decay and growth tables for naturally occurring radioactive series. *Anal. Chem.* 26:1063.
2. SILL, C. 1960. Determination of radium-226, thorium-230, and thorium-232, U. S. Atomic Energy Comm. Rep. No. TID 7616 (Oct.). USAEC, Washington, D.C.
3. GOLDIN, A.S. 1961. Determination of dissolved radium. *Anal. Chem.* 33:406.
4. HALLDEN, N.A. & J.H. HARLEY. 1960. An improved alpha-counting technique. *Anal. Chem.* 32:1961.

706 RADIUM 226 BY RADON IN WATER (SOLUBLE, SUSPENDED, AND TOTAL)

1. General Discussion

a. Introduction: The discussion of radium, particularly in drinking water, presented in Section 705 preceding, is also pertinent to the determination of radium 226 by radon 222. In this method, *total* radium 226 means the sum of suspended and dissolved radium 226. Radon means radon 222 unless otherwise specified.

b. Principle: The radium in water is concentrated and separated from sample solids by coprecipitation with a relatively large amount of barium as the sulfate. The precipitate is treated to remove silicates, if present, and to decompose insoluble radium compounds, fumed with phosphoric acid to remove SO_3, and dissolved in HCl. The completely dissolved radium is placed in a bubbler, which is then closed and stored for a period of several days to 4 wk for ingrowth of radon. The bubbler is connected to an evacuated system and the radon gas is removed from the liquid by aeration, dried with a desiccant, and collected in a counting chamber. The counting chamber consists of a dome-topped scintillation cell coated inside with silver-activated zinc sulfide phosphor; a transparent window forms the bottom (Figure 706:1). The chamber rests on a photomultiplier tube during counting. About 4 hr after radon collection, the alpha-counting rate of radon and decay products is at equilibrium, and a count is obtained and related to radium 226 standards similarly treated.

The counting gas used to purge radon from the liquid to the counting chamber

may be helium, nitrogen, or air. The gas should be freed of radon by aging. Although all these gases are satisfactory, the yield and pulse heights of scintillations are improved if helium is used.

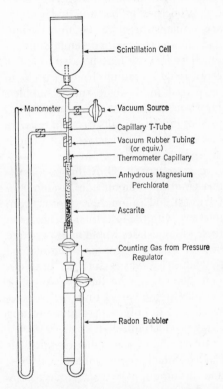

Scintillation Cell
Manometer
Vacuum Source
Capillary T-Tube
Vacuum Rubber Tubing (or equiv.)
Thermometer Capillary
Anhydrous Magnesium Perchlorate
Ascarite
Counting Gas from Pressure Regulator
Radon Bubbler

Figure 706:1. De-emanation assembly.

Various radon (emanation) technics for determining radon 226 are available. Some employ a minimum of chemistry but require high dilution of the sample solution and large chambers for counting of the radon 222.[1] Others involve more chemical separation, concentration, and purification of radium

226 before de-emanation into counting cells of either the ionization or alpha scintillation types.

The selected method[2] requires a moderate amount of chemistry coupled with a sensitive alpha scintillation count of radon 222 plus daughter products in a small chamber.[3]

c. Concentration technics: The chemical properties of barium and radium are similar; therefore, because barium does not interfere with de-emanation, as much as 100 mg may be used to aid in coprecipitating radium from a sample to be placed in a single radon bubbler. However, because some radium 226 is present in barium salts, reagent tests are necessary in order to account for radium 226 introduced in this way.

d. Interferences: Only the gaseous alpha-emitting radionuclides, radon 219 (actinon) and radon 220 (thoron), can interfere with the test. Interference from these radionuclides would be expected to be very rare in water not contaminated by industrial wastes such as uranium mill elements.[2] The half-lives of these nuclides are only 3.92 and 54.5 sec, respectively, so only their alpha-emitting decay products interfere.

Interference from stable chemicals is limited. Small amounts of lead, calcium, and strontium, which are collected by the barium sulfate, do not interfere. However, lead may cause deterioration of the platinum ware. Calcium at a concentration of 300 mg/l and other dissolved solids (in brines) at 269,000 mg/l cause no difficulty.[4]

The formation of precipitates in excess of a few milligrams during the radon 222 ingrowth period is a warning that modifications[2] may be necessary because radon 222 recovery may be impaired.

e. Minimum detectable concentration: The minimum detectable concentration depends on counter characteristics, background-counting rate of scintillation cell, length of counting period, and contamination of apparatus and environment by radium 226. Without reagent purification, the overall reagent blank (excluding background) should be between 0.03 and 0.05 pCi radium 226, which may be considered the minimum detectable amount under routine conditions.

2. Apparatus

a. Scintillation counter assembly with a photomultiplier (PM) tube 5 cm (2 in.) or more in diameter, normally mounted, face up, in a light-tight housing: The photomultiplier tube, preamplifier, high-voltage supply, and scaler may be contained in one chassis; or the PM tube and the preamplifier may be used as an accessory with a proportional counter or a separate scaler. A high-voltage safety switch should open automatically when the light cover is removed, to avoid damage to the photomultiplier tube.

The preamplifier should incorporate a variable gain adjustment. The counter should be equipped with a flexible ground wire attached to the chassis and to the neck of the scintillation cell by means of an alligator clip or similar device. The operating voltage is ascertained by determining a plateau using ^{222}Rn in the scintillation cell as the alpha source. The slope of the plateau should not exceed 2%/100 V. The counter and scintillation cell should be calibrated and used as a unit when more than one counter is available. The background-counting rate for the counter assembly without the scintillation cell in place should be of the order of 0.00 to 0.03 cpm.

b. Scintillation cells,[2, 3] Lucas-type, preferably having a volume of 95 to 140 ml, made in the laboratory, or commercially available.*

c. Radon bubblers, capacity 18 to 25 ml, as shown in Figure 706:1.† The glass stopcocks must be gastight and the fritted glass disk must be the equivalent of Corning's medium porosity. One bubbler is used for a standard ^{226}Ra solution and one for each sample and blank in a batch.[2]

d. Manometer, open-end capillary tube or vacuum gauge having volume that is small compared to volume of scintillation cell, 0 to 760 mm Hg.

e. Gas purification tube, 7 to 8 mm OD standard-wall glass tubing, 100 to 120 mm long, constricted at lower end to hold glass wool plug (Figure 706:1); thermometer capillary tubing.

f. Sample bottles, polyethylene, 2- to 4-l capacity.

g. Membrane filters.‡

h. Gas supply: Helium, nitrogen, or air aged in high-pressure cylinder with two-stage pressure regulator and needle valve.

i. Silicone grease, high-vacuum.

j. Sealing wax, "Pyseal"§ (or equivalent), low-melting.

k. Laboratory glassware: Excepting bubblers, all glassware must be decontaminated before and between uses by

---

*William H. Johnston Laboratories, 3617 Woodland Ave., Baltimore, Md. 21215.

†Available from Corning Glass Works, Special Sales Section, Corning, N.Y. 14830.

‡Type HAWP (Millipore Filter Corp., Bedford, Mass.), or equivalent.

§Available from Fisher Scientific Co., Pittsburgh, Pa.

heating for 1 hr in EDTA decontaminating solution at 90 to 100 C, then rinsed in water, $1N$ HCl, and again in distilled water to dissolve Ba(Ra)SO$_4$.

The removal of previous samples from bubblers and rinsing is described in Section 706.4*b*17). More extensive cleaning of bubblers requires removal of the wax from joints, silicone grease from stopcocks, and the last traces of barium-radium compounds.

l. Platinum ware: Crucibles (20 to 30 ml) or dishes (50 to 75 ml), large dish (for flux preparation), and platinum-tipped tongs (preferably Blair type). Platinum ware is cleaned by immersion and rotation in a molten bath of potassium pyrosulfate, removing, cooling, rinsing in hot tap water, digesting in hot $6N$ HCl, rinsing in distilled water, and finally flaming over a burner.

3. Reagents

a. Stock barium chloride solution: Dissolve 17.79 g barium chloride, BaCl$_2$•2H$_2$O, in distilled water and dilute to 1 l; 1 ml = 10 mg Ba.

b. Dilute barium chloride solution: Dilute 200.0 ml stock barium chloride solution to 1,000 ml in a volumetric flask, as needed; 1 ml = 2.00 mg Ba. Allow to stand 24 hr and filter through a membrane filter.

Optionally, approximately 40,000 dpm of ^{133}Ba may be added to this solution before dilution in the volumetric flask. Account must be taken of the stable barium carrier added with the ^{133}Ba and with the diluting solution, so that the final barium concentration is near 2 mg/l. (The use of ^{133}Ba provides a convenient means of checking on the recovery of ^{226}Ra from the sample (Section 706.6). The $BaCl_2$ solution containing ^{133}Ba is used in Sections 706.4b3), 4c8), and 4d3) and must be measured accurately from a pipet or buret. It is *not* used in ¶ *d* below; instead, a separate dilution of the stock barium chloride solution is used for preparing the ^{226}Ra standard solutions.

c. Acid barium chloride solution: To 20 ml conc HCl in a 1-l volumetric flask, add dilute barium chloride solution to the mark and mix.

d. Stock radium 226 solution: Take every precaution to avoid unnecessary contamination of the working area, equipment, and glassware, preferably by preparing the ^{226}Ra standards in a separate area or room reserved for this purpose. Obtain a National Bureau of Standards gamma ray standard containing 0.1 μg ^{226}Ra as of the date of standardization. Using a heavy glass rod, cautiously break the neck of the ampul, which is submerged in 300 ml acid barium chloride solution in a 600-ml beaker. Chip the ampul unit until it is thoroughly broken or until the hole is large enough to obtain complete mixing. Transfer the solution to a 1-l volumetric flask, rinse the beaker with acid barium chloride solution, dilute to the mark with the same solution, and mix; 1 ml = approximately 100 pg ^{226}Ra.

Determine the time in years since the NBS standardization of the original ^{226}Ra solution and multiply the time by 4.3×10^{-4}. Subtract the product from one; the resulting factor is multiplied by 100 pg/ml to correct the concentration of ^{226}Ra for decay. Multiply the last result by 0.990 ± 0.004 to convert pg ^{226}Ra to pCi ^{226}Ra.

e. Intermediate radium 226 solution: Add 100 ml stock radium 226 solution

to a 1-l volumetric flask and dilute to the mark with acid barium chloride solution; 1 ml = approximately 10 pCi ^{226}Ra.

f. Standard radium 226 solution: Add 30.0 ml intermediate radium 226 solution to a 100-ml volumetric flask and dilute to the mark with acid barium chloride solution; 1 ml = approximately 3 pCi ^{226}Ra and contains about 2 mg Ba. See ¶ *d* et seq above for correction factors.

g. Hydrochloric acid, conc, 6N, 1N, and 0.1N.

h. Sulfuric acid, conc and 0.1N.

i. Hydrofluoric acid, 48%, in a plastic dropping bottle. (CAUTION.)

j. Ammonium sulfate solution: Dissolve 10 g ammonium sulfate, $(NH_4)_2SO_4$, in distilled water and dilute to 100 ml in a graduated cylinder.

k. Phosphoric acid, 85%.

l. Ascarite, 8 to 20 mesh.

m. Magnesium perchlorate, anhydrous desiccant.

n. EDTA decontaminating solution: Dissolve 10 g disodium ethylenediaminetetraacetate dihydrate [also called (ethylenedinitrilo) tetraacetic acid sodium salt] and 10 g sodium carbonate in distilled water and dilute to 1 l in a graduated cylinder.

o. Special reagents for total and suspended radium:

1) *Flux*—Add 30 mg barium sulfate, $BaSO_4$, 65.8 g potassium carbonate, K_2CO_3, 50.5 g sodium carbonate, Na_2CO_3, and 33.7 g sodium tetraborate decahydrate, $Na_2B_4O_7 \cdot 10H_2O$, to a large platinum dish (500-ml capacity). Mix thoroughly and heat cautiously to expel water, then fuse and mix thoroughly by swirling. Cool the flux, grind in a porcelain mortar to pass a 10- to

12-mesh (or finer) screen, and store in an airtight bottle.

2) *Dilute hydrogen peroxide solution*—Dilute 10 ml 30% H_2O_2 to 100 ml in a graduated cylinder. Prepare daily.

4. Calibration of Scintillation Counter Assembly

a. Test bubblers by placing about 10 ml distilled water in them and passing air through them at the rate of 3 to 5 ml (free volume) /min. Air should form many fine bubbles rather than a few large ones; the latter condition indicates nonuniform pores. Bubblers requiring excessive pressure to initiate bubbling should not be used. Corning's "medium porosity" fritted-glass disks are usually satisfactory. Reject unsatisfactory bubblers.

b. Apply silicone grease to stopcocks of a bubbler and, with gas inlet stopcock closed, add 1 ml stock barium chloride solution and 10 ml (30 pCi) standard radium 226 solution, and fill the bubbler two-thirds to three-fourths full with additional acid barium chloride solution.

c. With the bubbler in a clamp or rack, dry the joint with lintfree paper or cloth, warm the separate parts of the joint, apply sealing wax sparingly to the male part of the joint, and make the connection with a twisting motion to spread the wax uniformly in the ground joint. Allow joint to cool. Establish zero ingrowth time by purging liquid with counting gas for 15 to 20 min according to ¶ 4*j* below and adjusting inlet pressure to produce a froth a few millimeters thick. Close stopcocks, record date and time, and store bubbler, preferably for 3

wk or more (with most samples) before collecting and counting the ^{222}Rn. A much shorter ingrowth period of 16 to 24 hr is convenient for a standard bubbler. An estimate of the ^{222}Rn present at any time may be obtained from the B columns in Table 706:I.

d. Attach scintillation cell as shown in Figure 706:1; ‖ substitute a glass tube with a stopcock for the bubbler so that the compressed gas can be turned on or off conveniently. Open stopcock on scintillation cell, close stopcock to gas, and gradually open stopcock to vacuum source to evacuate cell. Close stopcock to vacuum source and check manometer reading for 2 min to test system, especially the scintillation cell, for leaks.

e. Open stopcock to counting gas and cautiously admit gas to scintillation cell until atmospheric pressure is reached.

f. Center scintillation cell on photomultiplier tube, cover with light-tight hood and, after 10 min, obtain a background counting rate (preferably over a 100- to 1,000-min period, depending on concentration of ^{226}Ra in unknown samples). *Do not allow phototube to be exposed to external light with the high voltage applied.*

g. Repeat Steps *d* through *f* above for each scintillation cell.

h. If the leakage test and background are satisfactory, continue calibration.

i. With scintillation cell and standard bubbler [¶ 4*c*] on vacuum train, open

---

‖ The system as described and shown in Figure 706:1 is considered minimal. In routine work, the use of manifold systems and additional, more precise needle valves is warranted. An occasional drop of solution will escape from the bubbler; there should be enough free space beyond the outlet stopcock to accommodate this liquid, thus preventing its entrance into the gas-purifying train.

TABLE 706:I. FACTORS FOR DECAY OF RADON 222, GROWTH OF RADON 222 FROM RADIUM 226, AND CORRECTION OF RADON 222 ACTIVITY FOR DECAY DURING COUNTING

Time	Factor for Decay of Radon 222 $A = e^{-\lambda t}$		Factor for Growth of Radon 222 from Radium 226 $B = 1 - e^{-\lambda t}$		Factor for Correction of Radon 222 Activity for Decay during Counting $C = \lambda t/(1 - e^{-\lambda t})$
	Hours	Days	Hours	Days	Hours
0.0	1.0000		0.000 00		1.000
0.2	0.9985		0.001 51		1.001
0.4	0.9970		0.003 01		1.001
0.6	0.9955		0.004 52		1.002
0.8	0.9940		0.006 02		1.003
1	0.9925	0.8343	0.007 52	0.1657	1.004
2	0.9850	0.6960	0.014 99	0.3040	1.008
3	0.9776	0.5807	0.022 40	0.4193	1.011
4	0.9703	0.4844	0.029 75	0.5156	1.015
5	0.9630	0.4041	0.037 05	0.5959	1.019
6	0.9557	0.3372	0.044 29	0.6628	1.023
7	0.9485	0.2813	0.051 48	0.7187	1.027
8	0.9414	0.2347	0.058 61	0.7653	1.031
9	0.9343	0.1958	0.065 69	0.8042	1.034
10	0.9273	0.1633	0.072 72	0.8367	1.038
11	0.9203	0.1363	0.079 69	0.8637	1.042
12	0.9134	0.1137	0.086 62	0.8863	1.046
13	0.9065	0.0948	0.093 49	0.9052	1.050
14	0.8997	0.0791	0.100 31	0.9209	1.054
15	0.8929	0.0660	0.107 07	0.9340	1.058
16	0.8862	0.0551	0.1138	0.9449	1.062
17	0.8795	0.0459	0.1205	0.9541	1.066
18	0.8729	0.0383	0.1271	0.9617	1.069
19	0.8664	0.0320	0.1336	0.9680	1.073
20	0.8598	0.0267	0.1402	0.9733	1.077
21	0.8534	0.0223	0.1466	0.9777	1.081
22	0.8470	0.0186	0.1530	0.9814	1.085
23	0:8406	0.0155	0.1594	0.9845	1.089
24	0.8343	0.0129	0.1657	0.9871	1.093
25	0.8280	0.0108	0.1720	0.9892	1.097

TABLE 706:I. FACTORS FOR DECAY OF RADON 222, GROWTH OF RADON 222 FROM RADIUM 226, AND CORRECTION OF RADON 222 ACTIVITY FOR DECAY DURING COUNTING

Time	Factor for Decay of Radon 222 $A = e^{-\lambda t}$		Factor for Growth of Radon 222 from Radium 226 $B = 1 - e^{-\lambda t}$		Factor for Correction of Radon 222 Activity for Decay during Counting $C = \lambda t/(1 - e^{-\lambda t})$
	Hours	Days	Hours	Days	Hours
26	0.8218	0.0090	0.1782	0.9910	1.101
27	0.8156	0.0075	0.1844	0.9925	1.105
28	0.8095	0.0063	0.1905	0.9937	1.109
29	0.8034	0.0052	0.1966	0.9948	1.113
30	0.7973	0.0044	0.2027	0.9956	1.118
31	0.7913	0.0036	0.2087	0.9964	1.122
32	0.7854	0.0030	0.2146	0.9970	1.126
33	0.7795	0.0025	0.2205	0.9975	1.130
34	0.7736	0.0021	0.2264	0.9979	1.134
35	0.7678	0.0018	0.2322	0.9982	1.138
36	0.7620	0.0015	0.2380	0.9985	1.142
37	0.7563	0.0012	0.2437	0.9988	1.146
38	0.7506	0.0010	0.2494	0.9990	1.150
39	0.7449	0.0009	0.2551	0.9991	1.154
40	0.7393	0.0007	0.2607	0.9993	1.159
41	0.7338	0.0006	0.2662	0.9994	1.163
42	0.7283	0.0005	0.2717	0.9995	1.167
43	0.7228	0.0004	0.2772	0.9996	1.171
44	0.7173	0.0003	0.2827	0.9997	1.175
45	0.7120	0.0003	0.2880	0.9997	1.179
46	0.7066	0.0002	0.2934	0.9998	1.184
47	0.7013	0.0002	0.2987	0.9998	1.188
48	0.6960	0.0002	0.3040	0.9998	1.192
49	0.6908	0.0001	0.3092	0.9999	1.196
50	0.6856	0.0001	0.3144	0.9999	1.201
51	0.6804	0.0001	0.3196	0.9999	1.205
52	0.6753	0.0001	0.3247	0.9999	1.209
53	0.6702	0.0001	0.3298	0.9999	1.213
54	0.6652	0.0001	0.3348	0.9999	1.218
55	0.6602	0.0000	0.3398	1.0000	1.222
56	0.6552	0.0000	0.3448	1.0000	1.226
57	0.6503	0.0000	0.3497	1.0000	1.231
58	0.6454	0.0000	0.3546	1.0000	1.235
59	0.6405	0.0000	0.3595	1.0000	1.239
60	0.6357	0.0000	0.3643	1.0000	1.244

stopcock on scintillation cell and evacuate scintillation cell and purification system (Figure 706:1) by opening the stopcock to vacuum source. Close stopcock to vacuum source. Check system for leaks as in Step *d* above.

j. Adjust gas regulator (diaphragm) valve so that a very slow stream of gas will flow with the needle valve open. Attach gas supply to inlet of bubbler.

k. Note time as beginning of an approximately 20-min de-emanation period. Very cautiously open bubbler outlet stopcock to equalize pressure and transfer all or most of the fluid in the inlet side arm to the bubbler chamber.

l. Close outlet stopcock and very cautiously open inlet stopcock to flush remaining fluid from side arm and fritted disk. Close inlet stopcock.

m. Repeat Steps *h* and *l* above, four or five times, to obtain more nearly equal pressures on the two sides of the bubbler.

n. With outlet stopcock fully open, cautiously open inlet stopcock so that the flow of gas produces a froth a few mm thick at the surface of bubbler solution. Maintain flow rate by gradually increasing pressure with regulator valve and continue de-emanation until the pressure in the cell reaches atmospheric pressure. The total elapsed time for the de-emanation should be 15 to 25 min.

o. Close stopcocks to scintillation cell, close bubbler inlet and outlet, shut off and disconnect gas supply, and record the date and time as the ends of the ^{222}Rn ingrowth and de-emanation periods and as the beginnings of decay of ^{222}Rn and ingrowth of decay products.

p. Store the bubbler for another ^{222}Rn ingrowth in the event a subsequent de-emanation is desired (Table 706:I). The standard bubbler may be kept indefinitely.

q. Four hours after de-emanation, when daughter products are in virtual transient equilibrium with ^{222}Rn, place scintillation cell on photomultiplier tube, cover with light-tight hood, let stand for at least 10 min, then begin counting. Record date and time counting was started and finished.

r. Correct the net counting rate for ^{222}Rn decay (Table 706:I) and relate it to the picoCuries of ^{226}Ra in standard bubbler (see Section 706.6*a*). Unless the scintillation cell is physically damaged, the calibration will remain essentially unchanged for years. Occasional calibration is recommended.

s. Repeat Steps *h* through *r* above on each scintillation cell.

t. To remove ^{222}Rn and prepare scintillation cell for reuse, evacuate and cautiously refill with the counting gas. Routinely, repeat evacuation and refilling twice, and repeat process more times if the cells have contained a high activity of ^{222}Rn. (Decay products with a half-life of approximately 30 min will remain in the cell. Background on cells should not be checked until the activity of decay products has had time to decay to insignificance.)

5. Procedure

a. Soluble radium 226:

1) Using a membrane filter, filter at least 1 l of sample or a volume containing up to 30 pCi ^{226}Ra and transfer to a polyethylene bottle as soon after sampling as possible. Save the suspended matter for determination by the procedure described in Section 706.5*b* immediately following. Record volume of

sample actually filtered if suspended solids are to be analyzed as in the procedure for ^{226}Ra in suspended matter.

2) Add 20 ml conc HCl/l of filtrate and continue analysis when convenient.

3) Add 50 ml dilute barium chloride solution, with vigorous stirring, to 1,020 ml of acidified filtrate [Section 706.5a2) preceding] in a 1,500-ml beaker. In each batch of samples include a reagent blank consisting of distilled water plus 20 ml conc HCl.

4) Cautiously, with vigorous stirring, add 20 ml conc H_2SO_4. Cover beaker and allow overnight precipitation.

5) Filter supernate through a membrane filter, using $0.1N$ H_2SO_4 to transfer Ba-Ra precipitate to filter, and wash precipitate twice with $0.1N$ H_2SO_4.

6) Place filter with precipitate in a platinum crucible or dish, add 0.5 ml HF and 3 drops (0.15 ml) ammonium sulfate solution, and evaporate to dryness.

7) Carefully ignite filter and residue over a small flame until carbon is burned off; cool. (After filter is charred a Meker burner may be used.)

8) Add 1 ml H_3PO_4 with a calibrated dropper and heat on hot plate at about 200 C. Gradually raise temperature and maintain it at about 300 to 400 C for 30 min.

9) Swirl the vessel over a low Bunsen flame, adjusted to avoid spattering, while covering the walls with hot H_3PO_4. Continue to heat for a minute after precipitate fuses into a clear melt (just below redness) to insure complete removal of SO_3.

10) Fill cooled vessel one-half full with $6N$ HCl, heat on steam bath, then gradually add distilled water to within 2 mm of the top of the vessel.

11) Evaporate on boiling steam bath until there are no more vapors of HCl.

12) Add 6 ml $1N$ HCl, swirl, and warm to dissolve $BaCl_2$ crystals.

13) Close gas inlet stopcock, add a drop of water to the fritted disk of the fully greased and tested radon bubbler, and transfer sample from platinum vessel to bubbler by means of a medicine dropper. Use dropper to rinse the vessel with at least three 2-ml portions of distilled water. Add distilled water until bubbler is two-thirds to three-fourths full.

14) Dry, wax if necessary, and seal the joint. Establish zero ingrowth time as instructed in Section 706.4c preceding.

15) Close stopcocks, record date and time, and store bubbler for ^{222}Rn ingrowth, preferably for 3 wk for low concentrations of radium 226.

16) De-emanate and count ^{222}Rn as instructed for calibrations in ¶s 4 i through r, with unknown sample replacing the standard bubbler.

17) The sample in the bubbler may be stored for a second ingrowth or discarded and the bubbler cleaned for reuse. (A bubbler is readily cleaned while in an inverted position by attaching a tube from a beaker containing 100 ml $0.1N$ HCl to the inlet and attaching another tube from outlet to a suction flask. By alternately opening and closing outlet and inlet stopcocks, the acid rinse water is sequentially passed through the fritted disk, accumulated in the bubbler, and flushed into the suction flask. Drain bubbler with the aid of vacuum, heat the ground joint gently to melt the wax, and separate the joint. More extensive cleaning, as indicated in Section 706.2k above, may be necessary if the bubbler contained more than 10 pCi ^{226}Ra.)

b. Radium 226 in suspended matter:

1) Suspended matter in water usually contains siliceous materials that require fusion with an alkaline flux to insure recovery of radium. The suspended matter of the sample (up to 1,000 mg of inorganic material) retained on the membrane filter specified in ¶5a1) above from a known volume of water is dried in a tared platinum crucible and ignited as in ¶5a7).

2) Weigh crucible to estimate residue.

3) Add 8 g flux/g residue, but not less than 2 g flux, and mix with a glass rod.

4) Heat over a Meker burner until melting begins, being careful to prevent spattering. Continue heating for 20 min after bubbling stops, with an occasional swirl of the crucible to mix the contents and achieve a uniform melt. A clear melt is usually obtained only when the suspended solids are present in small amount or have a high silica content.

5) Remove crucible from burner and rotate as melt cools to distribute it in a thin layer on crucible wall.

6) When cool, place crucible in a covered beaker containing 120 ml distilled water, 20 ml conc H_2SO_4, and 5 ml dilute H_2O_2 solution for each 8 g of flux. (Reduce acid and H_2O_2 in proportion to flux used.) Rotate crucible to dissolve melt if necessary.

7) When melt is dissolved, remove and rinse crucible into beaker. Save crucible for Step 10) below.

8) Heat solution and slowly add 50 ml dilute $BaCl_2$ solution with vigorous stirring. Cover beaker and let stand overnight for precipitation. (Precipitation with cool sample solution is also satisfactory.)

9) Add about 1 ml dilute H_2O_2 and, if yellow color (from titanium) deepens, add additional H_2O_2 until there is no further color change.

10) Continue analysis according to Section 706.5a5) through 16).

11) Calculate result as directed in Section 706.6a and b, taking into account that the suspended solids possibly were contained in a sample volume of other than 1 l of sample [see Section 706.5a1)].

c. Total radium 226:

1) Total ^{226}Ra in water is the sum of soluble and suspended ^{226}Ra as determined in Sections 5a and b preceding, or it may be determined directly by examining the original water sample that has been acidified with 20 ml conc HCl for each liter of sample and stored in a polyethylene bottle.

2) Thoroughly mix the acidified sample and take 1,020 ml or a measured volume containing not more than 1,000 mg inorganic suspended solids.

3) Add 50 ml dilute $BaCl_2$ solution and slowly, with vigorous stirring, add 20 ml conc H_2SO_4/l of sample. Cover and allow to precipitate overnight.

4) Filter supernate through membrane filter and transfer solids to filter as in ¶ 5a5) preceding.

5) Place filter and precipitate in tared platinum crucible and proceed as in ¶s 5b2) through 10) above but with the following changes in the procedure given in ¶ 5b8): Omit the addition of dilute $BaCl_2$ solution, digest for 1 hr on a steam bath, and filter immediately after digestion without stirring up $BaSO_4$. (If these changes are not made, filtration will be very slow.)

6) Calculate total radium 226 concentration as directed in Sections 706.6 a and b immediately following.

6. Calculations

a. The ^{226}Ra in a bubbler, including reagent blank, is calculated as follows:

$$^{226}\text{Ra in pCi} = \frac{R_s - R_b}{R_e} \times \frac{1}{1 - e^{-\lambda t_1}}$$

$$\times \frac{1}{e^{-\lambda t_2}} \times \frac{\lambda t_3}{1 - e^{-\lambda t_3}}$$

where:

λ = decay constant for ^{222}Rn, 0.0755/hr,

t_1 = time interval allowed for ingrowth of ^{222}Rn, hr,

t_2 = time interval between de-emanation and counting, hr,

t_3 = time interval of counting, hr,

R_s = observed counting rate of sample in scintillation cell, cph,

R_b = (previously) observed background counting rate of scintillation cell with counting gas, cph,

R_e = calibration constant for scintillation cell (i.e., observed net counts per hour, corrected by use of ingrowth and decay factors (C/AB from below) per picoCurie of Ra in standard),

or:

$$^{226}\text{Ra in pCi} = \frac{(R_s - R_b)}{R_c} \times \frac{C}{AB}$$

where:

A = factor for decay of ^{222}Rn (see Table 706:I),

B = factor for growth of ^{222}Rn from ^{226}Ra (see Table 706:I), and

C = factor for correction of ^{222}Rn activity for decay during counting (see Table 706:I).

For nontabulated times, decay factors for ^{222}Rn are obtained by multiplying together the appropriate tabulated "day" and "hour" decay factors, interpolating for less than 0.2 hr if indicated by the precision desired. Radon 222 growth factors for nontabulated times are obtained most accurately, especially for short periods (e.g., in calibrations),

by calculation from ^{222}Rn decay factors given in Column A and using formula given in heading for Column B (of Table 706:I). Linear interpolations are satisfactory for routine samples. The decay-during-counting factors are obtained by linear interpolation for all nontabulated times.

In calculating cell calibration constants, the same equation is used, but the pCi of ^{226}Ra is known and R_c is the unknown.

b. Convert the activity into pCi/l of soluble, suspended, or total ^{226}Ra by the following equation:

$$^{226}\text{Ra, pCi/l} = \frac{(D-E) \times 1,000}{\text{ml sample}}$$

where:

D = pCi ^{226}Ra found in sample, and

E = pCi ^{226}Ra found in reagent blank,

7. Recovery of Barium (Radium 226) (Optional)

If ^{133}Ba was added in reagent *b*, the recovery of Ba can be checked by removing the solution of sample from the bubbler, adjusting its volume appropriately, gamma-counting it under standardized conditions, and comparing the result with the count obtained from a 50-ml portion (evaporated if necessary to reduce volume) of the dilute barium solution also counted under standardized conditions; 1 ml H_3PO_4 should be added to the latter portion before counting. The assumption that the Ba and ^{226}Ra are recovered to the same extent is valid in the method described.

It should be noted that ^{226}Ra and its decay products interfere slightly even if a gamma spectrometer is used. The technic works best when the ratio of ^{133}Ba to ^{226}Ra is high.

Determinations of recovery are particularly helpful with irreplaceable samples, both in gaining experience with the method and in applying the general method to unfamiliar media.

8. Precision and Accuracy

In a collaborative study, seven laboratories analyzed four water samples for dissolved radium 226 using the method. No result was rejected as an outlier. The average recoveries of added radium 226 from Samples A, B, C, and D (below) were 97.1, 97.3, 97.6, and 98.0%, respectively. At the 95% confidence level, the precision (random error) was 6% and 8% for the two sets of paired samples. Because of the small number of participating laboratories and the low values for random and total errors, there was no evidence of laboratory systematic errors. Neither radium 224 at an activity equal to that of the radium 226 nor dissolved solids up to 610 mg/l produced a detectable error in the results.

Test samples consisted of two pairs of simulated moderately hard and hard water samples containing known amounts of added radium 226 and other radionuclides. The composition of the samples with respect to nonradioactive substances was the same for a pair of samples but varied for the two pairs. The radiochemical composition of the samples is given in Table 705:I.

9. References

1. HURSH, J.B. 1954. Radium-226 in water supplies of the U.S. *J. Amer. Water Works Ass.* 46:43.
2. RUSHING, D.E., W.J. GARCIA & D.A. CLARK. 1964. The analysis of effluents and environmental samples from uranium mills and of biological samples for radium, polonium, and uranium. In: Radiological Health and Safety in Mining and Milling of Nuclear Materials. International Atomic Energy Agency, Vienna, Austria, Vol. II, p. 187.
3. LUCAS, H.F. 1957. Improved low-level alpha scintillation counter for radon. *Rev. Sci. Instrum.* 28:680.
4. RUSHING, D.E. 1967. Determination of dissolved radium-226 in water. *J. Amer. Water Works Ass.* 59:593.

707   TRITIUM IN WATER*

The American Public Health Association appreciates the permission granted to publish a revision of the method adopted by the Food and Agriculture Organization, the International Atomic Energy Agency, the World Health Organization, and the Association of Official Analytical Chemists.

1. Discussion

Tritium exists fairly uniformly in the environment as a result of natural production by cosmic radiation[3] and residual fallout from nuclear weapons tests. This background level is gradually being increased by the use of nuclear reactors to generate electricity. Current tritium from the nuclear power industry comprises a small proportion of environmental tritium in comparison with that from nuclear weapons fallout and naturally produced tritium. However, nuclear reactors and fuel-processing plants are localized sources of tritium because of discharges during normal operation. This industry is expected to become the major source of environmental tritium contamination some time after the year 2000 if present growth trends continue and nuclear explosions in the atmosphere are not resumed. Tritium is produced in light-water nuclear reactors by ternary fission, neutron capture in coolant additives, control rods and plates,

and activation of deuterium.[4] About 1% of the tritium in the primary coolant is released in gaseous form to the atmosphere[5]; the remainder is eventually released in liquid waste discharges.[6] Most of the tritium produced in reactors remains in the fuel and is released when the fuel is reprocessed.

Naturally occurring tritium is most abundant in precipitation such as rain and lowest in aged water because of its physical decay by beta emission to helium. The maximum beta energy of tritium is 0.018 MeV and its half-life is 12.26 yr.

a. Exposure criteria: The guidance given by both the NCRP[7] and the ICRP[8] on the maximum permissible concentrations of tritium in water for an individual in the general population sets a level of 3 μCi/l or, for the average of a suitable sample of the population, 1 μCi (1,000 nCi) /l.

b. Principle: A sample of water or waste is distilled to remove quenching materials and nonvolatile radioactivity. Complete transfer of tritiated water is assured by distillation to dryness. A subsample of distillate is mixed with scintillation solution and the beta activity is counted on a coincidence-type liquid scintillation spectrometer. The scintillation solution consists of 1,4-dioxane, naphthalene, POPOP, and PPO.†[9] The spectrometer is calibrated with standard solutions of tritiated water and background and unknown samples are prepared and counted alternately, thus nullifying errors that could result from

---

*This method is recommended by the Food and Agriculture Organization, the International Atomic Energy Agency and the World Health Organization[1]; collaboratively tested by a committee and adopted as Official First Action by the Association of Official Analytical Chemists[2]; and revised to conform to APHA format.

---

†POPOP = 1,4-di-2-(5-phenyloxazolyl) benzene; PPO = (2,5-diphenyloxazole).

instrument drift or from the aging of scintillation solution.

c. Interferences: Distillation of natural waters is effective in removing nonvolatile radioactivity and the usual quenching materials. For waters containing volatile organic or radioactive materials, additional precautions and measures are necessary. Steps should be taken to remove interference from quenching due to volatile organic material by wet oxidation (Section 421). Distillation at a pH about 8.5 may be required to hold back volatile radionuclides such as iodides and bicarbonates. Double distillation with an appropriate delay (10 half-lives) between distillations may be required to circumvent interference from the volatile daughters of radium isotopes. Some clear-water samples collected in the vicinity of nuclear facilities may be satisfactorily monitored for tritium without distillation, especially when the monitoring instrument is capable of discriminating against beta radiation energies higher than those in the tritium range.

2. Apparatus

a. Liquid scintillation spectrometer, coincidence-type.‡

b. Liquid scintillation vial: 20-ml; low-K glass, polyethylene, nylon, or equivalent bottles, available from manufacturers of liquid scintillation spectrometers.

---

‡Various manufacturers have one or more models of liquid scintillation spectrometers with features of merit, depending on specific needs—for example, Beckman Instruments, Inc., 2400 Harbor Boulevard, Fullerton, Calif. 92634; Nuclear-Chicago Corporation, 333 East Howard Avenue, Des Plaines, Ill. 60018; Packard Instrument Co., 2200 Warrenville Road, Downers Grove, Ill. 60515; and others.

3. Reagents

a. Scintillation solution: Thoroughly mix 4 g PPO (2,5-diphenyloxazole), 0.05 g POPOP [1,4-di-2-(5-phenyloxazolyl) benzene], and 120 g solid naphthalene in 1 l spectroquality 1,4-dioxane (available from manufacturers of liquid scintillation spectrometers). Store in dark bottles. Solution is stable for 2 months.

b. Standard solution of tritium: Pipet 4 ml H_2O of known ^3H activity and 16 ml scintillation solution into scintillation vial, cover vial tightly with screw cap, and mix thoroughly by shaking.

c. Background solution: Mix 4 ml distilled H_2O (free of ^3H activity to be measured in samples) with 16 ml scintillation solution as in paragraph preceding.

4. Procedure

a. Distill 20 to 30 ml sample to near dryness. Mix 4 ml sample distillate with 16 ml reagent (¶3a above) in vial with stopper.

b. Dilute known quantities of tritium standard solution to 4 ml with background water in vials and mix with 16 ml of reagent (¶3a above).

c. Keep samples in the dark until the counting rate is constant (within the counting error). Dark adaptation requires about 3 hr unless the samples have been exposed to sunlight. When using a freezer unit, cool all vials from Steps *a* and *b* preceding to a temperature of about 4 C. When using an ambient-temperature liquid scintillation spectrometer, dark-adapt all vials from Steps *a* and *b* for about 3 hr at ambient temperature. Count samples and standards.

5. Calculations and Reporting

a. Calculate and report the tritium, ^3H, in picocuries per milliliter (pCi/ml) or its equivalent, nanocuries per liter (nCi/l) based on the formula:

$$^3H = (C - B)/(E \times 4 \times 2.22)$$

where:

$(S - B)/D$ = counting efficiency, E,
   B = cpm rate for background count,
   $C - B$ = net cpm for sample,
   $S - B$ = net cpm for standard solution, and
   D = disintegrations per minute (dpm) of tritium activity in standard sample.

b. Calculate the counting error of the sample at the 95% confidence level based on the equation for $\sigma(R)$ given in Section 701F. A total count of 40,000 within 1 hr for a background count of about 50 cpm gives a counting error slightly in excess of 1% at the 95% confidence level.

6. Precision and Accuracy

In a collaborative study,[2] 12 samples of tap water containing tritium additions, a stock standard solution of tritium, and a background sample of tap water were supplied to seven colaborators, who reported results from the use of the above method. Two sub-samples each of six stock preparations to which had been added, respectively, 1.2, 2.9, 6.8, 17.1, 42.9, and 115.8 nCi tritium/l were furnished each collaborator. The theoretical minimum detectable activity was 0.2 to 0.5 pCi/ml based on a 99% confidence level with a 100-min counting time over a range of background counts from 9 to 67 cpm. However, the result for a practical detectable limit is about 1 to 2 pCi/ml, since the sample containing 1.2 pCi tritium/ml varied from 0 to 4.8 pCi/ml. Over the concentration range 2.9 to 116 pCi/ml, the minimum, maximum, and average recovery of tritium for the seven sets of samples are given in the following tabulation:

Tritium Taken (pCi/ml)	Recovery of Added Tritium		
	Minimum %	Maximum %	Average %
2.9	72	224	109
6.8	63	117	99
17.1	64	108	93
42.9	91	107	99
115.6	92	104	96
2.9	86	110	98[a]
6.8	89	117	101[b]
17.1	92	108	96[c]

a = four outlier results omitted.
b = one outlier result omitted.
c = two outlier results omitted.

At the 2.9 nCi/l level, which is roughly 0.1% of the maximum permissible concentration in water for an individual of the population, the test, based on all results, is not very precise. When outlier results are omitted,[10] the method produces satisfactory results, particularly from a public health standpoint.

7. References

1. FAO, IAEA & WHO. 1966. Methods of Radiochemical Analysis. World Health Organization, Geneva.
2. SODD, V.J. & K.L. SCHOLZ. 1969. Analysis of tritium in water; a collaborative study. *J. Ass. Offic. Anal. Chem.* 52:1.
3. LIBBY, W.F. 1946. Atmospheric helium-3 and radiocarbon from cosmic radiation. *Phys. Rev.* 69:671.
4. PETERSON, H.T.J., J.E. MARTIN, C.L.

WEAVER & E.D. HARWARD. 1969. Environmental tritium contamination from increasing utilization of nuclear energy sources. Seminar on Agricultural and Public Health Aspects of Environmental Contamination by Radioactive Materials. International Atomic Energy Ass., Vienna, pp. 35–60.

5. SMITH, J.M. 1967. The Significance of Tritium in Water Reactors. General Electric Co., San Jose, Calif. (Sept. 19).

6. WEAVER, C.L., E.D. HARWARD & H.T. PETERSON. 1969. Tritium in the environment from nuclear power plants. *Pub. Health Rep.* 84(4)363.

7. NATIONAL COUNCIL ON RADIATION PROTECTION, SUBCOMMITTEE ON PERMISSIBLE INTERNAL DOSE. 1959. Maximum Permissible Body Burdens and Maximum Permissible Concentrations of Radionuclides in Air and in Water for Occupational Exposure. NBS Handbook 69 (June). National Bureau of Standards, Washington, D.C.

8. INTERNATIONAL COMMISSION ON RADIATION PROTECTION. 1960. Report of Committee II on permissible dose for internal radiation, 1959. *Health Phys.* 3:41 (June).

9. BUTLER, F.E. 1961. Determination of tritium in water and urine. *Anal. Chem.* 33:409.

10. YOUDEN, W.J. 1967. Statistical Techniques for Collaborative Tests. Association of Official Analytical Chemists, Box 540, Benjamin Franklin Sta., Washington, D.C. 20044.

PART 800

BIOASSAY METHODS FOR

AQUATIC ORGANISMS

801   GENERAL PROCEDURES

During the past 20 yr, bioassays have become basic tools for the detection, evaluation, and abatement of water pollution. Before that time, they were used in only a few laboratories and by very few industries. The value of bioassays for detecting and evaluating the toxicity of industrial wastes in connection with their treatment and safe disposal is being realized increasingly. Chemical examination alone of complex industrial wastes does not provide sufficient information on their effects on the aquatic biota for the protection of the aquatic environment.[1,2] Moreover, the toxicity of the complex mixture of wastes and chemicals cannot be determined by chemical means. The toxicity of effluents can be influenced greatly by interactions between their individual components, by wastes already present, and by the dissolved minerals naturally occurring in widely varying amounts in receiving waters. Different kinds of aquatic organisms are not equally susceptible to toxic substances and much of the pertinent published information is based on experiments with hardy species. Therefore, the toxicity of industrial waste to local biota in a natural environment must be detected and evaluated directly through bioassays under appropriate experimental conditions.

During the past few years this fact has been much more widely appreciated and the use of bioassays has increased greatly. In addition, there has been a great increase in the kinds of organisms used in the bioassays and in the purposes for which these studies are undertaken.

During this period, the term "bioassay" has been used to designate a variety of studies and it no longer has only the narrow meaning of tests to determine the potency of drugs or vitamins. Neither is it restricted to short-term laboratory tests to measure lethal effects of industrial effluents on a selected species of fish. Through common usage, "bioassay", with an added prefix where needed, is used to indicate studies that determine: (a) the suitability of environmental conditions for aquatic life, (b) favorable and unfavorable concentrations or levels of environmental factors, such as DO, pH, temperature, salinity, or turbidity, for aquatic life, (c) the effects of various combinations of these environmental factors on the toxicity of wastes, (d) the relative toxicity of different wastes to a selected species or a number of species, (e) the relative sensitivity of aquatic organisms to an effluent or toxicant, (f) the amount of waste treatment needed to meet water pollution control requirements, (g) the effectiveness of different waste treatment methods, (h) permissible discharge rates for effluents, (i) water quality requirements for aquatic life, and (j) compliance with water quality standards, effluent requirements, and discharge permits.

Extensive studies are being made to determine the toxicity of effluents to aquatic life in receiving water and the effectiveness of different waste treatment methods as a basis for granting discharge permits. Marine organisms are being used increasingly in bioassay investigations that are no longer confined to fishes. Phytoplankton, zooplankton, worms, insects, mollusks, and crustaceans are being used widely in investigations of the toxicity of wastes to the biota of receiving waters.

Reasonable uniformity of bioassay procedures and of the manner of presenting the results is essential for effective use of acquired data. Widespread adoption of uniform methods will pro-

mote the accumulation of comparable data and increase its effective use. The standardization of bioassay methods and experimental procedures described herein will insure adequate uniformity, reproducibility, and general usefulness of bioassay results without interfering unduly with the adaptability of the tests to local circumstances and problems.

801 A.   Terminology

An aquatic bioassay is any test in which aquatic organisms are used to detect or measure the presence or effect of one or more substances, wastes, or environmental factors, alone or in combination, on aquatic organisms. As the number of people using bioassays has increased there has been an increase in the number of terms or symbols used to express results.

Lethal concentration (LC) is used to express the results of bioassays having lethality as the criterion of toxicity. A numeral is used with it (for example, LC10, LC50, or LC70) to indicate the percentage of the test animals killed at a given concentration of the test material. Effects of toxicants in the aquatic environment depend on both the concentration to which the test organisms are exposed and the length of exposure. Therefore time must be included in terms expressing results. For example, the 96-hr LC50 is the concentration of a material that is lethal to 50% of the test organisms in 96 hr. Results of bioassays are usually expressed as median lethal concentration (LC50) with a prefix in-

dicating the period of exposure, i.e., 168-hr LC50 or 10-day LC50.

Effective concentration (EC) is used when some effect other than lethality is being studied. The median effective concentration (EC50) is the concentration producing a specific effect or response, such as loss of equilibrium, paralysis, developmental abnormality, or deformity, in 50% of the test organisms. This effect, as measured, can involve any other percentage, such as 10 or 70%, i.e., EC10 or EC70. When using EC, clearly specify the effect being measured. In expressing the results of such tests, also indicate time, e.g., 96-hr EC50 or 96-hr median effective concentration.

Herein, median lethal concentration and median effective concentration will henceforth replace TL_m, median tolerance limit. In tests dealing with lethality, TL50 is the same as LC50 but TL10 is equivalent to LC90 and TL90 to LC10.

Incipient lethal level is the concentration at which acute toxicity ceases, that is, the concentration at which 50% of the population can live for an indefinite time. This measure has been described in different terms by different investigators: incipient lethal level,[3] ultimate median tolerance limit,[4] lethal threshold concentration,[5] and asymptotic LC50.[6] Incipient lethal level, as used herein, is synonymous with incipient LC50, the lethal concentration for 50% of the test organisms on long exposure[7] or the concentration at which 50% of the population can live indefinitely.

Safe concentration (SC) is the maximum concentration of a toxicant that has no observable harmful effects after long-term exposure over one or more generations. When the test species is the important local species that is most sensitive to the material or waste under consideration, the SC so determined serves as the basis for a water quality standard for that material or waste in that area. Most important species are those having economic (food), recreational, forage (important in the food chain), or ecological importance.

Maximum allowable toxicant concentration (MATC) is the concentration of toxic waste that may be present in the receiving water without causing significant harm to its productivity and all its various uses. The MATC is determined by a long-term bioassay of a partial life cycle with the sensitive life stages or a full life cycle of the test organism in which a range of concentrations of the toxicant under test that do not demonstrate significant harm to the test organism is determined.

The terms defined here are adequate for expressing nearly all results of bioassays in the aquatic environment. Use these terms as standard symbols for expression of bioassay results.

Complete life cycle bioassays have been made with only a few organisms. Partial life cycle bioassays have been conducted with a larger number. Various indirect methods for estimating MATC or SC for toxicants, including the use of an application factor, have been proposed by several workers including the National Technical Advisory Committee.[8] Generally, application factors have been estimated but the true value is the ratio between the MATC and the incipient LC50. Therefore,

$$AF = \frac{MATC}{\text{incipient LC50}} \quad \text{Application}$$

factors have been determined for only a few fishes and thus can be used only in the estimation of the MATC for fishes because results for invertebrates may be entirely different. The measured AF value for one toxicant for different fish species varies by a factor of 2 to 5. The amount of this variation attributable to experimental error and the amount due to real variation is not known. However, it is much better than arbitrarily selected AF's and is the best tool available for estimating MATC unless tests can be performed in the receiving water and with the species concerned. In using AF's with incipient LC50's for estimating MATC's for fishes it is assumed that the AF for a given toxicant is constant, which may or may not be true.

When the SC for a toxicant in the waters of a region is estimated, a different approach is taken. All available data on the sensitivity of aquatic organisms of the area to that particular toxicant are examined and short-term studies are made to determine the most sensitive of the important species to fill in blanks in the data. Then life-cycle bioassays to determine the SC for the most sensitive important species are carried out, using dilution water taken from the receiving water outside the zone of influence of the effluent. Because the SC is determined for the most sensitive important species in the area, the SC will protect all other important organisms in the biota with a certain degree of safety. This SC, so determined, is the water quality criterion for the waste studied and should be the water quality standard for that waste in that water.

Where other than the actual receiving water must be used in a bioassay and where the most sensitive important species in the biota for the toxicant under consideration is not known definitely, the MATC can be used for an estimate of the SC. When the SC for a waste or material has been determined for the local important most sensitive species,

$$\frac{SC}{\text{incipient } LC50} = AF \text{ to be used in the}$$

water of that area. This AF can then be used with the incipient LC50 determined for the selected most sensitive species, when the receiving water is used for dilution, to estimate the SC of the waste discharged into other wa-

ters of the area. Then SC=incipient LC50×AF and is the allowable concentration of that waste after mixing with the receiving water. The accuracy of this estimate depends on the accuracy with which the incipient LC50 measures the influence of changes in water quality and the effects of other wastes that may have been added on the toxicity.

The following is an example of the use of an application factor for estimating the SC for an effluent under conditions of long-term exposure. Because the quality of a receiving water and the wastes added to it influence the toxicity of an effluent discharged to that water, the incipient LC50 must be determined for the waste in each receiving water and at various times because the water quality may change substantially over a period of time. This incipient LC50 is determined for each effluent by using dilution water taken from the receiving body of water outside the zone of influence of the waste in question and using the selected most sensitive species as the test organism. Then, if the AF is 0.01, the calculated SC for the waste in that specific area outside the zone of mixing is 0.01 times the incipient LC50.

801 B.   Basic Requirements for Bioassays

The basic requirements and desirable conditions for conducting bioassay programs are: (a) an abundant supply of unpolluted water of the desired quality, (b) an adequate and effective flowing water system constructed of non-polluting materials, (c) adequate space and well-planned effective modern hold-

ing, culturing, and testing equipment and facilities, and (d) a nearby and adequate source of experimental organisms. Much valuable information and advice are available for planning and constructing water supply systems.[9-13] A complete chemical analysis should be made of all waters being considered for dilutants for bioassays to detect and measure any potential toxicants, especially those that may be the subject of toxicity studies.

The facilities, equipment, and water supplies needed for effective bioassay investigations depend on the type of bioassays being conducted and the objectives of the study. When effluent bioassays and those for monitoring compliance with standards and regulations are being conducted, take the dilution water from the receiving water outside the zone of influence of the waste. Ideally, conduct these bioassays on the site so that supplies of waste and dilution water will not be a problem. When bioassays are carried out for other purposes (e.g., to determine the most sensitive species and life stage, the relative toxicity of different toxicants, the effects of water quality and the environmental factors alone and in combination on the toxicity of a waste or material, the maximum concentration of a waste that does not taint the flesh of edible organisms), use a water supply free from pollution and choose facilities and equipment as indicated above.

801 C.   Preparing Organisms for Bioassays

1. Selecting Test Organisms

The prime considerations in the selection of test organisms for bioassays are: (a) their sensitivity to the material or environmental factors under consideration, (b) their geographical distribution, abundance, and availability throughout the year, (c) their recreational, economic, and ecological importance locally and nationally, (d) the availability of culture methods for their rearing in the laboratory and knowledge of their environmental requirements, (e) their general physical condition and freedom from parasites and diseases, and (f) their suitability for bioassay tests. Very few studies have been made to determine the important species most sensitive to a potential toxicant or waste. When selecting a test species for investigating a particular material, environmental factor, or effluent, consider the available information on sensitivity or determine sensitivity by short-term bioassays; then select on the basis of the considerations listed above. Because space usually is limited, consider the size of the organism and the length of the life cycle. Generally, smaller organisms not over 5 to 8 cm long and having a short life cycle are desirable for bioassay studies, but some studies require larger organisms with long life cycles.

When conducting studies for the determination of effluent requirements, use the most sensitive locally important species and the most sensitive life stage. When circumstances necessitate the use of some other species, make comparative tests with the effluent to relate the sensitivity of the selected test species to the most sensitive of the locally important species. For any one series of bioassays, obtain the test species from a common source and collect the organisms at one time. Use test organisms that are nearly uniform in size, with the largest individual not more than 50% longer than the shortest. Use organisms of the same age group or life stage. Determine and report any known unusual conditions to which the organisms have been exposed, such as exposure to pesticides or other toxic materials.

Determine the past history of test organisms, including when and where they were collected and methods of collection, transportation, and handling.

Do not take test organisms from polluted areas where the organisms are in poor condition or where they have unusually high body burdens of potential toxicants, especially those under test. Avoid taking organisms from areas where disease and parasites are prevalent or where deformed individuals are found.

Information is available on the laboratory holding and culturing throughout the life cycle for only a few organisms. In many instances, therefore, it will be necessary to collect certain life stages of selected organisms from the field for bioassays. Knowledge of the environmental requirements and food habits is important in the selection of test organisms.

2. Collecting Test Organisms

If laboratory-reared specimens are used, report the original source and strain. Test organisms can be secured from a variety of sources. Cultures of many species of algae are maintained by the following:

Graduate School of Oceanography
University of Rhode Island
Narragansett, R. I.

Department of Botany
University of Indiana
Bloomington, Ind.

Eutrophication Research Program
Pacific Northwest Environmental Research
  Laboratory
200 S. W. 35th Street
Corvallis, Ore. 97330

Virginia Institute of Marine Science
Gloucester Point, Va. 23062

Chesapeake Biological Laboratory
Box 38
Salomons, Md. 20688

Dr. Robert Guillard
Woods Hole Oceanographic Institution
Woods Hole, Mass.

Many of the smaller species of invertebrates and fishes can be collected along the shore in dip nets or in coarse plankton nets or by hand. The larger species that occur near shore can be caught in seines. Traps and fyke nets are good for freshwater areas but are selective for some species. Different types of trawls are used to sample different regions of the sea. Otter trawls are effective for the collection of benthic species and midwater trawls for pelagic species. Various types of dredges are available to sample benthic species occurring on different types of bottoms or to collect different sizes of organisms. Commercially important species such as the lobster, blue crab, and dungeness crab are caught in traps or are taken in deep water by trawls. Species that colonize surfaces, such as barnacles, may be secured by suspending plates of wood, plastic, glass, or other suitable material at selected depths for various periods of time and periodically harvesting the attached organisms.

When collecting organisms for bioassay purposes use great care to insure that the animals are not damaged in the collection, transfer, and transporting process. When seining or using trawls, make short hauls. Do not allow plant materials, debris, mud, sand, or gravel to collect in the net or in the bag of the seine. If these materials are present to any extent the animals will be injured. When seining, avoid those materials or, when they are noted, terminate the haul and collect in another area or make very short hauls. Always leave the bag of the seine in the water at the end of the haul, stretch out the wings of the seine, open the entrance to the bag, dip out the organisms with a bucket, and transfer directly to the holding tanks that have been prepared in advance with water from the collecting site. Do not expose delicate, easily damaged species to the air. Take out the larger, more hardy species with soft mesh dip nets. Do not collect too many animals at one time. If collections are being made with trawls, after bringing the trawl up to the boat, very quickly bring it over the side without letting the portion containing the catch hit against the side of the boat and then immerse that portion of the net containing the collection in a tank of water. Open up the trawl and remove the animals desired by dipping them out with a bucket or a hand net with small soft mesh. Have clean water available in adequate amounts in tanks before beginning a haul and transfer the organisms as rapidly and carefully as possible from the trawl or net to the holding containers or tanks. If the organisms are to be transported any distance by boat, provide live boxes where they can be held. If they are transported by truck, put them in large tanks supplied with water from the area in which they were collected. Provide for the aeration of the water and its cooling in summer or warming in winter.

Determine temperature, salinity, dissolved oxygen, and pH at the collecting site to indicate the water quality into which the organisms should be transferred on arrival at the laboratory. Do not handle organisms any more than necessary. Make transfers with suitable containers or hand nets, or if the organisms are small, by large-bore pipets into which they can be drawn without damage and transferred to holding containers. Use hand nets made of soft material with several layers around the rim of the net and free from sharp points or projections. Clean and sterilize all equipment before use. Do not crowd the organisms during transportation and watch them carefully for signs of distress.

Observe collected animals for possible injury as a result of the procedures in transport to the laboratory. Examine smaller forms under a disecting microscope. Criteria for assessing if an animal is injured depend on the species, and such assessment is more difficult for sluggish species. Useful criteria for denoting injury include loss of appendages, inability to maintain a normal body posture with dorsal side uppermost, abnormal locomotion, and uncoordinated movements of the mouth parts or other parts of the body.

For additional information on the collection of aquatic organisms, see Part 1000.

3. Handling, Holding, and Conditioning Test Organisms

During transport to the laboratory, organisms are often crowded, bruised, and otherwise stressed, thereby increasing their susceptibility to disease. To reduce mortality, do not crowd the organisms, supply plenty of oxygen, and maintain a favorable temperature. To avoid introduction of disease into stock tanks, treat the organisms during transit or on arrival in accordance with procedures in ¶5 below and as suggested for each of the different groups of organisms (Sections 803 through 810). Hold field-collected animals in quarantine for at least 7 days to observe them for parasites and disease in order to avoid the transfer of such infections to the laboratory stock holding tanks. If more than 10% of the collected animals die after the second day or they are heavily parasitized or diseased and the problem cannot be controlled, destroy the lot, clean and sterilize all contacted containers and equipment, and collect another supply from a different area if possible. To meet the problem of disease or parasites being brought in with test organisms or the water supply, provide for sterilization of the portion of the water supply used by susceptible organisms. Sterilization for the elimination of unwanted organisms is usually accomplished by means of ultraviolet light. Rapid sand filters are also desirable for the removal of unwanted organisms. When it is established that organisms from a given area are parasitized or diseased, collect from another area. Because it is not always possible to collect from unpolluted areas and the collector can not always be sure that a particular organism has not been exposed to a toxicant, use a sample of the individuals to determine if they have accumulated one or more potential toxicants in their body tissues. Check animals or materials collected as food for the test organisms for their content of pesticides or other toxic materials. Feed the organisms daily during their quarantine period.

At the end of the quarantine period, transfer animals that appear to be disease-free to the regular laboratory stock tanks. Discard organisms that touch dry surfaces or are dropped or injured during handling. To avoid unnecessary stress do not subject organisms to rapid changes in temperature or water quality. In general, keep changes in water temperature less than 3 C in any 24-hr period. Keep oxygen levels above 60% of saturation and preferably at or near saturation. Some organisms require high concentrations of DO, 80% of saturation or above. After the transfer to the stock holding tanks, begin a slow acclimation to laboratory conditions or to the temperature, salinity, hardness, and other conditions at which the bioassays are to be made. With forms having a life cycle of several months or more, an acclimation period of 2 wk is desirable. The period of acclimation will be governed by the type of organism and the extent of the desired changes in water quality. Inspect closely and frequently to determine any stress, unusual behavior, parasites or disease, changes in color, or failure to eat. Avoid crowding and take care in the loading of the holding tanks. Provide adequate flow-through water so that the dissolved oxygen, pH, carbon dioxide, salinity, hardness, and other characteristics are favorable. Do not allow metabolic products to accumulate. Generally, use flow-through equivalent to 6 to 10 tank volumes/day. Usually, greater amounts of flow-through water are required for the smaller organisms on a weight-volume basis. For small organisms, water flow should be at least 3 l/day/g. Aeration should be available to all holding tanks whenever its use is indicated. Check temperature and dissolved oxygen frequently. When holding brood stock, periodic or continuous treatment for the control of parasites and diseases is often desirable.[14,15] Clean tanks and equipment thoroughly and often and remove or flush out all growths and wastes daily or at least twice a week. Remove within 24 hr all uneaten food that collects on the bottom or in corners. Use different sets of nets and other equipment for different groups of organisms and clean and sterilize them between use. Cover the tanks and containers to prevent the organisms from jumping out. Shield the tanks with curtains or some other means to protect the organisms from nearby movements and noise. Provide photoperiods and light intensities favorable to the organisms (see Section 801D.3f).

Hold various groups of organisms in flow-through systems within their favorable range of temperature, dissolved oxygen, pH, salinity, and other environmental factors. One to two weeks before they are to be used in bioassays, begin their acclimation to the test conditions. There should be few or no deaths due to parasites and diseases during this period. Use only those groups of organisms that are free from gross parasitic infection and diseases and in which the mortality is less than 10% during the laboratory holding period. When handling is necessary, clean the hands and nets before touching the organisms. Do not drop, squeeze, or touch animals unnecessarily. Keep them submerged or moist at all times and away from harmful surroundings.

It is of utmost importance for bioassay studies that the test animals be kept in excellent condition before the tests. Never allow abrupt changes in environmental conditions; often it is helpful to follow the natural seasonal variations in environmental conditions such as temperature and the seasonal daylight patterns. There should be no supersaturation of gases. This most often occurs in the winter when very cold water is brought into the laboratory and the temperature is raised. If there is danger of gas bubble disease keep the incoming water in an open system and let it drop over baffles to bring the dissolved gases into equilibrium with the air.[16]

If the organisms in the holding tank are not exposed to the same water quality as that to be used in the bioassays, gradually acclimate them to temperature and other conditions to which they will be exposed in the actual bioassays. Acclimate freshwater arthropods, daphnids, and midge larvae to water quality and temperature by rearing in the dilution water at the test temperatures, unless temperature is one of the factors being studied. Acclimate other organisms to the dilution water and test temperatures by transferring the appropriate number of similar-length individuals from the holding facilities to an acclimation tank and gradually changing the water from 100% holding water to 100% dilution water over a period of several days. Keep all organisms in 100% dilution water for at least 2 days before they are used in the bioassays. Do not use a group of organisms for bioassays if more than 1% die during the 48 hr immediately before the beginning of the test. If a group fails to meet these criteria discard them or re-treat them, hold them an additional 10 days, and reacclimate them if necessary.

Make the necessary provisions for organisms requiring a special substrate, cover, or materials to use for clinging, support, the building of their cases, or hiding.

During long holding periods, hold most test organisms in the lower range of favorable temperatures rather than at higher temperatures because the metabolic rate and the number and severity of disease outbreaks are reduced in the cooler water. For example, the cold-water, freshwater organisms are best held between 5 C and 15 C, usually well below 15 C. Hold warm-water organisms at temperatures between 10 C and 25 C depending on the season. Hold aquatic invertebrates within the temperature range of the water from which they were obtained unless they are being acclimated for special temperature or other tests. If possible, follow the natural seasonal variation in temperatures.

4. Culturing Test Organisms

a. Facilities, construction materials, and equipment: The water delivery system from the water intake, through pipes and pumps to the laboratory and all components of the storage, holding, acclimation, and culturing systems must be constructed of nontoxic materials. Glass, stainless steel, plexiglass, silicone sealant, silicone tubing, schedule 40 PVC rigid piping and fitting, titanium, and fiberglass are all nontoxic materials. Fiberglass-reinforced polyester, polyester resin, and epoxy resins have been used widely with good results. However, it is desirable to test the toxicity of all materials before they are purchased in large quantities and introduced into the water supply and testing system. All plastics containing plasticizers must be suspect of toxicity and tested before use. Use a glass or titanium interface be-

tween the water and heating elements for marine waters and glass or stainless steel in fresh waters. If concrete tanks are used, leach them with frequent changes of water over a period of weeks before use. Wooden tanks are acceptable for fresh water after a period of leaching.

Construction materials that contact the dilution water should not contain leachable substances and should not absorb significant amounts of substances from the water. Stainless steel is probably the best construction material for fresh water. Glass significantly adsorbs some trace organics. Do not use rubber, plastics containing fillers, additives, stabilizers, plasticizers, etc. Teflon, nylon, and their equivalents should not contain leachable materials and should not absorb significant amounts of most substances. Unplasticized polyethylene and polypropylene usually do not contain leachable substances, but may absorb very significant amounts of trace organic compounds.

There should be adequate space for holding facilities for test organisms as well as water storage reservoirs and water supply systems. Provide for heating and cooling facilities and for the distribution of hot and cold water with facilities for mixing to obtain any desired temperature. Use air compressors with water seals to prevent oil from getting into the air lines and contaminating the rearing tanks. When large volumes of air are needed, use low-pressure blowers. Assure that air intakes are not in shops or furnace rooms or near outlets from hoods or chemical laboratories. Provide acclimation and culturing tanks with facilities for the control of water temperatures and for aeration.

Because cleaning presents a considerable labor cost, design all holding facilities for ease of cleaning and the prevention of growths. For holding and culturing fish and many macroinvertebrates, preferably use round tanks, 1 to 3 m (2 to 8 ft) or more in diameter. Larger tanks should be constructed of fiberglass over plywood to give strength. There should be a standpipe drain in the center, threaded below the tank floor so that, when the standpipe is removed, the opening is flush with the bottom of the tank. The tank bottom should slope gently to the center to facilitate draining and cleaning. The tanks should have a smooth surface to promote cleaning, to prevent injuries to the organisms, and to insure that no material will collect in corners, cracks, and crevices. Square or rectangular tanks also can be used for special purposes or when space is scarce. They should have standpipes at one end for draining, with threads for securing the pipe on the underside. Corners of the tank should be rounded and smooth to prevent the collection of organic material that might cause a polluting effect and to make cleaning more effective. For culturing plankton-feeders, water supplies should be jetted into the circular tank along the edge to create a circular movement of the water around the central standpipe. Another pipe with half-moon cutouts at its base should be fitted over the standpipe and covered with a screen so that the outflowing water passes out at the bottom, goes up through the outside pipe then down the standpipe. This results in a circular current and a certain amount of self-cleaning. Homogenized dry food simulating plankton can be dripped into the tank to feed plankton-feeding species.

b. Water supply: For successfully holding and culturing test organisms to be used in bioassays, the laboratory should have a flowing water system that has been used successfully for holding, spawning, and rearing a variety of aquatic organisms. In some laboratories reconstituted fresh water or artificial seawater is used, but such sources, if they are the only supplies, seriously limit the amount of work that can be done. They are unsatisfactory for large-scale rearing or flow-through bioassays because of the large amounts of water required. Natural water supplies, which are essential for most operations, should not be polluted. They should have low turbidity, high DO, low BOD, and an annual temperature cycle that requires a minimum of heating and cooling in order to meet the specific cyclic daily and seasonal requirements for the successful holding and culture of the test organisms. The annual cycle of pH should be favorable and require little or no adjustments.

1) Fresh water supplies—In laboratories for rearing purposes and special tests with fresh water organisms it is desirable to have a supply of both hard and soft waters. It is advantageous to have water with temperatures between 3 C and 7 C during the winter and between 20 C and 25 C at peak summer temperatures. For general use, the pH should fall within the range of 7 to 8.2 and carbon dioxide should be 1 mg/l or less although most organisms will acclimate to higher concentrations. Annual variations in water quality should be favorable and in line with the natural annual and seasonal variations in the natural waters of the area. The water supply must be appropriate or capable econom-

ically of being made appropriate for the organisms being reared. A good fresh water supply should be constant in quality and should not contain more than the designated amounts of the following: suspended solids <20 mg/l, total organic carbon or chemical oxygen demand (TOC or COD) <10 mg/l, un-ionized ammonia <20 μg/l, residual chlorine <0.5 μg/l, total organophosphorus pesticides <50 ng/l,* total organochloride pesticides plus PCB's <50 ng/l.* A water is considered to be of constant quality if the monthly ranges of hardness, alkalinity, conductivity, TOC or COD, and salinity are less than 10% of the respective averages and if the range of pH is less than 0.4 unit.

Municipal water supplies often contain unacceptable concentrations of copper, lead, zinc, fluoride, and chlorine or chloramines. If a satisfactory fresh water supply is not available or if a standard water is required for comparative toxicity studies, relative sensitivity tests, or tests to determine the effects of hardness, pH, or total alkalinity on the toxicity of various materials, use a reconstituted standard water of the desired quality.

Prepare the standard fresh water by adding specific amounts of reagent-grade chemicals to glass distilled and/or deionized water. For special studies, check to determine that the distilled and/or deionized water contains less than the designated amounts of the following materials:

Conductivity	<1 μsiemens/cm
Total organic carbon (TOC) or chemical oxygen demand (COD)	<2 mg/l
Boron, fluoride	<100 μg/l each
Un-ionized ammonia	<20 μg/l
Aluminum, arsenic, chromium, cobalt, copper, iron, lead, nickel, zinc	<1 μg/l each
Residual chlorine	<0.5 μg/l
Cadmium, mercury, silver	<100 ng/l each
Total organophosphorus pesticides	<50 ng/l*
Total organochlorine pesticides plus polychlorinated biphenyls (PCB's)	<50 ng/l*

Carbon-filtered deionized water usually is acceptable. Determine the conductivity of the distilled and/or deionized water for each batch of reconstituted water. Check the other constituents periodically whenever some change is suspected. If the water is prepared from a dechlorinated water, measure residual chlorine in each batch of water prepared. The pH and hardness of a receiving water influences the toxicity of some materials, especially the metals.

2) Marine water supplies—Marine waters used for culturing should be unpolluted and should have a salinity and pH favorable for the organisms being cultured as well as low turbidity and very little settleable solids. Annual variations of salinity should not be so wide as to be harmful to the organisms.

---

*No individual pesticide should exceed the allowable concentration limit set in the National Water Quality Guidelines, EPA as set in accordance with the Federal Water Pollution Control Act 92-500 as amended 1972.

If a suitable marine water supply is not available limited culturing can be carried on with artificial seawater. Standard artificial seawaters also can be used for a variety of purposes including comparative toxicity studies; relative sensitivity tests; studies to determine the influence of various levels of salinity, pH, and other environmental factors on the toxicity of materials and wastes; and the culturing of microorganisms.

TABLE 801:I. REAGENTS FOR PREPARING ARTIFICIAL SEAWATER[17]

Chemical	Concentration g/l
NaCl	23.50
Na₂SO₄	4.00
KCl	0.68
H₃BO₄	0.026
MgCl₂•2H₂O	10.78
CaCl₂•2H₂O	1.47
NaHCO₃	0.196
Na₂SiO₃•9H₂O*	0.030
Na₄EDTA†	0.0003

* Use for algal culture media only. Prepare stock solution in deionized water and adjust pH to 7.8. Add slowly with constant mixing.

† Tetrasodium ethylenediamine tetraacetate. Omit when conducting toxicity tests with metals. In bioassay tests with plankton or larvae, omit EDTA and strip medium of trace metals.[18] Na₂EDTA may be used in algal culture medium but at 0.300 mg/l [Section 801C.4c1)b)].

When artificial seawater is required for the culture of algae and other purposes, prepare it by adding to 890 ml glass-distilled, deionized water *in the given order* the reagent-grade chemicals listed in Table 801:I. Each chemical must be completely dissolved before another is added. When all chemicals are dissolved, add distilled, deionized water to make 1 l. The salinity should be $34\pm0.5^{0}/oo$ and pH 8.0 ± 0.2. Obtain desired salinity at time of use by dilution with deionized water.

Securing and maintaining a desired salinity often presents problems. If possible, obtain the water supply from an area of high salinity and obtain lower salinities by adding fresh water of a satisfactory quality. To increase salinity, use a strong natural brine. This can be secured by freezing and then partially thawing seawater. Such a procedure is satisfactory if only limited amounts of water are needed. For larger volumes, use commercial sea salts or a stronger solution of the recommended artificial seawater. In the preparation of artificial seawater, be sure that an undesirable concentration of metals does not occur. Even reagent chemicals contain traces of several metals and the extensive use of several chemicals can result in a buildup of metals. If large volumes of artificial seawater are not required the metals can be removed by passing the seawater through a column containing a deionizing resin.[18] Equipment has been devised for supplying flow-through water at a constant salinity.[19]

c. Food and feeding:

1) Culture of microorganisms—Phytoplankton and zooplankton are cultured for biostimulation, environmental requirements, and toxicity tests. They are also cultured as food for other organisms used in bioassay studies. Various species of algae are eaten by copepods, daphnia, and other microcrustaceans, the larvae and adults of mollusks, and young and adult fishes. Culture methods have been developed for growing freshwater and marine algae for bioassays and as food for other organisms used in bioassays.

a) Culture medium for freshwater algae—Prepare reconstituted fresh water by adding reagent-grade macro-nutrients to glass distilled and/or deionized water in the concentrations given in Table 801:II.

TABLE 801:II. MACRONUTRIENT STOCK SOLUTION

Compound	Concentration mg/l	Element	Resulting Concentration mg/l
NaNO₃	25.500	N	4.200
		Na	11.001
NaHCO₃	15.000	C	2.143
K₂HPO₄	1.044	K	0.469
		P	0.186
MgSO₄·7H₂O	14.700	S	1.911
		Mg	2.904
MgCl₂	5.700		
CaCl₂·2H₂O	4.410	Ca	1.202

In addition to the macro-nutrients, several other elements are needed in small quantities. The concentrations of the essential micro-nutrients are given in Table 801:III.

TABLE 801:III. MICRONUTRIENT STOCK SOLUTION

Compound	Concentration µg/l	Element	Resulting Concentration µg/l
H₃BO₃	185.520	B	32.460
MnCl₂	264.264	Mn	115.374
ZnCl₂	32.709	Zn	15.691
CoCl₂	0.780	Co	0.354
CuCl₂	0.009	Cu	0.004
Na₂MoO₄·2H₂O	7.260	Mo	2.878
FeCl₃	96.000	Fe	33.051
Na₂EDTA·2H₂O	300.000	—	—

Prepare a stock solution of each of the individual macro-nutrient salts in 1,000 times the specified final concentration in the nutrient medium in glass-distilled and/or deionized water. For the stock solution of micro-nutrients, combine the trace metals and EDTA in a single stock solution in glass distilled and/or deionized water at 1,000 times the final concentration of each in the nutrient medium.

To prepare the culture medium for the algae, add 1 ml of each of the macro-nutrient stock solutions to 900 ml of the glass-distilled and/or deionized water, then add 1 ml of the trace metal-FeCl₃-EDTA mixture and make up to 1 l by the addition of glass-distilled and/or deionized water.

Use sterile technics for bioassays with algae or other organisms when bacterial growth interferes with the tests.

Prepare the freshwater algal culture medium as follows: to 900 ml of glass-distilled and/or deionized water add 1 ml of each of the macro-nutrient stock solutions in the order listed with mixing between each addition. Filter-sterilize by passing through a sterile 0.22-µm-porosity membrane filter (pre-rinsed with 100 ml double-distilled water) into a suitable autoclave-sterilized container. Add 1 ml of the micro-nutrient solution, which has been sterilized in the same manner, and make up to 1 l with sterile distilled and/or deionized water.

Sterilization may not be required for some experiments carried out with freshly prepared culture medium because the recommended assay species are usually not axenic, containing symbiotic and commensal (nonparasitic) bacteria. However, maintain stock cultures in previously sterilized culture medium.

Store uninoculated sterile reference medium in the dark to avoid possible photochemical changes.

When sterility is desired in algal bioassays, check sterility periodically by adding 1 ml of the inoculated test culture into tubes of the sterility check medium and incubating in the dark at the test temperature for 2 wk. The appearance of opalescence in the test medium indicates the presence of contamination.

The sterile nutrient test medium is prepared so that each liter of test medium contains:

Sodium glutamate	250 mg
Sodium acetate	250 mg
Glycine	250 mg
Sucrose	250 mg
Sodium lactate	250 mg
L and D alanine	250 mg
Nutrient agar	50 mg

b) Culture medium for marine algae —To the artificial seawater formula given in Section 801C.4b2), including the Na_2SiO_3, add the nutrients listed in Table 801:IV to give the indicated concentrations in the algal culture medium.

TABLE 801:IV. NUTRIENTS FOR ALGAL CULTURE MEDIUM

Compound	Concentration	Concentration of Nutrient
NaNO₃	25.00 mg/l	4.2 mg N/l
K₂HPO₄	1.05 mg/l	0.19 mg P/l
FeCl₃	72.60 µg/l	
MnCl₂	2.30 µg/l	
ZnCl₂	2.10 µg/l	
Na₂MoO₄•-2H₂O	2.50 µg/l	
CuCl₂	0.20 µg/l	
Na₂EDTA	300.00 µg/l	
Vitamins:		
Thiamine HCl	0.100 mg/l	
Biotin	0.50 µg/l	
B₁₂	0.50 µg/l	

Culture medium for marine algae can be prepared by adding the micronutrients listed in Table 801:IV to artificial seawater. It is recommended, however, that when a good unpolluted seawater is available the medium be prepared by enriching filter sterilized natural seawater by addition of micronutrients at one half the above concentrations. If sterile technics are required in the bioassay, follow the procedures outlined for the fresh water medium. When sterilization is performed by autoclaving for 4 hr at 60 C, add the vitamins after autoclaving. When filter sterilization is used, use a positive pressure $<0.74 \, kg/cm^2$.

2) Mass production of algae as food for other organisms—The rearing of zooplankton, various filter-feeders, the larvae of crustaceans, and fishes requires large quantities of certain phytoplankters. Supplying these needs requires apparatus with the capability of producing continuous supplies of the desired organisms at high densities. An apparatus used for this purpose should permit easy assembly, cleaning, and sterilizing and efficient utilization of light energy, and be of a construction suitable for continuous use. An apparatus that meets these requirements has been constructed and used.†

A schematic diagram of this unit is given in Figure 801:1. The main body of the unit consists of a 60-cm section of 15-cm-diam pyrex drainage pipe. The top section is a 15-cm to 5-cm concentric reducer and the bottom section is a 15-cm to 5-cm ell. Each of these ac-

---

†For details of construction and use, contact Dr. Richard Steele, National Marine Water Quality Laboratory, Narragansett, R.I. 02882.

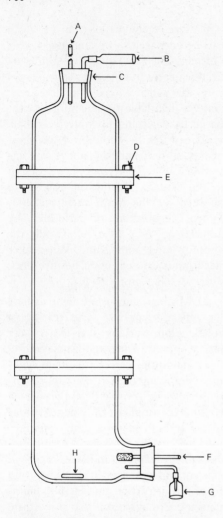

Figure 801:1. Algal culture units. A—inlet tube to allow medium into culture vessel; B—Exhaust tube for air; C—No. 12 silicone stopper with two holes (may be held in place with carboy clamp); D—aluminum flange clamp ring, an integral part of this type of plumbing; E—silicone tube, 3/32 in. (0.24 cm) OD in a groove between adjoining glass surfaces; F—inlet tube for sintered glass gas dispersion tube for aerating cultures; G—aseptic filling bell for withdrawing cells from culture; H—stirring bar with magnetic stirrer underneath to help keep organisms suspended.

This culture device can be used to supply cells on a periodic or continuous basis. As the cells are withdrawn, more medium is added. The following species have been grown at the indicated cell concentration per milliliter: *Skeletonema costatum*, 4.3×10^6; *Dunaliella tertiolecta*, 4.4×10^6; *Isochrysis galbana*, 7.0×10^6; *Monochrysis lutheri*, 5.0×10^6.

3) Food for macroinvertebrates and fishes—A suitable food is essential for rearing the various life stages of macroinvertebrates and fishes. It is necessary to distinguish carnivores from herbivores in order to supply the correct type of food. The organisms taken as food differ for the different life stages of a species but related species may take the same food. As organisms grow they take progressively larger food organisms that must be large enough to be recognized by the predator but small enough to be ingested easily. Many feed on pelagic organisms whose movements should be sufficient to attract the predator but slow enough so they can be readily caught.

commodates a No. 12 silicone rubber stopper held in place by a carboy or similar type clamp. The three sections are held together by aluminum ring clamps and adjoining surfaces are sealed by silicone "O" rings made from small-diameter tubing. All material is autoclavable and nontoxic. The assembly, light source, culture medium supply bottle, air filter, pumps, stands, and setup are shown in Figure 801:2.

Figure 801:2. Method of lighting, free-standing frames, and placement of medium source, air pumps, and other apparatus for mass algal culture device.

Food organisms should be nutritious, easily digested, and readily obtainable in nature or capable of being reared in the laboratory throughout the year. Distribution of zooplankton food in the rearing tanks must match distribution of the organisms using it. An adequate amount of food must be available; the ratio of number of prey required to predators varies from 50 : 1 to 200 : 1. If a small number of organisms is to be reared in a large tank, more food organisms must be provided to insure that enough are captured. Some of the algae and diatoms that are used for food have a tendency to settle to the bottom. Circular movement of the water in the rearing tanks, provided as described in Section 801C.4a, will serve to keep them and other food materials in suspension to the benefit of planktonic feeders.

Methods for rearing freshwater organisms have been described by Needham et al.[20] There are more recent articles on special groups. Methods for rearing larvae of marine animals with special reference to their food organisms have been summarized by Hirano and Oshima.[21] May[22] has reviewed the literature on feeding larvae of marine fishes in the laboratory. His paper lists many good references.

Algae serves as the principal food of the larval stages of many organisms. They are the food of the early life stages of many crustaceans and larval fishes as well as many mollusks. Facilities should be provided for passing the water supply directly from the source to the various holding tanks in order to provide natural plankton to the plankton feeders. In some instance, provisions should be made for pumping planktonic food organisms from the culturing tanks into the water supply of the holding, accli-mation, and testing tanks in which plankton feeders are being held. Adequate space should be provided for the production of food for plankton-feeders.

Provide test organisms with food that has been determined to be uncontaminated, palatable, and readily taken. Cold rooms and deep freezers are needed for food preparation and storage.

When using cultured microorganisms as food, be constantly aware of possible environmental changes caused by using them. In addition to the possible presence of toxic metabolites, algal blooms may occur that produce excess oxygen resulting in supersaturation and gas bubble disease.[16]

Use live food whenever possible. Analyze these food organisms to determine if they contain toxicants, especially pesticides and heavy metals, which may be harmful to the test organisms feeding on them. A knowledge of any accumulation of materials in the bodies of food organisms is especially important in studies of the effects of pesticides, bioaccumulation, and biological magnification.

Natural foods can be supplemented with several prepared dried and pelleted foods now on the market.‡ They are provided in different-sized pellets for different kinds and sizes of organisms. Such foods should be attractive to the organisms and high in protein and should supply the necessary other food elements and the trace elements and contain binders to insure pellet stability.[23] When homogenized in a blender, one part food to

---

‡Some foods that have been widely used include Glencoe Trout Food, Glencoe Mills, Glencoe, Minn. 53336; Biorell and Tetramine, available from local pet shops; Oregon Moist, Warrenton, Oregon; and Cerophyll, Cerophyll Laboratories, Inc., Kansas City, Mo. The latter has been used for the smaller forms and as a food for organisms providing food for the higher species.

two parts water, dry trout food can be dripped into tanks having circular water movement to supply the needs of plankton-feeders.

d. Cleaning containers and equipment:

1) Cleaning the holding, acclimation, testing, and dilution water tanks— Clean test containers and toxicant delivery systems before use. Wash new containers with detergent and rinse once with hydrochloric acid and acetone and twice with tap or other clean water. When the containers or delivery systems are to be used again for different organisms or for other tests, empty them, rinse with water, and clean with a material appropriate for removing the toxicant tested (for example, acid to remove metals and bases, detergent or organic solvent to remove organic compounds) then rinse twice with water. Acid can remove mineral deposits and hypochlorite, and at concentrations of 200 mg/l it is useful for removing organic matter and for disinfection. However, do not use acid and hypochlorite together. Rinse all containers with dilution water just before use. Hesselberg and Burress[24] have developed labor-saving devices useful when large numbers of bioassays are performed routinely.

2) Removal of unused food and wastes—Do not let unused food accumulate. Whenever possible, build holding and testing containers with sloping bottoms so food can be drained out or collected in a definite area and removed by a siphon. Remove fecal material and other organic wastes in the same way. Clean holding containers every day or every other day, depending on the organisms being held. If there are growths on the sides of the containers, dislodge them with a rubber spatula or rubber plate scraper and let settle for removal either by draining through the funnel-shaped bottom or by means of a siphon. The amount and frequency of cleaning needed depends on the organism being tested, the ratio of dilution water to the weight and volume of contained organisms, and the feeding schedule.

5. Parasites and Disease

a. Stress in relation to parasites and disease: Unexpected and often unexplained mortalities in experimental and control animals can interfere, sometimes seriously, with acute or chronic bioassay studies. While many factors may be responsible for the death of an animal, diseases due to specific pathogenic organisms can be among the most significant.

When large numbers of organisms are retained in a relatively small space, undesirable growths, diseases, and parasites become a problem. If the water supply is pure, such as might be obtained at an offshore island or from a shore area largely unaffected by the activities of man, problems produced by these organisms often can be controlled by strict sanitation practices. However, if the water supply is even somewhat enriched by organic materials and the concentration of potential toxicants is even slightly above normal, problems increase greatly. Pathogens and parasites that might be very rare in the natural waters become potential and ever-present dangers in an intensive culture operation. Bacteria that grow on uneaten food or fecal and other wastes compete for available dissolved oxygen and have a potential for unwanted growths, disease, and toxic products.

Even with a good flow-through, each corner, crevice, and dead area of a tank becomes a potential trouble area. Thus, circular tanks with smooth surfaces, free of corners, crevices, and dead current areas, should be used.

Filtration and/or sterilization of the water supply, regular cleaning of holding vessels, strict sanitation practices, and sterilization of equipment are the first lines of defense. Methods for uniform food distribution and limiting the amount of unused food and methods for the removal of unused food and waste materials are of prime importance.

When feral animals are used, infections, disease, and parasites are likely to be present. The deleterious effects of these factors will be enhanced by the usually crowded test conditions and test results can be significantly altered.

When organisms are exposed to a toxicant in bioassay studies they are stressed and weakened and become much more susceptable to parasites and disease. Often other environmental factors may contribute to reduced resistance of an animal to the effects of pathogens, so careful attention to nutrition, oxygen supply, and water quality is essential for maintaining a suitable stock of test organisms.

b. Control methods: Ultraviolet light and ozonation have been used successfully to control disease and parasites and improve water quality. Salinity and temperature are critical factors in larval survival and growth. Because larvae are often handled in static systems, some investigators have resorted to collection of large quantities of water from locations where the particular species of larva occurs naturally, even though this is often a laborious undertaking. Antibiotics have been used in holding tanks as a method of reducing bacterial populations.

To reduce mortality and to avoid introduction of disease into stock tanks, treat with a wide-spectrum antibiotic immediately after collection or during transport or on arrival at the laboratory. Holding in tetracycline, 15 mg/l for 24 to 48 hr, can be very helpful. Many types of chemotherapeutic agents are available, but use care in their application because some are toxic at low concentrations.[25]

Do not use treated organisms for bioassays for at least 10 days after treatment. Sterilize tanks and containers that may be contaminated with undesirable or harmful organisms with iodophore or with hypochlorite, 200 mg/l for 1 hr.

If adequate nutrition is provided and water quality is maintained, effects of disease can be minimized. Even with adequate sanitation, however, disease outbreaks may occur, so it is important to be able to recognize early signs of those diseases for which information is available. As yet, no manual for diagnosis and control of disease for marine fish and shellfish exists.

For larval bioassays, the best approach to disease control is in extraordinary measures to maintain water quality and adequate nutrition. Sanitary measures must be strict, and must include sterilization of utensils and containers, filtration and ultraviolet sterilization of water, and removal of metabolic products. If disease signs appear in larval cultures, the present method of choice is discarding the entire culture.

For bioassays using adult fish and shellfish, early diagnosis and prompt treatment, when available, can prevent loss of the entire culture.

801 D. Bioassay Systems, Test Materials, and Procedures

1. Water Supply Systems and Testing Equipment

All components of a testing system, including water heating and cooling units, pipes, constant-level troughs and head boxes, valves and fittings, diluters, pumps, mixing equipment, tanks, and exposure chambers must be constructed of nontoxic materials. Dilution water of the desired temperatures may be secured by mixing hot and cold water of constant temperature in the correct proportions, by heat exchangers, or by heaters or coolers in constant-level troughs and head boxes. A heated room with thermostatic controls is usually suitable for static bioassays with warm-water organisms. The dilution water can be held in tanks until it reaches ambient temperature. A specially insulated constant-temperature room or a large water bath equipped with temperature controls and adequate circulating water usually is required for conducting static bioassays with cold-water species. A satisfactory design for a small laboratory to conduct short-term static bioassays has been described.[26,27] Bioassays with different groups of organisms require special facilities and equipment to meet the special problems created by the different requirements. These are described in the various sections, 802 through 810.

Flow-through tests require metering pumps or other devices for accurate delivery of the toxicants or test material into the dilution water for the flow-through test chambers. Most toxicant delivery systems have been designed for introducing solutions of toxicants and solvents into fresh water and may not be applicable to all wastes. Many materials proposed for disposal at sea are not homogeneous mixtures and special toxicant delivery systems will be required to introduce representative samples into the test containers. Stirring may be required to maintain suspended solids and nonhomogeneous wastes in flow-through and static tests.

Dilution water and stock solutions of toxicants can be measured, mixed, and delivered to the exposure chambers by a variety of methods. Dilution water may be delivered from constant-head troughs or head boxes by means of siphons, constricted tubing, nozzles, or pumps, while toxicants may be delivered by means of siphons from constant-head reservoirs, special pumps, calibrated glass nozzles, or Mariotte bottles.[28] The dilution water and toxicant are mixed in tanks with baffles or stirrers or in mixing troughs.[29] Since the introduction of the serial diluter,[30] various methods and types of diluters have been described[31-39] but the proportional diluter[40] and its modifications has probably been used routinely in fresh water more than any other system.

The basic components of a continuous-flow bioassay system are shown in Figure 801:3. A much greater volume of diluent water is required for flow-through bioassays than for static bioassays. This necessitates a large, elevated diluent-water reservoir, Figure 801:3a, of sufficient volume to provide water for at least 5 days. When dilution water is added to this reservoir continuously, a reservoir of smaller capacity is

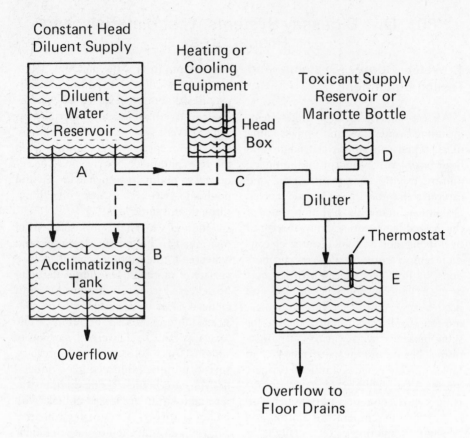

Figure 801:3. Basic components of continuous-flow bioassay system.

preferred. Diluent water flows at a constant rate by gravity from this reservoir to a constant-head diluent-supply head box through a nonmetallic float-controlled valve or other device and then to the diluter at a constant rate. The head box (c) should have heating or cooling equipment to maintain a constant temperature that is controlled by a thermostat in the test container (e). Test containers must have an overflow system designed to prevent the organisms from entering outlets. Such containers have been described by Lemke.[41] Cleaning of

the test containers is described in 801C.4d.

The constant-head toxicant supply (d) is a constant-level tank for the effluent, or it can be a Mariotte bottle or other device for materials of higher toxicity. If the toxicant stock solution is not stable, renew it before breakdown. If metering pumps are used, the toxicant supply system need not maintain a constant pressure.

Jackson and Brungs[42] described a device with a simple valve control system for regulation of flow rates of the diluent and toxicant solution. For more toxic materials, less volume of toxicant is required and a Mariotte bottle that delivers a very slow but constant flow is useful.[43] The assembly and operation of a Mariotte bottle has been described by Burrows.[44]

A diluter meters the dilution water from the constant-head box and the toxicant from the constant-head tank or other containers and mixes them in the proper proportions for each of the test chambers.

After proper calibration of the diluter, make the toxicant stock solutions to the proper concentration. When a Mariotte bottle is used insulate it against rapid temperature fluctuations to reduce variations of flow resulting from pressure changes. A constant-head device that is open to the atmosphere does not need to be insulated.

The proportional diluter is generally more useful and easier to construct, calibrate, and operate, but the serial dilution apparatus is more applicable when the desired dilution factor (i.e., the value by which a concentration is multiplied in order to obtain the next lower concentration) is less than 0.50. The proportional diluter has been modified to provide a very narrow range of concentrations with a dilution factor of 0.90.[45]

The proportional diluter[30] can deliver five toxicant dilutions and water for a control test at any desired flow rate up to 400 ml/min for each concentration, with dilution factors ranging from 0.75 to 0.50. Metering cells can be exchanged to provide dilution factors outside this range. Proportional diluters have been used that deliver up to 2,000 ml/min and can be made even larger.

Some examples of the precision of the proportional diluter are available in the literature.[45, 46]

Provide a chamber to promote mixing of toxicant-bearing water and dilution water between the diluter and the test container for each concentration. If duplicate test containers are used, run separate delivery tubes from the mixing chamber to each duplicate. Alterations in the design of the proportional diluter have been useful in some situations. Flow rates through the test containers must be at least 6 tank water volumes/24 hr and in many cases it is desirable to construct the toxicant delivery system so that it can provide 10 or more tank water volumes/24 hr. Do not let the flow rate through the test containers vary by more than ±10% from any one test container to any other, or from one time to another within a given test. Check the calibration of the toxicant delivery system carefully before, during, and after each test. Determine the volume of stock solutions and dilution water used in each portion of the toxicant delivery system and the flow rate through each test container. Check the general operation of the toxicant delivery system daily during the test.

The diluter is the best method for mixing the dilution water and the toxicants and delivering them to the test containers because it is fail-safe. If the dilution water is shut off, the system stops and no more toxicant is added.

Bioassays of effluents present several problems including suspended materials, and often the need for large volumes of the toxicant. A special diluter has been designed to meet these problems by Esvelt and Conners.[47] Because developments in the construction and use of diluters are continuing, those conducting long-term, flow-through bioassays should consult literature now available and keep abreast of current publications on the subject.

2. Preparing Test Materials

a. Dilution water: Whenever possible, make bioassays to determine the toxicity of effluents on site where ample supplies of the toxicant and dilution water are available.

The temperature, DO, pH, hardness or salinity, turbidity, and other qualities of the dilution water will be those of the receiving water and will vary with it daily and seasonally. This is essential if the effect of the waste discharge in the receiving water is to be determined accurately. Convey the water to the testing chambers with as little modification as possible. Do not aerate, heat, cool, or unnecessarily agitate it. If it is low in oxygen, flow-through and loading in the test chambers should be such that the DO is not significantly reduced in passing through the test; hold temperature at or near that of the receiving water.

When the receiving water already contains wastes from other sources it is especially important that water for dilution of the test effluent be taken from the receiving water just outside the area of effect of that effluent. The toxicity of the test waste in conjunction with the other contaminants must be ascertained when determining allowable discharge rates. This is especially necessary when effluents are known to contain metal salts, cyanide complexes, ammonium compounds, or other chemicals, the toxicity of which is known to be greatly influenced by changes in pH, hardness, and other characteristics. When wide variations occur in quality characteristics of receiving waters, determine the toxicity of the waste material at the upper and lower limits of the range, in short, at the conditions under which it is most toxic.

If the receiving water already causes stress on the aquatic biota because of wastes already added in other areas, this may be evaluated by using two controls, one with the receiving water and another with an unpolluted water of the same or very similar natural quality. The water for this control may be artificial seawater or fresh water or it may be water taken from a well or another source having a natural quality similar to that of the receiving water before the addition of toxicants. The calcium, magnesium, sulfate, and dissolved oxygen content for fresh-water controls should not differ by more than 10% from the natural content of the water receiving the test waste. Adjust the pH, alkalinity, and hardness to those of the receiving water before the addition of wastes. The purpose of this is to determine if the dilution water itself, before the addition of the effluent, is unfavorable for the more sensitive aquatic species that live or have lived in that area. In addition, evaluate existing information on the composition of the aquatic biota and study aquatic populations above and below the effluent and in other areas of the water to determine the qualitative and quantitative makeup of the populations. If an effluent discharged to a water over a long period has an adverse effect, this will be indicated by a change in the aquatic biota below the outfall. Such a discharge can be likened to a long-term bioassay on the whole biota. A study of the aquatic population above and below the outfall gives a measure of the long-term effects of the effluent. The best method for detecting and evaluating these effects is to make qualitative and quantitative population studies some distance above and below the outfall. Determine whether wastes added in another section of the stream, lake, reservoir, bay, estuary, or shore area are rendering conditions unfavorable for aquatic life, so that better equalization can be made of the capacity of the receiving water to purify the wastes without adversely affecting other desired uses. Conduct monitoring bioassays to determine compliance with standards or regulations either on site or at a source of unpolluted water for dilution and controls.

When the purpose of the bioassay is other than to determine the toxicity of an effluent, use for dilution water only a nonpolluted natural water or a synthetic water of a constant and reproducible quality and one that is favorable for aquatic life and of the quality described for holding, acclimating, and culturing aquatic organisms. Warm or cool dilution water to the desired test temperature and bring to equilibrium with the atmospheric gases before it is delivered to the exposure chambers.

Use standard water for comparative toxicity and sensitivity bioassays as well as standard conditions and organisms. Use standard reconstituted fresh or marine water as described in Sections 801C.4b1) and 2) if the natural supply is not suitable for these tests. Because of the effects of water quality on toxicity, have on hand both hard and soft water for bioassays with freshwater organisms.

Because many marine organisms spend a portion of their life cycle in es-tuaries, change the quality of dilution water used in life cycle bioassays in accordance with their special requirements at the different life stages. Select the dilution water temperature with consideration of the usual and maximum temperature of the waters to which the bioassay results are to apply. If the effects of temperature are not being studied, keep it within the favorable range, usually near the upper allowable level throughout the annual cycle.

Keep the dissolved oxygen content of the dilution water used in bioassays with warm-water species above 4 mg/l, 60% of saturation, or the DO standard, whichever is highest. For the cold-fresh-water species, keep minimum DO above 5 mg/l unless local standards differ. Some larval forms, such as those of marine crustaceans, require higher DO concentrations. Consider temperatures and dissolved oxygen together.

The pH of the dilution water can vary widely for some organisms while others require a narrow range. Therefore, determine the requirements of the organisms being studied. Generally, the CO_2 concentration should be less than 1 mg/l but many organisms can acclimate to higher concentrations. Avoid rapid changes in pH or CO_2 content. A rapid increase in the CO_2 content of marine waters indicates that some significant change has occurred that should be investigated at once. Freshwater organisms are more tolerant of pH changes and accommodate to much wider variations than do the strictly marine forms, which usually live in a narrow range. Changes in pH drastically alter the toxicity of some materials such as cyanide and ammonia. In long-term studies, other than effluent and monitoring studies, keep the pH relatively constant when the toxicity of the materials being studied is greatly influenced by pH. During a bioassay, do not let pH vary more than 0.1 unit from the normal daily and seasonal variations or the established level for the bioassay.

In bioassays with estuarine and marine organisms and different life stages that may be marine or estuarine, salinity is of prime importance. Use the natural salinity for each test species and its different developmental stages. Keep the selected salinity as near constant as possible[19] unless the bioassays are being conducted to determine the effects of different salinities or most favorable salinities. Unnatural variations in salinity are stressful and can seriously impair the results of bioassays.

The turbidity of the dilution water is an important environmental factor in determination of harmful concentrations of potential toxicants or the desired concentrations of other environmental factors because some toxicants are adsorbed or absorbed on particulate organic matter, suspended solids, and settleable solids. Where large amounts of settleable solids significantly remove the toxicants from the water, determine concentrations of toxicants in the bottom sediments and their toxicity by appropriate bioassays with benthic organisms. Turbid dilution water also may cause problems in the conduct of bioassays by limiting visibility for inspection, by limiting photosynthesis of algae, or by forming deposits and clogging water systems.

Keep acidity, total alkalinity, and hardness of dilution water essentially constant during bioassays. Hardness influences the toxicity of some metals and total alkalinity can be an important factor in photosynthesis and algal growth.

b. Preparation of toxicant solution: Prepare solutions of toxicants in advance so that they may be added immediately to the dilution water for static tests in the required amounts to obtain the different test concentrations. If a toxicant is unstable in solutions, determine its time to deterioration so that it may be replaced as necessary. Prepare all solutions required for each series of toxicity bioassays from the same sample of material. Disperse any undissolved material uniformly by shaking before withdrawal and addition to dilution water in the test containers.

Some effluents, especially oil, are very difficult to distribute evenly throughout the test solutions. Agitation may be necessary in the test containers to maintain solids in suspension. This may require a magnamix in the tank containing the stock solution of the effluent.

The nature of the material being tested governs the selection of test containers, size and shape, preparation of the test concentrations, and the frequency of a test medium replacement. Problems due to various wastes include insolubility, adsorption to exposed surfaces, decomposition, hydrolysis, photolysis, loss of volatile materials, high BOD, and bacterial growth. These can change the concentration of the material being tested and lead to reporting of erroneous results. Breakdown by hydrolysis, photolysis, bacteria, and chemical interactions produce breakdown products that may be more or less toxic than the original material.

Changes in pH must be taken into consideration. Volatilization, absorption, and adsorption, if extensive, indicate the need for special handling of the test material.

If the effluent bioassays are not conducted on site, the collection and handling of the samples and the preparation of the test solutions from them becomes an additional problem.

Collect samples of industrial or other effluents that are not constant in composition at different times; do not combine them unnecessarily to make composite samples because knowledge of the maximum, rather than average, toxicity of a variable effluent often is required in connection with the control of waste disposal in flowing waters.

Extreme damage to the aquatic life of a receiving stream can result from brief intermittent discharges of a highly toxic waste even if the toxicity of the effluent at other times and its average toxicity are negligible. Therefore, if the composition and toxicity of an effluent vary considerably, test a number of individual grab samples taken at times when the effluent is likely to be most toxic in order to determine the maximum toxicity or run a continuous-flow toxicity bioassay where the organisms are subjected to these variations in toxicity with a release at times being rapidly lethal. A composite sample of an effluent consisting of portions collected at regular time intervals can be useful only when average toxicity is to be evaluated. An average toxicity is not necessarily adequate for the protection of the biota because it is often the extremes and not the averages that are critical.

Store effluent samples in completely filled stoppered containers at a low temperature. If the waste contains organic matter subject to bacterial decomposition, refrigerate the samples and hold between 0 and 4 C. Determine allowable time of storage before testing by checking samples after given periods of storage. Do not store samples longer than absolutely necessary.

Many effluents are complex mixtures having solid, liquid, and gas components. When preparing test media, shake the waste toxicant thoroughly before use. Use the waste directly as a stock solution of the toxicant or prepare a stock solution by diluting with filtered seawater or fresh water to the desired concentration and volume for mixing with the dilution water. Make stock solutions on a volume-to-volume ratio of the dilution water and the waste effluent, if it is a liquid, so that the percentage of waste in each of the test concentrations can be designated. If it is a solid waste dilute on a weight-to-volume basis, for example, milligrams per liter. If a volume-to-volume basis is used and it is desired to express it as parts per million or weight per volume, correct for specific gravity of the material being tested.

If the waste contains both solids and liquids, shake thoroughly to insure that it is evenly dispersed, remove a desired volume, while it is still mixed, as a stock toxicant or dilute with water to the desired concentration or percentage of waste to be added to the dilution water in the test solutions. Provide agitation in the stock reservoir and in the test concentrations to keep the material in suspension. If small organisms are being used for the test, use a magnetic stirrer in the test chamber. If larger organisms are being tested in tanks, place a screen or perforated false bottom in the tank over a propeller that keeps the material in suspension. However, if the solids settle out quickly in nature and are not contacted by the pelagic organisms, test only the liquid portion. After thorough mixing, allow it to settle and then decant or drain off the liquid and use as the test toxicant. If the solid portion of the waste is toxic, set up test chambers having a certain weight-to-volume ratio of bottom material and expose benthic and burrowing organisms of the area to test possible toxic effects of the solid portion of the waste on the biota that would be exposed. Mix wastes and let settle before adding the organisms. Test organisms would include, for fresh water, tubifex worms and other silt-inhabiting annelids, burrowing mayflies, chironomids, and other diptera living in or on bottom materials. In marine waters, worms and other burrowing and benthic organisms that live on or in bottom materials or ingest these sediments or bottom detritus should be the test species.

If possible, use mechanical means to solve problems of extent and rate of solubility. If the waste contains materials only slightly soluble or insoluble in water, check solubility in milligrams per liter and, if it is below toxic levels or very low, use solvents and/or emulsifying agents or water-miscible solvents to disperse them throughout the toxic solutions being tested.

Acetone, dimethylformamide (DMF), ethanol, methanol, and triethylene glycol may be used as solvents for the preparation of stock solutions. If these are not satisfactory, use isopropanol acetonitrile, dimethylacetamide, or ethylene glycol. A suggested surfactant is Triton X-100, a product of Rohm and Haas Company, or equivalent. Use only the minimal amount of solvent necessary to disperse the toxicant, not to exceed 0.5 mg/l in static and 0.1 mg/l in flow-through test solutions.

When an additive is used, use two sets of controls, one containing no additives and one containing the highest concentration of additives to which any organisms in the test are exposed.

For preparation of test solutions with highly toxic substances, it may not be feasible to add measured quantities of the toxicants directly to the dilution water in test containers. Table 801:V can be useful in determining volumes of suitable stock solutions or dilutions to add. Effluents are added on a percent volume to volume basis.

c. Test organisms: Select test organisms as described in Section 801C.1 and handle as indicated in Sections 801C.3 and 4. For long-term tests, the condition of the test organisms is very important. They must be in excellent condition when placed in the test containers. At the end of the test they should be in good condition in the controls. Organisms to be used in these tests should have mortalities less than 2% during acclimation. No disease should occur and deaths should be less than 1% in the 4 days before the tests among macroinvertebrates and fishes. There should be no evidence of abnormalities or unusual behavior at the time of their transfer to the test containers. Select test animals and grade according to size in advance to avoid unnecessary handling just before introduction into the test containers. The largest organism in the test group of organisms should not be more than 50% longer than the shortest organism.

With the macroinvertebrates and fishes, deaths in the controls should be virtually absent during short-term tests. The test is not acceptable if 10% of the control organisms die of causes other than cannibalism.

TABLE 801:V. DILUTIONS FOR VARIOUS TEST SOLUTION CONCENTRATIONS

Test Solution Concentration Desired			Volume to Be Diluted to 1 l for Given Stock Solution Strength *ml*				
%	*mg/l*	*µg/l*	100 g/l	10 g/l	1 g/l	0.1 g/l	0.01 g/l
1.0	10,000		100				
0.56	5,600		56				
0.32	3,200		32				
0.18	1,800		18				
0.10	1,000		10	100			
0.056	560		5.6	56			
0.032	320		3.2	32			
0.018	180		1.8	18			
0.010	100		1.0	10	100		
0.0056	56			5.6	56		
0.0032	32			3.2	32		
0.0018	18			1.8	18		
0.0010	10			1.0	10	100	
0.00056	5.6				5.6	56	
0.00032	3.2				3.2	32	
0.00018	1.8				1.8	18	
0.00010	1.0	1,000			1.0	10	100
0.000056	0.56	560				5.6	56
0.000032	0.32	320				3.2	32
0.000018	0.18	180				1.8	18
0.000010	0.10	100				1.0	10
0.0000056	0.056	56					5.6
0.0000032	0.032	32					3.2
0.0000018	0.018	18					1.8
0.0000010	0.010	10					1.0

3. Test Procedures

a. Experimental design: Expose the test organisms in duplicate containers or the optimal number required to provide adequate volume for holding the test organisms and carrying out the bioassay test. The use of more organisms and replicate test containers for each toxicant concentration is often desirable to reduce variability. Replicates must be true replicates, with no water connection between the test containers. Normally each bioassay consists of a series of five test concentrations and a control or an additional control if solvents or emulsifiers are used. Because each concentration is run in duplicate, 11 or 12 containers are required for each test. Randomization of the test containers within the testing area is desirable. If replicates are used, random assignment of one test container for each test concentration in a row followed by random assignment of a second test container in a second row or an extension of the same row is recommended rather than total randomization. Distribute the organisms impartially to the test containers either by adding one at a time to each container if there are to be less than 11 organisms per container or 2 at a time if there are to be more. Repeat this process until each exposure chamber contains the desired number of test organisms. It is often convenient, especially in short-term static bioassays, to assign organisms to other containers and then add them to the test chambers containing the toxic solutions all at the same time.

It is desirable to repeat all short-term bioassays in order to determine if the information is reproducible and comparable. If short-term static tests are not comparable on the second series, repeat tests until a good agreement is reached.

In long-term flow-through tests, results are not acceptable if 10% of the test organisms in the control die, show the effect under study, fail to spawn, develop abnormally, or are in apparent poor condition. These percentages should not include cannibalism when it apparently takes place equally in the control and test chambers. When the larvae of some marine crustaceans are tested, it is often difficult to keep loses in the controls below 15%.

In short-term static or renewal tests with fishes, it has been the usual practice to use 10 or more test organisms in each toxicant concentration. In recent years, as the number of different organisms used in bioassays has increased, the tendency has been to use larger numbers of test organisms for each test concentration, especially with the smaller species such as the algae, protozoa, daphnids, copepods, and the larvae of marine crustaceans and mollusks.

The number of organisms to be exposed in each test concentration is governed by a number of considerations: (*a*) the size of the organisms; (*b*) the expected apparent normal mortality; (*c*) the extent of cannibalism; (*d*) the availability of dilution water, toxicant, and test organisms, and (*e*) the desired precision of the estimate of the toxicity of the test material. In turn the precision obtained also depends on a number of factors: (*a*) the variability of the organisms in their response; (*b*) the number of organisms exposed to each test concentration; (*c*) the number of replications being made; (*d*) the toxicant to which organisms are exposed; (*e*) how close the midconcentrations tested happen to be to the LC50 and how closely the concentrations of the toxicant solutions cluster around the LC50 concentration; and (*f*) in the case of an effluent, the variability of the toxicant being tested.

A number of factors govern the precision of the results of a bioassay and the arbitrary setting of the number of test organisms will not assure a certain precision for the results. For a given test under similar conditions, increasing the number of test organisms increases the precision. In a series of tests with sewage effluent, it was found that with 10 fish, the 95% confidence interval was within $\pm 20\%$ of the mean while when 20 fish were exposed in each test concentration it was within $\pm 14\%$ of the mean value. When a certain precision is demanded for the LC50 or EC50 values and the incipient LC50 or EC50 values, evaluate the results of the preliminary tests and with these results determine the number of test organisms to be exposed in each test concentration. Establish the standard mortality curve by plotting the probit or logit of the mortality against the log of the concentration to get an indication of the sample size necessary to secure a given precision.

Because the incipient LC50 or EC50 is used with an AF (application factor) to determine the SC (safe concentration) of that particular waste in that particular receiving water, determine them with an acceptable degree of precision. It is recommended that the 95% confidence interval be within less than ±30% of the mean value. The number of test organisms and test concentrations for each test will then be the number required to attain this precision. With test organisms for which culture methods have not been well worked out, this degree of precision may be difficult or impossible to attain. Use at least 10 test organisms for each test concentration, but 20 or more often are required when small organisms or larvae are used and cannibalism or natural mortality is high. The required degree of precision determines the number of test organisms and duplicate tests that must be used.

Because industrial effluents vary in their volume and toxicity, determine the incipient LC50 at periodic intervals and especially when there is reason to believe that there is some change in the effluent.

b. . Selection of test concentrations. Concentrations of test solutions of liquid industrial wastes (aqueous solutions, suspensions, and emulsions of complex or unknown compositions) are expressed as percent by volume on a volume-to-volume basis. For example, a 10% dilution equals 1 volume of wastewater in 9 volumes of diluent water. Concentrations of nonaqueous wastes and of individual chemicals (solids, liquids, or gases) usually are expressed in terms of milligrams or micrograms per liter. Indicate the inclusion of any water of hydration as part of the weight of the solute (e.g., $CuSO_4 \cdot 5H_2O$). Likewise, when an impure chemical is tested, especially a formulation containing added inert ingredients, indicate the chemical composition by weight and whether the LC value is based on concentration of total material or concentration of active ingredient.

TABLE 801:VI. GUIDE TO SELECTION OF EXPERIMENTAL CONCENTRATIONS, BASED ON PROGRESSIVE BISECTION OF INTERVALS ON LOGARITHMIC SCALE

Column 1	Column 2	Column 3	Column 4	Column 5
10.0				
				8.7
			7.5	
				6.5
		5.6		
				4.9
			4.2	
				3.7
	3.2			
				2.8
			2.4	
				2.1
		1.8		
				1.55
			1.35	
				1.15
1.0				

Although the LC may be determined by using any appropriate series of concentrations of the substance or waste being assayed, the logarithmic series of concentration values given in Table 801:VI is recommended for the test concentrations of the toxicant to be used. These values can represent concentrations expressed as percent by volume or milligrams per liter or as parts per million by weight. They may all be multiplied or divided, as necessary, by any power of 10. For example, the two values in the first column may be 10.0 and 1.0 as shown, or they may be 100 and 10, or 1.0 and 0.1, with the values in the other columns changed accordingly. The series of values 10.0, 5.6, 3.2, 1.8, and 1.0 (i.e., Columns 1 to 3), or 10.0, 7.5, 5.6, 4.2, 3.2, etc. (Columns 1 to 4), are evenly spaced when plotted on a logarithmic scale. The values in the first three columns are often sufficient, but precision can often be increased by including values from Column 4 in the test concentration series initially or by performing additional tests. Values in Column 5 are not often used. Values in the first three columns give concentrations each of which is 55 to 57% of the next highest concentration. When the values in the fourth column are included, each concentration is approximately 75% of the next higher concentration.

Some investigators prefer other, similar series of concentrations, such as those in Table 801:VII. The values in Column 1 may be used and are often sufficient but those in Column 2 are also used when it is deemed advisable to reduce the intervals between test concentrations. The reason for the selection of these concentrations is apparent from their logarithms. Successive dilution whereby the concentration of a solution is reduced stepwise by a constant factor, 0.5 for example, is a simple way to ob-

TABLE 801:VII. GUIDE TO SELECTION OF
EXPERIMENTAL CONCENTRATIONS, BASED ON
DECILOG INTERVALS

Concentrations		Log of Concentration
Column 1	Column 2	
10.0		1.00
	7.94 (or 7.9)	0.90
6.31 (or 6.3)		0.80
	5.01 (or 5.0)	0.70
3.98 (or 4.0)		0.60
	3.16 (or 3.15)	0.50
2.51 (or 2.5)		0.40
	1.99 (or 2.0)	0.30
1.58 (or 1.6)		0.20
	1.26 (or 1.25)	0.10
1.00		0.00

tain a geometric series of concentrations, such as 8, 4, 2, 1 and 0.5%.

The magnitude of suitable intervals between concentrations tested to establish an LC50 or EC50 by interpolation depends on the required degree of precision and on the nature of the experimental data.

c. Loading: For static bioassays, the weight of organisms in a test container must not exceed 1 g/2 l/day, preferably 1 g/3 l/day of test solution. In tests with small organisms and tropical forms, the volume of test solution per gram of test organisms must be increased significantly to as much as 1 g/10 l. To properly accomodate the larger test organisms, use at least duplicate test containers. Limit the number of test organisms per volume of test solution so that during the test (a) dissolved oxygen and the toxicant concentrations are not lowered significantly, (b) the concentrations of metabolic products (e.g., CO_2) do not become too high, and (c) the organisms are not stressed by crowding. See Table 801:VIII for concentrations of un-ion-

TABLE 801:VIII. PERCENTAGE OF AMMONIA UN-IONIZED IN DISTILLED WATER*

Temperature C	Percentage Un-ionized at Given pH								
	6.0	6.5	7.0	7.5	8.0	8.5	9.0	9.5	10.0
5	0.01	0.04	0.11	0.40	1.1	3.6	10	27	54
10	0.02	0.06	0.18	0.57	1.8	5.4	15	36	64
15	0.03	0.08	0.26	0.83	2.6	7.7	21	45	72
20	0.04	0.12	0.37	1.2	3.7	11	28	55	80
25	0.05	0.17	0.51	1.7	5.1	14	35	63	84
30	0.07	0.23	0.70	2.3	7.0	19	43	70	88

* Prepared from data given in Sillen and Martell.[49]

ized ammonia at different temperatures and pH. The concentration of un-ionized ammonia must not exceed 20 μg/l. Space needed to avoid stress and cannibalism will vary with the species. For flow-through studies, the volume of flow should be 6 to 10 tank volumes every 24 hr to maintain desirable temperatures, oxygen concentrations, and safe concentrations of metabolites. At the suggested loadings and flow-through rate, oxygen concentrations should not be significantly decreased. It is estimated that, at the maximum, the DO may be lowered an average of 2 mg/l.

d. Physical and chemical determinations:

1) Analysis of water quality—When carrying out bioassays to determine water quality criteria, comparative toxicity, relative sensitivity, and various other parameters, if a fresh water is used for dilution measure its hardness, alkalinity, pH, conductivity, TOC, COD, and suspended solids at the beginning of the test and at least once every 30 days thereafter. If the quality of the dilution water is constant, this is sufficient. If it is variable, test more frequently. If a city water is used, measure the residual chlorine.[48] The concentration of un-ionized ammonia can be calculated from the concentration of total ammonia, pH, and temperature by the use of Table 801:VIII. Analyze controls for each test concentration weekly for pH, alkalinity, and hardness to define variability of the test water. However, if any of these characteristics are affected by the toxicant, test each toxic concentration at least once every other week. When brackish or marine dilution water is used, measure its salinity, pH, suspended solids, and TOC or COD at least once every 30 days, and at the beginning and end of each test.

When the bioassays are used to determine the amount of an effluent that may be discharged to a particular receiving water, dilution water is taken from the receiving water and the analyses listed are to determine that the various test concentrations are correct. In this instance it is the toxicity of the effluent in the receiving water, whatever it might be during the course of the bioassay, that is important.

2) Analysis of the toxicant—When flow-through life cycle bioassays are conducted to determine effluent requirements for a specific waste discharge, routine detailed analyses of the effluent are not needed if the effluent is not being modified because the studies are in progress and the effluent is that normal-

ly discharged. However, make periodic tests to insure that the correct ratio of effluent to dilution water is being maintained in each of the exposure tanks.

For studies to determine water quality criteria measure the concentration of toxicants (*a*) in each test container at the beginning of the test and at least once during the test, (*b*) in at least one test container at the next-to-lowest toxicant concentration at least once every week, and (*c*) in at least one appropriate test container whenever a malfunction is detected in any part of the toxicant delivery system. For replicate test containers the ratio of the highest measured concentration to the lowest measured concentration should be less than 1.15; if it is not, check the toxicant delivery system and analyze additional samples from the proper test containers to determine if the sampling or analytical method is not precise enough. In addition, the measured concentrations of toxicants must be no more than 10 to 15% higher or lower than the concentration calculated from the composition of the stock solution and the calibration of the toxicant delivery system. When the concentrations of toxicants are not measured, the flow-through technic will be less useful.

Record temperatures at least hourly throughout the test in at least one test container; additional measurements of the dilution water and test solutions are often desirable. Measure dissolved oxygen concentration, pH, and salinity at the beginning of the test and every 24 hr thereafter in the control, high, medium, and low toxicant concentrations as long as test organisms are in them. Variation of 0.5 C from the temperature regime is allowable but ±1 C should not be exceeded. Correct any reduction in DO

below the minimum specified as soon as noted.

Take water samples for chemical analysis at the center of the exposure tank; do not include any surface scum or material from the bottom or sides of the tank. Daily, equal-volume, grab samples can be composited for a week if it has been shown that the results of the analysis are not affected by storage of the samples. Analyze enough grouped grab samples periodically throughout the test to determine whether the concentration of toxicant is reasonably constant from day to day in one tank and from one tank to its duplicate. If not, analyze enough samples weekly throughout the test to show the variability of the toxicant concentration. If methods are available, analyze to determine if the conditions of the test and the flow rate used are such that no more than 10% of the toxicant at the next-to-lowest concentration will degrade or volatilize or both and that at the loading used no less than 90% of the toxicant that would be present in the next-to-lowest concentration without test organisms in the test container will be present with test organisms in the test container. Both problems can be alleviated by using a faster flow rate; the latter problem can also be alleviated by using a lower loading.

When possible and necessary, analyze mature test organisms and possibly the eggs, larva, and juveniles obtained from the test for toxicant residues. For the larger organisms, analyze muscle and liver and possibly also gills, blood, brain, bone, kidney, GI tract, gonads, and skin. Analysis of whole organisms may be done, but for the higher organisms it should not replace analysis of individual tissues, especially muscle.

e. Biological data and observations:

In short-term bioassays with macroinvertebrates and fishes, count the number of dead or affected organisms in each test container at least every 24 hr after the first day of the test. More observations are desirable during the first day. Remove dead organisms as soon as they are observed. In addition, count the number often enough to define the shape of the toxicity curve. A suggested schedule for short-term acute tests is to count the number of dead or affected organisms in each test container 1.5, 3, 6, 12, and 24 hr after the beginning of the test and once or twice a day thereafter. It is more important to obtain data that will define the shape of the toxicity curve than to obtain data at prespecified times. Death is the adverse effect most often used to study acute toxicity with aquatic organisms. The usual criterion for death is no movement, especially no gill movement in fish, and no reaction to gentle prodding. Death is not easily determined for some invertebrates, and movement of antennae, mouth parts, or other organs may be used. When actual death can not be determined, EC50 is often used rather than LC50. The effect generally used for determining EC50 with daphnia, midge larvae, copepods, and other organisms is immobilization, which is defined as inability to move, except for minor activity of appendages. Other effects can be used to determine EC50, but always report the effect and its definition. Report such effects as erratic swimming, loss of reflex, discoloration, changes in behavior, excessive mucus production, hyperventilation, opaque eyes, curved spine, hemmorhaging, molting, and cannibalism.

In short-term tests, close observations of the reactions of the organisms during the first few hours may give an indication of the nature of the toxicant and serve as a guide for further tests. Determine length and weight of organisms by measuring representative organisms before the test and all live organisms after the test. After acclimation has begun, do not handle test organisms or remove them from the test chambers for weighing or measuring. However, to determine increases in growth rate or increases in weight, add more organisms initially for removal periodically to make the necessary determinations.

In long-term partial life cycle or life cycle bioassays, a photographic method for counting and measuring the small test organisms[50] is very satisfactory because it is rapid and accurate and does not entail handling of the organisms. With this method, the exposure chambers have glass bottoms and drains that allow the water level to be drawn down. When it is desired to count and measure the test organisms, the water in the test aquarium is drawn down to a depth of 2 to 3 cm and the aquarium is transferred to a light box having fluorescent lights under a square millimeter grid of adequate size to accomodate the exposure chambers. A photograph is then taken of the bottom of the aquarium; this shows the test organisms over the grid. With a proper enlargement of the picture, the organisms can be counted and measured by means of the grid. Periodic measurements can be taken in this way to determine the survival of various life stages.

f. Photoperiod and artificial light: In long-term studies to determine water quality requirements for those species that require the annual light cycle photoperiods, simulate the natural seasonal daylight and darkness periods, with appropriate twilight periods, at that local-

TABLE 801:IX. TEST (EVANSVILLE, IND.) PHOTOPERIOD FOR BROOK TROUT, PARTIAL LIFE CYCLE

Dawn to Dusk Time	Date	Day Length (hr & min)
6:00-6:15	Mar. 1	12:15
6:00-7:00	15	13:00
6:00-7:30	Apr. 1	13:30
6:00-8:15	15	14:15
6:00-8:45	May 1	14.45
6:00-9:15	15	15:15
6:00-9:30	June 1	15:30
6:00-9:45	15	15:45
6:00-9:45	July 1	15:45
6:00-9:30	15	15:30
6:00-9:00	Aug. 1	15:00
6:00-8:30	15	14:30
6:00-8:00	Sept. 1	14:00
6:00-7:30	15	13:30
6:00-6:45	Oct. 1	12:45
6:00-6:15	15	12:15
6:00-5:30	Nov. 1	11:30
6:00-5:00	15	11:00
6:00-4:45	Dec. 1	10:45
6:00-4:30	15	10:30
6:00-4:30	Jan. 1	10:30
6:00-4:45	15	10:45
6:00-5:15	Feb. 1	11:15
6:00-5:45	15	11:45

Juvenile-adult exposure (Mar. 1 – Sept. 15)
Spawning and egg incubation (Oct. 1 – Nov. 15)
Alevin-juvenile exposure (Dec. 1 – Feb. 15)

ity or some central location. Make adjustments in photoperiods on the first and fifteenth of every test month. Photoperiod adjustments for brook trout are shown in Table 801:IX, which is arranged so that adjustments need be made only in the dusk times. This schedule can be adapted for establishing photoperiods for other test organisms. The dawn and dusk times listed in the table need not correspond to the actual test times where the test is being conducted. To illustrate this point, a test started March 1 would require the use of the photoperiod for Evansville test date March 1 and the lights would go on any time on that day just as long as they remained on for 12 hr and 15 min. Fifteen days later, the photoperiod would be changed to 13 hr. Gradual changes in light intensity at dawn and dusk[51] may be included within the photoperiod as shown and should not last for more than 0.5 hr from full on to full off and vice versa.

Durotest vitalite (optima FS) lamps and wide spectrum Grow-lux fluorescent tubes are recommended as a light source similar to daylight. Different light intensities are required for different organisms and life stages. Some organisms require subdued light, others need some place where they can hide, and some, such as the eggs of lake trout, require darkness during certain life stages. Any test exposure to light must be based on what is normal to and required by the species. Measure light intensity at the water surface. In short-term tests a standard photoperiod of 14 hr light, 10 hr dark is suggested but often the usual laboratory lighting is adequate.

g. *Exposure chambers:* For organisms weighing more than 0.5 g, test solution should be between 15 and 30 cm deep. In short-term tests, these organisms are often exposed in about 15 l of solution in 19.6-l (5-gal) wide-mouth, soft-glass bottles. Test containers of other sizes can be fabricated by welding (not soldering) stainless steel, by gluing double-strength or stronger window glass with clear silicone adhesive, or by modifying glass bottles, battery jars, or beakers to provide screened overflow holes or v-notches. Silicone adhesive absorbs some organic chlorine and organophosphorus pesticides, which are difficult to remove. Therefore, as little of the adhesive as possible should come in contact with the water. Extra beads of ad-

hesive that give added strength should be placed only on the outside of containers. Smaller organisms may be exposed in 3.9-l (1-gal) wide-mouth, soft-glass bottles or battery jars that contain 2 to 3 l of solution. Daphnids, midge larvae, copepods, and other small organisms also may be exposed in loosely-covered beakers of desirable size or in flasks or other suitable containers.

Keep surface areas small in relation to volume in order to limit adsorption and absorption on the vessel walls. With flow-through tests keep the surface area of the liquid small in relation to volume to reduce the loss of volatiles.

The size and shape of exposure chambers and the depth of the test solutions are determined by the test organisms and the objectives of the bioassays. Different types of exposure chambers are used and recommended for the different groups of organisms in Sections 803 through 810.

801 E.   Conducting the Bioassay

1. Types of Bioassays, Their Uses, Advantages, and Disadvantages

Bioassays may be classified in a number of ways, (*a*) according to their length, as short-term, intermediate, and long-term, (*b*) according to the test solutions, as static, renewal, or flow-through, and (*c*) according to their kind or purpose, as effluent, monitoring, relative toxicity, relative sensitivity, taste or odor, growth rate, etc. Short-term bioassays are range-finding or explor-

atory and short-term definitive tests. The former are for determining the concentrations of the toxicant under investigation that should be used in the short-term definitive tests. The short-term acute or definitive tests are for the purpose of determining LC50 or EC50 and incipient LC50 and EC50 values. The results of these tests also are used to indicate the concentrations of the test toxicant that should be used in intermediate and long-term partial life cycle or life cycle tests.

Static bioassays are those in which the test organisms remain in the same test concentration for the duration of the test. In renewal bioassays the test organisms are transferred to newly prepared test toxicants at periodic intervals, usually every 24 hr. In the flow-through tests measured quantities of dilution water and the stock toxicant solution are mixed and delivered periodically to the test chambers to give a continuous flow-through of the test toxicants.

Intermediate tests are used when the determination of the incipient LC50 requires additional time, for studies of selected life stages of the long-life-cycle organisms or partial life cycles, and to indicate the toxicant concentrations to be used in life cycle tests. The long-term tests are almost always flow-through tests, the objectives of which are to determine MATC or SC for indicating water quality standards or effluent requirements or to provide data for the determination of AF's to be used in the estimation of MATC and SC in different water areas.

Short-term tests are valuable for supplying in a short time an idea of the toxicity of the material in question. They are also of value for indicating the relative toxicity of a variety of materials or wastes to a selected test organism or the relative sensitivity of a number of species to the same toxicant on short-term exposure. They are also used to indicate the maximum allowable levels or concentrations for very short exposures, such as passing through a thermal electric power plant or a zone of heated water.

Short-term static bioassays are not satisfactory for use with wastes having a large BOD because of oxygen depletion.

There are several other problems associated with the use of static short-term bioassays. If the toxicant is volatile or unstable or is broken down by hydrolysis or bacterial action, the amount or concentration of the toxicant in the test solution is unknown and the amount to which the test organisms are exposed becomes progressively less as the test progresses. Also, metabolic products build up and undesirable concentrations of CO_2 or ammonia may occur. Dissolved oxygen often decreases to low concentrations, putting additional stress on the test organisms. In addition, materials collect in the sediments and on the walls of the test chamber, or combine with the mucus or metabolic products of the test organisms and in their bodies, thereby reducing the concentration of the toxicant an unknown amount.

Flow-through tests are desirable for waste chemicals that have high biochemical oxygen demand and are unstable or volatile. Many test species of fish and macroinvertebrates have high rates of metabolism and are difficult to maintain in jars or tanks of standing water. Continuous-flow bioassays conducted under proper conditions provide for well oxygenated test solutions, nonfluctuating concentrations of the toxicant, and continual removal of metabolic wastes of the test organisms. Static bioassays are suitable for detecting and evaluating toxicity not associated with excessive oxygen demand and that due to relatively stable substances. Use flow-through studies whenever there is evidence or expectation of rapid changes of the toxicity of the test solution. Such a change is indicated when the survival time of test animals in a fresh solution is significantly shorter than the survival time in a corresponding 2-day-old solution, provided adequate dissolved oxygen is present throughout both tests. Flow-through bioassays are used to test industrial effluents and chemicals that are removed appreciably from solution by precipitation, by test organisms, or other means. The continuous-flow bioassay is preferable to the static bioassay and its modifications when such substances are being tested. These bioassays duplicate the natural conditions of receiving waters not far downstream from the waste outfall more precisely than do static bioassays in that they permit extended exposure to determine long-term toxicity or safe concentrations of the toxicants for the determination of permissible effluent discharge rates.

The LC50 values are useful measures of acute toxicity under certain experimental conditions but they obviously do not represent concentrations that are safe or harmless in aquatic habitats subject to pollution. Concentrations of wastes that are not demonstrably toxic to aquatic organisms within 96 hr may be very toxic under conditions of continuous exposure in a receiving water. Under extreme conditions and with prolonged exposure, the 96-hr LC50 may represent only a small fraction of the long-term toxicity. Therefore, when estimating safe discharge rates or dilution ratios for industrial effluents or other pollutants on the basis of acute toxicity evaluations, use application factors determined by life cycle tests. Even the provision of an apparently ample margin of safety can fail to accomplish its purpose when there is accumulative toxicity that cannot be predicted from acute toxicity bioassay results, and when

the choice of test animals, experimental water, or experimental procedures or the sampling of wastes for bioassays has been improper or unfortunate.

No single, simple application factor can be valid for all wastes or toxicants. The constituents of a complex waste responsible for the acute toxicity of the waste may be, but are not necessarily, the constituents responsible for the chronic or accumulative toxicity that may be demonstrable when the waste has been diluted enough so that it is no longer acutely toxic. The chronic toxicity may be lethal after a long time or it may cause only nonlethal impairment of functions or performance of the animals (e.g., decrease in ability to swim, appetite, growth, resistance to disease, reproductive capacity, or ability to compete with other organisms in the natural environment). The acute toxicity bioassay cannot be expected to reveal such effects nor to indicate reliably at what waste concentration they will or will not occur. Nevertheless, knowledge of the acute toxicity of a waste often can be very helpful in predicting or anticipating and preventing acute damage to aquatic life in receiving waters as well as regulating toxic waste discharges so as to avoid rapid mortality of aquatic organisms exposed to the toxicant for relatively short periods.

2. Short-Term Bioassays

a. Range-finding bioassays: When effluents or materials of unknown toxicity are tested, much time and effort can be saved by conducting small-scale range-finding or exploratory bioassays to determine the approximate range of concentration of the waste that should be covered in the full-scale short-term tests. Range-finding tests are usually short-term static bioassays of 24 hr duration. With effluents that have low toxicity or are slow acting, it may be necessary to continue the tests for 48 or 96 hr to determine the concentration range to be tested. The test organisms are exposed to a wide range of concentrations, usually in a logarithmic ratio, such as 0.01, 0.1, 10, and 100%. If the material under test is an effluent, the test concentrations are set up as a percentage of the effluent in the test concentration by volume. When a material is being investigated, the different test concentrations are in milligrams per liter. Five different concentrations are used in these tests with five organisms exposed in each concentration. These tests may be static, renewal, or flow-through, depending on the test organisms, the objectives, the equipment, the water supply, and the toxicant. It is desirable to have the concentrations tested include one that killed all the organisms and another that killed very few or none of the organisms. If the lowest concentration in the series killed all the organisms, set up another series in logarithmic ratio below the lowest concentration. In determining the concentration to be used in the short-term, full-scale tests, select the highest concentration that killed none or only a few of the test organisms and the lowest concentration that killed most or all of the test organisms and select a series of concentrations based on progressive bisections of intervals on the logarithmic scale, Table 801:VI, such as 2.4, 3.2, 4.2, 5.6, and 7.5, when the indicated concentrations were 10 and 1.8 as the concentrations to be used in the short-term definitive full-scale tests (See Sec-

tion 801D.3b). These bioassays are set up with five or more test concentrations and a control. Table 801:V is helpful in preparing the different test concentrations. The test concentrations are prepared as described in Section 801D.2b. Make exposures of intermediate-size organisms in small aquaria or 20-l (5-gal) wide-mouth soft-glass jars*; total weight of the five organisms should not be over 7 g. Expose smaller organisms in smaller exposure chambers (Section 801D.3g). If the test organisms are large, use renewal or flow-through bioassays. Select the test organisms for size, place in a container, and then randomly place in the five test concentrations and the control that have been prepared in advance. Make observations and record data as directed in Section 801D.3e.

b. Short-term definitive bioassays: In each series of five concentrations, set them up in a logarithmic ratio or at half or quarter points on the log scale (Section 801D.3b) and use a control. Because death is easily detected and obviously an important adverse effect, the most commonly used tests are the acute lethality tests. An acute test is one involving a stimulus severe enough to bring about a speedy response, usually within a few hours or in 4 to 7 days.

Short-term bioassays may be static, renewal, or flow-through. Static tests are often used when the test organisms are phyto- or zooplankton because it is difficult to prevent them from being carried away in flow-through tests. With these small organisms, it is not necessary

---

* These jars are now difficult to find but may be obtained from Owens Illinois Glass Container Division, P.O. Box 1035, Toledo, Ohio 43601. Catalog No. AT5062 (Type 132-K-450CH).

to renew the toxic solution before 96 hr; however, if there is an oxygen demand, it is desirable to renew the test solution every 24 hr. Renewal-type tests are most often required with the macroinvertebrates and fishes. If the test material has a high biochemical oxygen demand or is volatile or relatively unstable, use the renewal or flowthrough technic.

Several variables affect the results of bioassay studies. If bioassay results are to be comparable, more uniform, and easy to replicate, these variables must be taken into consideration in the planning of the bioassays. Among these variables are body size, age, stage of the life cycle, sex, stage of the reproductive cycle, molting stage, feeding and starvation, biorhythms including diurnal, tidal, seasonal, and annual, parasites and diseases, and previous acclimation history. Of outstanding importance is the condition of the test animals. Short-term bioassays may be made with adults or with any one of the life stages such as developing larvae or zoea of crabs and other crustaceans.

In tests with macroinvertebrates and fishes, do not feed test animals for 2 days before the test or during the test. Those feeding on live phytoplankton may be fed by maintaining a population in the test containers. Feed organisms that have cannibalistic tendencies, such as the larval stages of crabs and lobsters, throughout the tests. Feeding requirements are discussed in the descriptions of bioassays for different groups, 803 through 810.

The duration of these tests is determined by the toxicant under study, the objectives of the tests, and the precision desired. The duration of short-term bioassays is usually the same for the different groups of organisms but with short-life-cycle organisms such as phytoplankton, the usual exposure time can cover several generations. Duration of the tests should therefore be determined in part by the length of the life cycle. Generally, continue the tests until the toxicity curve shows a threshold. If this does not occur in a reasonable time, establish the shape of the toxicity curve as described by Sprague.[52]

The duration of short-term bioassays has been more or less arbitrarily limited to 96 hr, but more prolonged tests sometimes are desirable in as much as even acute toxicity does not always cause death within the 96-hr period. When some test animals are still alive but dying or evidently affected after a 96-hr exposure to some concentrations of a toxic material, the advisability of prolonging these tests is indicated. If tests are continued for longer periods, the test organisms will have to be fed.

Continue short-term tests with macroinvertebrates and fishes for at least 96 hr. Make longer tests when indicated by the results of tests and in order to secure the desired precision. The number of test organisms used in each of the concentrations tested also depends on the organisms being used and the precision desired.

Short-term tests are used to give an idea of the toxicity of effluents, wastes, or materials to specific aquatic organisms or to serve as the basis for the selection of concentrations of the effluent or waste material used in the long-term bioassays. They are used to determine the comparative toxicity of different wastes or effluents, to determine organisms most sensitive to a given material, waste, or effluent, and to determine short-term requirements for oxygen, pH, temperature, and other environmental factors alone and in various combinations. They also indicate the short-term effects of various environmental factors on the toxicity of effluents, wastes, or materials. Likewise, these short-term tests can be used to evaluate the effects of slugs or periodic discharges, the effects of dumping by successive bioassays with the same organisms to simulate periodic dumps, the relative toxicity of different materials to the same organism or organisms, and the most sensitive local species and life stage for a selected waste or material. They can, by the use of the species most sensitive to an effluent and the receiving water for dilution, determine the incipient LC50 for that effluent which, when used with its AF, will indicate the amount of that effluent that can be discharged to the receiving water without exceeding effluent requirements and established water quality standards.

Special tests may be conducted on altered or treated samples of the effluent or on other samples to obtain additional information about its toxicity. It may be desirable to prepare test solutions by mixing the effluent with dilution water and letting the mixture age for a period of time, such as 24 to 48 hr, before adding the test organisms, to determine if toxicity increases or decreases. When special tests are conducted, describe the exact methodology in detail. If possible, take frequent chemical and physical measurements of the intake water and effluent in order to detect changes. This is especially important for the effluent from certain industrial processes because of diel differences in production and sea-

sonal or other changes in production and waste discharge.

Routine physical and chemical analyses are conducted as described in Section 801D.3d. Make biological observations, collect and analyze data, and report results as described in Sections 801D.3e and 801F and G.

3. Intermediate-Term Bioassays

There is no sharp time separation between short- and intermediate- or between intermediate- and long-term bioassays. Usually bioassays of 14 days or less are considered short-term while intermediate ones may be from 15 to 90 days. However, 14 days can represent several life cycles for some algae as can 90 days for many zooplankters.

Intermediate-length tests may be static, renewal, or flow-through bioassays. Flow-through tests are recommended for most situations. The tests are set up as described in Section 801D.3a. Rate of flow, number of test concentrations and test organisms, and ratio of weight to volume are as have been described in Section 801D.

Intermediate-term bioassays can be used with organisms that have not been reared through their life cycle in the laboratory by field collection of the different stages. These tests are also used to determine how the effects of a stressing agent decrease with time and when the toxicity curve becomes almost asymptotic with the time of exposure axis.

4. Long-Term, Partial or Complete Life Cycle Bioassays

With few exceptions, mostly the short life-cycle forms (phyto- and zooplankton), these tests are flow-through bioassays with exposure extending over as much of the life cycle as possible. In those instances where the life cycle can be carried out, the tests are continued from egg to egg or beyond, or for several life cycles in the smaller forms, in order to determine the maximum concentrations of the effluent, waste, or material that does not produce harmful effects with continuous exposure. The overall objective of this type of effluent test is to determine the amount of an effluent or waste that may be discharged to a given water without violating the water quality standards. In general, the objectives of effluent bioassays are: (a) to establish the relative sensitivity of important aquatic species to the waste, (b) to identify the effects of physical and chemical variables such as temperature, DO, pH, and salinity on toxicity of the effluent, (c) to determine permissible effluent requirements, (d) to determine compliance with water quality standards, (e) to secure data for hearings and for legal actions to abate pollution, and (f) to collect data essential for granting discharge permits. The life cycle studies are also used for the determination of application factors to be applied to short-term studies for indicating safe concentrations of effluents in the receiving water.

Long-term studies are used to determine effects on growth, reproduction, development of sex products, maturation, spawning, success of spawning, hatching success, survival of larvae or fry, growth and survival of different life stages, behavior, and bioaccumulation.

In life cycle or partial life cycle bioassays of toxicants with some species, water quality factors such as temperature, pH, salinity, and dissolved oxy-

gen should follow the natural seasonal cycle in the area where the study is being carried out. In such bioassays it is essential that the natural annual cycle be duplicated if the development of sex products, spawning, and development of the eggs and larvae are to be normal. In studying the long-term effects of temperature or any other environmental factor, if their seasonal variation is vital to the development of the organism, the test solutions should follow the seasonal cycle throughout the year with a change in the factor under study being continually added to or subtracted from the normal seasonal levels to give realistic exposures and effective testing of the change in the environment. In this way, the range of the normal seasonal changes in environmental conditions are kept unchanged so that the effects of the actual change in the environmental factor can be evaluated. Water supply systems, diluters, and other equipment for these studies are as described in Section 801D.1. Dilution water, toxic solutions, and test organisms are prepared as described in Sections 801D.2a through c. The test procedures are as in Section 801D.3. The concentration of the toxicants in the flow-through studies should not vary by more than ±10 to 15% from the selected test concentration because of uptake by the test organisms, absorption, precipitation, and other causes.

In these tests, the five or more concentrations used for long-term exposure are selected on the basis of the results of the short- and intermediate-term bioassays. The five or more test concentrations are selected as described in Section 801D.3b and are set up in duplicate. Exposure chambers, spawning chambers, hatching containers, growth chambers, and other equipment are varied to meet the needs of the different organisms used in the tests and are described in Sections 802 through 810. Physical and chemical determinations, biological observations, and data taking and recording are as described in Sections 801D.3d and e.

5. Special-Purpose Bioassays

a. Bioassays to determine relative sensitivity to a toxicant: In tests to rank the sensitivity of different species to a toxicant, use a standard water and standard exposure conditions. Select exposure conditions (e.g., temperature, DO, pH, CO_2, and salinity) in a favorable range for the species in the different groups. Keep conditions constant for the different groups in all the exposures with the different species in those groups of organisms tested. Keep the dilution water for freshwater, estuarine, and marine forms constant and use it in all tests to evaluate the sensitivity of the different species to the toxicant. Do not let the toxicant vary in its toxicity. These tests should be flow-through following the standard routine method, and have an exposure period of 2 wk.

b. Bioassays to determine the relative toxicity of various toxicants to selected species: These bioassays resemble the sensitivity tests in that once selected, the test conditions and dilution waters are kept constant and standard. Also the selected test species must all be from the same group and in good condition, of uniform size, age, and life stage. It is especially important to prevent any change in the sensitivity of the test organisms throughout the period of the tests. In so far as possible, select species sensitive to the group of toxicants being rated. It is desirable to choose test species from several different groups, i.e., an alga, microcrustacean, macrocrustacean, insect, mollusk, or fish. These tests should be flow-through bioassays of 2 wk duration. Follow the routine bioassay methods as outlined for other tests.

c. Flesh tainting tests: The purpose of these studies is to determine the maximum concentrations of wastes and materials that do not taint the flesh of edible aquatic organisms. Exposures to effluents, wastes, or materials to determine if they taint the flesh of edible organisms and the maximum concentration that does not cause detectable tainting, are set up as described for other types of bioassays. However, the organisms exposed to the various concentrations are large enough to serve as food and to supply portions for the taste panel. The exposure tanks are set up as for other bioassays and are supplied with continuous flows of the odiferous materials in the different test concentrations by means of proportional diluters. Because the concentrations causing tainting are not well known, perform range-finding bioassays over a wide range of concentrations to determine the concentrations to be used in the second, more definitive, series of tests. All exposures should be for 2 wk.

At the completion of the exposure, prepare the test organisms for taste testing. Clean the organisms, prepare them for cooking, wrap in aluminum foil, and bake in an oven. When they are cooked, divide them into portions, wrap in the alumnium foil, give a code number, and distribute to the taste panel while still warm, along with samples of unexposed organisms, cooked, wrapped and coded in the same manner. The taste panel records the results of their taste tests on a prepared form. The data are analyzed and the highest concentration of the test material that did not cause detectable tainting is recorded as the safe concentration. Several tests may be necessary to gain a consensus. Further, a carefully selected and trained panel is essential for uniformity of results. Details of methods and results of tests are given elsewhere.[53-56]

d. Growth-rate determination: Studies of the effects of toxicants and environmental factors on growth can become very complicated and great care must be used in the evaluation of data in order that erroneous conclusions are not drawn. Data available on this subject are mostly related to fishes but findings are useful for studies with other organisms.

In studies of the influence of water quality and toxic substances on the growth of fishes, the manner of feeding is of utmost importance. Not only must the food offered be attractive and nutritious and be properly described in reporting test results, but also the feeding level, or the quantity of food offered to and consumed by the fish, must be reported carefully. Too often, the latter information has not been clearly provided, rendering the experimental results almost valueless, because observed effects may vary markedly with the food supplies. The level of feeding may be one of the following: (*a*) The fish may all be provided uninterruptedly with more food than they can consume of a kind that remains attractive and palatable to them at all times, usually live food such as tubificid worms or *Daphnia*. This feeding level is commonly referred to as an *unrestricted supply*. In order to make possible complete analysis and interpretation of test results, the food introduced into aquaria and any uneaten food removed from time to time or at the end of a test must be weighed to determine the amounts consumed. (*b*) The fish may be fed intermittently, usually once or twice a day, all the attractive food that they will consume at the time of feeding (i.e., to repletion). Any food remaining after the fish have ceased feeding is removed thereafter from each aquarium. This level of feeding may be referred to as an *intermittent satiation supply*. (*c*) Finally, all of the experimental fish, which initially should be as nearly as possible of equal size, may be provided once a day with equal amounts of food that they will all consume without exception (i.e., even under the most unfavorable conditions tested). Obviously, the amount of food provided must be decidedly less than the satiation supply for most of the test animals. The supply may be increased as the fish grow larger and their food requirement increases, but it must be increased uniformly so that it continues to be consumed fully by all the fish whose growth rates are to be compared. Any such level of feeding is called a *uniformly restricted supply*.

Although only unrestricted or intermittent satiation supplies have been provided in many studies of growth, performance of at least one series of comparative tests with a uniformly restricted food supply as an additional part of every such study is strongly recommended. Without information so obtained, reliable interpretation of the results of growth experiments usually is not possible and their ecological significance remains obscure. Differences of growth rates of fish that are provided unrestricted or intermittent satiation supplies of food, under different water quality conditions, can be due entirely to difference in appetite or food consumption rate. Knowledge of effects of water quality differences or toxic pollutants on the appetite or food consumption capacity of fish is important, and it cannot be gained through experiments with uniformly restricted food supplies or rations only. But knowledge of the influence of water pollutants on the efficiency of conversion of ingested food to body tissue when food consumption is uniformly restricted is also essential, because, under natural conditions, the availability of food is often limited. Fish exposed to solutions of some toxicants (e.g., cyanide, pentachlorophenol) in aquaria with an unlimited supply of food have been found to increase their food consumption rates, thus compensating partly or wholly for a loss of efficiency of their utilization of consumed food for growth. A limited availability of food in nature would render impossible such a compensatory increase of food consumption, but the adverse effects of the toxicants on growth under the natural conditions may not be fully revealed by the results of the laboratory experiments in which abundant food is provided, especially if the amounts of food consumed are not measured.

A loss of gross efficiency of food conversion can be a result simply of reduced food consumption. This is because if less food is consumed, a greater proportion is required for maintenance of body weight and therefore is unavailable for conversion to new body tissue. However, such a loss of conversion efficiency must be distinguished from a loss of metabolic efficiency, for it is important only when more food is readily available than the fish are able to consume. Ideally, laboratory experiments on growth should include a series of tests with unrestricted supplies of food (or, at least, with intermittent satiation supplies) and several series of tests with different, uniformly restricted supplies or rations. The lowest of these feeding levels should be near the maintenance level for the controls, which is the feeding level at which the controls neither gain nor lose weight. The effect of the variable under study on growth at any level of food availability and consumption then can be readily determined from a group of curves relating observed growth rates to toxicant concentrations or other water quality conditions at each of the several feeding levels (see Warren and Doudoroff,[57] Figures 11-22 and 11-23, pp. 165-166).

To ensure that each individual fish that is provided a restricted supply of food consumes its full allotment and none consumes more than this allotment, it is best to hold the fish separately in individual aquaria or compartments. However, experiments in which groups of fish held together are fed in such a manner that all are afforded nearly equal opportunity to consume the restricted rations provided may yield satisfactory results. Uniform temperatures and concentrations of dissolved oxygen in test solutions of toxic substances are essential, because both temperature and dissolved oxygen concentration have a pronounced influence on the food consumption and growth rates of fish.

Rapidly growing juvenile fish may gain enough weight in only 2 or 3 wk for satisfactory determination of differences in growth. However, effects of toxicants on growth after prolonged exposure thereto may be markedly different from those observed initially, because of acclimation or accumulative toxic action, so that more prolonged experiments with repeated weighing of the fish at suitable intervals of time (e.g., every 10 days) are advisable. Results are best reported in terms of growth rates, computed as weight gain in grams per day per gram of mean weight (the sum of their weights at the beginning and end of a time interval, divided by 2). Because of possible differences in water and fat content of fish that have grown under different conditions, determine dry weights, wet weights, and the fat content of the dry material (determined through extraction with solvent) at the conclusion of an experiment. Estimate the initial dry weight and fat content from the wet weight after determining the ra-

tios of dry weight and fat content to wet weight in a sample of test animals at the beginning of the experiment. Increased fatness (i.e., deposition of fat without corresponding increase in amount of protein) may not be regarded as true growth, and some investigators have insisted that only increase of protein (measurable as nitrogen), not overall weight increases, should be determined and reported as a measure of growth. However, from an ecological and bioenergetic standpoint, storage of fat, which can be utilized as a source of energy instead of protein during periods of malnutrition and weight loss, also is important.

For pertinent additional information that may be helpful, the chapter on experimental studies on growth (Chapter 9, pp. 361-400) of Brown[58] and the chapter on bioenergetics and growth (Chapter 11, pp. 135-167) of Warren and Doudoroff[57] can be consulted.

801 F. Calculating, Analyzing, and Reporting Results of Bioassays

In the past, simplified methods have been used for determining LC50 and EC50 values. Such methods of interpolation have given values that were generally accurate within the precision of the test. To handle data by the simpler methods, use the procedures described in Section 801F.1. Use the more sophisticated approaches described in Section 801F.2 for the more detailed and involved tests.

1. Calculating Results by Interpolation

An LC50, as defined in past editions, is an interpolated value based on percentages of test organisms dying at two or more concentrations, in at least one of which less than half and in another more than half died. Estimation of the LC50 by interpolation involves plotting the data on semilogarithmic coordinate

paper with concentrations on the logarithmic and percentage dead on the
arithmetic scale. A straight line is drawn
between two points representing the
percentage dead at the two successive

concentrations that were lethal to more
than half and to less than half of the test
organisms. The concentration at which
this line crosses the 50% lethality line is
the estimated LC50 value. Figure 801:4

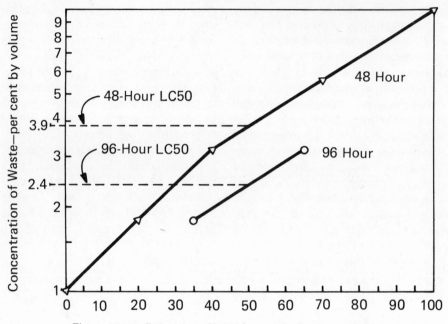

Figure 801:4. Estimation of LC50 by straight-line interpolation.

Experimental Data (Hypothetical) Plotted Above

No. of Test Animals	Concentration of Waste % by Volume	Test Animals Dying			
		48 hr		96 hr	
		No.	*%*	*No.*	*%*
20	1.0	0	0	2	10
20	1.8	4	20	7	35
20	3.2	7	40	13	65
20	5.6	14	70	19	95
20	10.0	20	100	20	100

* Although the dependent variable is plotted on the
horizontal axis, it is customary and probably best to
maintain this format. If such a graph were derived from
estimates of median lethal times at various concentrations, the graph would be correct inasmuch as time
would be the dependent variable axis. Since the same

set of observations could be used to produce either a series of LC50's or a series of median lethal times, there
would seem to be little reason to have two different
formats for toxicity curves and the form shown in Figure 801:4 is historically conventional.

illustrates this procedure, which is referred to as straight-line graphical interpolation. Hypothetical results used in developing the graph are given in the table. The LC50 values for 48 and 96 hr exposures are 3.9 and 2.4%, respectively. Another approach is plotting the data on logarithmic-probability paper with concentrations on the logarithmic and percentage dead on the probability scale.

The precision of a toxicity bioassay is limited by a number of factors including the normal biological variation among individuals of a species. Toxicity studies with a randomly selected species cannot be expected to give accurate information on the toxicity of that material to other species and life stages or to an entire biota. A toxicity bioassay with one species yields an accurate estimate of the toxicity only to others of that species of similar size, age, and physiological condition and in water with the same or similar characteristics and under similar test conditions. This is why it is so important to use as the test organism the most sensitive important species to the toxicant in the area under consideration when the objective is the protection of the biota.

2. Analyzing Results of Quantal Bioassays

Responses arising from bioassays are of two kinds, and methods of analysis are described for each. The first kind is the *quantal* test, in which a given organism either shows the response under study or does not show it, for example, it dies or does not die. Thus, at any concentration greater than that tolerated in the environment without effect, a certain percentage of test organisms will show the response within some stated time period. The second kind is the *quantitative* or graded test, in which each organism yields a response that is variable in degree, such as amount of growth.

a. Estimating LC50 and EC50: Methods for quantal bioassays are designed to estimate the concentration of a test material that just causes a response by the median or "typical" test organism.

The same procedure is used for estimating the median lethal concentration, or the median effective concentration (EC50) for any sublethal response. The latter might be immobilization, turnover, fatigue in a swimming test,[59] avoidance reaction,[60] or a significant effect on growth, fertility, or tissue structure. For the latter responses or effects, substitute "EC50" for "LC50" in the text below and substitute the word or phrase describing the sublethal response for "mortality."

Use the lethal concentration for 50% of the individuals (LC50) to report results of bioassays in which death is the criterion of effect. The quantal test is used for acute lethality, which usually is considered to occur within 4 to 7 days, depending on the test organism, or for any longer period such as 30 days or 3 months.

The LC50 may be estimated by probit analysis. In routine tests, this requires, as a minimum, that a line be drawn by eye to fit the results plotted on logarithmic-probability paper (Figure 801:5). Such plotting is always the first stage of analysis, even in the more complex methods described below.

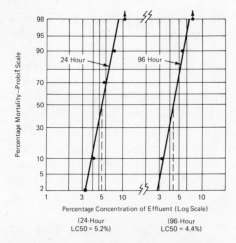

Figure 801:5. Examples of determining median lethal concentrations at two representative times by probit analysis and the line of best fit.

100% mortality value, the ones nearest the center of the range of concentrations.

To construct the graph, plot percentage mortality on the vertical axis against concentration on the horizontal axis. Death is on a *probit* or probability scale and concentration on a logarithmic scale (Figure 801:5). Because the probit scale never reaches 0 or 100%, plot any such points with an arrow indicating their true position.

Next, fit a line to the points by eye. Give most consideration to points between 16 and 84% mortality and try to minimize total vertical deviations of the line from the points. If there is doubt about placing the line, draw it as horizontally as possible (Figure 801:5) because this acknowledges more variability in the data.

Read the concentration causing 50% mortality from the fitted line; this is the estimated LC50 for the selected exposure time. Report this as the result of the bioassay. In the example, the estimated 96-hr LC50 is about 4.4%. This is the estimated concentration that

Observations of mortality are tabulated as in Table 801:X for at least one selected exposure time. The selected time ordinarily should be the longest one used in the test, often 96 hr. Use only one successive 0% and one successive

TABLE 801:X. EXPERIMENTAL DATA FROM HYPOTHETICAL BIOASSAY SUBJECTED TO PROBIT ANALYSIS

Concentration of Waste, % by Volume	No. of Test Organisms	Number of Test Organisms Dead at							
		2 hr	4 hr	6 hr	8 hr	24 hr	48 hr	72 hr	96 hr
10	10	1	4	7	9	10	10	10	10
7.5	10	0	1	2	6	9	9	10	10
5.6	10	0	0	0	2	7	7	8	9
4.2	10	0	0	0	0	1	4	4	4
3.2	10	0	0	0	0	0	1	1	1
0	10	0	0	0	0	0	0	0	0
LC50, %, estimated from graph		10	10	9	7.1	5.2	4.7	4.5	4.4
LC50, estimated by probit analysis		—	—	8.96	7.02	5.27	4.70	4.46	4.34
95% confidence limits		—	—	7.60	5.82	4.53	3.95	3.87	3.49
				10.5	8.42	6.12	5.59	5.14	5.40
Slope of probit line		—	—	10.9	8.42	10.1	7.03	9.54	11.3

would kill the average or typical test organism in 96 hr. The LC50 estimated by graphical procedures is almost always satisfactorily accurate. For example, the first graphical estimates shown in Table 801:X are very close to those obtained by formal probit analysis with a computer.

In order to estimate an LC50 satisfactorily, the data used to obtain it should satisfy certain guidelines. For reasonable accuracy, each concentration of the toxic material or effluent should be at least 55.5 to 57% of the next higher one. The use of five concentrations in the first three columns of Table 801:VI (Section 801D.3b) gives these percentages. In addition, it would usually be sufficient in routine tests to determine pollutional effects of wastewater discharges if one concentration produced lethality below 50% and a higher concentration produced lethality above 50%. Alternatively, one of these values could be exactly 50%.

In more exacting tests and for research purposes, it is desirable to have several partial mortalities at different concentrations. To secure these, it is necessary to test a larger number of concentrations and include those shown in Column 4 of Table 801:VI. This gives a set of concentrations each of which is 75% of the next highest concentration. Inclusion of the concentrations in Column 5 gives a series in which each concentration is 85 to 87% of the next highest concentration. In research studies, it is desirable to have at least one of the responses in the range of 16 to 84% mortality because these represent ±1.0 probit about the median response. At least two partial mortalities are required in order to estimate the LC50 and its

confidence limits by Finney's method of formal probit analysis, described below in the section on confidence limits.

b. Plotting toxicity curves: Most bioassays will provide information on mortality at times before the final selected time. It will usually be beneficial to the investigator to use such information, as soon as it becomes available, to plot a toxicity curve.

The procedure is to estimate the LC50, from a graph plotted in the same way as Figure 801:5, for each of the observation times. The series of LC50's should be used to construct a toxicity curve as the experiment proceeds, ending with something similar to Figure 801:6.

The purpose of a toxicity curve is to give the investigator an overall picture of the progress of the test and to indicate when acute lethality has stopped. This will be indicated by the curve becoming asymptotic to the time axis.[52] In Figure 801:6, the toxicity curve is closely approaching an asymptote of time but may not have quite reached it.

The LC50 for an exposure time that is in the asymptotic part of the curve could be termed the *threshold* or *incipient* LC50. Such a threshold of acute lethality for the median organism has greater theoretical significance than an LC50 for some arbitrary time.

Threshold LC50's usually can be determined for most macroinvertebrates and fish within a 96- to 168-hr exposure.[52] However, sometimes a threshold is not apparent in that time, especially with the mollusks. In such a case, the absence of a threshold for acute lethality is obviously of great practical interest. In research tests, it is advantageous to continue beyond 96 to 168 hr

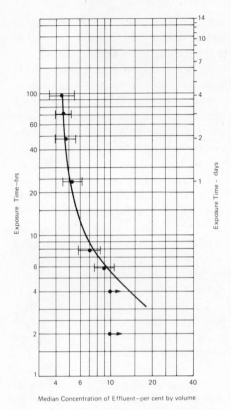

Figure 801:6. **Toxicity curve, drawn as the experiment proceeded, from LC50's determined as shown in Figure 5.** Curve has become almost asymptotic with the time axis. The 95% confidence limits are shown for each LC50, although in many bioassays they would be calculated only for the selected or final LC50.

to determine if a threshold exists. If no threshold is found, that should be reported.

c. Confidence limits of the LC50: Confidence limits of the LC50 are essential in research and helpful in routine testing also. They may be calculated by probit analysis.[61] Estimate confidence limits for the LC50 of the longest exposure time. It is not necessary to estimate

confidence limits at every exposure time, although this has been done in Table 801:X for illustrative purposes.

The simplified nomographic methods of Litchfield and Wilcoxon[62] are acceptable for field work or when use of a computer is impossible or inconvenient. Plot results for the selected time interval as in Figure 801:5. Use the Litchfield-Wilcoxon graphic procedures to estimate the goodness of fit of the eye-fitted line, its "sloped function", and the 95% confidence limits of the LC50. In doubtful cases, draw a number of different lines and choose the best-fitting one. Report the LC50, its limits, and the slope function. An approximate probit line may be constructed by this method, and confidence limits can be estimated even if there is only one partial lethality between 16% and 84% and one 0% or 100% response, as long as one of these is greater than 50%.

Use a computer when possible to carry out the otherwise tedious iterative calculations of Finney's probit analysis, which gives a maximum likelihood solution for the LC50, its confidence limits, slope of the probit line, and other data. There are many packaged computer programs; one that is easily available is BMD035[63] using the language FORTRAN. Unfortunately, the output of that program requires some modification to express in common terms statements of such desired parameters as confidence limits. Finney's procedures also may be used with other languages such as APL, in which the investigator can type in the data directly without the intermediate step of preparing punched cards.†

---

† Such a program in APL Plus may be obtained from the Institute of Computer Science, University of Guelph, Guelph, Ontario, Canada.

This formal arithmetic probit analysis requires partial lethality at two concentrations. If two are not obtained, analyze results by the Litchfield-Wilcoxon method described above, or the moving average or moving-average angle methods mentioned in Section 801F.2d.

Even when a formal probit analysis is carried out with a computer, *always* make a graph such as Figure 801:5 to check the reasonableness of the computed LC50. In some cases of variable responses or "split probits", the investigator's judgment must take precedence over a blindly-computed LC50.

Significant difference between two LC50's may be tested once confidence limits have been estimated. The simplest way is to look at the confidence limits of the two LC50's. If the limits do not overlap, then the two LC50's are significantly different. However, this is a conservative approach, and the LC50's may still be different if the confidence limits overlap. Significant differences may be tested more exactly by the formula:

$$1.96 \, SE_{Diff} = \text{Antilog} \, \sqrt{(\log f_1)^2 + (\log f_2)^2}$$

where f = the factor for the 95% confidence limits of the LC50, i.e., the confidence limits are LC50×f and LC50÷f (f is the antilog of two standard deviations of the log LC50). This formula has been adapted to simple nomogram use by Litchfield and Wilcoxon. If the ratio $\dfrac{\text{greater LC50}}{\text{smaller LC50}}$ exceeds the value for $1.96 \, SE_{Diff}$ then the LC50's are significantly different; otherwise, they are not.

The confidence limits about the LC50 do *not* describe variability of the LC50, if it were estimated with another stock of organisms at another time of year, or under other conditions. The limits merely indicate the accuracy of the estimate that would be expected from replicate bioassays carried out at the same time with exactly the same conditions and components. A precision within about 10% is sometimes attainable, but better than that is not to be expected, even under favorable circumstances, unless more than 10 organisms are exposed at each concentration.

d. Other methods of analyzing results: The graph for estimating the LC50 (Figure 801:5) is sometimes constructed with an arithmetic scale for percentage mortality instead of a probability scale. However, the probit scale is generally better since it usually gives a straight line.

Logits have been used instead of probits with equivalent results.[64] Reciprocal transformations also have been used and angle (=arcsine) transformations with estimation of the LC50 by a moving average also have been used.[65] All these methods have certain limitations[47,60] but the last one is recommended for estimating LC50 and confidence limits when fewer than two partial lethalities have been obtained.

Highly sophisticated computerized approaches describing multivariate response surfaces are available and are advantageous for advanced research.[66] Such factorial treatment of response surfaces has been done for toxicity of mercury to crab larvae at different temperatures and salinities after transformation of observed percentage mortality to arcsin.[67] However, for most work, the basic method given above has advantages of speed and simplicity.

For some purposes, it may be more informative to estimate the median effective time (ET50) for mortality at each concentration. This may be done by plotting percentage mortality on a probit scale against time on a logarithmic scale. The ET50's may then be estimated by technics of probit analysis similar to those given above.[61, 68-70] Bioassay procedures are the same, although somewhat more frequent observations of mortality may be required. For research purposes, this method sometimes allows for easier interpretation of irregular results. It may also be useful in assessing mixing zones or other situations involving high concentrations in which it would be desirable to estimate a time for passage of fish that would cause an insignificantly small percentage mortality.

e. *Mortality in controls:* Control mortality should be virtually absent. It should not be greater than 10% and preferably not more than 5%, representing an occasional weak organism in a group. Regard anything more than this as unsatisfactory and repeat the test under more suitable conditions. Make corrections for higher mortality in controls by Abbott's formula,[71]

$$P = \frac{P^*-C}{1-C}$$

where P and P^* = the corrected and observed proportions responding to the experimental stimulus and C = the proportion responding in the control test. However, this does not solve the problems of probable interaction of stress from the toxicant with whatever stress is causing mortality in the control. Sometimes with long tests or with some invertebrates that have considerable mortality under the best possible conditions, it is necessary to use Abbott's formula, or to consider the threshold lethal concentration as that in which mortality equals mortality in controls.

f. *Reporting results:* Always give the LC50 with specified exposure time. Also report, if they have been calculated, the confidence limits of the LC50 and the slope of the probit line (or the slope function of Litchfield and Wilcoxon).[62] These are the key data, and from them future investigators could reconstruct the probit line. Also highly useful is a figure showing the toxicity curve or a list of the LC50's for different exposure times. If neither of these is given, report the mortality in each concentration at the end of each 24-hr period. Always state mortality in controls.

Associated with these experimental results, provide descriptions of: (*a*) the species and number of the test organisms, their source, weight, and condition, acclimation to test conditions, treatment for disease and parasites before use, and observations on behavior during the test; (*b*) the tested material, its source, storage, and known physical and chemical properties; (*c*) the source of the experimental water or diluent, its physical and chemical properties and variations in these properties during the test, as well as any pretreatment, additives, unusual constituents, or known contaminants; (*d*) physical and chemical properties of the test solution, especially a complete description of the concentration of the toxic component, if measurable, and the temperature at which the tests were made; (*e*) brief mention of the method if standard, or its description if different, plus the specific experimental design; (*f*) type of test container with volume and depth of solution, number of organisms and loading rate, toxicant delivery system, flow rate, or frequency of renewal, and (g) the criterion of response and any observations on reaction or behavior of the organisms during tests.

3. Analyzing Results of Graded or Quantitative Bioassays

In quantitative or graded bioassays, each test organism gives a response that. is measurable on a continuous graded scale. For example, each organism in a test might show a measurable percentage increase in body weight.

Since there are usually many test organisms, a series of several graded measurements is generated for each test concentration. Such data are easily analyzed by standard technics. A simple one-way analysis of variance may be used initially to assess whether significant differences have been found.

If differences exist, the investigator may determine whether responses for a given concentration are significantly different from responses for the control. Several good technics are available and are described in most standard statistical textbooks. One sound test is the Student-Newman-Keuls test,[72] and a similar one is Duncan's new multiple-range test.[73] A particularly appropriate method is Dunnett's test,[74] in which responses at each concentration are compared to responses of the control.

These technics are applicable to most of the graded responses described for specific test organisms in the sections that follow. For example, they might be used for maximum specific growth rates or standing crops of algae and protozoans (Sections 802, 803, and 804), number of young or eggs produced by *Daphnia* (Section 804B), polychaetes (Section 806), crustaceans (Section 807), or mayflies (Section 808), growth of crustaceans or oysters (Sections 807 and 809). Discussions of the measurement of the toxicity of pollutants to aquatic life are available.[75,76]

801 G.   Interpreting and Applying Bioassay Results

The 48- and 96-hr LC50 values provide useful measures of the relative acute lethal toxicity of tested substances to organisms under certain experimental conditions, but these values do not represent concentrations that are safe in natural habitats. Long-term exposure to much lower concentrations may be lethal to fishes and other organisms and still lower concentrations may cause nonlethal impairment of their function or performance, such as swimming ability, appetite and growth, resistance to disease, reproductive capacity, or ability to compete with other species in the biota. A review[58] on the water quality requirements of fish serves as a general introduction to physiological, toxicological, and ecological fundamentals.

Formulas for estimating permissible discharge rates or dilution ratios for industrial effluents and other water pollutants based on evaluations of the acute toxicity have been proposed tentatively and their derivations have been discussed elsewhere.[77-81] The use of fractional "application factors" by which LC values are multiplied to arrive at permissible or presumably safe concentrations of toxic wastes or chemicals recently has been favored widely. Mount and Stephan[32] and Mount[82] have derived experimentally some tentative application factors, and these studies have demonstrated much variation, depending on the toxicant. Available data indicate that these factors must vary according to the toxicant if they are to be reasonable and equitable as well as effective. No single application factor can be equally appropriate to all toxic materials. Recognizing this fact, as well as our present lack of knowledge and the pressing need to use all available knowledge and experience, the National Technical Advisory Committee on Water Quality Requirements for Aquatic Life tentatively grouped toxicants into three general groups and suggested application factors for each of these groups.[8] In all approaches to this problem, possible synergism or antagonism, as well as the effects of the presence of two or more toxicants, should be taken into consideration. Several discussions of the uses and value of bioassays in the establishment of effluent requirements and water quality standards for meeting water pollution problems have appeared in the literature.[2, 83-86]

801 H. References

1. TARZWELL, C.M. 1958. The use of bioassays in the safe disposal of electroplating wastes. *Amer. Electroplaters Soc. 44th Annu. Tech. Proc.*:60.

2. TARZWELL, C.M. 1971. Bioassays to determine allowable waste concentrations in the aquatic environment, I. Measurement of pollution effects on living organisms. *Proc. Royal Soc. London. B.* 177:279.

3. FRY, F.E.J. 1947. Effects of the environment on animal activity. Univ. Toronto Stud. Biol. Ser. *55.*, *Publ. Ont. Fish. Res. Lab.* 68:1.

4. DOUDOROFF, P. et al. 1951. Bioassay methods for the evaluation of acute toxicity of industrial wastes to fish. *Sewage Ind. Wastes* 23:1380.

5. LLOYD, R. & D.H.M. JORDAN. 1963. Predicted and observed toxicities of several sewage effluents to rainbow trout. *J. Proc. Inst. Sewage Purif.* Pt.2:167.

6. BALL, I.R. 1967. The relative susceptibilities of some species of freshwater fish to poisons—I. Ammonia. *Water Res.* 1:767.

7. SPRAGUE, J.B. 1969. Measurement of pollutant toxicity to fish. I. Bioassay methods for acute toxicity. *Water Res.* 3:793.

8. Water Quality Criteria. Report of the National Technical Advisory Committee to the Secretary of the Interior. 1968. FWPCA, U.S. Dep. Interior, U.S. Government Printing Office I-X.

9. U.S. DEPARTMENT OF COMMERCE. 1970. Aquarium Design Criteria, Special ed. National Fish. Center Aquarium.

10. CLARK, J.R. & R.L. CLARK, eds. 1964. Sea water systems for experimental aquariums. U.S. Fish & Wildlife Service, Bur. Sports Fish & Wildlife, Res. Rep. 63:1.

11. SPOTTE, S. 1973. Marine Aquarium Keeping-The Science, the Animals, the Art. Wiley Interscience Publ., New York, N.Y.

12. LASKER, R. & L.L. VLYMER. 1969. Experimental seawater aquarium. U.S. Fish & Wildlife Service, Bur. Commercial Fisheries, Circ. 334:1.

13. TARZWELL, C.M. 1962. Development of water quality criteria for aquatic life. *J. Water Pollut. Control Fed.* 34:1178.

14. MOUNT, D.I. & W.A. BRUNGS. 1967. A de-

vice for continuous treatment of fish in holding chambers. *Trans. Amer. Fish. Soc.* 96:55.

15. CLINE, T.F. & G. POST. 1972. Therapy for trout eggs infected with *Saprolegnia. Progr. Fish-Cult.* 34:148.

16. RUCKER, R.R. & K. HODGEBOOM. 1953. Observations on gas-bubble disease of fish. *Progr. Fish-Cult.* 15:24.

17. KESTER, E., I. DREDALL, D. CONNERS & R. PYTOWICZ. 1967. Preparation of artificial seawater. *Limnol. Oceanogr.* 12:176.

18. DAVEY, E.W., J.H. GENTILE, S.J. ERICKSON & P. BETZER. 1970. Removal of trace metals from marine culture medium. *Limnol. Oceanogr.* 15:486.

19. BAHNER, L.H & D.R. NIMMO. 1975. A salinity controller for flow-through bioassays. *Trans. Amer. Fish. Soc.* (in press).

20. NEEDHAM, J.G., P.S. GALTSOFF, F.E. LUTZ & P.S. WELSH. 1937. Culture Methods for Invertebrate Animals. Comstock Publ. Co., Inc. Ithaca, N.Y. XXXII.

21. HIRANO, R. & Y. OSHIMA. 1963. Rearing of larvae of marine animals with special reference to their food organisms. *Bull. Jap. Soc. Sci. Fish.* 29:282

22. MAY, R.C. 1970. Feeding larval marine fishes in the laboratory, A review. Calif. Mar. Res. Comm., CalCOF1 Rep. 14:76.

23. MEYERS, S.P. & Z.P. ZEIN-ELDIN. 1972. Binders and pellet stability in development of crustacean diets. *Proc. 3rd Annu. Workshop World Mariculture Soc.*:351.

24. HESSELBERG, R.J. & R.M. BURRESS. 1967. Labor saving devices for bioassay laboratories. U.S. Bur. Sport Fish Wildl. Invest. Fish Control 21:1.

25. WILLFORD, W.A. 1967. Toxicity of 22 therapeutic compounds to six fishes. U.S. Bur. Sport Fish Wildl. Invest. Fish. Control 18:1.

26. HENDERSON, D. & C.M. TARZWELL. 1957. Bioassays for the control of industrial effluents. *Sewage Ind. Waste* 29:1002.

27. LENNON, R.E. & C.R. WALKER. 1964. Investigations in fish control I. Laboratories and methods for screening fish-control chemicals. U.S. Bur. Sport Fish Wildl. Circ. 185:1.

28. MCALLISTER, W.A., JR., W.L. MAUCH &

F.L. MAYER, JR. 1972. A simplified device for metering chemicals in intermittent-flow bioassays. *Trans. Amer. Fish. Soc.* 101:555.

29. LOWE, J.I. 1964. Chronic exposure of spot, *Leiostomus xanthurus,* to sublethal concentrations of toxaphene in seawater. *Trans. Amer. Fish. Soc.* 93:396.

30. MOUNT, D.I. & R.E. WARNER. 1965. A Serial Dilution Apparatus for Continuous Delivery of Various Concentrations of Material in Water. PHS Publ. No. 999-WP-23, Environmental Health Ser., U.S. Dep. HEW, Washington, D.C.

31. CHANDLER, J.H., H.O. SANDERS & D.F. WALSH. 1974. An improved chemical delivery apparatus for use in intermittent-flow bioassays. *Bull. Environ. Contam. Toxicol.* 12:123.

32. MOUNT, D.I. & C. STEPHAN. 1967. A method for establishing acceptable toxicant limits for fish—Malathion and the butoxyethanol ester of 2,4-D. *Trans. Amer. Fish. Soc.* 96:185.

33. SCHIMMEL, S.C., D.J. HANSEN & J. FORESTER. 1974. Effects of aroclor® 1254 on laboratory-reared embryos and fry of sheepshead minnows (*Cyprinodon variegatus*). *Trans. Amer. Fish. Soc.* 103:582.

34. FREEMAN, R.A. 1971. A constant flow delivery device for chronic bioassay. *Trans. Amer. Fish. Soc.* 100:135.

35. BENGTSSON, B.E. 1972. A simple principle for dosing apparatus in aquatic systems. *Arch. Hydrobiol.* 70:413.

36. GRANMO, A. & S.C. KOLLBERG. 1972. A new simple water flow system for accurate continuous flow tests. *Water Res.* 6:1597.

37. BENOIT, D.A. & F.A. PUGLISI. 1973. A simplified flow-splitting chamber and siphon for proportional diluters. *Water Res.* 7:1915.

38. LICHATOWICH, J.A., P.W. O'KEEFE, J.A. STRAND & W.L. TEMPLETON. 1973. Development of methodology and apparatus for the bioassay of oil. In: Proc. Joint Conf. Prevention and Control of Oil Spills, p.659. American Petroleum Inst., EPA, & U.S. Coast Guard, Washington, D.C.

39. ABRAM, F.S.H. 1973. Apparatus for control of poison concentration in toxicity studies with fish. *Water Res.* 7:1875.

40. MOUNT, D.I. & W.A. BRUNGS. 1967. A

simplified dosing apparatus for fish toxicology studies. *Water Res.* 1:21.

41. LEMKE, A.E. 1964. A new device for constant-flow test chambers. *Progr. Fish. Cult.* 26:136.

42. JACKSON, H.W. & W.A. BRUNGS. 1966. Biomonitoring of industrial effluents. *Proc. 21st. Ind. Waste Conf.*, Purdue Univ., Eng. Ext. Bull. 121:117.

43. SURBER, E.W. & T.O THATCHER. 1963. Laboratory studies of the effects of alkyl benzene sulfonate (ABS) on aquatic invertebrates. *Trans. Amer. Fish. Soc.* 92:152.

44. BURROWS, R.E. 1949. Prophylactic treatment for control of fungus, *Saprolegnia parasitica. Progr. Fish-Cult.* 11:97.

45. THATCHER, T.O. & J.F. SANTNER. 1966. Acute toxicity of LAS to various fish species. *Proc. 21st Ind. Waste Conf.*, Purdue Univ., Eng. Ext. Bull. No. 121:996.

46. BRUNGS, W.A. & G.W. BAILEY. 1966. Influence of suspended solids on the acute toxicity of endrin to fathead minnows. *Proc. 21st Ind. Waste Conf.*, Purdue Univ., Eng. Ext. Bull. No. 121:4.

47. ESVELT, L.A. & J.D. CONNERS. 1971. Continuous-flow fish bioassay apparatus for municipal and industrial effluents. In: Toxicity Removal from Municipal Wastewaters. (L.A. Esvelt, W.J. Kaufman and R.E. Selleck, eds.). Vol. IV of A Study of Toxicity and Biostimulation in San Francisco Bay-Delta Waters. p.155. Sanitary Engineering Research Lab., Univ. Calif., Berkeley.

48. ANDREW, R.W. & G.E. GLASS. 1974. Amperometric methods for determining residual chlorine, ozone and sulfite. U.S. EPA, National Water Quality Lab., Duluth, Minn.

49. SILLEN, L.C. & A.E. MARTELL. 1964. Stability constants of metal ion complexes. Spec. Publ. 17, Chemical Soc., London, England.

50. MCKIM, J.M. & D.A. BENOIT. 1971. Effect of long-term exposures to copper on survival, reproduction and growth of brook trout *Salvelinus fontinalis* (Mitchill). *J. Fish. Res. Board Can.* 28:655.

51. DRUMMOND, R.A. & W.F. DAWSON. 1970. An inexpensive method for simulating a diel pattern of lighting in the laboratory. *Trans. Amer. Fish. Soc.* 99:434.

52. SPRAGUE, J.B. 1970. Measurement of pollu-

tant toxicity to fish II. Utilizing and applying bioassay results. *Water Res.* 4:3.

53. SURBER, E.W., J.N. ENGLISH & G.N. MCDERMOTT. 1962. Tainting of fish by outboard motor exhaust wastes as related to gas and oil consumption. PHS Publ. No. 999-WP-25, Environmental Health Ser.:170. Washington, D.C.

54. AMAN, C.W. 1955. The relation of taste and odor to flavor. *Taste Odor Control J.* 21(10):1.

55. BALDWIN, R.E., D.H. STRONG & J.H TORRIE. 1961. Flavor and aroma of fish taken from four fresh-water sources. *Trans. Amer. Fish. Soc.* 90:176.

56. DAWSON, E.H. & B.L. HARRIS. 1951. Sensory methods for measuring differences in food quality. *U.S. Dep. Agr. Agr. Inform. Bull.* 34:1.

57. WARREN, C.E. & P. DOUDOROFF. 1971. Biology and Water Pollution Control. W.B. Saunders Co.

58. BROWN, M.E., ed. 1957. The Physiology of Fishes. Vol. 1, Metabolism. Academic Press Inc., New York, N.Y.

59. BRETT, J.R. 1967. Swimming performance of sockeye salmon (*Oncorhynchus nerka*) in relation to fatigue time and temperature. *J. Fish. Res. Board Can.* 24:1731.

60. SPRAGUE, J.B. 1968. Avoidance reactions of rainbow trout to zinc sulphate solutions. *Water Res.* 2:367.

61. FINNEY, D.J. 1971. Probit Analysis, 3rd ed. Cambridge Univ. Press, London and New York.

62. LITCHFIELD, J.T. & F. WILCOXON. 1949. A simple method of evaluating dose-effect experiments. *Pharmacol. Exp. Ther.* 96:99.

63. DIXON, W.J., ed. 1970. BMD biomedical computer programs. In: Automatic Computation Ser. No. 2, 2nd ed., Univ. of Calif. Press, Los Angeles.

64. BERKSON, J. 1953. A statistically precise and relatively simple method of estimating the bioassay with quantal response based on the logistic function. *J. Amer. Statist. Ass.* 48:565.

65. PICKERING, O.H. & W.N. VIGOR. 1965. The acute toxicity of zinc to eggs and fry of the fathead minnow. *Progr. Fish-Cult.* 27:153.

66. ALDERDICE, D.F. 1972. Factor combinations. Responses of marine poikilotherms to environmental factors acting in concert. In: Marine Ecology (O. Kinne, ed.). Vol. 1, Part 3:1659. Wiley-Interscience, London and New York.

67. VERNBERG, W.B., P. DE COURSEY & W.J. PADGETT. 1973. Synergistic effects of environmental variables on larvae of *Uca pugilator. Mar. Biol.* 22:307.

68. LITCHFIELD, J.T. 1949. A method for rapid graphic solution of time-percent effect curves. *Pharmacol. Exp. Ther.* 97:399.

69. SHEPARD, M.P. 1955. Resistance and tolerance of young speckled trout (*Salvelinus fontinalis*) to oxygen lack, with special reference to low oxygen acclimation. *J. Fish. Res. Board Can.* 12:387.

70. SPRAGUE, J.B. 1973. The ABC's of pollutant bioassay using fish. In: Biological Methods for the Assessment of Water Quality (J. Cairns and K.L. Dickson, eds). p.6. American Soc. for Testing and Materials, Philadelphia, Pa. ASTM STP 528.

71. TATTERSFIELD, F. & H.M. MORRIS. 1924. An apparatus for testing the toxic values of contact insecticides under controlled conditions. *Bull. Entomol. Res.* 14:223.

72. KEULS, M. 1952. The use of the "studentized range" in connection with an analysis of variance. *Euphytica* 1:112.

73. DUNCAN, D.B. 1955. Multiple range and multiple F tests. *Biometrics* 11:1.

74. DUNNETT, C.W. 1955. A multiple comparison procedure for comparing several treatments with a control. *J. Amer. Statist. Ass.* 50:1096.

75. SPRAGUE, J.B. 1970. Review paper, Measurement of pollutant toxicity to fish—II. Utilizing and applying bioassay results. *Water Res.* 4:3.

76. SPRAGUE, J.B. 1971. Review paper, Measurement of pollutant toxicity to fish—III. Sublethal effects and "safe" concentrations. *Water Res.* 5:245.

77. HART, W.B., P. DOUDOROFF & J. GREENBANK. 1945. The Evaluation of the Toxicity of Industrial Wastes, Chemicals and Other Substances to Fresh Water Fishes. Waste Control Laboratory, Atlantic Refining Co., Philadelphia, Pa.

78. DOUDOROFF, P. 1951. Biological observations of industrial waste disposal. *Proc. 6th Ind. Waste Conf.*, Purdue Univ., Eng. Ext. Bull. 76:88.

79. OHIO RIVER VALLEY WATER SANITATION COMMISSION. 1955. Aquatic life water quality criteria. *Sewage Ind. Wastes.* 27:321.

80. HENDERSON, C. 1957. Application factors to be applied to bioassays for the safe disposal of toxic wastes. In: Biological Problems in Water Pollution (C.M. Tarzwell, ed.). p.31. Robert A. Taft Sanitary Engineering Center, Cincinnati, Ohio.

81. WARREN, G.E. & P. DOUDOROFF. 1958. The development of methods for using bioassays in the control of pulp mill waste disposal. *TAPPI* 41:8.

82. MOUNT, D.I. 1968. Chronic toxicity of copper to fathead minnows, *Pimephales promelas*, (Rafinesque). *Water Res.* 2:215.

83. TARZWELL, C.M. 1962. The need and value of water quality criteria with special reference to aquatic life. *Can. Fish Cult.* 31:35.

84. TARZWELL, C.M. 1968. The determination, use, and value of water quality requirements. *Proc. 29th Annu. Int. Water Conf., Eng. Soc. Western Pa.*:1.

85. TARZWELL, C.M. 1966. Water quality requirements for aquatic life. National Symp. Quality Standards for Natural Waters Proc., p.185.

86. TARZWELL, C.M. 1969. Waste management in the marine environment. Proc. Civil Engineering in the Ocean II. Miami Beach, Fla., p.477.

802   BIOSTIMULATION (ALGAL PRODUCTIVITY)
802 A.   General Principles

This algal assay procedure for determining the primary productivity of a water is based on Liebig's "Law of the Minimum", which states that "growth is limited by the substance that is present in minimal quantity in respect to the needs of the organism."

The assay is a laboratory procedure in which effects of various substances on the maximum specific growth rate and maximum crop of selected algal species, cultured under specified conditions, are measured. Results are assessed by comparing growth in the presence of selected substances to growth in control flasks. Since some degree of variability is inherent in the test, experimental designs must incorporate sufficient replication to permit statistical evaluation of results.

The algal assays consist of three steps: (a) selection and measurement of appropriate factors or conditions during the assay (for example, biomass indicators such as total cell carbon), (b) presentation and statistical evaluation of the measurements made during the assay, and (c) interpretation of the results with respect to the specific problem being investigated.

1. Application of Technics

a. *General procedures:* Biostimula-

tion assay involves: (a) assessment of a receiving water to determine its nutritional status and its sensitivity to change, (b) evaluation of materials and products to determine their potential effects on algal growth in receiving waters; (c) assessment of effects of changes in waste treatment processes on algal growth in receiving waters, and (d) assessment of impact of nutrients in tributary waters on algal growth in lakes and receiving waters.

b. *Specific procedures:* After the general assessment, identify limiting algal nutrients, determine biologically the availability of those nutrients, the lowest concentration of which limits algal growth, and quantify the biological response to changes in concentrations of essential nutrients.

2. Determination of Growth Responses

The maximum specific growth rate and the maximum standing crop are determined. The maximum specific growth rate is related to the concentration of the rate-limiting nutrients present. The maximum standing crop is proportional to the initial amount of limiting nutrient available.

802 B.   Planning and Evaluating Algal Assays

The specific experimental design of each algal assay must be tailored to meet the actual situation. It is extremely important that all pertinent environmental factors be considered in the planning of an assay to insure that valid results and conclusions are obtained. As a minimum, follow the instructions given below.

1. Selecting Sampling Sites

The quality of water samples may vary greatly with time and point of collection. Establish sampling programs so that representative and comparable data will be obtained.

a. Spatial variations: It may be of value to sample both epilimnion and hypolimnion in stratified bodies of water. The use of transection lines is helpful in securing adequate samples and locating sampling stations. In rivers and streams, useful information can be obtained by taking samples upstream and downstream from suspected nutrient sources and from tributary streams. When conditions are evaluated, include samples from a number of natural waters having a range of representative water qualities.

b. Temporal variations: The nutrient contents of natural and wastewaters often vary daily and seasonally. Take this into consideration and consider the possible necessity of composite sampling, frequent grab sampling, or other sampling procedures.

2. Determining Limiting Nutrients

Deficiency of any essential nutrient may limit algal growth. Bioassays can be designed to examine in detail only a few nutrients which, by preliminary testing, have been shown to be the most likely to be limiting to growth.

3. Evaluating Materials

In a program for evaluating potential effect of a substance on receiving waters, consider the following factors: (*a*) distribution, e.g., local, regional, or national, (*b*) amount to be used, (*c*) chemical and/or physical nature, e.g., its theoretical potential for direct or indirect nutrient enrichment, (*d*) fate, e.g., its chemical change or biological degradation during waste treatment or in surface waters, (*e*) pathways by which it will reach the receiving water, e.g., include the test material in several waste treatment effluents or as a component of surface runoff, (*f*) dilution factor for the receiving body, e.g., an appropriate range of dilutions to represent the range in dilution due to changes in flow, and (*g*) selection of appropriate test water, e.g., use of appropriate test water for a material of local interest, but use of a full range of water qualities for material with broad distribution.

4. Assessment of Waste Treatment Processes

When the algal assay is used to measure stimulation of growth by a given effluent, overall evaluation must include consideration of the following: (*a*) typical and atypical conditions under which the type of effluent may enter the environment, (b) growth measurements and test organisms to be used, (c) concentration of the growth-limiting nutrient, (d) possible change in the available amount of the growth-limiting nutrient as a result of the sewage treatment process, and (e) the overall effects of a nutrient removal process or process changes.

802 C.   Apparatus

1. Sampling and Sample Preparation

The following equipment is required:
a. *Sampler*, non-metallic.
b. *Sample bottles*, borosilicate glass, linear polyethylene, polycarbonate or polypropylene, capable of being autoclaved.
c. *Membrane filter apparatus* for use with 47-mm petri prefilter pads and 0.45-μm porosity filters.
d. *Autoclave or pressure cooker* capable of producing 1.1 kg/cm² (15 psi) at 121 C.

2. Culturing and Incubation

a. *Culture vessels:* Erlenmeyer flasks of good-quality borosilicate glass such as Pyrex or Kimax. Use the same brand of glass throughout the laboratory. When trace nutrients are being studied, use special glassware such as Vycor, polycarbonate, or coated (e.g. silicone) glassware. While the flask size is not critical, the surface-to-volume ratios of the growth medium are, because of carbon dioxide limitation. The recommended surface-to-volume ratios are as follows:

40 ml sample in 125 ml flask
60 ml sample in 250 ml flask
100 ml sample in 500 ml flask.

It is desirable to number test flasks permanently in order that anomalous growth that appears to be related to specific flasks can be identified and those flasks eliminated from future tests.

b. *Culture closures:* Use foam plugs, loose-fitting aluminum foil, or inverted beakers to permit good gas exchange and prevent contamination. Each laboratory must determine for each batch of closures purchased whether that batch has any significant effect on the maximum specific growth rate and/or the maximum standing crop.

c. *Constant-temperature room:* A constant-temperature room, or equivalent incubator, capable of providing temperature control at 18±2 C is required. Control of temperature variation is important because of effects on growth rate, so either good temperature variation or a policy of random spatial shifting of flasks is necessary to randomize the effects or compensate for the allowable temperature range.

d. *Illumination:* Use "cool-white" fluorescent lighting to provide 4,304 lux (400 ft-c)±10% or 2,152 lux (200 ft-c)±10% measured adjacent to the flask at the liquid level. The energy level output of a bank of six 144-cm "cool white" fluorescent lamps (GE 40-W, @60 Hz) was approximately 1,300 μW/cm² (range, 380 to 760 nm) at a distance of 67 cm, as measured with an ISCO Model SRC spectroradiometer. With the same measurement geometry, a Weston Model 756 Illumination Meter read 4304 lux (400 ft-c). All reflecting surfaces were matte white. Therefore, utilizing a calibrated illumination meter with a foot-candle readout, one may, by adjusting the height of the lights, achieve a known energy level output of 1,300 μW/cm^2. For further discussion of the problems of the differences in absorption of light by photosynthesizing organisms and by man's eye and their measurement, see Tyler.[1]

e. Light meter: Several types may be used. Calibrate meter against a standard light source or light meter.

3. General Equipment

a. Analytical balance capable of weighing 100 g with a precision of ±0.1 mg.

b. Microscope and illuminator, good quality, general purpose.

c. Hemacytometer or plankton counting slide.

d. pH meter having a scale of 0-4 pH units with an accuracy of ±0.1 pH unit.

e. Dry heat oven capable of temperatures to 120 C.

f. Centrifuge capable of a relative centrifugal force of at least 1,000×g.

g. Spectrophotometer or colorimeter for use at 600 to 750 nm.

4. Optional Equipment

a. Electronic particle (cell) counter.

b. Fluorometer.

c. Shaker table, capable of 100 oscillations/min.

802 D.   Sample Handling

1. Collection

Use a nonmetallic water sampler and autoclavable storage container. Do not re-use containers when toxic or nutrient contamination is suspected.

2. Transportation

Leave a minimum of air space in the transport container and keep it in the dark and at 0 C.

3. Preparation

To enable the use of unialgal test species, "remove" the indigenous algae before assaying the sample. This "removal" necessitates either the separation or destruction of the indigenous algae. Fil-

ter and/or autoclave, according to the type of information being sought. In both cases, prepare the sample as soon as possible (within 24 hr) after collection. (See Section 802D.4 for discussion of storage.)

a. Membrane filtration: Use membrane filtration to remove indigenous algae before determining deficiencies in soluble nutrients that have not been taken up by filtrable organisms, or in order to predict the effect of added nutrients to a test water at a specific time. Pretreat 0.45-μm-porosity membrane filters by passing at least 50 ml of distilled water through them. Discard filtrate and use another collecting vessel. Then filter the quantity of the sample as needed under reduced pressure of 0.5 atm or less. If there is a large amount of suspended material in the sample, filter through an appropriate prefilter (for example, glass fiber), also pretreated as described above, before filtration through the 0.45 μm porosity filter.

b. Autoclaving: Use autoclaving to determine the amount of algal biomass that can be grown from all nutrients in the water, including those contained in filtrable organisms. Autoclave the sample at 1.1 kg/cm^2 (15 psi) and 121 C (250 F). The length of time of autoclaving will depend on the volume of the sample, e.g., 30 min or 10 min/l of sample, whichever is longer. After autoclaving and cooling the sample, allow it to equilibrate either in an air or carbon dioxide atmosphere in order to restore the carbon dioxide lost. If an electronic particle counter is to be used for all counting, pass the carbon-dioxide-equilibrated sample through a 0.45-μm membrane filter.

4. Storage

Changes occur in water samples during storage regardless of storage conditions. The extent or chemistry of these changes is not well known; therefore, keep the duration of storage to a minimum after sample preparation. Store samples in full containers (no air space). Before sample preparation, store samples in the dark at 0 to 4 C. If prolonged storage is anticipated, prepare sample first and then store in the dark at 0 to 4 C.

802 E. Synthetic Algal Culture Medium

The formula and instructions for the preparation of synthetic culture media for algae are given in Section 801C.4c1).

802 F. Inoculum

1. Recommended Test Algae

a. Fresh water:

1) *Selenastrum capricornutum* Printz.

2) *Microcystis aeruginosa* Kuetz. emend Elenkin (*Anacystis cyanea* Drouet and Daily).

3) *Anabaena flos-aquae* (Lyngb.) De Brebisson.

4) *Cyclotella* sp.

5) *Nitzschia* sp.

6) *Synedra* sp.

If any of the latter three are used, add 20 mg Si/l (101.214 mg Na$_2$SiO$_3 \cdot$9H$_2$O/l) to the culture medium as noted in Section 801C.4c.

b. Marine:

1) *Dunaliella tertiolecta* Butcher (DUN Clone).

2) *Thalassiosira pseudonana* (Hasle and Heimdal) (CN Clone) (old *Cyclotella nana*). Do not shake.

2. Sources of Test Algae

Algal cultures may be secured from National Eutrophication Research Program, Pacific Northwest Environmental Research Laboratory, National Environmental Research Center, Environmental Protection Agency, 200 S.W. 35th Street, Corvallis, Ore. 97330 and from Department of Botany, University of Indiana, Bloomington, Ind.

3. Maintenance of Stock Cultures

a. *Medium:* See Section 801C.4c1).

b. *Incubation conditions:*

1) Freshwater species—Temperature 24±2 C under continuous cool-white fluorescent lighting at 4,304 lux (400 ft-c)±10% for *S. capricornutum* and the diatoms; 2,152 lux (200 ft-c)±10% for *M. aeruginosa* and *A. flos-aquae;* shake at 110 oscillations/min.

2) Marine species—Temperature 18±2 C under continuous cool-white fluorescent lighting at 4,304 lux (400 ft-c)±10% for *D. tertiolecta,* (shake at 110 oscillations/min) and for *T. pseudonana* (do *not* shake but swirl once a day).

c. *First stock transfer:* Upon receipt of the inoculum species, transfer a portion to the algal culture medium (Section 801C.4c1). (Example: 1 ml of inoculum in 100 ml in a 500-ml erlenmeyer flask).

d. *Subsequent stock transfers:* Make a new stock transfer, using an aseptic technic as the first operation on opening a stock culture. The volume of the transfers is not critical so long as enough cells are included to overcome significant growth lag. Conduct a weekly routine stock transfer schedule as a means of providing a continuing supply of "healthy" cells for experimental work. Also, make a microscopic check of the algal cultures to insure that the stock cultures remain unialgal.

e. *Age of inoculum:* Use cultures 1 to 3 wk old as a source of inoculum. For *Selenastrum* and the diatoms, a 1-wk incubation is often sufficient to provide enough cells. The blue-green species require a longer time to achieve maximum crop than does *Selenastrum* and 2 to 3 wk may be required to provide inocula for assays.

4. Preparation of Inoculum

Centrifuge the cells from the stock culture and discard the supernatant. Resuspend the sedimented cells in an appropriate volume of glass-distilled water containing 15 mg $NaHCO_3/l$ and again centrifuge. Resuspend the sedimented algae again in the water-bicarbonate solution and use as the inoculum.

5. Amount of Inoculum

Count the cells suspended in the bicarbonate solution and pipet into the test water to give a starting cell concentration in the test waters as follows:

S. capricornutum	10^3 cells/ml
M. aeruginosa	50×10^3 cells/ml
A. flos-aquae	50×10^3 cells/ml
Diatoms	10^3 cells/ml

The volume of the transfer is calculated to result in the above concentrations in the test flasks (Example: for *S. capricornutum* 5×10^5 cells/ml in the stock culture requires a 0.2 ml transfer/100 ml of test water).

802 G.   Test Conditions and Procedures

1. Temperature

Keep temperature at 18±2 C for marine species and 24±2 C for freshwater species.

2. Illumination

See Section 802F.3b. Measure light intensity adjacent to the flask at the liquid level. A convenient and acceptable way to achieve these two light intensities is to set up the illumination for 4,304 lux (400 ft-c) and then place cheesecloth over the blue-green algal culture flask to reduce the light intensity at the liquid level to 2,052 lux (200 ft-c).

3. Procedure

a. Preparation of glassware: Wash all cylinders, flasks, bottles, centrifuge tubes, and vials with detergent or sodium carbonate and rinse thoroughly with tap water. Then rinse with a 10% solution by volume of warm reagent-grade hydrochloric acid (HCl). Fill vials and centrifuge tubes with the 10% HCl solution for a few minutes and fill all large containers to about one-tenth capacity with HCl solution and swirl so that the entire inner surface is bathed. After the HCl rinse, rinse the glassware five times with tap water, then five times with deionized water.

Place pipets in 10% HCl solution for 12 hr or longer and rinse at least 10 times with tap water in an automatic pipet washer, then rinse with deionized water. Disposable pipets may be used to eliminate the need for pipet washing and to minimize the possibility of contamination.

Dry cleaned glassware at 105 C in an oven and store either in closed cabinets or on open shelves with the tops covered with aluminum foil.

Before use, stopper culture flasks with plastic plugs or cover with aluminum foil and autoclave at 1.1 kg/cm² for 15 min. After autoclaving, prerinse the flasks with the type medium to be used for subsequent culturing and leave inverted on absorbent paper 20 to 30 min to drain.

b. pH control: To insure the availability of carbon dioxide, keep the pH below 8.5 by using optimum surface-to-volume ratios, continuously shaking the flask (approximately 100 oscillations/min), and ventilating with air or air/carbon dioxide mixture through the culture.

c. Growth measurements

Two measures are used to describe the growth of a test alga in the Bottle Test,[2] maximum specific growth rate and maximum standing crop. Either or both may be determined, depending on the objectives of the assay.

1) Maximum specific growth rate— The maximum specific growth rate (μ_{max}) for an individual flask is the largest specific growth rate (μ) occurring at any time during incubation. The μ_{max} for a set of replicate flasks is determined by averaging μ_{max} of the individual flasks.

The specific growth rate, μ, is defined by:

$$\mu = \frac{\ln(X_2/X_1)}{t_2 - t_1} \quad \text{days}^{-1}$$

where X_2 = biomass concentration at end of selected time interval, X_1 = biomass concentration at beginning of selected time interval, and $t_2-t_1 =$ elapsed time (days) between selected determinations of biomass.

If biomass (dry weight) is determined indirectly, e.g., by cell counts, compute the specific growth rate directly from these determinations without conversion to biomass, if the factor relating the direct determination to biomass remains constant for the time period considered. Cell counts, chlorophyll content, and other measures of biomass do not remain constant to one another or to dry weight.

a) Laboratory measurements—The maximum specific growth rate occurs during the logarithmic phase of growth, usually between day 0 and day 5; therefore, measure biomass at least daily during the first 5 days of incubation to determine this maximum rate. Indirect measurements of biomass, such as cell counts, normally will be required because of the difficulty in making accurate gravimetric measurements at low cell densities.

b) Computation of maximum specific growth rate—The maximum specific growth rate (μ_{max}) is determined by calculation using the equation in ¶1) to determine the daily specific growth rate (μ) for each replicate flask and averaging for all of the replicates the largest value for each flask. It also may be determined by preparing a semilog plot of biomass concentration versus time for each replicate flask. Ideally, the exponential growth phase is drawn on the plot. If it appears that the data describe two straight lines, use the line of steepest slope. A linear regression analysis of the data also may be used to determine the best-fit straight line. Select two data points that most closely fit the line and determine the specific growth rate (μ) according to the equation given in ¶1) above. Average the largest specific growth rates for the replicate flasks to obtain μ_{max}.

2) Maximum standing crop—The maximum standing crop in any flask is defined as the maximum algal biomass achieved during incubation. For practical purposes, it may be assumed that the maximum standing crop has been achieved when the increase in biomass is less than 5%/day.

After the maximum standing crop has been achieved, determine the dry weight of algal biomass gravimetrically by either the aluminum-dish or filtration technic. If biomass is determined indirectly, convert the results to an equivalent dry weight using appropriate conversion factors.

4. Biomass Monitoring

Several methods may be used, but they must always be related to dry weight.

a. Dry weight: Two methods may be used. To use the first, centrifuge a suitable portion of algal suspension, wash the sedimented cells three times in distilled water containing 15 mg $NaHCO_3/l$, transfer to tared crucibles or aluminum cups, dry overnight in a hot-air oven at 105 C, and weigh. This method is more sensitive than the second method but cells may be lost during washing.

The second method involves filtering a measured portion of algal suspension through a tared membrane filter with a 0.60-μm pore size. Dry filters for several hours at 60 C in an oven. Place filters in folded sheets of paper or aluminum weighing dishes on which the weights or codes may be written. Cool filters in a desiccator containing desiccant. Filter a suitable portion of the culture under a vacuum of 0.5 atm. Filter 50 ml, or less as the size of the culture dictates. Rinse the filter funnel with 50 ml distilled water using a wash bottle and allow the rinsings to pass through the filter. This serves to transfer all the algae to the filter and to wash the nutrient salts from the filter. Dry the filter at 60 C, cool in desiccator, and weigh. To correct for loss of weight of filters during washing, wash two blank filters with 50 ml of distilled water, pouring it through slowly under reduced vacuum. Dry and weigh filters and record weight loss. This correction is not large, but is essential for meaningful results on thin cultures. For example, if 50 ml have been filtered and yield a difference between tare and final of 5.58 mg and the blank has lost 0.02 mg, then the culture contains: $(5.58+0.02) \times 20 = 112$ mg/l dry weight.

b. Direct microscopic counting: A hemacytometer or plankton counting cell is used. For filamentous algae, facilitate microscopic counting of the individual cells by breaking up the algal filaments. Filament-breaking technics include the use of a syringe, an ultrasonic bath, a high-speed blender, and vigorous stirring with glass beads. While all of these technics have drawbacks, expelling the sample forcefully through a syringe against the inside of the flask is the most satisfactory way to break up tight clumps of filaments. Other methods of biomass measurement such as dry weight, absorbance, or chlorophyll fluorescence are often considered to be more

suitable than cell counts for growth assessment of filamentous algae.

c. Absorbance: Measure absorbance with a spectrophotometer or colorimeter at a wavelength of 600 to 750 nm. In reporting results, give the instrument make or model, the geometry and path length of the cuvette, the wave length used, and the equivalence to biomass.

In any photometric measure of absorbance, considerations of precision lead to the simple rule of thumb that measurements be limited to a range of $0.05 < D < 1.0$, where D represents optical density. A further reason for this restriction is that for particulate suspensions the linearity between D and concentration hold practically only over limited range. Hence, limit values measured to this range by concentration or dilution before measurement.

d. Chlorophyll: All algae contain chlorophyll *a*, and measuring this pigment can yield some insight into the relative amount of algal biomass present.[3, 4] Chlorophyll may be measured either in vivo or in vitro by fluorescence.

1) In vivo procedure—Swirl flasks to insure homogeneous suspension of algal cells. Pipet a portion of the cell suspension (5 ml minimum) into a small beaker or vial. Zero fluorometer with a distilled water blank before each sample reading and change in sensitivity setting. Pour well-mixed sample into cuvette and read fluorescence. If reading (scale deflection) is over 90 units, use lower sensitivity setting, e.g., $30 \times > 10 \times > 3 \times > 1$; conversely, if reading is less than 15 units, increase sensitivity setting. If samples fail to stay in range, dilute accordingly. Record fluorescence units, based on a common sensitivity factor,

e.g., a reading of 50 at $1 \times = 1,500$ at $30 \times$.

2) In vitro procedure—Filter a measured sample under vacuum (0.5 atm) through a glass fiber filter. Add approximately 1.0 ml of magnesium carbonate suspension (1.0 g finely powdered analytical-reagent-grade magnesium carbonate in 100 ml distilled water) and drain filter thoroughly under suction. Place filter in the bottom of a tissue grinding tube. Add 2 ml of 90% acetone to the grinding tube and insert pestle. Grind the sample 1 to 2 min (in subdued light) and wash pestle and grinding tube with 5 ml of 90% acetone into a 15 ml screw cap centrifuge tube. Centrifuge ($2,000 \times g$) for 1 to 5 min and allow to stand in the dark 1 to 2 hr to ensure complete removal of all extractable pigment. Measure fluorescence as outlined in the in vivo method. If pheophytin is to be measured, acidify with 2 drops 1 N HCl and reread fluorescence. Record fluorescence values as relative chlorophyll values or as chlorophyll a (mg/m^3) as calculated from the equation:

$$\text{chlorophyll } a \ (mg/m^3) = \frac{\dfrac{F_o/F_{a_{max}}}{(F_o/F_{a_{max}})-1} \ (kx)(F_o-F_a)}{\text{liters filtered}}$$

$$\text{pheophytin } a \ (mg/m^3) = \frac{\dfrac{F_o/F_{a_{max}}}{(F_o/F_{a_{max}})-1} \ (kx)[(F_o/F_{a_{max}})(F_a)-F_o]}{\text{liters filtered}}$$

where F_o = fluorescence before acidification, F_a = fluorescence after acidification, $F_o/F_{a_{max}}$ = maximum acid factor that can be expected in the absence of pheophytin, and kx = calibration constant for a specific sensitivity scale. Note that kx, $F_o/F_{a_{max}}$, and acid ratios are functions of the combination of photomultiplier and color filters.

e. Total cell carbon: Determine by carbon analyzer. Report equivalence between total cell carbon and biomass.

802 H.   Effect of Additions

1. Determination of Stimulatory or Inhibitory Effects

The quantity of cells produced in a given medium is limited by the nutrient that is present in the lowest relative quantity with respect to the needs of the organism. If a quantity of the limiting nutrient is added to the medium, cell production increases until this additional supply is depleted or until some other nutrient becomes limiting to growth. Additions of substances other than that which is limiting would yield no increase in cell production. Nutrient additions may be made singly or in combination and the growth response compared to that of untreated controls to identify those substances that limit growth rate or cell production. The selection of additives, e.g., nitrogen, phosphorus, iron, wastewater effluents, will depend on the requirements of the test.

In all cases, keep the volume of added nutrient solution as small as possible; concentrations will vary and must be matched to the waters being tested.

Keep the concentration small to minimize alterations of the sample, but at the same time make it sufficiently large to yield a potentially measurable response. Relate the concentrations of additions to fertility of the sample. To assess the effect of nutrient additions, compare the treated sample to an untreated control of the test water. If the control is quite fertile, cell production will be high and flask-to-flask variations in the controls might mask the effect of small additions of the limiting nutrient.

2. Auxiliary Additions

It is sometimes necessary to check for the possibility that the test water contains some toxic material that could influence results. To check for toxic materials, treat the test water with an appropriate dilution of the complete synthetic medium. If no, or less than expected, growth occurs, the presence of toxic materials is suspected. In some situations, dilution of the sample or the addition of a chelating agent will eliminate toxic effects.

802 I.   Data Analysis and Interpretation

The fundamental measure used in the algal assay to determine biostimulation is the amount of suspended solids (dry weight) produced and determined gravimetrically. Other biomass indicators may be used, but all results presented must include experimentally determined conversion factors and the dry weight of suspended solids. Use several biomass indicators whenever possible, because biomass indicators respond differently to any given nutrient-limiting condition.

1. Reference Curves

Report results of addition assays with results from two types of reference samples: the assay reference medium and unspiked samples of the water under consideration. Present the entire growth curves for each of the two types of reference sample. Report the results of individual assays as the maximum specific growth rate (with time of occurrence) and maximum standing crop (with time at which it was reached).

a. Maximum specific growth rate:
1) Identification of growth-rate-limiting nutrients by single-nutrient additions—Determine the nutrients that limit growth rate by treating a number of replicate flasks with single nutrients, determining the maximum specific growth rate for each flask, and comparing the averages by Student's t-test or other appropriate statistical tests.

2) Identification of growth-rate-limiting nutrients by treating with many nutrients—To determine significance of data from multiple-treatment tests, make analysis of variance calculations. It is important in multiple-nutrient treatment to account for the possible interaction between different nutrients. Such interactions can be detected by use of factorial analysis.[2]

b. Maximum standing crop: The methods for finding growth-rate-limiting nutrients are used to determine the nutrient that limits biomass of the maximum standing crop.

The available concentration of the growth-limiting nutrient is determined by comparing the maximum standing crop in an untreated sample with the maximum standing crop in reference media having various concentrations of the nutrient in question.

2. Confidence Intervals

Report both the maximum specific growth rate and the maximum standing crop with their confidence intervals. Base the calculation of confidence interval for the average values presented on at least five samples. Consequently, make a minimum of five replications when an unfamiliar source water is first analyzed. Use the results of these to calculate the standard deviation. Subsequent samples from the same source can be analyzed using only three replicates, and reported with the confidence interval established for that source water.

3. Rejecting Outliers

When algal assays are conducted it is often observed that one of the flasks among replicates shows a considerable growth difference from the remainder of the replicates. Eliminate such outliers from the results if they fall outside the 95% confidence limits.

4. Evaluating Assay Results

The overall evaluation of assay results consists of two parts. The first is determination of whether a given assay result is significant when considered as a laboratory measurement. Several methods are available such as the Student's t-test and analysis of variance technics. However, there is as yet no unique method available to determine significant responses. Each experimental evaluation must be based on specific objectives using valid statistical procedures.

The second part of the overall evaluation is the correlation of laboratory assay results to effects observed or predicted in the field. Specific guidelines are not yet available, but investigators should note the general considerations presented in Section 802B before planning any algal assay.

802 J. References

1. TYLER, J.E. 1973. Applied radiometry. *Oceanogr. Mar. Biol. Annu. Rev.* 11:11.
2. NATIONAL EUTROPHICATION RESEARCH PROGRAM. 1971. Algal Assay Procedure: Bottle Test. EPA, Pacific Northwest Environmental Research Lab., Corvallis, Ore.
3. JOINT INDUSTRY—GOVERNMENT TASK FORCE ON EUTROPHICATION. 1969. Provisional Algal Assay Procedure. EPA, Pacific Northwest Environmental Research Lab., Corvallis, Ore.
4. STRICKLAND, J.D.H. & T.R. PARSONS. 1965. A Manual of Sea Water Analysis, 2nd rev. ed. Fisheries Research Board Canada Bull. 125.

802 K.   Bibliography

McGauhey, P.H., D.B. Porcella & G.L. Dugan. 1970. Eutrophication of surface waters—Indian Creek reservoir. First Progress Rep., FWQA Grant No. 16010 DNY. EPA, Pacific Northwest Environmental Research Lab., Corvallis, Ore.

Maloney, T.E., W.E. Miller & T. Shiroyama. 1971. Algal responses to nutrient additions in natural waters. Spec. Symp., American Society Limnology & Oceanography. Special symposium on Nutrients and Eutrophication: Limiting-Nutrient Controversy 1:134.

Miller, W.E. & T.E. Maloney. 1971. Effects of secondary and tertiary wastewater effluents on algal growth in a lake-river system. J. Water Pollut. Control Fed. 43:2361.

Weiss, C.M. & R.W. Helms. 1971. Interlaboratory Precision Test—An Eight Laboratory Evaluation of the Provisional Algal Assay Procedure: Bottle Test. Dep. Environmental Science & Engineering, School of Public Health, Univ. North Carolina, Chapel Hill.

Maloney, T.E., W.E. Miller & N.L. Blind. 1972. Use of algal assays in studying eutrophication problems. Proc. 6th Int. Conf. Water Pollut. Res. p.205. Pergamon Press, Oxford, England and New York, NY.

Scherfig, J., P.S. Dixon, R. Appleman & C.A. Justice. 1973. Effect of Phosphorus Removal on Algal Growth, EPA Ecology Research Ser. 660/3-75-015.

Miller, W.E., T.E. Maloney & J.C. Greene. 1974. Algal productivity in 49 lakes as determined by algal assays. Water Res. 8:667.

803   BIOASSAY PROCEDURES FOR PHYTOPLANKTON (TENTATIVE)

The phytoplankton are primary producers in the aquatic community and, as such, are at the base of aquatic food chains. Because of this, they must be tested in bioassays that predict and determine the potential effects of a substance on the aquatic environment. The same general principles used in determining biostimulation (Section 802) are used to determine toxicity to phytoplankton. The procedure given here applies to freshwater estuarine and marine phytoplankton.

803 A.   Test Organisms and Materials

1. Algal Test Species

The basic principles for the selecting of test species are discussed in Section 801C.1. Freshwater species that can be used are: Selenastrum capricornutum Printz, Microcystis aeruginosa Kuetz., emend Elenkin (Anacystis cyanea Drouet and Daily), Anabaena flosaquae (Lyngb). Important marine and estuarine species are: Thalassiosira pseudonana Hasle and Hundal (Cyclotella nana Hustedt), Skeletonema costatum (Greville) Clevel., Monochrysis lutheri Droop, and Dunaliella tertiolecta Butcher.

2. Preparation of Culture Media and Test Materials

a. Water supplies:
1) Fresh water—See Section 801C.4*b*1).
2) Marine water—See Section 801C.4*b*2).

b. Preparation of culture media:

1) Freshwater species—See Section 801C.4*c*1)a).
2) Marine species—See Section 801C.4*c*1)b).

c. Preparation of test material:
1) Glassware—For type, see Section 802C.2*a*.
2) Preparation—See Section 802G.3*a*.

803 B. General Test Conditions and Bioassay Procedures

1. Test Conditions

a. Fresh water: See Sections 802G.1 and 2.

b. Marine and estuarine:
1) Light intensity, 4,304 lux (400 ft-c).
2) Temperature, 18 ± 2 C.

2. Maintaining Stock Cultures

a. Fresh water: See Section 802F.3.

b. Marine and estuarine: Maintain the test species in the full-strength medium. Test species must be in the logarithmic growth phase. Therefore, transfer them to fresh culture medium every 4 to 5 days.

3. Procedure

a. Preparation of glassware: See Section 802G.3*a*.

b. Additions to test vessels: Add the material to be tested to the test vessels to give the desired concentrations. Prepare triplicate vessels for each concentration. Dilutions of the culture medium may be used if it is desired to simulate the chemical conditions of specific receiving waters. For optimum surface-to-volume ratios, see Section 802C.2*a*.

c. Inoculum:
1) Fresh water—See Sections 802.F3, 4, and 5.
2) Marine and estuarine—Proceed as for the freshwater algae but use sufficient inoculum to give a final concentration of 1,000 cells/ml.

d. Laboratory measurements: The maximum specific growth rate (μ_{max}) occurs during the logarithmic phase of growth, usually between Day 0 and Day 5. Therefore, it is necessary that measurements of biomass be made at least daily during the first 5 days of incubation to determine this maximum rate. Indirect measurements of biomass, such as chlorophyll *a* or cell numbers, usually will be required because accurate gravimetric measurements at low cell densities are difficult. See Section 802G.4 for methods.

e. Calculation of maximum specific growth rate: See Section 802G.3*c*.

4. Concentrations of Toxicants Tested

Test a log series of concentrations (see Section 801D) initially. After this preliminary test, base the experimental concentrations on progressive bisection of intervals on a logarithmic scale (Section 801D). Narrow the test concentrations so that the concentration that reduces the maximum specific growth rate (μ_{max}) to 50% of that of the control can be determined. This requires that at least two of the concentrations tested should fall on each side of the concentration that inhibited (μ_{max}) to 50% of that of the control (see Section 801F.)

5. Conducting the Bioassay

a. Bioassay of receiving water quality: To determine quality of a receiving water, add algae as described in Section 803.B.3c and compare the maximum specific growth rate (μ_{max}) to that obtained in the synthetic fresh water or artificial seawater culture medium. Inoculate triplicate sets of test vessels.

Destroy indigenous algae and zooplankton before inoculation. For marine waters, filter through a 0.45-μm-porosity membrane filter or pasteurize for 4 hr at 60 C. For fresh water, autoclave at 1.1 kg/cm^2 (15 psi) at 121 C (250 F)

and filter through a 0.45-μm-porosity membrane filter. Equilibrate the media in air or a carbon dioxide atmosphere to restore the carbon dioxide lost during treatment.

b. Bioassay of specific toxicants: Regional and seasonal variations in the quality of natural waters make them unsuitable as a standard bioassay medium for comparative toxicity tests. Therefore, use the synthetic fresh water medium and/or the artificial seawater. Add various concentrations of the toxicants to the culture medium in triplicate and inoculate with the test species.

For other types of tests such as those to determine effluent requirements or compliance with water quality standards, take dilution water from the receiving body near the outfall but outside its influence. Treat such dilution waters to remove undesirable organisms before undertaking growth rate tests with selected sensitive species. Determine the maximum specific growth rates (μ_{max}) in the test vessels and compare them with those of the controls and EC50's and SC calculated based on percent of growth reduction.

6. Calculating, Reporting, and Significance of Bioassay Results

See Section 801F.

803 C.   Bibliography

ERICKSON, S.J., N. LACKIE & T.E. MALONEY. 1970. A screening technique for estimating copper toxicity to estuarine phytoplankton. *J. Water Pollut. Control Fed.* 42:R270.

NATIONAL EUTROPHICATION RESEARCH PROGRAM. 1971. Algal Assay Procedure: Bottle Test. EPA, Pacific Northwest Environmental Research Lab., Corvallis, Ore.

Walsh, G.E. 1972. Effects of herbicides on photosynthesis and growth of marine unicellular algae. *Hyacinth Control J.* 10:45.

Tyler, J.E. 1973. Applied radiometry. *Oceanogr. Mar. Biol. Annu. Rev.* 11:11.

Eutrophication and Lake Restoration Branch. 1974. Marine Algal Assay Procedure: Bottle Test. EPA, Pacific Northwest Environmental Research Lab., Corvallis, Ore.

804 BIOASSAY PROCEDURES FOR ZOOPLANKTON

804 A. Bioassay Procedures for Ciliated Protozoa (TENTATIVE)

Protozoa, algae, and bacteria form the broad base of aquatic food chains. Ciliated protozoa are the most numerous animals of the estuarine benthos[1,2] and may be more important as nutrient regenerators, particularly of nitrogen and phosphorus, than bacteria.[3,4] Further, some ciliates are able to concentrate certain persistent pesticides and related chemicals[5,6,7] and thereby aid in translocation to higher trophic levels. Thus, it is possible that effects of such toxicants could be exerted at higher trophic levels either through disruption of nutrient cycles or through biological concentration of the toxicants higher in the food chain.[8,9]

The procedures described herein have been used successfully for a number of years to test toxicity and bioaccumulation of a number of toxic materials.[5,6] Responses measured are (*a*) effect on population growth rate, (*b*) effect on maximum population density, and (*c*) degree of accumulation and concentration of toxicants from media. A recommended organism for these studies is *Tetrahymena pyriformis*. This species occurs in freshwater and salt marshes, has world-wide distribution, and is readily grown in axenic culture. Its

physiology has been studied extensively.[10,11] Strain W is used in this bioassay; however, several other strains can be used. These may be obtained for a small fee from the American Type Culture Collection (ATCC), 12301 Parklawn Drive, Rockville, Md. 20852. Instructions for cultivation will be furnished when requested. Strains other than those maintained by ATCC usually can be obtained through the courtesy of investigators using them. These investigators are generally willing to furnish a brief note on media and culture conditions they have found to give best growth.

1. Holding and Culturing of Test Organisms

a. Culture of test organisms: Use standard bacteriological technics to prepare and autoclave culture media and to transfer axenic cultures of *T. pyriformis*. Maintain stock cultures of the protozoan at 26 ± 0.5 C in a suitable incubator.*

---

*Revco Model IB-1650 (Revco, Inc., Scientific Industrial Div., 1100 Memorial Dr., West Columbia, S.C. 29169) has been found to be satisfactory for culturing these organisms.

Slant culture tubes containing 10 ml of medium at 60 degrees to enhance aeration. Keep duplicate stock cultures at room temperature to prevent losses due to incubator failure. Keep them upright to slow growth by decreasing aeration and thereby prolong the life of the culture. The cultures are grown axenically in 18×150 mm bacteriological culture tubes capped with polypropylene or stainless steel closures and supported in vinyl-coated 40-tube racks.

b. Culture medium: Methods for the culture of organisms for bioassays differ only in that the cultures are grown in optically matched culture tubes of the same size, capped in the same manner, and in that the medium contains known concentrations of a toxicant. The same medium is used for stock and experimental cultures. It consists of 2% (w/v) proteose peptone, 0.2% (w/v) yeast extract, 0.5% glucose, and 90 μM Fe:EDTA chelate per liter. Do not use Fe:EDTA chelate when testing metals because of the probability of chelation of the metal and consequent reduction of their effect. The addition of Fe:EDTA chelate eliminates population growth variation due to variations in the iron content of different lots of proteose peptone. Prepare chelate by the method of Conner and Cline.[12] Make up the medium in distilled water or the artificial seawater [Section 801C.4c1)b)] diluted to a lower salinity, dispense among culture tubes, and autoclave for 15 min at 1.1 kg/cm^2 (15 psi). Before inoculation let stand a sufficient time so the DO is restored. Best growth occurs in the distilled water formulation, although there is no statistically significant difference in growth rates of populations grown in

the medium prepared with distilled water or in that prepared with 5 ‰ salinity.

2. Bioassay Procedures

a. Preparation of stock solutions of toxicant: Prepare a sterile stock solution for each concentration to be tested as described in Section 801D.3*b*. For toxicants that are not water soluble, acetone and polyethylene glycol 200 have been used as solvents at a final concentration of 0.1% in the test medium without apparent harm to the organisms. Growth is not significantly different at this concentration from that of solvent-free control cultures, and there is no reason to suspect the effects of the solvent and toxicant are additive. Nevertheless, it is always wise in testing toxicants with which one has no experience, to test for interaction of toxicant and solvent at concentrations of solvent that will be used. This can be done during the range-finding tests for the determining concentrations that will be used in the full-scale tests.

b. Conducting the bioassays:

1) Test procedures—Test procedures are essentially those described in Section 801D. Select and prepare test concentrations of toxicants as described in Sections 801D.2b and 3b. Prepare 11 or 12 optically matched culture tubes for each concentration, 10 tubes for the test solution with a control and special controls for the solvent and emulsifier if these materials are used. The inoculum for each tube is 1 ml of a 65-hr culture of the organism that has been diluted 3:10 with sterile medium. The final volume in each tube after addition of tox-

icant and inoculum should be 10 ml. Tests are run for 96 hr. Conduct tests in an incubator in which the temperature may be kept constant or varied daily and seasonally in accordance with the natural temperature regime of the area. Run bioassays concurrently on five concentrations of the toxicant (see Section 801D.3b). In view of the large variations usually observed among replicates, use six replicates to insure statistical validity at p=0.05. Analyze the effects of the toxicant on growth rate and population density statistically by analysis of variance (see Section 801F.).

Run tests to determine bioaccumulation for 7 days in replicate using 10 cultures per concentration plus controls.

2) Analytical procedures—Make chemical analyses of toxicant solutions at the beginning and completion of the bioassay to determine the accuracy with which the concentrations of the test solutions were formulated (see Section 801D.3d).

At the termination of the bioassay, all cultures from each concentration are pooled and the cells concentrated by centrifugation at 1,000 g. Wash the cells twice in toxicant-free medium and store, if necessary, before analysis in sealed tubes at –20 C. One hundred milliliters of a 96-hr control culture typically yield about 1 g of packed cells. The media and cells then can be analyzed separately by standard analytical procedures.[5,13] Residues usually are calculated on a wet weight basis. Dry weight values can be obtained by preparing replicate cultures and drying the cells at 60 C for 65 hr. If the toxicant under investigation is thermolabile, freeze-drying would cause less error in dry weights of cells.

3. Reporting Results

Population density is measured in a spectrophotometer† as absorbance at 540 nm. The blanks consist of a sterile proteose-peptone medium with the appropriate concentration of the toxicant and carrier. Conversion of absorbance values to absolute numbers of ciliates is precluded by variation in volume of individuals with the phase of population growth.[14] Therefore, mean absorbance is used to estimate differences in population density in the cultures. The effects of the toxicants on growth rate and population density are estimated from absorbance measurement of control and experimental cultures at 0, 4, 8, 16, 24, 36, 48, 60, 72, 84, and 96 hr. These data are plotted to determine the period of exponential growth for each population. Since growth in this period is logarithmic, growth rate can be estimated by the quality b of the least squares estimate of the $y=a+bx$. The calculated line gives a close fit to the experimental data, generally r≥0.9. The effect of the toxicant on growth rate and population density is determined as described in Sections 801F.2 and 3.

4. References

1. Borror, A.C. 1963. Morphology and ecology of the benthic ciliated protozoa of Alligator Harbor, Florida. *Arch. Protistenk.* 106:465.

2. Fenchel, T. 1967. The ecology of marine

---

†The Bausch and Lomb Spectronic 20 has been used successfully in this type of study because it accepts the large culture tubes. Other available instruments that can be adapted to large tubes and should be satisfactory are Coleman Junior and Junior II and Turner Model 330 Spectrophotometers.

microbenthos. I. The quantitative importance of ciliates as compared with metazoans in various types of sediments. *Ophelia* 4:121.

3. JOHANNES, R.E. 1965. Influence of marine protozoa on nutrient regeneration. *Limnol. Oceanogr.* 10:434.

4. JOHANNES, R.E. 1968. Nutrient regeneration in lakes and oceans. In: Advances in Microbiology of the Sea (M.R. Droop & E.J. Ferguson Wood, eds.) 1:203. Academic Press, New York, N.Y.

5. COOLEY, N.R., J.M. KELTNER, JR. & J. FORESTER. 1972. Mirex and Aroclor® 1254: Effect on and accumulation by *Tetrahymena pyriformis* strain W. *J. Protozool.* 19:636.

6. COOLEY, N.R., J.M. KELTNER, JR. & J. FORESTER. 1973. The polychlorinated biphenyls, Aroclors® 1248 and 1260: Effect on and accumulation by *Tetrahymena pyriformis. J. Protozool.* 20:443.

7. GREGORY, W.W., JR., J.K. REED & L.E. PRIESTER JR. 1969. Accumulation of parathion and DDT by some algae and protozoa. *J. Protozool.* 16:69.

8. BURDICK, G.E., E.J. HARRIS, H.J. DEAN, T.M. WALKER, J. SKEA & D. COLBY. 1964. The accumulation of DDT in lake trout and the effect on reproduction. *Trans. Amer. Fish. Soc.* 93:127.

9. BUTLER, P.A. 1969. Monitoring pesticide pollution. *Bio-Science* 19:889.

10. CORLISS, J.O. 1970. The comparative systematics of species comprising the hymenostome ciliate genus *Tetrahymena. J. Protozool.* 17:198.

11. ELLIOTT, A.M., ed. 1973. Biology of *Tetrahymena*. Dowden, Hutchinson & Ross, Inc., Stroudsburg, Pa.

12. CONNER, R.L. & S.G. CLINE. 1964. Iron deficiency and the metabolism of *Tetrahymena pyriformis. J. Protozool.* 11:486.

13. HATCH, W.R. & W.L. OTT. 1968. Determination of sub-microgram quantities of mercury by atomic absorption spectrophotometry. *Anal. Chem.* 40:2085.

14. SLATER, J.V. & A.M. ELLIOTT. 1951. Volume change in *Tetrahymena* in relation to age of the culture. *Proc. Amer. Soc. Protozool.* 2:20.

804 B.   Bioassay Procedures for *Daphnia* (TENTATIVE)

Daphnia have been used in tolerance studies for over a century. *Daphnia magna* is the largest of the *Daphnia*, reaching a maximum size of over 5 mm. Large numbers can be reared in a relatively small space. Neonates (first instar young) are 0.8 to 1.0 mm long and can be observed without optical aids. This stage has been used most commonly for tolerance studies.

1. General Considerations

Individual female *Daphnia magna* have been known to live for as long as 4 months when reared at 20 C. They have been cultured in natural waters and in tap water dechlorinated with activated carbon. Foods include bacteria, algae, and yeast, together with soil extracts and organic materials such as cotton seed meal, herring meal, powdered dried grass, and enriched trout fry granules. *Daphnia* have been reared individually in small vessels and in mass culture in large aquariums.[1-5] No one seems to have a defined medium that is satisfactory for long-term cultures.

Reproduction can be restricted to the production of females by diploid parthenogenesis when suitable culture conditions are maintained, thereby insuring a supply of experimental animals whose genetic variability is limited to the heterozygosity of the parent.[6] Genetic uniformity is expected within parthenogenetic clones derived from a single female.[7] When culture conditions are good *Daphnia magna* females release their first broods of young within 10 days when reared at 20 C and 7 days at 25 C. After their first broods young are released every 3 to 4 days at 20 C and 2 to 3 days at 25 C. Twenty or more young per brood are produced as long as culture conditions remain adequate. A single female may release over 400 young during her lifetime.

Daphnia may be obtained from established cultures or by field collection. While *Daphnia* of any age can be available at any time, it is more convenient to use neonates than older animals for tolerance assays because they do not need to be subjected to additional culturing. When reared at 20 C, they undergo their first ecdysis about 30 hr after release from the brood chamber and at 25 C about 20 hr. Neonates can be obtained by segregation from stock animals at 24-hr intervals when reared at 20 C and at 12-hr intervals at 25 C. Neonates are less tolerant of many substances than older animals. *Daphnia* are more susceptible to most substances at ecdysis than between molts. The actual volume of ten neonates in 100 ml test solution as recommended for testing is about 1:100,000 in contrast to that usually recommended for fish of 1 to 3 g/l or 1:2000.

The Water Quality Criteria Data Book[8] suggests that results obtained by different investigators using *Daphnia* are comparable and in general, *Daphnia* are less tolerant of toxic substances than are fish.

2. Culturing

a. General procedures: Of the various culture media that have been used for rearing *Daphnia*, one of the simplest is the manure-soil medium developed by Banta and modified by Anderson[3,10] by supplementing it periodically with yeast. Make this medium by mixing 5 g dried sheep manure, 25 g garden soil or sandy muck, and 1 l pond, spring, or tap water. Let stand for 2 days at room temperature, then strain through bolting cloth with mesh openings of approximately 0.15 mm. During straining, work some of the finer soil particles through the cloth. Set the filtrate aside for a week or more and discard the residue. To make the final medium, mix one part filtrate with six to eight parts pond, spring, or dechlorinated tap water. The original filtrate may be kept indefinitely before the final medium is made.

The final medium can be used for individual or mass culturing. For individual rearing, dispense 100 ml medium into 125-ml (4-oz) wide-mouth flint glass bottles or equivalent vessels and inoculate with one daphnid per bottle. Beginning 1 day after inoculation, add 1 ml of a suspension containing 1 mg active dry yeast in water to each bottle on alternate days. This provides the optimum quantity of yeast for maximum reproduction. Mass rearing may be carried out conveniently in 3.8-l (1-gal) wide-mouth glass jars filled with 3 l medium to which a suspension of 30 mg active dry yeast is added on alternate days. Once the cultures are initiated, the culture medium need not be changed. Add water from time to time to replace that lost by evaporation and in removal of young. To retard evaporation, cover the vessels with a perforated cover that permits diffusion of air. Aeration is unnecessary since the critical oxygen concentration for *Daphnia* is less than 15% of saturation at 20 C.

The above method of culturing produces a good yield of neonates. With a stock of 100 individually reared stock females, over 300 neonates can be available daily. When the stock females begin reproducing, remove the young at periodic intervals, preferably every 24 hr at 20 C or 12 hr at 25 C. When the stock animals reach old age and the reproductive rate drops, replace them with young females in fresh media.

b. Alternative procedures: Other methods of culturing such as those using algae, developed by Parker and Dewey,[4] have been used with success. Biesinger and Christensen[5] have developed a medium consisting of a suspension of 0.5 g cerophyll and 10 g enriched trout fry granules in 250 ml of unpolluted lake, well, or river water mixed vigorously in a blender for 5 min. The suspension is then strained through a stainless steel screen with about 0.066-cm openings and an additional 50 ml water is added to rinse the blender. The suspension is refrigerated. Before a portion is withdrawn the suspension is thoroughly mixed. It is fed at the rate of 1 ml/wk/l.

3. Bioassay Procedures

a. Static tests:

1) Setting up the tests—Prepare test materials, dilution water, and toxicant solutions as described in Sections 801D.2 and 3. Select test concentration as described in Section 801D.3*b*. Make up the test solutions and controls in 100-ml quantities in 125-ml (4-oz) wide-mouth flint glass bottles or equivalent vessels.

2) Performing the assays—After the test solutions are prepared, segregate neonate *Daphnia* that have been released from the brood chambers of the mothers during the preceding 24 hr at 20 C or 12 hr at 25 C from the stock animals and collect in one vessel. Wash these in three changes of diluent water, allowing 5 min in each to reduce the carryover of materials from the culture medium to the test solutions. Introduce 10 neonates into each of the test vessels and the control. Use a piece of 8-mm glass tubing 20 cm long, with one end drawn to a diameter of 2 mm and the other end fire-polished and fitted with a 2-ml-capacity rubber bulb, for collecting and transferring neonates. Use tubing of the same diameter and length, with both ends fire-polished and fitted with a rubber bulb, for handling adults.

After the neonates are introduced to the test solutions, observe them periodically on a regular basis, usually after 1, 2, 4, 8, and 16 hr on the first day and daily thereafter. Record the number of motile animals in each test vessel. An animal is considered immotile if it shows no viable movement even after a test vessel is rotated. Nonmotile animals are not necessarily dead. At threshold concentrations of such substances as ethanol, acetone, and chlorobutanol, animals may show no movement and the heart may have ceased to beat but on transfer to the diluent water they will recover. Obviously, however, if such animals are maintained in the test medium they will die. Continue observations for 5 days or as long as most of the animals in some of the test solutions remain motile. Run tests in triplicate.

Do not feed the test animals during the tests. *Daphnia* will live for as long as a week without food in well-balanced salt solutions.[11] If the animals are not fed during the tests, food materials need not be taken into consideration in interpreting the results.

b. Long-term tests:

1) Determination of reproductive impairment—Reproduction may be impaired at much lower concentrations of toxicants than those causing acute toxicity, sometimes as low as 0.0003 of that producing acute toxicity. Precede these tests by acute tolerance tests to establish the maximum concentration to be used.

2) Preparation of the test medium—Prepare the test medium in the same way as the regular culture medium, except that the water should be representative of that receiving the effluent discharge in the case of a specific pollution problem. Prepare a series of six to ten 1-l quantities of the final medium to which graded amounts of the toxicant have been added. The highest concentration of the toxicant should be that required for the LC50 or EC50 at 96 hr. Reduce each successive concentration in a geometric progression by a factor of three or more in preliminary experiments. Finally, use one 1-l quantity of culture medium without toxicant for control. Dispense each liter of test medium in 100-ml quantities to each of 10 bottles.

3) Performing the assays—Segregate and collect neonate *Daphnia* as for static tests. Do not wash the animals because they are being transferred from one culture medium to another. Introduce one neonate into each bottle. On the following day and on alternate days thereafter, add a 1-ml suspension containing 1 mg active dry yeast to each bottle. Make daily observations and note dead or immobilized animals. As the animals grow and reproduce, remove the young and record the number. Replace water lost through removal of young and evaporation with diluent water. Continue the observations until the control animals have released at least six broods of young, which will take about 21 days at 25 C and 30 days at 20 C. In other respects, handle the animals as individual cultures of stock animals.

At the end of the observation period analyze the results and test for significance the differences in the number of young produced. Other items that may be considered are the time of appearance of the first broods and the number of broods.

If the number of young produced in the lowest concentration of the toxicant differ significantly from those in the controls, repeat the experiment with more reduced concentrations of the toxicant until no significant differences are obtained.

After reaching those concentrations of the toxicant where no differences are apparent between the experimentals and the controls in the number of young, number of broods, and time of appearance of the first broods, conduct a final set of experiments with 30 or more animals in each of four concentrations of the toxicant bracketed about the lowest concentration for which significant differences in young production were found with an equal number of animals for the control.

4. Reporting Results

Assemble, analyze, evaluate, and report data as described in Section 801F.

5. References

1. NEEDHAM, J.G. et al. 1937. Culture Methods for Invertebrate Animals. Comstock Publishing Company. Reprinted by Dover Publ., Inc. New York, N.Y.

2. NAUMANN, E. 1933. *Daphnia magna* Straus als Versuchstier. *Kgl. Fysiogr. Sallsk. Lund Forhandl.* 3:15.

3. ANDERSON, B.G. 1944. The toxicity thresholds of various substances found in industrial wastes as determined by the use of *Daphnia magna. Sewage Works J.* 16:1156.

4. PARKER, B.L. & J.E. DEWEY. 1969. Further improvements on the mass rearing of *Daphnia magna. J. Econ. Entomol.* 62:725.

5. BIESINGER, K.E. & G.M. CHRISTENSEN. 1972. Effects of various metals on survival, growth, reproduction and metabolism of *Daphnia magna. J. Fish. Res. Board Can.* 29:1691.

6. BACCI, G., G. COGNETTI & A.M. VACCARI. 1961. Endomeiosis and sex determination in *Daphnia pulex. Experientia* 17:505.

7. HEBERT, P.P. & R.D. WARD. 1972. Inheritance during parthenogenesis in *Daphnia magna. Genetics* 71:639.

8. KEMP, H.T., J.P. ABRAMS & R.C. OVERBECK. 1971. Water Quality Criteria Data Book Vol. 3. Effects of Chemicals on Aquatic Life, Selected Data from the Literature through 1968. EPA Water Pollution Center Research Ser. 18050GWV05/71, U.S. Government Printing Off. Washington, D.C.

9. ANDERSON, B.G. 1946. The toxicity thresholds of various sodium salts determined by the use of *Daphnia magna. Sewage Works J.* 18:82.

10. ANDERSON, B.G. 1950. The apparent thresholds of toxicity to *Daphnia magna* for chlorides of various metals when added to Lake Erie water. *Trans. Amer. Fish. Soc.* 78:96.

11. STAMPER, W.R. 1969. The determination of the optimal combination of concentrations of sodium, potassium, calcium and magnesium chlorides for the survival of *Daphnia pulex.* Ph. D. thesis, The Pennsylvania State Univ.

804 C.   Bioassay Procedures for the Calanoid Copepod, *Acartia tonsa* (Dana) (TENTATIVE)

This method provides bioassay data on the effects of toxicants on a marine copepod, *Acartia tonsa*. General bioassay procedures that apply to copepods are described in Sections 801C, D and E.

1. Collecting and Holding Test Organisms

a. Collection: Collect *Acartia tonsa* by towing at ≥4 km/hr a plankton net (aperture 150 to 250 μm) at a depth of 1 to 3 m. Transfer the animals carefully to insulated containers three-fourths filled with ambient seawater. Their density should not exceed 250/l to assure that the dissolved oxygen concentration remains adequate if the organisms are not returned to the laboratory within 1 to 2 hr. Measure and record the temperature, salinity, dissolved oxygen, and pH at the time of the collection because these values must be maintained during the initial stages of holding.

b. Holding: Immediately upon return to the laboratory, transfer the samples to 2.3 l (190×100 mm) borosilicate crystalizing dishes. Adjust the volume of water in each dish to 2 l with filtered seawater at ambient temperature and salinity and add the algal diet for adult copepods, described in ¶2*b* below, in the quantity necessary to attain the density of organisms listed in Table 804:I. Incubate the cultures at the temperature of the water at point of collection and illuminate as described in Section 801D.3*f*. After 24 hr, begin to acclimate the cultures to 20 C and 20 $^0/_{00}$ salinity. Salinity and temperature changes in increments of 3 $^0/_{00}$ and 3 C/day are satisfactory. If organisms are to remain in the original vessel during acclimation, alternately siphon off and then add seawater of a different salinity. Transfer organisms either by pipetting or siphoning to new vessels. During acclimation, maintain a daily feeding schedule to provide the density of algae listed in Table 804:I.

c. Sorting and identification: The plankton tows contain a mixture of species from which *Acartia tonsa* must be isolated. For basic information on the taxonomy and biology of the genus *Acartia* and other coastal calanoids consult other sources.[1-6] To facilitate capture of the copepods, reduce the culture volume from 2.0 l to 0.5 l by slowly siphoning the seawater, with a 150-μm

plankton netting screen over the siphon intake. Carefully draw individual adults up into a wide-bore (≥ 2 mm) transfer pipet and place in depression slides. Identify and transfer to food-enriched filtered seawater of 20 $^0/_{00}$ at 20 C [see ¶2*a*1) and Section 801C.4*c*1)b)]. Exclude all nauplii and juvenile forms in order to eliminate undesired species.

d. Water supply:

1) Natural water—Use Niskin or Van Dorn samplers to collect seawater from 3 to 10 m depth to avoid collecting contaminated surface water. Record salinity, dissolved oxygen, and pH at the time of collection. Transport collected seawater to the laboratory in glass or polyethylene carboys that have been aged in seawater. In the laboratory, filter the water through a 1.0-μm acid-washed filter (glass fiber, cellulose-acetate, nylon, or polycarbonate) to remove particulate matter. Rinse the containers with deionized water, fill with the filtered seawater, and store at 4 C.

2) Artificial seawater—See Section 801C.4*b*2) for standard artificial seawater. There are two seawater requirements for the maintenance and culturing of copepods and other zooplankters. First, there is the need for water to perform the bioassays. The seawater for this function should, if possible, be collected

TABLE 804:I. COMPOSITION OF ALGAL DIET AND RECOMMENDED CONCENTRATIONS FOR ADULT AND NAUPLIAR FEEDING AND EGG-LAYING

Species	Adult & Copepodite	Naupliar	Egg-Laying
Skeletonema costatum	5.0×10^6	5.0×10^5	1.5×10^7
Thalassiosira pseudonana	7.0×10^6	7.0×10^5	2.1×10^7
Isochrysis galbana	5.0×10^6	5.0×10^5	1.5×10^7
Rhodomonas baltica	3.0×10^6	3.0×10^5	9.0×10^6
Total cells/l of copepod culture	2.0×10^7	2.0×10^6	6.0×10^7

from the study area. Further, this seawater, when adjusted to 20 ^{0}/oo salinity and 20 C, must support survival of the adult copepod *Acartia tonsa* for at least 96 hr.

The second requirement is that the seawater must support the complete life cycle of the copepod and, with proper enrichments, the growth of food algae. If no suitable natural seawater is available, use the synthetic seawater formulation described in Section 801C.4*b*2). This formulation has been used for both whole life cycle cultures and numerous bioassay studies. Heinle[6] found the commercial seawater Instant Ocean® suitable for the culture of both *A. tonsa* and *Eurytemora affinis*. Algal bioassays indicate that this product is unsuitable for bioassays involving heavy metals. It is recommended only for culture and not for bioassays until more extensive comparative data are available.

2. Culturing of Test Organisms

a. Production of food for test organisms:

1) *Culture medium for algae*—See Section 801C.4*c*1)b) for the medium for the culture of marine algae.

2) Growth chambers—Algal cultures may be grown either in standard screwcapped test tubes, flask cultures, or in the fill-and-draw semicontinuous system described below.

3) Culturing and harvesting algae for food—Grow algae for feeding copepods and other zooplankton in filtered natural or synthetic seawater at 20 ‰ salinity and 20 C with 2,500 to 5,000 lux continuous illumination or 14 hr of daylight and 10 hr darkness (14L:10D).

Use the nutrient enrichments of Guillard and Ryther.[7]

Dispense enriched seawater [see Section 801C.4*c*1)b)] into screwcapped test tubes (50 ml) or Erlenmeyer flasks. After autoclaving for 15 min at 1.1 kg/cm^2 and 121 C, cool the medium and equilibrate with atmospheric gases for 48 hr. Make sterility checks as described in Section 801C.4*c*1)a).

The recommended algal culture system is a fill-and-draw type where cultures are easily maintained near their maximum log-phase cell density and growth rate (Figure 804:1) It is then a simple operation to draw off medium and organisms and replace with fresh medium so that the culture will have reached the same cell density within 24 hr. When longer than 24-hr intervals occur between harvests, proportionally greater amounts of culture are drawn off and replaced. Furthermore, it is easy to scale this system up or down depending on food needs, but most important, this system produces algal food that is physiologically and nutritionally consistent. Thus, the nutritional history of the test species is more effectively controlled. Keep a series of tube cultures of each of the four algal foods concurrently in case of contamination of the large cultures.

Algal cell densities may be determined by direct microscopic counts using a hemacytometer, Palmer-Maloney chamber, or Utermohl chamber (inverted microscope).[8,9] An electronic particle counter is an accurate and rapid method for determining unialgal densities. If visual counts are necessary, it is useful to relate these to specific absorbance at 400 nm or 665 nm with a spectrometer. A curve that compares cells

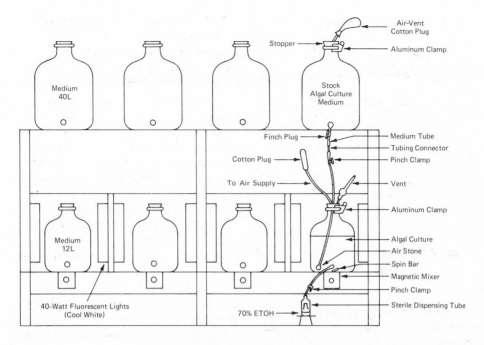

Figure 804:1. Algal culture system.

per milliliter with absorbancy can be used to replace the cell count.

b. Mass culture of test organisms: The objective of this system is to provide large quantities of *Acartia tonsa* of standard age for bioassays.

1) Growth chambers—The mass culture unit is derived from culture systems used by Mullin and Brooks[10] and Frost.[11] The culture vessel in Figure 804:2 is a pyrex aspirator bottle. Its size can range from 13 to 45 l, depending on the number of copepods needed. The contents are mixed gently by a low-rpm motor (≤ 25 rpm) with a stirring rod mounted above the culture vessel. The slow mixing maintains algal food in suspension where the planktonic copepods

normally feed. Water movement must be gentle and free of vortices such as those produced by magnetic stirrers. Cool white fluorescent lights provide 1,000 lux illumination incident to the culture surface on a 14L:10D cycle.

A continuous-flow system, Figure 804:3, with the following basic design criteria works equally well. A cylindrical vessel (15 to 40 l) is fitted with a standpipe and drain. The standpipe is collared with 200-μm nitex screen to prevent loss of eggs and nauplii. A low-rpm motor (≤ 25 rpm) with stirrer is mounted above the culture vessel. Filtered seawater is added by a peristaltic pump or siphon from a constant-head tank at a rate of 1 to 3 tank volumes ev-

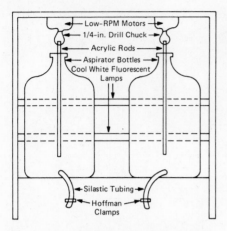

Figure 804:2. Apparatus for mass copepod culture (static).

ery 24 hr. Feeding is accomplished by mixing the four algal species (Table 804:I) in a single container and introducing them into the culture chambers by means of a pump, Figure 804:3, at a rate necessary to maintain a food cell density of 2 to 5×10^7 cells/l. The low-rpm stirring rod should be so placed in the culture vessel that the lower 25% of the vessel receives only gentle mixing. This permits a quiet area for mating and egg laying and keeps sediment from being stirred up and clogging the nitex screening. Drain and clean the system every 3 to 4 wk. Brush the nitex screen collar daily with a fine brush to avoid clogging.

2) Algal diet for copepods—Although various algal diets have been used for copepod cultures[9,12-14] the following modification of Wilson and Parrish's algal diet,[15] Table 804:I, is recommended. *Skeletonema costatum* has been added because it is a naturally-occurring food for *Acartia tonsa*.

3) Setting up cultures of test organisms—*Acartia tonsa* females are capable of producing more than 30 eggs each per day when fed the food ration recommended in Table 804:I. Thus, if 250 or more gravid females are kept as breeders, theoretically over 5,000 eggs will be produced within 24 hr. For this potential number of adults, a 40-l culture vessel would be desirable. Generally, the relationship between milliliters of culture and organism density is 10:1.

For the production and collection of copepod eggs, use generation cages (Figure 804:4). They consist of a plexiglass cylinder 125 mm in diameter and 90 mm high, one end of which is covered with plankton netting having an aperture size of 250 μm. Place this cylinder in a 2.3-l (190×100 mm) crystalizing dish with the covered end 25 mm from the bottom. Supply the crystalizing dish with 2 l of filtered seawater or artificial seawater. Place 50 to 100 gravid females in each screen-bottom cylinder and feed three times the adult algal diet (Table 804:I). The plankton netting allows eggs to pass through and hatch in the crystalizing dish where they are protected from predation by the adults. After 24 hr remove the adults by gently lifting each generation cage out of the crystalizing dish and quickly immersing it in another dish with three times the usual food density. Carefully siphon the remaining seawater from all dishes containing eggs and nauplii into a glass aspirator bottle containing filtered seawater. Adjust the final volume and feed the nauplioid culture as indicated in Table 804:I. If a second mass culture is desired, repeat the procedure after 24 hr, using the required number of generation cages to produce the needed organisms.

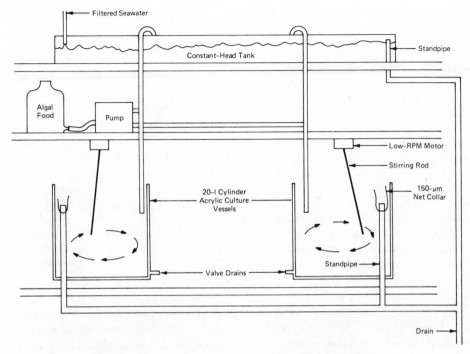

Figure 804:3. Apparatus for mass copepod culture (flowing).

The average length of each developmental stage in the life cycle of *Acartia tonsa* at 20 C and 20 °/oo is as follows:

Stage	Length in Days
Egg (newly oviposited)	1
Nauplius (6 instars)	7
Copepodite (6 instars)	6
Adult (until gravid)	3
Total life cycle	17

During the first 6 days of mass culture only naupliar stages are present. Daily feeding should be at 2×10^6 cells/l. On the third and seventh days, slowly siphon off 50% of the culture medium and replace with clean medium, with the intake end of the siphon covered with 60-μm netting to prevent loss of nauplii.

After the seventh day, copepodites should be present. From this time on, feed 2×10^7 cells/l/day with 50% replacement of the culture volume with filtered seawater every third day as described above. Within 16 to 17 days the population will have reached maturity and can be used for bioassays or to start new cultures. Average adult life span at 20 C is approximately 30 days.

It is desirable to maintain a non-age-standardized mass culture in reserve. Use gravid females from the original generation cages to start a 12-l (3.5-gal) system. Feed the adult food ration and replace 50% of the culture water every third day. In addition, harvest approximately one-third of the culture, including organisms, periodically (10 to 14

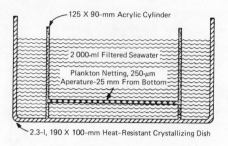

125 X 90-mm Acrylic Cylinder

2 000-ml Filtered Seawater

Plankton Netting, 250-μm
Aperature-25 mm From Bottom

2.3-l, 190 X 100-mm Heat-Resistant Crystallizing Dish

Figure 804:4. Generation cage (after Heinle).

days) to keep the population at about 50 adults and copepodites per liter. This precaution is worth the effort since high-density cultures occasionally experience precipitous decline in numbers for no apparent reason.

4) Harvesting test organisms—Harvest mass cultures of copepods that have reached the adult stage as follows: Reduce the culture volume 75% using a slow siphon with its intake covered with 60- μm plankton netting. Transfer carefully the remaining 25% of the culture, including organisms, to 2.3-l pyrex crystalizing dishes to provide a total volume of 2 l/dish. This transfer is critical and is best performed as follows. Because of the fragility of the organism, do not construct the discharge tube to reduce flow. Control the discharge flow through the ventral tubulation on the aspirator bottle (Figure 804:2) by minimizing the head pressure between the culture vessel and the crystalizing dish. A slow flow minimizes turbulence and the opportunity for organisms to collide with vessel walls.

Harvested animals can be further concentrated in the crystalizing dishes by siphoning off the culture medium. Cap-

ture is facilitated by using the positive photatic response of the test species.

5) Other organisms—The above culture system, while designed for *Acartia tonsa*, has worked well for *Eurytemora affinis* and *Pseudodiaptomus coronatus*. However, the generation cages were suitable only for *A. tonsa* because it releases eggs individually. Both *E. affinis* and *P. coronatus* produce egg sacs.

3. Bioassay Procedures

With adult *A. tonsa* and the previously described culture method, the short-term bioassays are performed as follows:

a. Range-finding bioassays: Use 10 adult *Acartia* per replicate with three replicates per test concentration and control. For a test container, use a suitable flat-bottom borosilicate glass dish containing 100 ml seawater. The depth of medium must be ≥2.0 cm. Generally, a broad range of concentrations is used (see Sections 801D.3b and 801E.2a). Prepare toxicant solutions as described in 801D.2b. Capture 10 adult *Acartia* for each test chamber from stock cultures with a wide-bore transfer pipet and transfer to a 20-ml beaker containing 5 ml filtered seawater. Adjust the final volume of this beaker to 15 ml. Add the animals and the 15 ml of medium to 85 ml of toxicant-dosed medium in the test chamber by immersing the beaker and gently rinsing. The exposure period is 96 hr. Observe and record the number of dead, moribund, and living copepods after 1.5, 3, 6, 12, 24, 48, 72, and 96 hr of exposure. To ascertain if a motionless animal is dead, touch it gently with a sealed glass capillary probe. Control mortalities in excess of 15% invalidate the experiment. Analyze results as directed in Section 801F.

b. Definitive short-term bioassays: General culture conditions and handling follow those described in Sections 801C and 801D. The specification for this assay is as follows. Test 15 adults in each of four replicate test vessels per toxicant concentration and control. Select test concentrations of toxicants as described in Section 801D.3*b*. Expose the animals and collect data as described in Sections 801D and E.

4. Calculating, Analyzing, and Reporting Results

Calculations, data presentation, and expression of results are as described in Section 801F.

5. References

1. CONOVER, R.J. 1956. Oceanography of Long Island Sound, 1952-1954. VI. Biology of *Acartia clausi* and *A. tonsa. Bull. Bingham Oceanogr. Coll.* 15:156.

2. HEINLE, D.R. 1966. Production of a calanoid copepod *Acartia tonsa*, in the Patuxent River Estuary. *Chesapeake Sci.* 7:59.

3. HEINLE, D.R. 1969. Effects of Temperature on the Population Dynamics of Estuarine Copepods. Ph.D. thesis, Univ. of Maryland, College Park.

4. WILSON, C.B. 1932. The Copepods of the Woods Hole Region, Massachusetts. Smithsonian Inst., U.S. National Museum Bull.

5. ROSE, M. 1933. Faune de France. No. 26. Copepodes Pelagiques. Librarie de la Faculte des Sci. Reprinted 1970 by Kraus Reprint, Nendeln Luchtenstein.

6. HEINLE, D.R. 1969. Culture of calanoid copepods in synthetic seawater. *J. Fish. Res. Board Can.* 26:150.

7. GUILLARD, R.R. & J.H. RYTHER. 1962. Studies of marine planktonic diatoms. I *Cyclotella nana* Hustedt and *Detonula confervacia* (Cleve) Grant. *Can. J. Microbiol.* 8:229.

8. PALMER, C.M. & T.E. MALONEY. 1954. A new counting slide for nannoplankton. *J. Amer. Soc. Limnol. Oceanogr.*, Spec. Publ. 21:1.

9. SCHWOERBEL, J. 1970. Methods of Hydrobiology. Pergamon Press, New York, N.Y.

10. MULLIN, M.M. & E.R. BROOKS. 1967. Laboratory culture, growth rate and feeding behavior of a planktonic marine copepod. *J. Amer. Soc. Limnol. Oceanogr.* 12:657.

11. FROST, B.W. 1972. Effects of size and concentration of food particles on the feeding behavior of the marine planktonic copepod *Calanus pacificus. J. Amer. Soc. Limnol. Oceanogr.* 17:805.

12. ZILLIOUX, E.J. & D.F. WILSON. 1966. Culture of a planktonic calanoid copepod through multiple generations. *Science* 151:996.

13. KATONA, S.K. 1970. Growth characteristics of the copepods *Eurytemora affinis* and *E. herdmani* in laboratory cultures. *Helgolander wiss. Meeresunters* 20:373.

14. NASSOGNE, A. 1970. Influence of food organisms on the development and culture of pelagic copepods. *Helgolander wiss. Meeresunters* 20:333.

15. WILSON, D.F. & K.K. PARRISH. 1971. Remating in a planktonic marine calanoid copepod. *Mar. Biol.* 9:202.

805   BIOASSAY PROCEDURES FOR SCLERACTINIAN CORAL (TENTATIVE)

The scleractinian corals* comprise one of the most conspicuous and important components of many tropical reef ecosystems. They are especially sensitive to environmental perturbations and are valuable indicator organisms for studies of water quality in shallow tropical marine environments.

The reef-forming corals flourish only within a narrow range of chemical and physical conditions. Those conditions generally considered favorable to coral reef development (clear water, low inorganic and organic nutrients, low sedimentation rate, tropical open-ocean temperature and salinity) are also widely regarded as desirable water quality.

In addition to their aesthetic value, corals are of great importance in the for-

mation of protecting reefs about islands and lagoons.[8] These massive structures provide an essential environment for many reef organisms that live on and within them and are the basis for an entire ecosystem. Unlike many other marine organisms, reef corals are slow to reestablish themselves; the process often requires decades. Once the rapidly calcifying corals have been killed, the unbalancing of the basic geomorphological process may lead to erosion and substantial environmental modification such that the area becomes permanently unsuited for coral recovery.

Corals lack the specialized circulatory and excretory systems of the higher animals that have been used in bioassays. This renders them highly sensitive to changes in their physical-chemical environment. Unlike most reef animals, corals cannot migrate or burrow to protect themselves from localized short-term environmental stress, nor can they isolate themselves temporarily from harsh conditions by withdrawing into a shell or tube.

---

*References for the identification of the scleractinian corals: Tropical Pacific—Unfortunately, no single reference exists for this region and in many respects the taxonomy is confused. The best introductory reference is Wells.[1] Other more comprehensive works are Wells,[2] Vaughan and Wells,[3] Crossland,[4] and Hickson.[5] The corals of Hawaii are described by Vaughan.[6] Tropical Atlantic—A complete general reference for this region has been published by Smith.[7]

---

805 A.   Selecting and Preparing Test Organisms

1. Suggested Test Species

a. *Tropical, Indo-Pacific Area* (species listed in order of their importance):

1) Branching *Acropora*
Acropora formosa (Dana)
Acropora is not present in Hawaii. The branching form of *Montipora verrucosa* Lamarck can be substituted.

2) Finely branched *Pocillopora*
Pocillopora damicornis (Linnaeus)
Synonyms: *Pocillopora caespitosa* Dana and *Pocillopora bulbosa*
Alternate: *Pocillopora brevicornis* Lamarck.

3) Branching *Porites*
Porites compressa Dana or small *Porites lobata* Dana
Alternate: *Porites andrewsi* Vaughan.

4) Recommended representative of the solitary hermatypic corals: *Fungia scutaria* Lamarck.

5) Recommended representative of the ahermatypic (lacking zooxanthellae) corals: *Tubastrea aurea* (Quoy and Giamard).

b. Tropical Atlantic Area (test groups listed in order of their importance):

1) Branching *Acropora*
Acropora cervicornis (Lamarck).

2) Branching *Porites*
Porites porites (Pallas)
Alternate: *Porites furcata* (Lamarck)
Pocillopora is not present in the Atlantic.

3) Other corals widely used in experimental work:
Meandrina meandrites (Linnaeus) forma *meandrites*
Montastrea annularis (Ellis & Solander)
Montastrea cavernosa (Linnaeus) forma *areolata*.

4) Recommended representative of the solitary hermatypic corals: *Scolymia lacera* (Pallas) formerly *Mussa lacera* (Pallas).

5) Recommended representative of the ahermatypic (lacking zooxanthellae) corals: *Tubastrea aurea* (Quoy and Giamard).

This list of recommended species is not intended to restrict the investigator's selection of test species, but rather to act as a guide in choosing test subjects.

2. Selecting Test Organisms

Because basic differences occur between the Caribbean and Indo-Pacific coral fauna, it can be difficult to find comparable species from the two areas. Wells[2] estimated that 36 species occur in the Caribbean as opposed to at least 500 for the Indo-Pacific area. Few of the coral species are common to both oceans. Genera intensively studied in the Indo-Pacific include *Acropora*, *Pocillopora*, *Porites*, and *Fungia*. The genera *Meandrina*, *Montastrea*, and *Manicina* are often used as laboratory subjects in the Caribbean.

Except for *Acropora cervicornis*, all of the suggested species have been used successfully as laboratory subjects. *Acropora cervicornis* is listed as the primary test species for the Atlantic because it is widely distributed, very sensitive, and similar to the important Indo-Pacific species *Acropora formosa*. Although *Acropora cervicornis* could eventually prove to be too delicate to maintain in some experimental systems, it has already been used in short-term laboratory studies[9] and in field transplants.[10] With proper care it should be possible to culture this species in the laboratory.

The ahermatypic corals do not contain symbiotic algae and long-term maintenance requires that *Tubastrea* be kept in flowing seawater with a source of plankton for food. Although this organism is not an important reef-former, it has been included in the list because it is common to both oceans and is lacking in symbiotic algae. It has been used as a comparison species in tests designed to assess the role of zooxanthellae in the hermatypic corals.[11]

Whenever possible, use the suggested species in order to allow for comparisons between various geographic locations. These species have been selected with regard to their previous use as laboratory subjects, widespread occurrence, and relative importance as reef-builders. The small-polyp forms have been given preference, since they tend to be sensitive to environmental disruption.[12]

In determining the adverse effects of water pollutants, the high species diversity of coral reefs dictates that intensive work be done on at least several genera. In addition to the recommended species, include members of other locally dominant species as well as species that may be suspected or determined to be the most sensitive to the stress or toxicant in question. Ideally, perform comparative tests to determine tolerance of all locally common species so that the most sensitive species can be used in the long-term studies.

3. Collecting, Handling, and Holding of Test Organisms

a. Field collection of corals: Guidelines for the operation of collecting boats in tropical reef areas are given by Domm.[13] Ideally, the field procurement program should produce large numbers of small, unattached specimens that are similar in size, morphology, genetic makeup, and environmental history. Extreme care must be taken in the selection of experimental specimens because corals display a wide variety of growth forms within a given species.[3, 14-16]

For the branching species, use a single large colony as the source of all specimens for a given experiment. Clip branch tips of approximately 10 g wet weight from the colony with pruning shears. Selection of specimens of solitary and massive corals will depend on local availability of specimens of suitable size. Unattached species, such as *Fungia*, are easily collected, whereas the massive and encrusting forms generally grow firmly attached to the reef and must be pried or

broken away with a pry bar or chisel. Because corals vary widely in size, morphology, and availability, it is difficult to give firm rules on methods of collection for all species. Often unattached specimens of massive and encrusting corals can be found in protected shallow areas having a gravel-like coral rubble bottom.

b. Field preparation: If the broken fragments are allowed to remain in a protected reef area where there is no heavy wave action to roll the fragments about, the coral tissue will cover the surface within a month and a small colony completely covered with living tissue is produced. The substrate in the holding area must consist of gravel-size reef rubble. The holding area should not be subject to abnormally high temperatures or to land runoff; thus, on unprotected coasts, it may be necessary to use a deep offshore area for holding. When facilities are available, the corals can be allowed to heal over in the laboratory seawater system.

Larger corals are easily tagged by tying commercially available vinyl "spaghetti" tags to the specimen. Monofilament tags can be used on small specimens. Small coral colonies readily overgrow a monofilament or vinyl strand and produces a solidly tagged colony.

c. Handling and holding corals: Because coral tissue is exposed and has no protection from damage by desiccation or abrasion, keep the animals submerged in seawater at all times and handle them lightly and only when necessary. When transferring corals from location to location, submerge the transfer container, place the coral in the container, and transport the submerged coral to its new location; then again submerge the container and remove the coral. If the coral is to be transported over a distance and must remain in a transfer container for more than 5 min, monitor dissolved oxygen and temperature. Oxygen should remain at saturation $\pm 10\%$ and temperature should not change by more than 1 C from ambient reef water conditions. A boat supplied with a live well is desirable for transportation. If a large volume of water is used to contain a small volume of coral, there is less danger of these limits being reached. Corals rapidly modify the chemistry of the water in containers and the tropical sun can cause rapid temperature increases in closed containers if they are not properly shaded.

It is better to renew the water in the containers at a rate sufficient to keep the dissolved oxygen and temperature within the safe levels, rather than to resort to aeration. It can be assumed that when dissolved oxygen has been altered adversely by coral metabolic activity, other biologically important characteristics of the water have also been affected adversely. Aeration will not correct these other changes, which can be equally important to the condition of the organisms.

d. Long-term holding: If corals are to be held for long periods of time in the laboratory, use a substrate of natural reef rubble with its associated organisms. Remove this material from the reef and use it to cover the bottom to a depth of 5 cm. Such a substrate prevents accumulation of detritus, allows circulation of water on the underside of the coral, and permits tissue to cover the fragment completely. In addition to the invertebrate herbivores that are included

with the coral rubble, it is useful to maintain small herbivorous fish (such as *Acanthurus triostegus*) in the tanks to control algal growth. Holding tanks should have a capacity of at least several hundred liters and be maintained by pumping a continuous flow of seawater favorable for coral growth at a rate sufficient to flush the tanks at a minimum of once every hour. If dissolved oxygen concentrations or temperatures between inlet and outlet change by more than 10% or 1 C, respectively, increase the flow rate so that these changes are not exceeded.

4. Culturing Test Organisms

a. Water supply: Take the seawater supply from an area that supports good, natural coral growths (Section 801C). For static studies, an artificial seawater can be used [Section 801C.4*b*2)].

Successful laboratory maintenance of corals requires the continuous flow of large amounts of uncontaminated open-ocean seawater. Use seawater system, pumps, piping, cleanouts, and delivery systems described in Sections 801C and D.

b. Food and feeding: The specific nutritional requirements of hermatypic corals are more complex than those of most other organisms. This is the result of the symbiotic relationship between the coral and the zooxanthellar algae contained within its tissue. It is also due to the rapid calcification process that produces the massive coral skeleton.

Symbiotic algae utilize sunlight to produce food. A portion of this material is transferred to the coral.[17] In addition, corals are known to capture plankton,[18] are capable of digesting bacteria[19, 20] and of absorbing dissolved organics from the water.[20,21] Coral also takes up various inorganic nutrients (e.g., bicarbonate ion) for the calcification process and certain inorganic plant nutrients.[22-25] Corals kept in full sunlight continue to grow in filtered, continuous-flow seawater systems but cease to grow and eventually die if deprived of light but still supplied with unfiltered seawater.[11,26] Presumably all nutritional requirements of corals can be met by keeping them in full sunlight and supplied with a constant flow of seawater from the reef.

Feeding behavior is an important response that should be observed during tests. The carnivorous feeding habits of 15 Pacific species of corals have been described by Abe.[27] In the Atlantic, *Manicina areolata*, *Montastrea carvernosa*, and *Porites porites* have been used in feeding studies[28,29] and will readily ingest freshly hatched nauplii of the brine shrimp, *Artemia*. Zooplankton captured with a fine mesh net also can be used.

5. Parasites and Predators

For a general discussion, see Section 801C.5.

The known coral parasites and predators have been reviewed by Robertson.[30] In the laboratory, these may become very damaging to experimental corals. Many such organisms can enter laboratory tanks in larval form from the seawater system and grow rapidly to maturity there while feeding on coral tissue. White patches will appear, especially on the undersides of the coral, when predators are present and feeding. Generally, predators will be attached to the coral adjacent to damaged areas. Several predators are potentially dangerous in laboratory situations. Corals of the genus *Montipora*, and possible other Acroporids, are attacked by the Polyclad flatworm *Prosthiostomum*.[31] *Porites* is eaten by the aeolid nudibranch *Phestilla sibogae*, while *Tubastrea* is eaten by a similar species, *Phestilla melanobranchia*.[32] *Fungia* is attacked by the wentletrap *Epitomium ulu*.[33] If predators of these types appear, it is generally quite easy to remove them by drawing them into an ordinary household basting pipet. Damaged specimens of larval corals, as well as adult corals, may be destroyed by holotrich ciliate protozoa,[34] although in most locations such infestations are rare.

805 B.   Bioassay Procedures

1. General Considerations

Many coral reef communities are "biologically accommodated," rather than "physically controlled."[35] Corals rapidly modify the water chemistry of closed systems with respect to components such as nutrients, dissolved oxygen, and CO₂, and special attention must be given to loading (Section 801D.3*d*). Although corals have been maintained for several months in closed recirculating systems using carbonate and charcoal filters,[36-38] the water chemistry of such systems may depart significantly from that of the natural environment. Laboratory lighting systems needed to simulate reef environments tend to elevate water temperatures greatly during the experimental period. Because of these factors, continuous-flow systems are required for long-term experiments. For facilities, equipment, and construction materials, see Sections 801C.3 and 4 and 801D.1.

2. Preparing Test Materials

a. Dilution water: Tropical open ocean surface water is generally available to most coral investigators and it is perhaps the best dilution medium for bioassay studies. Take the water from an offshore area, away from strong terrestrial influence (see Sections 801B, C, and D).

b. Toxicant solutions: See Section 801D.2*b*.

c. Test organisms: See Sections 801C and D for general procedures.

3. Test Procedures and Conditions

For general procedures, see Section 801D. Use at least 20 coral colonies in each of the concentrations being tested and in the controls. The number and size of the exposure chambers will be governed by the size of the colonies in the tests. Load as indicated in 801D.3*c*. Select toxic concentrations to be tested as described in Section 801D.3*b*. Because of the special requirements for corals, the volume of water delivered to the exposure chamber each hour should equal the volume of water in the chamber and should be constant in flow with variation of not more than 5%. Toxicant delivery systems for flow-through tests and test dilutions should be as described in Section 801D.1. Keep the test chambers clean. Maintain salinity at 33 to 35.0 $^o/_{oo}$ or that of the area from which the coral were collected. Hold temperatures at 27.0 ± 1 C or at those in the natural habitat. Keep dissolved oxygen at saturation in the water holding reservoirs and head boxes and do not let it vary more than $\pm 10\%$ in the test chambers. The pH may vary from 8.1 to 8.4. Use the light source described in Section 801D.3*f* with a mid-day intensity at the water surface. The top of the coral colonies should be at least 2 cm below the water surface. Illumination should be for tropical conditions, 12 hr light and 12 hr dark with appropriate twilight periods morning and evening (Section 801D.3*f*). Supply a source of nutrients in long-term studies. Some species need sources of energy other than sunlight. The need for animal food varies between species and probably with environmental conditions within a single species. When animal food is needed, feed as described in Section 805A.4*b*.

4. Conducting the Bioassays

Conduct the different types of bioassays as described in Section 801E. Conduct flow-through test of effluent under local conditions of light, temperature, and water chemistry. Carry out tests in large outdoor aquariums exposed to full sunlight. Supply tanks with a continuous flow of seawater pumped from the intended body of receiving water at a rate sufficient to maintain temperature within 1 C and DO within 10% of that of the receiving water body.

Measure the physical, chemical, and biological characteristics of the water frequently and include the results in the bioassay report. The light intensity (especially ultraviolet) in shallow tanks can be excessive. Light levels at the intended depth can be simulated by screening part of the natural light with a filter such as fiberglass window screening.[39, 40]

Treat coral colonies used in the bioassay tests as described in Sections 805A.3b and c. Acclimate coral fragments that have developed polyps on all sides in the holding facilities for 30 days before use in the bioassays. If more than 10% of the colonies exhibit damage, discard them and use a new group of colonies. Because it will not be known if corals used in a particular test are functionally autotrophic or heterotrophic[24] under stress conditions, it might be necessary in some cases to run duplicate series for each concentration with and without a source of zooplankton. Zooplankton may be field-collected or reared in the laboratory as described in Section 804C.2.

Uniformity in the size of colonies is desirable. Each should weigh approximately 10 g wet weight, or more when space permits.

The various life stages of corals have been photographed[34] and described.[41, 42] Coral planulae have been used successfully to assay relative wastewater toxicity.[43] The advantage of using larvae in bioassay tests is their small size, because small containers and large numbers of organisms can be used. However, the free planula is quite unlike the adult colonies; it is a noncalcifying, nonfeeding, solitary planktonic organism with a certain degree of mobility. Planulae may not predict accurately the effects of environmental alterations on adult colonies. In some species, planulae may be the most resistant life stage.[42]

Planulae are not always available because certain species show seasonal periodicity.[44-49] Attempts to obtain planulae from some species have failed,[42] probably because reproduction is infrequent. Planulae usually can be obtained from *Pocillopora damicornis* in the Pacific and from *Agaricia agaricites* in the Atlantic. Gather planulae by collecting mature coral heads and placing them in an aquarium with a continuous flow of seawater. Pass the outlet water from the aquarium into a submerged upright cylinder closed at the ends with plankton netting. Planulae expelled by the coral polyps are retained in the cylinder where they can be kept for several days until needed.[50] Release of planulae has been stimulated by warming the water to 35 C for a few minutes.[41, 42] However, this is not recommended because it tends to produce damaged and immature specimens.

Conduct static bioassays with planulae in 150-ml pyrex beakers containing 100 ml of the test solution and then hold in a water bath or air-conditioned room under conditions described previously in this section. Use flow-through systems for medium- and long-term studies. Conduct these bioassays in 100-ml or larger glass containers, tightly covered with plankton mesh and containing 20 organisms. Circulate the test solution through the container at a rate sufficient to renew the water every hour.

Because some planulae will settle in the containers, setting success can also be measured by this technic. The extremely high mortality involved in setting and early colony growth[50, 51] indicate that in many instances this life stage is most sensitive to environmental disruption.

Coral larvae can be settled on glass slides[4, 27] to produce new colonies for use as bioassay subjects. Newly settled corals can be subjected to the recommended test for planulae described previously.

805 C.   Evaluating and Reporting Results

1. Lethal Response

Most corals are colonial; therefore, they present a problem as to what should be counted as one individual organism. Although coral fragments differ in total number of polyps, a lethal concentration will generally kill all polyps and thus allow treatment of the colony as an individual. Interdependence between polyps has been suggested by various investigators.[50, 52] Exceptions seem to be the result of a strong gradient of a factor affecting only one portion of the colony. For example, accumulation of sediments around the base of the colony may kill only those polyps that it contacts. High light intensity may interact with other factors and kill only the exposed polyps. Generally, these problems do not occur with proper experimental design.

Death of the colony becomes obvious when the polyps are insensitive to stimulation and opaque in appearance. Within a few hours after death, corals begin to disintegrate. At the end of a test the corals can be returned to optimal conditions and observed for recovery.

2. Visible Sublethal Effects

Healthy corals generally contain dense concentrations of zooxanthellae, which contain plant pigments that give the polyps a characteristic coloration. In response to sublethal concentrations of certain forms of stress, the zooxanthellae are extruded over a period of hours or days, leaving the polyps transparent. This effect has been reported as a response to high temperature, low light intensity, and starvation,[26] as well as to runoff of fresh water and silt[53] and estuarine effluents.[54]

Under some conditions, the first sign of damage is destruction of the thin tissue covering the septae or cenosarc. In such cases the skeleton can be seen through lesions in the tissue. Some corals will extrude mesenterial filaments when subjected to stress.

Irritated or damaged corals may produce large amounts of mucus. Often, distressed corals will contract their polyps during periods when they normally would be expanded. Edmondson[55] and Mayer[56] reported that corals cease feeding long before lethal temperatures are reached and such information indicates that this is a realistic measure of safe temperatures. It has been observed that Samoan corals, which are exposed to pesticides, show abnormal feeding behavior long before death occurs.

A method of using carmine granules to observe ciliary currents on the surfaces of corals is described by Abe;[27] this offers a potentially useful technic for observing signs of distress (i.e., inhibited movement of materials over the tissue surface in some species of corals.)

805 D.   Other Types of Bioassays

In situ field measurement of biological response can be used in support of the laboratory bioassay. Often sophisticated laboratory systems needed to maintain corals for extended time periods are not available, necessitating field experiments. In other instances, it is useful to supplement laboratory work with field studies. Transplanting corals into a polluted or otherwise unfavorable environment is a powerful investigative technic that has frequently been used to evaluate coral response to various environmental factors or changes.[10, 14, 16, 57-59]

Location of the transplant stations should be based on the following criteria: (a) the stations should span extreme gradients of the factor to be studied, from an area where all living corals have been eliminated to an area of good coral development and (b) the stations should be similar in all respects (depth, wave action, salinity, substrate type, etc.) except for the specific gradient factors under study.

An ideal platform for attachment of transplanted coral is a section of commercially available vinyl-coated steel wire fencing material, firmly anchored to the reef with iron stakes or concrete blocks. The corals can be tied to the platform with plastic-coated electrical wire, allowing them to be replaced or removed for weighing or other analyses. In areas of fine sediment, the frame should be supported off the bottom, unless sedimentation is the factor being investigated.

Select, handle, tag, and field-prepare specimens in the same manner as for laboratory bioassay. Larger heads weighing several hundred grams can be used because space is not limited.

Continue such studies for a minimum of 1 yr and check the corals for mortality, growth, or other responses at monthly intervals. Monitor the physical environment of the transplanted corals and include measurements of all biologically significant water quality factors such as salinity, temperature, dissolved oxygen, light, sediment load, dissolved plant nutrients, particulate matter, carbon, and dissolved organic carbon. Data gathered by this method can be used to draw conclusions about the effects of toxic effluents or other factors.

In situ measurements of coral calcification and oxygen metabolism have been carried out in submerged enclosures.[57, 60] This approach can be used in connection with field transplants. Corals can be exposed in situ on a small scale to such substances as sewage sludge, sediment, heated effluent, or thermal brine to determine tolerance. Such studies are valuable for determining the effects of competition between species under the changed environmental conditions. Does organic enrichment that is not lethal to the corals cause overgrowths of algae that largely eliminate them? What are the effects of increases in temperature? Are desired species replaced by less desired species that are favored by the changed environmental conditions? Answers to these questions can be obtained most readily by field studies. Such experiments do not require extensive laboratory facilities and can be used as rapid tests under actual field conditions.

805 E.   Handling Data and Calculating Results

Follow the procedures described in
Section 801F.

805 F.   References

1. WELLS, J.W. 1954. Recent corals of the Marshall Island, Bikini and nearby atolls. Part 2, Oceanogr. (Biologic). *Geol. Survey Paper* 260:385. Pl. 94-185. Washington, D.C.

2. WELLS, J.W. 1956. Scleractinia. In: Treatise on Invertebrate Paleontology (R.C. Moore, ed.). Geol. Soc. Amer. F328-F444.

3. VAUGHAN, T.W. & J.W. WELLS. 1943. Revision of the suborders, families and genera of the Scleractinia. *Geol. Soc. Amer. Spec. Papers* 44:1.

4. CROSSLAND, C. 1952. Madreporaria, Hydrocorallinae, Heliopora and Tubipora. Great Barrier Reef Expedition. VI:86. British Museum (Natural History).

5. HICKSON, S.J. 1924. An Introduction to the Study of Corals. Manchester Univ. Press, London & New York.

6. VAUGHAN, T.W. 1907. Recent Madreporaria of the Hawaiian Islands and Laysan. Smithsonian Inst., U.S. National Museum, Bull. LIX, Washington, D.C.

7. SMITH, F.G. 1971. Atlantic Reef Corals. Univ. of Miami Press.

8. YONGE, C.M. 1963. The biology of coral reefs. *Advan. Mar. Biol.* I (4):209.

9. PEARSE, V.B. & L. MUSCATINE. 1971. Role of symbiotic algae (zooxanthellae) in coral calcification. *Biol. Bull.* 141:350.

10. SHINN, E.A. 1966. Coral growth rate, an environmental indicator. *J. Paleontol.* 40:233.

11. FRANZISKET, L. 1969. Riffkorallen konnen autotroph leben. *Naturwissenschaften* 56.144.

12. FISHELSON, L. 1973. Ecological and biological phenomena influencing coral-species composition on the reef tables at Eilat (Gulf of Aquaba, Red Sea). *Marine Biol.* 19:183.

13. DOMM, S.B. 1971. The safe use of open boats in the coral reef environment. *Atoll Res. Bull.* 143:1.

14. WOOD-JONES, F. 1907. On the growth forms and supposed species in corals. *Zool. Soc. London, Proc.*, 518.

15. WOOD-JONES, F. 1910. Corals and Atolls. L. Reeve, London.

16. MARAGOS, J.E. 1972. A Study of the Ecology of Hawaiian Reef Corals. Ph.D. thesis, Univ. of Hawaii, Honolulu.

17. MUSCATINE, L. & E. CERNICHIARI. 1969. Assimilation of photosynthetic products of zooxanthellae by a reef coral. *Biol. Bull.* 137:506.

18. YONGE, C.M. 1973. The nature of reef-building (hermatypic) corals. *Bull. Mar. Sci.* 23:1.

19. DiSALVO, L.H. 1971. Ingestion and assimilation of bacteria by two scleractinian coral species. In: Experimental Coelenterate Biology (H.M. Lenhoff, L. Muscatine & L.V. Davis, eds.). p. 129. Univ. Hawaii Press, Honolulu, Hawaii.

20. SOROKIN, Y.I. 1973. On the feeding of some scleractinian corals with bacteria and dissolved organic matter. *J. Amer. Soc. Limnol. Oceanogr.* 18:380.

21. STEPHENS, G.C. 1962. Uptake of organic material by aquatic invertebrates. I. Uptake of glucose by the solitary coral *Fungia scutaria*. *Biol. Bull.* 123:648.

22. FRANZISKET, L. 1973. Uptake and accumulation of nitrate and nitrite by reef corals. *Naturwissenschaften* 60:552.

23. FRANZISKET, L. 1974. Nitrate uptake by reef corals. *Int. Rev. Gesamten Hydrobiol.* 59:1.

24. GOREAU, T.F., N.I. GOREAU & C.M. YONGE. 1971. Reef corals: autotrophs or heterotrophs? *Biol. Bull.* 141:247.

25. KAWAGUTI, S. 1953. Ammonia metabolism of the reef corals. *Biol. J. Okayama Univ.* 1:171.

26. YONGE, C.M. & A.G. NICHOLLS. 1931. Studies on the physiology of corals. IV. The structure, distribution and physiology of the zooxanthellae. *Sci. Rep. Great Barrier Reef Exped.* 1:135.

27. ABE, N. 1938. Feeding behavior and the nematocyst of *Fungia* and 15 other species of corals. *Palau Trop. Biol. Sta. Stud.* 1:469.

28. Coles, S.L. 1969. Quantitative estimates of feeding and respiration for three scleractinian corals. *J. Amer. Soc. Limnol. Oceanogr.* 14:949.

29. Lehman, J.T. & J.E. Porter. 1973. Chemical activation and feeding in the Caribbean reef-building coral *Montastrea cavernosa. Biol. Bull.* 145:140.

30. Robertson, R. 1970. Review of the predators and parasites of stony corals with special reference to symbiotic prosobranch gastropods. *Pac. Sci.* 24:43.

31. Jokiel, P.L. & S.J. Townsley. 1974. Biology of the polyclad *Prosthiostomum sp.*, a new coral parasite from Hawaii. *Pac. Sci.* 28:361.

32. Harris, L.G. 1971. Nudibranch associations as symbioses, In: Aspects of the Biology of Symbiosis (T.C. Cheng, ed.). p. 77. Univ. Park Press, Baltimore, Md.

33. Bosch, H.F. 1965. A gastropod parasite of solitary corals in Hawaii. *Pac. Sci.* 19:267.

34. Sisson, R.F. 1973. Life cycle of a coral captured in color. *Nat. Geogr. Mag.* 143:780.

35. Sanders, H.L. 1968. Marine benthic diversity: A comparative study. *Amer. Natur.* 102:243.

36. Abe, N. 1937. Post-larval development of the coral *Fungia actiniformis* var. *palawensis* Doderlein. *Palao Trop. Biol. Sta. Studies* 1:73.

37. Yonge, C.M., M.J. Yonge & A.G. Nicholls. 1932. Studies on the physiology of corals. VI. The relationship between respiration and the production of oxygen by their zooxanthellae. Rep. Great Barrier Reef Exped., British Museum (Natural History) p. 213.

38. Catala, R. 1964. Carnival Under the Sea. R. Sicard, Paris, France.

39. Coles, S.L. 1973. Some Effects of Temperature and Related Physical Factors on Hawaiian Reef Corals. Ph.D. dissertation. Dep. Zool., Univ. of Hawaii, Honolulu (unpublished).

40. Jones, R.S. & R.H. Randall. 1973. A study of biological impact caused by natural and man-induced changes on a tropical reef. Univ. Guam Tech. Rep. No. 7:1.

41. Edmondson, C.H. 1929. Growth of Hawaiian Corals. B.P. Bishop Museum, Bull. No. 58:1. Honolulu, Hawaii.

42. Edmondson, C.H. 1946. Behavior of coral planulae under altered saline and thermal conditions. *Occas. Pap. Bernice Pauahi Bishop Mus.* 18:283.

43. Engineering Science, Inc. 1971. Water Quality Program for Oahu with Special Emphasis on Waste Disposal. Final Report of Work Area 5. Chapter III, Toxicity Bioassays. City and County of Honolulu, Dep. Pub. Works.

44. Wilson, H.V. 1888. On the development of *Manicina areolata. J. Morphol.* 2:191.

45. Duerden, J.E. 1904. The coral *Siderastrea radians* and its postlarval development. *Carnegie Inst. Wash. Publ.* 20:1. Washington, D.C.

46. Yabe, H & Eguchi. 1939. Ecological studies on *Rhizopsammia minuta* var. *mutsuensis*. Jubilee Publ. Prof. H. Yabe 60th Birthday Vol. 1:175. (Japanese with English summary.)

47. Yonge, C.M. 1935. Studies on the biology of Tortugas corals. I. Observations on *Meandrina areolata* Linn. *Carnegie Inst. Wash. Publ.* 452:185.

48. Marshall, S.M. & T.A. Stephenson. 1933. The breeding of reef animals. Part I. The corals. *Sci. Rep. Great Barrier Reef Exped.* 3:219.

49. Kawaguti, S. 1941. On the physiology of reef corals. V. Tropisms of coral planulae, considered as a factor of distribution of the reefs. *Palao Trop. Biol. Sta. Stud.* 2:319.

50. Harrigan, J.F. 1972. The Planulae Larvae of *Pocillopora damicornis:* Lunar Periodicity of Swarming and Substratum Selection Behavior. Ph.D. dissertation, Dep. of Zoology, Univ. of Hawaii.

51. Fishelson, L. 1973. Ecology of coral reefs in the Gulf of Aqaba (Red Sea) influenced by pollution. *Oecologia* (Berlin) 12:55.

52. Goreau, T.F. 1963. Calcium carbonate deposition by coralline algae and corals in relation to their roles as reef builders. *Ann. N.Y. Acad. Sci.* 109:127.

53. Goreau, T.F. 1964. Mass expulsion of zooxanthellae from Jamaican reef communities after Hurricane Flora. *Science* 145:383.

54. Wells, J.M., A.H. Wells & J.G. Vanderwalker. 1973. *In situ* studies in benthic reef communities. *Helgolander wiss. Meeresunters* 24:78.

55. Edmondson, G.H. 1928. The ecology of a Hawaiian coral reef. B.P. Bishop Museum, Bull. No. 45:1.

56. MAYER, J.W. 1915. On the development of the coral *Agaricia fragilis* Dana. *Amer. Acad. Arts Sci. Proc.* 51:483.

57. GLYNN, P.W. & R.H. STEWART. 1973. Distribution of coral reefs in the Pearl Islands (Gulf of Panama) in relation to thermal conditions. *Limnol. Oceanogr.* 18:367.

58. MARSHALL, S.M. & A.P. ORR. 1931. Sedimentation on Low Isles Reef and its relation to coral growth. *Sci. Rep. Great Barrier Reef Exped.* 1:93.

59. JOKIEL, P.L. & S.L. COLES. 1974. Effects of heated effluent on hermatypic corals at Kahe Point, Oahu. *Pac. Sci.* 28:1.

60. BARNES, D.J. & D.L. TAYLOR. 1973. *In situ* studies of calcification in the coral *Montastrea annularis. Helgolander wiss. Meeresunters* 24:284.

806 BIOASSAY PROCEDURES FOR MARINE POLYCHAETE ANNELIDS (TENTATIVE)

The polychaete annelids are an important component of the biota in marine and estuarine environments throughout the world. In the subtidal benthic environment, they comprise about 30 to 70% of the macroinvertebrate species and about the same percentage of the total number of individuals. As a group, they possess a variety of feeding types with the majority being either filter or detritus feeders. They are important food for snails, larger crustaceans, fishes, and birds.

Bioassay procedures utilizing polychaetes as test organisms have not been widely used. However, within the past decade, there has been a growing awareness of the importance of this group and species discussed herein represent those used to the greatest extent for bioassays in the past. The investigator may wish to use other species that are more sensitive to the material being studied, more readily available, more adaptable to the particular situation, or more important ecologically in a specific locality.

Polychaetes will be used more widely in bioassay studies for the determination of water quality criteria and the effectiveness of water pollution control measures because methods are now available for laboratory culture, many species have relatively short life cycles, they are an important food resource for fishes, and they are of great abundance and ecological importance.

The following procedures are intended to serve as guidelines for the use of polychaetes in various types of bioassays.

806 A. Selecting and Preparing Test Organisms

1. Selecting Test Organisms

In accordance with the criteria listed in Section 801C.1, the following organisms are recommended for bioassays:

a. *Family Nereidae:*

1) *Neanthes arenaceodentata* (New England, Florida, California coast).

2) *Neanthes succinea* (all U.S. coastlines).

3) *Neanthes virens* (East coast).

b. *Family Capitellidae:*
Capitella capitata (all U.S. coasts).

c. *Family Dorvilleidae:*
Ophryotrocha sp.

2. Collecting and Culturing Test Organisms

a. Collection technics: Neanthes arenaceodentata, N. succinea, and *Capitella capitata* inhabit intertidal mud flats in estuarine areas and in the fouling communities on pilings, boat floats, or submerged objects. To obtain worms, bring the substrate or fouling material into the laboratory, place in white enameled pans, and cover with seawater. After a period of time, the worms will come to the surface; remove them with a fine brush and transfer to petri dishes containing seawater. Examine each specimen under a dissecting microscope and discard all injured worms. Transfer uninjured specimens to 4-l aquariums or other suitable containers for holding and feeding.

b. Culturing:

1) Condition of animals—Because the physiology of many polychaetes is altered during gamete maturation, examine each animal microscopically for their presence. Discard specimens that contain gametes in the coelom and those that have been injured during collection.

2) Food and feeding—Provide food in all long-term experiments. The green alga, *Enteromorpha* sp., is the most convenient food. This alga grows abundantly in nearly all estuarine areas of the United States. It can be collected in quantity and be dried and stored indefinitely. Before use, soak the alga in seawater and knead so that the individual filaments separate when added to the aquariums. Vary the amount of alga used according to the species and number of individuals in the container. Usually, about 0.15 g dry weight (0.25 to 0.3 g wet weight) /wk, per specimen, is sufficient for worms weighing less than 100 mg wet weight. Feed this same amount of food twice a week to polychaetes weighing more than 100 mg. Because many polychaetes fail to feed in the presence of a toxicant, examine each experimental container daily to make certain the worms are feeding and the food is not spoiling. Accumulation of fecal pellets is an indication of feeding.

The species of polychaetes have a wide range in size. Whenever possible, use specimens large enough, at least 10 to 15 mm, so that feeding can be determined. *Ophryotrocha* sp. can be fed frozen spinach or finely ground *Enteromorpha* at the rate of 1.0 mg dry weight/worm/wk. Larvae or recently settled juveniles of *Neanthes arenaceodentata, N. succinea,* and *C. capitata* are fed living specimens of *Dunaliella* sp.

Use *Dunaliella* as the initial food source until the larvae settle. Culture it according to the procedures outlined for the culture of marine algae in Section 801C.4*c*1)b). Feed *Dunaliella* at the rate of 10 ml of culture (having a minimum cell count of 20,000 cells/ml)/l of the worm culture. Feed so as to maintain a green color in the growth chambers or test solution. After settling, the worms can be fed *Enteromorpha* until the larvae mature to the epitoke stage, which represents completion of the life cycle. The epitoke is a reproductive stage characterized by morphological modifications for swimming.

3) Producing test organisms

a) *Ophryotrocha*—Several species of the genus have been cultured by Akesson[1] for laboratory bioassays. They reproduce rapidly under laboratory conditions and because of their minute size can be transported with ease.

b) *Capitella capitata*—Laboratory-cultured specimens begin to mature in about 15 to 25 days, as indicated by the appearance of maturing eggs as white masses arranged segmentally from about segment 10 posteriorly in the female and the appearance of specialized setae on the dorsal surface of segments 8 and 9 in the male. Copulation occurs with the transfer of sperm to the female. The female lays fertilized eggs along the inside lining of her tube where larval development continues until the trochophore larvae emerge. Obtain free-swimming trochophore larvae from the tubes of females. Examine these tube masses under a dissecting microscope to detect those containing eggs or larvae. Recently fertilized eggs appear white, but as they mature become grey-green in color and can be seen moving about within their parent's tube. Place females containing larvae in a petri dish and under a disecting microscope and open the tubes to free the trochophores. One female provides 200 to 300 trochophores. Remove from the dish the parent and the tube containing the larvae that did not swim free, and discard them. Use the free-swimming larvae in tests or let them develop for later use.

c) *Neanthes succinea*—Take nearly mature epitokes from the field or laboratory colony and hold them in suitable containers until they complete sexual metamorphosis to the epitokal stage. Mature epitokes swim to the surface of the water and release gametes. If fertilization is successful, resulting in the production of zygotes, separate the zygotes into several 4-l jars provided with aerated water and allow them to develop to the three setiger stage. This requires about 1 wk. These larvae are then ready for experimental use. One fertilization provides a few thousand larvae. *Dunaliella* sp. is used as the initial food until the larvae settle, after which *Enteromorpha* can be used as food until larvae mature to the epitoke stage and complete their life cycle.

d) *Neanthes arenaceodentata*—Before spawning, either the male or female enters the tube or burrow of another worm. If these two worms are of the same sex, they begin to fight and the intruder leaves. Fighting consists of extending their proboscis and grapsing the other specimen with the terminal jaws. If the worms are of different sex, they remain together and spawn within the tube. The female dies within a day after spawning and the male incubates the eggs for about 3 wk, at which time they have 18 to 21 setigerous segments. At that time the young worms leave the tube, begin feeding, and construct their own tube. They are fed *Enteromorpha* as indicated in Section 806A.2*b*2). Under laboratory conditions sexual maturity is reached in 3 to 4 months. It is impossible to distinguish the sex of immature forms by morphological means; however, they can be distinguished by observing whether or not they fight when placed together as described above. By using a female with maturing eggs in her coelom as a known individual, it is possible to distinguish one sex from another. The most convenient time to obtain larvae is shortly after they have left the parent's tube and have begun to feed.

c. Parasites and diseases: Microbial growth can result from overfeeding, improper conditioning of food, or insufficient dissolved oxygen. Most fungal growths can be prevented by proper sanitation and periodic care. To minimize the possibilities of overfeeding, examine each aquarium before feeding to make certain food is required. Soak and knead *Enteromorpha* sufficiently so that the individual filaments separate when placed in the aquarium. Generally there is an adequate supply of dissolved oxygen in the 4-l aquariums; however, the aeration can be increased to correct any deficiency.

The internal protozoan parasitic gregarines have been observed by Akesson[1] to reduce the vitality of *Ophryotrocha* laboratory populations. Whether or not they cause similar problems in other polychaetes is unknown.

806 B.   Bioassay Procedures

1. General Procedures

Exploratory tests to determine the concentration of toxicants to be used in the short-term tests (acute static and renewal) and the intermediate and long-term tests can, in general, be carried out in accordance with instructions in Section 801E. Prepare the dilution water and test solutions of toxicants and introduce them into the test containers as described in Section 801D.

2. Water Supply

a. Artificial seawater: If artificial seawater is used, prepare as recommended in Section 801C.4*b*2). Use a salinity of approximately 35.5 ‰ and a pH of about 7.8 for marine populations; use lower salinities in bioassays with estuarine populations.

b. Seawater: When natural seawater is used as dilution water, determine its quality routinely and report as a part of the description of test procedures. Maintain the salinity of the dilution water at or near the selected or normal concen-tration. In a given test, salinity should not vary by more than ±3 ‰. In effluent bioassays, it will vary with the receiving water. Determine salinity periodically and, if it has varied, correct it by the addition of fresh water or sea salt as needed. In all instances, other than in effluent tests, filter the seawater through a membrane filter (45 μm) to insure complete removal of detritus and microscopic organisms.

3. Exposure Chambers

Aquariums or glass jars of 4-l capacity are recommended for short-term and intermediate static and renewal tests and for long-term tests where flow-through facilities are not available. Cover the aquariums with screen, glass, or some plastic material to prevent the entrance of foreign materials. Do not add more than 2,500 ml of the test solution to each 4-l exposure aquarium. Erlenmeyer flasks of 500 ml capacity, containing 100 ml seawater, are convenient for either short-term or long-term experims when only one organism is placed in each flask. Close the flask with a No. 7 teflon stopper supplied with a glass tube for aeration. Use small stender dishes (30 ml) for larval bioassays. For life-cycle, flow-through tests, use exposure chambers described in Section 807A.3*b*3).

4. Conducting the Bioassays

a. Setting up the test chambers: For static and renewal tests, set up the test concentrations and controls as described in Section 801D. When adult worms are used, place a minimum of two worms in each chamber and use 10 replicate test chambers to supply at least 20 worms for each test concentration. If larvae are used, use a minimum of four exposure chambers, each containing at least five larvae, for each test concentration and the controls. If a single adult organism is used per container, tests may be conducted in erlenmeyer flasks. If aeration is required, see Section 801D.3*c*.

In tests of short duration, it is not necessary to clean the exposure containers. In long-term tests in which the organisms are fed, remove unused food and other materials routinely by a siphon or other means as described in 801C.4*d*. For long-term flow-through bioassays, the test chambers are as described in 807A.3*b*3).

It has not been found necessary to provide a substrate in the test containers and as yet it has not been determined that certain light intensities or photoperiods are required. Keep temperatures within ±2 C of that of the natural habitat unless the effects of different temperatures are under investigation.

b. Duration and type of bioassays:

1) Short-term bioassays—The length of short-term or acute bioassays depends on the length of the life cycle of the organism under study [see Section 801D.3*a*)]. It may vary from 1 to 14 days, depending on the organisms and the purpose of the study. Short-term tests may be static if they are of 4 days or less duration or they may be renewal tests with the test solution renewed every 24 hr or at selected longer periods.

2) Intermediate-length bioassays—Tests of intermediate length are usually used for determining adult survival. For most species it is recommended that these tests be conducted for 28 days. They may be renewal or flow-through type tests. In order to avoid accumulation of metabolic products and reduction of the toxicant concentration through precipitation, collection on the sides of the containers, or volatilization, use the flow-through test for the adults.

3) Long-term bioassays—Long-term tests with worms may be of two types: (*a*) lifetime tests beginning with the trochophore larval stage and continuing through sexual maturity, and (*b*) life cycle tests beginning with the newly-settled larval stage and continuing through reproduction and subsequent larval settlement of the offspring. These tests should be the flow-through type.

Select and prepare test concentrations as described in Section 801D.2*b*. Measure and mix dilution water and stock solutions of toxicants by proportional diluters and deliver to the exposure chambers as described in Section 801D.1. Because it is essential to prevent the accumulation of wastes and the escape of small larvae and to count living and dead organisms periodically, conduct tests in flow-through exposure chambers similar to those used for the dungeness crab, Sections 807A.3*b*3) and 807B.4*c*2).

Renewal tests may be necessary where flowing seawater is not available. Test solutions can be conveniently renewed in the 4-1 exposure chambers when the water, which is poured off to facilitate counting the worms retained on the bottom, is replaced by fresh test solutions. The duration of the long-term tests depends on length of life cycle of the organisms under study. These tests will vary from about 1 wk with *Ophryotrocha*, to 1 month with *C. capitata*, to 3 or more months with *N. succinea, N. virens,* and *N. arenaceodentata.*

c. Test organisms:

1) Source and selection of organisms—If laboratory-reared specimens are used, state the original source and strain. In the laboratory, separate field-collected specimens from other species and place in holding containers for observation of their condition and general well-being. Examine each organism under a dissecting microscope to determine if gametes are present. Reject as test organisms individuals containing maturing gametes because at this stage they are easily injured by handling.

2) Holding and acclimation—Hold polychaetes at the test temperature for at least 1 wk after collection and observe for any unusual mortality or poor condition. Short-life-cycle species may be held until the next generation either in aerated aquariums or in covered petri dishes. The holding temperature should not vary more than ±2 C from that at which they were collected in the field. If more than 10% of the noninjured, nonreproductive field specimens die during the holding period, discard all the specimens and collect a new group of organisms.

3) Number of test organisms—In short- or intermediate-term survival studies with adult worms, follow the procedures outlined in Section 801D.3. For renewal-type survival or long-term tests with trochophore larvae, there should be a minimum of 25 larvae/4-1 test chamber with a minimum of four chambers per concentration. Use the same number of organisms in the untreated controls. Follow the same procedures for complete life cycle tests beginning with the newly settled larval stage. For flow-through tests described in Section 806B.4*b*3), place 10 organisms in each of the 10 exposure beakers.

d. Carrying out the tests:

1) Short-term bioassays—Static or renewal tests are set up and conducted as has been described in Section 801E.2. When determining survival of adults, check exposure chambers at 1.5, 3, 6, 12, and 24 hr and once or twice every 24 hr thereafter. Dead specimens are generally pale and swollen and lie on the bottom of the container. Live specimens usually move when the containers are rotated. If the tests are more than 4 days long, renew the solutions, preferably every 24 hr but at least every fourth day. In short-term tests with larvae, determine survival after 96 or 168 hr by examination of the water for larvae under a dissecting microscope. The absence of larvae generally indicates death because decomposition of small larvae is rapid.

2) Intermediate-length bioassays—In these studies, test chambers are set up as described in ¶4*a* and *c*. They are conducted for the determination of adult le-

thality expressed as LC50 or incipient LC50. Examine the test containers daily to determine survival during each of the first 5 days; thereafter, examine two to three times per week for the duration of the experimental period. Report results of these tests as the 28-day LC50. If no organisms are killed after a certain length of exposure, report the period beyond which there is no further kill and the percentage killed in each test concentration. Calculate incipient LC50.

3) Life-cycle tests beginning with the trochophore larval stages—Set up exposure chambers for these studies as described previously. In these studies the organisms are carried through sexual maturity and the test period will vary from 3 to 4 wk with *C. capitata*, and from 2 to 3 months or longer for *N. succinea* and *N. virens*. Feed the larvae as described in Section 806A.2*b*2). Observe to determine survival at least twice a week for *C. capitata* and once a week or more for *Neanthes*. During the early part of the study count the organisms on the bottom of the 4-l exposure chambers or the flow-through exposure chambers because of the small size of the juvenile worms. In order to do this most effectively for the 4-l chambers, decant the supernatant fluid and examine under a dissecting microscope or remove the flow-through chambers from the glass tray, count the organisms, and return the test chamber to the glass tray to continue the exposure [see Sections 807A.3*b*3) and 807B.4*c*2)]. After the counts are made in the 4-l chambers, replace the fluid with fresh test solution to insure that the organisms are exposed to the selected concentration of toxicant. If

no organisms are observed in the first or second examination, retain the test chamber until the third examination. If no organisms are then observed, terminate that particular test chamber. When *C. capitata* is the test organism, remove the test chambers after about 15 or 16 days of exposure and every 2 days thereafter to check with a dissecting microscope for the presence of eggs within the coelom and later for the presence of zygotes along the sides of the tube. Remove the females when developing eggs are in the trochophore stage and count the larvae. Discard the females and larvae after the number of larvae and other data such as length and number dead and deformed have been recorded. Continue to examine each exposure chamber every 2 days for the detection of females incubating larvae until all females have been removed and the total number of larvae recorded. The number of larvae produced in test chambers, when compared to those produced in controls, serves as the measure of effects of the different concentrations of toxicants on the reproductive process.

When *N. succinea* is the experimental organism, set up the various exposure chambers as described previously in ¶s 4*a* and *c* with 25 larvae in each 1-l exposure chamber or 10 larvae in each of the flow-through exposure chambers, 10 for each concentration tested. Because individuals of this species fight with and eat each other when crowded, after the first month set up additional exposure chambers or reduce the number in each test chamber in order to reduce the number of larvae in each exposure chamber to five individuals. This should provide sufficient space to prevent cannibalism. Continue tests until the specimens reach the epitoke stage. At that time, determine counts of individuals' lengths and total weights and compare with those in the control to determine effects of the toxicants on the completion of the life cycle and the condition of the populations.

4) Life-cycle tests beginning with the newly settled larval stage—These tests will vary from about 1 wk with *Ophryotrocha*, to 1 month for *C. capitata* and 3 months or more for *N. arenaceodentata*. Set up the tests as described previously with the newly settled larvae, with a minimum of two specimens per flask and ten flasks per concentration. As the tests progress, count the organisms as has been described. Because *Ophryotrocha* is very small, examine the chambers for survival only at the completion of the experimental period in the 4-l chambers. However, the larvae can be counted periodically in the flow-through chambers by simply removing the chambers from the glass trays, setting them on a grid under a microscope, and counting the larvae. For the other species, examine for survival as has been

outlined previously, ¶*d3*), once or twice a week.

When studies are carried out with *N. arenaceodentata*, use recently emerged larvae having approximately 18 to 21 setigerous segments. Place four specimens in each 4-l exposure chamber with 2,500 ml of the test solution. Set up five jars for each test concentration and with appropriate controls. If flow-through bioassays are used, place two larvae in each of 10 exposure chambers for each test concentration and the controls. At 25 days, examine the worms by viewing from the outside of the jar for the presence of eggs in the coelom of the worms. Mature eggs reach 450 μm in diameter and are yellowish-orange. Examine at 5-day intervals until the eggs are noted and then at 2- to 3-day intervals to determine whether or not the eggs are being laid. The females die within a day after laying the eggs and the males incubate them for about 3 wk. The life cycle is complete when the worm leaves the male's tube. Remove the males and count the larvae, making comparisons with those in the controls to determine the effects of the toxicant.

806 C.   Data Evaluation

1. Short-Term and Intermediate Adult Survival Studies

For these studies, determine the LC50 values for each exposure period as described in Section 801F.

2. Life-Cycle Studies Beginning with the Trochophore and Settled Larval Stages

Knowledge of effects of a toxicant on the life cycle is of special significance be-

cause it is the only true indicator of whether or not the substance is toxic. Subtle effects of a toxicant are indicated by reduction in the number of females forming eggs, the number laying eggs, and the number of offspring produced. The numbers obtained are inversely related to sublethal concentrations of the substance at levels below the LC50. They provide a more sophisticated measure of effects than the LC50. Record the life cycle data in tabular form for each concentration of the toxicant as follows: number of females forming eggs, number of females laying eggs, and number of eggs and live offspring produced, to obtain data on the effects of exposure to the various concentrations. Compare these data, expressed on a percentage basis, for all test concentrations with those obtained from the controls. When the percentages are the same, or practically the same in the test concentration and control, that concentration is considered safe under conditions of the test and is an estimate of the maximum allowable concentration of that material in the environment for the species studied. Analyze, evaluate, and report results as described in Section 801F and G.

806 D. Reference

1. AKESSON, B. 1970. *Orphryotrocha labronica* as a test animal for the study of marine pollution. *Helgolander wiss. Meeresunters.* 20:293.

806 E. Bibliography

EISIG, H. 1898. Zur Entwickelungsgeschichte der Capitelliden. *Zool. Stat. Neapel, Mitt.* 13:1.

THORSON, G. 1946. Reproduction and larval development of Danish marine bottom invertebrates with special reference to the planktonic larvae in the sound (Øresund). *Komm. Dan. Fisk.-Havundergelser. Ser. Plankton, Meddel.* 4:1.

REISH, D.J. 1957. The life history of the polychaetous annelid *Neanthes caudata* (delle Chiaje), including a summary of development in the Family Nereidae. *Pac. Sci.* 11:216.

REISH, D.J. & J.L. BARNARD. 1960. Field toxicity tests in marine waters utilizing the polychaetous annelid *Capitella capitata* (Fabricius). *Pac. Natur.* 1(21):1.

REISH, D.J. & T.L. RICHARDS. 1966. A technique for studying the effect of varying concentrations of dissolved oxygen on aquatic organisms. *Air Water Pollut. Inst.* 10:69.

RICHARDS, T.L. 1969. Physiological Ecology of Selected Polychaetous Annelids Exposed to Different Temperature, Salinity and Dissolved Oxygen Combination. Ph.D. dissertation, Univ. of Maine.

REISH, D.J. 1970. The effects of varying concentrations of nutrients, chlorinity and dissolved oxygen on polychaetous annelids. *Water Res.* 4:721.

BELLAN, G., D.J. REISH & J.P. FORET. 1972. The sublethal effects of a detergent on the reproduction, development and settlement in the polychaetous annelid *Capitella capitata. Mar. Biol.* 14:183.

807 BIOASSAY PROCEDURES FOR CRUSTACEANS (TENTATIVE)

Crustaceans are a large, important group of organisms, most of which live in the sea. The class, Crustacea, contains more than 25,000 species grouped into two subclasses, Entomostraca and Malacostraca. Many of the smaller Entomostraca, the copepods and cladocerans, are commonly referred to as microcrustaceans and are important macroplanktonic organisms in both marine and fresh waters. Bioassay methods for this group are under Zooplankton, Section 804. The subclass Malacostraca contains the larger and economically important crustaceans. The organisms in this subclass are mostly marine but there are some important freshwater forms. In the family Mysidae, *Mysis relicta* of the Great Lakes is an important food of the various species of salmonids.

The order Amphipoda, containing over 3,000 species, is almost exclusively marine but has important fresh water species in the genera *Hyalella, Gammarus, Crangonyx*, and *Pontoporeia*. The order Isopoda also is almost exclusively marine but has a few freshwater forms in the genus *Asellus*. Of greater economic importance is the order Decapoda, which contains the lobsters, spiny lobsters, crabs, shrimp, prawns, and crayfish. Various kinds of marine decapods have been used during the past 15 yr for bioassays. Crustaceans are especially relevant for determining the toxicity of pesticides in the aquatic environment because of their phylogenic relationship to the insects for whose control many pesticides have been developed.

807 A.   Selecting and Preparing Test Species

1. Selecting Test Organisms

The general principles governing the selection of test organisms are described in 801C.1. The following genera or species, which have been used in bioassay studies or have been cultured in the laboratory or for mariculture, are suggested as test organisms:

Freshwater species:
  Gammarus lacustris
  Gammarus pseudolimnaeus
  Gammarus fasciatus
  Hyalella azteca
  Pontoporeia affinis
  Mysis relicta

  Palaemonetes cummingi
  Palaemonetes paludosus
  Palaemonetes kadiakensis
  Crayfish—*Cambarus*
                Potamobius
                Orconectes rusticus

Marine and brackish water species:
  Palaemonetes pugio—grass shrimp
  Palaemonetes vulgaris
  Palaemonetes intermedius
  Crangon septemspinosa—sand
    shrimp
  Penaeus duorarum—pink shrimp
  Penaeus aztecus—brown shrimp
  Penaeus setiferus—white shrimp

Homarus americanus—American lobster
Callinectes sapidus—blue crab
Cancer irroratus—rock crab
Cancer borealis—jonah crab
Cancer magister—dungeness crab
Panopeus herbstii—mud crab
Rhithropanopeus harrisii—mud crab
Menippe mercenaria—stone crab

Accurate identification of experimental animals is absolutely necessary. Most of the inshore macrocrustaceans in the United States have been classified and regional keys are available to aid in identification.[1-5]

2. Collecting and Handling Test Organisms

The smaller forms can be taken in dip nets or coarse plankton nets. The larger forms occurring near shore can be taken in small mesh seines. Most of the marine forms can be taken by means of trawls. For methods of collecting and transporting test organisms see Sections 1005 B and 801 C.2.

3. Holding, Acclimating, and Culturing Test Organisms

a. Water supply: See Section 801C.4b.

b. Acclimation, holding, and maintenance of stock cultures: See Section 801C.3 and 4. Although risks in handling most adult crustaceans are usually not great because of their rigid exoskeleton and general durability, certain precautions are necessary. Both larval and adult forms of many species are cannibalistic and readily attack their fellows in the soft-shell stage. Hold juveniles and adults in individual compartments

in the test aquariums. These can be provided by the use of long troughs or tanks divided into compartments by perforated separators that slide into slots on the sides. These may be made with stainless steel for freshwater forms and with glass, acrylic plastic, or plywood covered with fiberglass for marine forms. The compartments should have rigid, transparent covers to prevent loss of the highly motile specimens. A flow of water through each compartment for the removal of metabolic products and the provision of dissolved oxygen can be achieved by having a large number of small openings in the separators so the water flows from one compartment to another. The crustacean growth process, which involves a periodic ecdysis or sloughing of the rigid exoskeleton, imposes a lack of uniformity in test animals that is not readily detectable in advance. In the pre-ecdysis stage and during ecdysis the animals are heavily stressed and more sensitive to unsatisfactory environmental conditions and toxicants.

1) Amphipods—Freshwater amphipods for bioassays may be collected from their natural habitat or they may be reared in the laboratory. A few species have been reared through three or more generations. By maintaining several stock cultures supplemented by collections from the natural habitat it is possible to provide a supply of organisms for testing purposes. In the laboratory, a new generation can be produced in about 8 to 20 wk, depending on the species and the water temperature.[6, 7, 8] For holding and for bioassays, a known favorable temperature generally has been used. A light intensity of 538 to 1,614 lux (50 to 150 ft-c) at the water surface is recommended.

Keep amphipods collected from the field for test purposes in flow-through systems with water temperatures held initially near the temperature of the water from which they were collected and then gradually phased into the temperature at which the bioassays are to be conducted. Handle the test animals carefully and as little as possible. Use small dip nets having no projections and soft flexible netting.

Both young and adults feed on aspen, maple, and birch leaves that have been soaked for several weeks in flowing water. Test leaves to insure that those used are free of pesticides or other toxicants. Supply the leaves in sufficient quantities to support a stable population but not to the extent that they cause oxygen depletion or excessive fungal growth. Some leaves should be present at all times to provide cover. Commercial fish chow can be used to supplement the leaf diet.

2) Crayfish—Collect specimens for testing or rearing from their natural habitat by trapping, seining, or hand collection (Section 801C.2) General procedures for holding and acclimation are as described in Sections 801C.3 and 4.

Because of their cannibalistic tendencies hold all but the young stages of crayfishes in separate compartments. Suitable holding, acclimating, and culturing chambers are provided by stainless steel, glass, fiberglass-covered wood, or plastic troughs, 180 cm long, 30 cm wide, and 20 cm deep, with a divider down the center to make two long troughs. Shallow channels are made on the sides and the central divider every 15 cm into which separators can be slipped to make 12 compartments on each side, each approximately 15×15 cm square and 20 cm deep. This size has been suitable for

crayfish but the number and size of the compartments will depend on the type and amount of work being carried out and the size of the organisms. When a large number of small crayfish is to be held the separators may be removed to make a tank of the length desired. The separators are provided with a large number of perforations so they operate as a screen. Water introduced into the two chambers at one end will flow through the 10 compartments and out through a standpipe in the last or twelfth compartment. The depth of water in the test chambers is governed by the standpipe in the last compartment of the trough.[9] The separators can be raised temporarily a short distance from the bottom during cleaning to allow excess food and wastes to be washed out. This is facilitated by removing the standpipe in the last compartment to insure a good current to carry away wastes. Clean routinely with a siphon and a brush to loosen materials from the screens, walls, and bottoms of the compartments. Water adjusted to the desired temperature and DO concentration is supplied to the two head compartments by means of a siphon from a constant-head box. There should be a minimum flow of 10 trough volumes per day, the volume being adjusted to the amount needed to maintain favorable water quality in each of the compartments. Water depth required in the compartments depends on the size of the organisms being held, but a depth of 15 cm is usually most desirable. Each set of troughs should be provided with a transparent lid to insure that each crayfish is kept in its assigned compartment.

For studies with eggs or newly hatched young or life-cycle studies, collect ovigerous females and place them in the flow-through troughs under conditions similar to those in the area from which they were taken. Acclimation to different conditions can be begun after 2 days. Hold the animals in the troughs until the young hatch. The compartment dividers can be left out to provide freedom of movement of the young throughout the trough. Clean as described in Section 801C.4*d*.

Molting periods are critical because the crayfish are much more sensitive to environmental factors and toxicants at ecdysis.[9]

Macerated fish is the recommended food for juveniles and adults but prepared dry fish food also may be used. Very finely divided pieces of fish and commercial fish food pellets serve as food for the newly hatched.

3) Crabs—Static culture of brachyuran crab larvae has been successfully accomplished for several species of crabs from the Atlantic coast.[10-13] Long-term toxicity bioassays with these species have been carried out in static or renewal tests.[14-16] Culture of the larvae of the dungeness crab *Cancer magister* has been reported.[17-19] The larvae of this species have been cultured successfully by a continual replacement flowing water method suitable for use in bioassays.[19]

Of prime importance in the culturing of crab larvae is a favorable water supply and the control of competitors, predators, and disease. This may be accomplished through filtration and sterilization by ultraviolet light treatment. The amount of treatment needed is governed by the quality of the seawater supply. If it is unpolluted open ocean water such as is available around offshore islands it will require little or no treatment. However, if the supply is taken from an estuary that has received organic wastes it may require much purification before use. In this case filter the seawater for the flow-through system by gravity flow through a coarse, quartz sand filter and adjust to the desired salinity, approximately 25 to 30 ‰, by the addition of fresh water. To insure the removal of other organisms, refilter under pressure through sequential layers of 40/60-mesh garnet, 20/30-mesh silica sand, and 0.3 cm hard coal.* Finish by using a polishing filter.† Finally, treat the filtered water with ultraviolet light to ensure freedom from spores and harmful bacteria. The amount of water needed will govern the size of the filters required. To obtain constant flows of the desired quantity and quality of water for the cultures use constant-level head boxes equipped with heating, cooling, and stirring devices, which deliver constant measured flows to holding and acclimation tanks, spawning compartments, and culture vessels by means of siphons, selected nozzles, or constant and accurate delivery pumps.

Collect ovigerous females from the field or purchase from fishermen and place in holding tanks or in flow-through troughs similar to, but larger than, those described for the crayfish. Acclimation and conditioning is essentially as described in Section 801C.3. When the eggs are ready to hatch, transfer the female crabs to static tanks provided with aerated and UV-sterilized water at 30 ‰ and 13 C. As the eggs

---

*Filter design patented by Microfloc Corp., Corvallis, Ore.

†The Commercial Filter Corp. Fulflo, Model F15-10 or equivalent.

hatch dip out the swimming first-stage larvae with beakers and transfer to culture beakers with large-bore pipets.

Dungeness crab larvae have long delicate spines that make their culture in flowing systems difficult. Spines are often damaged by catching on screens or impingement on hard surfaces due to currents and thus provide avenues of infection. The larvae have been cultured successfully to the fourth and fifth stage in 250-ml beakers that have a hole 15 mm in diameter blown through their sides near the bottom. A nitex screen having 360-μm openings is fastened over this hole on the inside of the beaker by means of silicone cement and a nitex screen having 210-μm openings is cemented over the hole on the outside.[19] Because of the lip created by blowing the glass, the two screens are 3 to 4 mm apart. The larger mesh screen on the inside is less likely to catch and damage the spines of the larval crabs while the smaller mesh screen on the outside does not come in contact with the larvae but does retain the food organisms of the crab larvae, brine shrimp nauplii. Further, the screen area is small in relation to the surface of the beaker and its placement at the sides rather than the bottom of the vessel minimizes the possibility of entrapping zoea that settle to the bottom.

The 250-ml culture beakers are set in glass trays or aquariums large enough to accomodate 10 beakers and provide a depth of at least 10 cm.[19] These trays are supplied with a constant flow of water by a tube that discharges near the bottom of the tray. The trays are provided with an automatic siphon at the outlet so there is continual fill and drawdown, which provides a constant but

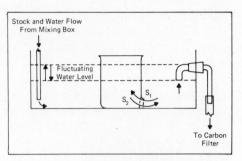

Figure 807:1. Rearing and exposure beaker and automatic siphon for dungeness crab larvae.[19]

gentle change of water in the beakers, Figure 807:1. The automatic siphon is constructed so that when the water reaches the high point and the siphon is activated the beakers contain approximately 200 ml and when the siphon is broken the beakers contain 150 ml; thus, at each cycle approximately 25% of the beaker contents is replaced. This fluctuating water level keeps the larvae dispersed throughout the beakers, frees any larvae that may have caught on the screen during the fill cycle, and tends to reduce bottom stagnation and the collection of organic material that may lead to undesirable bacterial growth.

The automatic siphon is made by blowing a 1.3-cm-diam hole through the side of the tray, inserting into this hole a silicone rubber stopper drilled to receive from the inside a right-angle glass tube of 8 mm ID to form the inner leg of the siphon and on the outside to receive a smaller-bore right-angle glass tube of 5 mm ID to form the outer leg (Figure 807:1). The hole in the side of the tray is placed at such a distance from the top of the tray that the upper interior surface of the inner leg of the siphon is on the plane of the 200 ml water level in the beakers. The inside arm is of such length that the intake hole is at the 150-ml level in the beakers. The outside arm extends to or below the bottom of the tray. It is critical that the intake hole of the siphon be perfectly flat and smooth to prevent air from being drawn into the siphon before the water level drops to the 150-ml level.[19] The bore of the tube delivering water from the head box to the tray and that of the inside and outside arms of the siphon that draws it down should be such that the tray is filled to activate the siphon in about 10 min and is drawn down to where the siphon is broken in about 5 min, making about a 15-min cycle.

When the culture chambers are set up and functioning, place 10 first-stage larvae in each culture beaker by means of smooth pipets of a bore larger than the larvae. The larvae can be fed non-living food but the best results are obtained by feeding first-stage brine shrimp nauplii at the rate of 70 for each crab larva three times a week through the third stage, at which time the feeding is increased to 100 brine shrimp per crab larva. Keep the density of crab larvae low and that of the food organism high to minimize crab larvae contacts with resulting cannibalism. Before feeding, transfer the larvae to clean chlorine-sterilized and rinsed beakers. A temperature of 12 to 13 C; a pH of 8, and a salinity of 25 to 30 ‰ are favorable for the culturing of the larvae. The photoperiod is adjusted to correspond with natural conditions or, if the cycle is off-season, to correspond to the normal annual cycle of light and dark. Natural light is excluded and fluorescent light (Section 801 D.3g) under controlled intensity is used. Under these conditions survival of 80 to 90% through the fourth zoeal stage has been attained. Larvae usually begin molting into the fifth zoeal stage by the 45th day and mortalities have been found to increase at about that time.

Juvenile and adult dungeness crabs are much less susceptible to disease and fungal and bacterial growths than are the larvae. By the practice of strict sanitation and the use of a clear, unpolluted open seawater the treatment of the water may be held to a minimum of sand filtration. The juvenile and adult crabs are held in trough compartments similar to, but larger than, those used for the crayfish.

To allow space for movement use compartments for each juvenile crab 15×15 cm and 15 to 20 cm deep, as suggested for crayfish. For adult crabs use 30×30-cm or 40×40-cm compartments with a depth of about 30 cm. Deeper water may be needed for large specimens. Necessary flow of water through a trough containing 10 compartments depends on the loading and should be sufficient to insure favorable dissolved oxygen levels. For ease of supplying water, arrange the troughs on stands having three shelves with space on each for two troughs. Feed cut-up or macerated fresh fish, clams, or mussels, or commercial dried fish foods to juveniles and adults. Remove unused food within 24 hr to reduce fouling.

Routinely clean the sides and bottoms of compartments to remove organic material, growths, and wastes. Remove such materials with vacuum or siphon cleaners; raise the screen separators a few millimeters and flush as suggested for the crayfish troughs.

4) American lobsters, *Homarus americanus*—Obtain adult lobsters by

trapping or purchase from lobster fishermen. Ovigerous females can most readily be obtained in the early spring from lobster fishermen who have been provided permits to have these lobsters. Select females with brownish eggs because these eggs will hatch within a few weeks to a few months depending in part on the temperature of the water in which they are held.[20] Place the ovigerous females in holding tanks immediately after receipt. Tanks 300×100×30 cm have been used for this purpose. While such a tank will hold more lobsters, use only 25 to 30. At a ratio of two females to one male these should be more than adequate to supply needed larvae. Hold the claws of these lobsters closed by elastic bands so that they cannot injure each other. Do not use wooden pegs because of injury to the claw and subsequent infection. Pass uncontaminated seawater continually through this tank at a rate that maintains the DO at or above 80% of saturation. A desirable salinity range is 30 ‰ to normal seawater. Maintain temperatures above 12 C and preferably at or above 15 C.[20] Feed clams, quahogs, bay scallop visera, fish (such as alewives), crabs, abalone scraps, squid, or commercial dry pelleted foods to the lobsters.

To provide an egg-hatching tank, place a partition across the lower end of the holding (described above) tank 30 cm from the end. Place standpipe of a height to maintain the desired water level to one side of this 100×30 cm area. Remove a piece 5 cm deep and 30 cm long from the top central portion of the partition for the outflow from the hatching tank. Fit screen box, 25 cm wide, 15 cm deep, and 30 cm long with a notch

5×30 cm in the top of one side of the frame, against the notch in the partition. Use plastic window screen with 2-mm-square[4] openings in the construction of the screen box. Place female lobsters with eggs about to hatch in this hatching box, which is supplied with a flow of seawater sufficient to maintain DO above 80% of saturation. Normally, in southern New England, hatching begins in May when water temperatures reach 15 C. At this temperature all the eggs of one individual female will hatch in 10 to 14 days. The peak of hatching intensity occurs when water temperatures reach 20 C. At this temperature all eggs of an individual female hatch in 2 to 3 days. Maintain temperatures in the larval rearing tanks above 18 C. Above this temperature the molting frequency is proportional to the temperature up to 25 C, beyond which the animals are stressed. Recommended temperatures are 19 to 20 C.

The stages in the larval development of *Homarus americanus* have been fully described by Herrick.[21, 22] The larval period is considered to extend from the time of hatching to the fourth molt or attainment of the fifth stage. Duration of the larval period depends somewhat on the temperature of the water. Templeman[23] reported that larvae held at a temperature of 19 to 20 C would require, on the average, 3.3 days for the completion of the first stage; 3.8 days for the second; 6.5 days for the third, or an average of 13.6 days for the fourth molt. During the first three stages the larvae live in a free-swimming state, move toward the light, and remain near the surface of the water. After the fourth stage they become bottom-crawlers and seek

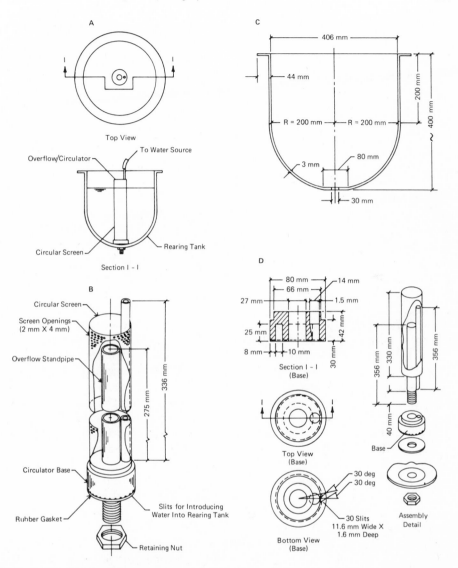

Figure 807:2. Hughes lobster-rearing tank.[24] A—general views; B—views of overflow/circulator; C—details of rearing tank construction; D—construction and assembly details for rearing tank and overflow/circulator. This is a 40-l tank. For bioassays, scale down to 5-l volume.

dark places, lead a nocturnal life, and acquire the defensive instincts of the adult lobster.

A special culture tank for rearing the larval stages[24] is of molded fiberglass and has a combined water circulator and overflow device at the center, as shown in Figure 807:2. A tank of this size is not required for the rearing of larvae for bioassays. For bioassays, use a tank one-eighth this size, i.e., one with a volume of 5 l. Water flow for this modified tank should be 0.5 to 1 l/min and should enter through the standpipe at the top and be discharged into the tank at the bottom through small slits in the manifold at the bottom of the overflow circulator. For details of construction and operation, see Figure 807:2 and consult Hughes et al.[24]

Temperature variations should be ±1 C. Flow rate can be regulated by means of ball valves.‡ If the water supply contains silt or much suspended matter pass it through a sand filter to remove particulate matter and invertebrate animals. If the supply is pure open ocean water, use without treatment. If the water is contaminated, use fine filtration and sterilization by ozone or ultraviolet light. A 10-μm wound polypropylene filter and an Aquafine (Aquafine Corp., Burbank, Calif.) PVCL-1 40-W UV unit has performed with near 100% efficiency for this purpose.[24] For more information on filtration refer to Spotte.[25] If a total flow of more than 40 l/min is required for all purposes a diatomaceous earth filter may be required. In some instances recirculating systems may be advantageous, especially when treatment with streptomycin is required to prevent harmful growths of filamentous bacteria or when large amounts of water are required for the flow-through systems and pumping and/or heating become a problem. The maximum concentration of lobster larvae for good results is about 45/l. At higher concentrations there are more lobster-to-lobster contacts and more cannibalism with a reduction in survival.

‡Chemcock ball valve or equivalent, Chemtrol Piping Co., Louisville, Ky.

As the eggs of the female lobsters placed in the hatching tank begin to hatch, the first-stage larvae are washed over the 5×30-cm notch in the partition into the screen box. Dip the larvae from this box with a small beaker and place in the modified Hughes larval rearing chamber by submerging the beaker and gently removing it. Stocking should be less than 225 larvae.

The newly hatched larvae can be fed a variety of foods such as clams, mussels, liver, or other meat chopped in a blender at a ratio of one part meat to two parts seawater. This mixture can be dripped continually into the rearing tanks from a stock bottle, the contents of which are mixed continually by means of a magnetic stirrer. To insure that the food is well dispersed and held in suspension for as long as possible by water currents in the rearing chamber, introduce the water under pressure through the openings in the overflow circulator. Because the lobster larvae are very cannibalistic the objective is to keep them dispersed by currents and by providing many food particles for each larva, thereby reducing larva-to-larva contact. Best results have been obtained by feeding newly hatched nauplii of brine shrimp *Artemia salina*, possibly because they swim about and are dispersed. Maintain a density of 50 to 200 brine shrimp nauplii to one lobster larva. An automatic brine shrimp feeder has been described by Smith et al.[26] Continual availability of food reduces cannibalism. By feeding live adult brine shrimp, a survival of 80 to 90% can be attained.[24]

When the lobster larvae reach the fifth stage they are placed in individual compartments formed by placing separators in a trough as described for the crayfish. For the fifth stage and juveniles, compartments 15 cm on a side are ample. As the lobsters grow they are placed in larger tanks. For those weighing 460 g or more, use a compartment 60×45×30 cm. Feed as recommended for the ovigerous females. It has been found that ground whole crabs improves coloration. During the spring, summer, and fall feed daily but during the winter feed once a week. Remove all unused food after 24 hr. Clean the sides and bottom of the tanks and siphon and flush out wastes, growths, and other materials as described for the crayfish tanks.

Growth rate depends not only on food and water quality but also on the size of the holding tank. Long before the lobster is physically restrained it reduces its growth in response to the size of the compartment in which it is held. During the first calendar year of life the lobster has an average of 10 molts in ambient temperatures. In nature, larval molting actively reaches a peak in the 15 to 20 C range; it seldom occurs below 5 C. Lobsters usually reach maturity at a weight of about 460 g. To accomplish mating, a male is placed in a compartment with a female immediately after she has molted and is in the soft stage. Success of mating decreases with time after molting and it should be accomplished within 48 hr after molting. When temperatures of 22 to 24 C are maintained, year round, lobsters reach maturity in 2 yr.[27] The rate of development of the eggs depends in part on the temperature at which the females are held. For extrusion of the eggs, the females must be placed in a special deeper tank because they need at least 45 cm of water over them or they will not extrude their eggs successfully. The egg-laying tank must be provided with a rough or non-slip bottom that will allow the female to assume and remain in the egg laying position until all the eggs are laid and attached to the non-plumose hairs of the swimmerets.

With reliable stable temperature control, it should be possible to maintain larval cultures year round. Non-ovigerous females and those bearing green eggs collected in the fall can be held at low temperatures to retard development. Before eggs are needed, some females are removed and gradually acclimated to egg-laying temperatures to bring about egg development. Even when the eggs have reached the brown stage, hatching can be spread out by different temperature regimes. Another method is to rear and mate the lobsters in the laboratory at different times and under different temperature regimes. Although culturing in the laboratory is expensive it has certain advantages: (a) the potential to produce larvae on a year-round basis; (b) the capability to produce larvae of a known genetic constituency, which can greatly reduce experimental variability in toxicity tests and; (c) the ability to carry out complete-life-cycle tests. A method is available to determine beforehand when lobster eggs will hatch.[28] Once the eye pigment has been formed the course and rate of development of lobster embryos may be monitored by the periodic measuring of the eye of the embryos. Further, because temperature has a direct effect on the development rate of lobster embryos that rate may be manipulated by adjusting the water temperature of holding tanks to insure periodic hatches of larvae throughout the year so that meaningful bioassays can be carried out year-round.

5) Shrimp-Natantia—A supply of shrimp may be obtained by collection, from another laboratory, or by purchase from bait dealers. Check the animals for parasites, disease, and general conditon. Shrimp of the genera *Penaeas*, *Palaemonetes*, and *Crangon* can be seined from local estuaries. For general instructions on collection, handling, transferring, holding, acclimating, and culturing, see Section 801C.

a) *Palaemonetes*—Three marine species and three freshwater species of the genus *Palaemonetes* have been reared through metamorphosis. They are therefore suitable for life-cycle studies and can be brought in from the field for direct studies or for rearing in the laboratory. Place field-collected adult shrimp in suitable aquariums provided with flow-through water favorable to the organisms. Feed the freshwater species macerated parts of any of several local fishes;[29] feed the marine forms macerated mollusks or fishes.[30] Observe and examine shrimp periodically to detect the ovigerous females. When it appears that the eggs are nearly ready to hatch, remove the desired number of females from the tank and put in individual containers for the hatching of the eggs. Keep females in these containers, preferably with flow-through water, until the eggs begin to hatch. During this period feed them macerated fish or other suitable food organisms. After the eggs hatch, remove the female and feed the prelarval or prezoeae on day-old *Artemia salina* nauplii. The rearing procedures for the larvae are essentially the same for all six species.[31] Rear larvae with equipment and procedures similar to those used for the dungeness crab, but use rearing chambers with a capacity of 1 l set in a deeper tray. Place 10 larvae

in each beaker and feed with newly hatched brine shrimp nauplii. Recommended rearing temperature is 25 C, although lower temperatures between 18 and 25 C can be used. Filter and sterilize water to remove other organisms, parasites, or diseases. Suggested illumination during the larval period is 14 hr light and 10 hr dark,[32] with the source of light the same as has been suggested for the other crustaceans (see Section 801D.3f). Inspect larvae daily and feed every 24 hr. If sediments or wastes tend to collect, remove them once a day with a siphon. At 25 C, the duration of the larval period is 16 to 24 days. The average length of larval life is between 19 and 20 days. If it is desired to rear through the entire life cycle, immediately place females that have laid and hatched their eggs in an aquarium with males. Mating takes place with the production of a second batch of fertilized eggs. The incubation period of the eggs depends on temperature; usually 24 to 28 days are required. The number of eggs laid varies. There are six larval stages, the first being the protozoea, with five other stages. The seventh stage is a post-larval or juvenile shrimp, which marks the end of the metamorphosis. The normal orientation of larvae is dorsal side down with the anterior end lower than the posterior. They usually swim with posterior end foremost. Form 7, the postlarval juvenile shrimp, swim with the dorsal side uppermost and in the regular manner of the adults. In studies made with *Palaemonetes kadiakensis* the larval phase lasted 16 to 30 days with a mean larval life of 21 ± 2 days.

Keep larvae of the marine species in seawater adjusted to 25 ‰ salinity by the addition of demineralized water or unpolluted fresh water. Feed them newly hatched *Artemia salina* nauplii. Rear at room temperatures varying between 23 and 27 C. Other rearing procedures are essentially the same as those used for the freshwater species. Larval development has been described by Faxon[33] and Broad.[34] Salinity and temperature optima for the larval development of *P. vulgaris* in the laboratory have been determined.[35] Remove the chelipeds of the ovigerous females by means of fine surgical scissors to prevent removal of the eggs. When rearing larvae to a particular age, maintain a 10 to 15% surplus to compensate for mortality and have sufficient numbers of larvae for desired uses. The larvae are relatively hardy to temperature and salinity and can be reared at 25 C and a salinity between 15 and 25 ‰.

b) *Penaeus*—Shrimp may be held in glass tanks of 30 l capacity or larger. Provide each tank with flow-through water, 2 to 3 cm of sand over the bottom, and a screen over the top to prevent the shrimp from jumping out. Avoid overloading; keep no more than 22 to 24 animals in a 30-l tank unless the flow-through maintains high DO levels. With species of the genus *Penaeus* a minimum of 7.5 l/g/day is required and larger flows up to 22 l/g/day may be desirable to insure dissolved oxygen concentrations above 60% of saturation and the removal of metabolic products. The period of acclimation to laboratory test conditions should be about 2 wk. If bioassays are restricted to short-term or medium-length tests with adults and juveniles, shrimp can be field-collected, brought into the laboratory, acclimated, and used in bioassay investigations. Cut-up fish is a satisfactory food. Cut a fillet from mullet, grouper, or other abundant species into pieces about 1 cm²; feed one piece for each shrimp every other day or every third day, depending on the size of the shrimp. Remove uneaten food every 24 hr to reduce fouling.

If it is desired to carry out tests with larvae or if life-cycle studies are to be made, collect gravid females offshore, allow them to spawn, and rear the larvae at least to the postlarval stage. Penaeid shrimp can be reared regularly from the egg to postlarvae in the laboratory. Cook and Murphy[36,37] have described in detail equipment and technics for conditioning, spawning, and rearing large numbers of shrimp larvae from the egg to the postlarval stage. Methods of rearing shrimp larvae for experimental studies have been described by Cook.[38] Mock and Murphy[39] have described improvements on the methods, equipment, and procedures for spawning the females, rearing the larvae, and culturing the diatom *Skeletonema* as food for the protozoeal stages. Air-lift pumps to prevent the accumulation of the diatoms in the corners of the rearing tanks are described by Salser and Mock.[40] Freshly hatched brine shrimp, *Artemia*, are fed to the mysis and postlarval stages. Additional data on the culture of algae and their feeding to shrimp are presented by Mock.[41] Equipment and procedures for the continuous mass culture of algae as a food for other organisms are described in Section 801C.4c2).

The protozoeal stages, one through three, of the penaeid shrimp require algae as food. Because the larval shrimp are pelagic and are not able to search for food during the early part of their life cycle, maintain the required density of phytoplankton to support a population.

Skeletonema costatum and *Tetraselmis* sp. are the preferred forms. Add these to the larval culture chambers according to the stage of development, the number of shrimp larvae present, and the volume of the water.

The number of algal cells necessary to rear a population of larval shrimp to the postlarval stage is as follows:

Protozoeal I	*Skeletonema*	50,000 cells/ml
Protozoeal II	*Skeletonema*	150,000 cells/ml
Protozoeal III	*Tetraselmis*	20,000 cells/ml
Mysis I	*Artemia* nauplii	3/ml
Mysis II	*Artemia* nauplii	3/ml
Mysis III	*Artemia* nauplii	3/ml
Postlarvae I-IV	*Artemia* nauplii	3/ml

The most difficult part of the operations is the culturing of the phytoplankton, which can be either maintained in continuous culture or harvested and frozen to be used at a later date. Algae culture production units shown in Figures 801:1 and 801:2, Section 801C.4c2), will produce daily, 7.5 l of culture containing 4.3×10⁶ *Skeletonema costatum*/ml or 7.0×10⁶ *Isochrysis galbana*/ml and several other species of algae at like concentrations.

Add algae as a food for the larval shrimp as a concentrate either fresh or frozen because the algal culture medium is toxic to the shrimp and also must be removed, otherwise the algae medium would soon constitute a large percentage of the exposure solutions. The algae can be concentrated by centrifugation.

A temperature range of 28 to 30 C and a salinity range of 27 to 35 ‰ are most satisfactory for penaeid larval culture. The omission of antibiotics from the larval culture medium may be possible when the chelator EDTA is substituted at a concentration of 10 mg/l of seawater.[42] As indicated, brine shrimp

have been used as food from the first mysis stage through the fourth postlarval stage. The juvenile shrimp are fed fresh pieces of fish, clams, or mussels.[42] Prepared dried foods also have been used with some success. Of great importance is the texture, protein content, and digestibility of these foods and their stability in the water.[43] Closed raceways and recirculated water with the removal of wastes and the provision of adequate oxygen and food have produced good growth and survival in postlarvae and juvenile shrimp.[44] Knowledge of environmental requirements is essential for the correct feeding and rearing of shrimp.[45]

4. Parasites, Diseases, and Harmful Growths

Much remains to be learned concerning harmful growths, parasites, and diseases of crustaceans.[46] For general problems and control procedures see Section 801C.5.

Adult shellfish in recirculated or flow-through systems are susceptible to biotoxins and pathogens in the water. Recirculating systems must provide for adequate removal of metabolites and dead individuals must be removed promptly or the entire system can be quickly fouled.

Juvenile and adult lobsters, crabs, and shrimps are subject to bacterial and fungal infections. *Gaffkya*, a bacterial pathogen, is particularly prevalent in tank-held lobsters, while *Vibrio* disease occurs in tank-held adult shrimps as well as in post-larvae. Most captive crustaceans are subject to "shell disease", produced by chitin-destroying bacteria. This disease, possibly augmented by other bacterial invaders, can produce mortalities in tank-held shrimp. A systemic fungal disease has been described in European prawns and several fungal infections occur in wild shrimp populations.

The larval stages of the lobster and several other crustaceans are prone to infections of the ubiquitous marine bacterium *Leucothrix mucor*, which has produced mortalities of over 90% in larval cultures.[47] The action on the larvae is epiphytic growth on external surfaces and gills that harasses the animal as it attempts to molt. The exuvia and the new exoskeleton become entangled in the long dense filaments of the bacteria and the larvae are unable to swim or feed adequately while only partly freed from the cast exoskeleton. This organism can also result in high mortalities by causing pelagic eggs to sink and by interfering with the filtering apparatus of larval forms and the functioning of the gills.[48]

If the introduction of *Leucothrix mucor* into the cultures can be prevented the problem is avoided. In some instances it may be necessary to culture the larvae in artificial seawater. Place ovigerous females in a bath of malachite green, 5 mg/l, for 1 min *only* or rinse or wash them several times in artificial seawater of the correct salinity that contains streptomycin, 2 ml/l, from a stock solution containing 2 g/l of the antibiotic. Streptomycin sulfate is a prophylactic for the infestation; it does not cure infected animals. Maintaining a 1 mg/l concentration of the antibiotic throughout the larval culture period prevents infections. Twice daily cleaning is also a good preventive method. Seawater, filtered and exposed to ultraviolet radiations, should be nearly bacteria-free.

A disease of lobster larva has tentatively been identified as the Phycomycete *Haliphtorus*. It appears as a scab on the first segment of the thoracic appendages up to and surrounding the first row of gills. Thorough cleaning and ultraviolet treatment of the water supply is the only known treatment at present. Mycelial growths have been observed underneath the carapace and down into the basal segments of the thoracic appendages. The basic reaction is a scablike encasement of the mycelium. In most cases these scabs adhere to both the old and new carapace and thus cause a mechanical impediment to the molting process. The mycelium is usually found in the white muscle tissue surrounding the hepatopancreas and occasionally in the tail muscle. Mortality appears to be restricted to larvae and young juveniles. No deaths of specimens with a carapace length over 27 mm have been observed. It is believed that the infection is spread by spores that have been observed in fecal material.

The fungus *Lagenidium* sp. causes serious problems in the rearing of larval shrimp.[49] The disease first becomes apparent in the second protozoeal stage and disappears as the shrimp reach the first mysis stage. The shrimp become immobilized by the near complete replacement of muscle tissue by the mycelium of the fungus.

Parasites have been found in many species of crustaceans and their presence can influence the results of bioassays. In *Uca*, an ectoparasitic isopod is found on the gills, nematodes in the gut, and metacercaria in the green glands. Species of *Lagenidium* similar to the one that occurs in shrimp occur in other marine crustaceans. *Lagenidium callinectes* occurs in the eggs and larvae of the blue crab.[50,51] The blue crab has a barnacle *(Octolasmus lowei)* living in association with its gills and gill chamber, metacercariae in various organs, and the sacculinid *Loxothylacus taxanas* lives beneath its abdomen.

Saprolegnia parasitica attacks larvae of the shrimp *Palaemonetes kadiakensis.*[52] Pure cultures of the fungus attack and kill healthy shrimp larvae and all larvae exposed to it develop severe localized infections. Amphipods sometimes are parasitized by larval stages of acanthocephalan worms.[53]

807 B.   Conducting the Bioasays

1. General Considerations

Bioassay procedures for crustaceans follow in general the methods outlined in Sections 801D and E for range finding or exploratory tests, short-term, static, renewal, and flow-through tests, and long-term or life-cycle tests. However, many adults of this group must be segregated into individual compartments because of their aggressive and cannibalistic tendencies. Special procedures must be used for many larval and juvenile stages, some of which are also due to their cannibalistic tendencies. As with most other groups, larval and juvenile crustaceans usually are significantly more sensitive than adults and therefore are preferred for short-term effluent and other tests. Bioassays involving these stages require considerable expertise in handling, feeding, and culturing. However, several decapod crustaceans have been reared and bioassays have been made with the larvae of grass shrimp, fiddler crabs, hermit crabs, blue crabs, dungeness crabs, commercial shrimps, and lobsters.

The determination of the effects of toxicants on decapods is complicated by three factors—initial paralysis, delayed response, and much greater sensitivity at molting periods. True sublethal effects may be shown either by increased irritability or by inactivity. Penaeid shrimp may lie motionless in the testing compartments for days without dying and become covered by silt, or they may be so irritable that they damage themselves by hitting the walls of the aquariums when lights are turned on or someone walks by. These effects may be reversible, disappearing when clean water is restored. A more definitive indication of toxicity is partial to complete paralysis of adults or cessation of swimming of larvae. Crabs may lie paralyzed for days before dying, and in general, paralysis is not a reversible effect. In nature, a paralyzed animal would be easy prey for predators and would not survive long. The second factor that may complicate the interpretation of crustacean bioassays may be termed the "delayed response." After short exposure to toxic materials, test animals may appear unharmed. If they are held in clean water, however, they may begin to die after a waiting period and the mortality eventually may reach 100% even though no deaths occur in the first few days after the exposure period.

Because of delayed mortality observed for some crustaceans, place all surviving individuals from each test exposure in compartmented tanks receiving clean dilution water and hold under favorable environmental conditions for 2 wk to detect any delayed effects.

If tests are being made to assess the effects of periodic spills, discharges, or dumping, results should be based not on one series of tests but on several series of short-term tests at the indicated exposures made over a period of weeks in order to gain a knowledge of the accumulative effects of intermittent exposure. This is essential because it has been observed that at least some decapods show accumulative effects and that three 8-hr exposures at a given concentration, even though they are as much as 3 wk apart, are equivalent to a 24-hr exposure to the same concentration.[9]

Bioassays utilizing embryonic and larval stages may last for periods ranging from a few hours to as much as 30 days, depending on the species and larval stages used. Toxicity criteria may include egg hatchability, rate and success of molting, swimming ability, tendency to lose appendages, and metamorphosis of the larvae as well as death. Tests with selected larvae, juveniles, and adults may measure acute toxicity with paralysis or death as the end point. Long-term and life-cycle tests usually measure effects on respiration, behavior, osmoregulation, growth, molting rates, reproduction, and general well-being.

2. Water Supply—Dilution Water and Water Distribution System

See Section 801D.1.

3. Equipment and Materials

Water storage reservoirs, troughs and head boxes, heating, cooling, and mixing equipment, delivery lines, dilution and conditioning systems, pumps, mixing troughs, diluters, and exposure chambers have been described in Section 801D and in cited references. These are satisfactory in general for tests with adults and some of the juvenile crustaceans but special procedures are needed for many of the larvae and some of the adult crustaceans.

4. Bioassay Procedures

a. Amphipods:

1) Short-term bioassays—Exploratory or range-finding tests as described in Section 801E.2 are conducted to determine the concentrations of the toxicants to be used in short-term definitive tests. Usually these are performed basically as described in Section 801E but certain special procedures are sometimes necessary to meet special conditions or requirements. These tests can be done either under flow-through or static conditions. Wide-mouth glass containers having a capacity of 5 to 6 l supplied with 4 l of the test solution have been used as static exposure chambers. Test chambers for the flow-through tests should be the same as those described for the long-term bioassays. Solutions of the toxicant at the selected test concentrations are prepared and placed in the exposure chambers as described in Section 801E. In exploratory and short-term definitive bioassays, water temperatures can be kept constant by the use of water baths or constant-temperature rooms and at levels favorable to the test organisms. Preferably, use a test temperature of 16 to 18 C. For effluent bioassays match the test temperature to that of the receiving water as described in Section 801E. Juveniles are recommended for these tests. Use five organisms in each of

the widely spaced concentrations for the exploratory tests. Use five or more concentrations of the toxicant in the definitive bioassays with duplicate test chambers for each concentration and the controls. Place 10 organisms in each test container, thus obtaining 20 test organisms for each control and concentration tested. Select the organisms randomly or impartially and place in the exposure chambers as described in Section 801D.3a immediately after the temperature-conditioned test solutions have been placed in the containers. Do not feed the organisms in these bioassays. A photoperiod of 16 hr light and 8 hr dark with changes from L to D and D to L in a 0.5 hr twilight period is suggested. Supply light as described in Section 801D.3f and at an intensity of 538 to 1,614 lux (50 to 150 ft-c) at the water surface. Dissolved oxygen concentrations depend on the type of test and should be as described in Section 801D.3a. Limit static bioassays in which the organisms are not fed to 4 days. Make observations and record mortality daily and record results of the analyses for the determination of toxic concentrations. Analyze and report the findings as indicated in Sections 801F and G.

2) *Partial or complete life-cycle bioassays*—A number of workers have used long-term bioassays for the determination of toxic effects of wastes and other materials to various species of amphipods.[54-59]

The water supply and testing systems are as described in the above publications and in Section 801D.1. Prepare toxic solutions as described in Section 801D.2b and select test concentrations on the basis of the results of the short-term tests and criteria in Section 801D.3b. When methods of analysis are available, take samples of the test concentrations immediately after the tests are begun and at monthly or more frequent intervals thereafter and analyze as described in Section 801D.3d to determine actual exposure concentrations.

The exposure tanks are preferably glass aquariums with a volume of 8 to 20 l. Rearing tanks for the young are of the same construction but about half the size. To enhance mixing, deliver the toxicant concentration near one end of the exposure chamber and position the screened standpipe at the other end. Depth of the test solution should be at least 15 cm. The flow rate of test solution to each chamber must be sufficient to maintain oxygen concentrations and remove metabolic products. Begin flow of the test solutions to the chambers before the introduction of test organisms so that conditions are stabilized before the beginning of the bioassays. With effluent bioassays, DO levels will be those of the receiving water. For other studies, keep DO concentrations above 60% of saturation. Amphipods are sensitive to supersaturation; do not let it occur in the test chambers.

Temperatures in effluent bioassays correspond to those occurring in the receiving water. Photoperiods may be those normally occurring in nature during the stages of development under investigation. Use a source of light as described in Section 801D.3f.

Partial or full life-cycle tests can be initiated with newly hatched young, juveniles, or adults. If the test is to be initiated with newly hatched young, collect ovigerous females about to shed young from the holding tanks of field collected specimens or from the culture tanks.

Place one each in clean 400- to 600-ml beakers containing the dilution water in which they have been acclimated to test temperatures, feed them as described in Section 807A.3b1), and hold until the young are shed. Record the number produced by each female. When sufficient newly hatched young are available, initiate the bioassays by selecting at random 30 young and place them in each of the duplicate growth aquariums, which have been set up and are in operation, for each test concentration and the controls. Feed the test organisms as described in Section 807A.3b1) and clean the aquariums as described in Section 801C.4d. Observe the test chambers daily; remove any dead organisms and preserve them for future study. At the end of 60 days siphon the contents of each test chamber into pans and record all living young for each duplicate exposure chamber for each test concentration; impartially select 15 from each exposure chamber and return them to their respective exposure chambers. Use the methods described by Clemens[6] for measuring the remaining organisms to determine growth. Preserve all organisms for toxicant accumulation and histopathological studies. Observe the test chambers daily and record behavior and number dead. As the amphipods approach maturity and mate, observe for gravid females about to shed their young. Place one in each beaker and handle as for the F$_1$ generation. Record the number of young produced by each female and randomly place 30 in each of the duplicate exposure growth chambers for each of the test concentrations and the controls. Terminate the adult exposure, record the number and the sex of each animal, measure the animals, and preserve them for additional studies.

Continue the exposure of the young and record the survival in each concentration at 1 month. Continue the exposure to 60 days and then terminate. Count, measure the length and weight, and record condition of all survivors and preserve for other studies. Analyze and report results as described in Section 801F.

b. Crayfish:

1) Short-term bioassays: These bioassays are carried out following the general procedures in Sections 801D and E for the range-finding and definitive bioassays for various purposes. General procedures, equipment, analytic methods, and data collection are similar to those described for other organisms but special modifications are necessary to adapt them to crayfishes. Preferably, make short-term tests with juveniles and young adults. All animals in a test series should be of about the same size, with the largest individual being no more than 50% longer than the shortest, and in approximately the same intermolt or molt stage during the period of exposure. Expose all organisms in individual compartments or containers. Duration of exposure depends on the objectives of the study and may be 96 hr, 168 hr, or 2 wk. Exposures can most readily be made in the compartmented troughs described in 807A.3b2) and can be static, renewal, or flow-through. If the duration of the test is more than 96 hr, use flow-through procedures with some feeding and thorough cleaning of the compartments. Make observations, analyze and evaluate data, and report results as described for other groups and in Section 801F.

2) Partial life-cycle bioassays—These studies cover a portion of the life cycle and may extend from newly hatched

young to the adult. Complete life cycles have not been carried out in the laboratory. Make exposures in the compartmented troughs described in Section 807A.3*b*2) with one trough used for each concentration tested and each control. Run tests in duplicate. Prepare dilution water and stock solutions of toxicants and arrange test troughs as described for similar studies with other crustaceans. Toxic solutions can be prepared and delivered to the various exposure chambers in the different ways described, but modified proportional diluters described in Section 801D.1 are recommended.

When newly hatched young are available in sufficient numbers, place the troughs for the selected test concentrations and controls in operation and place 100 young in each of the large chambers formed on each side by the removal of the screens to convert the 10 compartments into one large chamber. Adjust water quality to follow the normal seasonal cycle in local favorable waters or other selected conditions dictated by the objectives of the study. Water flow, feeding, and cleaning are as described for acclimation and culturing in Section 807A.3*b*2) and in the general procedures. Before the young become cannibalistic, remove them from the common exposure chamber and count; randomly select 20 individuals and place one in each of the 20 compartments of their respective exposure troughs. Count, measure, weigh, and preserve others for other studies. Make daily observations on mortality and condition and record results of the bioassay. Continue exposure until the test species become adults. At the completion of the tests, record numbers, weight, condition,

and sex and preserve the organisms for additional studies. Analyze results and report as described in Section 801F.

c. Brachyura—crabs: The literature on crab behavior, physiology, environmental requirements, and toxicology describes the research of a diverse group of investigators on a large number of species with different objectives in mind. A number of investigators have used short- and long-term bioassays in their research on selected species.[11,14-16,18,60-62] The basic procedures for conducting bioassays with crabs are those used for many years with fishes and other organisms and are outlined in Sections 801D and E. However, certain modifications and additions to the procedures are required to perform bioassays successfully with the various larval stages, juveniles, and adults of the different species of the group. Based on the various bioassay methods in current use, methods for bioassays with the dungeness crab are presented as a guide for conducting the bioassays with this and other species of the group.[63,64]

1) Short-term bioassays—Short-term bioassays may be carried out with any developmental stages of dungeness crabs. Tests with zoeal stages are more meaningful because the juveniles and adults are more resistant to toxicants. Conduct short-term studies for determining relative sensitivity, relative toxicity, or the test concentrations that are to be used in long-term bioassays under conditions of temperature, pH, salinity, etc., described for the rearing of the dungeness crab, Section 807A.3*b*3). Condition and prepare dilution water as described for crab rearing.

Because effluent bioassays take water for dilution from the receiving water, temperature, salinity, and other water quality factors are governed by the receiving water. Often it is necessary to use ultraviolet light for the control of bacterial growths, parasites, and diseases and sometimes filtration is required.

For short-term tests of the effects of toxicants on egg hatchability and early larval development to the first zoeal stage, ovigerous females with eggs nearing the hatching period are treated for the control of bacterial growths, parasites, and diseases (Section 807A.4) and then placed in tanks with flowing seawater at 12 to 13 C and a salinity of 25 to 30 ‰. At the time initial hatching occurs, carefully remove unhatched eggs from the egg mass and place 30 directly into each of the 250-ml test chambers described in Section 807A.3*b*3), which are set up 10 in each of the trays for each test concentration and the controls. Measure and mix dilution water and toxicant as described in Section 801D.1 and let the toxicant test solutions flow from the mixing chambers into the trays or aquariums holding the exposure beakers. The automatic siphon operates to exchange the test solution in the test chambers on a 15-min or longer cycle [Section 807A.3*b*3)]. Development from egg to prezoea stage to the first zoeal stages usually requires less than 24 hr. At the end of that period, determine the success of hatching, molting from the prezoeal to the first zoeal stage, and the percentage of motile first-stage zoea.

When it is desired to make short-term bioassay tests with the first zoeal stage or later zoeal stages, treat the female crab as in Section 807A.3*b*3) and place directly into filtered ultraviolet sterilized water at 13 C and 30 ‰ salinity and hold until hatching occurs. When large numbers of first-stage zoea come near the surface or collect in corners, dip them out with a beaker and place in the beaker exposure chambers, 10 larvae in each beaker, and 10 beakers for each concentration under test and for the controls. Exposure period is 96 hr or 168 hr as desired. All the larvae used in the bioassay series must be in a comparable stage of development so that some do not molt before the completion of the test while others do. The zoeal stages are much more sensitive before and at the period of molting and if part of the test organisms molt the variability of test results will be so great that significant conclusions can not be drawn. Generally, the first zoeal stage molts to the second stage in 12 to 13 days. During the bioassay, feed the larvae newly hatched brine shrimp at the rate of 70 nauplii to each crab larva.

To conduct tests with later zoeal stages, rear the larvae in seawater to the selected stage as described. Before beginning the bioassay, collect megalops stages for testing from the field or hold for short periods until they metamorphose into the early juvenile stage so that this stage can be used in the bioassay. Determine dissolved oxygen and pH during the test. When possible, make chemical analyses to determine concentrations to which the organisms are actually exposed. Use photoperiods normal for the season during which the larval stages develop. Because of the cannibalistic tendencies of crabs beyond the larval stages, expose each individual in a separate exposure chamber. The compartmented troughs described in Section 807A.3*b*3) provide the necessary exposure chambers and form a compact unit for testing of each effluent or toxicant concentration. With other than the effluent bioassays, which are carried out as described in Section 801E, recommended test conditions for these stages are 12 to 13 C, 25 to 33 ‰ salinity, and dissolved oxygen above 60% saturation. Feed the test organisms macerated fish or mollusks.

2) Partial life-cycle bioassays—These may be long-term bioassays covering a portion of the life cycle, such as from the hatching of the eggs to the fifth larval stage or from the fifth larval stage into the early juvenile stage. Conduct such tests as flow-through studies in the beaker test chambers as described for the rearing procedures. Dilution water and toxicants can be supplied by pumps or siphons from constant-head boxes and stock solution containers but procedures described in Section 801D.1 are recommended. Obtain eggs or first zoeal stage larva from the females as described for the short-term bioassays. If the long-term study is to begin with the egg, place 30 eggs in each of the 10 beaker tests chambers in the tray, making 300 eggs in all for each concentration. After hatching, determine the number of dead, deformed, and active first zoeal stage larva and reduce active larvae to 20 in each of the test beakers. Continue the exposure through the desired number of zoeal stages. Transfer the test organisms to clean beakers three times a week. At that time, feed them at the rate of 70 first-stage brine shrimp nauplii for each crab larva. After the third zoeal stage, increase feeding to 100 nauplii per crab larva. Check the test chambers regularly to determine if the automatic siphon is operating correctly and if there is an inflow and outflow of water in each of the test chambers that keeps the lar-

vae dispersed. Examine for any bacterial growths or disease. In some instances it may be necessary to treat the larva continuously with streptomycin as described in the rearing procedures. When bioassaying effluents, it may be necessary to pass the effluent or the test solutions through a filter to remove coarse materials so that the elements in the proportional diluter and screens in the beaker test chambers will not become clogged. In partial-life-cycle studies it is preferable to continue the bioassay studies from the egg stage through the fourth zoeal stages. Usually the zoea molt into the fourth zoeal stage by the 45th day. When culturing the dungeness crab, it was found that there was usually significantly more mortality during the molt to the fifth stage.[19] However, if the mortality in the controls is not excessive, carry on until the early juvenile stage if possible. In other than the effluent bioassays, condition the dilution water and keep the water quality the same as that used for the rearing of the crab larvae.

When the crabs reach the juvenile stage reduce the number to 20 in each concentration and the controls and transfer to the compartmented trough chambers, one to each compartment; continue exposure. Enumerate, measure, and weigh all crabs to be discarded and preserve them for any additional studies. Volume of flow-through should be sufficient to remove the metabolites and maintain dissolved oxygen concentrations at the specified level for the effluent bioassays and at 80% of concentration or above for other types of bioassays.

Feed juvenile crabs pieces of fish or some other marine animal every 2 or 3 days and remove excess food after 24 hr.

Clean the exposure chambers by scraping down the sides for the removal of algae and brush the crabs for the removal of algae or other growth twice a week. In tests with small juvenile crabs, provide a sand substrate if it is found that they have difficulty in shedding the old exoskeleton during their ecdysis. The criteria for death for the zoeae are cessation of heartbeat, cessation of swimming, failure to recover after transfer to pure water, and opaqueness. Criterion of death for the juveniles is absence of movement after stimulation. Terminate the bioassay at 4 months and record all data. Analyze and report data as specified in Section 801F.

d. American lobster, Homarus americanus: The American lobster has been reared through its life cycle. When they are reared in the laboratory with adequate facilities, experienced personnel, and a suitable water supply, it is possible to produce any life stage for short-term bioassays practically year-round.

1) Short-term bioassays—Short-term static, renewal, or flow-through bioassays with juvenile or adult lobsters can be conducted in the compartmented rearing troughs used for the rearing of the lobsters in the laboratory (Section 807A.3b4). Dilution water for effluent and other types of bioassays are as described in Section 801D.2a. The bioassay procedures are the same as those outlined in Sections 801D and E and for the dungeness crab and crayfish. While the bioassays may be static or renewal, because the compartmented troughs are designed for flow-through, it is suggested that even the short-term bioassays be of the flow-through type. This will eliminate many of the problems of static bioassays that arise with large test organisms. When the bioassays are of more than 96 hr duration, feed the lobsters and clean and carry out other necessary functions as described for the rearing activities [Section 807A.3b4)].

If the bioassays are conducted with larval stages, use the adaptation of the Hughes rearing chamber, Figure 807:2, previously described, as the exposure chamber. Filtration, sterilization, treatment for control of parasites and disease and the bioassay procedures are similar to those used with the dungeness crab larva. Obtaining eggs and larvae, handling, and transferring are as described in Section 807A.3b4). When conducting larval bioassays with effluents, filter the dilution water, which is taken from the receiving water, and the effluent for the removal of other organisms and materials that would clog the proportional diluters and the screens of the larval exposure chambers. Because a movement of water is necessary to keep the larvae separated and off the bottom, short-term bioassays must be of the flow-through type. The flow through the larval testing chambers should be 0.5 to 1 l/min. Meter stock toxic solutions and the dilution water by a proportional diluter discharged into a mixing chamber and then pump to the larval test chamber with some force to provide the necessary currents in the chamber. Feed with newly hatched nauplii of the brine shrimp as described for the rearing procedures in order to control cannibalism. The ratio of nauplii to lobster larvae should be at least 50 to 1. Use five concentrations and a control. Stock each 10-l exposure chamber with a minimum of 100 first-stage lobster larvae. Continue all tests for 96 to 168 hr, depending on the objective. For stocking each of the exposure chambers, which are set up in duplicate for each concentration, and the control, dip larvae from the screen box of the hatching tank with a small beaker and place in a glass tray for counting by the photographic method described in Section 801D.3e. At the completion of the bioassay count the survivors in the same way or by visual counting in the tray. Care, feeding, cleaning, etc., are the same as for rearing procedures. The controls will give an indication of cannibalism, which should be used in estimating kills at each toxicant concentration (see Section 801F, Abbott's formula). Analyze and report data as described in Section 801F.

2) Partial life-cycle and life-cycle bioassays—Determine test concentrations by the results of the short-term bioassays. In the long-term bioassays handle the test animals in the same manner as during rearing, with the mating, egg extrusion, adult holding, egg hatching, and larval and juvenile rearing carried out as described in Section 807A.3b4). The larval rearing chambers, compartmented troughs, mating chambers, egg-extrusion tanks, and the hatching tanks are the same as those used for rearing. In order to speed up the tests and complete the various life stages within a shorter time, exposures should be at temperatures of 22 to 24 C. Special procedures required for effluent bioassays are the same as those described for the short-term bioassays.

Proportional diluters for measuring dilution water and procedures for metering stock toxicant solution and mixing them to provide the different selected toxicant test concentrations are as described in Section 801D.1. Set up the testing system with duplicate larval rearing chambers for each test concentration and the control, and place in operation before introducing the test organisms.

Dip larvae from the screen box of the hatching tank with a small beaker and place in a glass tray for counting by the photographic method, Section 801D.3e. Place 150 first-stage larvae in each larval exposure chamber. An excess number is suggested so that some can be removed to check their condition and stage. Immediately after photographing, dip them from the tray and gently float them from the beaker into the larval exposure chamber. Concentrate the residue that cannot be dipped in one corner of the tray by tipping and emerse that corner in the exposure chamber to transfer all larvae. Feeding and cleaning have been described previously. Check the density of brine shrimp periodically by dipping out a measured amount of the test solution and counting them. The density should not drop below 750/l. Observe all exposure chambers daily for mortality, disease, unwanted growths, and general conditions. Check on the developmental stages. At the completion of the larval stages and the attainment of the fifth stage, shut off the water flow, reduce the volume by a screened siphon, dip the lobsters out, and place in a glass tray. To insure the recovery of all lobsters from the larval rearing chamber, disconnect it, remove the overflow circulator, and wash those not dipped out into a tray. Randomly select 20 lobsters and place one in each of the 20 compartments of the compartmented troughs and continue the exposure.

Anesthetize the remaining lobsters in the tray, photograph to measure length, remove, count, and preserve the remaining lobsters for further study.

Set up a compartmented trough for each larval exposure chamber, i.e., 40 lobsters for each exposure concentration and the controls. Feed and care for the lobsters and clean the troughs as described previously. Transfer the lobsters to larger compartmented troughs as they grow, reducing the number to 20 for each test concentration when they reach about 250 g in weight. Weigh and measure those discarded and preserve for additional study. Continue the exposure with the selected lobsters in each test concentration and the control until the objectives of the test are obtained or until maturity. When animals are mature and ready to mate, randomly select two pair, one from each side of the compartmented trough, and place in mating chambers immediately after the female has molted and is in the soft stage. After mating remove the males. Measure and weigh all lobsters from each exposure concentration and the controls and preserve for additional studies. Place the two females into the compartmented troughs for each concentration. Remove the separators so each has the entire length of one side of the trough. Continue the exposure until they give evidence that they are nearly ready to extrude the eggs. Place them in the deep egg-laying chambers with the special rough bottom until the eggs are extruded and fastened to the non-plumose hairs of the swimmerets. Then place them in the egg-laying tanks, one for each test toxicant and the controls. Continue exposure through the hatching of the eggs. Collect and place the desired number of larvae in larval exposure chambers, two for each test concentration and the controls, and expose as for the F_1 generation. Count and record all live larvae produced, all dead first-stage larvae, and all unhatched eggs. Measure, weigh, and preserve the females for further study. Continue the F_2 larvae through the fourth stage and discontinue the bioassay. Count and measure all larvae. Record the number of active larvae, the number deformed, and the number dead. Measure, weigh, and preserve for additional studies. Compare the lobsters from each concentration with those from the controls as follows: percentage of F_1 larvae reaching the fifth stage, the length, weight, and condition of all and the percentage dying, the survival, length, weight, and condition of all postlarvae to the adult stage, the number of eggs produced by control and exposed first-generation lobsters, the percentage hatching, percentage not hatching, and percentage deformed, and the length, weight, and condition of the F_2 larvae, and the percentage living, deformed, and dying. Also record and report the results of other studies such as those of histology, disease, and parasites and accumulation of toxicants. Analyze data and report as indicated in Section 801F.

e. Shrimp:

1) *Palaemonetes*—The species listed for this genus, three freshwater and three marine species, are easy to collect and maintain and they have been reared through their larval development in the laboratory. By manipulating temperature and photoperiods it has been possible to induce spawning in the laboratory.[65] This makes it possible to have the various life stages available for bioassays throughout the year. The salinity-tem-

perature optimum is known for larval development.[66] Their ability to live over a wide range of environmental conditions and their hardiness makes them easy to maintain in the laboratory but it makes them unsuitable for the determination of effects of environmental factors such as DO, temperature, and salinity essential for the well-being of an aquatic biota. They can be very useful in determining safe levels of certain toxicants.

a) *Short-term bioassays*—Adults and the six various larval stages can be used readily for short-term bioassays. These are performed in glass jars or aquariums in the routine manner as described in Section 801E. They may be static, renewal, or flow-through tests. Range-finding tests are carried out to indicate the concentrations to be used in the full-scale or definitive short-term tests. The definitive tests are conducted with effluents and other types of wastes or material for 96 or 168 hr with 20 or 30 test organisms for each concentration, depending on the objectives of the tests and the precision desired.

Adults and larvae for the tests are produced by the rearing operations described in Section 807A.3*b*5)a). A large number of ovigerous females is needed to produce the larvae required for the bioassay tests. The adults are fed macerated fish or mollusks and the larvae are fed brine shrimp daily before and during the tests. When rearing larvae to a particular age for a short-term test, rear a 10 to 15% surplus to insure an adequate number for the test. Ideally, larvae for a series of tests should be hatched at one time and reared in mass culture. However, *Palaemonetes* normally varies in molting and development rates during larval life and usually it is not feasible

to produce sufficient larvae of individual stages for testing. Therefore, conduct short-term tests with larvae of specified ages. Most first-stage larvae will metamorphose to postlarvae in 18 to 21 days. It is desirable, therefore, to set up two or more series of bioassays to cover the larval and post-larval stages. Because of the inherent variability of each age group of larvae and increased sensitivity before and during molting run two or three replicates simultaneously for each test concentration in each series of bioassays.

In static bioassays monitor dissolved oxygen in each test container and the control to indicate when and if the test solutions must be renewed. In bioassays of effluents do not let DO concentrations fall more than 0.5 mg/l below the minimum levels occurring at that period in the receiving water. For other types of tests, run the bioassays at the same oxygen concentration and temperature at which the test organisms are reared, about 25 C and 60% of saturation or above. For marine species salinities between 15 and 25 ‰ are favorable but in a test series salinity should not vary more than ±1 ‰. Use results of the short-term bioassays for selecting test concentrations for the life-cycle bioassays. Analyze data and present results as described in Section 801F.

b) *Life-cycle bioassays*—If feasible, begin these tests with ovigerous females. Place 25 females with well-developed eggs in a compartmented trough from which the separators have been removed so that there is a large compartment on each side of the center divider. Stock six or seven of these double compartmented troughs for the five test concentrations and for the controls. Supply the test solutions to the head chamber as described previously in Section 801D.1 and for the other crustaceans. Feed the test shrimp with macerated fish, mollusks, or other suitable organisms. Observe the test organisms daily to detect females with eggs nearly ready to hatch. Remove those females and place them in separate glass jars supplied with the appropriate test concentration and hold until the eggs hatch. Renew the test solutions as required. Supply brine shrimp nauplii as food for those larvae hatching first. When hatching is complete remove the females and transfer the larvae by pipet or gentle pouring into the test chambers, which are the same as the rearing chambers for the dungeness crabs. The toxicant delivery systems should already be in operation and test solutions passing in and out of the beakers through the action of the automatic siphons (Figure 807:1). If desired, rearing chambers like those used for the lobster larvae may be used as the exposure chambers. If the former is used, the exposure chambers should be 1 l in capacity, set up in duplicate, 20 exposure chambers in all for each concentration, stocked with five larvae each. If the exposure chamber for lobster larvae is used (Figure 807:2) stock with 50 larvae each in duplicate. After the transfer of active larvae, check the hatching chamber to determine percent of eggs that did not hatch, first-stage larvae that died, and the total number of live larvae. Count, measure, and preserve those not used for future exposure in the larval exposure chambers. Continue exposure with daily feeding of brine shrimp until the post-larval stage, which should occur in 18 to 21 days. Then randomly select 25 of the post-larvae from each duplicate group for each exposure concentration and place each group, one on each side of a compartmented trough similar to the ones in which the ovigerous females were exposed; thus there will be one compartmented trough and two groups of 25 post-larvae for each concentration being tested and the controls. Preserve those not needed for further exposure for determining lengths, weights, histopathological effects, and total body accumulation. Feed with macerated fish and/or mollusks and continue exposure until the eggs develop and are about to hatch. Then select at random and transfer five ovigerous females from each group to hatching chambers, continue the exposures, and determine success of hatching and number and percentage survival of active first-stage larvae. Count, measure, and weigh those not taken for further exposure and preserve. Compare with controls for egg hatching, survival of different larval stages, rate of development, size of adults in second generation, number of eggs produced, success of hatching, and survival to first larval stage. Analyze data and report results as described in Section 801F. Determine maximum concentration of effluent or toxicant that did not exert an apparent detrimental effect.

2) *Penaeus*—The three species listed for this genus have been held in laboratories as adults and reared from egg to the post-larval stage.

a) Short-term bioassays—Short-term bioassays can be carried out with juvenile or young shrimp following the routine procedure as described in Section

801E. While static or renewal bioassays could be carried out, very large aquariums would be required. Therefore, conduct flow-through short-term bioassays when penaeid shrimp are the test organisms. Hold, acclimate, and culture the test shrimp as described in Section 807A.3*b*5). The test concentrations may be metered, mixed, and delivered to the test chambers by a variety of methods; the system described in Section 801D.1 is recommended. For the flow-through tests, aquariums 60×30×30 cm high are recommended. Place 2 to 3 cm of sand, free of organic matter, in the bottom of the aquariums and cover the tops with screens so that the shrimp cannot jump out. After the exposure chambers are set up and the test concentrations have been flowing through long enough to stabilize conditions, place 20 to 22 juvenile shrimp having a total weight of not more than 50 g in each of the aquariums, which are in duplicate for each concentration and for the controls. Test shrimp should be uniform in size. Test concentrations should be at 25 C and have a selected salinity between 25 and 34 ‰ depending on the water supply. Monitor temperature and salinity and maintain salinity at the chosen concentration with a variation of not more than ±1 ‰.[67] If analytical methods are available, monitor concentrations of the toxicants under study in each of the aquariums at least once during the bioassay. In the two lowest concentrations under study, monitor the concentration twice, shortly after the beginning of the study to determine if the dilutions and the concentration are correct and at the completion of the bioassay. The flow-through should not be less than 7 l/day/g of organism and must be sufficient to maintain dissolved oxygen above 60% of saturation and to insure the removal of metabolites.

If the bioassays are for the purpose of testing effluents, the procedures are the same as those described in Section 801E with the test concentrations being determined by range-finding bioassays. Record, analyze, and report data in the routine manner.

Short-term bioassays may also be made with the larval stages of the shrimp. These are especially valuable for determining the concentrations of the effluent or toxicant to be used in the long-term studies. They are also of great value in tests to evaluate the effects of ocean dumping because the larval stages of the commercial shrimp are spent offshore where they are subject to exposure and because these larval stages are sensitive to a variety of toxicants and must be protected if one of the most valuable fisheries is to be protected from pollution.

The larval stages of shrimp for short-term bioassays are obtained from gravid females brought in from offshore. This is a time-consuming and expensive process but once they are secured the first protozoeal shrimp are obtained readily. Handle and feed as described in Section 807A.3*b*5)b). Equipment and technics for spawning and rearing shrimp larvae from egg to post-larvae are described elsewhere.[36-39]

To conduct the short-term bioassays, set up desired test toxicants in duplicate for the five test concentrations and the controls with 100 ml each in 250 ml beakers covered with a watch glass. For the range-finding bioassays, the five concentrations may be 0.01, 0.1, 1, 10, and 100%. Set up definitive acute tests at the concentrations indicated by the range-finding bioassays and as described in Section 801E. Place 10 larvae of the stage to be tested, taken up in a smooth-bore pipet, in each of the test beakers, which are put in a temperature-controlled shaker bath. Add the needed amount of food, algae for the protozoeal stages and brine shrimp for the mysis stages, as indicated in Section 807A.3*b5*)b). The duration of the test is governed by the length of the larval stage or stages it is desired to test. At the conclusion of the test examine the contents of the beakers in petri dishes under a microscope and note live larvae as well as deformed and dead. Analyze and report results as indicated in Section 801F. Use the results of these tests for the selection of concentrations of toxicants to be used in the partial-life-cycle tests.

b) Partial-life-cycle bioassays—Begin these bioassays with the egg and continue to the postlarvae or juvenile stage. In general, conduct the bioassays as recommended in Section 801E with certain modifications to meet the special requirements. The recommended temperature for the bioassays is 28 to 28.5 C and the salinity 28 to 30 ‰. Salinities between 25 and 34 ‰ may be used if the more desirable levels cannot be met. Survival of larvae is poor when spawning is at temperatures below 28 C.

Begin the acclimation of ovigerous females brought in from offshore as soon as possible to get them to 28 to 28.5 C before they are placed in the spawning tanks in the laboratory. While being brought in on the collecting boat they may be held in insulated chests, the temperature of which may be controlled ei-ther by cooling with sacks of ice or warming with a heater. Females usually spawn the first night after being brought into the laboratory. As soon as spawning is completed remove them from the spawning chamber and take samples to estimate the number of eggs in the chamber by methods described by Mock and Murphy.[39] Set up a series of exposure beakers as described for the dungeness crab bioassays, Section 807A.3*b3*). On the beakers use screens of a mesh that will retain the shrimp larvae and brine shrimp but allow the algae to pass through so the screens will not clog. Set up 10 test beakers in a glass tray for each test concentration and the controls. The larvae usually pass through the five nauplii stages to the protozoea stage in about 35 hr. On the basis of the egg count, take samples from the spawning tank after thorough mixing of a volume that should contain about 10 nauplii and put in each of the exposure beakers; this will give 100 larvae for each test concentration and the controls. Just before the nauplii metamorphose to the protozoea stage add the algal food to each of the tanks. The flow of toxicant test solutions through the exposure trays should be 50 ml/min. Add sufficient algae to each exposure tray to supply the quantities indicated in Section 807A.3*b5*)b). Add only the algae concentrate. After the desired concentration of algae is attained, add only enough to maintain the concentration of algal cells at the desired number per milliliter [Section 807A.3*b5*)b)]. Culture algae in the units shown in Section 801C.4*c2*). There should be sufficient production units to supply all the needs for the trays in the test series. Monitor concentrations of the algae cells in the exposure trays at least once a day by taking a sample and passing it through a Coulter Counter or equivalent, modified to count or determine the mass of filamentous algae.

Feed algae throughout the protozoeal stages. At transformation to the mysis stage, phase out feeding of the algae cultures and add newly hatched brine shrimp to the test beakers. Because the algae that were in the tanks during the protozoeal stage tend to remove byproducts, it may be necessary to increase the flow-through in the mysis stage. This can be done more readily because the algae will not need to be continually replaced. Feed brine shrimp nauplii to excess and do not let their concentration drop below 3/ml at any time. Take samples by pipet daily and count visually or by a mechanical counter to insure adequate concentrations of brine shrimp.[39] Pour samples into a graduated cylinder to determine the sample volume and the concentration of brine shrimp in each test chamber. Feed brine shrimp to the larvae through the fourth day of the post-larval stages. At that time remove them from the beakers, place in glass dishes, and count. Count active, deformed, and dead larvae. Record percentage living and dead. Transfer living post-larvae to the compartmented troughs, one trough for each concentration. Change the diet and feed them macerated fish or mollusks. Dry food may also be used. A tropical marine fish food, Tetra Marina, or similar, has been found to produce good results. This food comes in flakes that are readily taken by the post-larvae and the juvenile shrimp.[41, 44] If sediment and organic material tend to collect in the tanks, remove from areas of collection by a siphon or flush out as described previously. Throughout the tests, examine the test organisms to determine the presence of disease or parasites. If bacterial growth or fungi become evident, treat as indicated in Section 801C.5 and 807A.4. If the test chambers become too crowded as the shrimp develop, set up additional chambers in duplicate for the various test concentrations and the controls.

Tests can be continued into the juvenile stage. At the end of the study, collect all the organisms from each tank for weighing, measuring, and histological and accumulation studies. Compare populations in the test tanks with the controls and determine the maximum test concentration that apparently did not reduce the population over the period of exposure. Analyze and evaluate the data and report the results as recommended in Section 801F.

807 C.   References

1. SMITH, R.I., ed. 1964. Keys to Marine Invertebrates of the Woods Hole Region, 1st ed. Systematics-Ecology Program, Marine Biology Lab. Woods Hole, Mass.

2. WILLIAM, A.B. 1965. Marine decapod crustaceans of the Carolinas. *Fish Bull.* 65:10298.

3. WASS, M.L. 1955. The decapod crustaceans

of Alligator Harbor and adjacent inshore areas of northwestern Florida. *Quart. J. Fla. Acad. Sci.* 18:129.

4. LIGHT, S.F., R.I. SMITH, F.A. PIDELKA, E.P. ABBOTT & F.M. WEESNER. 1957. Intertidal Invertebrates of the Central California Coast, 2nd ed. Univ. of Calif. Press, Berkeley.

5. HALSINGER, J.R. 1972. The Freshwater Amphipod Crustaceans (Gammaridae) of North America. Biota of Freshwater Ecosystems, Identification Manual No. 5, Water Pollution Research Ser. No. 5, 18050 E.L.D.O. 4/72.

6. CLEMENS, H P. 1950. Life cycle and ecology of *Gammarus fasciatus* Say. Ohio State Univ., *Franz T. Stone Inst. Hydrobiol. Contrib.* 12:1.

7. COOPER, W.E. 1965. Dynamics and productivity of a natural population of a freshwater amphipod *Hyalella azteca. Ecol. Monogr.* 35:377.

8. SMITH, W.E. 1973. Thermal tolerances of two species of *Gammarus. Trans. Amer. Fish. Soc.* 102:431.

9. HUBSCHMAN, J.H. 1967. Effects of copper on the crayfish *Orconectes rusticus* (Girard). I. Acute toxicity. *Crustaceana* 12:33.

10. COSTLOW, J.D. & C.G. BOOKHOUT. 1960. A method of developing brachyuran crab eggs in vitro. *Limnol. Oceanogr.* 5:212.

11. COSTLOW, J.D., C.G. BOOKHOUT & R. MONROE. 1962. Salinity-temperature effects on the larval development of the crab *Panopeus herbstii* Milne-Edwards reared in the laboratory. *Physiol. Zool.* 35:78.

12. COSTLOW, J.D. & C.G. BOOKHOUT. 1962. The larval development of *Sesarma recticulatum* Say reared in the laboratory. *Crustaceana* 4:281.

13. COSTLOW, J.D. & C.G. BOOKHOUT. 1971. The effect of cyclic temperature on larval development in the mud-crab *Rhithropanopeus harrisii*. D.J. Crisp. 4th European Marine Biology Symp. :211. Cambridge Press, London.

14. BOOKHOUT, C.G., A.J. WILSON, JR., T.W. DUKE & J.I. LOWE. 1972. Effects of mirex on the larval development of two crabs. *Water, Air Soil Poll.* 1:165.

15. EPIFANIO, C.E. 1971. Effects of dieldrin in seawater on the development of two species of crab larvae, *Leptodius floridanus* and *Panopeus herbstii. Mar. Biol.* 11:356.

16. LOWE, J.I. 1965. Chronic exposure of blue crabs, *Callinectes sapidus* to sublethal concentrations of DDT. *Ecology* 46:899.

17. REED, P.H. 1969. Culture methods and effects of temperature and salinity on survival and growth of dungeness crab, *Cancer magister* larvae in the laboratory. *J. Fish. Res. Board Can.* 26:389.

18. BUCHANAN, D.V., R.E. MILLEMANN & N.E. STEWART. 1970. Effects of the insecticide sevin on various stages of the dungeness crab, *Cancer magister. J. Fish. Res. Board Can.* 27:93.

19. BUCHANAN, D.V., M.J. MYERS & R.S. CALDWELL. 1975. An improved flowing water apparatus for culture of brachyuran crab larvae. (unpublished).

20. HUGHES, J.T. & G.C. MATTHIESSEN. 1962. Observations on the biology of the American lobster, *Homarus americanus. Limnol. Oceanogr.*, 7:414.

21. HERRICK, F.H. 1896. The American lobster: A study of its habits and development. *Bull. U.S. Fish Comm.* 15:1.

22. HERRICK, F.H. 1911. Natural history of the American lobster. *Bull. U.S. Bur. Fish.* 29:147.

23. TEMPLEMAN, W. 1948. Growth per molt in the American lobster. *Bull. Newfoundland Govt. Lab.* 18:26.

24. HUGHES, J.T., R.A. SHLESER & G. TCHOBANOGLOUS. 1974. A rearing tank for lobster larvae and other aquatic species. *Progr. Fish-Cult.* 36:129.

25. SPOTTE, S.H. 1970. Fish and Invertebrate Culture, Water Management in Closed Systems. John Wiley and Sons, Inc., New York, N.Y.

26. SMITH, R.A., J.A. HOLMAN & R.H KRAMER. 1974. Automatic brine shrimp feeder. *Progr. Fish-Cult.* 36:133.

27. HUGHES, J.T., J.J. SULLIVAN & R. SHLESER. 1972. Enhancement of lobster growth. *Science* 177:1110.

28. PERKINS, H.C. 1972. Developmental rates at various temperatures of embryos of the northern lobster (*Homarus americanus* Milne-Edwards). *Fish. Bull.* 70:96.

29. BROAD, A.C. & J.H. HUBSCHMAN. 1963. The larval development of *Palaemonetes*

kadiakensis, M.J. Rathbun, in the laboratory. *Trans. Amer. Microsc. Soc.* 82:185.

30. HUBSCHMAN, J.H. & A.C. BROAD. 1974. The larval development of *Palaemonetes intermedius* Holthuis 1949 (Decapoda, Palaemonidae) reared in the laboratory. *Crustaceana* 26:89.

31. DOBKIN, S. 1963. The larval development of *Palaemonetes paludosus* (Gibbes 1850) (Decapoda Palaemonidae) reared in the laboratory. *Crustaceana* 6:41.

32. HUBSCHMAN, J.H. & J.A. ROSE. 1969. *Palaemonetes kadiakensis* Rathbun: Post embryonic growth in the laboratory (Decapoda, Palaemonidae). *Crustaceana* 16:81.

33. FAXON, W. 1879. On the development of *Palaemonetes vulgaris. Bull. Mus. Comp. Zool.* (Harvard) 5:303.

34. BROAD, A.C. 1957. Larval development of *Palaemonetes pugio* Holthuis. *Biol. Bull.* 112:144.

35. BROAD, A.C. 1957. The relationship between diet and larval development of *Palaemonetes. Biol. Bull.* 112:162.

36. COOK, H.L. & M.A. MURPHY. 1966. Rearing penaeid shrimp from eggs to postlarvae. *Proc. 19th Annu. Conf. S.E. Ass. Game Fish. Comm.* 19:283.

37. COOK, H.L. & M.A. MURPHY. 1969. The culture of larval penaeid shrimp. *Trans. Amer. Fish. Soc.* 98:751.

38. COOK, H.L. 1967. A method of rearing penaeid shrimp larva for experimental studies. *FAO (Food Agr. Organ. U.N.) Fish. Rep.* 3:709.

39. MOCK, C.R. & M.A. MURPHY. 1970. Techniques for raising penaeid shrimp from egg to postlarvae. *Proc. 1st Annu. Workshop World Maricult. Soc.* 1:143.

40. SALSER, B.R. & C.R. MOCK. 1973. An airlift circulator for algal culture tanks. *Proc. 4th Annu. Workshop World Maricult. Soc.* 4:295.

41. MOCK, C.R. 1974. Larval Culture of Penaeid Shrimp at the Galveston Biological Laboratory. NOAA Tech. Rep. NMFS Circ. 388:33.

42. MOCK, C.R. 1973. Shrimp culture in Japan. *Mar. Fish. Rev.* 35(3-4):71.

43. MEYERS, S.P. & Z.P. ZEIN-ELDIN. 1972. Binders and pellet stability in development of crustacean diets. *Proc. 3rd Annu. Workshop World Maricult. Soc.* 3:351.

44. MOCK, C.R., R.A. NEAL & B. R. SALSER. 1973. A closed raceway for the culture of shrimp. *Proc. 4th Annu. Workshop World Maricult. Soc.* 4:247.

45. ZEIN-ELDIN, Z.P. & G.W. GRIFFITH. 1969. An appraisal of the effects of salinity and temperature on growth and survival of postlarval penaeids. *FAO (Food Agr. Organ. U.N.) Fish. Rep.* 3:1015.

46. ANDERSON, J.I.W. & D.A. CONROY. 1968. The significance of disease in preliminary attempts to raise crustacea in sea water. *Bull. Off. Inform. Epizoot.* 69:1239.

47. BROCK, T.D. 1966. The habitat of *Leucothrix mucor*, a widespread marine organism. *Limnol. Oceanogr.* 11:303.

48. JOHNSON, P.W., J.M. SIEBURTH, A. SASTRY, C.R. ARNOLD & M.S. DOTY. 1971. *Leucothrix mucor* infestation of benthic crustacea, fish eggs and tropical algae. *Limnol. Oceanogr.* 16:962.

49. LIGHTNER, D.V. & C.T. FONTAIN. 1973. A new fungus disease of the white shrimp *Penaeus setiferus. J. Invertebr. Pathol.* 22:94.

50. COUCH, J.H. 1942. A new fungus on crab eggs. *J. Elisha Mitchell Sci. Soc.* 58:158.

51. ROGERS-TALBERT, R. 1948. The fungus *Lagenidium callinectes* Couch on eggs of the blue crab in Chesapeake Bay. *Biol. Bull.* 95:214.

52. HUBSCHMAN, J.H. & J.A. SCHMITT. 1969. Primary mycosis in shrimp larvae. *J. Invertebr. Pathol.* 13:351.

53. SPENCER, L.T. 1974. Parasitism of *Gammarus lacustris* (Crustacea; Amphipoda) by *Polymorphus minutus* (Acanthocephala) in Colorado. *Amer. Midland Natur.* 91:505.

54. ARTHUR, J.W. & E.N. LEONARD. 1970. Effects of copper on *Gammarus pseudolimnaeus, Physa integra* and *Campeloma decisum* in soft water. *J. Fish. Res. Board Can.* 27:1277.

55. ARTHUR, J.W. & J.G. EATON. 1971. Chloramine toxicity to the amphipod, *Gammarus pseudolimnaeus* and the fathead minnow, *Pimephales promelas. J. Fish. Res. Board Can.* 28:1841.

56. NEBEKER, A.V. & F.A. PUGLISI. 1974. Effect of polychlorinated biphenyls (PCB's) in survival and reproduction of *Daphnia, Gammarus* and *Tanytarsus. Trans. Amer. Fish. Soc.* 103:722.

57. OSEID, D.M. & L.L. SMITH. 1974. Chronic

toxicity of hydrogen sulfide to *Gammarus pseudolimnaeus. Trans. Amer. Fish. Soc.* 103:819.

58. ARTHUR, J.W. 1970. Chronic effects of linear alkylate sulfonate detergents on *Gammarus pseudolimnaeus, Campeloma decisum* and *Physa integra. Water Res.* 4:251.

59. ARTHUR, J.W., A.E. LEMKE, V.R. MATTSON & J.B. HALLIGAN. 1974. Toxicity of sodium nitrilotriacetate (NTA) to the fathead minnow and an amphipod in soft water. *Water Res.* 8:187.

60. COLLIER, R.S., J.E. MILLER, M.A. DAWSON & F.P. THURBERG. 1973. Physiological response of the mud crab *Eurypanopeus depressus* to cadmium. *Bull. Environ. Contam. Toxicol.* 10:378.

61. THURBERG, F.P., M.A. DAWSON & R.S. COLLIER. 1973. Effects of copper and cadmium on osmoregulation and oxygen consumption in two species of estuarine crabs. *Mar. Biol.* 23:171.

62. VERNBERG, W.B. & J. VERNBERG. 1972. The synergistic effects of temperature, salinity and mercury on survival and metabolism of the adult fiddler crab, *Uca pugilator. Fish. Bull.* U.S. Fish Wildl. Serv. 70:415.

63. ARMSTRONG, D.A., D.V. BUCHANAN, M.H. MALLON, R.S. CALDWELL & R.E. MILLIMAN. 1975. Toxicity of the insecticide methoxychlor to the dungeness crab, *Cancer magister* Dana. Oregon State Univ. Marine Science Center, Newport (unpublished).

64. CALDWELL, R.S., D.V. BUCHANAN, D.A. ARMSTRONG, M.H. MALLON, & R.E. MILLIMAN. 1975. Toxicity of pesticides to the dungeness crab *Cancer magister* Dana. I The fungicide captan. Oregon State Univ. Marine Science Center, Newport (unpublished).

65. LITTLE, G. 1968. Induced winter breeding and larval development in the shrimp, *Palaemonetes pugio* Holthuis (Caridea Palaemonidae) studies in decapod larval development. *Crustaceana Suppl.* 2:19.

66. SANDIFER, P.A. 1973. Effects of temperature and salinity on larval development of grass shrimp, *Palaemonetes vulgaris* (Decapoda Caridea). *Fish. Bull.* 71:115.

67. BAHNER, L.H., C.D. CRAFT & D.R. NIMMO. 1975. A temperature and salinity controlled method for marine flow-through bioassays. *Trans. Amer. Fish Soc.* (in press).

807 D.   Bibliography

HADLEY, P.B. 1906. Regarding the rate of growth of the American lobster, *Homarus americanus. 36th Annu. Rep., Comm. Inland Fish. R.I.*: 153.

TEMPLEMAN, W. 1934. Mating in the American lobster. *Contrib. Can. Biol. Fish.* 8:423.

TEMPLEMAN, W. 1936. Further contributions to mating in the American lobster. *J. Biol. Board Can.* 2:223.

MACKAY, D.C.G. 1943. Temperature and world distribution of the genus *Cancer. Ecology* 24:113.

GRUNBAUM, B.W., B.V. SIEGEL, A.R. SCHULZ & P.L. KIRK. 1955. Determination of oxygen uptake by tissue growth in an all glass differential microrespirometer. *Mikrochim. Acta.* 1955:1069.

ROBERTS, J.L. 1957. Thermal acclimation of metabolism of *Pachygrapsus crassipes* Randall.

II. Mechanisms and the influence of season and latitude. *Physiol. Zool.* 30:242.

BOUSFIELD, E.L. 1958. Fresh water amphipod crustaceans of glaciated North America. *Can. Field Natur.* 72:55.

VERNBERG, F.J. & R.E. TASHIAN. 1959. Studies on the physiological variation between tropical and temperate zone fiddler crabs of the genus *Uca.* I. Thermal death limits. *Ecology* 40:589.

COSTLOW, J., C.G. BOOKHOUT & R. MONROE. 1960. The effect of salinity and temperature on larval development of *Sesarma cinerium* (Boxc) reared in the laboratory. *Biol. Bull.* 118:183.

KINNE, O. 1963. The effect of temperature and salinity on marine and brackish water animals: *Oceanogr. Mar. Biol. Annu. Rev.* 1:301.

Costlow, J. & C.G. Bookhout. 1964. An approach to the ecology of marine invertebrate larvae. *Symp. Exp. Mar. Ecol., Occas. Publ.* 2:69. Grad. School Oceanog., Univ. R.I.

Vernberg, F.J. & J.D. Costlow. 1966. Studies on the physiological variation between tropical and temperate zone fiddler crabs of the genus *Uca*. IV. Oxygen consumption of larvae and young crabs reared in the laboratory. *Physiol. Zool.* 39:36.

Hughes, J.T. 1968. Grow your own lobsters commercially. *Ocean Ind.* 3(12):46.

Saila, S., J. Flowers & J.T. Hughes. 1968. Fecundity of the American lobster *Homarus americanus*. *Trans. Amer. Fish. Soc.* 98:537.

Ballard, B.S. & R.E. Tashian. 1969. Osmotic accomodation in *Callinectes sapidus* Rathbun. *Comp. Biochem. Physiol.* 29:671.

Eisler, R. 1969. Acute toxicities of insecticides to marine decapod crustaceans. *Crustaceana* 16:302.

Vernberg, F.J. 1969. Acclimation of intertidal crabs. *Amer. Zool.* 9:333.

Hargrave, G.T. 1970. The utilization of benthic microflora by *Hyalella azteca* (Amphipoda). *J. Anim. Ecol.* 39:427.

Nimmo, D.R., A.J. Wilson, Jr. & R. R. Blackman. 1970. Localization of DDT in the body organs of pink and white shrimp. *Bull. Environ. Contam. Toxicol.* 5:333.

Rice, A.L. & D.I. Williamson. 1970. Methods for rearing larval decapod crustacea. *Helgolander wiss. Meeresunters* 20.

Sastry, A.N. 1970. Culture of brachyuran crab larvae using a recirculating sea water system in the laboratory. *Helgolander wiss. Meeresunters* 20:406.

Sastry, A.N. 1971. Culture of brachyuran crab larvae under controlled conditions: In: The Ocean World (M. Uda). p. 475. Joint Oceanographic Assembly. Japan Soc. Promotion Science, Tokyo.

Hynes, H.B.N. & F. Harper. 1972. The life histories of *Gammarus lacustris* and *Gammarus pseudolimnaeus* in southern Ontario. *Crustaceana*, Suppl. 3:329.

Jenio, F., Jr. 1972. The *Gammarus* of Elm Spring, Union County, Illinois. (Amphipoda: Gammaridae). Ph.D. dissertation, Southern Ill. Univ.

Portman, J.E. 1972. Results of acute toxicity tests with marine organisms, using a standard method. In: Marine Pollution and Sea Life (M. Ruivo, ed.). Fishing News (Brooks) Ltd., London.

Rees, C.P. 1972. The distribution of the amphipod *Gammarus pseudolimnaeus* Bousfield as influenced by oxygen concentration, substratum and current velocity. *Trans. Amer. Microsc. Soc.* 19:514.

Strong, D.R., Jr. 1972. Life history variation among populations of an amphipod (*Hyalella azteca*). *Ecology* 53:1103.

Barlocher, F. & B. Kendrick. 1973. Fungi and food preferences of *Gammarus pseudolimnaeus*. *Arch. Hydrobiol.* 72:501.

Lockwood, A.P.M. & C.B.E. Inman. 1973. Changes in the apparent permeability to water at moult in the amphipod *Gammarus duebeni* and the isopod *Idotea linearis*. *Comp. Biochem. Physiol.* 44A:943.

Vernberg, W.B., P. DeCoursey & W.J. Padgett. 1973. Synergistic effects of environmental variables on larvae of *Uca pugilator*. *Mar. Biol.* 22:307.

Hynes, H.B.N., N.K. Kaushik, M.A. Lock, D.L. Lush, Z.S.J. Stocker, R.R. Wallace & D.P. Williams. 1974. Benthos and allochthonous organic matter in streams. *J. Fish. Res. Board Can.* 31:545.

Nilsson, L.M. 1974. Energy budget of a laboratory population of *Gammarus pulex* (Amphipoda). *Oikos* 25:35.

808   BIOASSAY PROCEDURES FOR AQUATIC INSECTS (TENTATIVE)

Aquatic insects are important components of the biota of lakes and streams. In trout streams, they comprise 50 to 90% of the species of macroinvertebrates. As a group, aquatic insects occupy an important position in the trophic structure of many types of aquatic habitats.[1] Such groups as mayflies, stoneflies, caddisflies, and midges are major food items for many species of fishes. Many aquatic insects on which fishes depend for food are much more sensitive to organic pesticides than are the fishes themselves.

The wide variety of aquatic insects, their abundance in unpolluted streams, their sensitivity to low concentrations of pollutants, and the ease of maintenance of many species under laboratory conditions make them very useful as test animals. Bioassay procedures utilizing aquatic insects have been developed for evaluating toxicity and determining acceptable concentrations of toxicants in the aquatic environment.[2] They are also valuable for determining such environmental requirements of aquatic insects as temperature, oxygen, and pH. Most studies conducted to date consisted of short-term toxicity tests, but the procedures can be used readily for long-term tests.

Toxicants may affect aquatic insects by interfering with their survival, growth, reproduction, emergence, and metabolism. Because effects of long-term exposure to sublethal concentrations of toxicants may be more important than effects of infrequent short-term exposure to higher concentrations, flow-through, long-term bioassays are recommended. The following test procedures are intended to serve as guidelines for carrying out toxicity tests with aquatic insects.

808 A.   Selecting and Preparing Test Organisms

1. Suggested Test Organisms

For bioassays, use insects that are important food for fishes, readily available and abundant, relatively easy to keep and culture in the laboratory and, on the basis of present knowledge, most sensitive to the materials under investigation. The following organisms are suggested:

a. Stoneflies: Pteronarcys dorsata
                   Pteronarcys californica
                   Acroneuria lycorias
                   Acroneuria pacifica

b. Mayflies: Hexagenia limbata
                   Ephemerella subvaria

c. Caddisflies: Brachycentrus americanus
                   Brachycentrus occidentalis

The above species were chosen because of their ease of collection, handling, and identification, sensitivity, and adaptability to laboratory conditions.

d. Other species that have been used are:

1) Stoneflies—
   Isogenus frontalis
   Perlesta placida
   Paragnetina media
   Phasganophora capitata
   Acroneuria californica

2) Mayflies—
   Ephemerella grandis
   Ephemerella doddsi
   Ephemerella needhami
   Ephemerella tuberculata
   Stenonema ithaca

3) Caddisflies—
   Hydropsyche betteni
   Macronemum zebratum
   Arctopsyche grandis
   Hydropsyche bifida

4) Diptera—
   Chironomus plumosus
   Chironomus attenuatus
   Chironomus tentans
   Chironomus californicus
   Glyptochironomus labiferus
   Goeldichironomus holoprasinus
   Tanypus grodhausi
   Tanytarsus (Paratanytarsus) dissimilis

All insects in a test should be of the same year class and, as nearly as possible, the same size. Use early instar (first-year) larvae or nymphs when possible, especially for growth studies. Many of the species listed complete a generation in one summer. Use late instars for adult emergence tests.

2. Collecting Test Animals

Collect all test specimens from clean, natural waters rich in aquatic insects (see Section 1005, Benthic Macroinvertebrates). The larger stream species are found in riffle areas of clean, well-aerated gravel rubble streams and are collected with hand screens or bottom samplers such as the Surber sampler by stirring the bottom and letting the current carry the dislodged insects downstream into the net.

Immediately after collection, gently place the contents of the collection nets into a 15- to 20-l insulated container partly filled with stream water, for transportation to the bioassay laboratory. Remove the larger rocks and discard after it has been determined that they are free of insects. If transportation time is more than 30 min, provide for aeration and temperature control to maintain favorable conditions for the insects. On reaching the laboratory, swirl the water in the containers and dip it out and pour through a screen-bottom container, (of a mesh that will retain the insects required) held partly submerged in a tank of water. Wash the contents of the screen into a holding tank or, if it is desired to separate the insects, wash the contents of the screen into a large white enamel pan containing 3 to 5 cm of water and remove the desired species of insects by means of large-bore pipets or small spoon-shaped screens and place in the holding tanks. Oval annular tanks[2] provided with rocks for cover having a flow-through of dilution water and a current produced by paddle wheels as described elsewhere[2] are satisfactory for holding the riffle insects. A slower method of collecting, but one less damaging to the insects, is to gently pick up rocks, rubble, and gravel and carefully wash or pick and place the desired insects into the insulated containers for transportation to the laboratory.

To secure insects associated with organic debris, silt, or mud in pools of streams, ponds, lakes, and reservoirs, take samples of the bottom materials with Eckman, Petersen, or Ponar dredges. Empty these dredge samples into a large pail or small tub, add water and swirl around with the hand. Partly submerge a washing screen having a mesh bottom of a size that will retain the insects, pour into it a portion of the swirling sample, and wash by jiggling it up and down in the water. Place the washed insects in the insulated container and continue the process until the desired number of insects is collected for transportation to the laboratory to be handled as described previously.

Chironomids will probably be the dominant insect species in bottom material taken from these areas. However, other important insects such as dragonflies, damsel-flies, several species of Diptera, beetle larvae, and mayflies may be found in and on silt bottoms. The mayfly, *Hexagenia limbata*, is a large species often occurring in great abundance in soft, unpolluted muds rich in organic matter that occur in deep pools, ponds, lakes, and reservoirs. They are obtained by collecting the top 8 cm of mud and washing it as described previously.

3. Holding, Acclimating, and Culturing

a. General considerations: As soon after collection as possible, examine the insects for injury. Place all uninjured specimens in suitable holding chambers, supply them with food, and hold for at least 1 wk for observation and acclimation to the desired temperature. Acclimate stream species in flowing water. Hold species from deep pools of streams having mud bottoms and those from lakes and reservoirs in aquariums provided with a 3- to 5-cm layer of unsterilized mud from the site where they were collected. *Hexagenia* require a substrate in which to burrow.[3] The highly organic ooze that overlays the bottom where they were collected is recommended as the substrate for *Chironomus plumosus* and other chironomids of similar habits. Keep stream insects in oval troughs that have a current of water or in stainless steel wire cages in running water.[2] These troughs should contain flat stones covered with attached algae as cover and food for herbivorous species. Supply the insects with materials to build larval and pupal cases. For the caddisflies, sand grains, small pieces of wood, and plant materials that are retained by a 16-mesh stainless steel or aluminum screen serve this purpose. It is critical that those insects that construct tubes or cases be allowed to do so.

Water supplies, dissolved oxygen, and other conditions should be as described in Section 801C and D. The final holding temperature should not be more than 3 C from that at which the organisms were collected, unless they are held for long periods; in that case natural seasonal temperatures should be maintained. When aquatic insects are collected in winter when water temperatures are often 1 C or lower, acclimate them to higher temperatures if they are to be used in short-term bioassays because at these low temperatures they are almost immobile. Different species require different light intensities. Stoneflies require stones under which they can hide from direct light. The light cycle may be fixed at a certain day length, or it may be varied seasonally to correspond with the natural annual photoperiod. For *Chironomus plumosus*, a 16-hr photoperiod is recommended for rearing and testing. Lamps and fixtures are described in Section 801D.3*f*.

b. Food and feeding: Acroneuria, Brachycentrus, Isogenus, and *Paragnetina* are predators and require live food. Feed to excess with small midges, blackfly larvae, mosquitoes, or small caddisfly larvae from an unpolluted environment.[4] *Pteronarcys* and *Ephemerella* should be fed to excess coarse, chopped maple, birch, or aspen leaves that have fallen naturally and have been dried and then soaked in test water for at least 2 wk before feeding. *Hexagenia, Hydropsyche,* and *Arctopsyche* should be fed finely ground leaves and fish-food pellets. If the substrate is rich in organic matter, additional food may not be required for *Hexagenia*. The amount of food needed will vary considerably with species, their number, size, and special metabolic needs, which must be determined by experimentation. Overfeeding with fish food will cause DO difficulties and must be avoided. The larvae of some Hydropsychidae are highly carnivorous and cannibalistic. Keep them well-fed with plankton, microcrustacea, blackfly larvae, and other organisms, which can be collected from fish hatchery ponds, ponds, lakes, and streams with a net of No. 20 bolting silk.

Feed chironomids twice a week. They may be kept in jars supplied with the algal culture medium described in Section 801C.4*c*1)a), which is inoculated with algae and diatoms that provide food and material for their cases. They also may be fed a mixture of 5 g of any good fish food plus 1 g of Cerophyll* (powdered dried grass) shaken in 1 l of water. Add about 100 ml of this suspension to each culture or test jar per feeding. If there is no flow-through, remove 100 ml of the test solution before feeding and replace the toxicant removed with the 100 ml of test solution. Recommended containers are 10-l culture jars containing 8 l or less of culture medium. They should have a screen cover to retain the adults[5,6] and be kept in a constant-temperature room at 21 to 24 C. If desired for long-term studies, temperatures can follow the natural temperature cycle of the water from which the chironomids were taken. Because the jars have a mud substrate, cleaning is not essential, but take care not to overfeed and cause undesirable dissolved oxygen conditions. Emerging adults can be collected for breeding purposes in wire screen cylinders over the culture jars.[7]

---

*Cerophyll Laboratories Inc., 4722 Broadway, Kansas City, Mo.

808 B.   Bioassay Procedures

1. Procedures

Conduct tests as described in Section 801E. Use a minimum of 20 specimens for each toxicant concentration. Use an additional 40 animals to provide specimens for growth studies. Two species may be tested in the same tank if precautions are taken to avoid predation.

Static testing is not recommended with stream insects because they require high oxygen concentration and a flow of water to promote diffusion of oxygen into their gills or tracheae. Static tests may be used with certain lake or reservoir species if required dissolved oxygen concentrations are maintained. For long-term tests, see Section 801E.

a. Test tanks: Aquariums (glass and stainless steel) of either 8 l or 20 l size can be used for quiet-water species. For stream species, use oval, annular troughs of stainless steel[2, 5, 8] in which natural stream flow can be simulated. A recommended size for this oval, annular trough is 90 cm long, 15 cm wide, and 15 cm deep. Set these tanks side by side so paddle wheels on one long shaft can be used to circulate water in all the tanks.[2]

b. Flow rate: The flow to each tank should be no less than 6 to 10 tank volumes/24 hr. If aquariums without water-circulating devices are used for stream species, much higher flows are needed to create water movement simulating stream flow. If oval test tanks are used, velocities near 0.5 cm/sec are recommended. For the quiet-water forms such as *Hexagenia* and *Chironomus*, water velocity should not disturb the mud substrate.

c. Aeration: Aeration of test solutions should not be necessary; however, it can be used with nonvolatile toxicants to increase or control water movement in aquariums. This is especially useful for tank tests with lake and reservoir species.

d. Cleaning: See Section 801C.4*d*. Siphon out detritus on the bottom of tanks weekly during long-term testing. If a mud substrate is used, as with *Hexagenia* and *Chironomus*, no cleaning will be necessary, but avoid overfeeding and accumulation of oxygen-demanding materials on the bottom.

e. Substrate: Fine-mesh stainless steel screens formed into cyclinders or cubes, which provide 10 to 15 cm²/insect, are ideal for acute toxicity tests for all stream riffle species. Place these cages in the oval, annular troughs or in glass cyclinders.[2] For 30- to 90-day adult emergence tests, obtain clean rocks 5 to 10 cm in diameter (one for every three insects) from the stream from which the animals were collected to be used as a substrate. Provide fine screen or sticks that protrude above the water surface for adult emergence tests to enable the insects to leave the water.

f. Light and photoperiod: See Section 801D.3*f*. Use the natural photoperiod at the time of testing for the region in which the test is conducted. Increase day length during adult emergence tests by 0.5 hr every 2 wk.

g. Temperature: See Section 801D.3*a*. Suggested winter testing temperature is 10 C. Summer temperatures for trout stream insects should be near 15 C. Increase temperature during adult emergence tests by 1.0 C each week up to a maximum of 5 C above initial temperature. When using warm-water stream or lake insects, follow the natural temperature cycle for toxicity tests.

b. Time of year: Because most of these species emerge as adults in the spring under natural conditions, start adult emergence tests no later than March 1. *Hexagenia limbata* is an exception, emerging all summer in most localities.

2. Toxicant Preparation

Detailed methodology for preparation of test solutions, determination of the concentrations to be tested, and delivery of solutions to test chambers is given in Sections 801D.1 and 2*b* and in papers cited elsewhere in this and other sections.

3. Test Procedures for *Hexagenia*

Hexagenia can be tested for short-term survival for 96 to 168 hr, survival for 5 to 60 days, adult emergence, or completion of the full life cycle (90 to 120 days). Use a minimum of 20 organisms per test tank and more if possible. Aquariums should be not less than 8 l capacity and preferably 20 l. Water depth should be 8 to 20 cm. The fine organic ooze substrate should be 4 to 5 cm deep and as similar as possible to that where the naiads occur naturally. When newly hatched *Hexagenia* are used to start a test, use 50/tank. When *Hexagenia* eggs are used as a source of larvae, pipet them into petri dishes, (ca. 200/dish) with 20 ml of test water at about 20 C and allow to hatch.

When the substrate is mud, determine survival by counting the number of dead animals that have left their burrows and/or by counting the number of new burrows formed after disturbing the mud surface sufficiently to destroy the entrances to old burrows. If the counts do not agree, use the latter, because some dead specimens may not be counted. For acute toxicity tests an artificial substrate of epoxy resin may be used in lieu of mud. This allows easy observation of test animals and more accurate monitoring due to lower turbidity in the test solution.[3] For growth or emergence tests, set up an additional set of containers so that naiads can be removed periodically for measurement. Remove 10 naiads from the burrows after 20 and 60 days to determine growth. Do not remove more than 50% of the surviving animals before the conclusion of these tests and keep a record of the total number removed. These animals are used to give additional data on growth and emergence tests. Body length, head capsule width, and live weight should be recorded.

In acute toxicity tests, determine survival after 1.5, 3, 6, and 12 hr and twice daily thereafter. Failure of specimens to respond by movement to gentle probing or flashlight illumination can be used as a sign of death. In longer-term studies, check the tanks daily to remove and record dead animals and cast naiad skins, which indicate successful molting.

For growth studies of the test animals, determine the initial size range and means of total length, head capsule width, and weight from specimens obtained from the holding tank. Kill all animals in warm water (40 to 50 C) before measurement. Take measurements twice during testing using animals that are to be discarded. Obtain final measurements for all survivors. Make two counts: the number of adults and the cast skins; if different, use cast skins because some adults may have escaped.

Determine and record the percentage of adults that emerge, their sex, the incidence of incomplete emergence (i.e., half out of nymphal skin, wings unsuccessfully unfolded, etc.), the adult length, weight, and head capsule width and the number of mature eggs.

4. Test Procedures for *Chironomus*

In tests with this group, follow the general procedures described in Section 801D. For each concentration under test with this organism, use duplicate 20-l aquariums with mud substrate and screen covers to retain adults. Maintain the flow into each test container at about 2 l/hr. The mud substrate should be similar to that for the *Hexagenia*. Lighting and photoperiod should be as described in Section 801D.3*f*. Do not feed the animals during the short-term tests. Food for the 30-day and emergence tests should be as described in Section

808A.3*b*. If the prepared food is used, add about 100 ml of the food suspension to each container twice a week.

For the long-term tests, place 50 first instar larvae (about 1.5 mm long and less than 24 hr old) in each test aquarium. Transfer the larvae by means of eyedroppers. Determine the number of emerging adult males and females. Count both the adults and the pupal cases. If the counts differ, use the pupal case count because some of the adults may have escaped. At 25±1 C this requires about 1 month. If the success of fertilization of eggs is to be evaluated, take 50 eggs and determine the percent hatchability. If it is impossible to separate and count the eggs, hatch fertilized egg masses in beakers with the same test water from which the adults emerged. Count 60 larvae into a petri dish and examine for any injured larvae. Often the transfer will injure the early instar larvae; if a correction for this is not made in the count, errors in the percent survival recorded will result. After examination, count 50 larvae back to the test chamber and rear them to the adult stage. End points for taking and analyzing data are emergence of adults, egg production, and hatching of young. Repeat the complete test at least once.

808 C.   Data Evaluation

Analyze, evaluate, and report the data from the various tests as described in Section 801F.

808 D.   References

1. HYNES, H.B. 1970. Ecology of Running Waters. Univ. of Toronto Press, Buffalo, N.Y. and Toronto, Ont., Canada.

2. SURBER, E.W. & T.O. THATCHER. 1963.

Laboratory studies of the effects of alkyl benzene sulfonate on aquatic invertebrates. *Trans. Amer. Fish. Soc.* 92:152.

3. FREMLING, C.R. & G.L. SCHOENING. 1973.

Artificial substrates for *Hexagenia* may-fly nymphs. In: Proc. 1st Int. Conf. Ephemeroptera: 209.

4. NEBEKER, A.V. & F.A. PUGLISI. 1974. Effect of polychlorinated biphenyls on survival and reproduction of *Daphnia, Gammarus* and the midge *Tantarus. Trans. Amer. Fish Soc.* 103:722.

5. NEBEKER, A.V. 1972. Effect of high winter water temperatures on adult emergence of aquatic insects. *Water Res.* 5:777.

6. BAY, E.C. 1967. An inexpensive filter-aquarium for rearing and experimenting with aquatic invertebrates. *Turtox News* 45:146.

7. BREVER, K.D. 1965. A rearing technique for the colonization of chironomid midges. *Ann. Entomol. Soc. Amer.* 58:135.

8. NEBEKER, A.V. & A.E. LEMKE. 1968. Preliminary studies on the tolerance of aquatic insects to heated waters. *J. Kans. Entomol. Soc.* 41:413.

808 E.   Bibliography

PENNAK, R. 1953. Fresh Water Invertebrates of the United States. Ronald Press, New York, N.Y.

USINGER, R.L., ed. 1956. Aquatic Insects of California—With Keys to North American Genera and California Species. Univ. of Calif. Press, Berkeley.

ROBACK, S.S. 1957. The Immature Tendipedids of the Philadelphia Area. Monographs Acad. Natural Science Philadelphia, No. 9.

EDMUNDSON, W.T. et al. 1959. Freshwater Biology, 2nd ed. John Wiley & Sons, Wiley Interscience, New York, N.Y.

MACAN, T.T. 1963. Freshwater Ecology. John Wiley & Sons, Wiley Interscience, New York, N.Y.

FREMLING, C.R. 1967. Methods for mass-rearing *Hexagenia* (Ephemeroptera: Ephemeridae). *Trans. Amer. Fish. Soc.* 96:407.

SANDERS, H.O. & O.B. COPE. 1968. The relative toxicities of several pesticides to naiads of three species of stone-flies. *Limnol. Oceanogr.* 13:112.

HYNES, H.B. 1970. Biology of Polluted Waters. Univ. of Toronto Press, Buffalo, N.Y. and Toronto, Ont., Canada.

GAUFIN, A.R. & S. HERN. 1971. Laboratory studies on tolerance of aquatic insects to heated waters. *J. Kans. Entomol. Soc.* 44:240.

Standard methods for detection of insecticide resistance of *Diabrotica* and *Hypera* beetles. 1972. *Bull. Entomol. Soc. Amer.* 18:179.

GAUFIN, A.R. 1972. Water Quality Requirements of Aquatic Insects. Final Rep. Contract 14-12-438, Water Quality Office, Environmental Protection Agency.

NEBEKER, A.V. 1972. Effect of low oxygen concentration on survival and emergence of aquatic insects. *Trans. Amer. Fish. Soc.* 101:675.

GAUFIN, A.R., R. CLUBB & R. NEWELL. 1974. Studies on the tolerance of aquatic insects to low oxygen concentrations. *Great Basin Natur.* 31:45.

809   BIOASSAY PROCEDURES FOR MOLLUSKS

Oysters, clams, scallops, and mussels are widely distributed and are of great value as food for man. Because of increased demand and decreased production due to water pollution and other causes, their market price has increased greatly during the past few years.

The increasing use of oysters, clams, scallops, mussels, and other mollusks in bioassay tests has demonstrated their suitability for evaluating the toxicity of potential pollutants in both short- and long-term exposures. Oyster and clam embryos have been used by marine biologists for more than a decade to measure the effects of chemical and environmental variables in estuarine and marine environments. The following test protocols are presented so that different workers can generate comparable data.

Guidelines for using freshwater mollusks in standard bioassay tests await the completion of basic studies now underway. However, standard methods for the laboratory culture and maintenance of some hydrobiid snails are available.[1]

The great variety of bivalve mollusks available in unpolluted estuarine areas, the sensitivity of certain of their life stages to low concentrations of pollutants, and the ease with which they are caught and maintained contribute to their usefulness as test animals.

Toxicants may affect bivalves by interfering with fertilization, normal embryonic development, growth (shell deposition), byssal thread secretion, reproduction, and normal tissue histology. These important toxic effects are the bases for the recommended short- and long-term toxicity tests. Adult bivalves are not generally suitable for the determination of acute lethal concentrations of toxicants because of their ability to close their shells and protect themselves from the toxicant for considerable periods.

809 A.   Selecting and Preparing Test Organisms

1. Selecting Test Organisms

Although bioassay tests have been conducted with a large number of species, intensive testing has been confined to relatively few species. Some studies have been made of the relative sensitivity of various members of this group to the same toxicant and considerable variation has been found. For oil and the heavy metals, the bay scallop is the most sensitive species tested to date. Some adult mollusks are resistant to many materials and often accumulate them to high concentrations. In comparison to fishes and other invertebrates, the larvae of oysters are more sensitive to some materials and considerably less sensitive to others, especially some of the organic pesticides. Species recommended for study at this time are based on their past use in bioassays and the availability of data on their culture and handling.

They are as follows:

Crassostrea gigas	Pacific Oyster
Crassostrea virginica	Eastern Oyster
Ostrea lurida	Olympia Oyster
Argopecten irradians irradians	Bay Scallop
Mytilus edulis	Mussel
Mercenaria mercenaria	Quahog
Spisula solidissima	Surf Clam
Mulinia lateralis	Coot Clam
Macoma balthica	
Rangia cuneata	

2. Water Supply and Water System

The bioassay tests described here require the availability of a well-equipped marine laboratory having an adequate and dependable supply of clean, unfiltered estuarine or open ocean water that can be maintained in the desired temperature and salinity range. The general requirements for a water supply and water system are described in Section 801C.4b and 801D.1 and 2a. If necessary, artificial seawater can be used for limited studies.

Filter-feeding mollusks require an abundant supply of natural seawater containing an adequate amount of the planktonic organisms on which they feed. In long-term growth tests, adult oysters require a minimum of 5 l, and preferably more, of unfiltered seawater per hour per oyster to satisfy food requirements. Clams and scallops require comparable amounts of natural seawater rich in plankton. In flow-through tests, the water should be distributed from a constant-head tank as described for flow-through bioassays, Section 801D.1.

3. Collecting, Conditioning, and Culturing Test Organisms

Test organisms may be collected from the field, purchased from commercial dealers, or reared.

The bivalve mollusks described are filter-feeders and require an abundant water supply rich in planktonic food organisms. When adults are held for bioassay tests or spawners for the production of embryos and larvae for testing purposes, an adequate flow of natural seawater rich in plankton is of prime importance. Clean intake pipes and the water system frequently to insure that growth in the pipes does not remove the plankton organisms before the water reaches the holding tanks. If there is not sufficient food, or if a continuous flow-through of unfiltered seawater results in

problems of competitors, parasites, and disease, planktonic food can be produced in rearing chambers, Section 801C.4c2), for supplying the needs of the test organisms. *Monochrysis lutheri*, *Phaeodactylum tricornutum*, and *Dunaliella tertiolecta* have been used with success but several other species may be used. Culture medium for algae is described in Section 801C.4c1)b).

a. Oysters: For tests with adults, or for the production of embryos for testing purposes, use adults of the Pacific or Eastern oyster, 7.5 to 15 cm in height. Cull the oysters selected to singles and bring to the laboratory for conditioning at 2- to 4-wk intervals, depending on the amount of bioassay work to be done. In the laboratory hold each lot of oysters used for a specific study as a separate population in the conditioning trays. Oysters collected from December to April need longer conditioning than those collected between April and July. After August, oysters begin resorbing their unspawned gametes. Once this process starts, attempts to use them for spawners will not be satisfactory. To have spawning oysters after August, collect them during the spring months and keep in an area of year-round cool water, or in refrigerated, flowing seawater in the laboratory. Temperatures below 12 C arrest gonad development and assure a supply of oysters that can be conditioned for spawning in any month of the year.[2]

When prepared for tests, the oysters should be cleaned of fouling organisms and other extraneous materials. Fifteen oysters per conditioning tray, about $58 \times 46 \times 8$ cm ($23 \times 18 \times 3$ in.) is a reasonable density. Each tray should receive a minimum of 7 l/hr of flowing seawater at 20 ± 1 C. Oysters require 2 to 6 wk of thermal conditioning (depending on degree of gonad development) before they are ready to spawn and can be held 2 to 4 wk for use as spawners, after which they should be discarded. Conditioned mature mollusks will spawn in either natural or artificial seawater. When they are induced to spawn in natural seawater, transfer them immediately to the receiving water or artificial medium for collection of gametes for the bioassays.

Check oysters daily and remove moribund individuals. If any die, empty the tray and clean with detergent and warm water. Scrub the remaining oysters with clean seawater, rinse several times, and put back in the tray after the water flow has been restored.

Clean accumulated feces and silt from the trays at least once a week, preferably twice a week. Should an unplanned spawning occur, discard all oysters in that tray. When fertilized eggs are required, rinse conditioned oysters with clean seawater and place individually in spawning dishes. Raise the water temperature 5 to 10 C to induce spawning and add a sperm suspension as a further inducement for the females to spawn. The sperm suspension is prepared by opening a male oyster, rupturing the gonad, and gently washing the sperm free from the gonadal tissue into a 1,000-ml beaker with a fine jet of 20 C seawater. Take care not to rupture other body organs during the process and use enough water so that dissolved oxygen remains near saturation in the sperm suspension. After a spawning attempt, oysters that have not spawned are returned to the conditioning trays. Discard females once they have spawned. Place any surplus males that spawn in a separate tray; they can be sacrificed for making sperm suspensions for subsequent bioassays.

b. Clams: Clams can be collected from the field or secured from commercial fishermen, preferably by accompanying them on their trips and selecting the desired specimens. Keep adults so collected in live boxes or in containers with adequate flow-through water until they reach the laboratory, then place in suitable holding trays. Such specimens may be used in long-term growth or other studies, or they may be used for the production of larvae for short-term tests like those described for oysters. If adults are not taken during the normal spawning season, they can be thermally conditioned for spawning by placing them in conditioning trays with flow-through seawater between 18 and 22 C, depending on the species, for 3 to 4 wk to ripen the gonads. To stimulate adult clams with ripe gonads to spawn naturally, increase the water temperature to 24 to 28 C, depending on the species, and add a sperm suspension to the water as described for oysters. Produce larvae only from naturally liberated eggs. A stock of 30 to 40 thermally conditioned adults is adequate to assure spawning at any time. Place eggs so produced in the test solutions as soon as possible, and not more than 2 hr, after fertilization.

If it is desirable to use the larvae in longer-term tests and the natural food is not sufficient, feed them a mixture of *Isochrysis galbana* and *Monochrysis lutheri* or some other cultured algae[3] grown in the standard enriched seawater described in 801C.4c1)b).

c. Mussels: Mytilus edulis is found in large numbers attached to pilings, rocks, floating boat docks, jetties, and other suitable habitats. Collections can be made with ease from any of these areas, but those from floating docks or platforms are preferred because they are easiest to collect and clean. Because the larger specimens may contain maturing gametes that may be freed during the experimental period, use only small specimens in intermediate-term tests with adults. Specimens used in the tests should be of uniform size, 15 to 20 mm in width.[4] This size class can be secured readily through the use of a piece of sheet metal in which two holes, 15 and 20 mm in diameter, have been drilled. Specimens should pass through the 20-mm hole but not the 15-mm opening. Discard all other specimens. Clean the surface of the mussel of attached organisms and trim the byssal threads. Do not remove the byssal thread stalk because this may injure the secretory gland.

Acclimate cleaned specimens in aquariums for 1 wk at not more than 4 C above field water temperature but below 26 C and at a density of about 10 specimens/4 l of seawater. Provide aeration and filtration if the aquarium is a static system. Observe the holding aquariums daily for deaths. Discard all specimens if more than 10% die during the acclimation period. Occasionally some of the 15- to 20-mm specimens have mature gametes and will spawn in the aquarium. Change the water to prevent fouling and remove the mature specimen if it can be identified. If spawning is widespread within the aquarium, discard all specimens.

d. Scallops: Bay scallops for use in bioassays can be collected from the field or purchased from fishermen if special precautions are taken to insure proper handling from the time of catch until they are brought to the laboratory. Adults so obtained may be used for various types of growth or toxicity tests or for production of embryos and larvae for development, growth, or toxicity tests, as described for the oyster.

The life history of the bay scallop, *Argopecten irradians irradians*, has been under study since early in this century[5] and numerous studies have been made to develop culture methods.[6] Loosanoff and Davis[2] and Castagna and Duggan[6] described methods for conditioning and spawning adults and raising the larvae to metamorphosis. Turner and Hanks[7] and Sastry[8] substantiated the feasibility of conditioning adults for spawning out of season in order to secure larvae at all seasons for bioassay studies. These publications give information essential for the collection, handling, and conditioning of scallops. Conditioning is accomplished, spawning induced, and fertilization obtained much as has been described for oysters. Conditioning is carried out at 20 to 22 C for 3 to 8 wk in the same type of tray used for oysters. Check the gonads periodically to determine development. This is done by placing a finger in a gaping scallop to hold the shells open so the gonads can be seen. The bay scallop is a functional hermaphrodite. The testis comprises the anterior border of the gonad and the ovary the posterior portion. When ripe, the ovarian portion is reddish orange and the testis cream-colored. After the gonads have ripened, spawning is induced by raising the water temperature to 27 to 30 C. Procedures for spawning, handling of the ova, fertilization, and the rearing of larvae are described by Castagna and Duggan.[6] Embryos may be used for tests described for oysters or the larvae may be used for various longer-term tests.

4. Parasites and Diseases

Different species of cyclopoid copepods may be present within the mantle cavity or digestive tract of mollusks. Their effect has been reviewed by Cheng.[9] Species inhabiting the mantle cavity do not cause any known pathological damage to the host. However, cyclopoid copepods, such as *Mytilicola intestinalis*, which inhabit the digestive tract, may cause histopathological damage to the cellular linings. A higher incidence of mortality may occur during the tests among the infected organisms because of the damage to their digestive system. Examine the digestive tracts of a randomly selected sample of 20 mollusks for cyclopoid copepods before use of a group taken in one collection, especially in geographical areas where *M. intestinalis* is known to occur. Do not use the mollusks if the incidence of infection exceeds 10%.

809 B.   Conducting the Bioassays

1. Short-Term Bioassays

a. Oyster embryo tests: Oyster eggs can be produced routinely in the laboratory and fertilized to initiate development. Under standard conditions, they become shelled, straight-hinge larvae in 48 hr. The normality of their development when cultured in receiving water samples is used to determine receiving water quality. When embryos are cultured in artificial seawater the normality of their development is used as a criterion of relative toxicity of added toxicants. The procedures for preparing artificial seawater[10] for spawning of adult mollusks and culturing their embryos is as follows:

Add the following reagent-grade chemicals in the amounts and order listed to 890 ml glass distilled deionized water. Dissolve each chemical completely before adding another.* When all chemicals are dissolved, add distilled deionized water to make 1 l.

Chemical	Concentration g/l
$SrCl_2$	0.02
H_3BO_4	0.03
KBr	0.10
KCl	0.70
$CaCl_2 \cdot 2H_2O$	1.47
Na_2SO_4	4.00
$MgCl_2 \cdot 6H_2O$	10.00
NaCl	23.50
$Na_2SiO_3 \cdot 9H_2O$	0.03
$NaHCO_3$	0.20
Na_2EDTA	0.003

---

*If the salts are not added in the sequence listed above and each completely dissolved before the next is added, the pH will be unsatisfactory and will require so much $NaHCO_3$ to correct it that the salt balance will be unsatisfactory. See Sections 801C.4*b*2) and *c*1)b) for further discussion.

This artificial seawater is satisfactory for spawning adults as well as for culturing embryos[11] and has been proposed as a standard testing medium.[12,13] Methodology for oyster embryo culture was developed in studies of the eastern oyster, *Crassostrea virginica*,[2] and adapted for bioassays using the Pacific oyster, *C. gigas*,[14] and the blue mussel, *Mytilus edulis*.[15] This method is suited to other bivalves whose spawning can be controlled under laboratory conditions.

The general steps followed in carrying out tests with fertilized oyster eggs on a year-round basis are as follows:

1) Two hours before spawning is desired, place 15 thermally conditioned ripe female oysters in an equal number of pyrex baking dishes about $22 \times 12 \times 8$ cm filled with filtered, ultraviolet-light-treated seawater or artificial seawater at 20 C.

2) To induce spawning raise the water temperature by placing the dishes in a water bath with a temperature of 28 to 30 C.

3) About 30 min before spawning is desired, add 20 ml of a sperm suspension, prepared as described in Section 809A.3a, to each dish. The combination of increased temperature and sperm usually induces accelerated pumping by the oysters and one or more of the ripe females to spawn. The sperm fertilizes the eggs as they are discharged.

4) If spawning is not achieved in about 1 hr, or the oysters stop vigorous pumping activity, replace the water in the spawning dishes with fresh 20 C water and repeat the process. Introduction of additional sperm suspension by pipet directly into the water being drawn in by the oyster frequently initiates spawning.

5) About 30 to 45 min after spawning, eggs from a single female (usually 6 to 40 million) are poured into a 2-l beaker. Egg density is determined from two counts, made in a Sedgwick-Rafter cell, of the number of eggs in 1-ml samples of a 1:99 dilution of the homogeneous egg suspension.

6) Bring the temperature of control and test water samples to 20 C±0.5 C, (25 C±0.5 C in southern areas), before inoculation with oyster embryos. Add enough embryo suspension to each test container to give a population density of 20,000 to 30,000/l. Establish at least 10% of the cultures as controls and at least two replicates of each experimental condition.

7) Incubate cultures in a 20±1 C water bath for 48 hr, (25±1 C in southern areas), and then pour through a 37-μm sieve to retain and concentrate the larvae.

8) Wash the larvae into a 100-ml graduate. From this, take a 2-ml sample containing 150 to 250 larvae with an automatic pipet. Preserve samples in vials with 3% neutral formalin for evaluation by a microscopic examination.

9) Count preserved larvae in a Sedgwick-Rafter cell and record the numbers of normal and abnormal larvae. Normal larvae are those that are fully shelled, even though they may be misshapen or undersized. This criterion avoids the necessity of making an excessive number of value judgments to classify a larva as normal or abnormal. The percentage of normal larvae is the basic measure of biological response used in the method. The response to any variable studied is described in terms of the percentage of oyster larvae that developed normally in the presence of the

variable. Woelke[14] presents further details and discusses test variability and computer methods for data processing and analysis.

b. Scallop, clam, and mussel embryo tests: Make tests with bay scallop, clam, and mussel embryos using the procedures described for oyster embryos.

c. Oyster shell deposition test:

1) General considerations—This 96-hr test demonstrates the comparative toxicity of pollutants to young oysters. This test is conducted in flowing, unfiltered seawater at a selected temperature between 15 and 30 C. Actively feeding oysters extend their mantle edges to the periphery of the shell or valves. However, the body can contract to occupy a much smaller area. If the peripheral valve edges are mechanically ground away, the oysters respond by depositing new shell to replace this loss.[16]

The growth of new shell is primarily linear during the first week and the rate of deposition is an index of the animals' reaction to ambient water quality. With acceptable water conditions, 25 mm and larger oysters deposit as much as 1.0 mm of peripheral new shell per day. Small oysters are more suitable than large ones because typically they form new shell deposits within a broader temperature range than mature oysters, which tend to become less active at temperature extremes. Interpretation of test data is independent of minor fluctuations in temperature and salinity during the 96-hr exposure because the simultaneous shell deposition in control oysters is considered to be the norm or 100%.

2) Procurement and preparation of oysters—Oysters about 25 to 50 mm in height (i.e., the long axis) with reasonably flat, rounded shape are culled to singles, brush cleaned, and maintained in trays in the natural environment. At the time of the test, reclean oysters and remove about 3 to 5 mm of the shell periphery by handholding the oyster against an electric disc grinder, using care to insure uniform removal from the shell rim to produce a smoothly rounded blunt profile. Removal of too wide a rim of shell will make an opening into the shell cavity; discard such damaged oysters.

Test aquariums may be fabricated of glass, plexiglass, or fiberglassed wood and should measure about $64 \times 38 \times 10$ cm deep ($25 \times 15 \times 4$ in.) to provide adequate space for 20 oysters. This size permits adequate circulation of the water while avoiding physical agitation of the oysters by the water current. The unfiltered seawater supply in a constant-head trough or head box should be delivered to the test aquariums by the fail-safe diluter system described in Section 801D.1 or by calibrated siphons via a mixing trough (Figure 809:1 and Lowe[17]) into which the toxicant in an appropriate solvent is metered. Prepare stock solutions of the toxicant so that a delivery of 1 or 2 ml/min by means of the proportional diluters or by a calibrated pump† will result in the desired concentration. When the latter method is used (Figure 809:1) baffles in the trough ensure adequate mixing and aeration before the water enters the test aquariums. The aquariums contain about 18 l at 75% capacity and with a flow rate of 100 l/hr will provide 5 l/

---

†Sage syringe pump, Sage Instruments, Inc., Cambridge, Mass., or MilRoyal[R] controlled pump, Milton Roy, St. Petersburg, Fla. Similar pumps may be obtained from other suppliers.

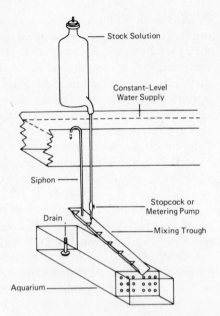

Figure 809:1. **Diagram of constant-flow apparatus.**[17]

hr/oyster. Small oysters feed and grow readily under these conditions.

3) Bioassay procedure—A preliminary exposure series is helpful in determining a suitable range of toxicant concentrations (see Section 801E.2a). In general, five oysters exposed for 48 hr to concentrations of 100, 10, 1.0, 0.1, and 0.01 mg/l will bracket the range of toxicant concentrations required to determine 96-hr EC50 data, although lower concentrations may need to be checked.

Prepare and distribute oysters randomly so that each control and test aquarium contains 20 individuals. Place oysters with the left, cupped valve down and the anterior hinged ends all oriented in one direction. Establish one control aquarium, another receiving only toxicant solvent, and one aquarium for each concentration of the toxicant being

tested. At the end of 96 hr, remove all oysters from the water and measure the shell increments. Shell deposition is not uniform on the periphery; record the length of the longest "finger" of new shell on each oyster, measured to the nearest 0.5 mm.

4) Calculation—The ratio of mean growth of a group of test oysters to mean growth of control oysters provides a percentage index of the response of the oysters to a toxicant concentration. For 96-hr exposure, one may calculate the concentrations causing 50% relative shell growth and 5% relative shell growth. These values are relative and may differ significantly under different salinity or temperature regimes.

2. Long-Term Bioassays

a. Oyster growth test:

1) General considerations—Oysters will grow from setting size to sexual maturity in about 3 to 4 months in laboratory aquariums if they are adequately supplied with flowing, unfiltered seawater containing planktonic food in adequate quantity. Small populations, 50 to 100 individuals, are useful for determining the effects of chronic exposure to toxicants or to physical factors causing stress, such as increased temperature or turbidity. Toxic effects may be manifested by the accumulation of chemical residues, changes in resistance to disease, or interference with reproduction. Growth rate changes are especially valuable for objective evaluation and are the basis for this bioassay test.

Oyster growth can be evaluated by recording weight increases. If oysters are weighed under water, day-to-day changes can be detected.[18] Oyster tissues have about the same density as seawater and such weight changes indicate primarily the deposition of new shell.

The value of weight data depends on the care exercised in cleaning the oysters. Remove all fouling organisms and debris, while taking care to maintain the integrity of the shells before each weighing. The oyster's valves must remain closed when it is exposed in the air and the shell must be free of air bubbles when weighed. Weighings can be replicated to 0.05 g and, under satisfactory conditions, a 15 g oyster (underwater weight), which weighs about 30 g in air, will gain 1 g or more per week. Andrews[19] discussed the weighing technic and proposed this method for assessing water quality in oyster-growing areas.

The sublethal effects of toxicants may become apparent only slowly. For example, Lowe et al.[20] did not observe statistically significant changes in growth rate in test oysters until after 22 wks of continuous exposure to low pesticide concentrations.

2) Bioassay procedure—Place small (2- to 3-cm) single oysters, randomly selected from a population of known approximate age, in test aquariums large enough to accommodate their anticipated growth. Supply water and toxicant as described for the 96-hr shell deposition test. A minimum of 5 l/hr of seawater per oyster provides adequate growing conditions. Select the concentration of the toxicant on the basis of available 96-hr tolerance data (Section 801E.2a).

Oysters are positioned on shallow compartmented racks to facilitate handling and identification of individual animals.[20] Groups of 50 oysters in each control and the test chambers are recommended. At weekly intervals remove the oysters, clean them, and keep immersed in water until weighed. Also clean test and control containers at this time.

Weigh individual oysters while they are immersed in water on a top-loading balance with suspension attachment. Estimate weights to the nearest 0.01 g. Appropriate analyses of weight increases will indicate the relative toxicity of the variable under test. It is desirable at each weighing to record changes in shell length to gain additional response data. A more thorough understanding of potential toxic effects can be gained if a suitable number of extra oysters is kept with test and control groups. These serve as periodic subsamples for determination of residue accumulations and histological changes.

b. *Scallop, clam, and mussel growth tests:* Bay scallops, clams, and mussels can be used in growth tests similar to those described for oysters if provisions are made to meet their special requirements with respect to exposure chambers, food, and handling.

809 C. Reporting and Analyzing Results

Except for special studies, analyze data, calculate results, and report results as described in Section 801F.

809 D.   References

1. Van der Schalie, H & G.M. Davis. 1968. Culturing *Oncomelania* snails (Prosobranchia: *Hydrobiidae*) for studies of oriental Schistosomiasis. *Malacologia* 6:321.

2. Loosanoff, V.L. & H.C. Davis. 1963. Rearing of bivalve mollusks. *Advan. Mar. Biol.* 1:1.

3. Chanley, P. & M. Castagna. 1966. Larval development of the pelecypod *Lyonsia hyalina. Nautilus* 79(4):123.

4. Reish, D.J. & J.C. Ayres, Jr. 1968. Studies on the *Mytilus edulis* community in Alamitos Bay, California. III. The effects of reduced dissolved oxygen and chlorinity concentrations on survival and byssal thread production. *Veliger* 10:384.

5. Belding, D.L. 1910. A Report upon the Scallop Fishery of Massachusetts, Including the Habits, Life History of *Pecten irradians*, Its Rate of Growth and Other Factors of Economic Value. Spec. Rep., Comm. Fish and Game, Boston, Mass.

6. Castagna, M. & W. Duggan. 1971. Rearing the bay scallop, *Argopecten irradians. Proc. Nat. Shellfish. Ass.* 61:80.

7. Turner, H. & J.E. Hanks. 1960. Experimental stimulation of gametogenesis in *Hydroides dianthus* and *Pecten irradians* during the winter. *Biol. Bull.* 119:145.

8. Sastry, A.N. 1966. Temperature effects in reproduction of the bay scallop, *Argopecten irradians* Lamarck. *Biol. Bull.* 130:118.

9. Cheng, T.C. 1967. Marine mollusks as hosts for symbiosis with a critical review of known parasites of commercially important species. *Advan. Mar. Biol. 5.*

10. Zaroogian, G.E., G. Pesch & G. Morrison. 1969. Formulation of an artificial sea water medium suitable for oyster larvae development. *Amer. Zool.* 9:1144.

11. Calabrese, A., R.S. Collier, D.A. Nelson & J.R. MacInnes. 1973. The toxicity of heavy metals to embryos of the American oyster *Crassostrea virginica. Mar. Biol.* 18:162.

12. Tarzwell, C.M. 1969. Standard methods for determination of relative toxicity of oil dispersants and mixtures of dispersants and various oils to aquatic life. In: Proc. Joint Conf. on Prevention and Control of Oil Spills. p.179. American Petroleum Inst.

13. LaRoche, G., R. Eisler & C.M. Tarzwell. 1970. Bioassay procedures for oil and oil dispersant toxicity evaluation. *J. Water Pollut. Control Fed.* 42:1982.

14. Woelke, C.E. 1972. Development of a Receiving Water Quality Bioassay Criterion Based on the 48-hr Pacific Oyster (*Crassostrea gigas*) Embryo. Tech. Rep. 9, Wash. Dep. Fisheries, Olympia.

15. Dimick, R.E. & W.P. Breese. 1965. Bay mussel embryo bioassay. In: Proc. 12th Pacific Northwest Industrial Waste Conf., Univ. of Wash., Seattle. p. 165.

16. Butler, P.A. 1965. Reaction of some estuarine mollusks to environmental factors. In: Biological Problems in Water Pollution (C.M. Tarzwell, ed.) U.S.PHS Pub. 999-WP-25, p. 92.

17. Lowe, J.I. 1964. Chronic exposure of spot, *Leiostomus xanthurus*, to sub-lethal concentrations of toxaphene in seawater. *Trans. Amer. Fish. Soc.* 93:396.

18. Havinga, B. 1928. The daily rate of growth of oysters during summer. *J. Cons. Perma. Int. Explor. Mer* 3:231.

19. Andrews, J.D. 1961. Measurement of shell growth in oysters by weighing in water. *Proc. Nat. Shellfish. Ass.* 52.1.

20. Lowe, J.I., P.D. Wilson, A.J. Rick & A.J. Wilson, Jr. 1971. Chronic exposure of oysters to DDT, toxaphene and parathion. *Proc. Nat. Shellfish. Ass.* 61:231.

809 E.   Bibliography

Gutsell, J.S. 1930. Natural history of the bay scallop. *Bull. U.S. Bur. Fish.* 46:569.

Loosanoff, V.L. & H.C. Davis. 1951. Delayed spawning of lamellibranchs by low temperature. *J. Mar. Res.* 10:197.

Davis, H.C. 1953. On food and feeding of larvae of the American oyster, *C. virginica. Biol. Bull.* 104:334.

Okubo, K. & T. Okubo. 1962. Study of the bioassay method for the evaluation of water pollution. II. Use of fertilized eggs of sea ur-chins and bivalves. *Bull. Tokai Reg. Fish. Res. Lab.* No. 32.

TUBIASH, H.S. & P.E. CHANLEY. 1963. Bacterial necrosis of bivalve larvae. *Bacteriol. Proc.* 1963.

DAVIS, H.C. & A. CALABRESE. 1964. Combined effects of temperature and salinity on devel-opment of eggs and growth of larvae of *M. mercenaria* and *C. virginica. U.S. Bur. Commer. Fish. Bull.* 63:643.

GALTSOFF, P.S. 1964. The American oyster, *Crassostrea virginica. U.S. Bur. Commer. Fish. Bull.* 64:1.

WOELKE, C.E. 1965. Bioassays of pulp mill wastes with oysters. In: Biological Problems in Water Pollution (C.M. Tarzwell, ed.) U.S. PHS Pub. 999-WP-25, p. 67.

WOELKE, C.E. 1965. Development of a Bioassay Method Using the Marine Alga, *Mono-chrysis lutheri.* Wash. Dep. Fish. Shellfish Prog. Rep., Olympia.

MATTHIESSEN, G.C. & R.C. TONER. 1966. Pos-sible Methods of Improving the Shellfish Industry of Martha's Vineyard, Duke's County, Massachusetts. Marine Research Foundation Inc., Edgartown, Mass.

WOELKE, C.E. 1967. Measurement of water quality with the Pacific oyster embryo bioassay. *Spec. Tech. Pub.* 416:112. Amer-ican Society for Testing and Materials, Philadelphia, Pa.

WOELKE, C.E. 1968. Application of shellfish bioassay results to the Puget Sound pulp mill problem. *Northwest Sci.* 42(4):125.

WOELKE, C.E., T.D. SCHINK & E.W. SANBORN. 1970. Development of an *in situ* marine bioassay with clams. Annu. Rep. Oct. 1, 1969-Sept. 30, 1970. July 6, 1970. Wash. Dep. Fish., Olympia.

BROWN, B.E. 1972. The effect of copper and zinc on the metabolism of the mussel *Mytilus ed-ulis. Mar. Biol.* 16:108.

FAVRETTO, L. & F. TUNIS. 1974. Typical level of lead in *Mytilus galloprovincialis* Lmk from the Gulf of Trieste. *Rev. Int. Oceanogr. Med.* 33:67.

810 BIOASSAY PROCEDURES FOR FISHES

Fish have been more widely used for bioassays than any other group of aquatic organisms. During the past 50 yr, more than 60 species have been used by various investigators for a wide vari-ety of bioassay investigations. However, only about 15 species have been used ex-tensively and only a portion of these have been employed in life-cycle bioassays. Among the latter group, most have been freshwater species.[1] This may be because methods for their culture had been developed. Until recently, few ma-rine fishes were cultured, reared in the laboratory, or used for bioassays. To date, most of the marine and estuarine fishes used in bioassays are hardy species readily maintained in the laboratory and most are very tolerant to a wide range of salinity, temperature, and dis-solved oxygen. Species that are tolerant of wide and rapid changes in DO, tem-perature, and salinity are not appropri-ate for bioassays to determine the suit-ability of those environmental factors essential for a well-rounded aquatic population. However, these species may be well suited for bioassays of some tox-icants. Within the past 10 yr there has been a great upsurge in the culturing of marine organisms and a few fishes have been reared through their life cycle, or several of their life stages, in the labora-tory.

810 A.   Selecting and Preparing Fishes for Bioassays

1. Selecting Test Species

General guidelines for selecting test organisms for bioassays have been presented in Section 801C.1. A prime consideration in the selection of fishes for bioassays is their sensitivity to the effluent, material, or environmental factor under consideration. To date, few studies have been made to determine the relative sensitivity of aquatic organisms to different potential toxicants and wastes in order to determine the most sensitive important local species. Because of the number of species that have been reared in hatcheries, it is possible to conduct life-cycle studies with a number of the freshwater fishes. For those that have not been reared in the laboratory, it is usually necessary to collect various life stages from the field for partial-life-cycle bioassays. Because only a very limited number of marine fishes have been spawned and reared in the laboratory, field collection and laboratory maintenance of larvae and juveniles is very often necessary.

The following is a partial list of the freshwater, estuarine, and marine fishes that have been used for bioassays by various investigators. Some of these have been used only in short-term bioassays while others have been used in long-term, partial-, or full-life-cycle studies. It is suggested that under present conditions one or more of these species can be used for specific bioassays. Some of the species listed are very hardy to changes in environmental factors and will survive under wide variations of temperature, oxygen, pH, and salinity

and thus are not well suited for determining favorable environmental factors for the survival of a biota. Further, certain levels of environmental factors and certain concentrations of toxicants under which adults may live indefinitely may not be suitable for the survival of the species and the most sensitive life stages should be used in the bioassays when possible. If data are not available on the relative sensitivity of the different species to the effluent or waste, use short-term bioassays with local species to determine the one most sensitive to the waste. Because of their previous use and importance the following species are suggested for toxicity testing.

a.   Freshwater fishes used for bioassays:

Clupeidae:

Alosa pseudoharengus	Alewife
Dorosoma petenense	Threadfin shad

Salmonidae:

Coregonus artedii	Lake herring
Coregonus clupeaformis	Lake whitefish
Prosopium williamsoni	Mountain whitefish
Oncorhynchus gorbuscha	Pink salmon
Oncorhynchus kisutch	Coho salmon
Oncorhynchus nerka	Sockeye salmon
Oncorhynchus tschawytscha	Chinook salmon
Salmo clarki	Cutthroat trout
Salmo gairdneri	Rainbow trout
Salmo salar	Atlantic salmon
Salmo trutta	Brown trout
Salvelinus fontinalis	Brook trout
Salvelinus namaycush	Lake trout

Osmeridae:

Osmerus mordax	Rainbow smelt

Esocidae:

   Esox lucius — Northern pike

Cyprinidae:

   Carassius auratus — Goldfish

   Cyprinus carpio — Carp

   Notropis atherinoides — Emerald shiner

   Pimephales notatus — Bluntnose minnow

   Pimephales promelas — Fathead minnow

Catostomidae:

   Catostomus commersoni — White sucker

Ictaluridae:

   Ictalurus melas — Black bullhead

   Ictalurus natalis — Yellow bullhead

   Ictalurus nebulosus — Brown bullhead

   Ictalurus punctatus — Channel catfish

Cyprinodontidae:

   Jordanella floridae — Flagfish

Poeciliidae:

   Gambusia affinis — Mosquitofish

   Poecilia reticulata — Guppy

Percichthyidae:

   Morone chrysops — White bass

Centrarchidae:

   Lepomis macrochirus — Bluegill

   Micropterus dolomieui — Smallmouth bass

   Micropterus salmoides — Largemouth bass

   Pomoxis annularis — White crappie

   Pomoxis nigromaculatus — Black crappie

Percidae:

   Perca flavescens — Yellow perch

   Stizostedion canadense — Sauger

   Stizostedion v. vitreum — Walleye pike

b. Marine and estuarine fishes used in bioassays:

Clupeidae:

   Brevoortia patronus — Gulf menhaden

   Brevoortia tyrannus — Atlantic menhaden

   Clupea harengus — Atlantic herring

   Harengula pensacolae — Scaled sardine

   Sardinops sagax — Pacific sardine

Engraulidae:

   Anchoa mitchilli — Bay anchovy

Cyprinodontidae:

   Cyprinodon variegatus — Sheepshead minnow

   Fundulus heteroclitus — Mummichog

   Fundulus similis — Longnose killifish

Atherinidae:

   Menidia beryllina — Tidewater silverside

   Menidia menidia — Atlantic silverside

Gasterosteidae:

   Gasterosteus aculeatus — Threespine stickleback

Percichthyidae:

   Morone saxatilis — Striped bass

Serranidae:

   Centropristis striata — Black sea bass

Sparidae:

   Lagodon rhomboides — Pinfish

Sciaenidae:

   Leiostomus xanthurus — Spot

   Micropogon undulatus — Atlantic croaker

Mugilidae:

   Mugil cephalus — Striped mullet

   Mugil curema — White mullet

Pleuronectidae:

   Pseudopleuronectes americanus — Winter flounder

2. Collecting, Handling, and Treating Test Fishes

Collecting equipment and methods are described in Sections 801C.2 and 1006A. Handling, holding, and treatment are discussed in Section 801C.3.

a. Freshwater fishes: While all the listed species and many of the different life stages may be collected from the field, it is usually more convenient to obtain from hatcheries species that are routinely raised there. Some minnows can be obtained from bait dealers. The larger species can be acquired with the cooperation of fishermen. The usual sources of supply of the salmonid fishes are private, state, and federal hatcheries. Whenever trout are to be used, obtain fish certified free of infectious pancreatic necrosis, furunculosis, kidney disease, and whirling disease. Collecting permits are usually required by state agencies.

b. Marine and estuarine fishes: Very often adequate numbers of the various life stages of marine fishes can be collected in the field and transported to the laboratory and held in good condition for bioassays on selected life stages. Vertical movement of early larval stages may necessitate night-time collecting, depending on the species desired. Most marine fish larvae are extremely fragile so care must be taken during collecting to prevent mechanical injury. Use a large-bore pipet, 3 to 5 mm ID, for sorting and transferring larvae during and after collection. Whenever possible, transfer by dipping or gently pouring. Fine-mesh dip nets are also suitable if transfers are made quickly.

3. Holding and Acclimation

General instructions for the holding, transfer, and acclimation of test organisms have been given in 801C.3. Water supply requirements have been discussed in Sections 801C.4b and 801D.2a. General instructions for holding and acclimation, the preparation of artificial seawater and reconstituted fresh water, the selection of safe construction materials, and choosing volume of flow and rate of change of water in the tanks, as well as information on such variables as loading and volume per unit weight of organisms have been presented in Sections 801C and D. Stocks of fish for bioassays may be kept in aquariums, small ponds, live boxes, screen pens, or tanks, depending on their size and number. The water in which they are held must be of a quality and quantity that will insure that they remain in good condition. Feed fish natural or prepared foods daily during accli-

mation. There are several good dried or pelleted fish foods on the market.* Detailed information on the handling, holding, care, and feeding of fish is available.[2-5] The type of food required varies with the fish; use care in selecting the diet. Fish obtained from the hatchery can be fed the food to which they are already accustomed. Many fish can be maintained for long periods on dried food but live food supplements are desirable. Overfeeding of fish is a common problem that leads to undesirable conditions in the holding tanks and should be avoided.

To maintain fish in good condition during holding and acclimation, watch carefully for signs of disease, stress, physical damage, and mortality. Remove dead and abnormal individuals immediately. If disease or parasites occur, treat at once in accordance with procedures described in Sections 801C.5 and 810A.5.

Perform necessary handling gently, carefully, and as quickly as possible, so that the fish are not unnecessarily stressed. Anesthetize† fish if they are to be handled for any period of time. This is especially important when weighing, measuring, or otherwise taking data from the fish. Anesthetics for fishes are discussed by Lewis.[4] Before fish from a given area are used in bioassays, analyze a sample of the whole fish for body burdens of pesticides, PCB's, heavy metals, and other toxicants that are to be studied. For short-term tests, fish weighing

---

*Examples are Oregon Moist Fish Food, Warrenton, Ore., and Glencoe Trout Food, Glencoe Mills, Glencoe, Minn. 55336.

†A widely used anesthetic is MS222, Sandoz (tricaine methanesulfonate) now marketed as Finquel by Ayerst.

between 0.5 and 5 g each are desirable. In one series of tests, all the test fish should be from the same year class and the standard length of the largest fish should not be more than 50% greater than that of the shortest fish.

Temperature and salinity regimes for laboratory holding of larval marine fishes should approximate the existing field conditions. Do not acclimate larvae to temperature or salinity combinations that differ from those normally encountered during the various phases of their life cycle. Many marine larvae migrate from saline to brackish water during the first few weeks of their development.[6,7] Others move from fresh water to tidal water during their development.[8] Desired temperature, salinity, turbidity, pH, dissolved oxygen, and other environmental factors essential for successful laboratory holding will vary according to the species, the life stages, and their seasonal occurrence.

Most larvae of marine fishes require special holding tanks. Prevent accumulation of toxic metabolites in holding tanks.[9] Proper shape, volume, depth, and color of holding tanks can be important. Correct lighting intensity, quality and duration are also essential for maintaining larvae in the laboratory.[10-13] Larvae have diverse and varying nutritional requirements; pay particular attention to the selection of the correct diet. Field-collected zooplankton have been used successfully as food for larval fishes.[12-16] Dense cultures of phytoplankton also have been used with some success.[11,17,18] See Section 801C.4c1) for the rearing of phytoplankton as food organisms. Live brine shrimp, *Artemia salina*, have been used successfully for feeding larval fishes.

4. Culturing of Test Fishes

a. Freshwater fishes: More than 30 species of freshwater fishes have been reared in hatcheries or rearing ponds for stocking fresh waters. Some are now being reared for production of high-protein foods. Fish cultural methods can be adapted to laboratory conditions for the production of different life stages of fishes for use in bioassays. Within recent years, many publications have appeared describing methods for the production of different species of fishes in the laboratory.[19-26] A few species have been reared through their entire life cycle in the laboratory in connection with bioassay studies.[27-32]

b. Marine and estuarine fishes: Considerable literature is now becoming available describing methods for the culture of marine and estuarine fishes and some literature is available on their culture in the laboratory. A good review on the feeding of larval marine fishes in the laboratory has been prepared by May.[33] Another review of the literature covers rearing of larvae of marine animals with special reference to their food organisms.[34]

Since very few of the marine fishes have been reared through their life cycle in the laboratory, either the different life stages must be field-collected or adults brought into the laboratories for spawning. Laboratory spawning, either natural or artificially induced by hormones, can be used to provide early life stages for use in bioassays. Technics are available for the laboratory rearing of herring, bay anchovy, scaled sardine, and Pacific sardine from eggs.[13,17,35-37] The sheepshead minnow and the common mummichog have been reared through their life cycle and the silverside through part of its life cycle.[38-40] Other species including the mullet, croaker, black sea bass, and spot have been cultured to or past yolk sac absorption with some success.[14,41-45] Difficulty in rearing many marine species past yolk sac absorption may limit the duration of tests. If hormones are used to ripen mature adults artificially, take care to avoid atrophy (over-ripeness), which will cause poor fertilization of eggs and emergence of larvae.[41,46] Handle developing eggs and pro-larvae with extreme care. Developing zygotes of some marine fishes are especially susceptible to mechanical damage[47] and even gentle handling can result in significant reduction of the percentage that emerge as larvae.[43] Hold adult brood stocks, eggs, and larvae under temperature, salinity, dissolved oxygen, and pH conditions approximating those encountered by adults spawning under natural conditions.

1) Sheepshead minnow — The sheepshead minnow thrives over a wide range of salinities and temperatures. To establish cultures, collect adult fish over 30 mm in standard length from wild populations and acclimate to laboratory temperatures. They should begin to spawn after holding in the laboratory for 2 wk at temperatures approaching 30 C. During this period feed liberally fresh or frozen adult brine shrimp. Sheepshead minnow eggs can also be obtained by injecting hormones to cause ripening of the sex products.[48] To induce egg production artificially, inject each female intraperitoneally with 50 IU of human chorionic gonadotrophic hormone. Two days later repeat the injection. On the third day most females

should produce eggs that are readily stripped. Strip or dissect the eggs into seawater in a beaker and add macerated testes.[48] Approximately 1 to 1.5 hr later check eggs for cleavage. Usually 90% or more of the eggs are fertile. Eggs from natural spawning can be collected by placing a pair of adult fish in a spawning chamber about $12 \times 18 \times 10$ cm high into which is fitted a 2-cm-deep tray covered with nylon screen having openings 2 mm square. As the eggs are laid they fall through the screen into the tray, formed by 0.5-mm nylon screen over a frame, which contains the eggs so they escape predation by the fish and are removed readily. A pair may spawn 100 eggs in a day but average production is about eight eggs per pair per day of which about 90% are fertile. Place the eggs in hatching chambers formed by fastening a 9-cm collar of 500-μm around petri dishes. Then place these in an aquarium having a flow-through of the toxicant.[49] The fry of the sheepshead minnow hatches after about 5 days incubation at 30 C. Sheepshead minnow eggs do not hatch below 22 C and hatching success is greatest at 24 to 35 C and a salinity between 15 and 20 $^0/oo$. As the fry hatch, transfer to a rearing aquarium and immediately feed newly hatched brine shrimp nauplii. Feed adults and juveniles adult brine shrimp, live or frozen, and a commercial dry food. It is desirable to supplement a dry food diet occasionally with live organisms. Very few deaths occur after the first week following hatching and survival from fertile eggs to 28 days is approximately 85%. Juveniles become sexually distinguishable at about 24 mm standard length and females produce eggs within 3 months after hatching, generally at a length of 27 to 30 mm standard length.

2) Atlantic silverside, *Menidia menidia*—The silverside, *Menidia menidia*, occurs in east coast estuarine areas throughout much of the year. Sexually mature and ripe individuals are readily collected from April to July at water temperatures above 15 C. Mature adults for spawning can be collected with a 5-mm-mesh bag seine. The silverside is ecologically significant as food for predacious fishes such as sea bass, mackerel, bluefish, striped bass, and sea trout.[50] The silverside can be maintained in the laboratory on a diet of chopped fish, mollusks or grass shrimp, and live brine shrimp. The Atlantic silverside spawns from March to August and produces approximately 500 eggs. Mature adults brought in from the field can be held in circular fiberglass tanks constructed as described in Section 801C.4*a*, 1 m in diameter and 60 cm deep and containing 45 cm of seawater. The interior surfaces of the tank should be almost glass-smooth. Adults placed in this rearing tank in early spring should be subjected to a temperature and daily light regime that follows that naturally occurring during the normal spring maturing period. Supply light as recommended in Section 801D.3*f* and give an illumination of 2,000 lux at the water surface. Raise temperatures gradually to 22 C and keep salinities between 24 and 26 ‰. Water temperature and photoperiod are important for maturing and ripening of the silverside. Adequate nutrition is also essential. Feed any live food and dry food to excess. Clean tanks and siphon unused food and wastes from the bottom of the tank daily. Informa-

tion on the rearing of the silverside is given elsewhere.[51, 52]

When the adults are ready to spawn either place them in spawning chambers or strip them to have better control of the eggs. The silverside, especially the larvae, are extremely sensitive to physical damage; do not handle any more than absolutely essential.

Strip the females into culture dishes 200 mm in diameter containing 1 cm of seawater. After four to six have been stripped, strip a few males and stir the milt and eggs gently to ensure fertilization. Immediately after fertilization the eggs of the silversides form gelatinous strands that bind them together in a mass.[39] Remove fertilized eggs from the culture dish by rolling a 25-cm length of nylon or polyethylene string around the gelatinous mass, which will adhere to the string. Suspend the eggs in a 2- to 4-l aerated, all-glass, flow-through aquarium. Water temperatures should range from 18 to 22 C and the salinity from 25 to 30 ‰ for optimal emergence of larvae. Hatching will begin 7 to 9 days after fertilization. Feed to newly hatched larval silversides either copepod nauplii or *Artemia* nauplii less than 8 hr old. Silversides are omnivorous feeders. Keep the brine shrimp nauplii at 200 to 800 nauplii/l. As the fish grow, increase the feed and vary the diet. Gradually increase the amount of dry food. Feed nauplii of *Balanus*, sea urchin eggs, copepods, rotifers, annelids, small bivalve larvae, and mysid shrimp. A transition from live food to dried food and other nonliving food can be accomplished with proper training but occasional live food is very desirable. When the larval fish begin to be crowded, transfer suitable numbers to the circular tanks described earlier and continue the feeding to adult stage.

5. Parasites and Diseases

When fish are held in confined quarters at unusually high densities parasites and disease become a very important factor that can alter bioassay results or even nullify bioassays by killing the test organisms after they are weakened by the stress of the toxicant or condition under study. Parasites and disease must be controlled if reliable bioassays are to be carried out for the evaluation of environmental factors and potential toxicants.

Larval fish are particularly vulnerable to fungi and parasites, such as copepods, that have direct life cycles and may quickly build to overwhelming numbers in the confined tank areas. Also, parasites transmitted to fish larvae by ingestion of phytoplankton may affect growth and survival of the larvae even when they occur in small numbers. Antibiotic treatment of fish in holding tanks reduces bacterial populations. Holding in a 15-mg/l tetracycline solution for 24 to 48 hr can be very helpful. Many types of chemotherapeutic agents are available but care should be exercised in their applications since some are toxic at low concentrations[53] and the long-term toxicity is not known for any of them.

a. Control methods for freshwater fishes: Freshwater fishes may be treated chemically to cure or prevent disease by the methods recommended in Table 810:I. The recommendations in Table 810:I do not imply that these treatments have been cleared or registered for these uses. Consult appropriate state and federal regulatory agencies to determine if treatment can be used and under what conditions the uses are permitted. Use treatments only on fish intended for bioassays. They have been found dependable, but efficacy against diseases and toxicity to fish may be altered by temperature or water quality. *Test treatments on small lots of fish before making large-scale applications.* Prevention of disease is preferred. Treat newly acquired fish with the formalin-malachite green combination on 3 alternate days if possible. However, do not treat fish on the first day they are in the facility. References 54-56 contain further information.

If fish are severely diseased, it is often better to destroy the entire lot.

In recent years a number of good reviews of fish diseases and parasites and methods for their control have been published.[57-63]

b. Control methods for marine and estuarine fishes: Species such as the clupeoids, with scales that are easily dislodged, are particularly susceptible to bacterial (usually *Vibrio*) infections, characterized by minute hemorrhages, fin erosion, and ulcerations. Infections often become systemic and mortalities result in a few days. Antibiotics (terramycin) in the food provide limited protection.

Ectoparasitic protozoa (particularly the ciliate *Cryptocaryon* and the dinoflagellate *Oodinium*) may multiply quickly to epizootic proportions in marine aquariums. Heavy infections can be fatal. An effective treatment using formalin and cupric acetate has been developed by Nigrelli and Ruggieri.[63]

Monogenetic trematodes on gills and body surfaces can be problems in main-

TABLE 810:I. RECOMMENDED PROPHYLACTIC AND THERAPEUTIC TREATMENTS FOR FRESHWATER FISHES

Disease	Chemical	Concentration* mg/l	Application
External bacteria	Benzalkonium chloride (Hyamine 1622®)	1-2 AI²	30-60 min in flow-through system†
	Nitrofurazone (water mix)	3-5 AI	30-60 min in flow-through system†
	Neomycin sulfate	25	30-60 min in flow-through system†
	Oxytetracycline hydrochloride (water-soluble)	25 AI	30-60 min in flow-through system†
Monogenetic trematodes, fungi, and external protozoa‡	Formalin *plus* zinc-free malachite green oxalate	25 0.1	1-2 hr in static system
	Formalin	150-250	30-60 min in flow-through system†
	Potassium permanganate	2-6	30-60 min in flow-through system†
	Sodium chloride	15,000-30,000 2,000-4,000	5-10 min dip 24 hr minimum, but may be continued indefinitely
	Dexon® (35% AI)	20	30-60 min in flow-through system†
Parasitic copepods	Trichlorfon (Masoten®)	0.25 AI	Weekly for up to 4 wk if necessary in static or flow-through systems. Do not use at >27C.

* AI=active ingredient.

† Add concentrated stock solution to the inflowing water by a drip system or by the technic of Brungs and Mount.[69]

‡ One treatment is usually sufficient except for *Ichthyophthirius*, which must be treated daily or every other day until no sign of the protozoans remains. This may take 4 to 5 wk at 5 to 10 C and 11 to 13 days at 15 to 21 C. A temperature of 32 C is lethal to *Ichthyophthirius* in 1 wk.

taining marine fish in captivity because they multiply rapidly and transmission from fish to fish is easy. Brine and sodium pyrophosphate dips have been found effective.

Other microbial and parasitic diseases (such as lymphocystis, fungus, and parasitic copepods) may occasionally occur in epizootic proportions in laboratory-held marine fish. For a general treatment of disease in marine aquariums see Sindermann.[64]

For a summary of advances and unsolved problems in marine fish larval culture and the description of a successful larval culture system, see Houde.[11, 65] For disinfection of water supplies, see Hoffman.[66]

810 B.   General Bioassay Procedures for Fishes

Types of bioassays and their uses, facilities and equipment, construction materials, the preparation of test materials including dilution water, various concentrations of toxicants, selecting and acclimating the test organisms, and various special test procedures for bioassays are described in Sections 801C through E.

1. Short-Term Bioassays

Range-finding bioassays for the determination of the concentrations of toxicants to be used in the short-term, acute, or definitive bioassays are conducted in the routine manner described in the General Procedures, Sections 801D and E, as are the definitive short-term acute bioassays. The handling of experimental organisms, acclimation, culturing, selection and preparation of test concentrations, conditioning and preparing test organisms, transferring test organisms, loading in the various concentrations, observations, recording of data and analyzing results are all described in Sections 801D through F and 810A.

2. Long-Term Partial- and Complete-Life-Cycle Bioassays

Recently, emphasis has been placed on the need for long-term partial- or complete-life-cycle bioassays in order to determine the effects of the discharge of wastes to the aquatic environment. Juveniles or adults prior to maturation of the gonads, newly spawned eggs, or newly hatched larval fishes are used to initiate these bioassays. The life stage selected depends on the species, its sensitivity in relation to other life stages, laboratory space and facilities, the availability of the different stages, and the purpose of the test. When space and the water supply permit, fish, in addition to the number required for the tests, may be exposed for special histological, residue, or other examinations. When holding mature adults for spawning, establish the sex ratio as soon as development of secondary sexual characteristics permits sex identification. Record total length and weight of all test fish at the beginning of a test, at selected intervals during the test, after mortality, and at the end of the test. To prevent injury, large fish may be anesthetized before handling. When large numbers of small fish are used in the test, they can be measured by the photographic method of McKim and Benoit.[67] Stop treatment of parental fish after stripping, at a fixed number of days after the last spawning, if the species spawns seasonally, or at a fixed number of days of spawning after the start of the test, if the species spawns continuously. Record sex and condition of the gonads along with the total length and weight at the end of the bioassay.

For egg viability and hatchability tests, incubate a selected number of eggs from each spawning at a temperature within the optimum range for the species. If effluent bioassays are being made, the temperature will be that of the receiving water. Count live and dead eggs and remove the dead eggs daily. Evaluate egg viability for all spawnings in all bioassays by incubating eggs until development can be determined. Determine egg hatchability for all spawnings in all exposure chambers or from a predetermined number of spawnings when the species tested is one that spawns continuously or multiple times per female. Count the number of dead, deformed, and normal larvae hatched daily.

For larval growth and survival bioassays, collect a uniform number of normal larvae, usually 20 to 50 or more, at random from two or more successful hatches and place in incubation chambers for each toxicant concentration being tested. If there is a prolonged hatching period use the median hatching date as the starting date for the survival and growth studies. Determine the length and number of the larvae upon transfer to the growth chambers if possible by the photographic method.[67] Determine total length of the larvae at selected intervals and at the end of the bioassay. Record deaths daily.

To start bioassays that begin with the eggs, use approximately equal numbers of eggs pooled from at least three or more females. For bioassays beginning with juvenile fish of species that have a long life cycle and spawn only once a year, use sexually immature fish that will spawn for the first time at the upcoming spawning season. Acclimate these juveniles for at least 1 month before the test begins (approximately 8 months before the time of spawning). For those fishes maturing and spawning more often, shorter periods are required.

Mixtures of the dilution water and the stock toxicant concentration can be delivered to the test chambers by a variety of methods, as described in Section 801D.1. However, proportional diluters are generally preferred. Install an automatically triggered emergency alarm system to alert the staff in case a diluter, temperature controller, or water supply fails.

The spawning tanks, exposure tanks, and growth chambers will vary in size according to the species under test. Generally it is desirable to have a depth of water of at least 15 to 30 cm. In growth chambers for larvae, lesser depths may be used. Each growth chamber should be designed so that the test solutions can be drained down to 2.5 to 3 cm and the chamber transferred to a fluorescent light box provided with a millimeter grid for photographing fish to record the size and number surviving.

Incubation cups or chambers can be made from 8-cm sections of 5-cm-OD plastic or glass tubing by cementing nylon screen of a mesh that will retain the eggs and larvae over one end of the tube. The incubation cups are oscillated in the test water by means of a rocker arm apparatus driven by a 2-rpm electric motor.[68]

Retain fish and eggs obtained during the bioassays for physiological, biochemical, histological, and other types of investigations, which may indicate direct or related effects of a toxicant. Report all pertinent data for each test container at the beginning, about a third of the way through the test, and at the end. Data should include the number and weight of individuals, the number of spawnings, the number of eggs, and the total lengths of normal, deformed, and injured mature and immature males and females. Record mortality during the test. Calculate the mean incubation time using date of spawning and the median hatch dates. Determine and record hatchability of the eggs and fry survival, growth, and deformities.

810 C.   Conducting the Bioassays

Although short- and long-term bioassays generally are conducted in a routine standard manner, certain small changes must be made in the long-term partial- and complete-life-cycle bioassays according to differences in size, environmental requirements, spawning, feeding, etc. Therefore, examples of partial-life-cycle and life-cycle bioassays are given for two freshwater and two marine fishes. These serve as models for bioassays with other fishes. A partial-life-cycle bioassay, as used here, is one that includes one to two life stages of the fish, such as egg and alevin, fry, juvenile, or adult. The life cycle means more than a generation, for example, exposed adult, egg, fry, juvenile, and adult to eggs.

1. Conducting Short-Term Bioassays

These bioassays are carried out as described in Sections 801C through E and as has been described for several other organisms.

2. Conducting Long-Term Partial- and Complete-Life-Cycle Bioassays

a. *Partial-life-cycle bioassays with the brook trout*, Salvelinas fontinalis: Salmonid fishes have been reared in hatcheries for over 100 yr. As a result, much is known about their spawning, rearing, and feeding. Rearing through their complete life cycle for research purposes has been a much later development.

1) Equipment and physical conditions—Several different methods have been outlined in Section 801D for measuring dilution water and stock toxicant solutions and mixing them in the desired proportions. Duplicate tanks are set up for each test concentration and the controls. When proportional diluters are used, a mixing tank or flow-splitting chamber[69] serves to mix each concentration before delivery to the duplicate spawning tanks and growth chambers.

Alevin to juvenile rearing facilities consist of an outer tank $55 \times 28 \times 15$ cm high, into which is set a tank made of glass or stainless steel with a glass bottom, which is $43 \times 25 \times 15$ cm high and divided lengthwise into two 12.5-cm-wide growth chambers. The water depth in each chamber should be about 13 cm. Each growth chamber has an opening so placed that the water drains down to a depth of 2 to 3 cm when the growth chambers are removed from the outer tank to allow the chambers to be placed over a millimeter grid in a fluorescent light box for photographing the fish as described in Section 801D.3e.

Flow rates through the growth chambers should be 6 to 10 tank volumes/day, depending on the amount needed to keep the dissolved oxygen above 60% of saturation. Siphon unused food and wastes from the growth chambers daily and brush and clean the interior surfaces and remove attached growths at least weekly.

The spawning tanks, preferably of stainless steel, should be not less than $90 \times 30 \times 40$ cm deep. Water depth should be about 30 cm. A spawning substrate or nest should be available to be placed in the spawning tanks at the appropriate time. The one described by

Benoit[70] has proven to be very effective for attracting spawning fish and for insuring fertilization. It is 33×28×13 cm deep and is made of double-strength glass or stainless steel. Larger fish will require a larger spawning substrate. Three 2.5-cm holes are drilled in each end 2.5 cm from the bottom and covered with 10 mesh stainless steel wire to allow the water in the box to drain down to 2.5 cm when the box is removed from the spawning tank. A 32×27×1.3 cm deep bottomless screen egg retainer with 2.5-cm-square compartments, constructed with 1.3-cm-wide strips of 7 mesh stainless steel screen, is placed in the spawning box. A 2.0 mesh stainless steel screen, 32×27 cm, to which 1.3 to 2.5 cm gravel is attached with silicone adhesive, is placed on top of the screen egg retainer. The attached gravel must have no sharp or jagged edges protruding upward. This spawning box is readily removed from the spawning tanks for the collection of eggs for transfer to the incubation cups described in Section 810B.2. Select yearling fish that will not grow too large for the spawning box, because this will result in poor fertilization. For the suggested spawning box size, fish should weigh not more than 50 to 70 g at time of selection and 150 g at spawning. If they weigh more than 150 g, use a larger box.

Lighting and photoperiod are described in Section 810D.3f. The photoperiod for brook trout should simulate dawn to dusk times at Evansville, Ind., or the local area, and should correspond to the actual dates of the bioassay in order to avoid putting natural production cycles out of phase (Table 801:IX).

TABLE 810:II. TEMPERATURE REGIME FOR BROOK TROUT LIFE CYCLE BIOASSAYS

Months	Stage	Temperature C	Comment
Mar.		9	
Apr.		12	
May		14	
June	Juvenile-adult exposure	15	
July		15	
Aug.		15	
Sept.		12	
Oct.		9	
Nov.	Spawning and egg incubation	9	Establish constant temperature just prior to spawning and egg incubation, and maintain throughout the 3-month alevin-juvenile exposure.
Dec.		9	
Jan.		9	
Feb.	Alevin-juvenile exposure	9	
Mar.		9	

The temperature regime during the study is indicated in Table 810:II. Temperature should not deviate from the specified test temperatures by more than 2 C and should not remain outside the specified temperature ±1 C for more than 48 hr at a time. Do not exceed the recommended temperature during juvenile-adult exposure, as the fish may outgrow the spawning substrate.

Cover spawning tanks and growth chambers with a screen to confine the fish and place behind curtains so the fish will not be disturbed. Shield the tanks and chambers from extraneous light that can affect the intended photoperiod or damage light-sensitive eggs and embryos.

Ideally, take the water for other than effluent studies from a well or spring or alternatively from an unpolluted surface source. If the water supply should be contaminated with fish pathogens, pass the water through an ultraviolet sterilizer immediately before it enters the test system.

2) Exposure procedures—When the bioassay is begun with juveniles, collect them no later than March 1 and acclimate to test temperature and water quality for at least 1 month. Judge suitability of fish for testing on the basis of their acceptance of food, apparent lack of disease, and 2% or less mortality during acclimation with no mortality during the 2 wk prior to the test. Set aside enough fish to supply an adequate number for use in short-term bioassays to determine incipient LC50's for use with the MATC to calculate the application factor (see Section 801A).

Begin exposure no later than April 1 by placing 12 acclimated yearling brook trout in each of the duplicate tanks for each test concentration and the controls using a stratified random assignment as described in Section 801D.3a. This allows about a 4-month exposure to the toxicant before the onset of the secondary or rapid growth phase of the gonads.

Extra test animals may be added at the beginning so that fish can be removed periodically for special examinations or for residue analysis.

Use a good pelletted trout food. Feed the fish the largest pellet they will take at least twice daily. Base the amount on a reliable hatchery feeding schedule. Analyze each batch of prepared food for pesticides.

Record mortalities daily and measure total length and weight of fish directly at initiation of the tests, after 3 months, and when the number of test fish are reduced. Do not feed fish for 24 hr before weighing. Lightly anesthetize them to facilitate measuring.

When secondary sexual characteristics are well developed (approximately 2 wk before expected spawning), separate males, females, and undeveloped fish in each tank and randomly reduce sexually mature fish to the desired number of two males and four females per tank. Record the number of mature, immature, deformed, and injured males and females in each tank and the number from each category to be discarded. After they have been thoroughly cleaned, sterilized and rinsed, place one spawning substrate in each spawning tank. As soon as spawning begins, set up the incubation cups to receive the eggs for hatching. Remove the eggs from the substrate at a fixed time each day (preferably after 1:00 PM, Evansville time, so the fish are not disturbed during the morning).

Randomly select 50 eggs from the first eight spawnings of 50 eggs or more in each duplicate spawning chamber and place them in an egg incubator cup for hatching. Count the remaining eggs from the first eight spawnings and all eggs from subsequent spawnings and place them in separate egg incubator cups for determining viability (formation of neural keel after 11 to 12 days at 9 C). Remove and record the number of dead eggs from each spawn. Never place more than 250 eggs in one egg incubator cup. All eggs incubated for viability and discarded after 12 days can be used for residue analysis and physiological measurements of toxicant-related effects.

Additional important information on hatchability and alevin survival can be gained by transferring control eggs immediately after spawning to test concentrations where spawning is reduced or absent, or to where an effect is seen on survival of eggs or alevin, and by transferring eggs from these test concentrations to the control tanks. Always reserve two growth chambers for each duplicate spawning tank for eggs produced in that tank.

Remove the dead eggs daily from the hatchability cups. When hatching begins, record number of alevins hatching daily in each cup. On completion of hatching in any cup, transfer fish to a culture dish and randomly select 25 alevins. Count dead or deformed alevins. Transfer 25 selected alevins to a growth chamber and place it over the light box to measure them by the photographic method, Section 801D.3e. After photographing, return the alevins to the incubation cup. Never net the alevins; transfer by gentle pouring and by large-bore pipets. Transport in the growth chambers containing the specified amount of the test solution, 2.5 cm. Preserve the unused alevins in formalin for physiological, histological, or body burden studies. Record the lengths and weights of discarded alevins separate from those of fish kept for subsequent exposure.

Randomly select from each of the duplicate incubation cups for each of the test concentrations and controls 25 alevins for the 90-day growth and survival exposures in the growth chambers. Because the hatching from one spawn may be spread out over a 3- to 6-day period,

use the median hatch date to establish the 90-day growth and survival period for each of the two groups of alevins selected from each duplicate cup for each concentration. If it is determined that the median-hatch dates for the eight groups will be more than 3 wk apart, select the two groups of 25 alevin from those that are less than 3 wk old. Use the remaining groups in the duplicate tests for the different test concentrations that do not hatch during the 3-wk period only for hatchability results. After photographing to determine lengths, preserve them for the determination of weights. In order to equalize any effects of the incubation cups on growth, keep all groups selected for the 90-day exposure in the incubation cups 3 wk after the median hatch date before they are released into the growth chambers. Begin feeding immediately after alevins are released from the cups. Keep the two groups selected from the duplicate exposure chambers for each test concentration separate during the 90-day period. Record mortalities daily, total lengths 30 and 60 days post-hatching by the photographic method, and total length and weight at 90 days post-hatching. At the end of the 90-day period cease feeding juveniles for 24 hr, then weigh. End survival and growth studies after 3 months and use the fish for tissue residue analysis and physiological measurements of toxicant-related effects.

End exposure of all parental fish when 3 wk pass in which no spawning occurs in any of the spawning tanks. Record mortality and weight, measure the total length of parental fish, and check the sex and the condition of the gonads (e.g., reabsorption, degree of maturation, spent ovaries).

Report, for each tank of a partial-life-cycle bioassay, the number and individual weights and total lengths of immature males and females at initiation of test, after 3 months, at reduction in numbers, and at the end of the test. Report individual weights and total lengths of normal, deformed, and injured fish, number maturing, mortality during the test, number of spawnings and eggs, hatchability and fry survival, growth, and deformities. Calculate a mean incubation time using date of spawning and the median hatch dates. Data are assembled and analyzed as recommended in Section 801F. Analyze results obtained in each of the test concentrations for significance and compare with those obtained in the controls to determine concentrations of the test toxicant that are not harmful to brook trout, at least over the period of exposure studied.

3) Measurement of toxicant concentrations—If analysis is possible, measure the concentration of the toxicant in one tank at each toxicant concentration at least every week for each set of duplicate tanks, alternating tanks in each set from week to week. Take water samples about midway between the top and bottom and the sides of the tank and do not include any surface scum or material stirred up from the bottom or sides of the tank. Equal-volume daily grab samples can be composited for a week if it has been shown that the results of the analysis are not affected by storage of the sample.

Analyze enough pooled grouped grab samples periodically throughout the test to determine whether or not the concentration of toxicant is reasonably constant from day to day in one tank and from one tank to its duplicate. If not, analyze

enough samples weekly throughout the test to show the variability of the toxicant concentration (see Section 801D.3d).

Record temperature continuously. Measure dissolved oxygen daily at least 5 days/wk on an alternating basis so that each tank is analyzed once each week. However, if the toxicant or an additive causes a depression in dissolved oxygen, analyze the toxicant concentration with the lowest dissolved oxygen concentration daily in addition to the above requirements.

Analyze control and one test concentration weekly for pH, alkalinity, hardness, acidity, and conductivity or more often, if necessary, to show the variability of the dilution or test water. However, if any of these characteristics is affected by the toxicant, analyze for that characteristic daily, at least 5 days/wk on an alternate basis so that each tank is analyzed once every other week. At a minimum, analyze the test water at the beginning and middle of the exposure period for calcium, magnesium, sodium, potassium, chloride, sulfate, conductivity, total solids, and total dissolved solids.

When possible and necessary, analyze mature fish and possibly eggs, larvae, and juveniles obtained from the test for toxicant residues. For fish, muscles should be analyzed and gills, blood, brain, liver, bone, kidney, GI tract, gonad, and skin should be considered for analysis. Analysis of whole organisms may be done in addition to, but should not be done in place of, analysis of individual tissues, especially muscle.

For additional information on life-cycle bioassays with brook trout consult other sources.[32, 67, 71-79] *b. Life-cycle bioassays with the fathead minnow*, (Pimephales promelas):

1) Physical system—Facilities and equipment, construction materials, the preparation of test materials including dilution water, toxic solutions, and test organisms, test procedures, and toxicant delivery systems are as described in Section 801D.1, 2, and 3 and 810B. The physical systems are in general like those described for the brook trout.

Two arrangements of test tanks (glass, or stainless steel with glass ends) can be used. The first arrangement is duplicate spawning tanks for each of the five or more test concentrations and the controls, measuring 30×30×90 cm long with a 30-cm-square portion at one end, screened off and divided in half as two larval chambers for the progeny. Test water is delivered separately to the larval and spawning chambers of each tank, with about one-third the water volume going to the larval chamber.

The alternate arrangement is duplicate spawning tanks measuring 30×30×60 cm long with duplicate progeny tanks for each spawning tank. The larval tank should be a minimum of 30×30×30 cm, divided to form two separate larval chambers with separate standpipes; separate 30×15×30-cm-high tanks also may be used. Test solutions and water for the controls are supplied as described in Section 801D.1. Maintain toxicant solutions in the test aquariums and the dilution water in the controls at a depth of 15 cm. Check periodically to determine any necessary adjustments in flow or in the concentration of the toxicant solutions.

Flow rate, dissolved oxygen requirements, aeration, cleaning, and operation of the system are as described for the brook trout.

Fathead minnows deposit their eggs on the underside of submerged objects. For the spawning substrates use inverted halves of tile 7.5 cm ID and 7 to 10 cm long or the equivalent. Place these tiles in the spawning tank so each end is readily accessible to the fish and they are parallel to the long axis of the spawning tanks.

Fasten egg incubation cups, such as those described for the brook trout, to a rocker arm as described by Mount.[68] The vertical travel distance of the cups should be 2.5 to 3.7 cm. Lamps and illumination are described in Section 801D.3f.

The photoperiods to be used (Table 810:III) simulate the dawn to dusk times at Evansville, Ind. Adjustments in day length are to be made on the first and fifteenth day of every Evansville test month. The table is arranged so that adjustments need be made only in the dusk times. Regardless of the actual date on which the experiment is started, adjust the Evansville test photoperiod so that the mean or estimated hatching date of the fish used to start the experiment corresponds to the Evansville test day length for December 1. This is to give a consistent prespawning exposure. The dawn and dusk times listed in the table need not correspond to the actual times where the experiment is being conducted. As an example, a bioassay started with 5-day-old larvae on August 28 (actual date) would require use of a December 5, Evansville test photoperiod and the lights could go on anytime on that day just so long as they remained on for 10 hr and 45 min. Ten days later (September 7 actual date, December 15, Evansville test date) the day length would be changed to 10 hr and 30 min. Gradual changes in light intensity at

TABLE 810:III. TEST PHOTOPERIOD FOR FATHEAD MINNOW LIFE CYCLE BIOASSAYS*

Dawn to Dusk Time	Date	Day Length (hr & min)
6:00-4:45	Dec. 1	10:45
6:00-4:30	15	10:30
6:00-4:30	Jan. 1	10:30
6:00-4:45	15	10:45
6:00-5:15	Feb. 1	11:15 5-month prespawning growth period
6:00-5:45	15	11:45
6:00-6:15	Mar. 1	12:15
6:00-7:00	15	13:00
6:00-7:30	Apr. 1	13:30
6:00-8:15	15	14:15
6:00-8:45	May 1	14:45
6:00-9:15	15	15:15
6:00-9:30	June 1	15:30
6:00-9:45	15	15:45 4-month spawning period
6:00-9:45	July 1	15:45
6:00-9:30	15	15:30
6:00-9:00	Aug. 1	15:00
6:00-8:30	15	14:30
6:00-8:00	Sept. 1	14:00
6:00-7:30	15	13:30
6:00-6:45	Oct. 1	12:45 post-spawning period
6:00-6:15	15	12:15
6:00-5:30	Nov. 1	11:30
6:00-5:00	15	11:00

* Based on Evansville, Ind. times.

dawn and dusk should be as described in Section 801D.3f.

Temperature should not deviate from 25 C by more than 2 C and should not remain outside the range of 24 to 26 C for more than 48 hr at a time. Record temperature continuously.

2) Biological systems—Test fishes are obtained from the laboratory cultures, collected from the field, purchased from bait dealers, or obtained from some other laboratory that maintains a stock of fathead minnows. Treat fish brought into the laboratory as necessary for control of parasites and disease as described in Sections 801C.5 and 810A.5. For starting the tests use a mixture of approximately equal numbers of eggs or larvae from at least three different females.

Set aside enough eggs or larvae at the start of the test to supply an adequate number of fish for the acute mortality bioassays used in determining application factors. Conduct all acute mortality tests to determine the concentrations to be used in the life-cycle bioassays with 2- to 3-months-old fish.

Begin the life-cycle bioassay by distributing 50 1- to 5-day-old larvae in each duplicate spawning tank for each test concentration by a stratified random assignment. If 1- to 5-day-old larvae are not available, fish up to 30 days of age may be used to start the test. Extra test fish may be added at the beginning so that fish can be removed periodically for special examinations such as residue analysis.

During the bioassay feed the fish once or twice a day, live brine shrimp nauplii for 30 to 60 days and then frozen adult brine shrimp as the main diet, supplemented by pelleted trout food, *Daphnia*, and chopped earthworms. One feeding each day of live young zooplankton from mixed cultures of small copepods, rotifers, and protozoans is recommended. Live food is especially important when larvae are just beginning to feed, or about 8 to 10 days after egg deposition. Check each batch of commercial feeds for pesticides and record the kinds and amounts.

When the test fish are 60 days old ±1 or 2 days, discard injured or crippled individuals and randomly reduce the number in each tank to 15. Record the number, length, and weight of deformed fish discarded from each tank. If necessary, in order to have 15 fish per tank, select one or two fish for transfer from one duplicate to the other. Continue routine feeding and cleaning until the fish mature and give indications that they are almost ready to spawn. Then place five spawning tiles in each duplicate spawning tank, separated fairly widely to reduce fighting between the guarding male fishes. Place the tiles so their undersides and the guard males can be seen from the end of the tank. During the spawning period, remove sexually maturing males so that there are no more than four per tank at any one time. Reserve the fifth tile as cover for the females. Do not remove those males having well-established territories under tiles where recent spawnings have occurred.

Remove the eggs from the spawning tiles starting at 12:00 noon Evansville test time (Table 810:III) each day. Loosen eggs from the spawning tiles and at the same time separate them from one another by lightly placing a finger on the egg mass and moving it in a circular pattern with increasing pressure until the eggs begin to roll. Wash the groups of eggs into separate, appropriately marked containers and return the tiles to the spawning aquariums. Count the eggs, select those needed for incubation, and discard the remainder after recording the necessary data. Check all eggs for different stages of development. If there is more than one distinct stage of development present, consider each stage as one spawning and handle separately as described below.

Randomly select 50 unbroken eggs from a single spawning and place them in an egg incubator cup to determine viability and hatchability. Count and discard the remaining eggs. Determine viability and hatchability on each spawning of more than 49 eggs until the number of spawnings (>49 eggs) in each tank equals the number of females in that tank. Subsequently, only eggs from every third spawning of more than 49 eggs (none of those obtained on weekends), need be set up to determine hatchability; however, always remove weekend spawns from the tiles and count the eggs. If unforeseen problems are encountered in determining egg viability and hatchability, sample additional spawnings before only every third spawning is used.

If no spawning occurs for a week, cease parental fish testing. Record the total lengths and weights of the parental fish, their sex, and gonad condition. The gonads of most parental fish will have begun to regress from the spawning condition, and the differences between the sexes will be less distinct than previously. Initially, select males and females that are readily distinguishable from one another because of their external secondary sexual characteristics for determining how to differentiate between the testes and ovaries. One of the more obvious external characteristics of females that have spawned is an extended, transparent anal canal (urogenital papilla). The gonads of both sexes are located just ventral to the kidneys. The ovaries will appear transparent, but perhaps containing some coarsely granular yellow pigment; they are larger than testes. The testes will appear as slender, slightly milky, and very fine granular strands. Do not freeze fish before making these sexing examinations.

Each day record the live and dead eggs in the incubator cups, remove the dead ones, and clean the cup screens. Total numbers of eggs accounted for should always add up to within two of 50; if not, discard the entire batch. After 4 to 6 days, when larvae begin to hatch, cease handling the eggs or removing them from the egg cups until all have hatched. At that time, if enough larvae are still alive, select 40 at random and transfer immediately to a larval growth chamber to determine survival and growth of the second generation. Count and discard entire egg-cup groups not used for survival and growth studies.

Important information on hatchability and larval survival can be gained by transferring, immediately after spawning, eggs from the control tanks to those having toxicant concentrations in which spawning is reduced or absent, or to those in which an effect is seen on survival of eggs or larvae and by transferring eggs from these high toxicant concentrations to the control tanks. Always reserve one larval chamber for eggs produced in the tank to which it was originally assigned.

From the early spawned eggs in each duplicate tank, use larvae for 30- and 60-day growth and survival exposures. Plan the distribution of eggs for hatchability tests so that a new group of larvae is ready to be tested as soon as possible after the previously tested group comes out of the larval chambers, is thinned down to 15, and placed in the larger spawning tanks. Record mortality and lengths of larvae at 30 and 60 days post-hatch. Weigh them when the larval test is ended. Do not feed fish (larvae, juveniles, or adults) for 24 hr before weighing.

Transfer 50 of the 60-day post-hatching fish from each growth chamber to the corresponding spawning chamber and adjust the photoperiod to December 1. Continue the bioassay with the different groups in their respective test concentrations. Follow procedures used for the F_1 generation to determine the survival of the eggs, larvae, and juveniles of the F_2 generation. Terminate the adult fish on completion of spawning. Continue the post-hatching study to 60 days.

Use the fish and eggs obtained from the test for physiological, biochemical, histological, and other tests that may indicate certain toxicant-related effects.

Record the following data for each of the test tanks and the controls: total number and length of normal and deformed individuals in each tank at the end of 30- and 60-day counts for each generation; total length, weight, and number of each sex, both normal and deformed, at the end of the tests; mortality during the tests; number of spawnings and eggs produced in each and total egg production by each generation; percentage of the eggs hatching; number and percentage of larvae surviving and growth of the fry as well as the deformities produced in each of the tanks. On the basis of these data and the calculations made as outlined in Section 801F, evaluate the results of the tests and prepare the reports. For additional information on the life cycle of the fathead minnow and flow-through life-cycle bioassays, consult the other sources.[27-29, 81-86]

3) *Chemical analyses*—Analyze test concentrations periodically to determine exposure as described in Section 801D.3*d* and for brook trout. Measurements of other variables and residue analyses are conducted as described for the brook trout bioassays.

Partial-life-cycle bioassays have been performed with the bluegill, *Lepomis macrochirus*, and the flagfish, *Jordanella floridae*.[30, 31, 87-91]

c. Tentative bioassay procedures for sheepshead minnow, Cyprinodon variegatus:

1) *Short-term bioassays*—Handle, hold, acclimate, and culture test fish as described in Section 810A. Perform bioassays in the manner described in Sections 801D and E. Water quality, water flow, loading, chemical analyses, biological observations, and collection and handling of data should be as previously described. Bioassays may be static, renewal, or flow-through, depending on the objectives of the tests. Use 10 or 20 fish in each test concentration, depending on the variability of test fishes

and the precision desired. Conduct range-finding tests and carry out the definitive acute studies at concentrations indicated by them. Complete short-term acute bioassays before beginning the life-cycle or partial-life-cycle bioassays to indicate the concentrations that should be used. It is recommended that two different age classes, for example, larvae and juveniles, be tested in order to secure more pertinent data on the toxicity of the material and the concentrations that should be used in the long-term studies.

2) *Life-cycle bioassays*—These bioassays may begin with adult fish or eggs. Because adult fish can be brought in from the field it is suggested that tests begin with the egg. Secure the eggs either by natural spawning or by induced spawning through the use of hormones as described in Section 810A.4*b*1). For natural spawning, place spawning pairs in individual aquariums at least 30×18×20 cm high. Keep water temperature above 22 C, preferably 30 C, with salinities above 15 ‰ Set up five or six spawning aquariums for each test concentration and the controls. Use breeding fish, all from the same stock, that have been kept in holding tanks for at least 2 wk, during which deaths were less than 2%. Feed the spawners a combination of frozen adult brine shrimp and dry trout food. Water flow through the spawning aquariums should equal 6 to 10 tank volumes/day and be natural seawater filtered to remove planktonic larva 15 μm and larger that might prey upon the eggs or fry of the sheepshead minnow.

The testing apparatus is similar to that used for the other fishes and consists of a dosing apparatus comprising constant-head boxes, modified proportional diluters with mixing tanks, duplicate exposure tanks for each test concentration and the controls, spawning chambers, and hatching chambers. The spawning chambers have a coarse screen with 2-mm-square openings in the bottom over a net tray as described in Section 810A.4b1) for the protection and collection of the eggs.

When eggs become available, remove them from the spawning chambers and place in each of eight hatching chambers for each concentration being tested and the controls. Start the dosing equipment so that the chosen toxicant concentrations are flowing through the respective exposure chambers before the hatching chambers are placed in them. The hatching chambers are formed by cementing a 9-cm-wide strip of 500- μm nitex screen around a petri dish. Place them in the 90×30×30 exposure chambers in 7 cm of water with flow-through of the toxicant. As the eggs hatch, feed the fry newly hatched brine shrimp nauplii. Clean the screens on the incubation cups or chambers daily. Check and record daily the survival of the embryos and fry, which constitute the parental stock F_1. On the first day post-hatch, remove each chamber and photograph for counting and measuring the fry as described in Section 801D.3e. During the first 2 wk feed them newly hatched brine shrimp nauplii. During the following 2 wk supplement this diet with dry trout pellets or dry mollie flakes. At 4 wk count and measure the fish by the photographic method (Section 801D.3e) and reduce the number to 50 for each test concentration and the controls. Record length, weight, condition, and the number of living, deformed, and dead fishes

remaining for each test concentration and the controls. Determine the total number dying in each test concentration and the controls. Preserve live specimens for future tests or discard. Place the 50 chosen fishes, 25 each, in growth chambers having a glass bottom and provisions for drawing the water level down to 1 to 2 cm. Feed them a mixed diet of brine shrimp and dry trout food twice daily and examine daily for dead specimens. At 8 wk measure again by the photographic method. Feed twice daily dry food supplemented with frozen adult brine shrimp until maturity. Check each batch of food for pesticides, PCB's, and other toxicants. Clean all exposure aquariums and spawning and hatching chambers as described for other forms 2 to 3 times/wk. Siphon out all wastes.

As the fish mature to adults and approach spawning as indicated by sexual dimorphism, territoriality, aggressive behavior, and courtship, place separate pairs in spawning chambers, five from each duplicate exposure chamber, that is, 10 pair for each test concentration and the controls, and continue the exposure. Count, measure, and weigh all unused fishes from each duplicate exposure chamber. Also record the deformed and dying in each test concentration and the controls, the condition of the fish, and other pertinent data. Preserve some for whole-body analyses. As fertilized eggs are produced, remove them at a specified time daily and place 25 each in incubation or hatching chambers as for the F_1 generation. Keep a record of all eggs produced in each chamber, time required to hatch, hatching success, and survival of embryos. Test those not placed in the hatching chambers for fertility and record the percent fertile and the percent from which the fry did not emerge.

If no spawning occurs in the higher concentrations, transfer eggs from the controls and incubate in the higher concentrations to gain additional information. Further, eggs from the high test concentrations can be placed in the control aquariums to determine if they contain materials toxic to the embryos or fry and if exposure of the parents and the eggs will have any toxic effect.

Keep the pairs in each of the spawning chambers until all eggs needed for additional exposure for the F_2 generation are obtained and until a sufficient number of eggs has been collected to insure statistical comparisons of fecundity, fertility, and survival of embryos and fry. At termination, measure and weigh the spawning pairs and record all data. Preserve for residue analyses for each test concentration and the controls.

Expose the eggs in the hatching chambers in their respective duplicate exposure chambers for each test concentration and the controls as before. Count and measure by photographic methods as for the F_1 generation. Feed fish and record results as before. At the end of 4 wk stop the test. Weigh and measure all fish; record the deformed and determine the number that died. Preserve for histological and accumulation studies. Determine the different effects of each test concentration and calculate indicated safe levels. Analyze, handle, and report data as indicated in Section 801F. During the course of the tests, record temperature, DO, pH, and salinity in the various test solutions and controls at periodic intervals. If possible, make analyses of the various test concentrations at the beginning, at various times during the course of the exposure as indicated by conditions and results of tests, and at the completion of the tests. Analyze lots of 10 fishes from the highest and lowest exposure concentrations and from the controls for body accumulation of the toxicant. Also analyze the dilution water, at least at the beginning and end of the test, as well as the effluent or material itself.

d. Tentative bioassay procedures for Atlantic silverside, Menidia menidia

1) Short-term tests—Perform range-finding and short-term acute or definitive bioassays with the silverside as has been described in General Procedures and for the other fishes. Handling, holding, transfer, and feeding of the silverside during the tests are the same as the procedures described for holding and culturing in Section 810A. The length of the tests, biological observations, chemical analyses, recording, analyzing and statistical handling of the data, and reports for the short-term bioassays are described in Sections 810D through F.

2) Partial-life-cycle tests—Because of their extreme sensitivity, when collecting adult silverside from the field take special care during handling to prevent injury. Bring the adult silversides into the laboratory in the early spring. Dip them from the transfer tank with a breaker or other suitable container, then submerge it in the circular holding tanks so the fish can swim free. These holding tanks are the same as those described in Section 801C.4a. Feed the fish dry food, adult brine shrimp, copepods, and minced clams or mussels. Siphon all unused food and waste from the tank daily to

prevent any contamination. When it appears that the fish are ready to spawn, strip sufficient females into a 200-mm-diam culture dish containing 1 cm of seawater to provide an estimated 400 eggs. Fertilize these with the milt from ripe males.

Allow 15 min for fertilization and then suspend the egg mass from a nylon or polyethylene string. After the eggs have been attached to the string, suspend them in the flow-through treatment aquariums, 30×45×30 cm high. The flow rate should be sufficient to keep the eggs well aerated. Prepare additional aquariums for the other four concentrations of toxic test solution being studied and for the controls. Be certain that the eggs are suspended so that they do not touch the sides or bottom of treatment aquariums. Place a 500-μm screen over the drain tube for each aquarium to prevent loss of larvae as they hatch.

Keep the dilution water and toxic solutions supplied to the hatching jars between 20 and 22 C and at a salinity between 25 and 30 ‰ or higher. The larvae begin to hatch after 6 to 9 days at 22 C. The maximum emergence generally occurs 8 days after fertilization.

With a pipet, transfer larvae that will be exposed continuously to toxicants to rearing aquariums 30×45×30 cm high. Stocking density should not exceed 100 larvae in these aquariums. Examine larvae not used in the rearing aquariums for deformities and then preserve. Shortly after the larvae have been added to the rearing tanks, determine their number and length by the photographic method.

Begin feeding newly hatched brine shrimp nauplii immediately and feed so that there are always first-stage nauplii present in the rearing aquariums. Observe the aquariums daily for any dead or deformed larvae. Remove these with a large-bore pipet for examinations and record the number and apparent condition. Clean the tank three times a week or daily if necessary, removing organic material and waste with a siphon. Cover the outlet (notch, hole, standpipe or a combination) of each rearing aquarium with a screen having a mesh that will retain the larval fish and brine shrimp nauplii. Arrange standpipes so that the water levels in the aquariums can be drawn down for a photographic count of the larvae.

All larvae in the hatching jars usually emerge before the 12th day. At the 12th day, examine the egg clumps and if it appears that no more will hatch, discontinue the procedure, count and record live active larvae, deformed larvae, and unhatched eggs. Examine the egg clumps thoroughly and record the number of viable eggs from which larvae failed to emerge. Note the developmental stage because some toxicants may not inhibit development but do prevent emergence of larvae.

Because of difficulty in maintaining silversides in the laboratory for long intervals, it may be desirable or necessary to conduct bioassays within a certain segment of their life cycle. Partial-life-cycle bioassays beginning with ripening adults or recently fertilized eggs and extending through the juvenile stage are most desirable if life-cycle tests are not feasible.

810 D.   References

1. KEMP, H.T., J.P. ABRAMS & R.C. OVER-BECK. 1971. Water Quality Criteria Data Book Vol. 3. Effects of Chemicals on Aquatic Life, Selected Data from the Literature Through 1968. EPA Water Pollution Center, Research Ser. 18050GWV05/71, U.S. Government Printing Off. Washington, D.C.

2. HUNN, J.B., R.A. SCHOETTGER & E.W. WHEALDON. 1968. Observations on the handling and maintenance of bioassay fish. Progr. Fish-Cult. 30:164.

3. INNES, W.T. 1966. Exotic Aquarium Fishes, 19th ed. Metaframe Corp., Maywood, N.J.

4. LEWIS, W.M. 1962. Maintaining Fishes for Experimental and Instructional Purposes. Southern Ill. Univ. Press., Carbondale.

5. HESSLEBERG, R.J. & R.M. BURRESS. 1967. Investigations in Fish Control. No. 21. Labor-Saving Devices for Bioassay Laboratories. Bur. Sport Fish. Wildlife, U.S. Dep. Interior.

6. MASSMAN, W.H. 1954. Marine fishes in fresh and brackish waters of Virginia rivers. Ecology 35:75.

7. RANEY, E.C. & W.H. MASSMAN. 1953. The fishes of the tidewater section of the Pamunkey River, Virginia. J. Wash. Acad. Sci. 43:424.

8. RANEY, E.C. 1952. The life history of the striped bass, Roccus saxatilis, Walbaum. Bull. Bingham Oceangr. Coll. 14:5.

9. SPOTTE, S.H. 1970. Fish and Invertebrate Culture. John Wiley and Sons, Inc., New York, N.Y.

10. GARSTANG, W. 1900. Preliminary experiments on the rearing of seafish larvae. J. Mar. Biol. Ass., U.K. 6:76.

11. HOUDE, E.D. 1973. Some recent advances and unresolved problems in the culture of marine fish larvae. Proc. World Maricult. Soc. 3:83.

12. SHELBOURNE, J.E. 1964. The artifical propagation of marine fish. Advan. Mar. Biol. 2:1.

13. BLAXTER, J.H.S. 1968. Rearing herring larvae to metamorphosis and beyond. J. Mar. Biol. Ass. U.K. 48:17.

14. KUO, C., Z.H. SHEHADEH & K.K. MILISEN. 1973. A preliminary report on the development, growth and survival of laboratory reared larvae of the grey mullet, Mugil cephalus L. J. Fish. Biol. 5:459.

15. KRAMER, D. & J.R. ZWEIFEL. 1970. Growth of anchovy larvae, Engraulis mordax, Girard in the laboratory as influenced by temperature. Rep. Calif. Coop. Oceanic Fish. Invest. 14:84.

16. O'CONNELL, C.P. & L.P. RAYMOND. 1970. The effect of food density on survival and growth of early post yolk sac larvae of the northern anchovy, Engraulis mordax, Girard, in the laboratory. J. Exp. Mar. Biol. Ecol. 5:187.

17. SASKENA, V.P. & E.D. HOUDE. 1972. Effect of food level on the growth and survival of laboratory reared larvae of the bay achovy, Anchoa mitchelli, Valenciennes and scaled sardine, Harengula pensacolae, Goode and Bean. J. Exp. Mar. Biol. Ecol. 8:249.

18. QASIM, S.Z. 1959. Laboratory experiments on some factors affecting the survival of marine teleost larvae. J. Mar. Biol. Ass. India 1:13.

19. HILDEBRAND, S.F. 1923. Notes on habits and development of eggs and larvae of the silversides Menidia menidia and Menidia beryllina. U.S. Bur. Fish. Bull. 38:113.

20. NATIONAL ACADEMY OF SCIENCES. 1973. Nutrient requirements of trout, salmon and catfish. 11:1. Publ. Off. NAS, Washington, D.C.

21. STALNAKER, C.B. & R.E. GRESSWELL. 1974. Early life history and feeding of young mountain white fish. EPA 660/3-73-019, Off. Research and Development EPA, U.S. Government Printing Off., Washington, D.C.

22. CARLSON, A.R. & J.G. HALE. 1972. Successful spawning of largemouth bass Micropterus salmoides (Lacepede) under laboratory conditions. Trans. Amer. Fish. Soc. 101:539.

23. HOKANSON, K.E.F., J.H. McCORMICK, B.R. JONES & J.H. TUCKER. 1973. Thermal requirements for maturation, spawning, and embryo survival of the brook trout, Salve-

linus fontinalis. J. Fish. Res. Board Can. 30:975.

24. McCormick, J.H., K.E.F. Hokanson & B.R. Jones. 1972. Effects of temperature on growth and survival of young brook trout, *Salvelinus fontinalis. J. Fish. Res. Board Can.* 29:1107.

25. Hokanson, K.E.F., J.H. McCormick & B.R. Jones. 1973. Temperature requirements for embryos and larvae of the northern pike, *Esox lucius* (Linnaeus). *Trans. Amer. Fish. Soc.* 102:89.

26. Siefert, R.E. 1972. First food of larval yellow perch, white sucker, bluegill, emerald shiner and rainbow smelt. *Trans. Amer. Fish. Soc.* 101:219.

27. Pickering, Q.H. 1974. Chronic toxicity of nickel to the fathead minnow. *J. Water. Pollut. Control Fed.* 46:760.

28. Mount, D.I. & C.E. Stephan. 1969. Chronic toxicity of copper to the fathead minnow (*Pimephales promelas*) in soft water. *J. Fish. Res. Board Can.* 26:2449.

29. Eaton, J.G.1973. Chronic toxicity of a copper, cadmium and zinc mixture to the fathead minnow (*Pimephales promelas,* Rafinesque). *Water Res.* 7:1723.

30. Eaton, J.G. 1974. Chronic cadmium toxicity to the bluegill (*Lepomis macrochirus* Rafinesque). *Trans. Amer. Fish. Soc.* 103:729.

31. Smith, W.E. 1973. A cyprinodontid fish, *Jordanella floridae,* as a laboratory animal for rapid chronic bioassays. *J. Fish. Res. Board Can.* 30:329.

32. McKim, J.M. & D.H. Benoit. 1974. Duration of toxicity tests for establishing "no effect" concentrations for copper with brook trout (*Salvelinus fontinalis*). *J. Fish. Res. Bd. Can.* 31:449.

33. May, R.C. 1970. Feeding larval marine fishes in the laboratory: A review. Calif. Mar. Res. Comm., CalCOFI Rep. 14:76.

34. Hirano, R. & Y. Oshima. 1963. Rearing of larvae of marine animals with special reference to their food organisms. *Bull. Jap. Soc. Sci. Fish.* (Japanese) 29:282.

35. Houde, E.D. & B.J. Palko. 1970. Laboratory rearing of the clupeid fish, *Harengula pensacolae,* from fertilized eggs. *Mar. Biol.* 5:354.

36. Saksena, V.P., C. Steinmetz & E.D. Houde. 1972. Effect of temperature on growth and survival of laboratory reared larvae of the scaled sardine *Harengula pensacolae,* Goode and Bean. *Trans. Amer. Fish. Soc.* 101:691.

37. Lasker, R. 1964. An experimental study of the effect of temperature on the incubation time, development and growth of Pacific sardine embryos and larvae. *Copeia* (2):399.

38. Boyd, J.F. & R.C. Simmons. 1974. Continuous laboratory production of fertile *Fundulus heteroclitus,* Walbaum eggs lacking chorionic fibrils. *J. Fish. Biol.* 6:389.

39. Middaugh, D.P. & J.M. Dean. 1974. The Toxicity of Cadmium to the Eggs, Larvae and Adults of the Mummichog, *Fundulus heteroclitus* and the Silverside, *Menidia menidia.* Bears Bluff Field Station, EPA (unpublished).

40. Bayliff, W.H. 1950. The life history of the silverside (*Menidia menidia* Linnaeus). *Chesapeake Biol. Lab. Publ.* 50:1.

41. Middaugh, D.P. & R.L. Yoakum. 1974. The use of chorionic gonadotropin to induce laboratory spawning of the Atlantic Croaker, *Micropogon undulatus,* with notes on subsequent embryonic development. *Chesapeake Sci.* 15:110.

42. Hoff, F.H. 1972. Artificial spawning of black seabass, *Centropristis striata,* aided by chorionic gonadotropin hormones. Florida Dep. Natural Resources Marine Research Lab (mimeograph).

43. Middaugh, D.P. & A.C. Badger. 1974. Laboratory Spawning, Development and Rearing of the Spot, *Leiostomus xanthurus,* Lacépède. Bears Bluff Field Station, EPA (unpublished).

44. Hildebrand, S.F. & L. Gable. 1931. Development and life history of fourteen teleostean fishes at Beaufort, N.C. *Bull. U.S. Bur. Fish.* 46:383.

45. Dawson, C.E. 1959. A study of the biology and life history of the spot *Leiostomus xanthurus* Lacépède with special reference to South Carolina. *Bears Bluff Lab. Contrib.* 28:1.

46. Stevens, R.E. 1966. Hormone-induced spawning of striped bass for reservoir stocking. *Progr. Fish-Cult.* 28:19.

47. BLAXTER, J.H.S. 1969. Development: Eggs and larvae. In: Fish Physiology, 3, Reproduction and Growth, Bioluminescence, Pigments and Poisons. Academic Press, New York, N.Y.

48. SCHIMMEL, S.C., D.J. HANSEN & J. FORESTER. 1974. Effects of Aroclor 1254 on laboratory-reared embryos and fry of sheepshead minnows (Cyprinodon variegatus). Trans. Amer. Fish. Soc. 103:582.

49. HANSEN, D.J., S.C. SCHIMMEL & J. FORESTER. 1973. Aroclor 1254 in eggs of sheepshead minnows: Effect on fertilization success and survival of embryos and fry. Proc. 27th Annu. Conf. S.E. Ass. Game Fish. Comm.:420.

50. BIGELOW, H.B. & W.C. SCHROEDER. 1953. Fishes of the Gulf of Maine. U.S. Bur. Fish Bull. 53.

51. RUBINOFF, I. 1958. Raising the atherinid fish Menidia menidia in the laboratory. Copeia (2):146.

52. RUBINOFF, I. & E. SHAW. 1960. Hybridization in two sympatric species of atherinid fishes, Menidia menidia Linnaeus and Menidia beryllina, Cope. Amer. Mus. Natur. Hist. No. 1999:1.

53. WILLFORD, W.A. 1967. Investigations in Fish Control, Toxicity of 22 Therapeutic Compounds to Six Fishes. U.S. Bur. Sport Fish Wildl. Pap. No. 18.

54. RUCKER, R.R. & K. HODGEBOOM. 1953. Observations on gas-bubble disease of fish. Progr. Fish-Cult. 15:24.

55. MARKING, L.L. & V.K. DAWSON. 1973. Toxicity of quinaldine sulfate to fish. U.S. Bur. Sport Fish. Wildl. Invest. Fish. Control 48:1.

56. BRUNGS, W.A. & D.I. MOUNT. 1967. A device for continuous treatment of fish in holding chambers. Trans. Amer. Fish Soc. 96:55.

57. SNIESZKO, S.F. 1970. A Symposium on Diseases of Fishes and Shellfishes. Spec. Publ. 5, American Fisheries Soc.

58. HOFFMAN, G.L. 1967. Parasites of North American Freshwater Fishes. Univ. of Calif. Press, Berkeley and Los Angeles.

59. VAN DUIJN, C., JR. 1973. Diseases of Fishes, 3rd ed. Charles C. Thomas Co., Springfield, Ill.

60. REICHENBACK-KLINKE, H. & E. ELKAN. 1965. The Principal Diseases of Lower Vertebrates. Academic Press, London and New York.

61. DAVIS, H.S. 1953. Culture and Diseases of Game Fishes. Univ. of Calif. Press, Berkeley and Los Angeles.

62. HOFFMAN, G.L. & F.P. MEYER. 1974. Parasites of Freshwater Fishes: A Review of Their Control and Treatment. T.F.H. Publications Inc., Ltd., Neptune City, N.J.

63. NIGRELLI, R.F. & G.D. RUGGIERI. 1966. Enzootics in the New York aquarium caused by Cryptocaryon irritans Brown, 1951 (=Ichthyophthirius marinus 1961) a histophagous ciliate in the skin, eyes and gills of marine fishes. Zoologica 51:97.

64. SINDERMANN, C.J. 1970. Principal Diseases of Marine Fish and Shellfish. Academic Press, New York, N.Y.

65. HOUDE, E.D. & A.J. RAMSEY. 1971. A culture system for marine fish larvae. Progr. Fish-Cult. 33:156.

66. HOFFMAN, G.L. 1974. Disinfection of contaminated water by ultraviolet irradiation with emphasis on whirling disease (Myxosoma cerebralis), and its effects on fish. Trans. Amer. Fish. Soc. 103:541.

67. McKIM, J.M. & D.A. BENOIT. 1971. Effect of long-term exposures to copper on survival, reproduction and growth of brook trout, Salvelinus fontinalis (Mitchell) J. Fish. Res. Board Can. 28:655.

68. MOUNT, D.I. 1968. Chronic toxicity of copper to fathead minnows, Pimephales promelas Rafinesque. Water Res. 2:215.

69. BENOIT, D.A. & F.A. PUGLISI. 1973. A simplified flow-splitting chamber and siphon for proportional diluters. Water Res. 7:1915.

70. BENOIT, D.A. 1974. Artificial laboratory spawning substrate for brook trout (Salvelinus fontinalis Mitchell). Trans. Amer. Fish. Soc. 103:144.

71. ALLISON, L.N. 1951. Delay of spawning in eastern brook trout by means of artificially prolonged light intervals. Progr. Fish-Cult. 13:111.

72. CARSON, B.W. 1955. Four years progress in the use of artificially controlled light to induce early spawning of brook trout. Progr. Fish-Cult. 17:99.

73. FABRICIUS, E. 1953. Aquarium observations on the spawning behavior of the char, *Salmo alpinus*. *Rep. Inst. Freshwater Res. Drottingholm* 34:14.

74. HALE, J.G. 1968. Observations on brook trout, *Salvelinus fontinalis* spawning in 10-gallon aquaria. *Trans. Amer. Fish. Soc.* 97:299.

75. HENDERSON, N.E. 1962. The annual cycle in the testes of the eastern brook trout, *Salvelinus fontinalis* (Mitchell). *Can. J. Zool.* 40:631.

76. HENDERSON, N.E. 1963. Influence of light and temperature on the reproductive cycle of the eastern brook trout *Salvelinus fontinalis* (Mitchell). *J. Fish. Res. Board Can.* 20:859.

77. HOOVER, E.E. & H.E. HUBBARD. 1937. Modification of the sexual cycle in trout by control of light. *Copeia* (4):206.

78. PYLE, E.A. 1969. The effect of constant light or constant darkness on the growth and sexual maturity of brook trout. Fish. Res. Bull. No. 31. The nutrition of trout, Cortland Hatchery Rep. No. 36:13.

79. WYDOSKI, R.S. & E.L. COOPER. 1966. Maturation and fecundity of brook trout from infertile streams. *J. Fish. Res. Board Can.* 23:623.

80. BRUNGS, W.A. 1969. Chronic toxicity of zinc to the fathead minnow, *Pimephales promelas* Rafinesque. *Trans. Amer. Fish. Soc.* 98:272.

81. BRUNGS, W.A. 1971. Chronic effects of low dissolved oxygen concentrations on the fathead minnow (*Pimephales promelas*). *J. Fish. Res. Board Can.* 28:1119.

82. CARLSON, D.R. 1967. Fathead minnow, *Pimephales promelas* Rafinesque, in the Des Moines River, Boone County, Iowa and the Skunk River drainage, Hamilton and Story Counties, Iowa. *Iowa State J. Sci.* 41:363.

83. MARKUS, H.C. 1934. Life history of the fathead minnow (*Pimephales promelas*). *Copeia* (3):116.

84. MOUNT, D.I. & C.E. STEPHAN. 1967. A method for establishing acceptable toxicant limits for fish—malathion and the butoxyethanol ester of 2,4-D. *Trans. Amer. Fish. Soc.* 96:185.

85. PICKERING, Q.H & T.O. THATCHER. 1970. The chronic toxicity of linear alkylate sulfonate (LAS) to *Pimephales promelas*, Rafinesque. *J. Water Pollut. Control Fed.* 42:243.

86. PICKERING, Q.H & W.N. VIGOR. 1965. The acute toxicity of zinc to eggs and fry of the fathead minnow. *Progr. Fish-Cult.* 27:153.

87. BREDER, C.M. 1936. The reproduction behavior of North American sunfish. *Zoologica* 21:1.

88. EATON, J.G. 1970. Chronic malathion toxicity to the bluegill, *Lepomis macrochirus*. *Water Res.* 4:673.

89. McCOMISH, T.S. 1968. Sexual differentiation of bluegills by the urogenital opening. *Progr. Fish-Cult.* 30:28.

90. FOSTER, N.R., J. CAIRNS, JR. & R.L. KAESLER. 1969. The flagfish *Jordanella floridae*, as a laboratory animals for behavioral bioassay studies. *Proc. Acad. Natur. Sci. Philadelphia* 121(5):129.

91. BENOIT, D.A. 1975. Chronic effects of copper on survival, growth and reproduction of the bluegill (*Lepomis macrochirus*). *Trans. Amer. Fish. Soc.* (in press).

PART 900

MICROBIOLOGICAL

EXAMINATION OF

WATER

901   INTRODUCTION

The following sections describe the procedures to be used in making microbiological examinations of samples of water to determine sanitary quality and suitability for general use. The methods are intended to indicate the degree of contamination of the water with wastes from human or animal sources. They are the best technics currently available; however, their limitations must be thoroughly understood.

Traditionally, tests for the detection and enumeration of indicator organisms, rather than of pathogens, have been used. The coliform group of bacteria, as herein defined, has been the principal indicator of the suitability of a particular water for domestic, dietetic, or other uses. The cultural reactions and characteristics of this group of bacteria have been studied extensively and can be found described in many texts on bacteriology, particularly on the bacteriology of water and sanitation.

Experience has established the significance of coliform group densities as criteria of the degree of pollution and thus of the sanitary quality of the sample under examination. Developments in bacteriologic technics and culture media have increased the sensitivity of the older multiple-tube fermentation test, resulting in acceptance of this test as a standard method. The significance of the tests and the interpretations of the results are well authenticated and have been used as a basis for standards of bacteriologic quality of water supplies.

The membrane filter technic, which involves a direct plating for the detection and estimation of coliform densities, is an equally effective method for the detection of bacteria of the coliform group. Modification of the details of this method, particularly of the culture medium, has made the results of this test comparable with those given by the multiple-tube fermentation procedure. Although there are limitations in the application of the membrane filter technic for the examination of all types of water, it can, when used with strict adherence to these limitations and to the specified technical details, be considered a method equivalent to the multiple-tube fermentation procedure. It is presented as an additional standard method for the detection of bacteria of the coliform group.

It has become the custom to report the results of the coliform test by the multiple-tube fermentation procedure as a Most Probable Number (MPN) index. It should be realized that this is merely an index of the number of coliform bacteria that, more probably than any other number, would give the results shown by the laboratory examination. It is not an actual enumeration of the coliform bacteria. By contrast, direct plating methods such as the membrane filter procedure permit a direct count of coliform colonies. In both procedures coliform density is reported conventionally as the MPN or membrane filter count per 100 ml. Either procedure is a valuable tool for appraising the sanitary quality of water and the effectiveness of treatment processes.

Increasing attention to the potential value of fecal streptococci as indicators of significant fecal pollution of water has prompted the inclusion of methods for the detection and enumeration of such microorganisms. Improvements in the technical details of these procedures, based on current research, have been incorporated. A tentative pour plate method is included.

Since the 13th edition, additional standard methods for the differentiation of that segment of the coliform group designated as fecal coliforms have been included. Such differentiation had in the past been considered of limited value in assessing the quality of water because the presence of either type of coliform bacteria renders the water potentially unsatisfactory and unsafe. Recent investigations strongly indicate that the portion of the coliform group that is present in the gut and feces of warm-blooded animals generally includes organisms capable of producing gas from lactose in a suitable culture medium at 44.5 ± 0.2 C. Inasmuch as coliform organisms from other sources generally cannot produce gas under these conditions, this criterion may be used to define the fecal component of the coliform group. Both the multiple-tube dilution technic and the membrane filter procedure have been modified to incorporate incubation in confirmatory tests at 44.5 C in order to provide estimates of the density of fecal organisms, as defined. The investigations cited suggest that this differentiation will yield valuable information concerning the possible source of pollution in water, and especially the remoteness of this pollution, inasmuch as the *nonfecal* members of the coliform group may be expected to survive longer than the *fecal* members in the unfavorable environment provided by the water.

Methods for determination of the standard plate count in water are retained because experience indicates that an approximate enumeration of total numbers of bacteria multiplying at 35 C may yield useful information about the quality of the water and may provide supporting data on the significance of coliform test results. The Standard Plate Count is useful in judging the efficiency in operation of various water treatment processes and may have significant application as an in-plant control test. It also is valuable for periodic checking of the quality of finished water in a distribution system.

Experience accumulated during recent years in the shipment of un-iced samples by mail indicates that changes in type or numbers of bacteria during such shipment for limited periods of time are not negligible. Therefore, requirements for storage and shipment of samples to a laboratory for bacteriological examination, which were set forth in previous (11th and 12th) editions, no longer apply and are not given in this edition. Refrigeration during transportation is recommended.

Tentative procedures for the isolation of certain pathogenic bacteria are presented in this edition. These procedures are tedious and complicated and are not recommended for routine use. Likewise, a tentative procedure for enteric viruses is included. Additional experience will determine whether it should be retained. Its routine use is not advocated at the present time.

The results of the examination of routine bacteriologic samples of water cannot be regarded as providing complete or final information concerning the quality of the water. Bacteriologic results must be considered in the light of information available concerning the sanitary conditions surrounding the source of any particular sample. Precise evaluation of the quality of a water supply can be made only when the results of laboratory examinations of the water are interpreted in the light of such sanitary survey data. Therefore, the results of the examination of a single sample from a given source must be considered inadequate. When possible, evaluation of the quality of a water supply must be based on the examination of a series of samples collected over a known and protracted period of time.

The rapidly increasing attention being given pollution problems of tidal estuaries and other bodies of saline water has focused attention on necessary modification of existing bacteriologic technics so that they may be used effectively in the examination of samples from such sources. In the following section, application of the specific technics to saline water has not been discussed because available experience suggests that the methods used for fresh waters also can be used satisfactorily with saline waters.

Methods for examination of the waters of swimming pools and other bathing places are included. The standard procedures for the plate count, total coliform group, fecal coliforms, and fecal streptococci are identical with those used for other waters. Procedures for *Staphylococcus* and *Pseudomonas aeruginosa*, organisms commonly associated with the upper respiratory tract or the skin, are included on a tentative basis. Further study of these tests will be necessary before their acceptability as standard procedures can be established.

Tentative procedures for aquatic fungi, actinomycetes, and nematodes have been added.

The various bacteriologic methods outlined in Part 900, developed primarily to permit the prompt and rapid examination of samples of water, have been considered frequently to apply only to routine examinations. These same methods, however, are the basic technics required for research investigations in problems of sanitary bacteriology and water treatment. Their value in routine studies must not be allowed to overshadow or limit their very great value in research studies. Similarly, all these technics should be the subject of experimental investigations to establish their specificity, improve their procedural details, and expand their application to the measurement of the sanitary quality of water supplies or polluted waters.

901 A.   Laboratory Quality Assurance

The concepts of precision and accuracy, discussed in the chemistry sections of this book, are, unfortunately, not directly applicable to the assessment of the validity of bacteriologic analysis. Quality assurance by federal or state authorities has relied more on evaluation of laboratory methods and personnel by qualified laboratory survey officers than by statistical analysis.[1] A very useful manual and a form to assist in such evaluations are available from the U.S. Environmental Protection Agency.[2,3] These are keyed to the methods herein described so that conformity to "Standard Methods" practice is readily established.

Interlaboratory comparisons may also be necessary, particularly since the errors inherent in the multipe-tube fermentation test are relatively large. Given several laboratories that are analyzing a common water source and obtaining differing results, it may be important to determine whether all laboratories are performing correctly and within expected statistical limits. As a first step, an intensive survey of each laboratory involved is appropriate. Experience has shown that causes for discrepancies may be categorized as due to inadequate equipment such as autoclaves or pH meters, defective media, incorrect procedure, or inadequately trained personnel. The failure to dechlorinate samples adequately and inaccurate temperature control during culture incubation are specific causes for discrepancies. The latter is especially important in the test for fecal coliform bacteria. If discrepancies cannot be explained by observable errors in technic, a statistical evaluation of the several laboratories may be required. A suitable model is available for comparison of laboratories, media, and methods.[4] This model is based on the analysis of randomly distributed split samples. Although it cannot pinpoint specifically the source of difficulty, it can establish the overall acceptability of a laboratory as compared to others (for example, the state laboratory serving as a referee) and indicate the general area of difficulty (media or method).

901 B. References

1. GELDREICH, E.E. 1971. Application of bacteriological data in potable water surveillance. *J. Amer. Water Works Ass.* 63:225.
2. U.S. PUBLIC HEALTH SERVICE. 1966. Evaluation of Water Laboratories. PHS Pub. No. 999-EE-1, Dept. of Health, Education, & Welfare, Washington, D.C.
3. ENVIRONMENTAL PROTECTION AGENCY. 1971. Bacteriological Survey for Water Laboratories. EPA form EPA-103 (Cin.) (Rev. 3-71).
4. GREENBERG, A.E., J.S. THOMAS, T.W. LEF & W.R. GAFFEY. 1967. Interlaboratory comparisons in water bacteriology. *J. Amer. Water Works Ass.* 59:237.

902   USEPA STANDARDS OF DRINKING WATER QUALITY

In the United States the quality of public water supplies is judged in terms of the 1975 U.S. EPA Drinking Water Standards. These standards provide for a minimum number of samples to be examined per month and establish the maximum number of coliform organisms allowable per 100 milliliters of finished water and the maximum bacterial plate count (Standard Plate Count) per milliliter of finished water.

1. Sampling

Bacteriologic examinations should be carried out on samples collected at representative points throughout the distribution system. The frequency of sampling and the location of sampling points should be such as to insure accurate determination of the bacteriologic quality of the treated water supply, which may be controlled in part by the known quality of the untreated water and thus by the need for treatment. The minimum number of samples to be collected and examined each month should be based on the population served by the supply. It is important to examine repetitive samples from a designated point, as well as samples from a number of widely distributed sampling points. Samples should be taken at reasonably evenly spaced time intervals. Daily samples collected after an unsatisfactory sample has been taken should be considered special samples and should not be counted in the total number of samples examined monthly.

2. Application

For the multiple-tube fermentation technic the maximum number of allowable coliform organisms is prescribed in terms of standard portion volume (10 ml or 100 ml) and the number of portions examined. The absence of gas in all tubes, when five 10-ml portions are examined by the fermentation tube method (equivalent to an MPN of less than 2.2 coliforms/100 ml), is generally interpreted to indicate that the single sample meets the standards. A positive Confirmed Test for coliform organisms in three or more tubes (10-ml portions) or five portions (100-ml portions) indicates the need for immediate remedial action and additional examinations. Repeat samples of finished water from the same location that consistently show 3 or more positive 10-ml portions should be analyzed by the completed test. Similarly, for the membrane filter technic, the standard portion volume is 100 ml or more, the quality limit is 1 coliform colony/100 ml, and the action limit is more than 4 coliform colonies/100 ml. Daily samples from the sampling point should be collected and examined promptly until the results obtained from at least two consecutive samples show the water to be of satisfactory quality. Repeat samples of finished water from the same location that consistently give positive results should be analyzed by the verification procedure.

The Standard Plate Count is to be measured when it is indicated that the coliform test is not fully reliable in determining distribution system quality. The standard calls for two 1-ml portions and two 0.1-ml portions to be examined per sample with a quality and action limit to 500 organisms/ml.

These standards also specify limiting concentrations of chemical and physical constituents of water as related to its safety and potability.

The World Health Organization has established International Standards of Drinking Water Quality. These are similar to the U.S. Drinking Water Standards, but they have been modified and liberalized to apply to water supply conditions in all parts of the world.

3. Bibliography

WORLD HEALTH ORGANIZATION. 1963. International Standards for Drinking-Water. WHO, c/o Amer. Pub. Health Ass., 1740 Broadway, New York, N.Y. 10019.

U.S. ENVIRONMENTAL PROTECTION AGENCY. 1975. Interim Primary Drinking Water Standards. *Fed. Reg.* 40(51):11990, Mar. 14, 1975.

903 LABORATORY APPARATUS

1. Incubators

Incubators must maintain a uniform and constant temperature at all times in all areas, that is, they must not vary more than ±0.5 C in the areas used. Such accuracy can be accomplished by the use of a water-jacketed or anhydric type of incubator with thermostatically controlled low-temperature electric heating units properly insulated and located in or adjacent to the walls or floor of the chamber and preferably equipped with mechanical means of circulating air.

Incubators equipped with high-temperature heating units are unsatisfactory, because such sources of heat, when improperly placed, frequently cause localized overheating and excessive drying of the media, with consequent inhibition of bacterial growth. Incubators so heated may be operated satisfactorily by replacing the high-temperature units with suitable wiring arranged to operate at a lower temperature and by installation of mechanical air-circulation devices. It is desirable, where ordinary room temperatures vary excessively, that laboratory incubators be kept in special rooms maintained at a few degrees below the recommended incubator temperature.

Special incubating rooms, well insulated and equipped with properly distributed heating units and with forced-air circulation, may be used provided that they conform to desired temperature limits. When such rooms are used, the daily range in temperature in areas where plates or tubes are incubated shall be recorded. Incubators shall be provided with shelves so spaced as to assure uniformity of temperature throughout the chamber. A 2.5-cm (1-in.) space shall be provided between walls and stacks of dishes or baskets of tubes.

An accurate thermometer (checked against one certified by the National Bureau of Standards) with the bulb continuously immersed in liquid (glycerine, water, or mineral oil) shall be maintained on each shelf within the incubator and daily readings of the temperature recorded. The NBS-certified thermometer always should be used with its certificate and correction chart. It is desirable, in addition, to maintain a maximum and minimum registering thermometer within the incubator on the middle shelf to record the gross range in temperature variations over a 24-hr period. Temperature variations within the incubator when filled to maximum capacity should be determined at intervals. It is recommended that a recording thermometer be installed in every incubator whenever possible, so that a permanent record of temperature variations within the incubating chamber may be maintained.

Adequate temperature control of an air incubator operated at 44.5 C is not ordinarily possible. To obtain this temperature and to maintain a variation within ±0.2 C, a water bath or solid heat sink incubator must be used. Most water baths equipped with a gabled cover to reduce water and heat loss are adequate. The water depth in the incubator should be sufficient to immerse tubes to the upper level of the media. In the event that satisfactory temperature control is not achieved, water recirculation should be provided.

2. Hot-Air Sterilizing Ovens

Hot-air sterilizing ovens shall be of sufficient size to prevent internal crowding; constructed to give uniform and adequate sterilizing temperatures; and equipped with suitable thermometers capable of registering accurately in the range 160 to 180 C. The use of a tem-perature-recording instrument is optional.

3. Autoclaves

Autoclaves shall be of sufficient size to prevent internal crowding; constructed to provide uniform temperatures within the chambers (up to and including the sterilizing temperature of 121 C); equipped with an accurate thermometer the bulb of which is located properly on the exhaust line so as to register minimum temperature within the sterilizing chambers (temperature-recording instrument is optional); equipped with pressure gauge and properly adjusted safety valves connected directly with saturated-steam power lines or directly to a suitable special steam generator (steam from a boiler treated with amines for corrosion control should not be used); and capable of reaching the desired temperature within 30 min.

A pressure cooker may be substituted for an autoclave, provided that it is equipped with an efficient pressure gauge and with a thermometer the bulb of which is 2.5 cm (1 in.) above the water level.

4. Gas Sterilizers

The sterilizers shall be equipped with automatic controls capable of carrying out a complete sterilization cycle. Ethylene oxide diluted to 10 to 12% with an inert gas shall be used. The automatic control cycle shall consist of evacuation of the sterilizing chamber to at least 64 cm (25 in.) of vacuum, which shall be held for 30 min; adjustment of humidity and temperature; charging with the ethylene oxide mixture to a pressure dependent on the mixture used; holding such pressure for at least 4 hr; venting of the gas; again, evacuation to 64 cm (25 in.) of vacuum; and finally bringing to atmospheric pressure with sterile air. The humidity, temperature, pressure, and time of the sterilizing cycle depend on the gas mixture used.

If sample bottles packaged for shipment are sterilized by gas, store them overnight before they are shipped, to allow the last traces of the gas mixture to dissipate. If media are sterilized by gas, incubate them overnight to insure dissipation of the gas.

In general, mixtures of ethylene oxide with chlorinated hydrocarbons such as freon are harmful to plastics, although with temperatures below 55 C, gas pressure not over 0.35 kg/cm² (5 psi), and time of sterilization less than 6 hr, the effect is minimal. Carbon dioxide as a diluent of the ethylene oxide is preferable for plastic, but the exposure time and pressure required are greater, depending on the temperature and humidity that can be used.

Determine the proper cycle and gas mixture for the particular objects to be sterilized and confirm by sterility tests of the object.

5. Colony Counters

Use standard apparatus such as a Quebec colony counter, dark-field model preferred, or one providing equivalent magnification (1.5 diameters) and satisfactory visibility.

6. pH Equipment

Use electrometric pH meters, accurate to at least 0.1 pH units, for determination of pH values of media.

7. Balances

Balances shall provide a sensitivity of at least 0.1 g at a load of 150 g, with appropriate weights. An analytical balance having a sensitivity of 1 mg under a load of 10 g shall be used for weighing small quantities (less than 2 g) of materials. Single-pan rapid-weigh balances are most convenient.

8. Media Preparation Utensils

Use borosilicate glass or other suitable noncorrosive equipment such as stainless steel. Glassware must be clean and free from foreign residues or dried particles of agar and also from toxic or foreign materials that may contaminate media, such as chlorine, copper, zinc, antimony, chromium, or detergents.

9. Pipets and Graduated Cylinders

Pipets may be of any convenient size, provided they deliver accurately and quickly the required amount. The error of calibration for a given manufacturer's lot must not exceed 2.5%. Pipets shall have graduations distinctly marked and have unbroken tips. For satisfactory work relating to enforcement of water quality regulations, calibrated and marked bacteriologic transfer pipets may be required. Pipets conforming to the APHA standards given in the latest edition of "Standard Methods for the Examination of Dairy Products" may be used. It is recommended that the mouth end of all pipets be protected— e.g., by a cotton plug—to eliminate hazards to the worker or possible contamination by saliva of the sample being pipetted.

Graduated cylinders meeting ASTM Standards (D-86 and D-216) and with accuracy limits established by the National Bureau of Standards may be used where appropriate.

10. Pipet Containers

Boxes shall be of aluminum or stainless steel, end measurement 5 to 7.5 cm (2 to 3 in.), cylindrical or rectangular, and length about 40 cm (16 in.). When these are not available, paper wrappings may be substituted. To avoid excessive charring during sterilization, best-quality sulfate pulp (kraft) paper should be used. *Copper or copper alloy cans or boxes should not be used as pipet containers.*

11. Dilution Bottles or Tubes

Bottles or tubes shall be of resistant glass, preferably borosilicate glass, closed with glass stoppers or screw caps equipped with liners that do not produce toxic or bacteriostatic compounds on sterilization. Do not use cotton plugs as closures. Graduation levels shall be indelibly marked on the side of the dilution bottle or tube. Plastic bottles constructed of nontoxic materials and of acceptable size may be substituted for glass provided that they can be sterilized properly.

12. Petri Dishes

For making the Standard Plate Count, use petri dishes about 100 mm in diameter, with the side wall of the bottom at least 15 mm high, and with glass or porous tops as preferred. The bottom of the dish shall be free from bubbles and scratches and shall be flat so that the medium will be of uniform thickness throughout the plate. Plastic dishes about 60 X 15 mm are convenient for use in the membrane filter technic. Plastic petri dishes, when found to be satisfactory and when presterilized by the manufacturer, may be substituted for glass dishes for single use only. Petri dishes may be sterilized and stored in metal cans (aluminum or stainless steel, but not copper), or they may be wrapped in paper—preferably best-quality sulfate pulp (kraft)—before sterilization.

13. Fermentation Tubes and Vials

Fermentation tubes of any type may be used, if their design permits conformance to the requirements for concentration of nutritive ingredients as described subsequently. Where tubes are to be used for a test of gas production, enclose a shell vial, inverted. The sizes of the tube and the vial shall be such that the vial is completely filled with medium and at least partly submerged in the tube.

14. Inoculating Equipment

Wire loops shall be made of 22- or 24-gauge Chromel, nichrome, or platinum-iridium where flame sterilization is used. Single-service transfer loops of aluminum or stainless steel are satisfactory. The diameter of all loops shall be at least 3 mm. Dry heat or steam may be used for sterilization. Single-service hardwood applicators also may be used. They should be 0.2 to 0.3 cm (1/12 to 1/8 in.) in diameter and at least 2.5 cm (1 in.) longer than the fermentation tube, and should be sterilized by dry heat and stored in glass or other nontoxic containers.

15. Sample Bottles

Bottles of glass or other material resistant to the solvent action of water, capable of being sterilized, and of any suitable size and shape may be used for samples intended for bacteriologic examination. Bottles shall hold a sufficient volume of sample for all the required tests, permit proper washing, and maintain the samples uncontaminated until the examinations are completed. Ground-glass-stoppered bottles, preferably wide-mouthed and of resistant glass, are recommended. Plastic bottles of suitable size, wide-mouthed, and made of nontoxic materials have been found satisfactory as sample containers and eliminate the possibility of breakage during shipment.

Metal or plastic screw-cap closures may be used on sample bottles provided that no volatile compounds are produced on sterilization and that they are equipped with liners that do not produce toxic or bacteriostatic compounds on sterilization.

Before sterilization, cover the tops and necks of sample bottles having glass closures with metal foil, rubberized cloth, heavy impermeable paper, or milk bottle cover caps.

Many plastic sample bottles are commercially available. These should not be used for repetitive sampling unless it has been demonstrated that they can be sterilized. Some types may be autoclaved once or twice at 121 C for 10 min, but only a few do not distort and leak when autoclaved repeatedly. Generally the neck of the bottle shrinks faster than the thicker cap, so that the threads no longer make a watertight seal. Resistance to distortion not only depends on the type of plastic used, but also is markedly affected by the method of molding. Polypropylene is a satisfactory material.

16. Bibliography

Collins, W.D. & H.B. Riffenburg. 1923. Contamination of water samples with material dissolved from glass containers. *Ind. Eng. Chem.* 15:48.

Clark, W.M. 1928. The Determination of Hydrogen Ion Concentration (3rd ed.). Williams & Wilkins, Baltimore, Md.

Archambault, J., J. Curot & M.H. McCrady. 1937. The need of uniformity of conditions for counting plates (with suggestions for a standard colony counter). *Amer. J. Pub. Health* 27:809.

Richards, O.W. & P.C. Heijn. 1945. An improved dark-field Quebec colony counter. *J. Milk Tech.* 8:253.

Cohen, B. 1957. The measurement of pH, titratable acidity, and oxidation-reduction potentials. In: Manual of Microbiological Methods. Society of American Bacteriologists. McGraw-Hill Book Co., New York, N.Y.

McGuire, O.E. 1964. Wood applicators for the confirmatory test in the bacteriological analysis of water. *Pub. Health Rep.* 79:812.

American Public Health Association. 1972. Standard Methods for the Examination of Dairy Products (13th ed.). APHA, New York, N.Y.

904   WASHING AND STERILIZATION

Cleanse all glassware thoroughly with a suitable detergent and hot water, rinse with hot water to remove all traces of residual washing compound, and finally rinse with distilled water. If mechanical glassware washers are used, influent plumbing preferably should be of stainless steel or other nontoxic material. Copper piping should not be used to distribute distilled water. Plumbing for the rinse system shall be of stainless steel or other nontoxic material.

1. Inhibitory Residues on Glassware

Certain wetting agents or detergents used in washing glassware may contain bacteriostatic or inhibiting substances that require 6 to 12 successive rinsings to remove all traces from the glass surface and insure freedom from residual bacteriostatic action. The following test procedure is recommended for the biological examination of glassware where bacteriostatic or inhibitory residues may be present. If prewashed, presterilized plasticware is used, it also should be tested for inhibitory residues.

a. Procedure for test:

1) Wash six petri dishes according to usual laboratory practice and designate as Group A.

2) Wash six petri dishes as above, rinsing 12 times with successive portions of distilled water, and designate as Group B.

3) Rinse six petri dishes with the detergent wash water (in use concentration), dry without further rinsing, and designate as Group C.

4) Sterilize the dishes in Groups A,

B, and C by the usual procedure. To test presterilized plasticware, set up Group D consisting of six sterile petri dishes and proceed.

5) Add not more than 1 ml of a water sample yielding 50 to 150 colonies and proceed according to the procedure described for the Standard Plate Count. If there is difficulty in obtaining a suitable sample, inoculate three plates of each group with 0.1 ml and the other three plates of each group with 1 ml.

b. Interpretation of results:

1) Difference in average number of colonies of less than 15% on plates of Groups A, B, C, and D indicates that the detergent has no toxicity or inhibitory characteristics or that the presterilized dishes are acceptable.

2) Difference in colony count of 15% or more between Groups A and B or D and B demonstrates inhibitory residue left on supplies and equipment by routine washing procedure.

3) Disagreement in averages of less than 15% between Groups A and B and greater than 15% between Groups A and C indicates that the cleaning detergent has inhibitory properties that are eliminated during routine washing.

2. Sterilization

Glassware, except when in metal containers, shall be sterilized for not less than 60 min at a temperature of 170 C, unless it is known from recording thermometers that oven temperatures are uniform, under which exceptional condition 160 C will suffice. Glassware in metal containers should be heated to 170 C for not less than 2 hr.

Sample bottles not made of plastic may be sterilized as above or in an autoclave at 121 C for 15 min.

For plastic bottles that distort on autoclaving, low-temperature ethylene oxide gas sterilization should be used.

905   PREPARATION OF CULTURE MEDIA
905 A.   General Procedures

1. Storage of Culture Media

Store dehydrated media (powders) in tightly closed bottles in the dark at less than 30 C in an atmosphere of low humidity. Do not use them if they discolor or become caked so as to lose their free-flowing power. It is advisable to purchase dehydrated media in small quantities that will be used within 6 months after opening. Additionally, stocks of dehydrated media containing selective agents such as sodium azide, bile salts or derivatives, antibiotics, sulfur-containing amino acids, etc., should be of a relatively current lot number (within a year of purchase) so as to maintain optimum selectivity.

Culture media should be prepared in batches of such size that the entire batch will be used in less than 1 wk.

Liquid media in fermentation tubes, if stored at refrigeration or even moderately low temperatures, may dissolve sufficient air to produce, upon incubation at 35 C, a bubble of air in the tube. It is imperative, therefore, that fermentation tubes that have been stored at a low temperature be incubated overnight before use and that those tubes containing air be discarded.

Fermentation tubes may be stored at approximately 25 C; but because evaporation may proceed rapidly under these conditions—resulting in marked changes in concentration of the ingredient—storage at this temperature should not exceed a period of 1 wk.

2. Adjustment of Reaction

The reaction of culture media should be stated in terms of hydrogen ion concentration, expressed as pH.

The increase in the hydrogen ion concentration (decrease in pH) during sterilization will vary slightly with the individual sterilizer in use, and the initial reaction required to obtain the correct final reaction will have to be determined. The decrease in the pH reading will usually be 0.1 to 0.2 but may occasionally be as great as 0.4. When buffering salts such as phosphates are present in the media, the decrease in pH value as determined will be negligible.

Make the tests to control the adjustment to the required hydrogen ion concentration with a pH meter. Measure the pH of the prepared medium as directed in pH Value, Glass Electrode Method (Section 424). Titrate a known volume of the medium with a solution of NaOH to the desired pH. Calculate the amount of NaOH solution that must be added to the bulk of the medium to reach this reaction. After addition and thorough mixing, check the reaction and adjust if necessary. The required final pH is given in the directions for preparing each medium. If a specific pH is not prescribed, adjustment will be unnecessary.

The pH of reconstituted dehydrated media will seldom require adjustment if made according to directions. Such factors as errors in weighing the dehydrated medium or overheating of the reconstituted medium may produce an unacceptable final pH. Measurement of pH, especially of rehydrated selective media, should be made regularly to insure quality control and media specifications.

3. Sterilization

Sterilize all media, except sugar broths or broths with other specifications, in an autoclave at 121 C for 15 min after the temperature has reached 121 C. When the pressure reaches zero, remove the medium from the autoclave and cool it quickly to avoid decomposition of sugars by prolonged exposure to heat. To permit uniform heating and rapid cooling, pack materials loosely and in small containers. The maximum elapsed time for exposure of sugar broths to any heat (from the time of closing the loaded autoclave to unloading) is 45 min. Preheating the autoclave before loading can reduce total needed heating time to within the 45-min limit.

4. Quality Control

Commercially prepared dehydrated media may vary in quality among manufacturers and even from lot to lot from the same manufacturer. For plate count agar, productivity tests have been designed and are described in "Standard Methods for the Examination of Dairy Products." A reference standard is available from APHA for use by manufacturers who, after appropriate testing, may certify that their medium meets the specifications and standards of APHA. Such standardization unfortunately is not available for any other medium described below. The user is cautioned to be alert to anomalous reactions, discoloration, decoloration, and unusually high or low counts. Coliform media may be checked for productivity by using appropriate modifications of the distilled water suitability test (Section 905 B.2). Parallel testing using natural samples with media lots of acceptable quality should be made when a supply of a new lot is obtained; at least 5 replicates for each of 10 samples should be tested.

Handling of dehydrated media within a laboratory may also affect quality. The precautions cited in Section 905 A.1 must be observed.

905 B. Materials

1. Water Characteristics

Only distilled or demineralized water that has been tested and found free from traces of dissolved metals and bactericidal or inhibitory compounds may be used for preparation of culture media and reagents. Toxicity in distilled water may be derived from flouridated water high in silica. Other sources of toxicity are silver, lead, and various unidentified organic complexes. Where condensate return is used as feed for a still, toxic amines or other boiler compounds may be present in the distilled water. Residual chlorine or chloramines also may be found in distilled water prepared from chlorinated water supplies. If chlorine compounds are found in the distilled water, they should be neutralized by addition of an equivalent amount of sodium thiosulfate or sodium sulfite.

Distilled water also should be free of contaminating nutrients. Such contamination may be derived from flashover of organics during distillation; continued use of exhausted carbon filter beds; deionizing columns in need of recharging; solder flux residues in new piping; dust and chemical fumes; and storage of water in unclean bottles. Distilled water preferably should be stored out of direct sunlight to prevent growth of algae. Good housekeeping practices will usually eliminate nutrient contamination.

2. Test for Bacteriological Quality of Distilled Water

a. Principle: The test is based on the growth of *Enterobacter aerogenes* in a chemically defined minimal growth medium. The presence of a toxic agent or a growth-promoting substance will alter the 24-hr population by an increase or decrease of 20% or more when compared to a control.

b. Apparatus and materials:

1) Glassware: All glassware used in this procedure should be borosilicate and must receive a final rinse in water freshly redistilled from a glass still prior to dry heat sterilization. Steam sterilization will recontaminate these specially cleaned glassware items. The sensitivity and reproducibility of the test depend in part on the cleanliness of the sample containers, flasks, tubes, and pipets. It is often convenient to use new

glassware, which is then used exclusively for this test.

2) Culture: Any strain of coliform IMViC type $--++$ (*E. aerogenes*). This can be obtained easily from any polluted river or sewage sample.

c. Reagents: Use only reagents of the highest purity. Some brands of potassium dihydrogen phosphate, KH_2PO_4, contain large amounts of impurities. Sensitivity of the test is controlled in part by the purity of the reagents used. Reagents should be made in water freshly redistilled from a glass still.

1) Sodium citrate solution: Dissolve 0.29 g sodium citrate, $Na_3C_6H_5O_7 \cdot 2H_2O$, in 500 ml redistilled water.

2) Ammonium sulfate solution: Dissolve 0.60 g ammonium sulfate, $(NH_4)_2SO_4$, in 500 ml redistilled water.

3) Salt mixture solution: Dissolve 0.26 g magnesium sulfate, $MgSO_4 \cdot 7H_2O$; 0.17 g calcium chloride, $CaCl_2 \cdot 2H_2O$; 0.23 g ferrous sulfate, $FeSO_4 \cdot 7H_2O$; and 2.50 g sodium chloride, NaCl, in 500 ml redistilled water.

4) Phosphate buffer solution: Stock phosphate buffer solution, Media Specifications, Section 905 C, following, diluted 1:25 in redistilled water.

5) Sterilization of reagents: All reagent solutions must be boiled 1 to 2 min to kill vegetative cells. These solutions may be stored in sterilized glass-stoppered bottles in the dark at 5 C for several months provided that they are tested for sterility before each period of use. Since the salt mixture solution will develop a slight turbidity within 3 to 5 days as the ferrous salt converts to the ferric state, it is advisable to prepare the salt-mixture solution without the ferrous sulfate for long-term storage. To use the mixture, add an appropriate amount of the freshly prepared and freshly boiled iron salt. Solutions with a heavy turbidity should be discarded and a new solution prepared. Bacterial contamination may cause turbidity in the phosphate buffer solution, which should be discarded if this occurs.

6) *Preparation of unknown distilled water sample:*
Collect 150 to 200 ml water sample in a sterile borosilicate glass flask and boil for 1 to 2 min to kill any vegetative cells present. Avoid longer boiling to prevent chemical changes in the sample.

d. *Procedure:*

1) Label 5 flasks or tubes, A, B, C, D, and E. Add water samples, media reagents, and redistilled water to each flask as indicated in the following protocol:

water. Make an initial bacterial count by plating triplicate 1-ml portions from each culture flask in plate count agar. Incubate Tests A through E at 35 C for 24 ± 2 hr. Prepare final plate counts from each flask, using dilutions of 1, 0.1, 0.01, 0.001, and 0.0001 ml.

e. *Preparation of bacterial suspension:*

1) Bacterial growth—On the day before performing the distilled-water suitability test, inoculate a strain of *E. aerogenes* onto a nutrient agar slant with a slope of approximately 6.3 cm (2-1/2 in.) length contained in a 125X16 mm screw-cap tube. Streak the entire agar surface to develop a continuous-growth film and incubate 18 to 24 hr at 35 C.

2) Harvesting of viable cells—Pipet 1 to 2 ml sterile dilution water from a 99-ml water blank onto the 18- to 24-hr culture. Emulsify the growth on the

Media Reagents	Control Test (ml)		Optional Tests (ml)		
	Control A	Unknown Distilled Water B	Food Available C	Nitrogen Source D	Carbon Source E
Sodium citrate solution	2.5	2.5	-	2.5	-
Ammonium sulfate solution	2.5	2.5	-	-	2.5
Salt-mixture solution	2.5	2.5	2.5	2.5	2.5
Phosphate buffer (7.3±0.1)	1.5	1.5	1.5	1.5	1.5
Unknown water	-	21.0	21.0	21.0	21.0
Redistilled water	21.0	-	5.0	2.5	2.5
Total volume	30.0	30.0	30.0	30.0	30.0

2) Add a suspension of *Enterobacter aerogenes* (IMViC type --++) of such density that each flask will contain 30 to 80 cells/ml, prepared as directed below. Cell densities below this range result in ratios that are not consistent, while densities above 100 cells/ml result in decreased sensitivity to nutrients in the test

slant by gently rubbing the bacterial film with the pipet, being careful not to tear the agar; then pipet the suspension back into the original 99-ml water blank.

3) Dilution of bacterial suspension— Make a 1:100 dilution of the original bottle into a second water blank, a fur-

ther 1:100 dilution of the second bottle into a third water blank, then 10 ml of the third bottle into a fourth water blank, shaking vigorously after each transfer. Pipet 1.0 ml of the fourth dilution ($1:10^7$) into each of Flasks A, B, C, D, and E. This procedure should result in a final dilution of the organisms to a range of 30 to 80 viable cells for each ml of test solution.

4) Verification of bacterial density— Variations among strains of the same organism, different organisms, media, and surface area of agar slopes will possibly necessitate adjustment of the dilution procedure in order to arrive at a specific density range between 30 and 80 viable cells. To establish the growth range numerically for a specific organism and medium, make a series of plate counts from the third dilution to determine the bacterial density. Then choose the proper volume from this third dilution, which, when diluted by the 30 ml in Flasks A, B, C, D, and E, will contain 30 to 80 viable cells/ml. If the procedures are standardized as to surface area of the slant and laboratory technic, it is possible to reproduce results on repeated experiments with the same strain of microorganism.

5) Procedural difficulties—Problems that often arise in this method are due to:

a) Storage of unknown distilled water sample in soft-glass containers or in glass containers without liners for metal caps.

b) Use of chemicals in preparation of reagents not of analytical-reagent grade or not of recent manufacture.

c) Contamination of reagent by distilled water with a bacterial background. To avoid this problem prepare a Standard Plate Count on all

media reagents before initiating the suitability test, as a check on stock solution contamination.

d) Failure to obtain desired initial bacterial concentration or incorrect choice of dilution used to obtain 24-hr plate count.

e) Prolongation of incubation time beyond 26-hr limit, resulting in desensitized growth response.

6) Calculation—

a) For growth-inhibiting substances:

$$\text{Ratio} = \frac{\text{colony count/ml Flask B}}{\text{colony count/ml Flask A}}$$

A ratio of 0.8 to 1.2 (inclusive) shows no toxic substances; a ratio of less than 0.8 shows growth-inhibiting substances in the water sample.

b) For nitrogen and carbon sources that promote growth:

$$\text{Ratio} = \frac{\text{colony count/ml Flask C}}{\text{colony count/ml Flask A}}$$

c) For nitrogen sources that promote growth:

$$\text{Ratio} = \frac{\text{colony count/ml Flask D}}{\text{colony count/ml Flask A}}$$

d) For carbon sources that promote bacterial growth:

$$\text{Ratio} = \frac{\text{colony count/ml Flask E}}{\text{colony count/ml Flask A}}$$

Do not calculate ratios b, c, or d when ratio a indicates a toxic reaction. For ratios b, c, or d, a value in excess of 1.2 indicates an available source for bacterial growth.

f. Interpretation of results: The colony count from Flask A after 20 to 24 hr at 35 C will depend on the number of organisms initially planted in Flask A and on the strain of *E. aerogenes* used in the test procedures. This is the reason the control, Flask A, must be run for each individual series of tests. However, for a given strain of *E. aerogenes* under identical environmental conditions, the terminal count should be reasonably constant when the initial plant is the same. The difference in the initial plant of 30 and 80 will be about three-fold larger for the 80 organisms initially planted in Flask A, providing the growth rate remains constant. Thus, it is essential that the initial colony counts on Flask A and Flask B be approximately equal to secure accurate data.

When the ratio exceeds 1.2, it may be assumed that growth-stimulating substances are present. However, this procedure is extremely sensitive and ratios up to 3.0 would have little significance in actual practice. Therefore, when the ratio is between 1.2 and 3.0, Tests C, D, and E do not appear to be necessary except in special circumstances.

Usually Flask C will be very low and Flasks D and E will have a ratio of less than 1.2 when the ratio of Flask B to Flask A is between 0.8 and 1.2. The limiting factors of growth in Flask A are the nitrogen and organic carbon present. An extremely large amount of ammonia nitrogen with no organic carbon could increase the ratio in Flask D above 1.2, or the absence of nitrogen with high carbon concentration could give ratios above 1.2 in Flask E, with a B:A ratio between 0.8 and 1.2.

A ratio below 0.8 indicates that the water contains toxic substances, and this ratio includes all allowable tolerances. As indicated in the preceding paragraph, the ratio could go as high as 3.0 from 1.2 without any undesirable consequences.

Specific corrective measures cannot be recommended in specific instances of defective distillation apparatus. However, careful inspection of the distillation equipment and a review of the production and handling of the distilled water should enable local laboratory personnel to correct the cause of the difficulty.

Feedwater to a still is often passed through a deionizing column and a carbon filter. If these columns are well maintained, most inorganic and organic contaminants will be removed. If maintenance is poor, the input water may be degraded to a quality lower than that of the raw tap water.

The best distillation system is made of stainless steel. Quartz, Vycor, and pyrex glass, in that order of preference, are also acceptable. Tin-lined hardware is least desirable because maintenance is difficult. All connecting plumbing should be stainless steel, pyrex, or special plastic pipes made of polyvinyl chloride (PVC). Storage reservoirs should be of stainless steel and should be protected from dust.

g. *Test sensitivity:* Taking copper as one relative measurement of distilled water toxicity, maximum sensitivity of the test will be 0.05 mg of copper/l in a distilled water sample.

3. Membrane Filter Characteristics

Membrane filters may vary in performance as a result of differences in manufacturing methods, materials, and quality control. Pores in the filters must be distributed uniformly and have a diameter of 0.45 ± 0.02 μm. Filters should be able to retain bacteria quantitatively on their upper surface, be free of bacterial-growth-inhibiting or stimulating substances, and be free of materials that directly or indirectly interfere with bacterial indicator systems in the medium. The filter and absorbent pad should not be degraded by sterilization at 121 C for 10 min. The ink used to delineate the surface grid should be non-toxic. Filter uniformity should be sufficient so that the variation in five filter culture replicates should be no more than 10% of the average.

905 C.   Media Specifications

The need for uniformity dictates the use of dehydrated media. Never prepare media from the basic ingredients when suitable dehydrated media are available. Follow the manufacturer's directions for rehydration and sterilization. Commercially prepared media in liquid form (sterile ampoule or other) also may be used if known to give equivalent results.

NOTE—The term "percent solution" as used in these directions is to be understood to mean "grams of solute per 100 ml of solution."

1. Dilution Water

a. Buffered water: To prepare stock phosphate buffer solution, dissolve 34.0 g potassium dihydrogen phosphate, KH_2PO_4, in 500 ml distilled water, adjust to pH 7.2 with $1N$ NaOH, and dilute to 1 l with distilled water.

Add 1.25 ml stock phosphate buffer solution and 5.0 ml magnesium sulfate (50 g $MgSO_4 \cdot 7H_2O/l$ distilled water) to 1 l distilled water. Dispense in amounts that will provide 99 ± 2.0 ml or 9 ± 0.2 ml after autoclaving for 15 min.

b. Peptone dilution water: Prepare a 10% solution of peptone in distilled water. Dilute a measured volume to provide a final 0.1% solution. Final pH should be 6.8.

Dispense in amounts to provide 99 ± 2.0 ml or 9 ± 0.2 ml after autoclaving for 15 min.

Bacteria should not be suspended in any dilution water for more than 30 min at room temperature since death or multiplication may occur.

2. Lactose Broth

Beef extract . . . . 3.0 g
Peptone . . . . 5.0 g
Lactose . . . . 5.0 g
Distilled water. 1   l

pH should be between 6.8 and 7.0, but preferably 6.9 after sterilization. Before sterilization, dispense in fermentation tubes of such dimensions that the liquid in the inoculated tube will cover the inverted vial at least partially after sterilization.

When fermentation tubes or other containers are prepared for the examination of 10-ml or 100-ml portions of sample, the lactose broth medium must be of such strength that the addition of that volume of sample to the medium in the fermentation tube will not reduce the concentration of ingredients in the mixture below that in the standard medium. Because dehydrated medium is used, the proper concentration of ingredients may be obtained by consulting the following tabulation:

Inoculum ml	Amount of Medium in Tube ml	Volume of Medium + Inoculum ml	Dehydrated Lactose Broth Required g/l
1	10 or more	11 or more	13.0
10	10	20	26.0
10	20	30	19.5
100	50	150	39.0
100	35	135	50.1
100	20	120	78.0

3. Lauryl Tryptose Broth

Tryptose . . . . 20.0 g
Lactose . . . . 5.0 g
Dipotassium hydrogen
  phosphate, K_2HPO_4 . . . . . 2.75 g
Potassium dihydrogen
  phosphate, KH_2PO_4 . . . . . 2.75 g
Sodium chloride, NaCl . . . . . . 5.0 g
Sodium lauryl sulfate . . . . . . 0.1 g
Distilled water . . . . 1 l

pH should be approximately 6.8 after sterilization. Before sterilization, dispense in fermentation tubes of such dimensions that the liquid in the inoculated tube will cover the inverted vial at least partially after sterilization.

As with lactose broth, the lauryl tryptose broth must be of such strength that the addition of 100-ml or 10-ml portions of the sample to the medium will not reduce the concentrations of the various ingredients below those of the standard medium. Prepare in accordance with the following tabulation:

4. Tryptone Glucose Extract Agar

Beef extract . . . . 3.0 g
Tryptone . . . . 5.0 g
Glucose . . . . 1.0 g
Agar . . . . 15.0 g
Distilled water . . . . 1 l

pH should be between 6.8 and 7.0 after sterilization.

5. Plate Count Agar (Tryptone Glucose Yeast Agar)

Tryptone . . . . 5.0 g
Yeast extract . . . . 2.5 g
Glucose . . . . 1.0 g
Agar . . . . 15.0 g
Distilled water . . . . 1 l

pH should be 7.0 ± 0.1 after sterilization.

6. Endo Agar

Peptone . . . . 10.0 g
Lactose . . . . 10.0 g

Inoculum ml	Amount of Medium in Tube ml	Volume of Medium + Inoculum ml	Dehydrated Lauryl Tryptose Broth Required g/l
1	10 or more	11 or more	35.6
10	10	20	71.2
10	20	30	53.4
100	50	150	106.8
100	35	135	137.1
100	20	120	213.6

Dipotassium hydrogen
phosphate, K₂HPO₄. . . . . . 3.5 g
Agar. . . . . 15.0 g
Sodium sulfite . . . . 2.5 g
Basic fuchsin . . . . 0.5 g
Distilled water . . . . 1 l

pH should be 7.4 after sterilization. The medium should be light pink when hot and almost colorless when cool.

7. Eosin Methylene Blue (EMB) Agar (Levine's modification)

Peptone . . . . 10.0 g
Lactose . . . . 10.0 g
Dipotassium hydrogen
phosphate, K₂HPO₄ . . . . 2.0 g
Agar. . . . . 15.0 g
Eosin Y . . . . 0.4 g
Methylene blue . . . . 0.065 g
Distilled water. . . . . 1 l

pH should be 7.1 after sterilization. Decolorization of the medium occurs during sterilization, but the color returns after cooling.

8. Brilliant Green Lactose Bile Broth

Peptone . . . . 10.0 g
Lactose. . . . . 10.0 g
Oxgall . . . . 20.0 g
Brilliant green . . . . 0.0133 g
Distilled water . . . . 1 l

pH should be 7.2 after sterilization. Before sterilization, dispense in fermentation tubes with sufficient medium to cover the inverted vial at least partially after sterilization.

9. EC Medium

Tryptose or trypticase . . . . . . 20.0 g
Lactose. . . . . 5.0 g
Bile salts mixture or
bile salts No. 3. . . . . 1.5 g
Dipotassium hydrogen
phosphate, K₂HPO₄. . . . . . 4.0 g

Potassium dihydrogen
phosphate, KH₂PO₄. . . . . . 1.5 g
Sodium chloride, NaCl. . . . . . 5.0 g
Distilled water . . . . 1 l

pH should be 6.9 after sterilization. Before sterilization, dispense in fermentation tubes with sufficient medium to cover the inverted vial at least partially after sterilization.

10. M-FC Broth*

Tryptose or biosate . . . . 10.0 g
Proteose peptone No. 3
or polypeptone. . . . . 5.0 g
Yeast extract . . . . 3.0 g
Sodium chloride . . . . 5.0 g
Lactose. . . . . 12.5 g
Bile salts No. 3 or
bile salts mixture. . . . . . . 1.5 g
Aniline blue . . . . 0.1 g
Distilled water. . . . . 1 l

Rehydrate in the distilled water containing 10 ml of 1% rosolic acid in 0.2N NaOH.† Heat the medium to the boiling point, promptly remove from heat and cool to below 45 C. Do not sterilize by autoclaving. Final pH should be 7.4.

The finished medium should be stored at 2 to 10 C and any unused medium discarded after 96 hr.

Note—This medium may be solidified by the addition of 1.2 to 1.5 percent agar before boiling.

---

*Dehydrated Difco M-FC Broth Base (No. 0883), dehydrated BBL m-FC Broth (No. 01-757), or equivalent may be used.

†Rosolic acid reagent will decompose if sterilized by autoclaving. The stock solution should be stored in the dark at 2 to 10 C and discarded after 2 wk, or sooner if its color changes from dark red to muddy brown. Rosolic acid may be omitted from the medium if minimal background colony counts occur and equivalent results are obtained without it.

11. M-Endo Medium

M-Endo broth contains the following ingredients per liter:

	g
Tryptose or polypeptone	10.0
Thiopeptone or thiotone	5.0
Casitone or trypticase	5.0
Yeast extract	1.5
Lactose	12.5
Sodium chloride	5.0
Dipotassium hydrogen phosphate	4.375
Potassium dihydrogen phosphate	1.375
Sodium lauryl sulfate	0.050
Sodium desoxycholate	0.10
Sodium sulfite	2.10
Basic fuchsin	1.05

Rehydrate in 1 l of distilled water containing 20 ml of 95% ethanol. Heat the medium to the boiling point, promptly remove from heat, and cool to below 45 C. Do not sterilize by autoclaving. Final pH should be between 7.1 and 7.3.

The finished medium should be stored in the dark at 2 to 10 C and any unused medium discarded after 96 hr.

NOTE—This medium may be solidified by the addition of 1.2 to 1.5% agar before boiling.

12. LES MF Holding Medium, Coliform

Tryptone	3.0 g
M-Endo broth MF	3.0 g
Dipotassium hydrogen phosphate	3.0 g
Sodium benzoate	1.0 g
Sulfanilamide	1.0 g
Paraaminobenzoic acid	1.2 g
Cycloheximide	0.5 g
Distilled water	1 l

Rehydrate in the distilled water without heating. Final pH should be 7.1±0.1.

13. LES Endo Agar

Yeast extract	1.2 g
Casitone or trypticase	3.7 g
Thiopeptone or thiotone	3.7 g
Tryptose	7.5 g
Lactose	9.4 g
Dipotassium hydrogen phosphate	3.3 g
Potassium dihydrogen phosphate	1.0 g
Sodium chloride	3.7 g
Sodium desoxycholate	0.1 g
Sodium lauryl sulfate	0.05 g
Sodium sulfite	1.6 g
Basic fuchsin	0.8 g
Agar	15.0 g
Distilled water	1 l

Rehydrate in the distilled water containing 20 ml 95% ethanol. Bring to a boil, cool to 45 to 50 C and dispense in 4-ml quantities into the lower section of 60-mm glass or plastic petri dishes. If dishes of any other size are used, adjust the quantity to give an equivalent depth. Plates may be stored in the dark up to 2 wk when held at 2 to 10 C. Do not expose to direct sunlight.

14. M-VFC Holding Medium

This medium may not be available in dehydrated form and may require preparation from the basic ingredients.

Casitone, vitamin-free	0.2 g
Sodium benzoate	4.0 g
Sulfanilamide	0.5 g
Ethanol (95%)	10.0 ml
Distilled water	1 l

Heat to dissolve medium and sterilize by filtration through a membrane filter (pore diameter, 0.22 μm). Final pH should be 6.7.

The finished medium should be stored at 2 to 10 C and any unused medium discarded after 1 month. To prepare 100 ml of medium, make a 1:100 aqueous solution of casitone and add 2 ml.

15. Azide Dextrose Broth

Beef extract.	4.5 g
Tryptone or	
polypeptone	15.0 g
Glucose	7.5 g
Sodium chloride, NaCl.	7.5 g
Sodium azide, NaN₃	0.2 g
Distilled water	1 l

pH should be about 7.2 after sterilization.

16. Ethyl Violet Azide Broth

Tryptone or biosate	20.0	g
Glucose	5.0	g
Sodium chloride	5.0	g
Dipotassium hydrogen		
phosphate, K₂HPO₄	2.7	g
Potassium dihydrogen		
phosphate, KH₂PO₄	2.7	g
Sodium azide, NaN₃	0.4	g
Ethyl violet	0.00083	g
Distilled water	1	l

pH should be about 7.0 after sterilization.

17. KF Streptococcus Agar‡

Proteose peptone No. 3	
or polypeptone	10.0 g
Yeast extract	10.0 g
Sodium chloride	5.0 g
Sodium glycero-	
phosphate	10.0 g
Maltose	20.0 g
Lactose	1.0 g
Sodium azide	0.4 g
Agar.	20.0 g
Distilled water	1 l

Mix 7.64 g of dehydrated medium with 100 ml of distilled water in a flask. Heat in a boiling water bath to dissolve the agar. After solution is complete heat for an additional 5 min. Cool to 50 to 60 C

‡Dehydrated Difco KF Streptococcus Agar (No. 0496), dehydrated BBL KF Streptococcal Agar (No. 01-690), or equivalent, may be used.

and add 1 ml sterile aqueous 1% solution of 2,3,5-triphenyltetrazolium chloride/100 ml. Adjust pH to 7.2 with 10% Na₂CO₃ if necessary. The medium may be held at 45 to 50 C for up to 4 hr before plates are poured. Poured plates may be stored in the dark up to 30 days when held at 2 to 10 C.

18. Pfizer Selective Enterococcus (PSE) Agar

Peptone C	17.0	g
Peptone B.	3.0	g
Yeast extract	5.0	g
Bacteriological bile	10.0	g
Sodium chloride, NaCl	5.0	g
Sodium citrate	1.0	g
Esculin	1.0	g
Ferric ammonium citrate	0.5	g
Sodium azide, NaN₃	0.25	g
Agar	15.0	g
Distilled water	1	l

pH should be 7.1 after sterilization. The medium may be held at 45 to 50 C for up to 4 hr before plates are poured.

19. Brain-Heart Infusion

Infusion of calf brains	200	g
Infusion of beef heart	250	g
Proteose peptone	10.0	g
Glucose	2.0	g
Sodium chloride, NaCl	5.0	g
Disodium hydrogen		
phosphate, Na₂HPO₄	2.5	g
Distilled water	1	l

pH should be 7.4 after sterilization.

20. Brain-Heart Infusion Agar

Brain-heart infusion agar contains the same ingredients as brain-heart infusion except that 15.0 g agar are added. The pH should be 7.4 after sterilization. Tube for slants.

21. Tryptophane Broth

Tryptophane broth contains 10.0 g tryptone or trypticase/l of distilled water. Dispense in 5-ml portions in test tubes. Sterilize by autoclaving at 121 C for 15 min.

22. Buffered Glucose Broth

Proteose peptone or
   equivalent peptone. . . . . . . 5.0 g
Glucose . . . . 5.0 g
Dipotassium hydrogen
   phosphate, K₂HPO₄. . . . . . 5.0 g
Distilled water . . . . 1 l

Dispense in 5-ml portions in test tubes and sterilize in an autoclave at 121 C for 12 to 15 min, making sure that the total time of exposure to heat is not longer than 30 min.

23. Salt Peptone Glucose Broth

Polypeptone or proteose
   peptone . . . . 10.0 g
Sodium chloride, NaCl. . . . . . 5.0 g
Glucose . . . . 10.0 g
Distilled water . . . . 1 l

pH should be 7.0 to 7.2 before sterilization. Dispense in 5-ml portions in test tubes and sterilize in an autoclave at 121 C for 12 to 15 min, making sure that the total time of exposure to heat is not longer than 30 min.

24. Koser's Citrate Broth

Sodium ammonium hy-
   drogen phosphate,
   NaNH₄HPO₄•4H₂O . . . . . 1.5 g
Dipotassium hydrogen
   phosphate, K₂HPO₄ . . . . . 1.0 g
Magnesium sulfate
   heptahydrate,
   MgSO₄•7H₂O . . . . 0.2 g
Sodium citrate
   dihydrate, crystals . . . . 3.0 g
Distilled water . . . . 1 l

Dispense in 5-ml portions in test tubes. Sterilize by autoclaving.

25. Simmons' Citrate Agar

Magnesium sulfate
   heptahydrate,
   MgSO₄•7H₂O . . . . 0.2 g
Ammonium dihydrogen
   phosphate, NH₄H₂PO₄ . . . 1.0 g
Dipotassium hydrogen
   phosphate, K₂HPO₄ . . . . . 1.0 g
Sodium citrate dihydrate . . . . 2.0 g
Sodium chloride, NaCl . . . . . 5.0 g
Agar . . . . 15.0 g
Bromthymol blue . . . . 0.08 g
Distilled water . . . . 1 l

Tube for long slants and sterilize by autoclaving.

26. Chapman Stone Agar

Yeast extract . . . . 2.5 g
Tryptone. . . . . 10.0 g
Gelatin. . . . . 30.0 g
d-Mannitol. . . . . 10.0 g
Sodium chloride, NaCl. . . . . 55.0 g
Ammonium sulfate, (NH₄)₂SO₄ . 75.0 g
Dipotassium phosphate, K₂HPO₄ . . .
                5.0 g
Agar . . . . 15.0 g
Distilled water . . . . 1 l

pH should be 7.0 after sterilization by autoclaving at 121 C for 10 min.

27. M-PA Agar

This agar medium may not be available in dehydrated form and may require preparation from the basic ingredients.

L-lysine HCl . . . . 5.0 g
Sodium chloride, NaCl . . . . . 5.0 g
Yeast extract . . . . 2.0 g
Xylose . . . . 2.5 g
Sucrose . . . . 1.25 g
Lactose . . . . 1.25 g
Phenol red . . . . 0.08 g
Ferric ammonium citrate . . . . 0.8 g
Sodium thiosulfate . . . . 6.8 g
Agar . . . . 15.0 g
Distilled water . . . . 1 l

Adjust pH to 6.5 and sterilize. Cool to 55 to 60 C; carefully readjust pH to

7.1±0.1 and add the following dry antibiotics per liter of agar base: sulfapyri-
dine,§ 176 mg; kanamycin,‖ 8.5 mg;
nalidixic Acid, # 37.0 mg; and Actidione,** 150 mg. After mixing dispense
in 3-ml quantities in 50- by 12-mm
petri plates. Poured plates of the medium may be stored at 2 to 10 C for 1
month.

28. Milk Agar (Brown and Scott Foster modification)

Mixture A:
Carnation Instant Non-Fat
  Milk 100   g
Distilled water 500   ml
Mixture B:
Nutrient broth . . . . 12.5   g
Sodium chloride, NaCl . . . . . 2.5   g
Agar . . . . 15.0   g
Distilled water 500   ml

Separately sterilize Mixtures A and
B; cool rapidly to 55 C; combine the
two mixtures and pour into 100- by 15-
mm petri plates, about 20 ml/plate.

29. Asparagine Broth

This medium may not be available in
dehydrated form and may require preparation from the basic ingredients.

Asparagine, DL . . . . 3.0 g
Anhydrous dipotassium phosphate,
  K₂HPO₄ . . . . 1.0 g
Magnesium sulfate,
  MgSO₄•7H₂O . . . . 0.5 g
Distilled water 1   l

Adjust pH to 6.9 to 7.2 before sterilization.

---

§Nutritional Biochemicals, Cleveland, Ohio.
‖ Bristol-Myers, Syracuse, N.Y.
#Calbiochem, La Jolla, Calif.
**Upjohn Company, Kalamazoo, Mich.

30. Acetamide Broth

This medium may not be available in
dehydrated form and may require preparation from the basic ingredients.

Acetamide. . . . . 10.0   g
Sodium chloride, NaCl . . . . 5.0   g
Anhydrous dipotassium phosphate,
  K₂HPO₄ . . . . 1.39   g
Anhydrous potassium dihydrogen
  phosphate, KH₂PO₄ . . . . 0.73   g
Magnesium sulfate,
  MgSO₄•7H₂O . . . . 0.5   g
Phenol red. . . . . 0.012 g
Distilled water. 1   l

Adjust pH to 6.9 to 7.2 before sterilization.

Prepare acetamide agar slants as
above, except add 15 g agar, boil to dissolve agar, and dispense in 8-ml quantities to 16-mm tubes. After autoclaving,
incline the tubes while cooling to provide a large slant surface.

31. Neopeptone-Glucose-Rose Bengal-Aureomycin Agar

This medium may not be available in
dehydrated form and may require preparation from the basic ingredients.

Neopeptone . . . . 5.0   g
Glucose . . . . 10.0   g
Rose bengal . . . . 0.035 g
Agar. . . . . 20.0   g
Chlortetracycline (Aureomycin) or
  tetracycline . . . . 35.0   μg
Distilled water 1   l

pH should be about 6.5 after sterilization. Prepare the rose bengal in advance by dissolving 1 g of rose bengal,
aqueous, in 100 ml distilled water. Add
3.5 ml of this solution/l of medium before autoclaving.

Prepare the antibiotic chlortetracycline (or tetracycline) separately and add
after autoclaving but just before plates
are poured. Add 1 g of the water-soluble

antibiotic to 150 ml distilled water to prepare the stock solution. Refrigerate. Sterilize by filtration before each use. Add 0.05 ml of the sterile solution/10 ml of the agar medium.

Since this medium is used for the preparation of pour plates, the basal agar may be prepared and stored either in bulk, or more conveniently, in tubes in 10-ml amounts. After melting stored medium, cool to about 45 C, add 0.05 ml of the antibiotic solution/10 ml, and pour the plate.

Dehydrated Cooke's rose bengal agar may be used in place of neopeptone-glucose-rose bengal agar base.

32. Neopeptone-Glucose Agar

Neopeptone (or equivalent). . . . 5.0 g
Glucose . . . . 10.0 g
Agar . . . . 20.0 g
Distilled water 1   l

pH should be about 6.5 after sterilization.

This medium is known also as Emmons' Sabouraud Agar or Emmons' Sabouraud Dextrose Agar.

33. Czapek (or Czapek Dox) Agar

Sucrose. . . . . 30.0 g
Sodium nitrate, NaNO₃. . . . . 3.0 g
Dipotassium phosphate,
    K₂HPO₄ . . . . .1.0 g
Magnesium sulfate, MgSO₄ . . 0.5 g
Potassium chloride, KCl . . . . 0.5 g
Ferrous sulfate, FeSO₄ . . . . . 0.01 g
Agar . . . . .15.0 g
Distilled water 1   l

pH should be 7.3 after sterilization.

34. Yeast Nitrogen Base-Glucose Broth

Yeast nitrogen base. . . . . . . 13.4 g
Distilled water 1   l

Sterilize by filtration. Prepare 500 ml each of 2% and 40% aqueous glucose solutions. Sterilize each separately by filtration. To use the final medium, aseptically add to a sterile 250-ml Erlenmeyer flask 25 ml of the yeast nitrogen base and 25 ml of either the 2% or the 40% glucose solutions to make 1% or 20% final glucose concentrations. Stopper the flask with a gauze-wrapped cotton stopper and store until used.

35. Yeast Extract-Malt Extract-Glucose Agar

Yeast extract . . . . 3.0 g
Malt extract . . . . 3.0 g
Neopeptone (or equivalent). . . . 5.0 g
Glucose . . . . .10.0 g
Agar . . . . .20.0 g
Distilled water 1   l

No pH adjustment of this medium is required.

36. Diamalt Agar

Diamalt . . . . .150.0 g
Agar . . . . 20.0 g
Distilled water 1   l

No pH adjustment of this medium is required. The medium will be turbid but filtration is not required.

37. Starch-Casein Agar

Soluble starch. . . . . .10.0 g
Casein . . . . 0.3 g
Potassium nitrate, KNO₃ . . . . 2.0 g
Sodium chloride, NaCl . . . . . 2.0 g
Dipotassium phosphate,
    K₂HPO₄ . . . . 2.0 g
Magnesium sulfate, hydrate,
    MgSO₄•7H₂O . . . . 0.05 g
Calcium carbonate, CaCO₃. . . 0.02 g
Ferrous sulfate, hydrate,
    FeSO₄•7H₂O . . . . 0.01 g
Agar . . . . .15.0 g
Distilled water 1   l

No pH adjustment of this medium is required. Since the medium is used to prepare double-layer plates, the medium for the bottom layer may be stored in bulk or in tubes in about 15-ml amounts. Medium for the surface layer should be stored in tubes containing 17.0 ml. One milliliter of Actidione (1 mg/ml, sterilized at 121 C for 15 min) should be added to the liquefied surface medium at the time of inoculation.

38. Casitone-Glycerol-Yeast Autolysate Broth (CGY)

This medium may not be available in dehydrated form and may require preparation from the basic ingredients. It may be solidified by the addition of 1.5% agar.

Casitone	5.0	g
Glycerol	10.0	g
Yeast autolysate	1.0	g
Distilled water	1	l

39. Isolation Medium (Iron Bacteria)

This medium may not be available in dehydrated form and may require preparation from the basic ingredients.

Glucose	0.15	g
Ammonium sulfate, (NH₄)₂SO₄	0.5	g
Calcium nitrate, Ca(NO₃)₂ . . .	0.01	g
Dipotassium hydrogen phosphate, K₂HPO₄.	0.05	g
Magnesium sulfate, MgSO₄•7H₂O	0.05	g
Potassium chloride, KCl	0.05	g
Calcium carbonate, CaCO₃ . . .	0.1	g
Agar	10.0	g
Vitamin B₁₂.	0.01	mg
Thiamine.	0.4	mg
Distilled water	1	l

40. Maintenance (SCY) Medium (Iron Bacteria)

This medium may not be available in dehydrated form and may require preparation from the basic ingredients.

Sucrose	1.0	g
Casitone	0.75	g
Yeast extract	0.25	g
Trypticase soy broth without dextrose	0.25	g
Agar	10.0	g
Vitamin B₁₂.	0.01	mg
Thiamine.	0.4	mg
Distilled water	1	l

41. Mn-Agar

This medium may not be available in dehydrated form and may require preparation from the basic ingredients.

Manganous carbonate, MnCO₃	2.0	g
Beef extract.	1.0	g
Ferrous ammonium sulfate, Fe(NH₄)₂(SO₄)₂	150	mg
Sodium citrate	150	mg
Yeast extract	75	mg
Cyanocobalamin	0.005	mg
Agar	10.0	g
Distilled water	1	l

Prepare and sterilize the medium without cyanocobalamin. Separately sterilize the cobalamin by filtration and aseptically add just before the medium solidifies.

42. Iron Oxidizing Medium *(Thiobacillus ferrooxidans)*

This medium may not be available in dehydrated form and may require preparation from the basic ingredients.

Basal salts:

Ammonium sulfate, (NH₄)₂SO₄	3.0	g

Potassium chloride, KCl . . . .   0.10 g
Dipotassium hydrogen phosphate,
  K_2HPO_4 . . . .   0.50 g
Magnesium sulfate,
  $MgSO_4$•$7H_2O$. . . . . .   0.50 g
Calcium nitrate, $Ca(NO_3)_2$ . .   0.01 g
H_2SO_4, 10 N . . . .   1.0   ml
Distilled water. 700   ml
Energy source:
Ferrous sulfate, $FeSO_4$•$7H_2O$,
  14.74% solution (w/v) . . . 300   ml

Separately sterilize the basal salts and energy source and combine when cool. The medium can be stored for at least 2 wk in the refrigerator. A precipitate will form and the medium will be opalescent and green. The pH should be 3.0 to 3.6.

43. Ferrous Sulfide Agar (*Gallionella ferruginea*)

This medium may not be available in dehydrated form and may require preparation from the basic ingredients.

Agar layer:
Ferrous sulfide (washed precipitate
  and liquid) 500   ml
Sodium sulfide, Na_2S . . . . . 15.6 g
Ferrous ammonium sulfate,
  $Fe(NH_4)_2(SO_4)_2$•$6H_2O$ . . . 78.4 g
Boiling distilled water.   1   l
Agar (liquid) (30 g/l). 500   ml
Liquid overlay:
Ammonium chloride, NH_4Cl . .   1.0 g
Dipotassium phosphate,
  K_2HPO_4 . . . .   0.5 g
Magnesium sulfate,
  $MgSO_4$•$7H_2O$ . . . .   0.2 g
Calcium chloride, $CaCl_2$ . . . .   0.1 g
Distilled water   1   l

Prepare ferrous sulfide by reacting equal molar quantities of sodium sulfide and ferrous ammonium sulfate in boiling distilled water. Let the resulting precipitate settle from the hot solution in a completely filled and stoppered bottle. Wash the ferrous sulfide precipitate four times by decanting the supernatant and

replacing with boiling water. The ferrous sulfide can be stored in a glass stoppered bottle completely filled with additional boiling distilled water.

Add equal volumes of ferrous sulfide and 3% agar at 45 C. Prepare slants in screw-capped tubes. Prepare the liquid overlay, bubble carbon dioxide through it for 10 to 15 sec, and add several milliliters to the agar slant.

A variation of the basic medium requires the addition of 0.5 ml formalin (40% formaldehyde solution) to a screw-capped dilution bottle containing 10 ml of ferrous sulfide agar and 100 ml of the liquid overlay. Add 0.001% bromthymol blue and 0.004% bromcresol purple to the liquid overlay.

44. Sulfate-Reducing Medium

This medium may not be available in dehydrated form and may require preparation from the basic ingredients.

Sodium lactate. . . . . 3.5   g
Beef extract . . . . 1.0   g
Peptone . . . . 2.0   g
Magnesium sulfate,
  $MgSO_4$•$7H_2O$. . . . . . . 2.0   g
Sodium sulfate, Na_2SO_4. . . . 1.5   g
Dipotassium phosphate,
  K_2HPO_4. . . . . 0.5   g
Ferrous ammonium sulfate,
  $Fe(NH_4)_2(SO_4)_2$•$6H_2O$ . . 0.392 g
Calcium chloride, $CaCl_2$ . . . . 0.10   g
Sodium ascorbate . . . . 0.10   g
Distilled water. 1   l

pH should be 7.5±0.3 after sterilization. Prepare medium excluding ferrous ammonium sulfate and sodium ascorbate, dispense in screw-capped test tubes, and sterilize. For use, the tubes must be completely filled; therefore, in a flask sterilize extra medium to be added to the tubes for filling. On the day the medium is to be used prepare separate solutions of ferrous ammonium sulfate (3.92 g/100 ml) and sodium ascorbate (1.00 g/100 ml), sterilize by filtration through a 0.45-μm membrane filter, and aseptically add 0.1 ml of each solution/10 ml of the basal medium.

45. Sulfate-Reducing Medium (*Thiobacillus thioparus*)

This medium may not be available in dehydrated form and may require preparation from the basic ingredients.

Sodium thiosulfate,
  $Na_2S_2O_3 \cdot 5H_2O$ . . . . . .   10.0   g
Dipotassium hydrogen phosphate,
  K_2HPO_4 . . . .   2.0   g
Magnesium sulfate,
  $MgSO_4 \cdot 7H_2O$ . . . . . .   0.1   g
Calcium chloride,
  $CaCl_2 \cdot 2H_2O$ . . . .   0.1   g
Ammonium sulfate,
  $(NH_4)_2SO_4$ . . . .   0.1   g
Ferric chloride, $FeCl_3 \cdot 6H_2O$.   0.02 g
Distilled water   1   l

pH should be 7.8 after sterilization.

Separately sterilize the sodium thiosulfate and ammonium sulfate and add before use of the medium.

46. Sulfur Medium (*Thiobacillus thiooxidans*)

This medium may not be available in dehydrated form and may require preparation from the basic ingredients.

Sulfur, elemental . . . .   10.0   g
Potassium dihydrogen phosphate,
  KH_2PO_4 . . . .   3.0   g
Magnesium sulfate,
  $MgSO_4 \cdot 7H_2O$ . . . . . .   0.5   g
Ammonium sulfate,
  $(NH_4)_2SO_4$ . . . .   0.3   g
Calcium chloride,
  $CaCl_2 \cdot 2H_2O$ . . . .   0.25 g
Ferric chloride, $FeCl_3 \cdot 6H_2O$.   0.02 g
Distilled water   1   l

pH should be 4.8 after sterilization. Weigh the sulfur into 250-ml flasks using 1 g/flask. Add 100 ml of the medium to each flask and sterilize with intermittent steam (30 min for each of 3 consecutive days).

905 D. Bibliography

Levine, M. 1918. Differentiation of *B. coli* and *B. aerogenes* on a simplified eosine methylene blue agar. *J. Infect. Dis.* 23:43.

Levine, M. 1918. A simplified fuchsin sulphite (Endo) agar. *Amer. J. Pub. Health* 8:864.

Levine, M. 1921. Further observations on the eosine methylene blue agar. *J. Amer. Water Works Ass.* 8:151.

Levine, M. 1921. Bacteria fermenting lactose and their significance in water analysis. *Iowa State Coll. Agr. Mech. Arts Bull.* 62:117.

Bunker, G.C. & H. Schuber. 1922. The reaction of culture media. *J. Amer. Water Works Ass.* 9:63.

Jordan, H.E. 1932. Brilliant green bile for *Coli-Aerogenes* group determinations. *J. Amer. Water Works Ass.* 24:1027.

Ruchhoft, C.C. 1935. Comparative studies of media for the determination of the *Coli-Aerogenes* group in water analysis. *J. Amer. Water Works Ass.* 27:1732.

Ruchhoft, C.C. & J.F. Norton. 1935. Study of selective media for *Coli-Aerogenes* isolations. *J. Amer. Water Works Ass.* 27:1134.

McCrady, M.H. 1937. A practical study of procedures for the detection of the presence of coliform organisms in water. *Amer. J. Pub. Health* 27:1243.

Darby, C.W. & W.L. Mallmann. 1939. Studies on media for coliform organisms. *J. Amer. Water Works Ass.* 31:689.

Kelly, C.B. 1940. Brilliant green lactose bile and the *Standard Methods* completed test in isolation of coliform organisms. *Amer. J. Pub. Health* 30:1034.

RICHEY, D. 1941. Relative value of 2 per cent and 5 per cent brilliant green bile confirmatory media. *J. Amer. Water Works Ass.* 33:649.

HOWARD, N.J., A.G. LOCHHEAD & M.H. McCRADY. 1941. A study of methods for the detection of the presence of coliform organisms in water. *Can. J. Pub. Health* 32:29.

MALLMANN, W.L. & C.W. DARBY. 1941. Uses of a lauryl sulphate tryptose broth for the detection of coliform organisms. *Amer. J. Pub. Health* 31:127.

MALLMANN, W.L. & R.S. BREED. 1941. A comparative study of standard agars for determining bacterial counts in water. *Amer. J. Pub. Health* 31:341.

HOWARD, N.J., A.G. LOCHHEAD & M.H. McCRADY. 1942. Report of the committee on bacteriological examination of water and sewage. *Can. J. Pub. Health* 33:49.

ARCHAMBAULT, J. & M.H. McCRADY. 1942. Dissolved air as a source of error in fermentation tube results. *Amer. J. Pub. Health* 32:1164.

WATTIE, E. 1943. Coliform confirmation from raw and chlorinated waters with brilliant green bile lactose broth. *Pub. Health Rep.* 58:377.

McCRADY, M.H. 1943. A practical study of lauryl sulfate tryptose broth for detection of the presence of coliform organisms in water. *Amer. J. Pub. Health* 33:1199.

LEVINE, M. 1944. The effect of concentration of dyes on differentiation of enteric bacteria on eosin methylene blue agar. *J. Bacteriol.* 45:471.

MALLMANN, W.L. & E.B. SELIGMANN. 1950. A comparative study of media for the detection of streptococci in water and sewage. *Amer. J. Pub. Health* 40:286.

LITSKY, W., W.L. MALLMANN & C.W. FIFIELD. 1955. Comparison of the most probable numbers of *Escherichia coli* and enterococci in river waters. *Amer. J. Pub. Health* 45:1049.

STRAKA, R.P. & J.L. STOKES. 1957. Rapid destruction of bacteria in commonly used diluents and its elimination. *Appl. Microbiol.* 5:21.

SLANETZ, L.W. & C.H. BARTLEY. 1957. Numbers of enterococci in water, sewage, and feces determined by the membrane filter technique, with an improved medium. *J. Bacteriol.* 74:591.

FIFIELD, C.W. & C.P. SCHAUFUS. 1958. Improved membrane filter medium for the detection of coliform organisms. *J. Amer. Water Works Ass.* 50:193.

KENNER, B.A., H.F. CLARK & P.W. KABLER. 1961. Fecal streptococci. I. Cultivation and enumeration of streptococci in surface waters. *Appl. Microbiol.* 9:15.

McCARTHY, J.A., J.E. DELANEY & R.J. GRASSO. 1961. Measuring coliforms in water. *Water Sewage Works* 108:238.

DELANEY, J.E., J.A. McCARTHY & R.J. GRASSO. 1962. Measurement of *E. coli* Type I by the membrane filter. *Water Sewage Works* 109:289.

GELDREICH, E.E., H.F. CLARK, C.B. HUFF & L.C. BEST. 1965. Fecal coliform-organism medium for the membrane filter technique. *J. Amer. Water Works Ass.* 57:208.

GELDREICH, E.E. & H.F. CLARK. 1965. Distilled water suitability for microbiological applications. *J. Milk Food Technol.* 28:351.

AMERICAN PUBLIC HEALTH ASSOCIATION. 1972. Standard Methods for the Examination of Dairy Products, 13th ed. APHA, New York, N.Y.

MacLEOD, R.A., S.C. KUO & R. GELINAS. 1967. Metabolic injury to bacteria. II. Metabolic injury induced by distilled water or Cu++ in the plating diluent. *J. Bacteriol.* 93:961.

ISENBERG, H.D., D. GOLDBERG & J. SAMPSON. 1970. Laboratory studies with a selective enterococcus medium. *Appl. Microbiol.* 20:433.

LEVIN, M.A. & V.J. CABELLI. 1972. Membrane filter technique for enumeration of *Pseudomonas aeruginosa*. *Appl. Microbiol.* 24:864.

TAYLOR, R.H., R.H BORDNER & P.V SCARPINO. 1973. Delayed incubation membrane filter test for fecal coliforms. *Appl. Microbiol.* 25:363.

906   SAMPLES

906 A.   Collection

1. Containers

Samples for bacteriologic examination must be collected in bottles that have been cleansed and rinsed with great care, given a final rinse with distilled water, and sterilized as directed in Section 903, Laboratory Apparatus, and Section 904, Washing and Sterilization.

2. Dechlorination

A dechlorinating agent should be added to bottles intended for the collection of water containing residual chlorine unless they contain broth for direct planting of the sample therein. Sodium thiosulfate is a satisfactory dechlorinating agent. Its presence at the instant of collection of a sample from a chlorinated supply will neutralize any residual chlorine and will prevent a continuation of the bactericidal action of the chlorine during the time the sample is in transit to the laboratory. The bacteriologic examination will then indicate more probably the true bacterial content of the water at the time of sampling.

The sodium thiosulfate should be added to the clean sample bottle before sterilization in an amount sufficient to provide an approximate concentration of 100 mg/l in the sample. This can be accomplished by adding to a 120-ml (4-oz) bottle 0.1 ml of a 10% solution of sodium thiosulfate (this will neutralize a sample containing about 15 mg of residual chlorine/l). The bottle is then stoppered, capped, and sterilized by either dry or moist heat, as directed previously.

Water samples high in copper or zinc and wastewater samples high in heavy metals should be collected in sample bottles containing a chelating agent that will reduce metal toxicity. This is particularly significant when such samples are in transit for 24 hr or more. Ethylenediaminetetraacetic acid (EDTA) is a satisfactory chelating agent. A concentration of 372 mg/l has been found adequate. The EDTA may be added separately to the sample bottle before bottle sterilization (0.3 ml of a 15% solution in a 120-ml bottle) or it may be combined with the sodium thiosulfate solution before addition.

3. Sampling Procedures

When the sample is collected, leave ample air space in the bottle (at least 2.5 cm or 1 in.) to facilitate mixing of the sample by shaking, preparatory to examination. Care must be exercised to take samples that will be representative of the water being tested and to avoid contamination of the sample at the time of collection or in the period before examination.

The sampling bottle shall be kept unopened until the moment it is to be filled. Remove the stopper and hood or cap as a unit, taking care to avoid soiling. During sampling, do not handle the stopper or cap and neck of the bottle, and protect them from contamination. Hold the bottle near the base, fill it without rinsing, replace the stopper or cap immediately, and secure the hood around the neck of the bottle.

If the sample of water is to be taken from a distribution-system tap without attachments, it should be ascertained that the tap chosen is supplying water from a service pipe directly connected with the main, and is not, for example, served from a cistern or storage tank. The tap should be opened fully and the water allowed to run to waste for 2 or 3 min, or for a time sufficient to permit clearing of the service line. The flow from the tap should then be restricted to one that will permit filling the bottle without splashing. Leaking taps that allow water to flow over the outside of the tap must be avoided as sampling points.

In collecting samples directly from a river, stream, lake, reservoir, spring, or shallow well, the aim must be to obtain a sample representative of the water that will be the source of supply to consumers. It is therefore undesirable to take samples too near the bank or too far from the point of drawoff, or at a depth above or below the point of drawoff.

The location of sampling sites and the frequency of sampling are critical factors in obtaining reliable information about bacterial pollution in any body of water. Single or unscheduled grab samples from a river, stream, or lake can often be collected for control data or to satisfy regulatory requirements. A grab sample can be taken near the surface.

For extensive stream studies whereby the source and extent of pollution are to be determined, more representative samples must be taken, with consideration of the site, the method, and the time of sampling. In many instances, the number of sampling sites may represent a compromise based on the physical limitations of the laboratory, detection of pollution peaks, and frequency of sample collection. The number of samples to be processed depends on whether the survey objective is to measure cycles of immediate pollution, the duration of peak pollution, or the probable average pollution. Sites for measuring cyclic pollution and its duration are immediately below the pollution source. Sampling should be done as frequently as possible.

The site designated to measure estimated average pollution conditions should be far enough downstream to insure complete mixing of the pollutant and the water. Sampling at such points does not eliminate all the variations that may occur but will minimize any sharp fluctuations in quality. Downstream site sampling need not be done as frequently as cyclic pollution sampling.

Samples may be collected one-quarter, one-half, or three-quarters the width of the stream at each site or at other distances, depending on the objectives of the survey. Areas of relative stagnation should be avoided. Often only one sample, which is usually taken near the surface, may be collected in the stream channel.

Samples of bathing-beach water should be collected at locations and times of the greatest bather load, and, in natural bathing places, periods of stormwater runoff during the bathing season.

Samples from a river, stream, lake, or reservoir can often be taken by holding the bottle near its base in the hand and plunging it, neck downward, below the surface. The bottle should then be turned until the neck points slightly upward, the mouth being directed toward the current. If there is no current, as in the case of a reservoir, a current should be created artificially by pushing the bottle forward horizontally in a direction away from the hand. When sampling from a boat, obtain samples from the upstream side of the boat. If it is not possible to collect samples from these situations in this way, a weight may be attached to the base of the bottle, which can then be lowered into the water. In any case, care must be taken to avoid damage to the bank or stream bed; otherwise, fouling of the water may occur.

Special apparatus that permits mechanical removal of the bottle stopper below the water surface is required to collect samples from the depths of a lake or reservoir. Various types of deep sampling devices are available. The most common of these is the ZoBell J-Z sampler. This sampler utilizes a sterile 350-ml bottle and a rubber stopper through which a piece of glass tubing has been passed. This tubing is connected to another piece of glass tubing by a rubber connecting hose. The unit is mounted on a metal frame containing a cable and a messenger. When the messenger is released, it strikes the glass tubing at a point that has been slightly weakened by a file mark. The glass tube is broken by the messenger and the tension set up by the rubber connecting hose is released and the tubing swings to the side. Water is sucked into the bottle as a consequence of the partial vacuum created by sealing of the unit at the time of autoclaving. Commercial adaptations of this sampler and of others are available.

Bottom sediment sampling also requires special apparatus. The sampler described by Van Donsel and Geldreich has been found effective for a variety of bottom materials for remote (deep water) or hand (shallow water) sampling. This sampler preferably should be of stainless steel and fitted with a sterile plastic bag. A nylon cord closes the bag after the sampler penetrates the sediment. A slide bar keeps the bag closed during descent and is opened, thereby opening the bag, during sediment sampling.

If the sample is to be taken from a well fitted with a hand pump, water should be pumped to waste for about 5 min before the sample is collected. If the well is equipped with a mechanical pump, the sample should be collected from a tap on the discharge. If there is no pumping machinery, a sample can be collected directly from the well by means of a sterilized bottle fitted with a weight at the base; in this case care should be taken to avoid contaminating samples by any surface scum.

For sampling wastewaters or effluents the technics described above generally are adequate but the comments in Section 105 should be noted.

4. Size of Sample

The volume of a sample should be sufficient to carry out all the tests required, preferably not less than 100 ml of water for samples intended for bacteriologic examination.

5. Identifying Data

All samples should be accompanied by complete and accurate identifying and descriptive data. Samples not so identified should not be accepted for examination.

906 B. Preservation and Storage

The bacteriological examination of a water sample should be started promptly after collection to avoid unpredictable changes. If samples cannot be processed within 1 hr after collection, the use of iced coolers for storage of water samples during transport to the laboratory is recommended.

The temperature of all stream pollution samples should be held below 10 C during a maximum transport time of 6 hr. Such samples should be refrigerated upon receipt in the laboratory and processed within 2 hr. When local conditions necessitate delays in delivery of samples longer than 6 hr, consideration should be given to field examinations by the use of field laboratory facilities located at the site of collection or by use of the tentative delayed-incubation total coliform procedure. If it is known that the results will be used in legal action, a special messenger should be used to deliver samples to the laboratory within 6 hr.

Since these requirements are seldom realistic in the case of individual potable water samples sent to the laboratory by mail service, the time elapsing between collection and examination should in no case exceed 30 hr. Where refrigeration of individual water samples sent by mail is not possible, the use of a thermos-type insulated sample bottle that can be sterilized is recommended as an option. The time and temperature of storage of all samples should be recorded and should be considered in the interpretation of data.

906 C. Bibliography

CALDWELL, E.L & L.W. PARR. 1933. Present status of handling water samples—Comparison of bacteriological analyses under varying temperatures and holding conditions, with special reference to the direct method. *Amer. J. Pub. Health* 23:467.

ZoBELL, C.E. 1941. Apparatus for collecting water samples from different depths for bacteriological analysis. *J. Mar. Res.* 4:173.

Cox, K.E. & F.B. CLAIBORNE. 1949. Effect of age and storage temperature on bacteriological water samples. *J. Amer. Water Works Ass.* 41:948.

PUBLIC HEALTH LABORATORY SERVICE WATER SUB-COMMITTEE. 1952. The effect of storage on the coliform and *Bacterium coli* counts of water samples. Overnight storage at room and refrigerator temperatures. *J. Hyg.* 50:107.

PUBLIC HEALTH LABORATORY SERVICE WATER SUB-COMMITTEE. 1953. The effect of storage on the coliform and *Bacterium coli* counts of water samples. Storage for six hours at room and refrigerator temperatures. *J. Hyg.* 51:559.

PUBLIC HEALTH LABORATORY SERVICE WATER SUB-COMMITTEE. 1953. The effect of sodium thiosulphate on the coliform and *Bacterium coli* counts of non-chlorinated water samples. *J. Hyg.* 51:572.

SHIPE, E.L. & A. FIELDS. 1956. Chelation as a method for maintaining the coliform index in water samples. *Pub. Health Rep.* 71:974.

McCARTHY, J.A. 1957. Storage of water sample for bacteriological examinations. *Amer. J. Pub. Health* 47:971.

HOATHER, R.C. 1961. The bacteriological examination of water. *J. Inst. Water Eng.* 61:426.

COLES, H.G. 1964. Ethylenediamine tetra-acetic acid and sodium thiosulphate as protective agents for coliform organisms in water samples stored for one day at atmospheric temperature. *Proc. Soc. Water Treat. Exam.* 13:350.

LONSANE, B.K., N.M. PARHAD & N.U. RAO. 1967. Effect of storage temperature and time on the coliform in water samples. *Water Res.* (Britain) 1:309.

LUCKING, H.E. 1967. Death rate of coliform bacteria in stored Montana water samples. *J. Environ. Health* 29:576.

VAN DONSEL, D.J. & E.E. GELDREICH. 1971. Relationships of Salmonellae to fecal coliforms in bottom sediments. *Water Res.* 5:1079.

907   STANDARD PLATE COUNT

1. Introduction

The Standard Plate Count procedure provides a standardized means of determining the density of aerobic and facultative anaerobic heterotrophic bacteria in water. This is an empirical measurement because bacteria occur singly, in pairs, chains, clusters, or packets, and no single growth medium or set of physical and chemical conditions can satisfy the physiological requirements of all bacteria in a water sample. Consequently, the number of colonies may be lower substantially than the actual number of viable bacteria present. To facilitate the collection of reliable data for water quality control measurements, especially for comparative and legal purposes, a standardized plate count procedure is essential.

2. Work Area

A level table or bench top with ample area should be available in a clean, draft-free, well-lighted room. Table and bench tops should have a nonporous surface and should be disinfected before any analysis is conducted.

3. Samples

Potable water samples from a distribution system should be collected as directed in Section 906A. Initiate sample analysis as soon as possible to minimize changes in the bacterial population. The recommended maximum elapsed time between collection and examination of unrefrigerated samples is 8 hr (maximum transit time 6 hr, maximum processing time 2 hr). When analysis cannot begin within 8 hr, maintain the sample at a temperature below 10 C. The maximum elapsed time between collection and analysis shall not exceed 30 hr.

Bottled water samples obtained from retail outlets may be held or transported unrefrigerated provided the temperature does not exceed 20 to 25 C. Examine freshly bottled samples (less than 48 hr old) within 6 hr of collection if unrefrigerated and within 30 hr if refrigerated.

4. Sample Preparation

Mark each plate with sample number, dilution, date, and any other necessary information before sample examination. Prepare duplicate plates for each volume of sample or sample dilution examined.

Thoroughly mix all samples by making 25 complete up-and-down (or back-and-forth) movements of about 0.3 m (1 ft) in 7 sec. Optionally, use a mechanical shaker to shake the dilution blanks for 15 sec.

5. Sample Dilution

Prepare water used for dilution blanks as directed in Media Specifications, Section 905 C.

a. Selecting dilutions: Select the dilution(s) so that the total number of colonies on a plate will be between 30 and 300 (Figure 907.1). For example,

pet becomes contaminated before the transfers are completed, replace it with a sterile pipet. Use a separate sterile pipet for transfers from each different dilution. Do not prepare dilutions and pour plates in direct sunlight. Use caution when removing sterile pipets from the container; to avoid contamination of the pipet, do not drag the tip across the ex-

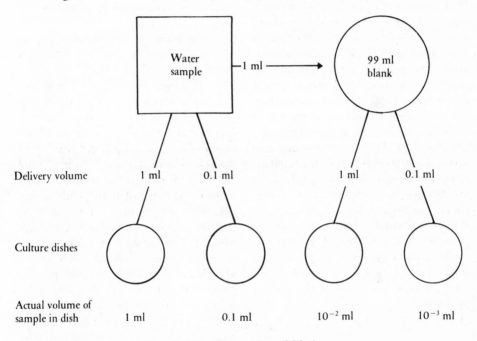

Figure 907:1. Preparation of dilutions.

where a Standard Plate Count as high as 3,000 may be suspected, prepare plates containing 1:100 dilution.

For most potable water samples, plates suitable for counting will be obtained by planting 1 ml and 0.1 ml of undiluted sample and 1 ml of sample diluted 1:100.

b. Measuring sample portions: Use a sterile pipet for initial and subsequent transfers from each container. If the pi-

posed ends of pipets or across the lips and necks of dilution bottles. When removing sample, do not insert pipets more than 2.5 cm (1 in.) below the surface of the sample or dilution.

c. Measuring dilutions: When measuring diluted samples of water, hold the pipet at an angle of about 45° with the tip touching the inside cover of the petri dish or the inside neck of the dilution bottle. Lift the cover of the petri dish just high enough to insert the pipet. Allow 2 to 4 sec for the liquid to drain from the 1 ml graduation mark to the tip of the pipet. If the pipet is not a blow-out type, touch the tip of the pipet *once* against a dry spot in the petri plate. If the pipet is, less preferably, a blow-out type, it must have a cotton plug in the mouthpiece; gently blow out the remaining volume of sample dilution. When 0.1-ml quantities are measured, let the diluted sample drain from the chosen reference graduation until 0.1 ml has been delivered. Remove the pipet without retouching it to the plate. Pipet 1 ml, 0.1 ml, or other suitable volume of the dilution to be used for plating in the sterile petri dish before adding the melted culture medium. It is recommended that decimal dilutions be used in preparing sample volumes of less than 1 ml; in the examination of sewage or turbid water, do not measure a 0.1-ml inoculum of the original sample, but prepare an appropriate dilution. Prepare at least two replicate plates for each sample dilution used. After depositing test portions for each series of plates, pour the culture medium.

6. Plating

a. Melting medium: Melt sterile solid agar medium in boiling water or by exposure to flowing steam in a partially closed container, but avoid prolonged exposure to unnecessarily high temperatures during and after melting. Do not resterilize the plating medium. If the medium is melted in two or more batches, use all of each batch in order of melting, provided that the contents in separate containers remain fully melted.

Discard melted agar that contains precipitate.

Temper the melted medium in a water bath between 44 C and 46 C until used. In a separate container place a thermometer in water or medium that has been exposed to the same heating and cooling as the plating medium. Do not depend on the sense of touch to indicate the proper temperature of the medium when pouring agar.

Use tryptone glucose extract agar or plate count agar, as specified in Section 905 C.

b. Pouring the plates: Limit the number of samples to be plated in any one series so that no more than 20 min (preferably 10 min) elapse between dilution of the first sample and pouring of the last plate in the series. Pour at least 10 to 12 ml of liquefied medium at 44 to 46 C into each plate by gently lifting the cover of the petri dish just high enough to pour the medium. Carefully avoid spilling the medium on the outside of the container or on the inside of the plate lid when pouring. As each plate is poured mix the melted medium thoroughly with the test portions in the petri dish, taking care not to splash mixture over the edge, by rotating the dish first in one direction and then in the opposite direction, or by rotating and tilting the dish. Allow the plates to solidify (within 10 min) on a level surface. After the medium solidifies, invert the plates and place them in the incubator.

c. Sterility controls: Check the sterility of the medium and the dilution water blanks by pouring control plates for each series of samples. Additional controls also may be prepared to determine contamination of plates, pipets, and room air.

7. Incubation

Incubate for the Standard Plate Count for all water samples except bottled water at a temperature of 35 ± 0.5 C for 48 ± 3 hr.

For the Standard Plate Count of bottled water, the plates shall be incubated at 35 ± 0.5 C for 72 ± 4 hr. Since many of the bacteria found in bottled water demonstrate a prolonged lag phase during adaptation to growth on tryptone glucose extract agar or plate count agar, such bacteria do not form colonies that can be counted after 48 hr incubation so that an additional 24 hr incubation is required to obtain a reliable Standard Plate Count.

Plates should be packed as directed under Laboratory Apparatus, Section 903, without crowding in the incubator. Any deviation from this method must be stated in the examination report.

8. Counting and Recording

Count all colonies on selected plates promptly after the incubation period. If counting must be delayed temporarily, store plates at 5 to 10 C for a period of no more than 24 hr, but avoid this as routine practice. Record the results of sterility controls on the report for each lot of samples.

Use an approved counting aid, such as the Quebec colony counter, for manual counting. If such equipment is not available, counting may be done with any other counter provided that it gives equivalent magnification and illumination. Automatic plate counting instruments are now available. These generally use a television scanner coupled to a magnifying lens and an electronics package. Their use is acceptable if evaluation in parallel with manual counting gives comparable results.

In preparing plates, volumes of sample should be planted that will give from 30 to 300 colonies on a plate. The aim should be to have at least one dilution for which the replicate plates give colony counts between these limits, except as provided below.

Ordinarily, it is not desirable to plant more than 1.0 ml of water in a plate; therefore, when the total number of colonies developing from 1.0 ml is less than 30, it is necessary to disregard the rule above and record the result as observed. With this exception, only plates showing 30 to 300 colonies should be considered in determining the Standard Plate Count. Compute the bacterial count per milliliter by multiplying the average number of colonies per plate by the dilution used. Report as the "Standard Plate Count" per milliliter.

If there is no plate with 30 to 300 colonies, and one or more plates have more than 300 colonies, use the plate(s) having a count nearest 300 colonies. Compute the count by multiplying the average count per plate by the dilution used and report as the "Estimated Standard Plate Count" per milliliter.

If plates from all dilutions of any sample have no colonies, report the count as less than one (<1) times the corresponding lowest dilution. For example, if no colonies develop on the $1:100$ dilution, report the count as "less than 100 (<100) Estimated Standard Plate Count" per milliliter.

If the number of colonies per plate far exceeds 300, do not report the result as "too numerous to count" (TNTC). If there are fewer than 10 colonies/cm^2, count colonies in 13 squares (of the colony counter) having representative colony distribution. If possible, select seven consecutive squares horizontally across the plate and six consecutive squares at right angles, being careful not to count a square more than once. Multiply the sum of the colonies in 13 representative cm^2 by 5 to compute the estimated colonies per plate when the area of the plate is 65 cm^2. When there are more than 10 colonies/cm^2, count four representative squares, take the average count per square cm and multiply by the appropriate factor to estimate the colonies per plate (usually about 65). When bacterial counts on crowded plates are greater than 100 colonies/cm^2, report the result as greater than ($>$) 6,500 times the highest dilution plated.

If spreading colonies (spreaders) are encountered on the plate(s) selected, count colonies on representative portions only when (a) colonies are well distributed in spreader-free areas, and (b) the area covered by the spreader(s) does not exceed one-half the plate area.

When spreading colonies must be counted, count each unit of the following types as one: (a) The first is a chain of colonies that appears to be caused by disintegration of a bacterial clump as the agar and sample were mixed. Count each such chain as a single colony, do not count each individual colony in the chain; (b) The second type of spreader develops as a film of growth between the agar and the bottom of the petri dish; (c) The third type forms in a film of water at the edge or over the surface of the agar. Types b and c largely develop because of an accumulation of moisture at the point from which the spreader originates. They frequently cover more than half the plate and interfere with obtaining a reliable plate count.

If plates prepared from the samples have excessive spreader growth, report as "Spreaders" (Spr). When plates are uncountable because of missed dilution, accidental dropping, and contamination, or the control plates indicate that the medium or other material or labware was contaminated, report as "Laboratory Accident" (LA).

9. Computing and Recording Counts

To compute the Standard Plate Count, multiply the total number of colonies or the average number (if duplicate plates of the same dilution) per plate by the reciprocal of the dilution used. Record the dilutions used and the number of colonies on each plate counted or estimated.

When colonies on duplicate plates and/or consecutive dilutions are counted and the results are averaged before being recorded, round off counts to two significant figures only at the time of conversion to the Standard Plate Count.

Avoid creating fictitious ideas of precision and accuracy when computing Standard Plate Counts, by recording only the first two left-hand digits. Raise the second digit to the next highest number only when the third digit from the left is 5, 6, 7, 8, or 9; use zeros for each successive digit toward the right from the second digit. For example, a count of 142 is recorded as 140, and a count of 155 as 160, whereas a count of 35 is recorded as 35.

10. Reporting Counts

Report counts as "Standard Plate Count" or "Estimated Standard Plate Count" per milliliter.

11. Personal Errors

Avoid inaccuracies in counting due to carelessness, damaged or dirty optics that impair vision, or failure to recognize colonies. Laboratory workers who cannot duplicate their own counts on the same plate within 5% and the counts of other analysts with 10%, should discover the cause and correct such disagreements.

12. Bibliography

BREED, R.S. & W.D. DOTTERER. 1916. The number of colonies allowable on satisfactory agar plates. Tech. Bull. 53, N.Y. Agr. Exp. Sta.

BUTTERFIELD, C.T. 1933. The selection of a dilution water for bacteriological examinations. J. Bacteriol. 23:355; Pub. Health Rep. 48:681.

ARCHAMBAULT, J., J. CUROT & M.H. McCRADY. 1937. The need of uniformity of conditions for counting plates (with suggestions for a standard colony counter). Amer. J. Publ. Health 27:809.

RICHARDS, O.W. & P.C. HEIJN. 1945. An improved darkfield Quebec colony counter. J. Milk Technol. 8:253.

BERRY, J.M., D.A. McNEILL & L.D. WITTER. 1969. Effect of delays in pour plating on bacterial counts. J. Dairy Sci. 52:1456.

AMERICAN PUBLIC HEALTH ASSOCIATION. 1972. Standard Methods for the Examination of Dairy Products, 13th ed. APHA, New York, N.Y.

GELDREICH, E.E., H.D. NASH, D.J. REASONER & R.H. TAYLOR. 1972. The necessity of controlling bacterial populations in potable waters: Community water supply. J. Amer. Water Works Ass. 64:596.

GELDREICH, E.E., H.D. NASH, D.J. REASONER & R.H. TAYLOR. 1975. The necessity for controlling bacterial populations in potable waters: Bottled water and emergency water supplies. J. Amer. Water Works Ass. 67:117.

908 MULTIPLE-TUBE FERMENTATION TECHNIC FOR MEMBERS OF THE COLIFORM GROUP

The coliform group comprises all of the aerobic and facultative anaerobic, gram-negative, nonspore-forming, rod-shaped bacteria that ferment lactose with gas formation within 48 hr at 35 C.*

The standard test for the coliform group may be carried out either by the multiple-tube fermentation technic (presumptive test, confirmed test, or completed test) described herein or by the membrane filter technic described under a separate heading, each technic being applicable within the limitations specified and with due consideration of the purpose of the examination.

As applied to the membrane filter technic, the coliform group may be redefined as comprising all the aerobic and facultative anaerobic, gram-negative, nonspore-forming, rod-shaped bacteria that produce a dark colony with a metallic sheen within 24 hr on an Endo-type medium containing lactose.

It has been adequately demonstrated that, even after the prescribed shaking,

---

* The "coliform group" as defined above is equivalent to the "B. coli group" as used in the third, fourth and fifth editions of this manual, and to the "coli-aerogenes group" as used through the eighth edition.

the distribution of bacteria in water is irregular. It is entirely possible to divide a given volume of water into portions and after testing find that the number of organisms in any portion may be none, or at least less than the arithmetic average based on examination of the total volume might indicate. It is also quite probable that the growth in a fermentation tube may result not from one organism but from many organisms. It is reasonable, however, to assume that growth develops from a single individual.

It is convenient to express the results of the examination of replicate tubes and dilutions in terms of the Most Probable Number (MPN). This term is actually an estimate based on certain probability formulas. Theoretical considerations and large-scale replicate determinations indicate that this estimate tends to be greater than the actual number and that the disparity tends to diminish with increasing numbers of tubes in each dilution examined.

The accuracy of any single test will depend, then, on the number of tubes used. The most satisfactory information will be obtained when the largest portion examined shows gas in some or all of the tubes and the smallest portion shows no gas in all or a majority of the tubes. The numerical value of the estimation of the bacterial content is determined largely by the dilution that shows both positive and negative results. The number of portions scheduled, especially in the critical dilution, will be governed by the desired accuracy of the result. The increased interest in the multiple-tube technic, the numerous investigations into its precision, and the expression of test results as MPNs should

not lead the analyst to regard this method as a statistical exercise rather than a means of estimating the coliform density of a water and thereby an aid to establishing its sanitary quality. The best assessment of the sanitary quality of a water still must depend on the interpretation of results of the multiple-tube technic—or of other methods, possibly more precise—and of all other information regarding a water that may be obtained by surveys or otherwise.

1. Water of Drinking Water Quality

When water is examined for evidence of quality that meets the standards of the U.S. Environmental Protection Agency, it is necessary to use five fermentation tubes of the presumptive medium, each containing 10 ml or 100 ml of the water sample. Practical considerations generally militate against the use of larger portions. The Confirmed Test or the Completed Test shall be the test of choice.

For water examined frequently, or even daily, the common practice of inoculating five 10-ml or five 100-ml portions generally provides sufficient definite information. In the examination of other waters presumed to be of drinking-water quality, the use of at least five tubes in each of at least three dilutions is desirable to provide acceptable precision and reasonably satisfactory information; in no case should less than three tubes per dilution be used.

For the routine examination of most potable water supplies, particularly those that are disinfected, the object of the test is to determine the presence or absence of coliform organisms as a measure of either the efficiency of operation or the presence of bacterial contamination. The safety of the water is generally judged by a knowledge of the sanitary condition of the supply and monitored by the number of samples yielding positive or negative results. It is expected that more than 95% of all samples examined yield negative results. An occasional positive result, unless repeated from the same sampling point, or unless it is one yielding three or more positive tubes when five tubes are inoculated, is usually of limited significance. What is important is an increase in the number of positive samples over a period of time or an abrupt increase in a short period of time. Either increase indicates a change in the quality of the water, the significance of which should be studied, with correction made as necessary.

2. Water of Other than Drinking Water Quality

In the examination of waters of other than drinking water quality, a series of lactose broth or lauryl tryptose broth tubes should be inoculated with decimal quantities of the water, the selection of portion sizes depending on the probable coliform density as indicated by the experience of the analyst and how much is known about the character of the water. The object of the examination of non-potable water is generally to estimate the density of bacterial contamination or determine a source of pollution. Either objective requires a numerical value for reporting results. The multiple-tube fermentation technic may be used; however, to obtain statistically valid MPN values, a minimum series of three, but preferably five, tubes—each inoculated with decimal quantities of sample—should be run. A sufficient number of samples must be examined to yield representative results for the sampling station. Generally, the log average or median value of the results of a number of samples will yield a value in which the effect of individual extreme values is minimized. The membrane filter technic may prove the better procedure to accomplish this objective.

3. Other Samples

The multiple-tube fermentation technic is applicable to the analysis of salt or brackish waters as well as muds, sediments, or sludges. The precautions given above on portion sizes and numbers of tubes per dilution should be followed. Solid or semisolid samples should be weighed and diluted initially with an equal weight of diluent. Mixing should be done in a sterile blender jar in accordance with the APHA recommended procedures for shellfish.

908 A.   Standard Total Coliform MPN Tests

1. Presumptive Test

Lactose broth or lauryl tryptose broth may be used in the Presumptive Test.

a. Procedure:

1) Inoculate a series of fermentation tubes ("primary" fermentation tubes) with appropriate graduated quantities (multiples and submultiples of 1 ml) of the water to be tested. Bottles to contain 100-ml sample portions should be pre-warmed in a water bath at 35 C; after adding the sample mix thoroughly and aseptically add a sterile fermentation vial. The concentration of nutritive ingredients in the mixture of medium and added portion of sample must conform to the requirements given in Section 905C, Media Specifications, Media 2 and 3. The portions of the water sample used for inoculating the lactose or lauryl tryptose broth fermentation tubes will vary in size and number with the character of the water under examination, but in general should be decimal multiples and submultiples of 1 ml. These should be selected in accordance with the discussion of the multiple-tube test above.

2) Incubate the inoculated fermentation tubes at 35±0.5C. At the end of 24±2 hr, shake each tube gently and examine it and, if no gas has formed and been trapped in the inverted vial, repeat this step at the end of 48±3 hr. Record the presence or absence of gas formation at each examination of the tubes, regardless of the amount.

b. Interpretation: Formation within 48±3 hr of gas in any amount in the inner fermentation tubes or vials constitutes a positive Presumptive Test.

The appearance of an air bubble must not be confused with actual gas production. If the gas is formed as a result of fermentation, the broth medium will become cloudy. Active fermentation may be shown by the continued appearance of small bubbles of gas throughout the medium outside the inner vial when the fermentation tube is gently shaken.

The absence of gas formation at the end of 48±3 hr of incubation constitutes a negative test. An arbitrary limit of 48 hr for observation doubtless excludes from consideration occasional members of the coliform group that form gas very slowly and are generally of limited sanitary significance; for the purpose of a standard test based on the definition of the coliform group, exclusion of these occasional slow gas-forming organisms does not compromise the value of the test.

2. Confirmed Test

Lactose broth or lauryl tryptose broth may be used for the primary fermentation; however, lauryl tryptose broth is recommended when experience shows a high proportion of false positive tubes of lactose broth.

Use brilliant green lactose bile broth fermentation tubes for the Confirmed Test.

a. Procedure: Submit all primary fermentation tubes showing any amount of gas at the end of 24 hr of incubation to the confirmed test. If active fermentation appears in the primary fermentation tube before expiration of the 24-hr period of incubation, it is preferable to transfer to the confirmatory medium without waiting for the full 24-hr period to elapse. If additional primary fermentation tubes show gas production at the end of 48-hr incubation, these too shall be submitted to the confirmed test.

b. Alternative procedure: Where three or more multiple portions of a series of three or more decimal dilutions of a given sample are planted, submit to the Confirmed Test all tubes of the two highest dilutions (smallest volumes) of the original samples showing gas formation in 24 hr.

All tubes producing gas in 24 hr that have not been submitted to the Confirmed Test must be recorded as containing organisms of the coliform group—that is, as positive—even though all the confirmed tests actually performed yield negative results.

Submit to the Confirmed Test all tubes of all dilutions of the original sample in which gas is produced only at the end of 48 hr.

If less than three portions of any dilution (volume), or if a series of less than three decimal dilutions of the original sample is planted, submit all tubes producing gas at 24 or 48 hr to the confirmed test.

c. Procedure with brilliant green lactose bile broth:

1) Either:

a) Gently shake or rotate primary fermentation tube showing gas and with a sterile metal loop, 3 mm in diameter, transfer one loopful of medium to a fermentation tube containing brilliant green lactose bile broth, or

b) Gently shake or rotate primary fermentation tube showing gas and insert a sterile wood applicator at least 2.5 cm (1 in.) into the medium. Promptly remove and plunge applicator to bottom of fermentation tube containing brilliant green lactose bile broth. Remove and discard applicator.

2) Incubate the inoculated brilliant green lactose bile broth tube for 48 ± 3 hr at 35 ± 0.5 C.

The formation of gas in any amount in the inverted vial of the brilliant green lactose bile broth fermentation tube at any time within 48 ± 3 hr constitutes a positive Confirmed Test.

3. Completed Test

The Completed Test is used as the next step following the Confirmed Test. It is applied to the brilliant green lactose bile broth fermentation tubes showing gas in the Confirmed Test.

a. Procedure:

1) Streak one or more Endo or eosin methylene blue plates from each tube of brilliant green lactose bile broth showing gas, as soon as possible after the appearance of gas. It is essential that the plates be so streaked as to insure the presence of some discrete colonies, separated by at least 0.5 cm from one another. Careful attention to the following details when streaking plates will result in a high proportion of successful isolations if coliform organisms are present: (*a*) Use an inoculating needle slightly curved at the tip; (*b*) tap and incline the fermentation tube to avoid picking up any membrane or scum on the needle; (*c*) insert the end of the needle into the liquid in the tube to a depth of approximately 5.0 mm; (*d*) streak the plate by bringing only the curved section of the needle in contact with the agar surface so that the latter will not be scratched or torn.

Incubate the plate (inverted, if with glass or plastic cover) at 35 ± 0.5 C for 24 ± 2 hr.

2) The colonies developing on Endo or eosin methylene blue agar may be described as *typical* (nucleated, with or without metallic sheen); *atypical* (opaque, unnucleated, mucoid, pink after 24 hr incubation), or *negative* (all others). From each of these plates fish one or more typical well-isolated coliform colonies or, if no typical colonies are present, fish two or more colonies considered most likely to consist of organisms of the coliform group, transferring each fishing to a lactose broth or a lauryl tryptose broth fermentation tube and to a nutrient agar slant.

The use of a colony counter is recommended to provide optimum magnification when colonies are fished from the plates of selective medium.

If possible, when transferring colonies, take care to choose well-isolated colonies separated by at least 0.5 cm from other colonies and barely to touch the surface of the colony with a flame-sterilized, air-cooled transfer needle, so as to minimize the danger of transferring a mixed culture.

The agar slants and secondary broth tubes are incubated at 35 ± 0.5 C for 24 ± 2 or 48 ± 3 hr if gas is not produced in 24 hr. Gram-stained preparations (see Section 908A.4 below) from those agar slant cultures corresponding to the secondary lactose broth tubes that show gas are examined microscopically.

b. Interpretation: The formation of gas in the secondary lactose broth tube and the demonstration of gram-negative nonspore-forming rod-shaped bacteria in the agar culture may be considered a satisfactory Completed Test, demonstrating the presence of a member of the coliform group in the volume of sample examined.

If, after 48 ± 3 hr, gas is produced in the lactose and no spores or gram-positive rods are found on the slant, the test may be considered completed and the presence of coliform organisms demonstrated.

4. Gram-Stain Technic

The Completed Test for coliform-group organisms requires the determination of gram-stain characteristics of the organisms isolated, as discussed above.

There are various modifications of the Gram stain, many of which have been listed by Hucker and Conn (Section 908E). The following modification by Hucker is valuable for staining smears of pure culture. It is desirable to use a gram-positive and a gram-negative culture as controls for the staining process.

a. Reagents:

1) *Ammonium oxalate-crystal violet* (Hucker's)—Dissolve 2 g crystal violet (90% dye content) in 20 ml 95% ethyl alcohol; dissolve 0.8 g of ammonium oxalate monohydrate in 80 ml distilled water; mix the two solutions and age for 24 hr before use; filter through paper into a staining bottle.

2) *Lugol's solution, Gram's modification*—Grind 1 g iodine crystals and 2 g potassium iodide in a mortar. Add distilled water, a few milliliters at a time, and grind thoroughly after each addition until solution is complete. Rinse the solution into an amber glass bottle with the remaining water (using a total of 300 ml).

3) *Counterstain*—Dissolve 2.5 g safranin dye in 100 ml of 95% ethyl alcohol. Add 10 ml of the alcoholic solution of safranin to 100 ml of distilled water.

4) *Acetone alcohol*—Mix equal volumes of ethyl alcohol, 95%, with acetone.

b. Procedure: Prepare a light emulsion of the bacterial growth on an agar slant in a drop of distilled water on a glass slide. Air-dry or fix by passing the slide through a flame and stain for 1 min with the ammonium oxalate-crystal violet solution. Rinse the slide in tap water; apply Lugol's solution for 1 min.

Rinse the stained slide in tap water. Decolorize with acetone alcohol by holding slide between the fingers and letting acetone alcohol flow across the stained smear until no more stain is removed. Do not over-decolorize. Counterstain with safranin for 15 sec, then rinse with tap water, blot dry with bibulous paper, and examine microscopically.

Cells that decolorize and accept the safranin stain are pink and defined as gram-negative in reaction. Cells that do not decolorize but retain the crystal violet stain are deep blue and are defined as gram-positive.

908   B.   Application of Tests to Routine Examinations

The following basic considerations apply to the selection of the Presumptive Test, the Confirmed Test, or the Completed Test in the examination of any given sample of water or wastewater.

1. Presumptive Test

The Presumptive Test without confirmation should not be used routinely; however, it may be applied to the examination of:

a. Any sample of waste, sewage, or water known to be heavily polluted, the fitness of which for drinking water is not under consideration.

b. Any routine sample of raw water in a treatment plant, provided records indicate that the Presumptive Test is not too inclusive for the development of pertinent data.

2. Confirmed Test

The Confirmed Test should be applied as a minimum to all samples.

3. Completed Test

The Completed Test should be applied in the examination of water samples where the results are to be used for the control of the quality of raw or finished waters; or if not applied to all samples, then to such a proportion of them as to establish beyond reasonable doubt the value of the Confirmed Test in determining the sanitary quality of such water supplies. Repeat samples of finished water from the same location that consistently show three or more positive 10-ml portions should be analyzed by the Completed Test.

NOTE: Schematic outlines of the Presumptive, Confirmed, and Completed Tests are shown in Figures 908: 1a and 908: 1b.

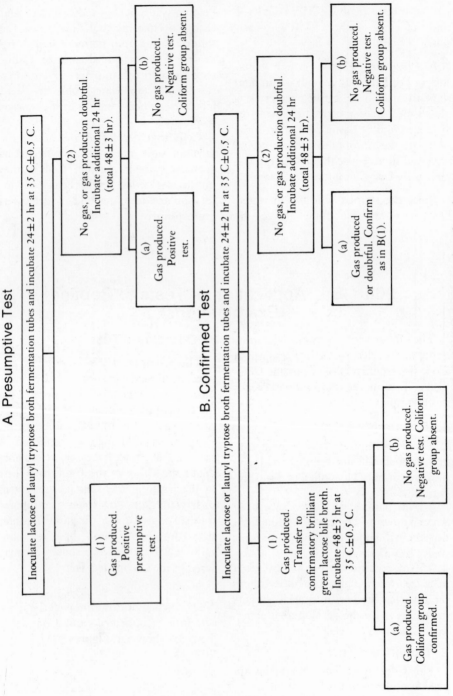

Figure 908:1a. Schematic outline of presumptive and confirmed tests.

C. Completed Test

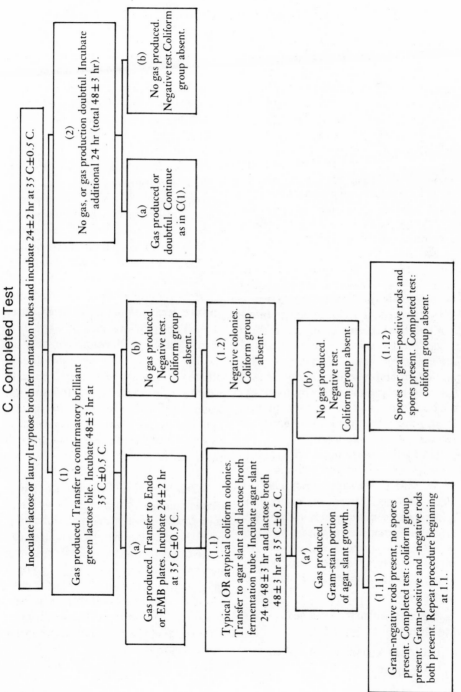

Inoculate lactose or lauryl tryptose broth fermentation tubes and incubate 24±2 hr at 35 C±0.5 C.

(1) Gas produced. Transfer to confirmatory brilliant green lactose bile. Incubate 48±3 hr at 35 C±0.5 C.

(2) No gas, or gas production doubtful. Incubate additional 24 hr (total 48±3 hr).

(a) Gas produced. Transfer to Endo or EMB plates. Incubate 24±2 hr at 35 C±0.5 C.

(b) No gas produced. Negative test. Coliform group absent.

(a) Gas produced or doubtful. Continue as in C(1).

(b) No gas produced. Negative test. Coliform group absent.

(1.1) Typical OR atypical coliform colonies. Transfer to agar slant and lactose broth fermentation tube. Incubate agar slant 24 to 48±3 hr and lactose broth 48±3 hr at 35 C±0.5 C.

(1.2) Negative colonies. Coliform group absent.

(a') Gas produced. Gram-stain portion of agar slant growth.

(b') No gas produced. Negative test. Coliform group absent.

(1.11) Gram-negative rods present, no spores present. Completed test: coliform group present. Gram-positive and -negative rods both present. Repeat procedure beginning at 1.1.

(1.12) Spores or gram-positive rods and spores present. Completed test: coliform group absent.

Figure 908:1b. Schematic outline of completed test.

908 C.   Fecal Coliform MPN Procedure

Elevated temperature tests for the separation of organisms of the coliform group into those of fecal origin and those derived from nonfecal sources have been used in many parts of the world and with various modifications. Recent modifications in technical procedures, standardization of methods, and detailed studies of members of the coliform group found in the feces of various warm-blooded animals compared with those from other environmental sources have established the value of a fecal coliform determination. This test may be performed either by a multiple-tube procedure as described here or by membrane filter methods as described in the section on the membrane filter technic. The following procedure yields adequate information about the source of the coliform group (fecal or nonfecal) when used as a *confirmatory* test procedure. This multiple-tube procedure cannot be used for direct isolation of coliforms from water but requires prior enrichment in a Presumptive Test medium for optimum recovery of fecal coliforms.

The fecal coliform test is applicable to investigations of stream pollution, raw water sources, sewage treatment systems, bathing waters, seawaters, and general water-quality monitoring. The procedure is not recommended as a substitute for the coliform test in the examination of potable waters, since no coliform bacteria of any kind should be tolerated in a treated water.

1. Fecal Coliform Test (EC Medium)

The fecal coliform test, when exe-cuted as described, may be expected to differentiate between coliforms of fecal origin (intestines of warm-blooded animals) and coliforms from other sources. Use EC medium as described in Section 905C, Media Specifications, No. 9, preceding.

a. Procedure: Make transfers from all positive presumptive tubes from the total coliform MPN test to EC medium. This examination may be performed simultaneously with the confirmatory procedure using brilliant green lactose bile broth. Use a sterile metal loop with a minimum 3-mm diam or a sterile wooden applicator to transfer from the positive fermentation tube to EC medium. When making such transfers, first gently shake the presumptive tube or mix by rotating. Inoculated tubes are incubated in a water bath at 44.5 ± 0.2 C for 24 ± 2 hr. Place all EC tubes in the water bath within 30 min after planting. The water depth in the incubator should be sufficient to immerse tubes to the upper level of the medium.

b. Interpretation: Gas production in a fermentation tube within 24 hr or less is considered a positive reaction indicating fecal origin. Failure to produce gas (growth sometimes occurs) constitutes a negative reaction indicating a source other than the intestinal tract of warm-blooded animals. Fecal coliform densities are calculated as described under Estimation of Bacterial Density (Section 908D below).

908 D.   Estimation of Bacterial Density

1. Precision of Fermentation Tube Test

It is desirable to bear in mind that unless a large number of portions of sample are examined, the precision of the fermentation tube test is rather low. For example, even when the sample contains 1 coliform organism/ml, about 37% of 1-ml tubes may be expected to yield negative results because of irregular distribution of the bacteria in the sample. When five tubes, each with 1 ml of sample, are used under these conditions, a completely negative result may be expected less than 1% of the time.

Even when five fermentation tubes are used, the precision of the results obtained is not of a high order. Consequently, great caution must be exercised when interpreting, in terms of sanitary significance, the coliform results obtained from the use of a few tubes with each dilution of sample, especially when the number of samples from a given sampling point is limited.

2. Computing and Recording of MPN

The number of positive findings of coliform group organisms (either presumptive, confirmed, or completed) resulting from multiple-portion decimal-dilution plantings should be computed as the combination of positives and recorded in terms of the Most Probable Number (MPN). The MPN, for a variety of planting series and results, is given in Tables 908:I and 908:II. Included in these tables are the 95% confidence limits for each MPN value determined.

The sample volumes indicated in Table 908:II relate more specifically to finished waters. The values may be used in computing the MPN in larger or smaller portion plantings in the following manner: If, instead of portions of 10, 1.0, and 0.1 ml, a combination of portions of 100, 10, and 1 ml is used, the MPN is recorded as 0.1 times the value given in the applicable table.

If, on the other hand, a combination of corresponding portions at 1.0, 0.1,

TABLE 908:I. MPN INDEX AND 95% CONFIDENCE LIMITS FOR VARIOUS COMBINATIONS OF POSITIVE AND NEGATIVE RESULTS WHEN FIVE 10-ML PORTIONS ARE USED

No. of Tubes Giving Positive Reaction out of 5 of 10 ml Each	MPN Index /100 ml	95% Confidence Limits	
		Lower	Upper
0	<2.2	0	6.0
1	2.2	0.1	12.6
2	5.1	0.5	19.2
3	9.2	1.6	29.4
4	16.	3.3	52.9
5	>16.	8.0	Infinite

TABLE 908:II. MPN Index and 95% Confidence Limits for Various Combinations of Positive
Results When Various Numbers of Tubes Are Used per Dilution (10 ml, 1.0 ml, 0.1 ml)

Combination of Positives	Tubes per Dilution					
	3			5		
	MPN Index /100 ml	95% Confidence Limits		MPN Index /100 ml	95% Confidence Limits	
		Lower	Upper		Lower	Upper
0-0-0	<3			<2		
0-0-1	3	<0.5	9	2	<0.5	7
0-1-0	3	<0.5	13	2	<0.5	7
0-2-0	—			4	<0.5	11
1-0-0	4	<0.5	20	2	<0.5	7
1-0-1	7	1	21	4	<0.5	11
1-1-0	7	1	23	4	<0.5	11
1-1-1	11	3	36	6	<0.5	15
1-2-0	11	3	36	6	<0.5	15
2-0-0	9	1	36	5	<0.5	13
2-0-1	14	3	37	7	1	17
2-1-0	15	3	44	7	1	17
2-1-1	20	7	89	9	2	21
2-2-0	21	4	47	9	2	21
2-2-1	28	10	150	—		
2-3-0	—			12	3	28
3-0-0	23	4	120	8	1	19
3-0-1	39	7	130	11	2	25
3-0-2	64	15	380	—		
3-1-0	43	7	210	11	2	25
3-1-1	75	14	230	14	4	34
3-1-2	120	30	380	—		
3-2-0	93	15	380	14	4	34
3-2-1	150	30	440	17	5	46
3-2-2	210	35	470	—		
3-3-0	240	36	1,300	—		
3-3-1	460	71	2,400	—		
3-3-2	1,100	150	4,800	—		
3-3-3	≥2,400			—		
4-0-0	—			13	3	31
4-0-1	—			17	5	46
4-1-0	—			17	5	46
4-1-1	—			21	7	63
4-1-2	—			26	9	78
4-2-0	—			22	7	67
4-2-1	—			26	9	78
4-3-0	—			27	9	80
4-3-1	—			33	11	93
4-4-0	—			34	12	93

TABLE 908:II. *(Continued)*

Combination of Positives	Tubes per Dilution					
	3			5		
	MPN Index /100 ml	95% Confidence Limits		MPN Index /100 ml	95% Confidence Limits	
		Lower	Upper		Lower	Upper
5-0-0	—			23	7	70
5-0-1	—			31	11	89
5-0-2	—			43	15	110
5-1-0	—			33	11	93
5-1-1	—			46	16	120
5-1-2	—			63	21	150
5-2-0	—			49	17	130
5-2-1	—			70	23	170
5-2-2	—			94	28	220
5-3-0	—			79	25	190
5-3-1	—			110	31	250
5-3-2	—			140	37	340
5-3-3	—			180	44	500
5-4-0	—			130	35	300
5-4-1	—			170	43	490
5-4-2	—			220	57	700
5-4-3	—			280	90	850
5-4-4	—			350	120	1,000
5-5-0	—			240	68	750
5-5-1	—			350	120	1,000
5-5-2	—			540	180	1,400
5-5-3	—			920	300	3,200
5-5-4	—			1,600	640	5,800
5-5-5	—			≥2,400		

and 0.01 ml is planted, record 10 times the value shown in the table; if a combination of portions of 0.1, 0.01, and 0.001 ml is planted, record 100 times the value shown in the table; and so on for other combinations.

When more than three dilutions are used in a decimal series of dilutions, the results from only three of these are used in computing the MPN. To select the three dilutions to be used in determining the MPN index, taking the system of five tubes of each dilution as an example, the highest dilution that gives positive results in all five portions tested (no lower dilution giving any negative results) and the two next succeeding higher dilutions should be chosen. The results at these three volumes should then be used in computing the MPN index. In the examples given below, the significant dilution results are shown in boldface. The number in the numerator represents positive tubes; that in the denominator, the total tubes planted; the combination of positives simply represents the total number of positive tubes per dilution:

Example 1 ml	0.1 ml	0.01 ml	0.001 ml	Combination of positives
(a)	5/5	5/5	2/5	0/5	5-2-0
(b)	5/5	4/5	2/5	0/5	5-4-2
(c)	0/5	1/5	0/5	0/5	0-1-0

In c, the first three dilutions should be taken, so as to throw the positive result in the middle dilution.

When a case such as shown below in line d arises, where a positive occurs in a dilution higher than the three chosen according to the rule, it should be incorporated in the result for the highest chosen dilution, as in e:

Example 1 ml	0.1 ml	0.01 ml	0.001 ml	Combination of positives
(d)	5/5	3/5	1/5	1/5 }	5-3-2
(e)	5/5	3/5	2/5	0/5 }	

When it is desired to summarize with a single MPN value the results from a series of samples, the geometric mean, the arithmetic mean, or the median may be used.

Table 908:II does not include all positive combinations; however, the most likely ones are shown. If unlikely combinations occur with a frequency greater than 1% it is an indication that the technic is faulty or that the statistical assumptions underlying the MPN estimate are not being fulfilled. The MPN for combinations not appearing in the table, or for other combinations of tubes or dilutions, may be estimated by Thomas' simple formula:

$$MPN/100 \text{ ml} = \frac{\text{no. of positive tubes} \times 100}{\sqrt{\left(\begin{array}{c}\text{ml sample in}\\\text{negative tubes}\end{array}\right) \times \left(\begin{array}{c}\text{ml sample in}\\\text{all tubes}\end{array}\right)}}$$

While the MPN tables and calculations are described for use in the coliform test, they are equally applicable to determination of the MPN of any organisms provided a suitable test is available.

908 E. Bibliography

Standard Tests

MEYER, E.M. 1918. An aerobic spore-forming bacillus giving gas in lactose broth isolated in routine water examination. *J. Bacteriol.* 3:9.

HUCKER, G.J. & H.J. CONN. 1923. Methods of gram staining. N.Y. State Agr. Exp. Sta. Tech. Bull. No. 93.

NORTON, J.F. & J.J. WEIGHT. 1924. Aerobic spore-forming lactose fermenting organisms and their significance in water analysis. *Amer. J. Pub. Health* 14:1019.

HUCKER, G.J. & H.J. CONN. 1927. Further studies on the methods of gram staining. N.Y. State Agr. Exp. Sta. Tech. Bull. No. 128.

PORTER, R., C.S. McCLESKEY & M. LEVINE. 1937. The facultative sporulating bacteria producing gas from lactose. *J. Bacteriol.* 33:163.

COWLES, P.B. 1939. A modified fermentation tube. *J. Bacteriol.* 38:677.

BREED, R.S., E.G.D. MURRAY & N.R. SMITH. 1957. Bergey's Manual of Determinative Bacteriology, 7th ed. Williams & Wilkins, Baltimore, Md.

American Society for Microbiology. 1957. Manual of Microbiological Methods. McGraw Hill, New York, N.Y.

Skerman, V.B.D. 1967. A Guide to the Identification of the Genera of Bacteria. Williams & Wilkins, Baltimore, Md.

American Public Health Association. 1970. Recommended Procedures for the Examination of Sea Water and Shellfish, 4th ed. APHA, New York, N.Y.

Fecal Coliform Tests

Perry, C.A. & A.A. Hajna. 1933. A modified Eijkman medium. *J. Bacteriol.* 25:419.

Perry, C.A. & A.A. Hajna. 1944. Further evaluation of EC medium for the isolation of coliform bacteria and *Escherichia coli. Amer. J. Pub. Health* 34:735.

Vaughn, R.H et al. 1951. A buffered boric acid lactose medium for enrichment and presumptive identification of *Escherichia coli. Food Res.* 16:10.

Levine, M., R.H. Tanimoto, H. Minette, J. Arakaki & G. Fernandes. 1955. Simultaneous determination of coliform and *Escherichia coli* indices. *Appl. Microbiol.* 3:310.

Clark, H.F., E.E. Geldreich, P. W. Kabler, R.H. Bordner & C.B. Huff. 1957. The coliform group. I. The boric acid lactose broth reaction of coliform IMViC types. *Appl. Microbiol.* 5:396.

Geldreich, E.E., H.F. Clark, P.W. Kabler, C.B. Huff & R.H Bordner, 1958. The coliform group. II. Reactions in EC medium at 45 C. *Appl. Microbiol.* 6:347.

Geldreich, E.E., R.H. Bordner, C.B. Huff, H.F. Clark & P.W. Kabler. 1962. Type distribution of coliform bacteria in the feces of warm-blooded animals. *J. Water Pollut. Control Fed.* 34:295.

Geldreich, E.E. 1966. Sanitary significance of fecal coliforms in the environment. FWPCA Publ. WP-20-3 (Nov.). U.S. Dep. Interior, Washington, D.C.

Numerical Interpretation

McCrady, M.N. 1915. The numerical interpretation of fermentation tube results. *J. Infect. Dis.* 17:183.

Greenwood, M. & G.U. Yule. 1917. On the statistical interpretation of some bacteriological methods employed in water analysis. *J. Hyg.* 16:36.

Wolman, A. & H.L. Weaver. 1917. A modification of the McCrady method of the numerical interpretation of fermentation tube results. *J. Infect. Dis.* 21:287.

McCrady, M.H. 1918. Tables for rapid interpretation of fermentation tube results. *Can. J. Pub. Health* 9:201.

Reed, L.J. 1925. *B. coli* densities as determined from various types of samples. *Pub. Health Rep.* 40:704 (Reprint 1029).

Hoskins, J.K. 1933. The most probable number of *B. coli* in water analysis. *J. Amer. Water Works Ass.* 25:867.

Hoskins, J.K. 1934. Most Probable Numbers for evaluation of *Coli-Aerogenes* tests by fermentation tube method. *Pub. Health Rep.* 49:393 (Reprint 1621).

Hoskins, J.K. & C.T. Butterfield. 1935. Determining the bacteriological quality of drinking water. *J. Amer. Water Works Ass.* 27:1101.

Halvorson, H.O. & N.R. Ziegler. 1933-35. Application of statistics to problems in bacteriology. *J. Bacteriol.* 25:101; 26:331, 559; 29:609.

Swaroop, S. 1938. Numerical estimation of *B. coli* by dilution method. *Indian J. Med. Res.* 26:353.

Dalla Valle, J.M. 1941. Notes on the most probable number index as used in bacteriology. *Pub. Health Rep.* 56:229.

Thomas, H.A., Jr. 1942. Bacterial densities from fermentation tube tests. *J. Amer. Water Works Ass.* 34:572.

American Public Health Association, American Water Works Association & Federation of Sewage and Industrial Wastes Associations. 1955. Standard Methods for the Examination of Water, Sewage, and Industrial Wastes, 10th ed. APHA, New York, N.Y.

Woodward, R.L. 1957. How probable is the Most Probable Number? *J. Amer. Water Works Ass.* 49:1060.

McCarthy, J.A., H.A. Thomas & J.E. Delaney. 1958. Evaluation of reliability of coliform density tests. *Amer. J. Pub. Health* 48:12.

U.S. Environmental Protection Agency. 1975. Interim primary drinking water standards. *Fed. Reg.* 40(51):11990 (Mar. 14, 1975).

909   MEMBRANE FILTER TECHNIC FOR MEMBERS OF THE COLIFORM GROUP

The membrane filter technic was presented as a tentative procedure in the 10th Edition of this work. The information obtained by subsequent use of this technic led to its adoption as a standard procedure in the 11th Edition, with the proviso that it be used for determining the potability of drinking waters only after parallel testing had shown that it would afford information equivalent to that obtainable by the standard multiple-tube test. Certain limitations were noted, especially with regard to its effectiveness for testing waters high in turbidity and in noncoliform bacteria.

Since publication of the 11th Edition, widespread use of the technic has confirmed its value, especially its high degree of reproducibility, the possibility of testing relatively larger volumes of sample, and its ability to yield definite results more rapidly than the standard tube procedure. The method has proved particularly valuable in the routine analysis of a given water after its applicability has been established. The U. S. Environmental Protection Agency has approved its use for certain water supplies. The membrane filter technic has also been shown to be extremely useful in emergencies and in the examination of waters not used for drinking. However, it is still desirable to conduct parallel tests in order to demonstrate applicability and to familiarize the worker with the procedures involved.

It must be recognized that turbidity caused by the presence of algae or other interfering material may not permit testing of a sample volume sufficient to yield significant results and that low coliform estimates may be caused by the presence of high numbers of noncoliforms or of substances toxic to the procedure. Experience indicates that the membrane filter technic is applicable to the examination of saline waters, but not wastewaters that have received only primary treatment followed by chlorination or wastewaters containing toxic metals or phenols. Chlorinated secondary or tertiary effluents should be analyzed by the two-step procedure (Section 909A. 5c).

909 A.   Standard Total Coliform Membrane Filter Procedure

1. Laboratory Apparatus

All glassware and other apparatus required for bacteriologic analyses using the membrane filter should be composed of material free from agents having unfavorable effects on bacterial growth. Any deviations from the recommendations presented below must be carefully noted, and quantitative tests will be necessary to demonstrate that such deviations have not introduced agents or factors resulting in conditions less favorable for growth.

Glassware should be sterilized as in Washing and Sterilization, Section 904.

a. Sample bottles should be of the type described in Laboratory Apparatus, Section 903.15.

b. Dilution bottles should be of the type described in Laboratory Apparatus, Section 903.11.

c. Pipets and graduated cylinders may be of any convenient size or shape provided they meet the requirements described in Laboratory Apparatus, Section 903.9.

The opening of graduated cylinders should be covered, before sterilization, with metal foil or a suitable paper substitute.

d. Containers for culture medium should be of clean borosilicate glass, presterilized to reduce bacterial contamination. Although they may be of any size or shape, erlenmeyer flasks with metal caps, metal foil covers, or screw caps are recommended for ease of mixing adequately the medium contained and for convenience of storage.

e. Culture dishes of the petri dish type, 60 by 15 mm, should be used. The bottom of the dish should be flat and should be 5 to 6 cm in diameter so that the absorbent pad for the culture nutrient will lie flat. The glass should be borosilicate or equivalent grade. Clean culture dishes may be wrapped, before sterilization, singly or in convenient numbers, in metal foil or suitable paper substitute. If glass petri dishes are used, precautions must be taken (*a*) to prevent possible loss of medium by evaporation, with resultant change in medium concentration, since covers for such dishes are loose-fitting; and (*b*) to maintain a humid environment for optimum colony development.

Disposable plastic dishes that are tight fitting and meet the specifications noted above may also be used for routine laboratory analyses. Suitable sterile plastic dishes are available commercially. If reuse is necessary, these culture dishes should be treated by exposure of the opened dishes to immersion in 70% ethanol for 30 min, air-dried on a sterile towel, protected from dust, and reassembled. Ultraviolet radiation or other appropriate chemical or physical agents may be used for sterilization purposes. Choice of means of sterilization should be governed not only by convenience but also by actual tests demonstrating the effectiveness of such methods. Freedom of the culture containers from residual growth-suppressive effects of the particular method used must be demonstrated. After sterilization and removal of the sterilizing agent, close the containers, using sterile technics, and store in a dustproof container until needed.

f. Filtration units: The filter-holding assembly should consist of a seamless funnel that fastens to a receptacle bearing a porous plate for support of the filter membrane. The funnel unit should be attachable to the receptacle by a convenient locking device. The construction should be such that the membrane filter will be securely held on the porous plate of the receptacle without mechanical damage and all the fluid will pass through the membrane during filtration of the sample. The filter-holding assembly may be constructed of glass, porcelain, or any noncorrosive, bacteriologically inert metal. It is recommended that the two parts of the assembly be wrapped separately in heavy wrapping paper for sterilization and storage until use. Sterilization may be done by boiling, autoclaving, or ultraviolet radiation. Field units may be sterilized by igniting methyl alcohol.

For filtration, the receptacle of the filter-holding assembly is mounted in a 1-l filtering flask with a side tube or other suitable device such that a pressure differential can be exerted on the filter membrane. The filter flask should be connected by the side arm to an electric vacuum pump, a filter pump operating on water pressure, a hand aspirator, or other means of securing a pressure differential. An additional flask may be connected between the filtering flask and the vacuum source to trap carry-over water.

g. Filter membranes: Membrane filters should have a rated pore diameter of 0.45 μm. Use only those filter membranes that have been found, through adequate quality control testing and certification by the manufacturer, to exhibit full bacterial retention, stability in use, freedom from chemical extractables inimical to the growth and development of bacteria, a satisfactory speed of filtration, and no significant influence on medium pH. They preferably should be grid-marked in such a manner that bacterial growth is neither inhibited nor stimulated along the grid lines. Several different brands of membrane filters meeting these specifications can be obtained from manufacturers and suppliers of laboratory equipment. Membrane filters held in stock should be stored in an environment without extremes of temperature and humidity. No more than a year's supply should be obtained at any one time.

Filter membranes must be sterilized before use, preferably by autoclave. The paper separators—but not the absorbent paper pads—should be removed from the packaged filters. The filters should be divided into groups of 10 to 12, or other convenient units, and placed in 10-cm petri dishes or wrapped in heavy wrapping paper. The membranes are then autoclaved for 10 min at 121 C. At the end of the sterilization period, the steam is allowed to escape rapidly to minimize the accumulation of water of condensation on the filters. Suitable packaged filters designed for autoclave sterilization—or if desired, presterilized—can be purchased. Presterilized filters are most commonly used now. The manufacturer should certify that his sterilization technic has neither induced toxicity nor altered the chemical or physical properties of the membrane.

h. Absorbent pads for nutrients should consist of disks of filter paper or other material known to be of high quality and free of sulfites or other substances that could inhibit bacterial growth. These should be approximately 48 mm in diameter and of a thickness sufficient to absorb 1.8 to 2.2 ml of nutrient. Presterilized absorbent pads or pads subsequently sterilized in the laboratory should release less than 1 mg of total acidity (calculated as $CaCO_3$) when titrated to the phenolphthalein end point, pH 8.3, using 0.02N NaOH. The pads may be sterilized simultaneously with membrane filters available in resealable kraft envelopes, or separately in other suitable containers. They must be free of visible moisture before use, a qualification best insured by the sterilization procedure described for membrane filters.

i. Forceps should be round-tipped, without corrugations on the inner sides of the tips. They may be sterilized before use by dipping in 95% ethyl or absolute methyl alcohol and then igniting the fluid.

j. Incubators: Facilities for incubation of membrane filter cultures must provide a temperature of 35±0.5 C and maintain a high level of humidity (approximately 90% relative humidity).

k. Microscope and light source: Membrane filter colonies are best counted with a magnification of 10 to 15 diameters and the light source adjusted to give maximum sheen. A binocular wide-field dissecting microscope is recommended as the best optical system. However, a small fluorescent lamp with magnifier is acceptable. Colony differentiation is best made with diffused daylight developed from cool white fluorescent lamps. The use of a microscope illuminator with optical system for light concentration from an incandescent light source is specifically unsatisfactory for coliform colony identification on Endo-type media.

2. Materials and Culture Media

Refer to Preparation of Culture Media, Sections 905A, B, and C.

Test each medium lot for satisfactory productivity by preparing dilutions of a culture of *Enterobacter aerogenes* (Section 905 B.2e) and filtering appropriate volumes to give 20 to 80 colonies per filter. With each new lot of Endo-type medium, verify enough colonies, obtained from natural samples, to establish the absence of false positives due to noncoliforms.

3. Samples

Samples should be collected and stored as directed previously under Samples, Sections 906 A and B.

4. Definition

All organisms that produce a colony with a golden-green metallic sheen within 24 hr of incubation are considered members of the coliform group. The sheen may cover the entire colony or may appear only in a central area or on the periphery. The coliform group thus defined is not necessarily the same as the group defined as the "coliform group" and described in the multiple-tube fermentation technic, but it probably has the same sanitary significance, particularly if suitable studies have been conducted to establish the relationship between the results obtained by the filter and those obtained by the standard tube dilution procedure.

Coliform organisms may occasionally produce atypical colonies. If only atypical forms are found, their identity as coliform bacteria should be verified by transfer of doubtful colonies to tubes of lactose or lauryl tryptose broth, followed by transfer of positives to brilliant green lactose bile broth. Gas formation in the confirmatory medium within 48 hr of incubation at 35±0.5 C is deemed evidence of coliform colonies.

5. Procedures

Generally, an enrichment procedure will give the best assessment of the quality of drinking waters. However, this step may be eliminated in the routine examination of drinking water where repeated determinations have shown that adequate results are obtained by a single-step technic. Enrichment is usually not necessary in the examination of nonpotable waters or sewages. Repeat samples of finished water from the same location that consistently give positive results should be verified as described above.

In the following sections, methods are offered with and without enrichment that provide for use of the agar-based medium or the M-Endo medium without agar. In the report of results, the method followed should be stated.

a. Selection of sample size: Size of the sample will be governed by the expected bacterial density, which in finished-water samples will be limited only by the degree of turbidity. [See Table 909:I.]

bacterial suspension over the entire effective filtering surface.

b. Filtration of sample: Using sterile forceps, place a sterile filter over the porous plate of the apparatus, grid side up. Carefully place the matched funnel unit over the receptacle and lock it in place. Filtration is then accomplished by passing the sample through the filter under partial vacuum. With the filter still in place, rinse the funnel by filtering three 20- to 30-ml portions of sterile dilution water between samples. Unlock and remove the funnel, immediately re-

TABLE 909:I. SUGGESTED SAMPLE VOLUMES FOR MEMBRANE FILTER TOTAL COLIFORM TEST

Water Source	Volume to be Filtered							
	100	50	10	1	0.1	0.01	0.001	0.0001
Drinking water	X							
Swimming pools	X							
Wells, springs	X	X	X					
Lakes, reservoirs	X	X	X					
Water supply intake			X	X	X			
Bathing beaches			X	X	X			
River water				X	X	X	X	
Chlorinated sewage				X	X	X		
Raw sewage					X	X	X	X

An ideal quantity will result in the growth of about 50 coliform colonies and not more than 200 colonies of all types. Finished waters may be examined by the filtration of duplicate portions of the same volume, such as 100 to 500 ml or more, or by filtration of two diluted volumes. All other waters should be examined by the filtration of three different volumes, depending on the expected bacterial density. When less than 20 ml of sample (diluted or undiluted) will be filtered, a small amount of sterile dilution water should be added to the funnel before filtration. This increase in water volume aids in uniform dispersion of the

move the filter with sterile forceps, and place it on the sterile pad or agar with a rolling motion to avoid the entrapment of air.

Filtration units should be sterile at the beginning of each filtration series as a minimum precaution to avoid accidental contamination. A filtration series is considered to be interrupted when an interval of 30 min or longer elapses between sample filtrations. After such interruption, any further sample filtration is treated as a new filtration series that requires resterilization of all membrane filter holders in use. Rapid decontamination of this equipment between successive filtrations may be accomplished by use of an ultraviolet (UV) sterilizer, flowing steam, or boiling water. In the UV sterilization procedure, a 2-min exposure of the filtration unit to UV radiation is sufficient. Do not subject membrane-filter culture preparations to any random UV radiation leaks that might emanate from the sterilization cabinet. Eye protection is recommended. Either safety glasses or prescription-ground glasses afford adequate eye protection against stray radiation from a UV sterilization cabinet that is not light-tight during the exposure interval. The UV tube should be cleaned regularly and checked periodically for effectiveness to insure that it will produce a 99.9% bacterial kill in a 2-min exposure.

c. Enrichment technic: Place a sterile absorbent pad in the upper half of a sterile culture dish and pipet enough enrichment medium (1.8 to 2.0 ml lauryl tryptose broth) to saturate the pad. Carefully remove any surplus liquid. Aseptically place the filter through which the sample has been passed on the pad. Incubate the filter, without inverting the dish, for 1-1/2 to 2 hr at 35±0.5 C in an atmosphere of at least 90% relative humidity.

If the agar-based medium is used, the final culture dish is prepared as directed under Preparation of Culture Media, Section 905C, No. 13. The enrichment culture is removed from the incubator and the filter is stripped from the enrichment pad and rolled onto the surface of the agar. Incorrect placement of the filter is at once obvious, because patches of unstained membrane indicate entrapment of air. Where such patches occur, realign the filter carefully. The used pad may be transferred to the dish (by ex-

changing covers) to aid in maintaining humidity.

If the liquid medium is used, the final culture is prepared by removing the enrichment culture from the incubator and separating the dish halves. A fresh sterile pad is placed in the bottom half of the dish and saturated with 1.8 to 2.0 ml of the final M-Endo medium (Section 905C, No. 11). The filter is transferred, with the same precautions as above, to the new pad. The used pad may be discarded.

With either the agar or the liquid medium, invert the dish and incubate for 20 to 22 hr at 35±0.5 C. Proceed to Counting (*e* below).

d. Alternative single-step direct technic: If the agar-based medium is used, the prepared filter is placed directly on the agar as described in the preceding section. The filter is incubated for 22 to 24 hr at 35±0.5 C.

If the liquid medium is used, a pad is placed in the culture dish and saturated with 1.8 to 2.0 ml of M-Endo medium. The prepared filter is placed directly on the pad and incubated for 22 to 24 hr at 35±0.5 C.

e. Counting: The typical coliform colony has a pink to dark-red color with a metallic surface sheen. The sheen area may vary in size from a small pinhead to complete coverage of the colony surface. The count is best made with the aid of a low-power (10 to 15 magnifications) binocular wide-field dissecting microscope or other optical device, with a daylight fluorescent light source above, and approximately perpendicular to, the plane of the filter. A total count on Endo-type medium has no relation to the total number of bacteria present in the original sample and, so far as is known, no significance can be inferred or correlation made with the pollution or purity of the water sample.

6. Calculation of Coliform Density

Report the coliform density in terms of (total) coliforms/100 ml. Compute the count, using membrane filters with 20 to 80 coliform colonies and not more than 200 colonies of all types per membrane, by the following equation:

(Total) coliform colonies/100 ml $=$

$$\frac{\text{coliform colonies counted} \times 100}{\text{ml sample filtered}}$$

a. *Water of drinking water quality:* Ideally, membranes selected for counting should have 20 to 80 coliform colonies and less than 200 total bacterial colonies per membrane. With water of good quality, the number of coliform colonies will be less than 20 per membrane. In this event, count all coliform colonies and use the formula given above to obtain the coliform density.

If confluent growth occurs, that is, growth covering the entire filtration area of the membrane with no discrete colonies, report results as "confluent growth." If the total number of bacterial colonies, coliforms plus non-coliforms, exceeds 200 per membrane, or if the colonies are too indistinct for accurate counting, report results as "too numerous to count (TNTC)." In either of these cases, request a new sample and select more appropriate volumes to be filtered per membrane, remembering that the standard drinking water portion is 100 ml. Thus, instead of filtering 100 ml/membrane, 50-ml portions may be filtered through each of two membranes,

25-ml portions may be filtered through each of four membranes, etc. Coliform colonies observed on each membrane are totaled and reported per 100 ml.

b. *Water of other than drinking water quality:* Ideally, membranes selected for counting should have 20 to 80 coliform colonies and less than 200 total bacterial colonies. As with potable water samples, if no filter has a number of coliform colonies falling in the ideal range, total the coliform counts on all filters and report per 100 ml. For example, if duplicate 50-ml portions were examined and the two membranes had 5 and 3 coliform colonies, respectively, report the count as 8 coliform colonies/100 ml, i.e.,

$$\frac{[(8+3) \times 100]}{(50+50)}$$

Similarly, if 50-, 25-, and 10-ml portions were examined and the counts were 15, 6, and <1 coliform colonies, respectively, report the count as 28/100 ml, i.e.,

$$\frac{[(15+6) \times 100]}{(50+25)}$$

On the other hand, if 10-, 1.0-, and 0.1-ml portions were examined with counts of 40, 9, and <1 coliform colonies, respectively, select the 10-ml portion only for calculating the coliform density because this filter had a coliform count falling in the ideal range. The result is 400/100 ml, i.e.,

$$\frac{(40 \times 100)}{10}$$

In this last example, if the membrane with 40 coliform colonies also had a total bacterial colony count of greater than 200, report the coliform count as >400/100 ml.

Report confluent growth or membranes with colonies too numerous to count as in *a* above. Request a new sample and select more appropriate volumes for filtration.

c. Statistical reliability of membrane filter results: Although the statistical reliability of the membrane filter technic is greater than that of the MPN procedure, membrane counts are not really absolute numbers. Table 909:II illustrates some 95% confidence limits.

TABLE 909:II. 95% CONFIDENCE LIMITS FOR MEMBRANE FILTER RESULTS USING A 100 ML SAMPLE

Number of Coliform Colonies Counted	95% Confidence Limits	
	Lower	Upper
1	0.05	3.0
2	0.35	4.7
3	0.81	6.3
4	1.4	7.7
5	2.0	9.2

909 B.   Delayed-Incubation Total Coliform Procedure

Modification of the standard membrane filter technic permits shipment or transport of the membrane after filtration to a distant laboratory for incubation and completion of the test. This delayed-incubation test may be used where it is impractical to apply conventional procedures. It may be used where it is not possible to maintain the desired sample temperature during transport; when the elapsed time between sample collection and analysis would exceed the approved time limit; where the sampling location is remote from laboratory services; when it is necessary to monitor streams for water quality or pollution control activities by a standardized procedure; or for other reasons that prevent analysis of the sample at or near the sample site.

Data secured by the delayed-incubation test have yielded results consist-ent with those from the immediate standard test in independent studies of samples from both fresh and salt waters. The applicability of the delayed-incubation test for a specific water source can be determined by comparison with results of test procedures using conventional methods.

The delayed-incubation test consists of filtering the sample in the field immediately after collection, placing the filter on the transport medium, and shipping to the laboratory. The coliform determination is completed in the laboratory by transferring the membrane to a growth medium, incubating at 35 ± 0.5 C for the stipulated time, and counting the typical coliform colonies so developed. The transport media are designed to keep the coliform organisms viable and generally do not permit visible growth during the time of transit. Bacteriostatic agents suppress growth of micro-organisms en route but allow normal coliform growth after transfer to a fresh growth medium.

The delayed-incubation test follows the methods outlined for the Total Coliform Membrane Filter Procedure, except as indicated below. Two alternative methods are given, one using the M-Endo preservative medium and the other the LES MF holding medium.

1. Apparatus

a. Culture dishes: Disposable, sterile, moisture-tight plastic petri dishes (50 by 12 mm) are recommended for use during shipping and also during incubation where a high humidity is not otherwise available. Such containers are light in weight and are less likely to break in transit. In an emergency, sterile glass petri dishes wrapped in plastic film or similar material may be used. Specifications for culture dishes are described in Section 909A.1*e.*

b. Field filtration units: Units should conform to the performance characteristics described under Section 909A.1 *f.* They may be sterilized by adding methyl alcohol to the filtering chamber, igniting, and covering to produce formaldehyde. Use a hand aspirator to obtain necessary vacuum.

2. Materials and Transport Media

a. M-Endo methods:

1) *M-Endo preservative medium:* Prepare as described in Media Specifications, No. 11, but add 3.84 g sodium benzoate (USP grade)/l or 3.2 ml of a 12% sodium benzoate solution/100 ml of medium.

2) *Sodium benzoate solution:* Dissolve 12 g sodium benzoate in sufficient distilled water to make 100 ml. This solution may be sterilized by autoclaving or filtration. Discard the solution after 6 months.

3) *Cycloheximide:** The addition to M-Endo preservative medium of cycloheximide is optional. It may be used for samples that previously have shown overgrowth of molds or fungi. Add 500 mg/l. A cycloheximide solution must be stored in the refrigerator and discarded after 6 months. Cycloheximide is a powerful skin irritant and should be handled with caution according to the manufacturer's directions.

b. LES method:

LES MF holding medium, coliform: Prepare as in Media Specifications, No. 12.

3. Procedure

a. Sample preservation and shipment: Place an absorbent pad in the bottom of a sterile petri dish and saturate with the selected coliform holding medium in accordance with the procedures given in Section 909A. *5c* above. Remove the membrane filter from the filtration unit with sterile forceps and roll it, grid side up, onto the surface of the absorbent pad that has been saturated with the transport medium. Protect the membrane from moisture loss. High humidity is maintained by tight closure of the plastic petri dish. While it is important to see that the membrane does not become dehydrated during transit, an excess of liquid in the dish is

---

*Actidione, manufactured by the Upjohn Company, Kalamazoo, Mich., or equivalent.

also undesirable. Place the culture dish containing the membrane in an appropriate shipping container and send to the laboratory for completion of the examination. The sample can be held without visible growth for a maximum of 72 hr on the transport medium, which usually allows use of the U.S. mails and common carriers. Visible growth occasionally is initiated on the transport medium when high temperatures are encountered.

b. Transfer: At the laboratory, transfer the membrane from the plastic dish in which it was shipped to a second sterile petri dish containing the growth medium. Another culture dish is used in this step to avoid any residues of sodium benzoate.

c. Incubation:

1) M-Endo method—Transfer the membrane from M-Endo preservative medium to a pad and petri dish containing M-Endo medium without the growth-suppressing reagents (Media Specifications, No. 11) and incubate at 35 ± 0.5 C for 20 to 22 hr.

2) LES method—Transfer the membrane from the LES MF holding medium to LES Endo agar (Media Specifications, No. 13) and incubate at $35 \pm .05$ C for 20 to 22 hr. If distinct colonies are observable without the aid of magnification at time of transfer, it is recommended that the petri dish containing the transferred membrane be refrigerated until it can be incubated at 35 ± 0.5 C for a 16- to 18-hr period. This manipulation of incubation time will permit the analyst a measure of control over the problems of overgrowth and sheen dissipation, which interfere with the coliform colony count.

4. Estimation of Coliform Density

Proceed as in Section 909A. 6 above. Record times of collection, filtration, and laboratory examination, and calculate the elapsed time.

909 C.   Fecal Coliform Membrane Filter Procedure

Determination of fecal coliform bacterial densities may be made either by the multiple-tube procedure or by a membrane filter technic. The choice of method should be governed by the methodology used for total coliform enumeration. The following procedure gives 93% accuracy for differentiating between coliforms from warm-blooded animals and coliforms from other sources. The membrane filter procedure calls for an enriched lactose medium that depends on an incubation temperature of 44.5 ± 0.2 C for its selectivity. Since incubation temperature is critical, membrane filter cultures must be placed in watertight plastic bags and submerged in a water bath for incubation at the elevated temperature or an appropriate, accurate solid heat sink incubator may be used. Areas of application for this method are stated in the introduction to the multiple-tube fecal coliform procedures.

1. Materials and Culture Medium

a. M-FC medium: Prepare as described in Media Specifications, Section 905C, No. 10.

Test each medium lot for satisfactory productivity by preparing dilutions of a culture of *Escherichia coli* (compare Section 905B. 2*e*) and—filtering appropriate volumes to give 20 to 80 colonies per filter. With each new lot of medium verify enough colonies, obtained from natural samples, to establish the absence of false positives.

b. Culture dishes: Tight-fitting plastic dishes are essential because these membrane-filter cultures must be submerged in a water bath during incubation. Enclosing groups of fecal coliform cultures in plastic bags is recommended to reduce further the occurrence of leakage during submersion. Specifications for plastic culture dishes are described in Section 909A.1*e* above.

c. Incubator: The specificity of the fecal coliform test is directly related to the incubation temperature. Air incubation is undesirable because of heat layering within the chamber and the slow recovery of temperature each time the incubator is opened during daily operations. Therefore, the need for greater temperature control must be met with a water bath or a heat sink incubator. A temperature tolerance of 44.5 ± 0.2 C can be obtained with most types of water baths that also are equipped with a gable top for the reduction of water and heat losses. A circulating water bath is excellent but may not be essential to this test if the maximum permissible variation of ± 0.2 C in temperature can be maintained with existing equipment.

2. Procedure

a. Selection of sample size: The volume of water sample to be examined by the membrane filter technic must receive careful consideration before filtration is started. [See Table 909:III.]

When the bacterial density of the sample is totally unknown, it is necessary to filter several decimal quantities of sample to establish the true coliform density. The best method is to estimate the ideal quantity expected to yield a countable membrane and select two additional quantities representing one-tenth and ten times this quantity, respectively. Sample quantities that will yield counts between 20 and 60 fecal coliform colonies result in greater accuracy of density determination.

b. Filtration of sample: Observe the same procedure and precautions as prescribed under Section 909A.5*b* above.

c. Preparation of culture dish: Place a sterile absorbent pad in each culture dish and pipet approximately 2 ml of M-FC medium, prepared as directed under Media Specifications (Section 905C) to saturate the pad. Carefully remove any surplus liquid from the culture dish. Place the prepared filter on the medium-impregnated pad as described under Section 909A above.

d. Incubation: Place the prepared cultures in waterproof plastic bags for protection during submersion in the water bath for the 24-hr incubation period at 44.5 ± 0.2C. These dishes must be anchored below the water surface during incubation to maintain critical temperature requirements. All prepared cultures should be placed in the water bath within 30 min after filtration. An

TABLE 909:III. SUGGESTED SAMPLE VOLUMES FOR MEMBRANE FILTER FECAL COLIFORM TEST

Water Source	Volume to be Filtered						
	100	50	10	1	0.1	0.01	0.001
Lakes, reservoirs	X	X					
Wells, springs	X	X					
Water supply, intake		X	X	X			
Natural bathing waters		X	X	X			
Sewage treatment plant, secondary effluent			X	X	X		
Farm ponds, rivers				X	X	X	
Stormwater runoff				X	X	X	
Raw municipal sewage					X	X	X
Feedlot runoff					X	X	X

appropriate, accurate solid heat sink incubator may be used instead of a water bath.

e. Counting: Colonies produced by fecal coliform bacteria are blue. The nonfecal coliform colonies are gray to cream-colored. Background color on the membrane filter will vary from a yellowish cream to faint blue, depending on the age of the rosolic acid salt reagent. Normally, few nonfecal coliform colonies will be observed on M-FC medium because of the selective action of the elevated temperature and addition of the rosolic acid salt reagent. The colony count is best made with the aid of a low-power (10 to 15 magnifications) binocular wide-field dissecting microscope or other optical device.

3. Calculation of Fecal Coliform Density

The density is computed from the sample quantities that produced membrane filter counts within the desired 20 to 60 fecal coliform colony range. This colony density range is more restrictive than the 20 to 80 total coliform range because of larger colony growth on M-FC medium. Proceed with the calculation as stated under Section 909A.6 above. Record densities as fecal coliforms/100 ml.

909 D. Delayed-Incubation Fecal Coliform Procedure (TENTATIVE)

This delayed incubation procedure is comparable to the Delayed-Incubation Total Coliform Procedure (Section 909 B). It eliminates the need for a field water bath incubator and frees the field investigator from the time-consuming task of counting colonies. Examination at a central laboratory, rather than in the field, permits colony confirmation and complete biochemical identification of the organisms, as necessary.

Results obtained by this delayed method have been consistent with results from the immediate standard test under varying laboratory and field use conditions. However, the applicability of this test for a specific water source must be determined by comparison with the standard membrane filter test. This is especially true with saline waters. Use of this delayed incubation test is suggested only when the standard immediate fecal coliform test cannot be performed.

The delayed-incubation test consists of filtering the sample in the field immediately after collection, placing the filter on the transport medium, and shipping to the laboratory. The fecal coliform test is completed in the laboratory by transferring the filter to M-FC medium, incubating at 44.5 C for 24 hr, and counting the fecal coliform colonies.

The transport medium keeps fecal coliform organisms viable but prevents visible growth during transit. Membrane filters can be held for up to 3 days on the VFC holding medium with little effect on the fecal coliform counts.

1. Apparatus

a. Culture dishes: Disposable, sterile, tight-lid plastic petri dishes (50 by 12 mm) are recommended for use during shipping. These containers are light and will not break easily in transit. Plastic tight-lid dishes should also be used for incubation, after transfer of the filter to M-FC medium.

b. Field filtration units: Units should conform to the performance characteristics described in Section 909A.1*f*. They may be sterilized by adding methyl alcohol to the filtering chamber, igniting, and covering to produce for-

maldehyde. Use a hand aspirator to obtain necessary vacuum.

2. Materials and Transport Medium

a. VFC holding medium: Prepare as directed under Media Specifications, Section 905 C. No. 14.

b. M-FC medium: Prepare as in Media Specifications, No. 10.

3. Procedure

a. Membrane filter transport: Place an absorbent pad in a tight-lid plastic petri dish and saturate with VFC holding medium. After filtering the sample remove the filter from the filtration unit and place it on the medium-saturated pad. It is important to use tight-lid dishes to prevent moisture loss from the pad and filter. At the same time, however, it is undesirable to have excess liquid in the dish. Place the culture dish containing the membrane in an appropriate shipping container and send to the examining laboratory. Membranes can be held on the transport medium at ambient temperature for a maximum of 72 hr with little effect on the fecal coliform counts.

b. Transfer: At the laboratory remove the membrane from the holding medium and place it in another dish containing M-FC medium (broth-saturated pad or agar).

c. Incubation: After transfer of the filter to M-FC medium, place the tight-lid dishes in waterproof plastic bags and submerge in a water bath at 44.5

C±0.2 C for 24 hr or use a solid heat sink incubator.

d. Counting: Colonies produced by fecal coliform bacteria are blue. Nonfecal coliform colonies are gray to cream-colored. The colony count is best made with the aid of a binocular widefield dissecting microscope at 10 to 15 magnifications.

4. Calculation of Fecal Coliform Density

Fecal coliform density is computed from the sample quantity that produces membrane filter counts within the desired 20- to 60-colony range. Calculate as in Section 909A. 6. Record densities as fecal coliforms /100 ml.

909 E. Bibliography

CLARK, H.F., E.E. GELDREICH, H.L. JETER & P.W. KABLER. 1951. The membrane filter in sanitary bacteriology. *Pub. Health Rep.* 66: 951.

GOETZ, A. & N. TSUNEISHI. 1951. Application of molecular filter membranes to bacteriological analysis of water. *J. Amer. Water Works. Ass.* 43:943.

VELS, C.J. 1951. Graphical approach to statistics. IV. Evaluation of bacterial density. *Water Sewage Works* 98:66.

TASK GROUP REPORT. 1953. Technic of bacterial examination of water. *J. Amer. Water Works Ass.* 45:1196.

TAYLOR, E.W., N.P. BURMAN & C.W. OLIVER. 1953. Use of the membrane filter in the bacteriological examination of water. *J. Appl. Chem.* (London) 3:233.

KABLER, P.W. 1954. Water examinations by membrane filter and MPN procedures. *Amer. J. Pub. Health* 44:379.

GELDREICH, E.E., P.W. KABLER, H.L. JETER & H.F. CLARK. 1955. A delayed incubation membrane filter test for coliform bacteria in water. *Amer. J. Pub. Health* 45:1462.

THOMAS, H.A. & R.L. WOODWARD. 1956. Use of molecular filter membranes for water potability control. *J. Amer. Water Works Ass.* 48:1391.

CLARK, H.F., P.W. KABLER & E.E. GELDREICH. 1957. Advantages and limitations of the membrane filter procedure. *Water Sewage Works* 104:385.

FIFIELD, C.W. & C.P. SCHAUFUS. 1958. Improved membrane filter medium for the detection of coliform organisms. *J. Amer. Water Works Ass.* 50:193.

McCARTHY, J.A. & J.E. DELANEY. 1958. Membrane filter media studies. *Water Sewage Works* 105:292.

McKEE, J.E., R.T. McLAUGHLIN & P. LESGOURGUES. 1958. Application of molecular filter technics to the bacterial assay of sewage. III. Effects of physical and chemical disinfection. *Sewage Ind. Wastes* 30:245.

McCARTHY, J.A., J.E. DELANEY & R.J. GRASSO. 1961. Measuring coliforms in water. *Water Sewage Works* 108:238.

JUDIS, J. 1962, 1963, 1964, 1965 a, b. Studies on the mechanism of action of phenolic disinfectants. I-V. *J. Pharm. Sci.* 51:261, 52:126, 53:196, 54:417, 541.

RHINES, C.E. & W.P. CHEEVERS. 1965. Decontamination of membrane filter holders by ultraviolet light. *J. Amer. Water Works Ass.* 57:500.

GELDREICH, E.E., H.F. CLARK, C.B. HUFF & L.C. BEST. 1965. Fecal-coliform-organism medium for the membrane filter technic. *J. Amer. Water Works Ass.* 57:208.

PANEZAI, A.K., T.J. MACKLIN & H.G. COLES. 1965. *Coli-Aerogenes* and *Escherichia coli* counts on water samples by means of transported membranes. *Proc. Soc. Water Treat. Exam.* 14:179.

McCARTHY, J.A. & J.E. DELANEY. 1965. Methods for measuring the coliform content of water. Sec. III. Delayed holding procedure for coliform bacteria. PHS Res. Grant WP 00202 NIH Rep. (Nov. 26).

GELDREICH, E.E., H.L. JETER & J.A. WINTER. 1967. Technical considerations in applying the membrane filter procedure. *Health Lab. Sci.* 4:113.

BREZENSKI, F.T. & J.A. WINTER. 1969. Use of the delayed incubation membrane filter test for

determining coliform bacteria in sea water. *Water Res.* 3:583.

LIN, S. 1973. Evaluation of coliform test for chlorinated secondary effluents. *J. Water Pollut. Control Fed.* 45:498.

TAYLOR, R.H., R.H. BORDNER & P.V. SCARPINO. 1973. Delayed incubation membrane-filter test for fecal coliforms. *Appl. Microbiol.* 25:363.

910   TESTS FOR THE FECAL STREPTOCOCCAL GROUP

The terms "fecal streptococcus" and "Lancefield's Group D Streptococcus" have been used synonymously. When used as indicators of fecal contamination the following species and varieties are implied: *S. faecalis, S. faecalis* var. *liquefaciens, S. faecalis* var. *zymogenes, S. faecium, S. faceium* var. *durans, S. bovis, and S. equinus.* Other streptococci may grow on the recommended media. These were formerly considered as biotypes of *S. faecalis* and *S. faecium* but current information indicates that they belong to Lancefield's serological Group Q. Group Q streptococci are found in the feces of humans and other warm-blooded animals, especially chickens. The Group Q antigen occurs in the cell wall of these organisms, and in addition, the Group D antigen is present between the cell wall and the cytoplasmic membrane where it naturally occurs in the established Group D species. Because of the close physiological relationship between Group D and Group Q organisms, they were understandably called "biotypes" or "intermediate strains" of the Group D streptococci.

The normal habitat of fecal streptococci is the intestines of man and ani-

mals; thus, these organisms are indicators of fecal pollution. Assays for fecal streptococci may provide valuable supplementary data on the bacteriological quality of lakes, streams, and estuaries but because of their survival characteristics it is not recommended to use *only* the fecal streptococci when investigating or determining water quality. Other fecal indicators should be used concurrently.

Since certain fecal streptococci are host-specific, biochemical characterization or speciation may provide valuable additional information about the source of pollution. For example, a predominance of *S. bovis* and *S. equinus* would indicate pollution due to the excrement of non-human, warm-blooded animals. Investigations have demonstrated high numbers of these species associated with pollution involving meat-processing plants, dairy wastes, and feedlot and farmland runoff. *S. bovis* and *S. equinus* have limited or short survival times outside of their natural habitat so that their presence in water indicates very recent contamination.

S. faecalis var. *liquefaciens* is not restricted to the intestines of man and animals. It has been found associated with vegetation, insects, and certain types of soils. Since media currently in use do not selectively exclude such strains of limited sanitary significance, care must be exercised in the use of the test and the interpretation of data. When studying various waters, especially recreational waters, fecal streptococci should be characterized biochemically to eliminate the possibility of predominance of *S. faecalis* var. *liquefaciens*, thus avoiding a situation where face-value streptococcal data may erroneously indicate gross fecal contamination.

910 A.   Multiple-Tube Technic

1. Presumptive Test Procedure

a. Inoculate a series of tubes of azide dextrose broth (Media Specifications, No. 15) with appropriate graduated quantities of the sample. Use 10 ml single-strength broth for inocula of 1 ml or less and 10 ml double-strength broth for 10-ml inocula. The portions of the sample used will necessarily vary in size and number with its character and should be decimal multiples of 1 ml. Refer to the section on tests for the presence of members of the coliform group (Section 908) for suggestions concerning suitable amounts of inocula in order to have some negative tubes in the higher dilution.

b. Incubate inoculated tubes at 35±0.5 C. Examine each tube for the presence of turbidity at the end of 24±2 hr. If no definite turbidity is present, reincubate, and read again at the end of 48±3 hr.

2. Confirmed Test Procedure

All azide dextrose broth tubes showing turbidity after 24- or 48-hr incubation must be subjected to the Confirmed Test.

a. Transfer three loopfuls of growth or use a wood applicator to transfer growth from each azide dextrose broth tube to a tube containing 10 ml ethyl violet azide broth (Media Specifications, No. 16). The wire loop should have a minimum diameter of 3 mm. A single inoculating wire, fashioned to have three individual 3-mm loops in a row, may be used to eliminate need for three separate loopfuls. Do not discard positive tubes, but hold in the incubator.

b. Incubate the inoculated tubes for 24 hr at 35±0.5 C. The presence of fecal streptococci is indicated by the formation of a purple button at the bottom of the tube, or occasionally by a dense turbidity. Record all positive results and discard those tubes. If no growth occurs in ethyl violet azide broth in 24 hr, reinoculate the tubes with an additional three loopfuls from the original positive azide broth cultures and reincubate for a second 24-hr period. Record results as final.

3. Computing and Recording of MPN

Refer to Tables 908:I and II and to Section 908D, Estimation of Bacterial Density.

4. Test Application

This test is designed primarily for the raw sewage and chlorinated sewage effluent samples. It is applicable to other fresh, but not saline, waters.

910 B.   Membrane Filter Technic

1. Laboratory Apparatus

Refer to membrane filter assembly and laboratory apparatus given in Standard Total Coliform Membrane Filter Procedure, Section 909A.1 preceding.

2. Materials and Culture Media

a. Culture media: Refer to Preparation of Culture Media, Sections 905A and B, and Media Specification No. 17 for KF Streptococcus agar formulation.

b. Culture dish preparation: Pour or pipet 4 to 5 ml liquefied medium into culture dishes (60 by 15 mm); flame the surface if necessary to eliminate bubbles. If tight-fitting plastic dishes are used, a stock of prepared dishes may be made in advance and stored at 4 to 10 C for use within a 4-wk period.

3. Procedure

a. Selection of sample size and filtration: Filter samples of water through a

sterile membrane to give 20 to 100 colonies on the membrane surface. Amounts varying from 100 to 10, 1, 0.1, or 0.01 ml may be necessary, depending on the amount of pollution in the water sample (refer to Section 909A.5a, Standard Total Coliform Membrane Filter Procedure). Transfer the filter directly to the agar medium in the petri dish, avoiding air bubbles.

b. Incubation: Invert culture plates and incubate at 35 ± 0.5 C for 48 hr.

c. Counting: Colonies produced by fecal streptococci are dark red to pink. Make the count with the aid of a low-power (10 to 15 magnifications) binocular wide-field dissecting mircoscope or equivalent optical device.

4. Calculation of Fecal Streptococcal Density

Compute the density from the sample quantities producing membrane filter counts within the desired 20- to 100-fecal streptococcus colony range. This colony density range is greater than the 20- to 80-total coliform range because of the increased selectivity of fecal streptococci media. Calculate as given under Standard Total Coliform Membrane Filter Procedure, Section 909A.6. Record densities as fecal streptococci/100 ml.

5. Confirmed Test

In the examination of samples of water from sources other than swimming pools, results reported to date indicate that practically 100% of the red and pink colonies that grow on filters placed on KF agar are fecal streptococci. If further confirmation is indicated, use the following procedures:

a. Fish selected typical colonies from membrane and inoculate onto a brain-heart infusion agar slant (Media Specifications, No. 20). Incubate at 35 ± 0.5 C for 24 to 48 hr. When growth is detected continue as in paragraphs *b* and *c.*

b. Transfer a loopful of growth from the brain-heart infusion agar slant to a clean glass slide and add a few drops of freshly tested 3% hydrogen peroxide to the smear. The absence of bubbles constitutes a negative catalase test, indicating a probable streptococcus culture. Continue confirmation as indicated below. The presence of bubbles constitutes a positive catalase test, which indicates the presence of non-streptococcal species. Do not continue confirmation.

c. Transfer a loopful of growth from the brain-heart infusion agar into brain-heart infusion broth and incubate at 45 C for 48 hr. Also transfer a loopful of growth into bile broth medium and incubate at 35 C for 3 days. Prepare this latter medium by adding 40 ml sterile 10% oxgall solution to 60 ml sterile brain-heart infusion broth.

d. Growth in the above media constitutes a positive test for fecal streptococci.

6. Differentiation of Fecal Streptococcal Organisms

Further identification of the distribution of fecal streptococcal types present within a given sample requires additional biochemical tests. See schematic outline in Figure 910:1 for identification of fecal streptococci.

7. Test Application

This test may be used for the examination of fresh and saline water samples. Like other membrane filter technics, it is not appropriate for highly turbid waters and chlorinated sewage.

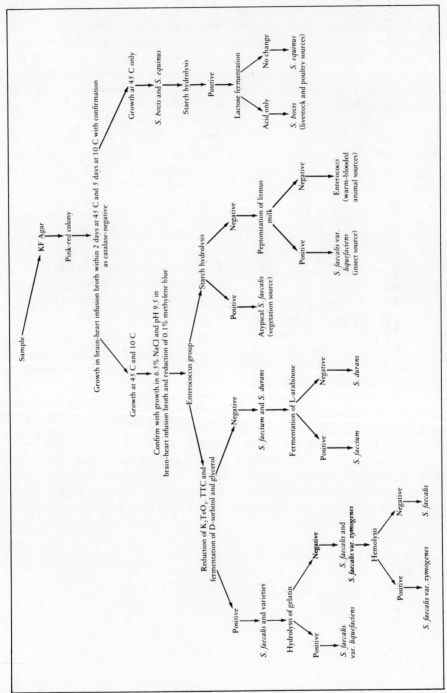

Figure 910:1. Schematic outline for identification of fecal streptococci.

910 C.   Fecal Streptococcal Plate Count
(TENTATIVE)

Fecal streptococcal densities may also be determined by the pour-plate technic using KF Streptococcus agar or Pfizer Selective Enterococcus Agar (PSE). This direct count procedure may be considered an alternative to the membrane filter technic and should be used preferentially for those samples containing few fecal streptococci associated with significant turbidity.

1. Preparation and Dilution

Refer to Standard Plate Count, Section 907.5.

2. Plating

Prepare KF Streptococcus agar or PSE as stated in Preparation of Culture Media, Section 905C., 17 or 18, and hold in a water bath at 45 C before making pour plates. Discard any liquid agar medium held over 4 hr.

First, place 1 ml, 0.1 ml, or other suitable volume of the sample or dilution to be used for plating in the culture dish. It is recommended that dilutions be used in preparing volumes less than 1 ml; in the examination of sewage or turbid water, a 0.1-ml inoculum of the original sample shall not be measured but an appropriate dilution should be prepared. Do not allow more than 20 min to elapse between making the dilution and pouring the plate.

Pour 12 to 15 ml liquefied agar medium into each culture dish containing the measured sample. Lift the cover of the dish just enough to permit introduction of the pipet or the culture medium. Throughly mix the agar and sample together for a uniform dispersion of organisms and medium over the bottom of the dish. This is best accomplished by gently tilting and rotating the dish, taking care not to splash the upper portion of the culture dish. Solidify the plates as rapidly as possible after pouring and place immediately, in inverted position, in the incubator.

3. Incubation

Incubate KF fecal streptococcal pour plates at a temperature of 35 ± 0.5 C for 48 ± 3 hr. Incubate PSE fecal streptococcal pour plates for 18 to 24 hr at 35 to 37 C.

4. Counting

Surface and subsurface colonies produced by fecal streptococci on KF are dark red to pink with entire edges. Subsurface colonies frequently are ellipsoidal or lens-shaped. Normally, few nonfecal streptococcus colonies will be observed on KF streptococcus agar because of the selectivity of the medium. However, occasional stream samples may contain gram-positive soil organisms, such as *Corynebacterium* species, which develop yellow or orange colonies on this medium. Infrequently, *Bacillus* species may produce fuzzy-white colonies with or without minute red-dot centers.

Fecal streptococci on PSE agar give brownish-black colonies with brown halos. PSE agar is a selective and differential medium that inhibits the proliferation of gram-negative bacteria. The only gram-positive cocci that will grow and exhibit esculin hydrolysis are the Group D streptococci. *Listeria monocytogenes* shows only pinpoint colonies at 24 hr and small (0.5-mm) brown-black colonies with brownish halos at the end of 48 hr. Coloration of colonies due to esculin hydrolysis is less marked with *Listeria* than with the fecal streptococci.

Count with either a Quebec colony counter or a low-power (10 to 15 magnifications) binocular wide-field dissecting microscope and suitable light source—preferably cool white fluorescent lamps.

5. Calculation of Fecal Streptococcal Density

Refer to Standard Plate Count, Section 907.8. Report results as fecal streptococci/100 ml.

910 D.   Bibliography

SHERMAN, J.M. 1937. The streptococci. *Bacteriol. Rev.* 1:3.

SKAUDHAUGE, K. 1950. Studies on Enterococci, with Special Reference to the Serological Properties. Einar Munksgaards, Copenhagen.

MALLMANN, W.L. & E.B. SELIGMANN. 1950. A comparative study of media for the detection of streptococci in water and sewage. *Amer. J. Pub. Health* 40:286.

LITSKY, W., W.L. MALLMANN & C.W. FIFIELD. 1953. A new medium for the detection of enterococci in water. *Amer. J. Pub. Health* 43:873.

LITSKY, W. 1955. Comparison of the Most Probable Number of *Escherichia coli* and enterococci in river waters. *Amer. J. Pub. Health* 45:1049.

SHATTOCK, P.M.F. 1955. The identification and classification of *Streptococcus faecalis* and some associated streptococci. *Ann. Inst. Pasteur* (Lille) 7:95.

COOPER, K.E. & F.M. RAMADAN. 1955. Studies in the differentiation between human and animal pollution by means of fecal streptococci. *J. Gen. Microbiol.* 12:180.

LAKE, D.E., R.H. DEIBEL & C.F. NIVEN, JR. 1957. The identity of *Streptococcus faecium. Bacteriol. Proc.*, p. 13.

BARNES, E.M. 1957. Reduction as a means of differentiating *Streptococcus faecalis* from *Streptococcus faecium. J. Gen. Microbiol.* 14:57.

BUCHANAN, R.E. & N.E. GIBBONS, eds. 1974. Bergey's Manual of Determinative Bacteriology, 8th ed., Williams & Wilkins, Baltimore, Md.

MORELIS, P. & L. COLOBERT. 1958. Un milieu selectif permettant l'identification et le denombrement rapides de *Streptococcus faecalis. Ann. Inst. Pasteur* 95:667.

SUREAU, P. 1958. Isolation and enumeration of faecal streptococci in waters by means of filtering membranes. *Ann. Inst. Pasteur* 95:6.

MEDREK, T.F. & W. LITSKY. 1959. Comparative incidence of coliform bacteria and enterococci in undisturbed soil. *Appl. Microbiol.* 8:60.

CROFT, C.C. 1959. A comparative study of media for detection of enterococci in water. *Amer. J. Pub. Health* 49:1379.

BARTLEY, C.H. & L.W. SLANETZ. 1960. Types and sanitary significance of fecal streptococci isolated from feces, sewage and water. *Amer. J. Pub. Health* 50:1545.

KENNER, B.A., H.F. CLARK & P.W. KABLER. 1960. Fecal streptococci. II. Quantification of streptococci in feces. *Amer. J. Pub. Health* 50:1553.

KENNER, B.A., H.F. CLARK & P.W. KABLER. 1961. Fecal streptococci. I. Cultivation and enumeration of streptocci in surface waters. *Appl. Microbiol.* 9:15.

NIVEN, C.F., JR. 1963. Microbial indices of food quality: Fecal streptococci. In: Proc. Conf. Microbiol. Qual. Foods. Academic Press, New York, N.Y.

SHATTOCK, P.M.F. 1963. Enterococci: Chemical and Biological Hazards in Food. Iowa Univ. Press, Des Moines.

MUNDT, J.C. 1963. Occurrence of enterococci on plants in a wild environment. *Appl. Microbiol.* 11:141.

NOWLAN, S.S., & R.H. DEIBEL. 1967. Group Q Streptococci. I. Ecology, serology, physiology, and relationship to established enterococci. *J. Bacteriol.* 94:291.

GELDREICH, E.E. & B.A. KENNER. 1969. Concepts of fecal streptococci in stream pollution. *J. Water Pollut. Control Fed.* 41:R336.

PAVLOVA, M.T., F.T. BREZENSKI & W. LITSKY. 1972. Evaluation of various media for isolation, enumeration and identification of fecal streptococci from natural sources. *Health Lab. Sci.* 9:289.

PAVLOVA, M.T., E. BEAUVAIS, F.T. BREZENSKI & W. LITSKY. 1973. Rapid assessment of water quality by fluorescent antibody identification of fecal streptococci. In: Int. Conf. Water Pollut. Res., 6th, Jerusalem, Proc., Pergamon Press, New York, N.Y.

PAVLOVA, M.T., E. BEAUVAIS, F.T. BREZENSKI & W. LITSKY. 1972. Fluorescent-antibody techniques for the identification of Group D streptococci: Direct staining method. *Appl. Microbiol.* 23:571.

PFIZER DIAGNOSTICS DIVISION, Pfizer Selective Enterococcus (PSE) Agar. Pfizer Diagnostics Tech. Bull., Pfizer Diagnostics Div., 235 E. 42nd Street, New York, N.Y.

911   DIFFERENTIATION OF COLIFORM GROUP OF ORGANISMS (TENTATIVE)

The methods previously given for the detection and estimation of the coliform group of bacteria provide full information on the pollution and sanitary quality of the water supply under examination. Differentiation of the fecal coliform organisms as a group has been described in the test procedures given in preceding sections.

Occasionally, it is of value to differentiate the coliform strains and identify them according to genera and species for research purposes or for special study. Tentative methods for such differentiation are presented.

911 A.   Culture Purification

It is well known that the accuracy of the Completed Test and of differential tests is at times impaired by failure to purify cultures. It is essential that a pure culture be obtained. This may be accomplished by streaking the culture

from the completed lactose broth tube to an eosin-methylene blue agar plate, which is then incubated at 35 ± 0.5 C for 24 hr. A single well-isolated colony fished to an agar slant is incubated at 35 ± 0.5 C for 24 hr and gram-stained to confirm the presence of gram-negative, nonspore-forming rods.

Variation in organisms of the coliform group, particularly the "unstable" variation characteristic of the *mutabile* type, is occasionally encountered. It is therefore advisable, when purification of cultures is attempted, to be on the lookout for this phenomenon. An apparent mixture of organisms may, in reality, consist of a single strain that is showing variation. However, persistent plus-minus reactions may very well indicate inadequate purification of the culture.

911 B.   IMViC Tests

The differentiation of the coliform group into *Escherichia coli, Enterobacter (Aerobacter) aerogenes,* and *Citrobacter (Escherichia) freundii* species long has been carried out on the basis of the results of four tests (indole, methyl red, Voges-Proskauer, and sodium citrate) often referred to collectively as the "IMViC tests." These tests are tentatively recommended for differential determination. A simplified grouping of the organism types according to the outcome of the four tests is given in Table 911:I. Additional tests are required for the separation of *Klebsiella* and *Enterobacter.*

all types of coliform organisms may occur in feces. Although *E. coli* will nearly always be found in fresh pollution derived from warm-blooded animals, some other type or types of coliform organisms, not accompanied by *E. coli,* may occasionally be found in fresh pollution from a particular source.

It is well to keep in mind, however, the possibility of occasional multiplication of coliform organisms on leather washers, wood, swimming pool ropes, or jute packing, as well as in slime formation inside of pipes. In fact, differentiation of coliform types finds one of its most . practical applications in the

TABLE 911:I. INTERPRETATION OF IMViC REACTIONS

Organism	Indole	Methyl Red	Voges-Proskauer	Citrate
Escherichia coli	+ or −	+	−	−
Citrobacter freundii	−	+	−	+
Klebsiella-Enterobacter group	+ or −	−	+	+

The significance of finding various types of coliform organisms in water samples has been and still is a subject of considerable study (see discussion under Fecal Coliform MPN Procedure, Section 908C). It must be remembered that study of unexpected coliform densities that may be explained by multiplication on or in organic materials. The presence of a large number of coliform organisms of the same type in water from a well or spring—or from a single tap on a distribution system, for example—is quite suggestive of such multiplication.

1. Indole Test

a. Reagents:

1) *Medium*—Use tryptophane broth as described under Media Specifications, No. 21.

2) *Test reagent*—Dissolve 5 g para-dimethylaminobenzaldehyde in 75 ml isoamyl (or normal amyl) alcohol, ACS grade, and add 25 ml conc HCl. The reagent should be yellow. Some brands of paradimethylaminobenzaldehyde are not satisfactory and some good brands become unsatisfactory on aging.

The amyl alcohol solution should have a pH value of less than 6.0. Both amyl alcohol and benzaldehyde compound should be purchased in as small amounts as will be consistent with the volume of work to be done.

b. Procedure: Inoculate 5-ml portions of medium from a pure culture and incubate at 35±0.5 C for 24±2 hr. Add 0.2 to 0.3 ml test reagent and shake. Let the tube stand for about 10 min and observe the results.

A dark red color in the amyl alcohol surface layer constitutes a positive indole test; the original color of the reagent, a negative test. An orange color probably indicates the presence of skatole and may be reported as a ± reaction.

2. Methyl Red Test

a. Reagents:

1) *Medium*—Use buffered glucose broth as described under Media Specifications, No. 22.

2) *Indicator solution*—Dissolve 0.1 g methyl red in 300 ml of 95% ethyl alcohol and dilute to 500 ml with distilled water.

b. Procedure: Inoculate 10-ml portions of medium from a pure culture. Incubate at 35 C for 5 days. To 5 ml of the culture add 5 drops methyl red indicator solution.

Record a distinct red color as methyl red-positive and a distinct yellow color as methyl red-negative. A mixed shade should be recorded as questionable and possibly indicative of incomplete culture purification.

3. Voges-Proskauer Test

a. Reagents:

1) *Media*—This test may be carried out using the medium as described for the methyl red differential test or, if desired, an alternative salt peptone glucose medium may be used as described under Media Specification, No. 23.

2) *Naphthol solution*—Dissolve 5 g purified α-naphthol (melting point 92.5 C or higher) in 100 ml absolute ethyl alcohol. This solution should be prepared fresh each day.

3) *Potassium hydroxide solution*—Dissolve 40 g KOH in 100 ml distilled water.

b. Procedure: Inoculate 5 ml of either culture medium and incubate at 35± 0.5 C for 48 hr. To 1 ml of culture add 0.6 ml naphthol solution and 0.2 ml KOH solution. Development of a pink to crimson color in the mixture from 2 to 4 hr after adding the reagents constitutes a positive test. Results should not be read after this period of time.

4. Sodium Citrate Test

a. Alternate media: Use either Koser's citrate broth as described under

Media Specification, No. 24 or Simmons' citrate agar as described under the same heading, No. 25.

b. Procedure:

1) Make the inoculation into the liquid medium only with a straight needle; it should be a light inoculum. Never use a pipet because of the danger of invalidating the result by the introduction of nutrient material with the transfer. Incubate at 35 ± 0.5 C for 72 to 96 hr. Record visible growth as positive, no growth as negative.

2) Inoculate the agar medium with straight needle, using both a stab and a streak. Incubate 48 hr at 35 ± 0.5 C Growth on the medium with (usually) a blue color constitutes a positive reaction; the absence of growth is recorded as negative.

911 C. *Klebsiella* Differentiation

The coliform group as defined herein includes the genus *Klebsiella*. *Klebsiella* strains exhibit seven different IMViC patterns with $--++$, $++++$, and $-+++$ being the most common.[1] Much of the confusion about *E. aerogenes* and *Klebsiella pneumoniae* has resulted because of their identical $--++$ IMViC pattern. Obviously, more biochemical tests are necessary to separate these two organisms.

Klebsiella pneumoniae is the most important species because of its association with human respiratory and genitourinary infections.[2-9] In addition, *K. pneumoniae* infects approximately 30% of the human population, being found in human excretions (feces, urine, and sputum) and, consequently, in sewage.[10-13] *Klebsiella* occurrences, in both healthy livestock and infected animals, have been estimated to range from 30 to 40%.[14, 15]

Large concentrations of *Klebsiella* in certain industrial wastes such as pulp and paper, sugar beet, and food-processor effluents are significant because they reflect the high bacterial nutrient levels in these wastes. Such wastewaters presumably contain large amounts of carbohydrates and are capable of supporting significant "aftergrowth" of these organisms in the effluents and receiving stream.[12] Aftergrowth may also occur in potable water.[16]

1. Procedure

Following culture purification (Section 911 A above), differentiation may be accomplished by streaking on a nitrogen-deficient medium[17] on which *Klebsiella* colonies are larger, more convex, and gummier in appearance than *Enterobacter*. More detailed and definitive differentiation requires biochemical testing for oxidase and the HOMoC series (hydrogen sulfide and ornithine decarboxylase production, motility, and citrate utilization).[18] Commercially available differential test kits may be used in preliminary screening prior to serological confirmation.[16] These kits give 95 to 98% agreement with conventional tests, although more significant differences occasionally occur. In some instances supplementary tests will be necessary to differentiate further among strains of

Enterobacteriaceae. *Klebsiella* is oxidase-negative, does not produce H_2S, does not decarboxylate ornithine, is nonmotile, and utilizes citrate as the sole source of carbon.[18-20]

2. References

1. BROWN, C. & R.J. SEIDLER. 1973. Potential pathogens in the environment: *Klebsiella pneumoniae*, a taxonomic and ecological enigma. *Appl. Microbiol.* 25:900.

2. TALERMAN, A. 1968. Multiple liver abscesses caused by *Klebsiella aerogenes*. *J. Med. Microbiol.* 1, 164.

3. CRUICKSHANK, R. 1965. Medical Microbiology, A Guide to Laboratory Diagnosis and Control of Infection. Williams and Wilkins, Baltimore, Md.

4. EICKHOFF, T.C., B.W. STEINHAUER & M. FINLAND. 1966. The *Klebsiella-Enterobacter-Serratia* division. Biochemical and serologic characteristics and susceptibility to antibiotics. *Ann. Intern. Med.* 65:1163.

5. HENSHAW, V., J. PUNCH, M.J. ALLISON & H.P. DALTON. 1969. Frequency of R factor-mediated multiple drug resistance in *Klebsiella* and *Aerobacter*. *Appl. Microbiol.* 17:214.

6. KAYYALI, M.Z., D.P. NICHOLSON & I.M. SMITH. 1972. A *Klebsiella* outbreak in a pediatric nursery: emergency action and preventive surveillance. *Clin. Pediat.* 11:422.

7. ROONEY, J.C., D.J. HILL & D.M. DANKS. 1971. Jaundice associated with bacterial infection in the newborn. *Amer. J. Dis. Child.* 122:39.

8. PARKKULAINEN, K.V. & T.V KOSUNEN. 1971. A follow-up study of bacteriuria in female patients treated for recurrent urinary tract infections using dip-slides. *Ann. Clin. Res.* 3:163.

9. GAVRILLA, I. 1969. Current clinico-bacteriological and therapeutic aspects of enterocolitis in children. *Pediatria* (Bucur) 18:63.

10. THONE, B.T. 1970. *Klebsiella* in faeces. *Lancet* 2:1033.

11. SELDEN, R., S. LEE, W.L. LOW, J.V. BENNETT & T.C. EICKHOFF. 1971. Nosocomial *Klebsiella* infections: intestinal colonization as a reservoir. *Ann. Intern. Med.* 74:657.

12. BORDNER, R.H. & B.J. CARROLL, eds. 1972. Proc. Seminar on the Significance of Fecal Coliforms in Industrial Wastes. EPA, Office of Enforcement. National Field Investigations Center, Denver, Colo.

13. BERGERSEN, F.J. & E.H. HIPSLEY. 1970. The presence of N_2-fixing bacteria in the intestines of man and animals. *J. Gen. Microbiol.* 60:61.

14. CARROLL, E.J. 1970. Bactericidal activity of bovine serum against coliform organisms isolated from milk of mastitic udders, udder skin, and environment. *Amer. J. Vet. Res.* 32:689.

15. SHIMAKURA, S., H. IWAMORI & K. HIRAI. 1970. Studies on the omphalitis in baby chicks. I. On the organisms isolated from baby chicks with omphalitis. *Jap. J. Poult. Sci.* 7:57.

16. PTAK, D.J., W. GINSBURG & B.F. WILLEY. 1973. Identification and incidence of *Klebsiella* in chlorinated water supplies. *J. Amer. Water Works Ass.* 65:604.

17. ELLER, C. & F.F. EDWARDS. 1968. Nitrogen-deficient medium in the differential isolation of *Klebsiella* and *Enterobacter* from feces. *Appl. Microbiol.* 16:896.

18. CLOSS, O. & A. DIOGRANES. 1971. Rapid identification of prompt lactose-fermenting genera within the family *Enterobacteriaceae*. *Acta Pathol. Microbiol. Scand.* Sec. B 79:673.

19. CORVAN, S.T. & K.J. STEEL. 1965. Manual for the Identification of Medical Bacteria. Cambridge Univ. Press, New York, N.Y.

20. TRAUB, W.H., E.A. RAYMOND & J. LINEHAN. 1970. Identification of *Enterobacteriaceae* in the clinical microbiological laboratory. *Appl. Microbiol.* 20:303.

911 D.   Bibliography

CLARK, W.M. 1915. The final hydrogen ion concentrations of cultures of *Bacillus coli*. *Science* 42:71.

CLARK, W.M. & W.A. LUBS. 1915. The differentiation of bacteria of the colon-aerogenes family by the use of indicators. *J. Infect. Dis.* 17:160.

LEVINE, M. 1916. On the significance of the Voges-Proskauer reaction. *J. Bacteriol.* 1:153.

LEVINE, M. 1921. Notes on *Bact. coli* and *Bact. aerogenes*. *Amer. J. Pub. Health* 11:21.

KOSER, S.A. 1924. Correlation of citrate utilization by members of the colon-aerogenes group with other differential characteristics and with habitat. *J. Bacteriol.* 9:59.

SIMMONS, J.S. 1926. A culture medium for differentiating organisms of typhoid-colon-aerogenes groups and for isolation of certain fungi. *J. Infect. Dis.* 39:309.

KOVACS, N. 1928. A simplified method for detecting indol formation by bacteria. *Z. Immunitatsforsch.* 56:311; *Chem. Abstr.* 22:3425.

RUCHHOFT, C.C., J.G. KALLAS, B. CHINN &
E.W. COULTER. 1930 and 1931. Coli-aerogenes differentiation in water analysis. *J. Bacteriol.* 21:407; 22:125.

EPSTEIN, S.S. & R.H. VAUGHN. 1934. Differential reactions in the coli group of bacteria. *Amer. J. Pub. Health* 24:505.

BARRITT, M.W. 1936. The intensification of the Voges-Proskauer reaction by the addition of alpha-naphthol. *J. Pathol. Bacteriol.* 42:441.

VAUGHN, R., N.B. MITCHELL & M. LEVINE. 1939. The Voges-Proskauer and methyl red reactions in the coli-aerogenes group. *J. Amer. Water Works Ass.* 31:993.

BORMAN, E.K., C.A. STUART & K.M. WHEELER. 1944. Taxonomy of the family Enterobacteriaceae. *J. Bacteriol.* 48:351.

EWING, W.H. 1966. Enterobacteriaceae: Taxonomy and Nomenclature. U.S. Dep. HEW, Nat. Center for Disease Control, Atlanta, Ga.

WOLFE, M.W. & D. AMSTERDAM. 1968. New diagnostic system for the identification of lactose-fermenting gram-negative rods. *Appl. Microbiol.* 16:1528.

912   DETECTION OF PATHOGENIC MICROORGANISMS IN WATER AND WASTEWATER

The most common and important pathogenic microorganisms that can be demonstrated in wastewater and, under certain conditions, surface and groundwaters of the United States, are *Salmonella*, *Shigella*, enteropathogenic *Escherichia coli*, *Leptospira*, and the enteric viruses. Organisms such as hookworm larvae, the cysts of *Endamoeba histolytica*, and other animal parasites may on occasion find their way into poorly constructed wells, particularly in areas where the infections they cause are endemic. Other organisms not normally associated with the climate in this country might also be found in water because of extensive and rapid world travel. Perhaps the most important of these "foreign" organisms, as far as waterborne transmission is concerned, is *Vibrio cholerae*.

Routine examination of water and wastewater for pathogenic microorganisms cannot be recommended at this time. There is no single procedure that can be used to isolate and identify these microorganisms. Salmonellae are extremely common in the environment and are probably responsible for most recognized waterborne disease outbreaks. Unfortunately, isolation technics even for these ubiquitous organisms involve relatively complicated procedures that will exceed the capabilities of all but a few water laboratories. Certainly monitoring of water or wastewater for enteric viruses cannot be carried out except in very well-equipped laboratories and then usually as a special research study. Thus, a combination of factors— among them lack of facilities, lack of trained personnel, lack of laboratory time, high costs, and lack of adequate methods—makes the routine examination of water for pathogens impossible. In view of the foregoing, it is apparent that there is a strong need for intensive research in this area, research that should be encouraged at every opportunity.

Some suspicion has been cast on the validity of the coliform test as an indicator of the biological safety of water.[1-3] These reports suggest that under unusual circumstances pathogenic bacteria can be isolated from waters containing few if any coliform bacteria. *The circumstances surrounding these isolations are not at all clear and it should not be concluded that the coliform test is unreliable or even needs to be supplemented by routine examinations for pathogens at this time.* This coliform test has, over the years, clearly proven its value. The discussion of pathogen isolation procedures that follows is offered for the specialist who may wish to initiate a research study—for example, to obtain background data on the numbers, types, and frequency of occurrence of pathogens in water as related to the coliform or fecal coliform index.

912 A.   General Qualitative Isolation and Identification Procedures for *Salmonella* and *Shigella*

The recommended methods presented below for the isolation of *Salmonella* and *Shigella* from water or wastewater are not standardized and must be considered research procedures that may need modification to fit a particular set of circumstances. The recovery efficiency of given lots of media should be checked by using several recently isolated strains of *Salmonella* or *Shigella*.[4,5]

Rather than recommend a specific protocol for *Salmonella* and *Shigella* detection in water, this presentation will give a brief summary of suitable methods for recovery of these organisms from water. This approach is necessary be-

cause some critical areas of procedural details require further study in the research laboratory before a specific protocol can be established. However, methods currently available have been used in numerous field investigations to demonstrate *Salmonella* in both fresh and estuarine water environments. It is further recommended that the technics available be carefully evaluated for the development of a protocol that will yield optimum isolation of these organisms in a specific investigation. Finally, it must be remembered that the occurrence of *Salmonella* in water is highly variable and that there are limitations and variations in sensitivity and selectivity of accepted *Salmonella* isolation procedures for the detection of the 900 to 1,200 different *Salmonella* serotypes currently recognized. Thus, a negative result by any of these methods does not imply the absence of all salmonellae, nor does it imply the absence of other pathogens.

1. Concentration Technics for Waterborne Pathogens

Generally, it is necessary to examine a relatively large sample in order to isolate pathogenic organisms. These organisms are usually present in small numbers as compared to coliforms, because their sporadic occurrence is related to the incidence of disease or infection at a given period.

a. Swab technic: Swabs may be prepared from cheesecloth 23 cm (9 in.) wide, folded five times at 36-cm (14-in.) lengths and cut lengthwise to within 10 cm (4 in.) from the head into strips that are 4.5 cm (1-3/4 in.) long. The uncut or folded end of the swab is then securely wrapped with 16-gauge wire and placed just below the surface of the stream, lake, or estuary sampling location for from 3 to 5 days. Gauze pads of similar thickness—for example, maternity pads—may be substituted for cheesecloth swabs. During the period of sampling, particulate matter and microorganisms are concentrated from the water passing through or over the swab. After the exposure period, the swab is retrieved, placed in a plastic bag, iced, and sent to the laboratory. Maximum storage time allowable is 6 hr. At the laboratory, the sample water is expressed from the pad into suitable enrichment media, or the pad itself or por-

tions of it may be placed in enrichment media.

b. Diatomaceous earth technic: The filtration capacity of diatomaceous earth is used to concentrate a relatively large proportion of the microorganisms present in a sample. This is accomplished by placing an absorbent pad (not a membrane filter) on a membrane filter funnel receptacle, assembling the funnel, then adding sufficient diatomaceous earth* to pack the funnel neck loosely. Two liters of sample are poured slowly through the diatomaceous earth filter and vacuum is applied. After filtration, the funnel is disassembled and the resulting "plug" of diatomaceous earth can be divided with a sterile spatula into portions that may be added to suitable enrichment media.

c. Membrane filter technic: In the examination of samples relatively free from turbidity, sample volumes of several liters may be passed through a sterile membrane filter (see Section 909, Membrane Filter Technic), which can be divided with sterile scissors into sections for inoculation into suitable enrichment media. Filters larger than 47 mm also may be used.

2. Enrichment

The concentrated sample must be enriched selectively in a growth medium that simultaneously suppresses the growth of coliform bacteria. Enrichment of the initial sample is essential, since the pathogens are usually present in low numbers and solid selective media for colony isolation are often somewhat toxic, even to the pathogens. There is no

---

*Johns-Mansville's "Celite" or equivalent.

single enrichment medium that can be recommended to give optimum growth of both the *Salmonella* and the *Shigella* groups. Tetrathionate broth is excellent for primary enrichment of *Salmonella*, but it is very toxic to *Shigella* strains. Media containing selenite are strongly inhibitory to *Shigella flexneri* and, in lesser degree, to *Shigella sonnei*. *Shigella* enrichment has been found to be satisfactory only in media containing bile salts for coliform suppression.

a. Dulcitol selenite broth has the advantage of inhibiting the nonpathogenic colon bacilli during the early hours of incubation following inoculation, while allowing the *Salmonella* strains to multiply rather rapidly. Optimum incubation time for maximum recovery of *Salmonella* is 24 hr. However, recovery of relatively slow-growing organisms like *S. montevideo*, *S. enteritidis*, and *S. worthington* will necessitate longer incubation periods. Therefore, repeat streaking from the same inoculated medium after each 24-hr period may be necessary. Broth cultures that develop turbidity and any orange-red color resulting from selenite reduction are streaked onto suitable selective solid media.

b. Tetrathionate broth may yield more salmonellae than selenite broth. However, incubation should be extended beyond 48 hr, with repeat streaking from the same tube several times during the first day and daily up to 5 days to insure recovery of all serotypes that may be present. Suppression of nonpathogenic organisms is improved by the addition of 1 : 100,000 brilliant green. Sensitivity is improved by the addition of 3 mg L-cystine/l of tetrathionate broth.

c. GN broth has been found to permit good growth of various *Shigella* species and is recommended for investigations of water pollution involving this pathogenic group. This medium will suppress not only the coliform group but also fecal streptococci, which may be numerous in polluted water. Incubation time should not be extended beyond 24 hr because longer incubation favors the growth of *Pseudomonas aeruginosa* and *Proteus* species.

3. Selective Growth

Further separation of pathogens from the surviving nonpathogenic bacterial population may be accomplished by the proper choice of incubation temperature for primary enrichment and secondary differentiation on selective solid media. These two factors—that is, temperature and choice of media—are interrelated. More *Salmonella* may be recovered at 37 C with bismuth sulfite agar than at other temperatures with other media. However, great skill at screening for these pathogens is necessary because of the competing growth of various nonpathogens. Use of an incubation temperature of 41.5 C and brilliant green agar reduces the number of interfering organisms, but some *Salmonella* serotypes will not grow at this elevated temperature.

Solid media commonly used for enteric pathogen detection may be classed into three groups: (*a*) differential media with little or no inhibition toward nonpathogenic bacteria, such as EMB (containing sucrose) and MacConkey's agar; (*b*) selective media containing brilliant green dye, such as brilliant green agar or bismuth sulfite agar; and (c) selective media containing bile salts inhibitors such as desoxycholate citrate agar or xylose lysine desoxycholate agar (*Salmonella-Shigella*, SS, agar contains a combination of these two selective agents). Any medium selected must provide optimum suppression of coliforms while permitting good recovery of the pathogenic group. Since *Shigella* organisms are among the more fastidious enteric bacteria in their growth requirements, media suitable for *Salmonella* recovery may not be optimum for *Shigella*. Therefore, the protocol must include several selective media for optimum recovery of both *Salmonella* and *Shigella* from water. Streaking duplicate plates, one heavily and one lightly, often aids in the recognition of enteric pathogens in the presence of large numbers of interfering organisms.

a. *Brilliant green agar:* Typical well-isolated *Salmonella* colonies grown on this medium form a pinkish white colony with a red background. *Salmonella typhi* and a few other species of *Salmonella* grow poorly on this medium because of the brilliant green dye content. Those lactose-fermenters whose growth is not suppressed will form greenish colonies, or they may at times produce other colorations. Occasionally, slow lactose-fermenters (*Proteus, Citrobacter,* and *Pseudomonas*) will produce colonies that resemble those of a pathogen. In some instances, *Proteus* has been observed to "swarm." This medium should be incubated a full 48 hr to permit any slow-growing or partially inhibited organisms to develop visible colonies. If no typical colonies are observed or if the streak plate is crowded, it may be necessary to transfer a few isolated colonies for further processing through the biochemical tests. Nonlactose-fermenting colonies may be masked by bordering lactose-fermenting colonies.

b. *Bismuth sulfite agar:* Luxuriant growth of many *Salmonella* species (including *S. typhi*) can be expected on this medium after 48 hr of incubation. Typical colonies usually develop a black color, with or without a metallic sheen, and frequently this blackening extends beyond the colony to give a "halo" effect. A few species of *Salmonella* have been observed that develop a green coloration. Therefore, it may be necessary to isolate some of these colony types when the typical forms are absent. As with brilliant green agar, typical colony coloration may be masked by the presence of numerous bordering colonies. A black color is also developed by other hydrogen sulfide-producing colonies— for example, *Proteus* and certain coliforms. A membrane filter procedure also has been described.

c. *Xylose lysine desoxycholate agar:* This medium is recommended for isolation of *Shigella* species when used in conjunction with GN enrichment broth. Media containing brilliant green dye are unsuited to *Shigella* recovery. Sodium desoxycholate is far less toxic to *Shigella* and the fastidious *Salmonella*. Colonies of *Shigella* grown on this medium are red, while *Salmonella* and *Arizona* organisms produce black-centered red colonies. Coliform bacteria, *Citrobacter, Proteus,* and most paracolons produce yellow colonies. Optimum incubation time is 24 hr. If plates are incubated longer, there is an alkaline reversion and subsequent blackening by H_2S-positive nonpathogens (*Citrobacter, Proteus vulgaris,* and *P. mirabilis*).

4. Biochemical Reactions

Numerous enteric organisms of little or no pathogenicity have some major biochemical characteristics in common with *Salmonella* and *Shigella*. The identification of pathogens by colony characteristics on selective media has limitations inherent in the biological variations of certain organisms. Suspected colonies grown on selective solid media must be purified and further classified by biochemical reactions and finally verified by serological identification. Usually the number of cultures obtained from the screening procedure will be large. Commercially available differential media kits may be used in preliminary screening, as an alternative to Phases 1, 2, and 3 described below, before serological confirmation. These kits give 95 to 98% agreement with conventional tests, although more significant differences occasionally occur. In some instances supplementary tests will be necessary to differentiate further among strains of *Enterobacteriaceae*.

When such kits are not used it is recommended that a sequential pattern of biochemical testing be followed that will result in a great saving of media and time for laboratory personnel. The following schedule of testing is suggested:

PHASE 1: *Urea agar or urea broth*

Urea-positive cultures should be discarded immediately as indicative of the *Proteus* group or other nonpathogenic forms. The urea-negative cultures should be subjected to the biochemical tests of Phase 2. A 24-hr incubation period will be sufficient to indicate most positive cultures. Cultures negative after 24 hr also may be incubated for an additional 24 hr to detect the occasional slow urease-producer.

PHASE 2: *Biochemical tests*

Medium	Purpose of Test
Decarboxylase media	Presence or absence of enzyme system
Citrate	Utilization of citrate as carbon source
TSI	Fermentation pattern; H_2S production
Lactose broth	Fermentation capability
Saccharose broth	Fermentation capability
Salicin broth	Fermentation capability
KCN broth	Growth capability in the presence of CN^- group
SIM	Production of indole, motility, H_2S production
Raffinose broth	Fermentation capability

Conformance to the typical biochemical patterns of the *Salmonella-Shigella* will determine whether the cultures are to be processed further (Phase 3). Aberrant cultures may be encountered that will not satisfy all the classical reactions attributed to each of the pathogenic groups. In all cases, therefore, it will be necessary to review all the reactions as a whole and not to discard cultures on the basis of a small number of apparent anomalies.

PHASE 3: *Fermentation reactions*

Fermentation reactions in dextrose broth, mannitol broth, maltose broth, dulcitol broth, xylose broth, rhamnose broth, and inositol broth are tested to characterize further the biochemical capabilities of the isolates. This additional sorting of the isolates will reduce the possible number of positive cultures that are to be processed for serological confirmation. If the testing laboratory is equipped for flagellar analysis, this series of biochemical tests may be eliminated.

5. Identification by Serological Technics

Serological identification of *Salmonella* or *Shigella* involves complex, highly specialized procedures which, if called for, should be carried out as described by Edwards and Ewing.[6]

912 B.   Immunofluorescence Technic for Detection of *Salmonella*

The direct fluorescent antibody (FA) technic is a rapid and effective means of detecting salmonellae in fresh and seawater samples. It may be used as a screening technic to provide rapid results for large numbers of samples, such as recreational or shellfish harvesting waters. Sample volume used will depend on the degree of contamination. Where gross pollution is present, smaller samples are used. When background information is absent, analyze a 2-l sample.

1. Apparatus for Fluorescence Microscopy

Standard fluorescent antibody microscopy equipment may be obtained separately or in a package containing the essential instrumentation:

a. Light microscope with microscope stand.

b. Very bright light source, providing energy in the short wavelength region of the spectrum. A high-pressure mercury arc enclosed in a quartz envelope satisfies this requirement. A significant por-

tion of the energy should be emitted in the ultraviolet and blue region of the spectrum.

c. Power pack to provide constant voltage output while maintaining constant wattage for the high-pressure mercury bulb. This should include a starter button that ignites the bulb when released.

d. Basic filters including heat-absorbing filter (KG-1 or KG-2, or equivalent); red absorbing filter (BG-38, or equivalent); exciter filter (BG-12, or equivalent, BG-12 being also a blue filter); and barrier filter (OG-1 or blue absorbing filter).

e. Cardioid dark field condenser for illuminating the specimen. A 95 X oil immersion objective with built-in iris diaphragm is desirable. True dark field illumination can be achieved only if the numerical aperture of the objective is smaller than the numerical aperture of the condenser, i.e., of the illuminating cone of light. (Difference in numerical aperture between objective and condenser should be at least 0.05). The numerical aperture of an oil immersion objective usually is reduced by using the built-in diaphragm or by putting a funnel stop into the objective.

2. Reagents for Fluorescent Microscopy

a. Cargille non-drying immersion oil: type A (low fluorescence).*

b. Fluorescent antibody pre-cleaned micro slides: 7.6 by 2.5 cm (3 by 1 in.), 0.8 to 1.0 mm thickness.

c. Cover glass for FA slides: No. 1-1/2, 0.16 to 0.19 mm thickness.

d. FA Kirkpatrick fixative.†

e. Phosphate buffered saline (PBS): Add 10 g of buffer‡ to 1,000 ml freshly prepared distilled water. Stir until the powder dissolves completely. Adjust with NaOH to pH 8.0.

f. FA mounting fluid: Use a standardized reagent-grade glycerine adjusted to pH 9.0 to 9.6 intended for mounting slides to be viewed with the FA microscope.

g. Distilled water: Use double distilled water made from all-glass still.

h. Staining assembly consisting of dish, cover, and slide rack with handle. Five dishes are required, for Kirkpatrick's Fixative; 95% ethanol; first PBS rinse; second PBS rinse; and distilled water.

i. FA Salmonella Panvalent conjugate is a fluorescein conjugated anti-*Salmonella* globulin.§ To rehydrate, add 5 ml distilled water to a vial of conjugate. Determine working dilution (see *5e*). Store unused rehydrated conjugate

in a freezer, preferably at –60 C. Avoid repeated freezing and thawing of conjugate.

j. Moist chamber is used to incubate slides containing smears that have conjugate added to them. A simple chamber consists of water-saturated toweling with a culture dish bottom (150 by 20 mm) placed over the wet toweling.

3. Concentration Technic

Place an absorbent pad on a membrane filter funnel and add sufficient sterile diatomaceous earth ‖ to pack the funnel neck loosely. Filter 2 l of sample. Wash down the funnel with 50 to 100 ml sterile buffered dilution water. Disassemble funnel and remove the resulting "plug" of diatomaceous earth and the absorbent pad. Repeat with a second 2-l sample.

4. Enrichment

Immerse one plug and absorbent pad in a flask containing 300 ml selenite cystine broth. Immerse the second plug and absorbent pad in a flask with 300 ml tetrathionate broth containing 3 ml of 1:1,000 aqueous solution of brilliant green dye and 3 mg of L-cystine. Incubate at 37 C for 24 hr.

5. Fluorescent Antibody Reaction and Analysis

a. Prepare spot plates of brilliant green agar (BGA) and xylose lysine brilliant green agar (XLBG) by placing one drop (about 0.01 ml) of the enrichment medium at each of four separate points on the surface of the agar. The drops on the agar plate should be spaced

---

*R.P. Cargille Laboratories, Inc., Cedar Grove, N.J., or equivalent.

†Difco (No. 3188), or equivalent.

‡Difco Bacto-FA Buffer, Dried, or equivalent.

§Difco, or equivalent.

‖ Celite, Johns Manville Co., or equivalent.

so that an FA microscope slide will cover two inoculation points. This is essential, since glass slide impression smears of the inoculated points will be made after incubation of the plates.

b. Incubate the BGA and XLBG plates at 37 C for 3 hr. After incubation make impression smears by taking a *clean* FA microscope glass slide and placing it over two inoculated points on the medium. Press down lightly, being careful not to move the glass slide horizontally. Do not apply too much pressure, since it will cause movement of the slide and the collection of additional agar on it. Repeat this process for the remaining two inoculation points and for the inoculation points on the second agar medium. Prepare a total of four FA slides.

c. Air-dry the smears and fix for 2 min in Kirkpatrick's fixative. Rinse slides briefly in 95% ethanol and allow to air dry. *Do not blot.*

d. Cover fixed smears with one drop of Salmonella panvalent conjugate. Before use, dilute the commercial conjugate and determine the appropriate working dilution. Experience shows that most batches are effective at a 1:4 dilution. This will vary depending on the type of fluorescence equipment used, light source, alignment, magnification, cultures, etc. Each laboratory must determine the working dilution (titer) of the conjugate.

e. To determine the titer of the conjugate use a known 18- to 24-hr *Salmonella* culture grown in veal infusion broth and make smears on a FA glass slide. Dilute the conjugate and treat as outlined in *c* and *d* above. For example, if the following results were obtained:

Dilution of Conjugate	Fluorescence
1:2	4+
1:4	4+
1:6	4+
1:8	2+
1:10	1+

then a 1:4 dilution of conjugate should be used. Diluting the conjugate reduces cross-reactions to a minimum. Prepare only enough diluted conjugate for use in a day's run.

f. After covering each smear with one drop of the *appropriate dilution of conjugate,* place the slides in a moist chamber to prevent evaporation of the staining reagent. After 30 min wash away excess reagent by dipping the slides into phosphate buffered saline (pH 8.0). Place slides in second bath of buffered saline for 10 min. Remove, rinse in distilled water, and allow to drain dry. *Do not blot.*

g. Place a small drop of mounting fluid (pH 9.0-9.6) on the smear and cover with a No. 1-1/2 coverslip. Seal *edges* of coverslip by using fingernail polish. Sealed slides can be stored for years with minimal losses of fluorescence.

h. Examine under a fluorescence microscope unit fitted with appropriate filters.

6. Recording of Results and Interpretation

The number of organisms fluorescing in any given field is important in assessing positive *Salmonella* smears. If the majority of cells present fluoresce (4+ or 3+) the smear is considered positive. Smears showing only a few scattered fluorescing cells should be scrutinized carefully. Critical examination of cellu-

Reaction	Description	Fluorescence Intensity
Positive	Brilliant yellow-green fluorescence, cells sharply outlined.	4 +
Positive	Bright yellow-green fluorescence, cells sharply outlined with dark center.	3 +
Negative	Dull yellow-green fluorescence, cells not sharply outlined.	2 +
Negative	Faint green fluorescence discernible in dense areas, cells not outlined.	1 +
Negative	No fluorescence.	0

lar morphology may distinguish between these and the *Salmonellae*. In summary, the number of cells fluorescing and the degree of fluorescence are criteria on which positivity is based. Weakly fluorescing cells (2+ and 1+) are considered negative. All positive FA results should be confirmed by conventional cultural technics (see Section 912A).

7. Bibliography

SCHULTE, S.J., J.S. WITZEMAN & W.M. HALL. 1968. Immunofluorescent screening for *Salmonella* in foods: Comparison with culture methods. *J. Amer. Org. Agr. Chem.* 51:1334.

THOMASON, B.M. & J.G. WALLS. 1971. Preparation and testing of polyvalent conjugates for F.A. detection of *Salmonellae. Appl. Microbiol.* 22:876.

THOMASON, B.M. 1971. Rapid detection of *Salmonella* microcolonies by fluorescent antibody. *Appl. Microbiol.* 22:1064.

CHERRY, W.B., J.B. HANKS, B.M. THOMASON, A.M. MURLIN, J.W. BIDDLE & J.M. CROOM. 1972. *Salmonellae* as an index of pollution of surface waters. *Appl. Microbiol.* 24:334.

KATZ, I.J. & F.T. BREZENSKI. 1973. Detection of *Salmonella* by fluorescent antibody.' U.S. EPA, Edison, N.J.

912 C.   Quantitative *Salmonella typhi* Procedure

A quantitative procedure for *Salmonella* is available only when *Salmonella typhi* is suspect. The method utilizes M-bismuth sulfite broth and the membrane filter procedure for bacterial concentration. This method of concentration can be used only with samples low in organic and particulate materials, since quantities of 100 ml or more are generally filtered. After filtration (see Membrane Filter Technic, Section 909A.5), the filter is incubated on a pad containing M-bismuth sulfite broth for 18 to 20 hr at 35 C and transferred to a fresh pad saturated with M-bismuth sulfite broth. Incubation at 35 C is continued, to give a total of 30 hr. Suspected colonies (smooth glistening colonies with jet-black centers surrounded by a thin clear white border) are transferred to triple sugar iron agar (TSI) for incubation at 35 C for 18 hr. Proceed with additional biochemical and serological procedures as described under qualitative methods.

912 D.   Enteropathogenic *Escherichia coli*

Enteropathogenic *E. coli* has been isolated from tap water,[7] drinking water sources,[8] and mountain streams.[9] It is unlikely that *E. coli* organisms could initiate disease by transmission through a properly treated potable water. Additionally, at least in the United States, these organisms reportedly cause disease almost exclusively in infants. Since infants are normally given boiled or sterilized water, waterborne infections by enteropathogenic *E. coli* appear quite improbable.

Examination of potable water supplies for enteropathogenic *E. coli* can be made by use of the membrane filter technic (Section 909 A), preferably with M-FC broth.[10] Pick characteristic blue colonies, purify, and determine IMViC reactions (Section 911 B.). Test IMViC reactive strains $++--$, which produce gas from lactose, by the serological technics of Edwards and Ewing.[6]

Three classes of antigens are important in serological grouping of *E. coli*: the heat-stable and major grouping factor, which is the "O" antigen and is associated with the cell; the envelope or capsule "K" antigen; and the "H" flagellar antigen. Slide agglutination is used for "O" and "K" antigen determinations. The microscopic tube test is recommended for confirmation of "O" antigens.

912 E.   Pathogenic Leptospires

The occurrence of pathogenic leptospires in natural waters is extremely variable. Many factors make interpretation of results difficult, for example, intermittent leptospire discharge from infected wildlife or farm animals and the effects of stormwater runoff and flooding of contaminated land.[11] Persistence in warm, slow-moving waters having a pH of 6.0 to 8.0[12-15] and moderate levels of bacterial nutrients[16] also complicates interpretation. Even when pathogenic leptospires are present, their detection is difficult because of the competitive growth of other organisms[17] and the need to differentiate between pathogenic and saprophytic strains.[13,17-20] Failure to isolate pathogenic leptospires from natural waters does not necessarily indicate their absence.

These factors explain why qualitative methodology has evolved to concentrate leptospires from water. Long-term incubation on various media is necessary because of the relatively slow growth of the organisms. During incubation, inoculated media are checked repeatedly for the appearance of leptospires and for culture contamination. Upon detection, the leptospire isolates must be characterized further by various biochemical and serological tests to separate pathogenic and saprophytic strains. Animal tests for pathogenic leptospires are also recommended but should be done on primary pure-culture isolates since pathogenic strains may become avirulent through subsequent culture passages.

1. Preliminary Concentration Technic

Pathogenic leptospires tend to be concentrated in nearshore bottom sediments of streams and farm ponds. Gently agitate bottom sediment before sampling to insure collection of bacteria-laden material from the sediment-water interface. The bacteriological bottom sampler or standard sample bottles (see Section 906 A) may be used to collect this finely suspended material. Upon return to the laboratory (or preferably at a field site) shake the sample vigorously to release entrapped bacteria from the sediment and prefilter immediately through either a Whatman No. 1 filter paper or a membrane filter absorbent pad. Pass the prefiltered sample through a Swinney hypodermic adapter containing a fiberglass prefilter and a membrane filter of 0.45-μm pore size to separate leptospires (which can pass through the pores into the filtrate) from other organisms present in the sample (which are retained by the membrane filter). Rinse with an equal volume of sterile dilution water.

2. Enrichment

Inoculate portions of sample filtrate (1 ml and 0.1 ml) into Fletcher's semisolid medium containing 10 percent rabbit serum.[21] Incubate the inoculated medium at 30 C for 6 wk. Examine each tube at least weekly for leptospiral growth and culture contamination; use darkfield illumination and 250 × magnification.[22] Strains of *Vibrio, Spirillum,* or *Paraspirillum* are the most common contaminants observed, particularly when filtrate volumes greater than 0.1 ml are examined.[21]

Leptospires are helicoidal, usually 6 to 20 μm long with each coil about 0.2 to 0.3 μm in diameter. The coils of leptospires are more compact than those of other spirochaetes.[22] If leptospires are not observed microscopically within a 6-wk incubation period, consider the test negative.

As an alternate enrichment procedure, inoculate spread plates of SM agar[23] or bovine albumin polysorbate 80 medium[24, 25] with 0.1 to 1.0 ml of sample filtrate. Incubate at 30 C for 7 to 9 days. When bovine albumin polysorbate 80 medium is used, an agar overlay of 0.7% distilled water agar is recommended. Regardless of the choice of agar medium, prepare it 1 to 2 days before inoculation to condition the agar and promote even spreading of the inoculum over the agar surface. Identify all colonies morphologically by darkfield microscopy before conducting biochemical and serological tests or animal inoculations.

3. Differentiation of Leptospires

Detection of pathogenic leptospires in lakes and streams indicates leptospirosis in domestic or wild animals that frequent these waters, and signals a health risk to bathers. It is critically important to differentiate pathogenic from saprophytic leptospire strains.

a. Culture reactions: Saprophytic leptospires grow well in Stuart's medium containing 10% rabbit serum supplemented with 10 μg copper sulfate/ml[14, 15] or 100 μg 8-azaguanine/ml.[12, 15] Only saprophytic leptospires grow in a 10% rabbit serum medium at 13 C.[13] Saprophytic strains demonstrate higher oxidase response[26] and higher egg yolk decomposition activity[27] than pathogenic leptospires. Optimum incubation temperature for pathogenic leptospires is 30 C. All tests must be incubated for 5 days. No single test should be used to differentiate saprophytic from pathogenic leptospires.[28]

b. Verification of pathogenicity: Commercial antisera are available that permit tentative identification of path-ogenic leptospires. Final verification of the suspect pathogenic strain by animal testing should be conducted, but only by laboratories with established expertise in these procedures.

912 F.　Vibrios, *Endamoeba histolytica* Cysts, Hookworm Larvae

Isolation and identification of these organisms require highly specialized procedures. Accordingly, if it is suspected that any of these organisms may be involved in waterborne disease, the services of a medical bacteriologist working in a state or local health department should be requested.

912 G.　References

1. AHMED, Z., I.A. POSHNI & M.A. SIDIQUI. 1964. Bacteriological examination of drinking water of Karachi and isolation of enteric pathogens. *Pakistan J. Sci. Ind. Res.* 7:103.
2. SELIGMANN, R. & R. REITLER. 1965. Enteropathogens in water with low *Esch. coli* titers. *J. Amer. Water Works Ass.* 57:1572.
3. GREENBERG, A.E. & H.J. ONGERTH. 1966. Salmonellosis in Riverside, California. *J. Amer. Water Works Ass.* 58:1145.
4. READ, R.B. & A.L. REYES. 1968. Variation in plating efficiency of Salmonella on eight lots of brilliant green agar. *Appl. Microbiol.* 16:746.
5. KING, S. & W.L. METZGER. 1968. A new medium for the isolation of enteric pathogens. I. Hektoen enteric agar. *Appl. Microbiol.* 16:577.
6. EDWARDS, P.R. & W.H. EWING. 1972. Identification of Enterobacteriaceae, 3rd ed. Burgess Publ. Co., Minneapolis, Minn.
7. EWING, W.H. 1962. Sources of *Escherichia coli* cultures that belong to O-antigen groups associated with infantile diarrheal disease. *J. Infect. Dis.* 110:114.
8. SEIGNEURIN, R., R. MAGNIN & M.L. ACHARD. 1951. Types d'*Escherichia coli* isolés des eaux d'alimentation. *Ann. Inst. Pasteur* 89:473.
9. PETERSEN, N. & J.R. BORING. 1960. A study of coliform densities and *Escherichia coli* serotypes in two mountain streams. *Amer. J. Hyg.* 71:134.
10. GLANTZ, P.J. & T.M. JACKS. 1968. An evaluation of the use of *Escherichia coli* serogroups as a means of tracing microbial pollution of water. *Water Resour. Res.* 4:625.
11. CRAWFORD, R.P., J.M. HEINEMANN, W.F. McCULLOCH & S.L. DIESCH. 1971. Human infections associated with waterborne leptospires, and survival studies on serotype pomona. *J. Amer. Vet. Med. Ass.* 159:1477.
12. GALTON, M.M., R.W. MENGES & J.H. STEELE. 1958. Epidemiological patterns of leptospirosis. *Ann. N.Y. Acad. Sci.* 70:427.
13. JOHNSON, R.C., & V.G. HARRIS. 1967. Differentiation of pathogenic and saprophytic leptospires. I. Growth at low temperatures. *J. Bacteriol.* 94:27.
14. OKAZAKI, W. & L.M. RINGEN. 1957. Some

effects of various environmental conditions on the survival of *Leptospira pomona*. *Amer. J. Vet. Res.* 18:219.

15. Ryu, E. & C.K. Liu. 1966. The viability of leptospires in the summer paddy water. *Jap. J. Microbiol.* 10:51.

16. Diesch, S.L., W.F. McCulloch, J.L. Braun & R.P. Crawford, Jr. 1969. Environmental studies on the survival of leptospires in a farm creek following a human leptospirosis outbreak in Iowa. Proc. Annu. Conf., *Bull. Wildlife Dis. Ass.* 5:166.

17. Chang, S.L., M. Buckingham & M.P. Taylor. 1948. Studies of *Leptospira icterohemorrhagiae* IV. Survival in water and sewage: Destruction in water by halogen compounds, synthetic detergents and heat. *J. Infect. Dis.* 82:256.

18. Johnson, R.C. & P. Rogers. 1964. Differentiation of pathogenic and saprophytic leptospires with 8-azaguanine. *J. Bacteriol.* 88:1618.

19. Fuzi, M. & R. Csoka. 1960. Differentiation of pathogenic and saprophytic leptospire by means of a copper sulfate test. *Zentrabl. Bakteriol. Parasitenk Infektionskr. Hyg. Abt. Orig.*, I. 179:231.

20. Crawford, R.P., J.L. Braun, W.F. McCullogh & S.L. Diesch. 1969. Characterization of leptospires isolated from surface waters in Iowa. *Bull. Wildlife Dis. Ass.* 5:157.

21. Braun, J.L., S.L. Diesch & W.F. McCulloch. 1968. A method for isolating leptospires from natural surface waters. *Can. J. Microbiol.* 14:1011.

22. Turner, L.H. 1970. Leptospirosis III. Maintenance isolation and demonstration of leptospires. *Trans. Roy. Soc. Trop. Med. Hyg.* 64:623.

23. Baseman, J.B., R.C. Henneberry & C.D. Cox. 1966. Isolation and growth of leptospira on artificial media. *J. Bacteriol.* 91:1374.

24. Ellinghausen, H.C., Jr. & W.G. McCullough. 1965. Nutrition of *Leptospira pomona* and growth of 13 other serotypes: Fractionation of oleic albumin complex and a medium of bovine albumin and polysorbate 80. *Amer. J. Vet. Res.* 26:45.

25. Tripathy, D.N. & L.E. Hanson. 1971. Agar overlay medium for broth of leptospires in solid medium. *Amer. J. Vet. Res.* 32:1125.

26. Fuzi, M. & R. Csoka. 1961. Rapid method for the differentiation of parasitic and saprophytic leptospire. *J. Bacteriol.* 81:1008.

27. Fuzi, M. & R. Csoka. 1961. An egg-yolk reaction test for the differentiation of leptospira. *J. Pathol. Bacteriol.* 82:208.

28. Kmety, E., I. Okesji, P. Bakass & B. Chorvath. 1966. Evaluation of methods for differentiating pathogenic and saprophytic leptospira strains. *Ann. Soc. Belge. Med. Trop.* 46:111.

912 H.   Bibliography

Müller, G. 1947. Der Nachweis von Keimen der Typhus-Paratyphusgruppe im Wasser. H.H. Nölke Verlag, Hamburg, Germany.

Clark, H.F., E.E. Geldreich, H.L. Jeter & P.W. Kabler. 1951. The membrane filter in sanitary bacteriology—Culture of *Salmonella typhosa* from water samples on a membrane filter. *Pub. Health Rep.* 66:951.

Greenberg, A.E., R.W. Wickenden & T.W. Lee. 1957. Tracing typhoid carriers by means of sewage. *Sewage Ind. Wastes* 29:1237.

Kabler, P. 1959. Removal of pathogenic microorganisms by sewage treatment processes. *Sewage Ind. Wastes* 31:1373.

McCoy, J.H. 1964. Salmonella in crude sewage, sewage effluent, and sewage polluted natural waters. In: Int. Conf. Water Pollut. Res., 1st, London, 1962. Vol. 1:205, Macmillan, New York, N.Y.

BREZENSKI, F.T., R. RUSSOMANNO & P. DE-FALCO, JR. 1965. The occurrence of *Salmonella* and *Shigella* in post-chlorinated and nonchlorinated sewage effluents and receiving waters. *Health Lab. Sci.* 2:40.

TAYLOR, W.I. 1965. Isolation of Shigellae, I. Xylose-lysine agars; new media for isolation on enteric pathogens. *Amer. J. Clin. Pathol.* 44:471.

TAYLOR, W.I., & B. HARRIS. 1965. Isolation of Shigella, II. Comparison of plating media and enrichment broths. *Amer. J. Clin. Pathol.* 44:476.

RAJ, H. 1966. Enrichment medium for selection of Salmonella from fish homogenate. *Appl. Microbiol.* 14:12.

SPINO, D.E. 1966. Elevated-temperature technique for the isolation of *Salmonella* from streams. *Appl. Microbiol.* 14:591.

BREZENSKI, F.T. & R. RUSSOMANNO. 1968. The detection and use of Salmonella in studying polluted tidal estuaries: A correlation of coliform and fecal coliform indices with the presence of Salmonella in shellfish and overlying waters. Presented at the 41st Annual Conference, WPCF, Chicago, Ill. (Sept. 22-27).

GALTON, M.M., G.K. MORRIS & W.T. MARTIN. 1968. Salmonella in foods and feeds. Review of isolation methods and recommended procedures. PHS Bureau of Disease Prevention & Environmental Control, NCDC, Atlanta, Ga.

TAYLOR, W.I. & D. SCHELHART. 1968. Isolation of Shigella. V. Comparison of enrichment broths and stools. *Appl. Microbiol.* 16:1383.

TAYLOR, W.I. & D. SCHELHART. 1968. Isolation of Shigella. VI. Performance of media with stool specimens. *Appl. Microbiol.* 16:1387.

913　DETECTION OF ENTERIC VIRUSES IN WATER AND WASTEWATER

Viruses excreted with feces or urine from any species of animal may pollute water. Especially numerous, and of particular importance to health, are the viruses that infect the gastrointestinal tract of man and are excreted with the feces of infected individuals. These viruses are present in domestic sewage which, after various degrees of treatment, enters waterways to become a part of the rivers and streams that serve as the source of water for most large communities. The viruses known to be excreted in relatively large numbers with feces include polioviruses, coxsackieviruses, echoviruses, adenoviruses, reoviruses, and the virus(es) of infectious hepatitis. Each group or subgroup consists of a number of different serological types so that more than 100 different human enteric viruses are recognized. Other viruses may be present in human excretions, but not usually in large numbers.[1-5]

Most of the enteric viruses, probably transmitted most frequently by the fecal-oral route, may be found in sewage predominantly during the warmer months of the year. Infectious hepatitis virus(es) may be an important exception because the incidence of the disease it produces increases in the colder months. No etiological agent of this disease has been isolated yet.

Viruses are not normal flora in the intestinal tract; they are excreted only by infected individuals, mostly young preschool and school-age children. Infection rates vary considerably from area to area, depending on sanitary and socioeconomic conditions. Viruses are usually excreted in numbers several orders of magnitude lower than those of coliform bacteria; because viruses multiply only within living susceptible cells, their numbers cannot increase in sewage. Sewage treatment, dilution, natural inactivation, and water treatment further reduce viral numbers by the time water is consumed for drinking purposes. Thus, although large outbreaks of waterborne viral disease may occur when massive sewage contamination of a water supply takes place,[6] transmission of viral infection and disease in technologically advanced nations depends on whether minimal quantities of viruses are capable of producing infections. It has been demonstrated that infection can be produced by a very few virus units.[7] However, the risk of infection incurred by the individual in a community with a water supply containing a very few virus units has not been determined.[2]

It has been argued that transmission of small numbers of viruses through water supplies may produce inapparent infections. However, the subsequent transmission of viruses from these inapparent infections to contacts probably involves large quantities of viruses. This may result in a considerable amount of disease transmission in a community, epidemiologically consistent with contact and not with transmission from a common source (e.g., water).

Direct demonstration and quantitation of viruses in relatively clean or finished waters requires sample concentration because the numbers present are likely to be small; thus, volumes of 400 l or more of such waters must be sampled to increase the probability of detection. Quantitation of viruses in wastewater and natural waters is more difficult be-

cause of suspended particulates. For such samples, the aqueous polymer two-phase separation technic may be used directly as a primary method for virus recovery.[8] When this is the sole method used, sample size is limited to 2 to 4 l.[8,9]

The most promising method[10] for concentrating small quantities of viruses, i.e., one infectious unit or less/4 l, from volumes of 400 l or more of water depends on adsorbing viruses to microporous filters as originally described by Metcalf[11] and adapted to water by Cliver[12] and Hoff and Jakubowski.[13] Subsequent development and application of the microporous filter virus adsorption technic has been described by Wallis and Melnick[14,15] and Rao and Labzoffsky.[16] Water is passed under pressure through 293-mm-diam microporous filters to which viruses adsorb. Adsorption of many of the enteroviruses occurs at pH 3.5 to 4.5. The presence of cations, i.e., Mg^{2+} or Al^{3+}, has been recommended,[17] but the conditions under which cations might be needed to enhance virus adsorption have not been determined unequivocally. Viruses may be eluted from microporous filters by pressure-filtering in situ with an alkaline protein solution. Nutrient broth, at a concentration five times the usual and pH 9.0, has been used successfully,[18] as have 3% beef extract and 10% bovine serum in borate buffer at pH 9.0.[19-21] One disadvantage of the protein eluants is that they cannot be reconcentrated readily by simple technics. For this reason, 0.05 M glycine buffer at pH 11.5 is the recommended eluant. The resulting eluate may be reconcentrated simply and rapidly by further filtration followed by elution with smaller volumes.[22]

The microporous filter technic is the most quantitative method available but it does have limitations, particularly when the sample is turbid. The problem of filtering large volumes of turbid water is eased by the addition of filter aid to the sample.[23] Wallis and coworkers[21] have developed a portable virus concentrator device that consists of several yarn-wound clarifying filters coupled with a 293-mm size membrane filter that shows promise for recovering enteric viruses from large volumes of tap water heavily contaminated with suspended solids. More recently, Wallis and coworkers[24] modified the portable virus concentrator device and are using a fiberglass textile depth filter or a cellulose acetate filter as the virus adsorbent. A commercial device that both concentrates the viruses from the water sample and elutes them for subsequent virological examination is available.*

For those who must determine the virus content of waters quantitatively, the microporous filter technic is recommended as a tentative procedure because the equipment is commercially available at a moderate cost, the method has been investigated by a number of workers, and it has been determined to satisfy, tentatively, the basic criteria for a good method by being simple, rapid, sensi-

tive, and reliable.[9, 11, 12, 14, 20, 25] For waters that are grossly polluted and highly turbid, the aqueous polymer two-phase separation technic offers certain advantages over the microporous filter technic, particularly from the standpoint of economy of application. For potable waters, the microporous filter technic presently holds the most promise for detecting viruses occurring at extremely low concentrations.

The microporous filter technic has been evaluated primarily with attenuated strains of poliovirus in a limited variety of waters. Since inherent differences in water quality with respect to dissolved and suspended materials do exist, the examination of a particular water with the tentative procedure should include an evaluation of virus recovery efficiency with that water. This may be accomplished by the addition of known quantities of a given virus to the required volume of the selected water with subsequent processing of the sample. The routine examination of potable water or wastewater for enteric viruses is not recommended at the present time. A tentative method for the examination of finished water is included because the human health concern for viruses in water is primarily with potable water. Nevertheless, in special circumstances, e.g., wastewater reclamation, disease outbreaks, or special research studies, it may be prudent to initiate virus testing but then only by competent virologists having adequate facilities.

---

*Aquella™, available from Water Management Group, The Carborundum Co., Niagara Falls, N.Y. 14302.

913 A.   Microporous Filter Technic for Enteric Virus Concentration and Detection in Finished Waters (TENTATIVE)

1. Laboratory Apparatus

   a. Virus-concentrator apparatus[26] *(Figure 913:1):*
   1) Virus-adsorbent filter holders.*
   2) Fluid Proportioner, duplex model and mixing chamber.†
   3) Pressure-relief valve.
   4) Water flow-meter.

   5) Pressure gauge.
   6) Pressure hose and connections.
   7) 20-l (5-gal) containers.
   b. Laboratory balance.
   c. pH meter.
   d. 1,500-ml beakers.
   e. Vertical-flow laminar-air hood.
   f. 4-l (1-gal) pressure vessel.

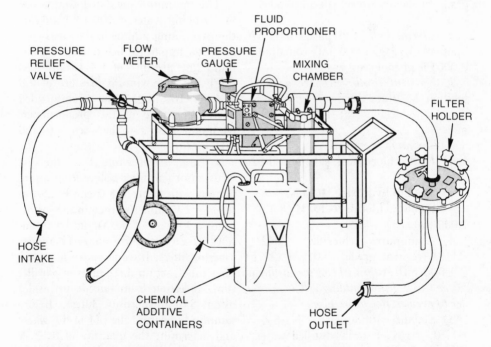

Figure 913:1. Diagrammatic view of the virus-concentrator apparatus. Ancillary component parts are shown mounted on a two-wheeled dolly constructed of angle iron. Note: Use stainless steel fittings for all connections.

---

*293 mm membrane filter holder, Millipore Corp.; Series 710 filter holder, Cox Instrument Div. Lynch Corp.; or Balston polycarbonate bowl type 92, with stainless steel support cores, Balston, Inc.

†Johanson & Son Machine Corp., Clifton, N.J., or equivalent.

Sterilize the proportioner section of the apparatus by rinsing thoroughly with a solution containing 25 mg/l free chlorine and then allowing the chlorine solution to remain within the proportioner section for at least 30 min. Sterilize all glassware and other sampling apparatus, including the virus-adsorbent filter holder setups, by autoclaving at 121 C for 45 min. At the sampling site, rinse the proportioner section with source water until it is free from residual chlorine, then connect the selected virus-adsorbent filter holder. Use aseptic technic during all operations.

2. Materials and Reagents

All reagents should be analytical grade or better unless specified otherwise.

a. Glycine buffer: Prepare a 0.05 *M* solution (3.75 g/1,000 ml) containing 0.0005% phenol red.

b. Nutrient broth: Prepare a stock solution 10 times usual strength. Sterilize by autoclaving at 121 C for 15 min.

c. Inorganic chemicals:

1) Hydrochloric acid, 0.12 *N* and 12 *N*.

2) Sodium hydroxide, 10.0 *N*.

3) Sodium chloride, 0.15 *M* (8.7 g/1,000 ml).

4) Aluminum chloride, $AlCl_3 \cdot 6H_2O$ (reagent grade), 0.05 *M* (21.1 g/1,000 ml). *Adjust pH of the distilled water to 3.5 before adding $AlCl_3$ in order to prevent floc formation.*

5) Sodium thiosulfate, $Na_2S_2O_3 \cdot 5H_2O$, 5 g/l of sterile distilled water. (Prepare 5 l for each 400-l sample).

d. Virus adsorbents: Use 293-mm cellulose nitrate membranes‡ of 8.0 and 1.2 μm porosity, or 267-mm epoxy-fiberglass-asbestos filters of 5.0 and 1.0 μm porosity,§ or epoxy-fiberglass filter

tubes of 8.0 μm porosity.‖ Use 47-mm epoxy-fiberglass-asbestos filters§ for re-concentration, adsorption, and elution. Porosities of 5.0, 1.0, and 0.45 μm are required.

e. Eluant: Add 5.4 ml of 10.0 *N* NaOH/l of 0.05 *M* glycine buffer to obtain a pH of 11.3 to 11.5. Add 12 ml of 12 *N* HCl/l of 0.05 *M* glycine buffer to obtain a pH of 1.1 to 1.5. Use both buffers within 2 hr after pH adjustment.

3. Procedures

The minimum suggested sample size for drinking water is 400 l.# Calibrate the two dosing pumps of the virus-concentrator apparatus before use. A minimum line pressure of 1.4 kg/cm² (20 psig) and a maximum pressure of 7.0 kg/cm² (100 psig) is the recommended operating range of the proportioner. Maintain flow rate between 4.0 and 10.0 l/min.

a. Sample collection: Load the disc virus-adsorbent filter holder from top to bottom with either a 8.0 μm+1.2 μm stack of 293-mm-size membrane (nitrocellulose) filters or a 5.0 μm+1.0 μm stack of 267-mm-size epoxy-fiberglass-asbestos filters. If using epoxy-fiberglass filter tubes, set up three units in parallel (flow direction from outside to inside) using 8.0-μm-porosity filters. Before sampling, measure the pH of the water and determine the quantity of 0.12 *N* HCl required to adjust the pH of 1 l to 3.5. Add an equal volume of 12 *N* HCl to each liter of acid-dosing solution. (Prepare 5 l of acid-dosing solution for each 400 l sample). Adjust the acid-dos-

---

‡Millipore filter or equivalent.
§AA Cox M-780 or equivalent.

‖ Balston filters or equivalent.
#Samples of 2,000 l (500 gal) may be necessary to detect 1 to 2 infectious virus units/400 l.[27]

ing pump of the proportioner to give a final dilution of 1:100. At the same time, adjust the other proportioner dosing pump to add the sodium thiosulfate solution to a final dilution of 1:100. Flame the spigot and connect the proportioner section to it. Rinse free of chlorine. Connect the virus-adsorbent filter holder to the proportioner section, read the flow meter, and turn on the water. Periodically check the filtrate to assure that the pH is 3.5 and that there is no residual chlorine. After filtering the sample, read the flow meter, disconnect the filter holder, pack in ice** and transport to the laboratory for virus elution.

b. Elution of virus from microporous filters: Use aseptic technic for elution procedures and carry out elution in a vertical-flow laminar-air hood. Remove residual water (usually about 200 ml) from the void area in the disc filter holders by applying air pressure to the filter holder. Discard the residual water. Drain residual water from the Balston units by opening the manual drain valve at the bottom of each unit. Add 1 l of 0.05 M glycine (pH 11.5) eluant to a 4-l pressure vessel connected to the inlet of the filter holder. Open pressure-release valve on the disc filter holders. Apply pressure to the system. When the void area of the filter holder is full (as evidenced by the appearance of eluant), close the pressure-release valve and filter the remaining eluant through the filter (complete filtration within 2 min). For the Balston units, apply pressure and permit the eluant to fill the chambers in the upright position (outside to inside direction of flow). After the chambers are

filled, invert the units until elution is complete. (NOTE: It has been found advantageous to re-filter the eluates simultaneously during elution by passing the primary eluates through a single 0.9-µm-porosity Balston unit in order to facilitate the reconcentration step; see *3c* below). Collect the eluate in a sterile 1,500-ml beaker. During eluate collection, *immediately* add portions of 0.05 M glycine buffer (pH 1.1) to reduce eluate pH from 11.5 to about 9.5.

c. Reconcentration of primary eluate: Reconcentrate the primary eluate as follows: adjust pH of eluate to 3.5 with 0.05 M glycine (pH 1.1); add 0.05 M AlCl$_3$ to give a final concentration of 0.0005 M; and filter the eluate through a stack of 47-mm size AA Cox M-780 fiberglass filters (or equivalent). From top to bottom, use filter porosities of 5.0 and 1.0 µm. After filtration, rinse the filters with 25 ml of 0.15 M sodium chloride solution (pH 3.5). For the elution step aseptically add a sterile 0.45 µm porosity filter under the 1.0 µm porosity filter. Re-elute the virus with two 7.0-ml portions of 0.05 M glycine buffer (pH 11.5). Collect the final eluate in a solution containing 2.5 ml of 0.05 M glycine buffer (pH 1.1 to 1.5), 1.5 ml of 10× Hanks Balanced Salt solution, and 2.0 ml of 10× nutrient broth or 2.0 ml of a 20% fetal calf serum. Add appropriate antibiotics and adjust pH to 7.4 for cell culture assay (final volume will be approximately 20 ml).

d. Assay of sample-concentrates for viruses: Conduct all virus assay procedures in a vertical-flow laminar-air hood. A complete virus assay system will require several cell culture types and the use of suckling mice for isolation

---

**Caution:* Seal off openings of the filter holder to prevent filter contamination.

of most of the coxsackievirus group A serotypes. The use of mice as well as the selection of specific cell cultures is left to the discretion of the virologist. Primary African Green monkey kidney cells and human embryonic kidney cells are recommended unless evidence is available indicating that suitable substitute cells have equivalent spectral sensitivity for enteric virus replication. Include uninoculated cell culture controls with each cell culture type.

Assay the entire sample-concentrate for virus. When suckling mice are used, inoculate at least two litters. Inoculate the remaining sample-concentrate onto the cell culture monolayers at a volume not to exceed 0.06 ml/cm^2 of cell surface area, e.g., the 18 to 20-ml sample-concentrate could be distributed equally onto three 60-cm^2 cell surface area bottles of each of two cell types. After an adsorption period of 2 hr at 36 ± 0.5 C, decant the inoculum and add maintence medium to the cells. Incubate the cell culture monolayers at 36 ± 0.5 C and observe microscopically, daily for the first 3 days and then periodically, for cytopathic effects (CPE) for 14 days. Do not change the medium during the holding period unless it is necessary to maintain healthy cells. Freeze and thaw once cell cultures that are negative for CPE (including cell controls) on the 14th day. Pool the harvest-fluids from a single cell culture type. Passage 20% of the pooled harvest-fluid to a second cell culture monolayer of the same cell culture type. Cell cultures negative for CPE on the 14th day of the second passage are considered negative for virus. Confirm all cell cultures positive for CPE for virus by additional passages. Identify virus isolates by appropriate serologic procedures.

When suckling mice are used, they should be less than 24 hr old. Inoculate a portion of the original sample-concentrate into 2 litters or more of suckling mice by the intraperitoneal (0.05 ml), and the intracerebral (0.02 ml) routes. Examine mice daily for 14 days. Mice exhibiting no pathology by the 14th day of the first passage are considered negative for coxsackievirus group A. Sacrifice mice exhibiting any pathology (e.g. flaccid or spastic paralysis of the extremities) and passage a second time in suckling mice (following those procedures outlined in Diagnostic Procedures for Viral and Rickettsial Diseases[28]).

913 B.   References

1. BERG, G. 1966. Virus transmission by the water vehicle. I. Viruses. *Health Lab. Sci.* 3:86.

2. BERG, G. 1966. Virus transmission by the water vehicle. II. Virus removal by sewage treatment procedures. *Health Lab. Sci.* 3:90.

3. BERG, G. 1966. Virus transmission by the water vehicle. III. Removal of viruses by water treatment procedures. *Health Lab. Sci.* 3:170.

4. CLARKE, N.A. & S.L. CHANG. 1959. Enteric viruses in water. *J. Amer. Water Works Ass.* 51:1299.

5. CLARKE, N.A., G. BERG, P.W. KABLER & S.L. CHANG. 1962 and 1964. Human enteric viruses in water: Source, survival and removability. In: Int. Conf. Water Pollut.

Res., 1st, London, 1962. Proc. Vol. 2:523. Macmillan, New York, N.Y.

6. VISWANATHAN, R. 1957. Epidemiology. *Indian J. Med. Res.* 45:1 (supplementary number).

7. PLOTKIN, S.A. & M. KATZ. 1967. Minimal infective doses of viruses for man by the oral route. In: Transmission of Viruses by the Water Route, G. Berg, ed. Interscience Publ., New York, N.Y.

8. SHUVAL, H.I. 1969. Detection and control of enteroviruses in the water environment. In: Developments in Water Quality Research. Ann Arbor-Humphrey Sci. Publ., Ann Arbor, Mich.

9. HILL, W.F., JR., E.W. AKIN & W.H. BENTON. 1971. Detection of viruses in water: A review of methods and application. *Water Res.* 5:967.

10. BERGER, B.B., (Chmn.) COMMITTEE ON ENVIRONMENTAL QUALITY MANAGEMENT. 1970. Engineering evaluation of virus hazard in water. *Jour. San. Eng. Div., Proc. Amer. Soc. Civil Eng.* 96:111.

11. METCALF, T.G. 1961. Use of membrane filters to facilitate the recovery of virus from aqueous suspensions. *Appl. Microbiol.* 9:376.

12. CLIVER, D.O. 1967. Enterovirus detection by membrane chromatography. In: Transmission of Viruses by the Water Route, G. Berg, ed. Interscience Publ., New York, N.Y.

13. HOFF, J.C. & W. JAKUBOWSKI. 1966. Studies on membrane filtration of bacteriophage. In: 1965 Proceedings Northwest Shellfish Sanitation Research Planning Conference. USPHS Publ. No. 999-FP-6, Environmental Health Ser., Food Protection.

14. WALLIS, C. & J.L. MELNICK. 1967. Concentration of enteroviruses on membrane filters. *J. Virol.* 1:472.

15. WALLIS, C. & J.L. MELNICK. 1967. Concentration of viruses from sewage by adsorption on Millipore membranes. *Bull. World Health Org.* 36:219.

16. RAO, N.U. & N.A. LABZOFFSKY. 1969. A simple method for the detection of low concentration of viruses in large volumes of water by the membrane filter technique. *Can. J. Microbiol.* 15:399.

17. WALLIS, C., M. HENDERSON & J.L. MELNICK. 1972. Enterovirus concentration on cellulose membranes. *Appl. Microbiol.* 23:476.

18. HILL, W.F., JR., E.W. AKIN, W.H. BENTON & T.G. METCALF. 1972. Virus in water. II. Evaluation of membrane cartridge filters for recovering low multiplicities of poliovirus from water. *Appl. Microbiol.* 23:880.

19. BERG, G., D.R. DAHLING & D. BERMAN. 1971. Recovery of small quantities of viruses from clean waters on cellulose nitrate membrane filters. *Appl. Microbiol.* 22:608.

20. RAO, V.C., U. CHANDORKAR, N.U. RAO, P. KUMARAN & S.B. LAKHE. 1972. A simple method for concentrating and detecting viruses in wastewater. *Water Res.* 6:1565.

21. WALLIS, C., A. HOMMA & J.L. MELNICK. 1972. Apparatus for concentrating viruses from large volumes. *J. Amer. Water Works Ass.* 64:189.

22. SOBSEY, M.D., C. WALLIS, M. HENDERSON & J.L. MELNICK. 1973. Concentration of enteroviruses from large volumes of water. *Appl. Microbiol.* 26:529.

23. HILL, W.F., JR., E.W. AKIN, W.H. BENTON, C.J. MAYHEW & T.G. METCALF. 1974. Recovery of poliovirus from turbid estuarine water on microporous filters by the use of celite. *Appl. Microbiol.* 27:506.

24. WALLIS, C., A. HOMMA & J.L. MELNICK. 1972. A portable virus concentrator for testing water in the field. *Water Res.* 6:1249.

25. JAKUBOWSKI, W., J.C. HOFF, N.C. ANTHONY & W.F. HILL, JR. 1974. Epoxy-fiberglass adsorbent for concentrating viruses from large volumes of potable water. *Appl. Microbiol.* 28:501.

26. HILL, W.F., JR., E.W. AKIN, W.H. BENTON, C.J. MAYHEW & W. JAKUBOWSKI. 1974. Apparatus for conditioning unlimited quantities of finished waters for enteric virus detection. *Appl. Microbiol.* 27:1177.

27. CLARKE, N.A., W.F. HILL, JR. & W. JAKUBOWSKI. 1974. Detection of viruses in water: Tentative standard method. Proc. AWWA Water Quality Technology Conf. Dec. 1-4, 1974, Dallas, Tex.

28. MELNICK, J.L., H.A. WENNER & L. ROSEN. 1964. The Enteroviruses. In: Diagnostic Procedures for Viral and Rickettsial Diseases, E.H. Lennette & N.J. Schmidt, eds. 3rd ed., American Public Health Association, New York, N.Y. pp. 217-218.

914   BACTERIOLOGICAL EXAMINATION OF RECREATIONAL WATERS

Recreational waters can be categorized as "fresh-water swimming pools" and "naturally" occurring fresh and marine surface waters. Historically, they have been examined for coliform bacteria and/or Standard Plate Count. The approach taken herein has been to describe acceptable, available methods for the microorganisms most frequently suggested as indicators of recreational water quality. In addition, the type of water being examined must be considered in the selection of the microbiological method to be used.

914 A.   Swimming Pools

A swimming pool is a body of water of limited size contained in a holding structure. The modern pool has a recirculating system so that the water can be filtered and disinfected. Microorganisms of concern are typically those from the bather's body and its orifices. Water quality depends on the efficacy of disinfection, the number of bathers in the pool at any one time, and the total number of bathers per day.

Residual levels of disinfectant should be determined periodically. Microbiological testing is directed at (a) evaluating the disinfection process; (b) obtaining a measure of the effects of bather density, that is, the potential for pathogen transmission; (c) enumerating fecal contamination; and (d) enumerating pathogens that derive from the skin and respiratory tract of the bather or that can multiply in waters low in nutrients. These objectives can be accomplished by measuring (a) the total viable bacterial density as determined by the Standard Plate Count; (b) the total number of staphylococci; (c) the total coliform density; and (d) the numbers of *Staphylococcus aureus* and *Pseudomonas aeruginosa*. The determination of *S. aureus*

and *P. aeruginosa* densities may be the most important measurements made, because skin, ear, eye, nose, and throat infections account for a large percentage of swimming-pool-associated illnesses and because these two organisms are relatively resistant to the effect of chlorine.

1. Samples

a. Containers: Samples for bacteriologic examination of swimming pool waters should be collected as directed in Section 906A (Samples, Collection). Containers of from 120 to 480 ml (4 to 16 oz) capacity may be used, depending on the analyses to be made. Sodium thiosulfate should be added in an amount sufficient to provide an approximate concentration of 100 mg/l in the sample. This can be accomplished by adding from 0.1 ml to a 120-ml (4-oz) bottle to 0.4 ml to a 480-ml (16-oz) bottle of 10% solution of sodium thiosulfate (this will neutralize about 15 mg of residual chlorine/l). The bottle is then stoppered, capped, and sterilized as outlined in Section 904.2.

b. Sampling procedure: Samples always should be collected in the area of, and during the time of, maximum bather density. Information on the bathing load also will be helpful in subsequent interpretation of laboratory results. To collect sample, carefully remove the cap and hold the sterile bottle near its base and at a 45-deg angle. Fill, in one slow sweep down through the water with the mouth of the bottle always ahead of the hand, making sure that the dechlorinating agent is not lost from the bottle. Care should be taken to avoid contamination of the specimen by floating debris.

It is essential that the residual chlorine or other disinfectant be determined at poolside, at the time of sample collection. If the residual chlorine level exceeds 15 mg/l, additional sodium thiosulfate must be added to the sample bottle before collection of the sample.

c. Sample storage: The samples should be refrigerated immediately upon collection and held at less than 10 C during transport to the laboratory. The samples should be tested within 6 hr of collection.

2. Standard Plate Count

The total bacterial count should be determined as directed under Standard Plate Count, Section 907. At least two plates per dilution should be used.

3. Tests for Total Coliforms

Tests for total coliforms should be performed as directed under the Multiple-Tube Fermentation Technic (Section 908) or the Membrane Filter Technic (Section 909).

4. Tests for *S. aureus*

Methods that could be used to enumerate the relatively low densities of *S. aureus* found in swimming pool waters are available. They have not been included here because there are insufficient data documenting their accuracy, selectivity, specificity, sensitivity, and precision when applied to the examination of swimming pool waters.

5. Tests for Other Organisms

Tests for other organisms are presented below in Sections 914C, D, and E. They include a membrane filter procedure for staphylococcus and a membrane filter and multiple-tube technic for *P. aeruginosa*.

914 B.   Natural Bathing Beaches

A natural bathing beach may be defined as any shoreline area of a stream, ocean, or inland lake that is used for recreation. A wide variety of pathogenic microorganisms are potentially transmissible to man through his use of natural fresh and marine recreational waters that may be contaminated by wastewater. These include: (*a*) enteropathogenic agents, such as salmonellae, shigellae, enteroviruses, and multicellular parasites; (*b*) human pathogens or "opportunists", such as *P. aeruginosa, Klebsiella, Vibrio parahemolyticus,* and *Aeromonas hydrophila,* which may multiply in recreational waters in the presence of sufficient nutrients; (*c*) organisms carried into the water from the skin and upper orifices of the recreationists, such as *S. aureus,* and (*d*) other organisms arising from a variety of sources, which are either less frequently encountered or found under restricted environmental conditions, e.g., pathogenic mycobacteria and leptospira, *Pasteurella tularensis,* and pathogenic *Naegleria* species (amoebic meningoencephalitis; these organisms may also be found in swimming pools).

Methods suitable for the routine examination of recreational waters are not currently available for most of the above organisms. Even with the methods described herein, and particularly with reference to the marine environment, there may be local conditions that compromise the accuracy or selective and differential characteristics of these methods.

The best available bacteriologic method for monitoring fecal contamination of naturally occurring recreational waters is the fecal coliform test. Total coliform measurements may be used as an alternative; however, such data are subject to a wide range of density fluctuations of doubtful sanitary significance.

The most valuable application of the fecal streptococcus test is in the development of fecal coliform:fecal streptococcus ratios. Fecal coliform:fecal streptococcus ratios of 4.0 or higher typically indicate domestic waste while ratios of 0.6 or lower are common to discharges from farm animals or stormwater runoff. Because several bio-

types of *S. faecalis* are known to be ubiquitous in the environment, it may be difficult to interpret the sanitary significance of densities of fecal streptococci below 100 organisms/100 ml.

Methods are available for *P. aeruginosa, Salmonella,* and *Klebsiella.* The enumeration of *P. aeruginosa* and *Klebsiella* species in recreational waters can be of considerable value with reference to the discharge of highly nutritive wastes into receiving waters, e.g., pulp mill wastes, effluents from textile finishing plants, etc.

1. Samples

a. Containers: Samples for bacteriologic examination should be collected as directed in Section 906 A. The size of the container will vary with the number and variety of tests to be performed. Addition of sodium thiosulfate to the bottle is unnecessary.

b. Sampling procedure: Collect samples just below the surface of the water in the areas of greatest bather density. Samples should be taken over the range of environmental and climatic conditions, especially during times when maximal pollution can be expected, i.e., periods of stormwater runoff, sewage by-passing, tidal, current, and wind influences, etc. The method of sample collection is given in Section 914A.1*b*.

c. Sample storage: As prescribed in the section on Swimming Pools. (Section 914A.1).

2. Tests for Fecal Coliforms

Tests for fecal coliforms should be performed as directed under the Multiple-Tube Fermentation Technic (Section 908C) or the Membrane Filter Technic (Section 909C).

3. Tests for Total Coliforms

Tests for total coliforms should be performed as directed under the Multiple-Tube Fermentation Technic (Section 908) or the Membrane Filter Technic (Section 909).

4. Tests for Fecal Streptococci

Tests for fecal streptococci should be performed as directed under Multiple-Tube Technic (Section 910A) or Membrane Filter Technic (Section 910B).

5. Tests for *Pseudomonas aeruginosa*

Tests for *P. aeruginosa* should be performed as directed below. The multiple-tube test is necessary for use with turbid samples.

6. Tests for Salmonella

Tests for salmonella can be performed as recommended in Section 912.

7. Tests for Enterovirus

Tests for enteroviruses can be performed as recommended in Section 913.

8. Tests for *Klebsiella*

Tests for *Klebsiella* should be made as directed under *Klebsiella* Differentiation, Section 911C.

914 C.   Membrane Filter Procedure for Staphylococci (TENTATIVE)

1. Laboratory Apparatus

Refer to membrane filter assembly and laboratory apparatus under Standard Total Coliform Membrane Filter Procedure (Section 909A.)

2. Materials and Culture Media

Refer to Chapman-Stone Agar in Section 905C.26.

3. Procedure

a. Filter 10- and 100-ml quantities of the sample through sterile membrane filters (see Section 909A for filtering procedure). Transfer the filters directly to plates so that there are no air bubbles between the filter and the surface of the agar.

b. Invert plates and incubate at 35 ± 0.5 C for 48 hr.

c. Count all colonies that develop except those that are extremely mucoid or rough; these latter colonies are rare and are usually spore-formers. An appropriate optical device, such as a low-power dissecting microscope, may be used to aid in colony counting. Where possible, the count should be obtained from filters containing 20 to 80 colonies.

4. Confirmation

Confirmation generally is not required. Questionable colonies may be verified as staphylococci by the Gram stain (Gram positive), microscopic morphology, the catalase test (positive), and the fermentation of dextrose with the production of acid.

5. Interpretation and Calculation of Density

Calculate and record as the number of staphylococci/100 ml.

914 D.   Membrane Filter Technic for *Pseudomonas aeruginosa* (TENTATIVE)

1. Laboratory Apparatus

Refer to membrane filter assembly and laboratory apparatus under Standard Total Coliform Membrane Filter Procedure (Section 909 A).

2. Culture Media

Refer to Media Specifications, M-PA and milk agar (Section 905C.27 and 28).

3. Procedure

a. Filter 200 ml or smaller portions of natural waters or up to 500 ml of swimming pool waters through sterile membrane filters. Place each membrane on a poured plate of M-PA agar so that there is no air space between the membrane and surface of the agar.

b. Invert the plates and incubate at 41.5 ± 0.5 C for 48 hr.

c. Typically, *P. aeruginosa* colonies are 0.8 to 2.2 mm in diameter and flat in appearance with light outer rims and brownish to greenish-black centers. Count the typical colonies, preferably from filters containing 20 to 80 colonies. A 10- to 15-power magnifier may be used as an aid in colony counting.

4. Confirmation

Confirm a number of typical and atypical colonies by use of milk agar. Make a single streak (2 to 4 cm long) from an isolated colony on a milk agar plate, which is incubated at 35 C for 24 hr. *P. aeruginosa* hydrolyzes the casein and produces a yellowish to green diffusible pigment.

5. Interpretation and Calculation of Density

Except as noted above, confirmation will not be required routinely. In the absence of confirmation, results should be reported as "presumptive". Calculate and record as the number of *P. aeruginosa*/100 ml.

914 E.   Multiple-Tube Technic for *Pseudomonas aeruginosa* (TENTATIVE)

1. Laboratory Apparatus

Refer to Multiple-Tube Technic for total coliforms (Section 908).

2. Materials and Culture Media

Refer to asparagine broth and acetamide medium in Section 905C.29 and 30.

3. Procedure

a. Presumptive test: Inoculate five 10-ml, five 1-ml, and five 0.1-ml samples into asparagine broth. Use 10 ml of single-strength broth for inocula of 1 ml or less and 10 ml of double-strength broth for 10-ml inocula. For artificial swimming pools these sample sizes are usually adequate; for natural recreational waters, higher dilutions may be necessary. Incubate inoculated tubes at 35 to 37 C. After 24 and again after 48 hr of incubation, examine tubes under long-wave ultraviolet light (black light) in a darkened room. Production of a greenish fluorescent pigment constitutes a positive presumptive test.

b. Confirmed test: Confirm positive tubes of asparagine broth by inoculating 0.1 ml of the culture into acetamide broth or onto the surface of acetamide agar slants. A positive confirmed reaction is the development of a high pH as indicated by a purple color within 24 to 36 hr of incubation at 35 to 37 C.

c. Computing and recording MPN: Refer to Table 908:II and to Estimation of Bacterial Density, Section 908 D.

914 F.   Bibliography

ROBINTON, E.D., E.W. MOOD & L.R. ELLIOTT. 1957. A study of bacterial flora in swimming pool water treated with high-free residual chlorine. *Amer. J. Pub. Health* 47:1101.

MALLMAN, W.L. 1962. Cocci test for detecting mouth and nose pollution of swimming pool waters. *Amer. J. Pub. Health* 52:2001.

McLEAN, D.M. 1963. Infection hazards in swimming pools. *Pediatrics* 31:811.

FAVERO, M.S., C.H. DRAKE & G.B. RANDALL. 1964. Use of staphylococci as indicators of swimming pool pollution. *Pub. Health Rep.* 79:61.

BØE, J., C.O. SOLBERG, T.M. VOGELSANG & A. WORMNES. 1964. Perianal carriers of staphylococci. *Brit. Med. J.* 2:280.

FAVERO, M.S. & C.H. DRAKE. 1964. Comparative study of microbial flora of iodated and chlorinated pools. *Pub. Health Rep.* 79:251.

COWAN, S.T. & K.J. STEEL. 1965. Manual for the Identification of Medical Bacteria. Cambridge Univ. Press, New York, N.Y.

WORKING PARTY OF THE PUBLIC HEALTH LABORATORY SERVICE. 1965. A bacteriological survey of swimming baths in primary schools. *Monthly Bull. Min. Health & Pub. Health Lab. Serv.* 24:116.

DRAKE, C.H. 1966. Evaluation of culture media for the isolation and enumeration of *Pseudomonas aeruginosa. Health Lab. Sci.* 3:10.

ROBINTON, E.D. & E.W. MOOD. 1966. A quantitative and qualitative appraisal of microbial pollution of water by swimmers: A preliminary report. *J. Hyg.* 64:489.

ROBINTON, E.D. & E.W. MOOD. 1967. An evaluation of the inhibitory influence of cyanuric acid upon swimming pool disinfection. *Amer. J. Pub. Health* 57:301.

KEIRN, M.A. & H.D. PUTNAM. 1968. Resistance of staphylococci to halogens as related to a swimming pool environment. *Health Lab. Sci.* 3:180.

BROWN, M.R.W., & J.H. SCOTT FOSTER. 1970. A simple diagnostic milk medium for *Pseudomonas aeruginosa. J. Clin. Pathol.* 23:172.

FAVERO, M.S., L.A. CARSON, W.W. BOND &

N.J. PETERSEN. 1971. *Pseudomonas aeruginosa:* growth in distilled water from hospitals. *Science* 173:836.

LEVIN, M.A. & V.J. CABELLI. 1972. Membrane filter technique for enumeration of *Pseudomonas aeruginosa. Appl. Microbiol.* 24:864.

GRUN, L. & H. KLEYBRINK. 1972. Staphylokokken-Mikrokokken im Badewasser. *Zentralbl. Bakteriol. Parasitenk. Infektionskr. Hyg. Abt. Orig. B.* 155:384.

915   DETECTION OF FUNGI IN WATER AND WASTEWATER

Fungi are ubiquitously distributed achlorophyllous organisms with an organized nucleus. They may be found wherever nonliving organic matter occurs. In spring water near the source, the number of fungus spores is usually minimal. Unpolluted river water will have large numbers, representing the true aquatic fungi (including flagellated zoospores and gametes), aquatic Hyphomycetes, and soil fungi. Moderately polluted water may carry spores or cells of the three types; however, there will be fewer true aquatic fungi and Hyphomycetes and more numerous soil fungi. Heavily polluted water will have large numbers of soil fungi only. The group designated as soil fungi includes the yeasts, many species of which have been isolated from polluted waters.

The association between fungus numbers and organic loading suggests that fungi may be useful indicators of pollution. Unfortunately, no single species or group of fungi has been identified as important in this role. There may be some

special cases that are exceptions; for example, the distinction between *Candida lambica* and *C. krusei* is the ability to utilize pentose sugars. Since the former fungus grows well on pentoses, it could be used as an indicator of paper mill wastes, which are high in such sugars. Yeasts and filamentous fungi can grow well at elevated temperatures and may be useful indicators of thermal pollution. The amount of chlorine, or other disinfectant, required for fungus control is essentially unknown.

In water there are two basic types of fungal growth patterns related to movement. True aquatic fungi produce zoospores or gametes which are motile by means of flagella, either of the whiplash or tinsel type. Some fungi, particularly the trichomycetes, have amoeboid stages. Collection of aquatic fungi is typically by means of exposing suitable baits (solid foodstuffs) in the habitat being examined or in a sample within the laboratory. Relatively little work on these fungi has been done in the U.S. although they have been extensively studied in polluted waters in England, Germany, and Japan.

The second fungal growth form is nonmotile in all stages of the life cycle. Growth and reproduction are usually asexual. Three growth processes have been recognized: (*a*) filamentous growth with blastic spores or spores produced in special structures; (*b*) filamentous growth with the mycelial filaments breaking up to form separate spores called arthroconidia; and (*c*) single-celled growth with buds produced on each parent cell. The fungus *Geotrichum* and its relatives belong to the

second type, while yeasts have the budding form.

Identification of fungi, which are considerably larger than bacteria, is dependent on colonial morphology on a solid medium, growth and reproductive morphology, and, for yeasts, physiological activity in laboratory cultures. Increasing numbers of fungi are usually indicative of increasing organic leadings in water or soil. Large numbers of similar fungi suggest excessive organic load while a highly diversified flora is indicative of population adjusted to the environmental organics.

915 A.   Technic for Fungi (TENTATIVE)

1. Samples

a. Containers: Samples for the detection of fungi should be collected as directed in Section 906A (Samples, Collection). Alternatively, cylindrical plastic vials with snap-on caps may be used. These vials are usually sterile as received. They should be transported in an erect position to minimize the chance of leakage and should be discarded after use.

b. Sample storage: Samples should not be held more than 24 hr. If analysis is not begun promptly after sample collection, refrigerate the samples.

2. Fungus Plate Count and Inventory, Procedure

Experience has shown that as many as 40 samples can be analyzed simultaneously by the following procedure.

About 20 samples represent the optimum number.

a. Preparation and dilution: To a sterile 250-ml Erlenmeyer flask add 135 ml sterile distilled water and 15 ml sample. Use a sterile measuring device for each sample or, less preferably, rinse the measure with sterile distilled water between samples. Be sure that the sample is well mixed before withdrawing the 15-ml portion (this is especially important in analyzing samples of sediments, sludges, or other solid or semi-solid materials). Shake flask on a rotary shaker at about 120 to 150 oscillations/min for about 30 min or transfer flask contents to a blender jar and blend at low speed for 1 min or high speed for 30 sec. Wash blender jar thoroughly between samples and rinse with sterile distilled water. Further dilutions may be made by adding 45 ml of sterile distilled water to 5 ml of the 1:10 diluted suspension.

For stream water samples a dilution of 1:10 is usually adequate. Samples with large amounts of organic material, such as sediments, should be diluted to 1:100 or 1:1,000. Stream bank or soil samples should be diluted 1:1,000 or 1:10,000.

b. Plating: Prepare five plates for each dilution to be examined. Neopeptone-glucose-rose bengal-aureomycin agar is the medium of choice, although experience may indicate that Czapek agar (for *Aspergillus, Penicillium,* and related fungi) and yeast extract-malt extract-glucose agar or Diamalt agar (for yeasts) may be preferable. Refer to Media Specifications, Section 905 C. To use noepeptone-glucose-rose bengal-aureomycin agar, aseptically transfer 10 ml of the medium at 45 C, containing 0.05 ml aureomycin solution that has been filter-sterilized, to a 9-cm-diam petri dish. Add 1 ml of the appropriate sample dilution and mix thoroughly by tilting and rotating the dish (see plating procedure under Standard Plate Count, Section 907). Alternatively add 1 ml sample, 0.05 ml aureomycin solution, and 10 ml of liquefied agar medium at 43 to 45 C, to the petri dish. Solidify the agar as rapidly as possible.

c. Incubation: Stack plates but do not invert. Incubate at room conditions of temperature and lighting but avoid direct sunlight. Examine and count plates after 5 to 7 days.

d. Counting and inventory: The fungus plate count will provide the basis for rough quantitative comparisons among samples; the inventory will give relative importance of at least the more readily identifiable species or genera.

In preparing plates, amounts of sample should be plated that will give about 50 to 60 colonies on a plate. Estimates of up to 300 colonies may be made but more crowded plates should be discarded. The medium containing rose bengal tends to produce discrete colonies and permits slow-growing organisms to develop.

The inventory includes the direct identification of fungi based on colonial morphology and the counting of colonies assignable to various species or genera. When discrete colonies cannot be identified and identification is important, pick from each selected colony and streak on a slant of neopeptone-glucose agar with a nichrome wire the end of which is bent in an L-shape. If five plates are used per sample then the average number of colonies on all plates (total number of colonies counted/5), times the reciprocal of the dilution (10/1, 100/1, 1,000/1, etc.) equals the fungus colony count per ml of the original sample. For solid or semisolid samples, a correction for the water may be used to report fungus colonies per gram dry weight of sample.

915 B.   Technic for Yeasts (TENTATIVE)

Of the total number of fungal colonies obtained from polluted waters, as many as 50% may be yeast colonies. Solid media such as those described above do not permit growth of all yeasts; thus, a qualitative enrichment technic may be useful in addition to the plate count.

1. Sample Preparation and Dilution

Prepare the sample as directed under Fungus Plate Count and Inventory.

2. Enrichment

In 250-ml Erlenmeyer flasks prepare one flask each of yeast nitrogen base medium containing 1% and 20% glucose (refer to Media Specifications, Section 905C). Inoculate with 1 ml of the appropriate sample dilution and incubate at room temperature on a rotary shaker operating at 120 to 150 oscillations/min for at least 64 hr. Shaken cultures are necessary to prevent overgrowth by filamentous fungi.

3. Isolation

Remove flasks from shaking machine and let settle 4 to 5 hr. Yeast cells, if present, will settle to the bottom, bacteria will remain in suspension, and filamentous fungi will remain in suspension, will float on the surface, or be attached to the glass. With a nichrome wire loop remove a loopful of the sediment at the sediment-supernatant interface and smear-streak on malt extract-yeast extract-glucose agar. Use three plates per flask. Incubate at room temperature but out of direct sunlight for 2 to 3 days. Do not invert plates. To obtain pure cultures, pick from reasonably isolated colonies and restreak on the same medium or on Diamalt agar plates. Obtain pure cultures of as many different colonies as can be recognized.

4. Counting

It is impossible to obtain a meaningful plate count after enrichment isolation. Assuming that one cell in the original sample will produce one or more colonies on the plates following enrichment, it can be stated that yeasts, or specific types of yeasts, occur at a minimal number dependent on the highest positive dilution. The reciprocal of this dilution is the indicated number of yeasts in the sample.

915 C.   Pathogenic Fungi

Routine isolations of fungi from polluted streams and sewage treatment plants usually have yielded four species known to be pathogenic to man; however, there is no evidence that they are associated with human disease or disease transmission by this route. These include: *Geotrichum candidum*, which is isolated almost universally and is known as *Endomyces* if a sexual stage is present; *Rhinocladiella mansonii*, which is equally widespread and is known also as *Phialophora jeanselmei* and *Tri-chosporium heteromorphum; Aspergillus fumigatus*, which produces large numbers of spores, is abundantly present, and may produce aspergillosis when not in an aqueous environment; and *Petriellidium boydii*, which may cause a bone infection called Madura foot when introduced through deep wounds. The asexual form of the last fungus is the common form and is known also as *Monosporium apiospermum* or *Scedosporium apiospermum*. About 20 different plant pathogens also have been isolated but there is no evidence for their involvement in the spread of plant diseases.

915 D.   Bibliography

EMERSON, R. 1958. Mycological organization. *Mycologia* 50:589.

COOKE, W.B. 1958. Continuous sampling of trickling filter populations. I. Procedures. *Sewage Ind. Wastes* 30:21.

COOKE, W.B. & A. HIRSCH. 1958. Continuous sampling of trickling filter populations. II. Populations. *Sewage Ind. Wastes* 30:139.

COOKE, W.B. 1959. Trickling filter ecology. *Ecology* 40:273.

COOKE, W.B. 1961. Pollution effects on the fungus population of a stream. *Ecology* 42:1.

ALEXOPOULOS, C.J. 1962. Introductory Mycology, 2nd ed. John Wiley & Sons, New York, N.Y.

COOKE, W.B. 1963. A Laboratory Guide to Fungi in Polluted Waters, Sewage, and Sewage Treatment Systems. Their Identification and Culture. USPHS Publ. 999-WP-1, Cincinnati, Ohio.

COOKE, W.B. 1965. The enumeration of yeast populations in a sewage treatment plant. *Mycologia* 57:696.

COOKE, W.B. & G.S. MATSUURA. 1969. Distribution of fungi in a waste stabilization pond system. *Ecology* 50:689.

COOKE, W.B. 1970. Our Mouldy Earth. FWPCA Res. Contract Ser. Publ. No. CWR-.

COOKE, W.B. 1970. Fungi in the Lebanon sewage treatment plant and in Turtle Creek, Warren Co., Ohio. *Mycopathol. Mycol. Appl.* 42:89.

BROCK, T.D. 1970. Biology of Microorganisms. Prentice-Hall, Englewood Cliffs, N.J.

LODDER, J., ed. 1970. The Yeasts, a Taxonomic Study, 2nd ed. North-Holland Publ. Co., Amsterdam.

COOKE, W.B. 1971. The role of fungi in waste treatment. *CRC Critical Rev. Environ. Control* 1:581.

916   DETECTION OF ACTINOMYCETES

Earthy-musty odors are reportedly among the most persistent and difficult for water plant operators to eliminate. As early as 1929, it was assumed that these odors could be attributed to volatile metabolites formed during normal development of actinomycetes.[1] Only recently has appreciable progress been made in evaluating the relationship between volatile products of actinomycetes and the musty-earthy odor problems affecting water supplies across the nation.

Modern research technics have led to the isolation from these organisms of two major earthy-musty-smelling compounds, both of which have been identified and independently confirmed.[2-8] The two compounds, geosmin and 2-methylisoborneol, have since been demonstrated as the agents responsible for earthy-musty odor problems in surface waters.[8, 9]

In areas periodically plagued by this problem, it has been prudent to enumerate actinomycetes. Identification of their relative abundance in a drinking water source can provide yet another parameter in the assessment of water quality. The methods described are well-established technics that have been used with considerable success in the isolation and enumeration of actinomycetes related to public water supplies.[10, 11]

Of the general properties of actinomycetes, the most striking is their fungal-type morphology. Although they were initially looked upon as fungi, later research revealed that actinomycetes are filamentous, branching bacteria.[12]

The actinomycetes are most commonly represented by saprophytic forms that have an extensive impact on the environment by bringing about the decomposition and transformation of a wide variety of complex organic residues. Widely distributed in nature, actinomycetes constitute a considerable proportion of the population of soil and lake and river muds. In these habitats, actinomycetes undoubtedly have the capacity to produce quantities of odoriferous substances that can be detected in the immediate area. Geosmin and 2-methylisoborneol have been isolated from laboratory-grown cultures of numerous actinomycetes, most of which belonged to the genus *Streptomyces,* a genus long considered as the most likely of the actinomycetes to be of particular consequence in water supply problems.

916 A.   Technic for Actinomycetes (TENTATIVE)

1. Samples

a. Samples for the detection of actinomycetes should be collected as directed in Section 906A (Samples, Collection).

b. Sample storage: Analyze samples as promptly after collection as possible. Refrigerate samples held more than 24 hr.

2. Actinomycete Plate Count

A plating method using a double-layer agar technic has been adapted for determining actinomycete density. Since only the thin top layer of the medium is inoculated with the sample, surface colonies predominate and the identification and counting of colonies is facilitated.

a. Preparation and dilution: Prepare and dilute samples as directed in Section 907.2 (Standard Plate Count) or 915A.2 (Fungus Plate Count and Inventory). Dilutions up to 1:1,000 are usually suitable for water while for soil samples, dilutions from 1:1,000 (10^{-3}) to 1:1,000,000 (10^{-6}) should be used.

b. Plating: Prepare three plates for each dilution to be examined. Aseptically transfer 15 ml of sterile starch-casein agar (refer to Media Specifications, Section 905C) to a petri dish and solidify the agar to form the bottom layer. To a test tube containing 17.0 ml of liquefied starch-casein agar at 45 to 48 C add 2 ml of the appropriately diluted sample and 1 ml of the antifungal antibiotic, Actidione, prepared in distilled water (1 mg/ml) and sterilized by autoclaving

magnification of 100× may be necessary to verify identity. Actinomycete colonies, because of filamentous growth, typically have a fuzzy colonial border. Table 916:I lists the distinguishing characteristics commonly used to differentiate actinomycete and bacterial colonies. Actidione generally suppresses fungal growth. However, fungus colonies, if present, can be recognized by their woolly appearance. Microscopically, the fungi can be seen to have considerably larger cell diameter than the actinomycetes.

TABLE 916:I. GENERAL MACROSCOPIC PROPERTIES OF ACTINOMYCETE AND BACTERIAL COLONIES ON SOLID MEDIUM

Characteristic	Bacterial Colony	Actinomycete Colony
Appearance	Shiny or opalescent	Dull, chalky when colony covered with aerial mycelium
Texture	Soft	Tough and leathery
Degree of adherance to solid medium	Weak	Strong
Edge of colony	Generally no distinction from the colony as a whole	Appears less dense, producing a halo effect

for 15 min at 121 C. Pipet 5 ml of the inoculated agar over the hardened bottom layer with gentle swirling to obtain even distribution of the surface layer.

c. Incubation: Incubate at 28 C until no new colonies appear. Usually this requires 6 to 7 days; however, all plates should be retained for 14 days.

d. Counting: Plates suitable for counting contain 30 to 300 colonies. Since the gross appearance of actinomycete and bacterial colonies may be similar, microscopic examination at a

e. Calculation: Report actinomycetes per milliliter of water or gram (dry weight) of soil. If three plates are used per sample then the average number of colonies on all plates (total number of colonies/3), times 2, times the reciprocal of the dilution (10/1, 100/1, 1,000/1, etc.) equals the actinomycete colony count per milliliter of the original sample. For solid or semisolid samples use a correction for the water to report actinomycete colonies per gram dry weight of sample.

916 B.   References

1. ADAMS, B.A. 1929. *Cladothrix dichotoma* and allied organisms as a cause of an "indeterminate" taste in chlorinated water. *Water & Water Eng.* 31:327

2. GERBER, N.N. & H.A. LECHEVALIER. 1965. Geosmin, an earthy-smelling substance isolated from actinomycetes. *Appl. Microbiol.* 13:935.

3. GERBER, N.N. 1968. Geosmin, from microorganisms, is trans-1,10-dimethyltrans-9-decalol. *Tetrahedron Lett.* 25:2971.

4. MARSHALL, J.A. & A.R. HOCHSTETLER. 1968. The synthesis of (±)-geosmin and the other 1,10-dimethyl-9-decalol isomers. *J. Org. Chem.* 33:2593.

5. ROSEN, A.A., R.S. SAFFERMAN, C.I. MASHNI & A.H. ROMANO. 1968. Identity of odorous substances produced by *Streptomyces griseoluteus*. *Appl. Microbiol.* 16:178.

6. MEDSKER, L.L., D. JENKINS & J.F. THOMAS. 1969. Odorous compounds in natural waters: 2-exo-hydroxy-2-methylbornane, the major odorous compound produced by several actinomycetes. *Environ. Sci. Technol.* 3:476.

7. GERBER, N.N. 1969. A volatile metabolite of actinomycetes, 2-methylisoborneol. *J. Antibiot.* 22:508.

8. ROSEN, A.A., C.I. MASHNI & R.S. SAFFERMAN. 1970. Recent developments in the chemistry of odour in water: the cause of earthy/musty odour. *Water Treat. Exam.* 19:106.

9. PIET, G.J., B.C.J. ZOETEMAN & A.J.A. KRAAYEVELD. 1972. Earthy-smelling substances in surface waters of the Netherlands. *Water Treat. Exam.* 21:281.

10. SAFFERMAN, R.S. & M.E. MORRIS. 1962. A method for the isolation and enumeration of actinomycetes related to water supplies. USPHS, Robert A. Taft Sanitary Eng. Center Tech. Rep. W62-10, Cincinnati, Ohio.

11. KUSTER, E. & S.T. WILLIAMS. 1964. Selection of media for isolation of *Streptomyces*. *Nature* 202:928.

12. LECHEVALIER, H.A. & M.P. LECHEVALIER. 1967. Biology of actinomycetes. *Annu. Rev. Microbiol.* 21:71.

917   DETECTION OF NEMATODES

Nematodes, commonly known as round- or threadworms, are invertebrates without appendages. The parasitic forms are macroscopic in size: the smallest, such as pinworms and hookworms, are about 1 cm in length. Freshwater and soil nematodes are usually microscopic but visible under a powerful hand-lens. Identification can be done only under a microscope. Most of them are about 1 mm long and 0.05 mm wide with both ends tapered. Sexes are separate in most genera; however, a few are parthenogenetic, with females producing diploid eggs. Most freshwater and soil nematodes are aerobic and free-living although a few genera parasitize plants. Free-living nematodes feed on bacteria, small algae or fungi, or dead zoomicrobes.

A nematode has a head, a body, and a tail, which are not separated externally. The head consists of a six-lipped mouth and a buccal cavity. The tail is posterior to the anus, tapered, and may end abruptly or extend into a long filament. Between the head and tail is the lengthy body, which contains the oesophagus, oesophageal bulb, and intestine, and the reproductive system.

The life cycle of free-living nematodes consists of egg, larval, and adult stages. Eggs are hard to recognize in microscopic examination of water or sewage effluent. Larvae resemble adults but are only about one-fifth adult size when newly hatched, with size approaching that of an adult before the last molt. Larvae can be distinguished from adults by the lack of reproductive organs. These stages are illustrated in Figure 917:1.

Free-living nematodes are not indicators of fecal pollution. They are present in small numbers in raw sewage, originating from land runoff, fresh vegetable washings, and the like. Those that feed on bacteria thrive in biological wastewater treatment processes and are present in large numbers in the effluent, even though many of the larger ones are removed during secondary settling.

Very few nematodes are present in clean or remotely polluted surface waters.[1] There is an insignificant increase in numbers following heavy runoff.[2]

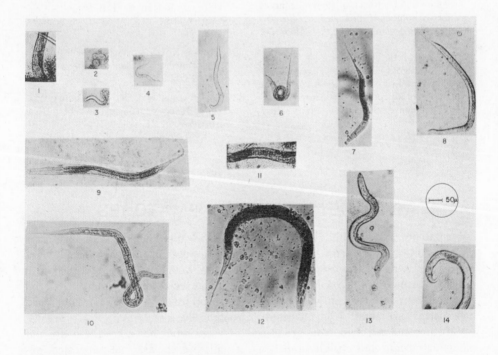

Figure 917:1. Life cycle of nematodes. 1. Section of female worm showing 3 ova. 2. Ovum freed from a female worm with a well formed larva. 3. Larva hatching out from an ovum. 4. 1st stage larva with tail. 5. 2nd stage larva. 6-7. 3rd stage larvae. 8. 4th stage larva. 9-10. Female worms. 11. Section of mature female worm showing striated cuticle. 12. Mature female worm with fully developed uterus and one ovum. 13. Male worm with spicules and gubernaculum. 14. Posterior section of male worm showing spicules on side view.

Most nematodes in surface water come from the discharge of secondary sewage treatment plant effluents [2, 3, 4]; therefore, free-living nematodes are useful indicators of pollution by secondary effluent. Data from nematological examination may provide useful information on the pollutional history but typically bear little relationship to disease transmission potential.[1]

917 A. Technic for Nematodes (TENTATIVE)

1. Samples

All samples should be collected from sampling stations where bacteriologic samples are taken so that findings can be interpreted together. If the examination is intended to obtain data on stream pollution, sampling stations should be located above and below an outfall. When samples are taken for plankton analysis, nematodes may be included but recorded separately.

a. Sample collection: Samples should be collected in the same manner as for bacteriological examination (Section 906A, Samples, Collection) with the following modifications. The sample size should be not less than 2 l, preferably 4 l. Square plastic containers are convenient for collection and shipment of samples. The containers need not be sterilized but should be thoroughly washed with tap water and rinsed with distilled water. For the examination of potable water, samples of 100 l may be used.

b. Sample storage: It is preferable to examine living material for nematodes. Although sample refrigeration is unnecessary, the analysis should be made as soon as possible and at least within 2 days of collection. If samples cannot be examined within 2 days they should be preserved in the same manner as plankton samples (see Section 1002B.).

2. Nematode Count Procedure

a. Sample concentration: Filter the sample as directed under Section 1002C.2, Membrane Filter Concentration Technic except that a woven nylon strainer (pore size 25 to 30 μm) replaces the membrane filter. It usually will be possible to filter 4 l of polluted water through a single strainer in a reasonable time. If strainer clogging occurs, two or more strainers may be used for the total sample. As the last amount of water disappears from the surface, disconnect the holder top. Remove the strainer with a pair of forceps and place it on the wall of a clean 100-ml beaker containing 2 to 4 ml of phosphate buffered dilution or distilled water. Using a capillary pipet repeatedly flush the surface of the strainer with the water. When the water is forced out of the pipet under some pressure, 8 to 10 flushings are sufficient to dislodge the nematodes. If more than one strainer is used to concentrate a single sample, pool the washings.

After a sample is filtered, wash the strainer-holding assembly in running tap water and rinse with distilled water before reuse. Sterilization is unnecessary.

b. Counting: Transfer 1 ml of thoroughly mixed wash water from the beaker to a Sedgwick-Rafter counting chamber. Scan the entire chamber using 100× magnification and count all nematodes. If the number of nematodes counted per milliliter of concentrate exceeds 10, multiply the number by the milliliters of concentrate, divide by the liters of sample, and report nematodes per liter. If the number of nematodes is less than 10/ml of concentrate, count the nematodes in the entire volume of concentrate. It may be useful to count living and dead nematodes separately; this can be done only in unpreserved samples.

3. Interpretation

Since the presence of free-living nematodes in open waters of lakes and rivers is chiefly, if not entirely, attributable to pollution by secondary effluents, their concentration provides a rough, but reliable, indication of levels of pollution by such effluents. The rapidity of obtaining results gives this analysis an obvious advantage in assessing water quality.

When the nematological results are examined in conjunction with bacteriological findings, inferences can be made as to the pollution history. For example, a combination of high fecal bacterial count and very low nematode count suggests that the water was polluted by a secondary effluent from an anaerobic biological treatment plant or that the secondary effluent had been further treated by detention in a stabilization pond prior to discharge into the receiving water; a very low fecal bacteria count and a high nematode count strongly indicates that the water had been used as a carrier of disinfected secondary effluents since nematodes are more resistant to chlorine

than most bacteria; a moderately high fecal bacteria count and a low nematode count indicates that the polluted water is stagnant or very slow-flowing, thus permitting settling of nematodes.

If nematodes are included in the examination of a raw water source, and if the water treatment includes sedimentation or filtration, results obtained in examination of the finished water can be interpreted for efficiency of the treatment. Nematodes are highly resistant to free chlorine[5] and since they can be removed by flocculation and/or sand filtration if they are completely or partially immobilized, their elimination requires pre-superchlorination. In such a treatment practice, the following can be used as a guide to the treatment efficiency:

% Nematode Removal	Efficiency of Treatment
>90	Very good
75-90	Good
50-74	Fair
<50	Poor

It has been reported that free-living nematodes are capable of ingesting enteric pathogenic bacteria and enteroviruses and that the ingested pathogens have remained viable for 2 days under laboratory conditions.[5] Under field conditions there may be a significant probability of finding 1 virus particle/200 worms.[6] Salmonellae also have been isolated from nematodes obtained from sewage treatment plants.[7] When repeated examination reveals nematode counts greater than about 20/l of raw water, consideration should be given to reducing the nematode load in the finished water by special treatment.

917 B. References

1. CHANG, S.L. 1972. Zoomicrobial indicators of water pollution. Presented at 72nd Annual Meeting of the Amer. Soc. Microbiol., Philadelphia, Pa:, Apr. 23-28, 1972.

2. CHAUDHURI, N., R. SIDDIQI & R.S. ENGELBRECHT. 1964. Source and persistence of nematodes in surface waters. *J. Amer. Water Works Ass.* 56:73.

3. CHANG, S.L. & P.W. KABLER. 1962. Free-living nematodes in aerobic treatment effluent. *J. Water Pollut. Control Fed.* 34:1356.

4. BALIGA, K.Y., J.H. AUSTIN & R.S. ENGELBRECHT. 1969. Occurrence of nematodes in benthic deposit. *Water Res.* 3:979.

5. CHANG, S.L., G. BERG, N.A. CLARKE & P.W. KABLER. 1960. Survival and protection against chlorination of human enteric pathogens in free-living nematodes isolated from water supplies. *Amer. J. Trop. Med. Hyg.* 9:136.

6. CHANG, S.L. 1970. Interactions between animal viruses and higher forms of microbes. *J. San. Eng. Div., Proc. Amer. Soc. Civil Eng.* 96:151.

7. WALTER, J. V. & R.R. HOLCOMB. 1966. Isolation of enteric pathogens from sewage-borne nematodes. Presented at 5th Annual Meeting of Soc. of Nematology, Daytona Beach, Fla., Aug. 23-26, 1966.

917 C. Bibliography

CHITWOOD, B.G. & M.B. CHITWOOD. 1950. An Introduction to Nematology Section I: Anatomy. Monumental Printing Co., Baltimore, Md.

SCHIEMER, F., H. LÖFFLER & H. DOLLFUSS. 1969. Benthic communities of Neusiedersee (Austria). *Verh. Int. Ver. Theor. angew., Limnol.* 17:201.

CHITWOOD, B.G. & M.W. ALLEN. 1959. Nemata, Chap. 15 in Freshwater Biology, 2nd ed. (W.T. Edmondson, ed.). John Wiley & Sons, New York, N.Y.

WHIPPLE, G.C., G.M. FAIR & M.C. WHIPPLE. 1927. Microscopy of Drinking Water. John Wiley & Sons, New York, N.Y.

918 IDENTIFICATION OF IRON AND SULFUR BACTERIA

The group of nuisance organisms collectively designated as iron and sulfur bacteria is neither morphologically nor physiologically homogeneous, yet it may be characterized by the ability to transform or deposit significant amounts of iron or sulfur, usually in the form of objectionable slimes. Iron and sulfur bacteria are not, however, the sole producers of bacterial slimes.

The organisms that are placed in this group may be filamentous or single-celled, autotrophic or heterotrophic, aerobic or anaerobic. According to conventional bacterial classification, these organisms are assigned to a variety of orders, families, and genera. They are studied as "iron and sulfur bacteria" because these elements and their transformations may be important in water treatment and distribution systems and may be especially bothersome in waters for industrial use, as in cooling and boiler waters. Iron bacteria may cause fouling and plugging of wells and distribution systems and sulfate-reducing bacteria may cause rusty water and tuberculation of pipes. These organisms also may cause odor, taste, frothing, color, and increases in turbidity in waters.

The food supply of iron and sulfur bacteria may be wholly or partly inorganic and they may extract it, if attached or in a gelatinous substrate, from a low concentration in flowing water.

This seems quite important in the case of certain sulfur bacteria utilizing small amounts of hydrogen sulfide or in the case of organisms such as *Gallionella*, which obtain their energy from the oxidation of ferrous iron. Temperature, light, pH, and oxygen supply also affect the growth of these organisms. Under different environmental conditions some bacteria may appear either as iron or as sulfur bacteria.

918 A.   Iron Bacteria

1. General Characteristics

"Iron bacteria" are considered to be capable of withdrawing iron present in their aqueous habitat and of depositing it in the form of hydrated ferric hydroxide on or in their mucilaginous secretions. A somewhat similar mechanism is employed by bacteria utilizing manganese. The large amount of brown slime so produced will impart a reddish tinge and an unpleasant odor to drinking water, which may render the supply unsuitable for domestic or industrial purposes. Such bacteria also may initiate pitting and tuberculation of pipes. Bacteria of this type, to obtain energy, oxidize ferrous to ferric iron, which is precipitated as ferric hydrate. Iron may be obtained from the pipe itself or from the water being carried. The amount of ferric hydrate deposited is very large in comparison with the enclosed cells.

Some bacteria that do not oxidize ferrous iron nevertheless may cause it to be dissolved or deposited indirectly. In their growth, they either liberate iron by utilizing organic radicals to which the iron is attached or they alter environmental conditions to permit the solution or deposition of iron. In consequence, less ferric hydrate may be produced, but taste, odor, and fouling may be encouraged.

2. Collection of Samples and Identification

Identification of nuisance iron bacteria has usually been made on the basis of microscopic examination of the suspected material. Bulked activated sludge, masses of microbial growth in lakes, rivers, and streams, and slime growths in cooling-tower waters may be examined directly. Suspected development of iron bacteria in wells or in distribution systems may require special efforts to secure samples useful for identification. Continued heavy deposition of iron caused by the oxidation of ferrous iron by air or by other environmental changes often hides the sheaths or stalks of iron bacteria. The cells within the filaments often die and disintegrate and the filaments tend to be fragmented or

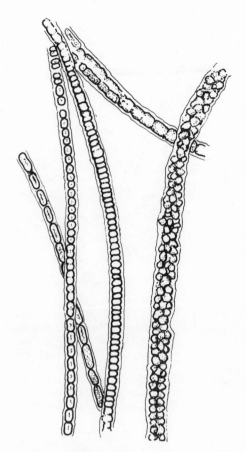

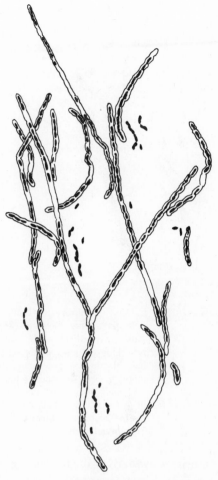

Figure 918:1. Filaments of *Crenothrix poly-spora* showing variation of size and shape of cells within the sheath. Note especially the multiple small round cells, or "conidia," found in one of the filaments. This distinctive feature is the reason for the name *polyspora*. Young growing colonies are usually not encrusted with iron or manganese. Older colonies often exhibit empty sheaths that are heavily encrusted. Cells may vary considerably in size: Rod-shaped cells average 1.2 to 2.0 μm in width by 2.4 to 5.6 μm in length; coccoid cells of "conidia" average 0.6 μm in diameter.

Figure 918:2. Filaments of *Sphaerotilus na-tans*, showing cells within the filaments and some free "swarmer" cells. Filaments show false branching and areas devoid of cells. Individual cells within the sheath may vary in size, averaging 0.6 to 2.4 μm in width by 1.0 to 12.0 μm in length; most strains are 1.1 to 1.6 μm wide by 2.0 to 4.0 μm long.

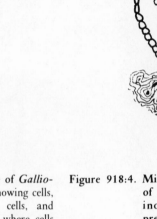

Figure 918:3. Laboratory culture of *Gallio-nella ferruginea*, showing cells, stalks excreted by cells, and branching of stalks where cells have divided. A precipitate of inorganic iron on and around the stalks often blurs the outlines. Cells at tip of stalk average 0.4 to 0.6 μm in width by 0.7 to 1.1 μm in length.

Figure 918:4. Mixture of fragments of stalks of *Gallionella ferruginea* and inorganic iron-manganese precipitate found in natural samples from wells. Fragmented stalks appear golden yellow to orange when examined under the microscope.

crushed by the mass of the iron precipitate.

Samples of water drawn directly from wells may be settled or centrifuged and the sediment examined microscopically. Place a portion of the sediment on a microscope slide, cover with a cover slip, and examine under a low-power microscope for filaments and iron-encrusted filaments. The material trapped by filters placed in front of back-surge valves often has yielded excellent specimens of iron bacteria. Water pumped from the well may be passed through a 0.45-μm membrane filter

and the filter examined microscopically. Phase-contrast microscopes have made possible the examination of unstained culture material. India ink or lactophenol blue may be used for staining when conventional light microscopy is used. A useful technic to dissolve iron deposits is to place several drops of 1 N HCl at one edge of the cover slip and to draw it under the cover slip by applying filter or blotting paper to the opposite edge. Reducing compounds such as sodium ascorbate also may be used to dissolve deposits and permit observation of cellular structure. To verify that the material is iron add a solution of potassium ferro-cyanide to a sample on a slide, cover, and draw 1 N HCl under the cover slip. A blue precipitate of Prussian blue will form as the iron around cells or filaments is dissolved.

Identification is made by comparing the material with available drawings or photographs of iron bacteria.[2-14] Some examples are given in Figures 918:1 through 918:5. A single-celled autotrophic bacterium, *Thiobacillus ferrooxidans*, which contributes to the problems of acid mine drainage, can be identified only by tests for its physiologic transfor-

Figure 918:5. Single-celled iron bacterium *Siderocapsa treubii*. Cells are surrounded by a deposit of ferric hydrate. Individual cells average 0.4 to 1.5 μm in width by 0.8 to 2.5 μm in length.

mation of ferrous to ferric iron or oxidation of reduced sulfur compounds.

918 B.   Sulfur Bacteria

1. General Characteristics

The bacteria that oxidize or reduce significant amounts of inorganic sulfur compounds exhibit a wide diversity of morphological and biochemical characteristics. One group, the sulfate-reducing bacteria, consists of single-celled forms that grow anaerobically and reduce sulfate to hydrogen sulfide. A second group—the green photosynthetic and the purple sulfur bacteria—grows anaerobically in the light and uses hydrogen sulfide as a hydrogen donor for photosynthetic activity. The sulfide is oxidized to sulfur or sulfate. A third group, the aerobic sulfur oxidizers, oxidizes reduced sulfur compounds aerobically to obtain energy for chemoautotrophic growth.

The sulfur bacteria of most importance in the water and wastewater field are the sulfate-reducing bacteria, which include *Desulfovibrio*, and the single-celled aerobic sulfur oxidizers of the genus *Thiobacillus*. The sulfate-reduc-ing bacteria contribute greatly to tuberculations and galvanic corrosion of water mains and to taste and odor problems in water. The *Thiobacillus*, by its production of sulfuric acid, has contributed to the destruction of concrete sewers and the acid corrosion of metals.

2. Collection of Samples and Identification

Identification of nuisance sulfur bacteria has usually been made on the basis of microscopic examination of the suspected material. Samples of slimes suspended in waters, scrapings from exposed surfaces, or sediments may be examined directly.

Three groups of sulfur bacteria may be recognized microscopically: green and purple sulfur bacteria; large, colorless filamentous sulfur bacteria; and large, colorless nonfilamentous sulfur bacteria. A fourth group cannot be identified by appearance alone.

a. Green and purple sulfur bacteria:

1) Green sulfur bacteria most frequently occur in waters high in hydrogen sulfide. They are small, ovoid to rod-shaped nonmotile organisms, generally less than 1 μm in diameter, and with a yellowish green color in masses. Sulfur globules are seldom if ever deposited within the cells.

2) Purple sulfur bacteria (see Figure 918:6 for examples) occur in waters containing hydrogen sulfide. They are large, generally stuffed with sulfur globules, and often so intensely pigmented as to make individual cells appear red. Large, dense, highly colored masses are easily detected by the naked eye.

b. Colorless filamentous sulfur bacteria: Colorless filamentous sulfur bacteria (see Figures 918:7 and 918:8 for examples) occur in waters where both oxygen and hydrogen sulfide are present. They may form mats with a

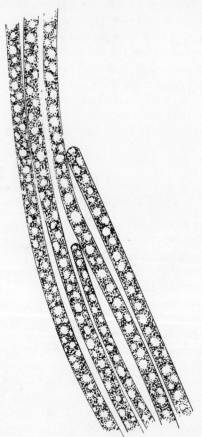

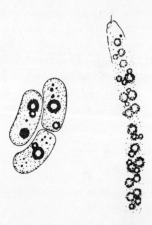

Figure 918:6. Photosynthetic purple sulfur bacteria: Large masses of cells have brown-orange to purple color—may appear chalky if there is a large amount of sulfur within the cells. Left: cells of *Chromatium okenii* (5.0 to 6.5 μm wide by 8 to 15 μm long) containing sulfur granules. Right: *Thiospirillum jenense* (3.5 to 4.5 μm wide by 30 to 40 μm long); cell contains sulfur granules and polar flagellum is visible.

Figure 918:7 Colorless filamentous sulfur bacteria: *Beggiatoa alba* trichomes, containing granules of sulfur. Filaments are composed of a linear series of individual rod-shaped cells that may be visible when not obscured by light reflecting from sulfur granules. Trichomes are 2 to 15 μm in diameter and may be up to 1,500 μm long; individual cells, if visible, are 4.0 to 16.0 μm long.

slightly yellowish white appearance due to the deposition of internal sulfur globules. They are generally large and may be motile with a characteristic gliding movement. Identification may be made by comparing the material with available photographs.[15-17]

c. Colorless nonfilamentous sulfur bacteria: Colorless, nonfilamentous sul-

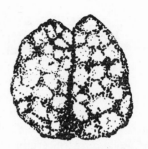

Figure .918:9. Colorless nonfilamentous sulfur bacteria: dividing cell of *Thiovolum majus*, containing sulfur granules. Cells may measure 9 to 17 μm in width by 11 to 18 μm in length and are generally found in nature in a marine littoral zone rich in organic matter and hydrogen sulfide.

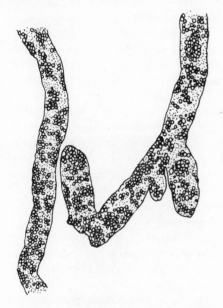

Figure 918:8. Colorless filamentous sulfur bacteria: portion of a colony of *Thiodendron mucosum*, showing branching of the mucoid filament. Individual cells (1.0 to 2.5 μm wide by 3 to 9 μm long) have been found within the jelly-like material of the filaments. The long axis of the cells runs parallel to the long axis of the filaments.

fur bacteria (see Figure 918:9 for example) are usually associated with decaying algae. They are extremely motile, ovoid to rod-shaped with sulfur globules and possible calcium carbonate deposits. They are generally very large.

d. Colorless small sulfur bacteria and sulfate-reducing bacteria: The small single-celled sulfur bacteria, the *Thiobacilli*, and the sulfate-reducing bacteria, such as *Desulfovibrio*, cannot be identified by direct microscopic examination. *Thiobacillus* types are small, colorless, motile, and rod-shaped and are found in an environment containing hydrogen sulfide. Sulfur globules are absent. *Thiobacillus* types and *Desulfovibrio* or other sulfate-reducing bacteria must be identified physiologically.

918 C.   Enumeration, Enrichment, and Isolation of Iron and Sulfur Bacteria (TENTATIVE)

There are no good means of enumerating iron and sulfur bacteria other than the sulfate-reducing bacteria and the *Thiobacilli*. Laboratory cultivation and isolation of pure cultures is difficult and successful isolation is uncertain. This is especially true of attempts to isolate filamentous bacteria from activated sludge or other sources where many different bacterial types are present.

1. Iron Bacteria

a. Sphaerotilus-Leptothrix:

1) Iron bacteria, especially those belonging to the *Sphaerotilus-Leptothrix* group, will thrive in media too dilute to support the proliferation of more rapidly growing organisms. One medium[18] is partially selective for *Sphaerotilus*. It is BOD dilution water supplemented with 100 mg/l sodium lactate. Dispense 50 ml of this medium in French square bottles and autoclave at 0.7 kg/cm^2 (10 psi) for 15 min. To inoculate the sample add 25-ml portions of stream water or 1-, 5-, and 10-ml portions of settled sewage or process liquor to duplicate bottles of the medium. Incubate at 22 to 25 C for 5 days and observe for filamentous growth. Isolate pure cultures by picking a filament from the BOD-lactate broth and streaking on 0.05% meat extract agar. After incubation for 24 hr at 25 C, pick typical curling filaments with the aid of a dissecting microscope and transfer to casitone-glycerol-yeast autolysate (CGY) broth (refer to Media Specifications, Section 905C.38). If a pellicle with no underlying turbidity develops in

2 to 3 days, transfer a filament to a CGY agar slant, incubate at 25 C until growth is visible, and store in a refrigerator.

A detailed key for identifying filamentous microorganisms in complex mixtures such as sewage and activated sludge is available.[19]

2) Isolation and maintenance media (see Media Specifications, Section 905C.39 and 40) have proven quite successful for identifying various groups of filamentous organisms, including iron bacteria.[20] Prepare agar slants of these media and aseptically pipet 3 ml sterile tap water onto the surface of the slants. Inoculate tubes and incubate at room temperature until turbid growth has developed in the liquid layer. The cells will remain viable for 3 months in the refrigerator.

3) Another good maintenance medium for cultivating the *Sphaerotilus* group is CGY (see Media Specifications, Section 905C.38).[9]

4) *Leptothrix (Sphaerotilus discophorous)* can be distinguished from *Sphaerotilus natans* by its ability to oxidize manganous ion. Use Mn-agar as the differential medium (see Media Specifications, 905C.41).[21]

b. Thiobacillus ferrooxidans: Although this organism is also a sulfur-oxidizing bacterium,[22, 23] its main importance has been in acid mine drainage. A medium suitable for enumeration of the MPN is available (see Media Specifications, 905C.42).[24] Some oxidation of iron occurs during sterilization but the loss of ferrous iron is not appreciable. The medium has a precipitate (probably ferrous and ferric phosphates), is opalescent and green, has a pH of 3.0 to 3.6, and contains 9,000 mg/l ferrous iron. Growth of the organism is manifested by a decrease in pH and an increase in the concentration of oxidized iron. With practice and the use of uninoculated controls, an increase of deep orange-brown color can be seen in positive enrichment tubes or flasks as compared to negative ones. Test-tube dilutions should be shaken daily because these organisms are highly aerobic.

c. Gallionella ferruginea: For the cultivation of this organism use ferrous sulfide agar[4, 6] (see Media Specifications, Section 905C.43). Inoculate the tubes with a drop of suspension of a suspected *Gallionella* deposit. Growth at room temperature usually occurs in 18 to 36 hr and appears as a white deposit on the sides of the test tube. The ring of colonies occurring at a certain level reflects a balance between the upward diffusion of ferrous ions and the downward diffusion of oxygen molecules. The ferrous sulfide agar may be used for isolation of pure cultures after supplementation with formalin.[25]

d. Other iron bacteria: An acid-tolerant (pH 3.5 to 5.0) filamentous iron oxidizing *Metallogenium* has been isolated using a medium[26] containing: $(NH_4)_2SO_4$, 0.1%; $CaCO_3$, 0.01%; $MgSO_4$, 0.02%; K_2HPO_4, 0.001%; potassium acid phthalate, 0.4%; and 250 mg/l ferrous iron from an acidified $FeSO_4 \cdot 7H_2O$, solution. Add 0.4% formalin to 100 ml of the isolating medium in a 250-ml Erlenmeyer flask.

For heterotrophic iron-precipitating bacteria[27] use a ferric ammonium citrate medium consisting of: $(NH_4)_2SO_4$, 0.5 g/l; $NaNO_3$, 0.5 g/l; K_2HPO_4, 0.5 g/l; $MgSO_4 \cdot 7H_2O$, 0.5 g/l; and ferric ammonium citrate, 10.0 g/l. Adjust pH to 6.6 to 6.8 and sterilize. To make the medium solid add 15 g/l of agar.

2. Sulfur Bacteria

a. Sulfate-reducing bacteria:

1) To enumerate sulfate-reducing bacteria such as *Desulfovibrio*, use the medium described by Lewis[28] (see Media Specifications, Section 905C.44). Inoculate the tubes and fill completely with sterile medium to create anaerobic conditions. For comparative purposes, incubate one or two uninoculated controls with each set of inoculated tubes. To sample volumes greater than 10 ml, pass the water sample through a 0.45-μm membrane filter and transfer this filter to the screw-cap test tube with the medium. If sulfate-reducing bacteria are present the tubes will show blackening within 4 to 21 days of incubation at 20 to 30 C.

2) An agar medium suitable for the growth and enumeration of sulfate-reducing bacteria also is available.[29] The medium consists of trypticase soy agar (4.0%), fortified with additional agar (0.5%) to which is added 60% sodium lactate (0.4% v/v), hydrated magnesium sulfate (0.2%), and ferrous ammonium sulfate (0.2%). Adjust pH to 7.2 to 7.4 and sterilize. The medium is clear and free from precipitate. Inoculate all plates within 1 or at the most 4 hr after the agar hardens to prevent saturation with oxygen. To prevent moisture condensation on the petri dish covers, replace the covers with sterile absorbent tops until 10 to 15 min after the agar hardens. Place the plates in dessicator jars or Brewer jars (plates not inverted) and replace the atmosphere with tank hydrogen or nitrogen by successive evac-

uation and gas replacement. Incubate at room temperature (21 to 24 C) or at 28 to 30 C, the optimum temperature for these organisms. Growth and blackening around the colonies is typical of sulfate-reducing bacteria and may occur between 2 and 21 days although the usual time is 2 to 7 days.

3) Media suitable for the enumeration of various species of sulfate-reducing bacteria have been evaluated.[30]

b. Photosynthetic purple and green sulfur bacteria: Because these organisms are so specialized and rarely cause problems in water and wastewater treatment processes, methods for their isolation and enumeration are not included here. An excellent review is available.[31]

c. Thiobacilli: The growth and physiology of the different species of the single-celled sulfur-oxidizing bacteria of the genus *Thiobacillus* have been carefully evaluated.[32,33] Media[34] suitable for the enumeration, by an MPN technic, of *Thiobacillus thioparus* and *Thiobacillus thiooxidans* are listed in Media Specifications, Section 905C.45 and 46. Inoculate the medium and incubate for 4 to 5 days at 25 to 30 C. Growth of *Thiobacilli* leads to sulfur sinking to the bottom, a decrease in pH, and turbidity. Chemical tests for the formation of sulfate are necessary to confirm presence of *Thiobacillus.*

d. Beggiatoa: Methods for the enrichment and isolation of *Beggiatoa* depend on the use of a hay extract.[16,35] To prepare the medium, extract dried hay at 100 C in large volumes of water, changing the water three times during the extraction. The final wash water has an amber color. After draining the extracted hay, dry it on trays at 37 C. The enrichment medium is 0.8% extracted and dried hay in tap water, dispensed 70 ml/125-ml Erlenmeyer flask and sterilized by autoclave. Inoculate 5-ml portions of mud containing decaying plant material from small ponds, lakes, and streams and incubate at room temperature. In successful enrichments a strong odor of H_2S is noticeable in the flasks and *Beggiatoa* growth appears within 10 days as a white film on the surface of the medium and the submerged upper walls of the flask. To isolate the organism, wash portions of the white surface film several times in sterile tap water and place on the surface of agar plates (1% agar and 0.2% beef extract). Incubate at 28 C. From those plates in which filaments have migrated to the periphery of the agar surface and away from contaminants, cut out agar blocks containing single, isolated filaments of *Beggiatoa* and place, filament side down, on fresh plates of the same medium. Incubate again at 28 C. After growth has progressed to the extent that isolated single filaments are present, repeat the isolation procedure.

An inorganic medium for *Beggiatoa* also has been described.[36]

918 D. References

1. LUESCHOW, L.A. & K.M. MACKENTHUN. 1962. Detection and enumeration of iron bacteria in municipal water supplies. *J. Amer. Water Works Ass.* 54:751.

2. STARKEY, R.L. 1945. Transformations of iron by bacteria in water. *J. Amer. Water Works Ass.* 37:963.

3. STOKES, J.L. 1954. Studies on the filamentous sheathed iron bacterium *Sphaerotilus natans. J. Bacteriol.* 67:278.

4. KUCERA, S. & R.S. WOLFE. 1957. A selective enrichment method for *Gallionella ferruginea. J. Bacteriol.* 74:344.

5. WAITZ, S. & J.B. LACKEY. 1958. Morphological and biochemical studies on the organism *Sphaerotilus natans. Quart. J. Fla. Acad. Sci.* 21:335.

6. WOLFE, R.S. 1958. Cultivation, morphology, and classification of the iron bacteria. *J. Amer. Water Works Ass.* 50:1241.

7. WOLFE, R.S. 1960. Observations and studies of *Crenothrix polyspora. J. Amer. Water Works Ass.* 52:915.

8. WOLFE, R.S. 1960. Microbial concentration of iron and manganese in water with low concentrations of these elements. *J. Amer. Water Works Ass.* 52:1335.

9. DONDERO, N.C., R.A. PHILIPS & H. HEUKELEKIAN. 1961. Isolation and preservation of cultures of *Sphaerotilus. Appl. Microbiol.* 9:219.

10. MULDER, E.G. 1964. Iron bacteria, particularly those of the *Sphaerotilus-Leptothrix* group, and industrial problems. *J. Appl. Bacteriol* 27:151.

11. DRAKE, C.H. 1965. Occurrence of *Siderocapsa treubii* in certain waters of the Niederrhein. *Gewässer Abwässer* 39/40:41.

12. BUCHANAN, R.E. & N.E. GIBBONS, eds. 1974. Bergey's Manual of Determinative Bacteriology, 8th ed. Williams & Wilkens Co., Baltimore, Md.

13. EDMONDSON, W.T., ed. 1959. Ward & Whipple's Fresh Water Biology, 2nd ed. John Wiley & Son, New York, N.Y.

14. SKERMAN, V.B.D. 1967. A Guide to the Identification of the Genera of Bacteria, 2nd ed. Williams & Wilkens Co., Baltimore, Md.

15. LACKEY, J.B. & E.W. LACKEY. 1961. The habitat and description of a new genus of sulphur bacterium. *J. Gen. Microbiol.* 26:28.

16. FAUST, L. & R.S. WOLFE. 1961. Enrichment and cultivation of *Beggiatoa alba. J. Bacteriol.* 81:99.

17. MORGAN, G.B. & J.B. LACKEY. 1965. Ecology of a sulfuretum in a semitropical environment. *Z. Allg. Mikrobiol.* 5:237.

18. ARMBRUSTER, E.H. 1969. Improved technique for isolation and identification of *Sphaerotilus. Appl. Microbiol.* 17:320.

19. FARQUHAR, G.J. & W.C. BOYLE. 1971. Identification of filamentous microorganisms in activated sludge. *J. Water Pollut. Control Fed.* 43:604.

20. VAN VEEN, W.L. 1973. Bacteriology of activated sludge, in particular the filamentous bacteria. *Antonie van Leeuwenhoek* (Holland) 39:189.

21. MULDER, E.G. & W.L. VAN VEEN. 1963. Investigations on the *Sphaerotilus-Leptothrix* group. *Antonie van Leeuwenhoek* (Holland) 29:121.

22. UNZ, R.F. & D.G. LUNDGREN. 1961. A comparative nutritional study of three chemoautotrophic bacteria: *Ferrobacillus ferrooxidans, Thiobacillus ferrooxidans,* and *Thiobacillus thiooxidans. Soil Sci.* 92:302.

23. MCGORAN, C.J.M., D.W. DUNCAN & C.C. WALDEN. 1969. Growth of *Thiobacillus ferrooxidans* on various substrates. *Can. J. Microbiol.* 15:135.

24. SILVERMAN, M.P. & D.C. LUNDGREN. 1959. Studies on the chemoautotrophic iron bacterium *Ferrobacillus ferrooxidans. J. Bacteriol.* 77:642.

25. NUNLEY, J.W. & N.R. KRIEG. 1968. Isolation of *Gallionella ferruginea* by use of formalin. *Can. J. Microbiol.* 14:385.

26. WALSH, F. & R. MITCHELL. 1972. A pH dependent succession of iron bacteria. *Environ. Sci. Technol.* 6:809.

27. CLARK, F.M., R.M. SCOTT & E. BONE. 1967. Heterotrophic, iron-precipitating bacteria. *J. Amer. Water Works Ass.* 59:1036.

28. LEWIS, R.F. 1965. Control of sulfate-reducing bacteria. *J. Amer. Water Works Ass.* 57:1011.

29. IVERSON, W.P. 1966. Growth of *Desulfovibrio* on the surface of agar media. *Appl. Microbiol.* 14:529.

30. MARA, D.D. & D.J.A. WILLIAMS. 1970. The evaluation of media used to enumerate sulphate reducing bacteria. *J. Appl. Bacteriol.* (England) 33:543.

31. PFENNIG, N. 1967. Photosynthetic bacteria. *Ann. Rev. Microbiol.* 21:285.

32. HUTCHINSON, M., K.I. JOHNSTONE & D. WHITE. 1965. The taxonomy of certain thiobacilli. *J. Gen. Microbiol.* 41:357.

33. HUTCHINSON, M., K.I. JOHNSTONE & D.

WHITE. 1966. Taxonomy of the acidophilic thiobacilli. *J. Gen. Microbiol.* 44:373.

34. STARKEY, R.L. 1937. Formation of sulfide by some sulfur bacteria. *J. Bacteriol.* 33:545.

35. SCOTTEN, H.L. & J.L. STOKES. 1962. Isolation and properties of *Beggiatoa. Arch. Mikrobiol.* 42:353.

36. KOWALLIK, U. & E.G. PRINGSHEIM. 1966. The oxidation of hydrogen sulfide by beggiatoa. *Amer. J. Bot.* 53:801.

PART 1000

BIOLOGICAL EXAMINATION

OF WATER

1001 INTRODUCTION

Water quality affects the abundance, species composition and diversity, stability, productivity, and physiological condition of indigenous populations of aquatic organisms. Therefore, an expression of the nature and health of the aquatic communities is an expression of the quality of the water. Biological methods used for measuring water quality include the collection, counting, and identification of aquatic organisms; biomass measurements; measurements of metabolic activity rates; measurements of the toxicity, bioaccumulation, and biomagnification of pollutants; and processing and interpretation of biological data.

Information from these types of measurements may serve one or more of the following purposes:

1. To explain the cause of color and turbidity and the presence of objectionable odors, tastes, and visible particulates in water;

2. To aid in the interpretation of the various chemical analyses, for example, in relating the presence or absence of certain biological forms to oxygen deficiency or supersaturation in natural waters;

3. To identify the source of a water that is mixing with another water;

4. To explain the clogging of pipes, screens, or filters, and to aid in the design and operation of water and wastewater treatment plants;

5. To determine optimum times for the treatment of surface water with algi-

cides and to check treatment effectiveness;

6. To determine the effectiveness of various drinking water treatment stages and to aid in determining effective chlorine dosage within the water treatment plant as such dosage is related to organic materials in water;

7. To indicate the nature, extent, and biological effects of pollution;

8. To indicate the progress of the self-purification of bodies of water;

9. To aid in explaining the mechanism of biological wastewater treatment methods or to serve as an index of the effectiveness of treatment;

10. To aid in determining the condition and effectiveness of the various units in the wastewater treatment plant;

11. To document short- and long-term variability in water quality as influenced by natural and/or man-induced changes;

12. To provide data on the status of an aquatic system on a regular basis.

The specific nature of a problem and the reasons for collecting samples will dictate which communities of aquatic organisms will be examined and which sampling and analytical technics will be used.

The following communities of aquatic organisms are considered in specific sections that follow:

1. PLANKTON: A community of plants (phytoplankton) and animals (zooplankton), usually swimming or suspended in water, nonmotile or in-

sufficiently motile to overcome transport by currents. In fresh water they are generally small or microscopic; in salt water, larger forms are observed more frequently.

2. PERIPHYTON (AUFWUCHS): A community of microscopic plants and animals associated with the surfaces of submersed objects. Some are attached, some move about. Many of the protozoa and other minute invertebrates and algae that are found in the plankton also occur in the periphyton.

3. MACROPHYTON: The larger plants of all types. They are sometimes attached to the bottom (benthic), sometimes free-floating, sometimes totally submersed, and sometimes partly emergent. "Higher" types usually have true roots, stems, and leaves; the algae are simpler but may have stem- and leaf-like structures.

4. MACROINVERTEBRATES: The larger invertebrates, defined here as those retained by the US Standard No. 30 sieve. They are generally bottom-dwelling organisms (benthos).

5. FISH: As used in this publication, only the finned fish.

6. AMPHIBIANS, AQUATIC REPTILES, BIRDS, AND MAMMALS: These vertebrates also may be affected directly or indirectly by spills or other discharges of pollutants and may be useful in monitoring the presence of toxic pollutants or long-term changes in water quality. Discussions of these organisms are not included.

Large numbers of bacteria and fungi also are present in the plankton and periphyton and constitute an essential element of the total aquatic ecosystem. Although their interactions with living and dead organic matter profoundly affect

the larger aquatic organisms dealt with below, technics for their investigation are not included herein.

Field observations are indispensable for meaningful biological interpretations, but many biological parameters cannot be evaluated directly in the field. These must be examined as field data or field samples within the laboratory. Because the significance of the analytical result depends on the representativeness of the sample taken, attention is given to field methods as well as to associated laboratory procedures. In biological examinations, field and laboratory personnel are often the same; if they are not, their activities must be coordinated closely.

Before sampling begins, study objectives must be defined clearly. For example, the frequency of a repetitive sampling program may vary from hourly, for a detailed study of diel variability, to every third month (quarterly) for a general assessment of seasonal conditions, depending on the objectives. The scope of the study must be adjusted to limitations in personnel, time, and money. An examination of historic data for the study area and a literature search of work by previous investigators should precede the development of a study plan.

Whenever practicable, a biologist should collect his own samples. Much of the value of an experienced biologist lies in his personal observations of conditions in the field and in his ability to recognize signs of environmental changes as reflected in the various aquatic communities.

Many specialized items of biological collecting equipment may not be available from the usual laboratory supply houses. The American Society of Limnology and Oceanography has compiled a list of manufacturers and distributors of such equipment entitled "Special Publication No. 1, Sources of Limnological and Oceanographic Apparatus and Supplies," which is available on request from the secretary of the society (consult a current issue of *Limnology and Oceanography* for the current name and address). The American Association for the Advancement of Science (AAAS) also prepares an equipment/supplier index that is published annually as an issue of *Science*.

The primary orientation of Part 1000 is toward field collection and associated laboratory analyses to aid in determining the status of aquatic communities under existing field conditions and to aid in interpreting the influence of past and present environmental conditions. Many other types of studies may be, and are being, conducted that are oriented more toward laboratory re-

search. Such laboratory studies will develop further basic knowledge of community and/or organism responses under controlled conditions and will aid in predicting effects of future changes in environmental conditions on the aquatic communities. However, such studies are not within the scope of this presentation.

The complex interrelationships existing in an aquatic environment are reflected in the organization of the following sections. Field and laboratory procedures relating to one section also may be appropriate for other sections; consequently, frequent cross-references between sections have been made.

The methods selected for description are necessary for the appraisal of water quality. Principal emphasis is on methods and equipment, rather than on interpretation or application of results. Preference is given to procedures used in assessing water quality rather than to those used in aquatic resources management.

1002   PLANKTON

1002 A.   Introduction

The term "plankton" refers to those microscopic aquatic forms having little or no resistance to the currents and living free-floating and suspended in open or pelagic waters. The planktonic plants are referred to as "phytoplankton" and the animals as "zooplankton." The phytoplankton (microscopic algae and bacteria) occur as unicellular, colonial, or filamentous forms. Many carry on photosynthesis and are grazed upon by

zooplankton and other aquatic organisms. The zooplankton in fresh water comprise principally protozoans, rotifers, cladocerans, and copepods; in marine waters, a much greater variety of organisms is encountered.

Plankton, particularly phytoplankton, long have been used as indicators of water quality.[1,2,3,4] Some species flourish in highly eutrophic waters while others are very sensitive to organic and/or chemical wastes. Phytoplankton reported to be indicators of clean water include *Melosira islandica*,[5] *Cyclotella ocellata*, and species of *Dinobryon*. Species reported to be indicators of polluted water include *Nitzschia palea*, *Microcystis aeruginosa*, and *Aphanizomenon flos-aquae*. The latter two species may form noxious blooms in polluted waters, giving off toxins and offensive odors.[6] As with the phytoplankton, the species assemblage of zooplankton in a given area is useful in assessing water quality.

Because of their short life cycles, plankters respond quickly to environmental changes, and hence the standing crop and species composition indicate the quality of the water mass in which they are found. Also, because of their small size and often great numbers, they not only strongly influence certain non-biological aspects of water quality (such as pH, color, taste, and odor), but in a very practical sense, they *are* a part of water quality. Certain taxa often are useful in determining the origin, or recent history, of a given water mass. Because of their transient nature, however, plankton communities may be of limited value in assessing water quality. In rivers, their origin can be uncertain and the duration of their exposure to pollutants unknown.

1002 B.   Sample Collection

1. General Considerations

Locate sampling stations as near as possible to those selected for chemical and bacteriological sampling to insure maximum correlation of findings. Establish a sufficient number of stations in as many locations as necessary to define adequately the kinds and quantities of plankton in the waters studied. The physical nature of the water (standing, flowing, or tidal) will influence greatly the selection of the sampling stations. The use of sampling sites selected by previous investigators usually will assure the availability of historic data that will lead to a better understanding of current results and provide continuity in the study of an area.

In stream and river work, locate stations upstream and downstream from suspected pollution sources and major tributary streams, and at appropriate intervals throughout the reach under investigation. If possible, locate stations on both sides of the river because lateral mixing of river water may not occur for great distances downstream. Some effects of pollution on plankton populations may not be apparent for distances downstream as great as several days stream flow. In a similar manner, investigate tributary streams suspected of being polluted but take care in the interpretation of data from a small stream since much of the plankton may be periphytic in origin, arising from scouring of natural substrates by the flowing water. Plankton contributions from adjacent lakes, reservoirs, and backwater areas, as well as soil organisms carried into the stream by runoff, also can influence data interpretation. The depth from which water is discharged from upstream stratified reservoirs also can affect the nature of the plankton.

Because the waters of rivers and streams usually are well mixed vertically, subsurface sampling often is adequate for collection of a representative sample at a given point. Always sample in the main channel of a river and avoid sloughs, inlets, or backwater areas that reflect local habitats rather than river conditions. In rivers that are mixed vertically and horizontally, plankton populations can be ascertained by examining periodic samples collected at midstream 0.5 to 1 m (about 1 to 3 ft) below the surface.

Use a grid network or transect lines in sampling a lake or reservoir. Take a sufficient number of samples to make the data meaningful. Sample a circular lake basin at strategic points along a minimum of two perpendicular transects extending from shore to shore; include the deepest point in the basin. Sample a long, narrow basin at several points along a minimum of three regularly spaced parallel transects that are perpendicular to the long axis of the basin, with the first near the inlet and the last near the outlet. Sample a large bay along several parallel transects originating near shore and extending to the lake proper. Because of the large number of samples required to appraise completely the plankton assemblage, it may be necessary to restrict sampling to strategic points, such as the vicinity of water intakes and discharges, constrictions within the water body, and major bays that may influence the main basin.

In lakes, reservoirs, and estuaries where plankton populations can vary with depth, collect samples from all major depth zones or water masses. The sampling depths will be determined by the water depth at the station, the depth of the thermocline or an isohaline, or other factors. In shallow areas of 2 to 3 m (about 5 to 10 ft) depth, subsurface samples usually are adequate. In deeper areas, collect samples at regular depth intervals. Sample estuarine plankton at regular intervals from the surface to the bottom. Collect offshore marine samples at intervals of 3 to 6 m or more throughout the euphotic zone, and to the bottom if zooplankton are to be included. The compromise sampling depths for marine waters may be an arbitrary depth between the thermocline and the euphotic zone, above and below an isohaline, or other boundary.

Samples usually are referred to as "surface" or "depth" (subsurface) samples. The latter are samples taken from some stated depth, whereas surface samples may be interpreted as samples collected as near the water surface as possible. A "skimmed" sample of the surface film can be revealing, but ordinarily a disproportionate quantity of surface film should not be included in a surface sample because plankton often are trapped on top or at the surface film together with pollen, dust, and other detritus.

The frequency of sampling is dictated by the purpose and scope of the study as well as the range of seasonal fluctuations, the immediate meterological conditions, adequacy of equipment, and availability of personnel. Frequent plankton sampling is desirable because of the normal temporal variability and migratory character of the plankton community. Daily vertical migrations occur in response to sunlight and random horizontal migrations or drifts are produced by winds, shifting currents, and tides. Ideally, collect daily samples and, when possible, sample at different times during the day and at different depths. When this is not possible, weekly, biweekly, monthly, or even quarterly sampling still may be useful for determining major population changes.

In tidal areas of fresh-water streams, in saline reaches of tributaries and estuaries, and in marine waters, collect plankton in accordance with tidal oscillations at each preselected depth during the flood and ebb tides for more than one tidal cycle. Data derived from these waters frequently are most meaningful when the samples have been collected near the end or beginning of both the flood and the ebb tides, but some sampling should be carried out at all tidal stages.

2. Sampling Procedures

Once sampling locations, depths, and frequency have been determined, preparation for field sampling can proceed. Label sample containers with sufficient information to avoid confusion or error. Indicate date, sampling station, study area (river, lake, reservoir), type of sample, and depth on the label. Use waterproof labels. When possible, enclose collection vessels in a protective container to avoid breakage. If samples are to be preserved immediately after collection, add the preservative to the container before sampling. Sample size depends on the type and number of

determinations to be made; the number of replicates depends on the statistical design of the study and the statistical analyses selected to assist in data interpretation. In a field record book note sample location, depth, type, time, meteorological conditions, turbidity, water temperature, and other observations of ecological significance. These field data are invaluable when analytical data are interpreted, and often help to explain unusual changes caused by the variable character of the aquatic environment.

3. Phytoplankton

When phytoplankton densities are less than 500 units/ml, collect a 6-l sample. In richer waters, a sample of 1 to 2 l is sufficient.

For qualitative and quantitative evaluations collect whole (unfiltered and unstrained) water samples with a device consisting of a cylindrical tube with stoppers at each end and a closing device. Lower the open sampler to the desired depth and close by dropping a weight, called a messenger, which slides down the supporting wire or cord and trips the closing mechanism. The most commonly used samplers that operate on this principle are the Kemmerer,[7] Van Dorn[8] (Figure 1002:1), and Nansen samplers. The Kemmerer and Van Dorn samplers are similar except for the closure mechanisms. The Nansen reversing water bottle[9] is used for sampling at greater depths.

Sometimes it is useful to divide plankton on the basis of size regardless of the type of collection equipment used. "Net plankton" is generally defined as plankton with a diameter of 60 μm or more (mesh openings of the common No. 20

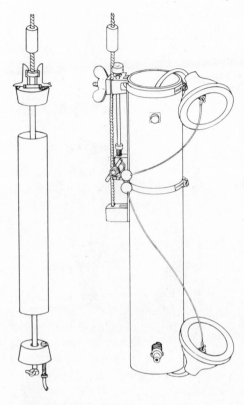

Figure 1002:1. Structural features of the Kemmerer (left) and Van Dorn (right) water samplers.

plankton net). Organisms smaller than 60 μm in diameter are termed "nanno-plankton" and those smaller than 10 μm in diameter are called "micro-" or "ultraplankton". If such a classification system is used, it should be described carefully or referenced in the report. Because the Kemmerer and Van Dorn samplers collect whole water samples, both the net and nannoplankton are collected.

The Van Dorn usually is the preferred sampler because its design offers no inhibition to the free flow of water

through the cylinder. Also, the samplers can be cast in a series on a single line for simultaneous sampling at multiple depths with the use of auxiliary messengers. Since the triggering devices of these samplers are very sensitive, avoid rough handling. Always lower the sampler into the water; do not drop. The capacity of the Kemmerer and Van Dorn samplers varies from 0.5 to 5 l or more. Polyethylene or polyvinyl chloride sampling devices are preferred to metal samplers because the latter liberate metallic ions that may contaminate the sample. Polyethylene or glass sample storage bottles are recommended. Metallic ion contamination can lead to significant errors when algal assays or productivity measurements are made.

Sampling phytoplankton with nets provides data of limited value since the total count, volume, biomass, and species composition are not measurable. Because of selectivity of the mesh size, the smaller plankton (nannoplankton), which may contribute as much as 60% of the total biomass, are not collected. However, the simplicity of this collection device encourages its continued use. Various types of plankton nets are shown in Figures 1002:2 and 1002:3. For primary productivity determinations, bottle samplers are recommended because all organisms present are collected. For greater speed of collection and for obtaining large quantities of organisms, use a pump. Lower a long, weighted hose, attached to a suction pump, to the desired depth, and pump water to the surface. The pump is advantageous because it can supply a homogeneous sample from a given depth or an integrated sample from the surface to a particular depth, but the possible

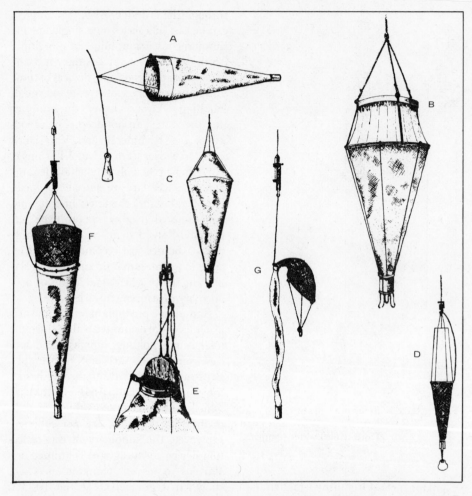

Figure 1002:2. Plankton sampling nets. (a) Simple conical tow-net; (b) Hensen net; (c) Apstein net; (d) Juday net; (e) Apstein net with semicircular closing lids; (f) Nansen closing net, open; (g) Nansen closing net, closed. Source: TRANTER, D.J., ed. 1968. Reviews on Zooplankton Sampling Methods. UNESCO, Switzerland.

damaging of organisms by the pump impeller must be investigated.

For shallow waters use the Jenkins surface mud sampler[10] or one of the bottle samplers modified so that it is held horizontally for sampling in shallow waters.[11] Like many of the other samplers mentioned, the water core sampler[12] is applicable to phytoplankton and zooplankton sampling.

If live samples are to be examined, fill the containers only partially to reduce inhibition of metabolic activities and store in a portable refrigerator or ice chest. Examine specimens within 3 hr of collection.

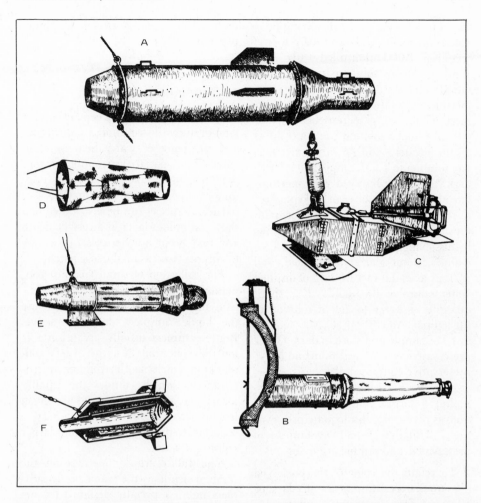

Figure 1002:3. **High-speed, oceanographic and/or quantitative zooplankton samplers.** (a) Gulf III sampler; (b) Clarke-Bumpus sampler; (c) Hardy continuous plankton recorder; (d) Sheard high-speed sampler; (e) Icelandic plankton sampler; (f) Clarke jet net (section). Source: TRANTER, D.J., ed. 1968. Reviews on Zooplankton Sampling Methods. UNESCO, Switzerland.

If it is impossible to examine living material, preserve the sample. For a sample that will be preserved, fill the container completely. There are numerous preservatives for phytoplankton work of which the most universally used is formalin. For delicate forms such as naked flagellates, Lugol's solution is a more suitable preservative.

To preserve the samples with formalin, add 40 ml buffered formalin to 1 l of the sample immediately after collection. Other popular preservatives are Lugol's solution and merthiolate. Prepare Lugol's solution by dissolving 60 g potassium iodide (KI) and 40 g iodine crystals in 1,000 ml distilled water. Add 1 ml of Lugol's solution to 100 ml of sample and store in dark. Prepare the merthiolate solution by dissolving 1.0 g merthiolate, 1.5 g sodium borate, and 1.0 ml Lugol's solution in 1,000 ml of distilled water. Add 36 ml of merthiolate solution to 1 l of sample and store in dark. Samples preserved with merthiolate are not sterile, but can be kept effectively for 1 yr, after which time formalin must be added.[13] Prepare "M³" fixative by dissolving 5 g potassium iodide, 10 g iodine, 50 ml glacial acetic acid, and 250 ml formalin in 1,000 ml of distilled water (dissolve the iodide in a small quantity of water to aid in solution of the iodine). Add 20 ml of "M³" fixative to 1 l of sample and store in dark. Other preservatives are 95% alcohol and 6-3-1 preservative composed of 6 parts water, 3 parts 95% alcohol, and 1 part formalin. A larger volume of these solutions is necessary for adequate preservation. Usually, equal volumes of preservative and sample are used.

To retain the color of the preserved plankton, store samples in the dark or add 1 ml of saturated cupric sulfate solution/l.

Most preservatives distort and disrupt certain cells, especially those of delicate forms such as *Euglena*, *Synura*, *Chromulina*, and *Mallamonas*. An experienced taxonomist is aware of these structural changes. A novice should become familiar with live specimens and the distortions associated with preservation. A reference collection supplied by a biological supply house or compiled by an experienced co-worker may be very

useful in identifying preserved phytoplankton.

4. Zooplankton

The choice of sampler depends on the kind of study (distribution, productivity) and the body of water being investigated. The spatial distribution of zooplankton in a lake is normally nonuniform. In certain situations, a particular species can be distributed in a thin, continuous layer at a specific depth and may occur nowhere else, or it may be limited to occasional dense patches.

For collection of small (nanno) zooplankters, such as protozoa, small rotifers, and immature microcrustacea, use the bottle samplers described above. Bottle samplers usually are unsuitable for the collection of larger (net) zooplankton (such as the mature microcrustacea) which, unlike the smaller forms, can avoid capture and are much less numerous. Usually it is necessary to concentrate the organisms from a larger volume of water.

The Juday trap[14] operates on the same principle as the water bottle samplers but is especially designed for net zooplankton sampling. It has a capacity of 10 l.

The larger zooplankton commonly are sampled with a No. 8 mesh plankton net.[15,16] However, the mesh size, type of material, orifice size, length, hauling methods, and volume sampled will depend on the particular needs of the study. The mesh size and net material determine filtration efficiency, clogging tendencies, velocity, drag, and the condition of the sample after collection. Most nets are made of nylon or silk.

These materials are stiff yet flexible, durable, and resistant to swelling. Long nets with wide mouths are recommended because they permit maximum filtering surface area and cause minimal disruption of the population.

Three types of tows are used: vertical, horizontal, and oblique. To make a vertical tow, lower the weighted net to a given depth, then raise vertically at an even speed; 0.5 to 1.0 m/sec is recommended. Estimate the volume (m^3) of water filtered through the net as $V = \pi r^2 d$ where r is the radius of the net's orifice and d is the depth to which the net is lowered. For oblique and horizontal tows, the types of samplers shown in Figure 1002:3 are more suitable.

To collect a sample, tow the plankton net from a boat. The boat should be equipped with a davit, meter wheel, angle indicator, and winch. Attach a 3- to 5-kg (about 7- to 10-lb) weight to hold the net down. Determine the depth of the net by multiplying the length of the extended wire by the cosine of the wire's angle with the vertical direction. Maintain the wire angle by controlling the boat's speed.

For oblique tows, lower the net or sampler to some predetermined depth and then raise at a constant rate as the boat moves forward. For horizontal tows, lower the net to the preselected depth, tow at that depth for 5 to 8 min, then close, and raise the net. Vertical and oblique tows collect a composite sample, whereas horizontal tows collect a sample at a particular horizon. For an estimation of both distribution and abundance, use the horizontal tow.

The Clarke-Bumpus sampler[17] is recommended for quantitative collection of zooplankton because it is more versatile than other devices and can be used in various sampling patterns. In standing waters, collect tow samples by filtering 1 to 5 m^3 of water.

For an estimate of net zooplankton populations in flowing waters, collect 20 l of surface water by bucket and filter through a mesh of appropriate size. The rim of the net should not be held more than a few centimeters above the surface of the water to prevent the organisms from being driven through the net.

Preserve zooplankton samples with 70% ethanol, 5% buffered formalin, or Lugol's solution. The formalin preservative is preferred but may cause distortion of plastic forms such as protozoans and rotifers. To prevent evaporation, add 5% glycerin to the concentrated sample. In turbid samples, differentiate animal and vegetative material by adding 0.04% rose bengal stain, which is chemically specific for the carapace (shells) of zooplankters.

1002 C.   Concentration Technics

The organisms contained in water samples sometimes must be concentrated in the laboratory before analysis. Three technics for concentrating, namely, sedimentation, membrane filtration, and centrifugation, are described below.

1. Sedimentation

Sedimentation usually is the preferred method of concentration because it is nonselective (unlike filtration) and nondestructive (unlike centrifugation). The volume concentrated varies inversely with the abundance of organisms and is affected by sample turbidity. It may be as small as 10 ml for use with an inverted microscope to as much as 1 l for general phytoplankton and zooplankton enumeration.

The settling rate may be accelerated by the addition of a liquid household detergent. For an untreated sample allow 1 hr settling/mm of sample depth. For a treated sample (10 ml detergent/l) allow about 0.5 hr settling/mm depth. The sample may be concentrated in a series of steps by quantitatively transferring the sediment from the initial container to sequentially smaller ones. Fill settling chambers without forming a vortex, keep them vibration-free, and move them carefully to avoid nonrandom distribution of settled matter. Siphon or decant the supernatants to obtain the desired final volume (5 ml for diatom mounts). Store the concentrated sample in a closed, labelled glass vial.

2. Membrane Filtration

The filtration method is used primarily for phytoplankton. It is not recommended when populations are dense and the content of detritus is high because the filter clogs quickly and silt may crush the organisms or obscure them from view. Pour a measured volume of the well-mixed sample into a funnel equipped with a membrane filter having a pore size of 0.45 μm. Apply a vacuum of less than 0.5 atm to the filter.

Certain features of this method make it particularly adaptable for use on waters with a low phytoplankton and silt content. Primarily, the method permits the use of high magnification for enumeration of small plankters, does not require counting of individual plankters to assemble enumeration data, and increases the probability of observing the less abundant forms.[18]

3. Centrifugation

Plankton can be concentrated by batch or continuous centrifugation. Centrifuge batch samples at 1,000 G for 20 min. The Foerst continuous centrifuge* is no longer generally recommended as a quantitative device but it may be desirable to continue its use in existing programs in order to assure continuity with previously collected data. For a specifically designed program of limited scope, its speed and convenience may outweigh its disadvantages. Although centrifugation accelerates sedimentation, it may damage fragile organisms.

---

*Foerst Mechanical Specialities Co., 2407 N. St. Louis Ave., Chicago, Ill. 60647 or Limnological Apparatus Co., 2406 N. Bernard St., Chicago, Ill. 60647.

1002 D. Mounting and Preparation for Examination

1. Phytoplankton Semi-permanent Wet Mounts

Agitate the settled sample concentrate and withdraw a subsample with an accurate automatic pipet if one is available. Prepare wet mounts by transferring 0.1 ml to a glass slide, placing a cover slip over the sample, and ringing the cover slip with an adhesive such as clear nail polish to prevent evaporation. For semipermanent slides, mix glycerin with the sample; as the sample ages the water evaporates, leaving the organisms imbedded in the glycerin. If the cover slip is ringed with adhesive, the slide can be retained for a few years if stored in the dark.

2. Phytoplankton Membrane Filter Mounts

Place two drops of immersion oil on a labeled slide. Immediately after filtering place the filter on top of the oil with a pair of forceps and add two drops of oil on top of the filter. The oil impregantes the filter and makes it transparent. Impregnation time is 24 to 48 hr. Once the filter has cleared, place a few additional drops of oil on the cleared filter and cover with a cover slip. The mounted filter is now ready for microscopic examination.

3. Diatom Mounts

Samples concentrated for diatom analysis by settling or centrifugation may contain dissolved materials, such as marine salts, formalin, and detergents, that will leave interfering residues and must be well washed with distilled water before slide preparation. Transfer several drops of the washed concentrate by means of a disposable pipet or a large-bore dropper to a cover slip on a hot plate warmed sufficiently to increase the evaporation rate, but not hot enough to boil. Evaporate to dryness. Repeat addition and evaporation until a sufficient quantity of sample has been transferred to the cover slip. Avoid producing a residue so dense that organisms cannot be recognized. If in doubt about the density, examine under a compound microscope. After evaporation, incinerate the residue on the cover slip on the hot plate at 300 to 500 C. This usually requires 20 to 45 min. Mount in Hyrax as described below.

Treat samples concentrated for diatom analysis by membrane filtration as described by Patrick and Reimer.[19] Mix an equal volume of concentrated nitric acid with the sample. Add a few grains of potassium dichromate[20] to facilitate digestion of the filter and cellular organic matter. Add more dichromate if solution color changes from yellow to green. Place the sample on a hot plate and boil down the contents to approximately one-third the original volume. Alternatively, let the treated sample stand overnight. This cleaning process destroys organic matter and leaves only the diatom shells (frustules). Cool the boiled samples, wash with distilled water, and mount as described above. CAUTION: When working with concentrated nitric acid, wear safety goggles and an acid-resistant apron and gloves, and work under a hood for protection. Transfer the cleaned frustules to a cover glass and dry as described above. Mount in Hyrax.

Place a drop of mounting medium in the center of a labeled slide. Use 25-mm by 75-mm slides with frosted ends. Commercially available Hyrax* microscopic mounting medium assures permanent, easily handled mounts for examination under oil immersion. Heat the slide to near 90 C for 1 to 2 min before applying the heated cover slip with its sample residue to hasten evaporation of solvent in the mounting medium. Remove the slide to a cool surface and apply a firm but gentle pressure to the cover glass by means of a broad flat instrument during cooling (5 to 10 sec) to reduce the mount thickness.

4. Zooplankton Mounts

For zooplankton analyses, withdraw a 5-ml subsample from the concentrate and dilute or concentrate further as necessary. Transfer the sample to a counting cell or chamber (see below) for analysis as a wet mount. Use polyvinyl lactyl phenol† for preparing semi-permanent zooplankton mounts. The mounts are good for about a year, after which time the clearing agent causes deterioration of entire organisms. For permanent mounting, use Turtox CMC-10‡ mountant, or equivalent.

---

*Custom Research and Development Inc., #5 Richmond Industrial Village, South Tenth and Wright Avenue, Richmond, Calif. 94804.

†Bio-Medical Specialists, Box 48641, Riggs Station, Los Angeles, Calif. 90048.

‡General Biological Inc., 8200 South Hoyne Avenue, Chicago, Ill. 60620.

1002 E.   Microscopes and Calibrations

1. Compound Microscope

Although most workers prefer the binocular compound microscope, the monocular type can be used. Equip either type with a mechanical stage capable of moving all parts of a counting cell past the aperture of the objective. Standard equipment includes 10× oculars (paired when a binocular microscope is used) and objectives in the following ranges (manufacturers differ slightly in exact specification):

Type of Objective	Approximate Overall Magnification with 10× Ocular
16 mm (low power, 10×)	100×
8 mm (medium power, 20×)	200×
4 mm (high power, dry 43×)	430×
1.8 mm (oil immersion, 90×)	900×

The 8 mm (20×) objective with a working distance of approximately 1.6

mm commonly is used with a standard plankton-counting cell 1 mm deep.

2. Stereoscopic Microscope

The stereoscopic microscope is essentially two complete microscopes assembled into a binocular instrument to give a stereoscopic view and an erect rather than an inverted image. This microscope is indispensable for the study and counting of large plankters such as the mature microcrustacea. The optical equipment of this microscope should include 10× to 15× paired oculars in combination with 1× to 8× objectives. This combination of lenses bridges the gap between the hand lens and the compound microscope and provides magnifications ranging from 10× to 120×. A good-quality zoom-type instrument with comparable magnifications is equally useful.

3. Inverted Compound Microscope

The inverted compound microscope is used routinely for plankton counting in many laboratories.[21] This instrument is unique in that the objectives are below a movable stage and the illumination comes from above. Samples are placed directly into a cylindrical settling chamber having a thin, clear glass bottom. Chambers of various capacities are available; the appropriate size depends on the density of organisms in the sample. After a suitable period of settling (see above), the samples are counted in the settling chambers.

The major advantage of the inverted microscope is that by a simple rotation of the nosepiece a specimen can be examined (or counted) directly in the settling chamber at any desired magnification. No other preparations or manipulations are required. An important disadvantage is that floating organisms, such as buoyant blue-green algae, would not be included in the count.

4. Microscope Calibration

Microscope calibration is essential. The usual equipment for calibration is a Whipple grid (ocular micrometer, reticle, or reticule), which is placed in an eyepiece of the microscope, and a stage micrometer that has a standardized, accurately ruled scale on a glass slide. Purchasers of microscopes for plankton counting should make certain that the eyepiece will accept a standard Whipple disc. The Whipple disk (Figure 1002:4) has an accurately ruled grid that has been subdivided into 100 squares. One of the squares near the center is subdivided further into 25 smaller squares. The outer dimensions of the grid are such that with a 10× (16-mm) objective and a 10× ocular, it delimits an area of approximately 1 mm^2 on the stage of the microscope. Because this area may differ from one microscope to another, the Whipple grid must be calibrated carefully for each microscope before use in counting plankton.

With the ocular and stage micrometers parallel and in part superimposed, match the line at the left edge of the Whipple grid with the zero mark on the stage micrometer scale (Figure 1002:5). Determine the width of the Whipple grid image to the nearest 0.01 mm from the stage micrometer scale. Should the width of the image of the Whipple grid

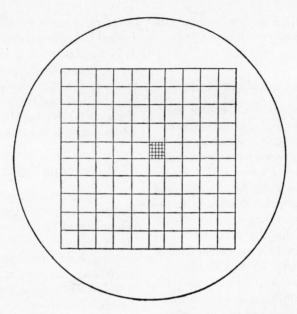

Figure 1002:4. Ocular micrometer ruling. A Whipple micrometer reticule is illustrated.

be exactly 1 mm (1,000 μm), the larger squares will be 1/10 mm (100 μm) on a side and each of the smallest squares 1/50 mm (20 μm).

When the microscope is calibrated at higher magnifications, the entire scale on the stage micrometer will not be seen and measurements should be made to the nearest 0.001 mm. Additional details for calibration are available.[7,22]

With a 10× eyepiece, magnification with the 10× objective lens (giving a total magnification of 10 × 10, or 100×) is not adequate for examination and enumeration of plankters 10 μm or less in diameter because they will appear as unidentifiable dots. Use objective lenses with a magnification of at least 20× (8 mm) when counting nannoplankton.

When a 20× objective lens is used, each smallest square on the Whipple micrometer field is approximately 10 × 10 μm, or 100 μm². Conventional objective lenses with magnifications greater than 20× cannot be used to examine plankton in the Sedgwick-Rafter counting chamber discussed below because their working distance is less than 1 mm and they will break the cover slip on the chamber when in position. Microscopes with the "zoom" mechanism may give the same magnification as a 20× objective when using a 10× objective, but will not provide the same resolution. Special "long working distance" objectives providing magnifications greater than 20× are available. The inverted microscope, as noted above, obviates these problems.

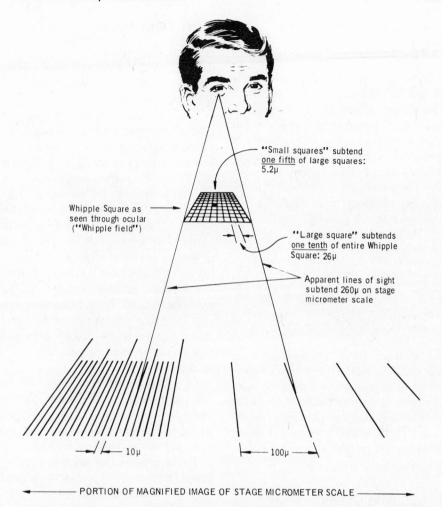

Figure 1002:5. Calibration of Whipple Square, as seen with 10× ocular and 43× objective (approximately 430× total magnification).

1002 F.   Counting Technics

1. Phytoplankton Counting Units

Some phytoplankton are unicellular while others are multicellular (colonial). The variety of configurations poses a problem in enumerating organisms. For example, should a four-celled colony of *Scenedesmus* (Plate 3, A) be reported as one colony or four individual cells? Listed below are a few approaches to the reporting of enumeration data:

Enumeration Method	Counting Unit	Reporting Unit
Total cell count	one cell	cells/ml
Natural unit count[23] (clump count)	one organism (any unicellular organism or natural colony)	units/ml
Areal standard unit count*	400 μm^2	units/ml

A total cell count is time-consuming and tedious, especially when colonies consist of thousands of individual cells. The natural unit or clump is the most easily used system and perhaps gives the most reliable and meaningful data. Whatever the method chosen, it must be identified in reporting results.

2. Counting Chambers

Enumeration of plankton is best performed by using a counting cell or chamber that limits the volume and area for ready calculation of population densities. When enumerating phytoplankton, do not count dead cells or diatoms with broken frustules. Tally empty centric and pennate diatoms separately

---

*Areal standard unit equals area of four small squares in Whipple grid at a magnification of 200X.

as "dead centric diatoms" or "dead pennate diatoms" for use in converting the diatom species proportional count to count per milliliter.

When counting with a Whipple grid, establish a convention for tallying organisms lying on an outer boundary line. For example, in counting a "field" (entire Whipple square), designate the top and left boundaries as "no-count" sides, and the bottom and right boundaries as "count" sides. Thus, every plankter touching a "count" side from the inside or outside is tallied, whereas any touching a "no-count" side is ignored. If there are present significant numbers of filamentous or other large forms that cross two or more boundaries of the grid, count them separately at a lower magnification and include their number in the total count.

In strip counting (see below), the top and bottom of the grid are the "count" and "no-count" boundaries, respectively, and plankters are counted as they move across the center vertical line.

To identify organisms use standard bench references (see section on Selected Taxonomic References below).

a. Sedgwick-Rafter (S-R) counting cell: The S-R cell is the device most commonly used for plankton counting because it is easily manipulated and provides reasonably reproducible data when used with a calibrated microscope equipped with an eyepiece measuring device such as the Whipple grid. The S-R cell is approximately 50 mm long by 20 mm wide by 1 mm deep. The total area of the bottom is approximately 1,000 mm² and the total volume is approximately 1,000 mm³ or 1 ml. The exact length and depth of the cell should be checked carefully with a micrometer and calipers before use.

The greatest disadvantage associated with the cell is that objectives providing high magnification cannot be used.

1) Filling the cell—Before filling the S-R cell with sample, place the cover glass diagonally across the cell and transfer the sample with a large-bore pipet (Figure 1002:6). Placing the cover slip in this manner will help prevent formation of air bubbles in the corners of the cell. The cover slip often will rotate slowly and cover the inner portion of the S-R cell during filling. Do not overfill the cell since this would yield a depth greater than 1 mm and an invalid count would result. Do not permit large air spaces caused by evaporation to develop in the chamber during a lengthy examination. To prevent formation of air spaces, occasionally place a small drop of distilled water on the edge of the cover glass.

Before proceeding with the count, allow the S-R cell to stand for at least 15 min to permit settling of the plankton. Count the plankton on the bottom of the S-R cell. Some phytoplankton, notably some blue-green algae, may not settle but instead may rise to the underside of the cover slip. When this occurs, count these organisms and add to the total of those counted on the bottom of the cell to derive the total number of organisms in the sample.

2) Strip counting—A "strip" the length of the cell constitutes a volume approximately 50 mm long, 1 mm deep, and the width of the total Whipple grid. When 10× eyepieces and 20× or greater objectives are used and the width of the total Whipple grid is calibrated to be 0.5 mm (500 μm),

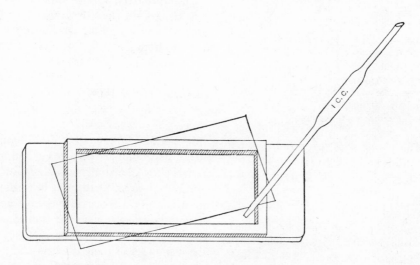

Figure 1002:6. Counting cell (Sedgwick-Rafter), showing method of filling. Source: WHIPPLE, G.C., G.M. FAIR and M.C. WHIPPLE. 1927. The Microscopy of Drinking Water. John Wiley & Sons, New York, N.Y.

the volume of one strip is 25 mm³, or 1/40 (2.5%) the total volume of the cell. For making a strip count, use a magnification of at least 200✕. Calculate the total number of plankters in the S-R cell by multiplying the actual count of plankton in the "strip" by the number (enumeration factor) representing the portion of the S-R cell counted.

Usually count two or four strips, depending on the density of the plankters; the fewer the plankton, the greater the number of strips to be counted. When 10✕ eyepieces and a 20✕ objective are used, the enumeration factor for plankton counted along two strips would be approximately 20, and for four strips approximately 10, depending on the calibration. Derive the number of plankton in the S-R cell from the following:

$$\text{No./ml} = \frac{C \times 1{,}000 \text{ mm}^3}{L \times D \times W \times S}$$

where:

C = number of organisms counted,
L = length of each strip (S-R cell length), mm,
D = depth of a strip (S-R cell depth), mm,
W = width of a strip (Whipple grid image width), mm, and
S = number of strips counted.

Multiply or divide the number of cells per milliliter by a correction factor to adjust for dilution or concentration of the sample.

3) Field counting—On samples containing many plankton (10 or more plankters per field), make field counts rather than strip counts. Count plankters in 10 or more random fields each consisting of one Whipple grid. The number of fields counted will depend on the plankton density and variety and the statistical accuracy desired. Use the following formula to calculate the numbers per milliliter from field counts:

$$\text{No./ml} = \frac{C \times 1{,}000 \text{ mm}^3}{A \times D \times F}$$

where:

C = number of organisms counted,
A = area of a field (Whipple grid image area), mm²,
D = depth of a field (S-R cell depth), mm, and
F = number of fields counted.

Multiply or divide the number of cells per milliliter by a correction factor to adjust for dilution or concentration of the sample.

b. Palmer-Maloney (P-M) nannoplankton cell: The P-M nannoplankton cell[24] is designed specifically for nannoplankton enumeration. It has a circular chamber with a 17.9-mm diam, 0.4-mm depth, and 0.1-ml volume. Use a magnification of 450✕ with the P-M cell. Do not use the P-M cell for routine examination unless the sample contains a dense population (10 or more plankters per field).

Introduce the sample with a pipet into one of the 2-mm by 5-mm channels on the side of the chamber with the cover slip in place. After a 10-min settling period examine 10 to 20 Whipple fields, depending on the density and variety of the plankton and the statistical accuracy desired. Strips may be counted in this or any other circular cell by measuring the effective diameter and counting two perpendicular strips that cross at the center. Calculate the number of plankters per milliliter as follows:

$$\text{No./ml} = \frac{C \times 1{,}000 \text{ mm}^3}{A \times D \times F}$$

where:

C = number of organisms counted,
A = area of a field (Whipple grid image), mm^2,
D = depth of a field (P-M cell depth), mm, and
F = number of fields counted.

Multiply or divide the number of cells per milliliter by a correction factor to adjust for dilution or concentration of the sample.

c. Other counting cells: The most readily available chamber is the standard medical hemacytometer used for enumerating blood cells. It has a ruled grid machined into a counting plate and is fitted with a ground glass cover slip. The grid is divided into square millimeter divisions; the chamber is 0.1 mm deep. Introduce sample by pipet and view under 450× magnification. Count all cells within the grid. A similar chamber, the Petroff-Hausser, designed for bacterial counts, also can be used for phytoplankton enumeration. Each of these chambers comes from the manufacturer with a detailed instruction sheet containing directions on calculations and proper usage. The disadvantage to these counting cells is that the sample must have a very high density of plankton to yield statistically reliable data.

d. Inverted microscope counts: Prepare a sample for examination by filling the settling chamber. After the desired settling time (see above), transfer the chamber to the microscope stage. Count two perpendicular strips across the center of the bottom and average the values. Random fields also can be examined until at least 100 units of the dominant species are counted. Calculate the number of plankters per milliliter:

$$\text{Strip count (no./ml)} = \frac{C \times TA}{L \times W \times S \times V}$$

where:

C = number of organisms counted,
TA = total area of bottom of settling chamber, mm^2,
L = length of a strip, mm,
W = width of a strip (Whipple grid image width), mm,
S = number of strips counted, and
V = volume of sample settled, ml.

$$\text{Field count (no./ml)} = \frac{C \times TA}{F \times A \times V}$$

where:

C = number of organisms counted,
TA = see above,
A = area of a field (Whipple grid image area), mm^2,
F = number of fields counted, and
V = volume of sample settled, ml.

3. Lackey Drop Microtransect Counting Method

The Lackey drop (microtransect) method[25] is a simple method of obtaining counts of considerable accuracy with samples containing a dense plankton population. It is similar to the S-R strip count.

Pipet 0.1 ml on to a glass slide and cover with a 22- by 22-mm glass cover slip. Count the organisms in three or four strips the width of the cover slip. Calculate the number of organisms per milliliter as follows:

$$\text{No./ml} = \frac{C \times TA}{A \times S \times V}$$

where:

TA = area of the cover slip, mm^2,
A = area of one strip, mm^2,
C = number of organisms counted,
S = number of strips counted, and
V = volume of sample under the cover slip, ml.

4. Membrane Filter Counts

Examine samples, concentrated on a membrane filter and mounted in oil as described above, at a magnification of 200X to 450X. Select the magnification level and size of the microscope field (quadrat) such that the most abundant species will appear in at least 70% but not more than 90% of the microscopic fields examined (80% is optimum). Adjust the microscope field size by using part or all of the Whipple grid. Examine 30 random microscope fields and record the number of fields in which each species occurred. Determine the percent occurrence (F %) and the density per field (DN) from Table 1002:I. In this method, ignore any markings on the membrane filter. Report the results as organisms per milliliter, calculated as follows:

$$\text{No./ml} = \frac{DN \times Q}{V \times DF}$$

where:

DN = density (organisms/field) from Table 1002:I,
Q = number of fields per filter,
V = milliliters filtered, and
DF = dilution factor (0.96 for 4% formalin preservative).

5. Particle Counters

Several types of particle counters have been marketed.[26] These instruments can be used very effectively for counting pure cultures but are not suited for enumerating natural plankton communities in surface water grab samples because they do not discriminate between the plankton and particles of silt or organic detritus. At present, these systems can detect particles only in a spe-

TABLE 1002:I. CONVERSION TABLE FOR
MEMBRANE FILTER TECHNIC
(Based on 30 Scored Fields)

Total Occurrence	F%	DN
1	3.3	0.03
2	6.7	0.07
3	10.0	0.10
4	13.3	0.14
5	16.7	0.18
6	20.0	0.22
7	23.3	0.26
8	26.7	0.31
9	30.0	0.35
10	33.3	0.40
11	36.7	0.45
12	40.0	0.51
13	43.3	0.57
14	46.7	0.63
15	50.0	0.69
16	53.3	0.76
17	56.7	0.83
18	60.0	0.91
19	63.3	1.00
20	66.7	1.10
21	70.0	1.20
22	73.3	1.32
23	76.7	1.47
24	80.0	1.61
25	83.3	1.79
26	86.7	2.02
27	90.0	2.30
28	93.3	2.71
29	96.7	3.42
30	100.0	?

Where:

$$F = \frac{\text{total number of species occurrences} \times 100}{\text{total number of fields examined}}$$

and
DN = number of organisms per field.

cific size range. To accommodate the wide range of sizes encountered in the plankton community they would have to be equipped with numerous orifice settings.

6. Diatom Species Proportional Count

Examine diatom samples prepared as directed above under oil immersion at a magnification of at least 900×. Scan lateral strips the width of the Whipple grid until at least 250 cells are counted. Time and degree of accuracy dictate the number of cells to be counted. Determine the percentage abundance of each species from the tallied counts and calculate the counts per milliliter of each species by multiplying the percent abundance by the total live and dead diatom count obtained from the plankton counting chamber.

7. Zooplankton

Enumerate the small (nanno) zooplankton in a counting chamber during the routine phytoplankton count. Report as organisms/per milliliter. Count the larger (net) zooplankton, such as the mature cladocera and copepoda, as concentrates and report as organisms per cubic meter. For larger forms, use a counting chamber 80 mm by 50 mm and 2 mm deep. The chamber can be used with or without a cover. An open chamber is difficult to move because the slightest jarring will disrupt the count. An advantage of the open chamber, however, is the accessibility of the exposed plankton. When using the larger counting chamber, adjust the volume of the concentrate to 8 ml and transfer to the chamber. Count and identify rotifers and nauplii in 10 strips scanned at 100× magnification using a compound microscope equipped with an ocular Whipple grid. Count large organisms, such as the mature microcrustacea, by scanning the entire chamber under a binocular dissecting microscope at 20 to 40× magnification. Where necessary, identify larger organisms after dissection and subsequent examination under a compound microscope. Calculate the number of organisms per cubic meter:

$$\text{No.}/\text{m}^3 = \frac{C \times V'}{V'' \times V'''}$$

where:

C = number of organisms counted,
V' = volume of the concentrated sample, ml,
V'' = volume counted, ml, and
V''' = volume of the grab sample, m^3.

1002 G.   Chlorophyll

The characteristic algal pigments are chlorophylls, xanthophylls, and carotenes. The three chlorophylls commonly found in planktonic algae are chlorophylls a, b, and c. Chlorophyll a constitutes approximately 1 to 2% of the dry weight of organic material in all planktonic algae and is, therefore, the preferred indicator for algal biomass estimates. Two methods for determination of chlorophyll a in phytoplankton are available, the spectrophotometric[8,27,28] and fluorometric.[8,29,30,31] The fluorometric method is more sensitive, requires less sample volume, and has been adapted for in vivo measurements.[32] A specific method for chlorophyll c, more sensitive than the trichromatic method described below, especially for samples of low pigment content, is available[33] but is not included here.

Pheophytin a, a common degradation product of chlorophyll a, can interfere with the spectrophotometric or fluorometric determination of chlorophyll *a* because it absorbs light and fluoresces in the same region of the spectrum as chlorophyll *a* and, if present, may cause errors in chlorophyll *a* values.[34,35] When performing chlorophyll *a* determinations, therefore, measure the concentration of pheophytin *a* in the sample. The ratio of chlorophyll *a* to pheophytin *a* serves also as a good indicator of the physiological condition of the phytoplankton. Another useful water quality indicator is the ratio of biomass to chlorophyll *a* (Autotrophic Index). In unpolluted waters the plankton population is composed largely of autotrophic (food-producing), chlorophyllous algae. As waters become organically enriched, the proportion of heterotrophic (consuming), nonchlorophyllous organisms, such as the filamentous bacteria and stalked protozoa, increases. The Autotrophic Index is a means of relating changes in plankton species composition to changes in water quality.[36] The Autotrophic Index (AI) is calculated as:

$$AI = \frac{\text{Biomass (ash-free wt of organic matter), mg/m}^3}{\text{Chlorophyll } a, \text{mg/m}^3}$$

Normal AI values range from 50 to 200. Larger AI values indicate poor water quality.

1. Spectrophotometric Determination of Chlorophyll *a*, *b*, and *c* (Trichromatic Method)

The pigments are extracted from the plankton concentrate with aqueous acetone and the optical density of the extract is determined with a spectrophotometer. When immediate pigment extraction is not possible, the samples may be stored frozen for as long as 30 days if kept in the dark. The ease with which the chlorophylls are removed from the cells varies considerably with different algae. To achieve complete extraction of the pigments, it is usually necessary to disrupt the cells mechanically with a tissue grinder.

a. Equipment and reagents:

1) *Spectrophotometer*, preferably a narrow-band (0.5 to 2 nm) instrument. Wide-band instruments are commonly used but are less accurate because they cannot resolve the narrow chlorophyll *a* peak. A spectrophotometer having a 20-nm band width will underestimate the chlorophyll *a* by as much as 25%.

2) *Cuvettes* with 1 cm, 4 cm, and 10 cm path length.

3) *Clinical centrifuge.*

4) *Tissue grinder.**

5) *Centrifuge tubes*, 15 ml, graduated, screw-cap.

6) *Filtration equipment*, filters, membrane (0.45 μm porosity, 47-mm diam) or glass fiber (GF/C or GF/A, 4.5-cm diam); vacuum pump.

7) *Magnesium carbonate suspension:* Add 1.0 g finely powdered magnesium carbonate to 100 ml distilled water.

8) *Aqueous acetone solution:* Mix 90 parts acetone (reagent grade BP 56 C) with 10 parts water (v/v).

b. Procedure:

1) Concentrate the sample by centrifuging or filtering (membrane or glass fiber filter). Add 0.2 ml magnesium car-

---

*Kontes Glass Company, Vineland, N.J. 08360: Glass/glass grinder, Model No. 885500; Glass/teflon grinder, Model No. 886000; or equivalent.

bonate suspension before centrifuging or during the final phase of filtering. Store concentrated samples frozen in a desiccator in the dark when extraction is delayed.

2) Place the sample in a tissue grinder, cover with 2 to 3 ml aqueous acetone solution.

3) Macerate the sample with the tissue grinder; use the teflon/glass grinder for a glass-fiber filter and the glass/glass grinder to macerate a membrane filter.

4) Transfer the sample to a screw-cap centrifuge tube and bring the volume up to 5 ml with aqueous acetone solution. Use solvent sparingly and avoid excessive dilution of the pigments. Steep the samples overnight at 4 C in the dark.

5) Clarify the extract by centrifuging in closed tubes for 20 min at 500 G. Decant the clarified extract into a clean, calibrated, 15-ml, screw-cap centrifuge tube and measure the total volume of extract.

6) Transfer the clear extract to a 1-cm cuvette and determine the optical density (OD) at 750, 663, 645, and 630 nm. If the OD 663 is less than 0.2, select longer cuvettes.

c. Calculations: Use the optical density readings at 663, 645, and 630 nm for the determination of chlorophyll *a*, *b*, and *c*, respectively. The OD reading at 750 nm serves as a correction for turbidity. Subtract this reading from each of the pigment OD values of the other wavelengths before they are used in the equations. The OD of the extract at 750 nm is very sensitive to changes in the acetone-to-water proportions; therefore, it is essential to adhere rigidly to the 90 parts acetone: 10 parts water (v/v) formula for pigment extraction. Use of

the 750-nm reading may be avoided if the pigment solution is cleared by centrifuging for 20 min at 500 G and the light path is limited to 1 cm.

1) Calculate the concentrations of the chlorophylls by inserting the (corrected) optical densities in the following equations:

a) $C_a = 11.64D_{663} - 2.16D_{645} + 0.10D_{630}$
b) $C_b = 20.97D_{645} - 3.94D_{663} - 3.66D_{630}$
c) $C_c = 54.22D_{630} - 14.81D_{645} - 5.53D_{663}$

where:

C_a, C_b, and C_c = concentrations of chlorophyll *a*, *b*, and *c*, respectively, in the extract, mg/l, and
D_{663}, D_{645}, and D_{630} = optical densities (with a 1-cm light path) at the respective wavelengths.

2) When the concentration of pigment in the extract has been determined, calculate the amount of pigment per unit volume of sample as follows:

$$\text{Chlorophyll } a, \text{mg/m}^3 = \frac{C_a \times \text{volume of extract, l}}{\text{volume of sample, m}^3}$$

2. Fluorometric Method for Chlorophyll *a*

The fluorometric method for chlorophyll *a* is more sensitive than the spectrophotometric method, requires a smaller sample, and does not require the wavelength resolution needed for the spectrophotometric method. Optimum sensitivity for in vitro chlorophyll *a* measurements is obtained at an excitation wavelength of 430 nm and an emission wavelength of 663 nm. A method for continuous measurement of chlorophyll *a* in vivo is available,[32] but is reported to be less efficient than the in vitro method given here, yielding about one-tenth as much fluorescence per unit weight as the same amount in solution.

Pheophytin *a* can also be determined fluorometrically.[8]

a. *Equipment and reagents:*

1) *Fluorometer,* Turner Model 111 or equivalent, equipped with a high-intensity F4T.5 blue lamp, photomultiplier tube R-136 (red sensitive), sliding window orifices 1×, 3×, 10×, and 30×, and filters for light emission (CS-2-64) and excitation (CS-5-60).

2) Other equipment and reagents as specified for the Spectrophotometric Determination of Chlorophyll, above.

b. *Procedure:*

1) Calibrate the fluorometer with a chlorophyll solution of known concentration as follows:

a) Prepare chlorophyll extract and analyze spectrophotometrically.

b) Prepare serial dilutions of the extract to provide concentrations of approximately 0.002, 0.006, 0.020, and 0.060 mg/l chlorophyll *a*.

c) Make readings for each solution at each sensitivity setting (sliding window orifice): 1×, 3×, 10×, and 30×.

d) Using the values obtained above, derive calibration factors to convert the fluorometric readings in each sensitivity level to concentrations chlorophyll *a*, as follows:

$$F_s = \frac{C_a}{R_s}$$

where:

F_s = calibration factor for sensitivity setting S,

R_s = reading of the fluorometer for sensitivity setting S, and

C_a = concentration of chlorophyll *a* determined spectrophotometrically, mg/l.

2) Measure the fluorescence of the unknown samples at a sensitivity setting that will provide a mid-scale reading. Convert the fluorescence readings to concentrations of chlorophyll *a* by multiplying the readings by the appropriate calibration factor.

3. Spectrophotometric Determination of Pheophytin a

The amount of pheophytin *a* is determined by reading the optical density of the extract before and after acidification. The addition of acid to a chlorophyll solution results in the loss of magnesium ion from the chlorophyll *a* molecule and converts it to pheophytin *a*. Since pheophytin has a lower specific absorption, acidification of chlorophyll causes a lowering of the optical density of the extract at 663 nm, which is generally used for chlorophyll *a* determinations. Acidification of a solution of pure chlorophyll *a* results in a 40% reduction in optical density at 663 nm, yielding an OD ratio $(663_b/663_a)$ of 1.70. Field samples with a $663_b/663_a$ ratio of 1.70 are considered to contain little if any pheophytin *a* and to be in excellent physiological condition. Solutions of pure pheophytin show no reduction in OD_{663} upon acidification and have a $663_b/663_a$ ratio of 1.0. Thus, mixtures of chlorophyll *a* and pheophytin *a* have OD_{663} ratios ranging between 1.0 and 1.7.

a. *Equipment and reagents:* In addition to the equipment and reagents used for the Spectrophotometric Determination of Chlorophyll (see above), provide 1*N* HCl.

b. *Procedure:*

1) Extract the pigment with 90% acetone (v/v) and clarify by centrifuging, as described above.

2) Read the OD at 663 and 750 nm before and after adding 0.02 ml of 1*N* HCl/ml of extract.

3) Subtract the 750 nm OD value from the 663 nm reading in each pair.

4) Use the corrected 663 nm readings to calculate the OD_{663b}/OD_{663a} ratio and concentration of chlorophyll and pheophytin in the sample.

c. *Calculations:* Calculate the chlorophyll a (C) and pheophytin a (P) per cubic meter as follows:

a) $C, mg/m^3 = \dfrac{26.73\,(663_b - 663_a) \times V_1}{V_2}$

b) $P, mg/m^3 =$
$\dfrac{26.73\,[1.7\,(663_a) - 663_b] \times V_1}{V_2}$

where:

663_b and 663_a = optical densities of the 90% acetone extract before and after acidification, respectively, when a 1-cm light path is used,

V_1 = volume of the extract, l, and

V_2 = sample volume, m^3.

4. Fluorometric Determination of Pheophytin a

To determine fluorometrically the concentration of pheophytin a requires the measurement of the fluorescence of acetone extracts before and after acidification. Acidification of acetone extracts of chlorophyll a and the resultant conversion of chlorophyll a to pheophytin a causes a reduction in fluorescence, which can be used to determine the concentration of pheophytin a in the extract.

a. *Equipment and reagents:* In addition to the equipment and reagents for the fluorometric determination of chlorophyll a (see 1002G.2a), provide 1N HCl and a solution of pure chlorophyll a† or a plankton chlorophyll extract with a before-after acidification ratio (OD_{663b}/OD_{663a}) of 1.70.

b. *Procedure:* Calibrate the fluorometer as described above. Determine the fluorescence of the extract at each sensitivity setting before and after acidification. Calculate the calibration factors (F_s) and the before-after acidification fluorescence ratio by dividing the fluorescence reading obtained before acidification by the reading obtained after acidification.

c. *Calculations:* Determine the "corrected" chlorophyll a and pheophytin a in extracts of plankton samples, using the following equations:[31]

$$\text{Chlorophyll } a, \; mg/m^3 = F_s\,\frac{r}{r-1}\,(R_b - R_a)$$

$$\text{Pheophytin } a, \; mg/m^3 = Fs\,\frac{r}{r-1}\,(rR_a - R_b)$$

where:

F_s = conversion factor for sensitivity setting "S" (see 1002G.2b),

R_b = fluorescence of the extract before acidification,

R_a = fluorescence of the extract after acidification, and

$r = R_b/R_a$.

---

†Purified chlorophyll a, Sigma Chemical Company, St. Louis, Mo., or equivalent.

1002 H.   Determination of Biomass (Standing Crop)

The standing crop of plankton can be expressed as numbers of organisms per unit volume. However, since plankton populations vary greatly in their size distribution, numbers alone do not give an adequate picture of population dynamics and the diversity and structure of the ecosystem. Methods available to provide more complete information on biomass include the determination of total carbon, nitrogen, oxygen, hydrogen, lipids, carbohydrates, phosphorous, silica (diatoms), chitin (zooplankton), and chlorophyll (algae). The only practical methods for assessment of zooplankton biomass are volume and dry weight determinations. Recently, the ATP (adenosine triphosphate)[37] and DNA (deoxyribonucleic acid)[38,39] contents of plankton have been evaluated as an estimate of viable biomass. Biomass estimates based on ATP appear to be in excellent agreement with estimates based on measurements such as chlorophyll a and cell volume. The DNA determination, however, is not recommended as an accurate indicator of biomass because of the occurrence of large amounts of detrital DNA in surface water, which can cause errors in biomass estimates.

1. Chlorophyll a

Chlorophyll a is an algal biomass indicator.[40] By assuming that chlorophyll a constitutes, on the average, 1.5 percent of the dry weight organic matter (ash-free weight) of the algae, one can estimate the algal biomass by multiplying the chlorophyll a content by a factor of 67.

2. Biovolume (Cell Volume)

Plankton data derived on a volume-per-volume basis are often more useful than data given as numbers per milliliter.[41] Determine the volume of a cell by using the simplest geometric configuration that best fits the shape of the cell being measured (such as sphere, cone, cylinder).[11] Cell sizes of an organism can differ substantially in different waters and from the same waters at different times during the year; therefore, it is necessary to average measurements from 20 individuals of each species for each sampling period. Calculate the total biovolume of any species by multiplying the average cell volume in cubic micrometers by the number per milliliter.

Compute the total wet algal volume as:

$$PV = \sum_{i=1}^{n} (PN_i \times SV_i)$$

where:

PV = total plankton cell volume, mm^3/l,

PN_i = number of organisms of the ith species/l, and

SV_i = average volume of cells of ith species.

3. Cell Surface Area

An estimation of cell surface area is valuable in analyzing interactions between the cell and the surrounding waters. Compute the average surface area in square micrometers and multiply by the numbers per milliliter of the species being considered.

4. Gravimetric Methods

The biomass of the plankton community can be estimated from gravimetric determinations, although silt and organic detritus interfere. Determine dry weight by placing 100 mg of the wet concentrated sample in a tared porcelain crucible and drying at 105 C for 24 hr. Obtain ash-free weight by igniting the dried sample at 500 C for 1 hr. Cool, rewet the ash with distilled water, and bring to a constant weight at 105 C. The ash is rewetted to restore the water of hydration of clays and other minerals in the sample; this may amount to as much as 10% of the weight lost during incineration.[42] The ash-free weight is preferred to the dry weight when comparisons are made that involve mixed assemblages. The ash content may constitute 50% or more of the dry weight in phytoplankton having inorganic structures, such as the diatoms. In other forms the ash content is only about 5% of the dry weight.

5. Adenosine Triphosphate (ATP)

Recently developed methods of measuring adenosine triphosphate (ATP) in plankton provide the only means of determining the total viable plankton biomass. ATP occurs in all plants and animals, but only in living cells; it is not associated with nonliving particulate material. The ratio of ATP to biomass varies somewhat from species to species, but appears to be constant enough to permit reliable estimates of biomass from ATP measurements.[36] The method is simple and relatively inexpensive and the instrumentation is stable and reliable. The method also has many potential applications in entrainment and bioassay work, especially plankton mortality studies.

a. Equipment and reagents:

1) *Glassware:* clean, sterile, dry Pyrex flasks, beakers, and pipets.

2) *Filters:* 47 mm, 0.45-μm porosity membrane filters.

3) *Filtration equipment.*

4) *Freezer (−20 C).*

5) *Boiling water bath.*

6) *Detection instruments* designed specifically for measuring ATP are currently available.*

7) *Microsyringes:* 10, 25, 50, 100, 250 μl.

8) *Reaction cuvettes and vials.*

9) *Tris buffer* (0.0 2M, pH 7.75): Dissolve 7.5 g trishydroxymethylaminomethane in 3,000 ml distilled water, adjust pH to 7.75 with 20% HCl, and autoclave 150-ml portions at 115 C for 15 min.

10) *Luciferin-luciferase enzyme preparation:*† Rehydrate frozen (−20 C) lyophilized extracts of firefly lanterns with Tris buffer as directed by the supplier; let stand at room temperature 2 to 3 hr, then centrifuge at 300 G for 1 min and decant the supernatant into a clean, dry test tube; let stand at room temperature for 1 hr.

11) *Purified ATP standard* for instrument calibration: Dissolve 12.3 mg disodium ATP in 1 l of distilled water and dilute 1.0 ml to 100 ml with Tris buffer (0.2 ml = 20 ng ATP).

b. Procedure: To determine the calibration factor (*F*), prepare a series of dilutions of the ATP standard, record the

---

*Dupont, Beckman, JRB, etc.

†Dupont, Sigma Chemical, or equivalent.

light emission (see section on sample analysis) from several portions of each concentration of the standard. Correct the mean area of the standards by subtacting the peak reading or the mean area of several blanks using 0.2 ml Tris buffer. Calculate the calibration factor F_s as:

$$F_s = \frac{C}{SA}$$

where:

F_s = calibration factor at sensitivity S,
SA = peak reading or mean area under standard ATP curve corrected for blank, and
C = concentration of ATP in standard solution, ng/ml.

Collect a 1- to 2-l sample in a clean, sterile sampler. Pass sample through a 250-μm net to remove large zooplankton[43] and extract ATP immediately. Extract at least three replicate portions of each sample.

Pass the sample through a 47-mm, 0.45-μm-porosity filter by applying about 0.3 atm vacuum. (Important: Break the suction before the last film of water is pulled through the filter). Quickly place filter in a small beaker. Immediately cover filter with 3 ml of boiling Tris buffer, using an automatic pipet. Place beaker in boiling water bath for 5 min and transfer the extract to a clean, dry, calibrated test tube with a Pasteur pipet. Rinse filter and beaker with 2 ml of boiling Tris buffer; combine extracts, record volume, bring volume up to 5 ml with Tris buffer, cover tubes with parafilm and, if samples cannot be analyzed immediately, freeze at –25 C. Extracts may be stored for many months in a freezer.

The analytical procedure depends on the detection equipment used. If a scintillation counter is used, pipet 0.2 ml of enzyme preparation into a glass vial. Measure the light emission of the enzyme preparation (blank) for 2 to 3 min at sensitivity settings near that anticipated for the sample. Add 0.2 ml of the sample extract to the vial, record the time, and swirl the contents of the vial. Start recording the light output 10 sec after combining the ATP extract and the enzyme preparation; record the output for 2 to 3 min, using the same time period for all samples. Determine the mean of the areas under the curves obtained from the sample and correct by subtracting the mean of the areas under the curves obtained from the blanks (blanks are prepared according to Strickland and Parsons[8]).

c. Calculations: The concentration of ATP in a sample is calculated as:

$$ATP, \text{ng/l} = \frac{CA \times EV \times F_s}{V}$$

where:

CA = mean corrected area under extract curves,
EV = extract volume, ml,
V = volume of sample, l, and
F_s = calibration factor.

Total living plankton biomass is given as:

$$PB, \text{mg/l}\ddagger = \frac{(\text{ng} \, ATP/\text{l})}{(2.4)(1,000)}$$

where:

PB = plankton biomass as dry weight organic matter.

---

‡Assuming an ATP content of 2.4 μg ATP/mg dry weight organic matter.[36]

1002 I. Metabolic Rate Measurements

The physiological condition of the aquatic community and the spectrum of biological interactions must be considered. In early studies, numbers, species composition, and biomass were the prime considerations. Recognition of the limitations of this approach, however, led to the measurement of rates of metabolic processes such as photosynthesis (productivity), nitrogen fixation, respiration, and electron transport. These provide a better understanding of the complex nature of the aquatic ecosystem.

1. Nitrogen Fixation

The ability of an organism to fix nitrogen is a great competitive advantage and plays a major role in population dynamics. The two most recent and reliable methods for estimating nitrogen fixation rates in the laboratory are the ^{15}N isotope tracer method [44,45] and the acetylene reduction method.[46] Because the rate of nitrogen fixation varies greatly with different types of organisms and with the concentration of combined nitrogen in the water, it is not possible to use nitrogen fixation rates to estimate biomass of nitrogen-fixing organisms in surface waters. However, the acetylene reduction method is useful in measuring nitrogen budgets and in algal assay work.[47]

2. Productivity, Oxygen Method

Productivity is defined as the rate at which inorganic carbon is converted to an organic form. The chlorophyll-bearing plants (phytoplankton, periphyton, macrophytes) serve as the primary producers in the aquatic food chain. Photosynthesis results in the formation of a wide range of organic compounds, the release of oxygen, and the depletion of carbon dioxide in the surrounding waters. Primary productivity[48] can be determined by measuring the changes in the oxygen and CO_2 concentration in the water.[49] In poorly buffered waters, pH can be a sensitive property for detecting variations in the system. As carbon dioxide is removed from the aquatic system during photosynthesis, the pH rises. This shift can be used to estimate both photosynthesis and respiration.[50] The sea and many fresh waters are too highly buffered to make this useful, but it has been applied successfully to productivity studies in some lake waters.

Two well-established methods of measuring the rate of carbon uptake and net photosynthesis in situ are: (*a*) the oxygen method of Gaarder and Gran[51] and (*b*) the carbon 14 method of Steeman-Nielsen.[52] In both methods, clear (light) and darkened (dark) bottles are filled with water samples and suspended at regular depth intervals for an incubation period of several hours.

The basic reactions in algal photosynthesis involve the uptake of inorganic carbon and the release of oxygen, summarized by the equation:

$$CO_2 + H_2O \rightarrow CH_2O + O_2$$

The chief advantages of the oxygen method are that it provides estimates of gross and net productivity and respiration and that analyses can be performed with inexpensive laboratory equipment and common reagents. The concentration of dissolved oxygen is determined at the beginning and end of the incubation period. Productivity is calculated on the assumption that one atom of carbon is assimilated for each molecule of oxygen released.

a. Equipment:

1) *BOD bottles*, numbered, 300-ml, clear pyrex or borosilicon, with ground-glass stopper and flared mouth, for sample incubation. Acid-clean the bottles, rinse thoroughly with distilled water, and just before use, rinse with the water being tested. Do not use phosphorus-containing detergents.

If suitable opaque bottles are not commercially available, make clear BOD bottles opaque by painting them black and wrapping with black waterproof tape. As a further precaution, wrap the entire bottle in aluminum foil or place in a light-excluding container during incubation.

2) *Supporting line or rack* that does not shade the suspended bottles.

3) *Nonmetallic opaque Lucite or Uscolite Van Dorn sampler* or equivalent, of 3- to 5-l capacity.

4) *Laboratory equipment and reagents for dissolved oxygen determinations* (see Section 422).

5) *Pyrheliometer.*

6) *Submarine photometer.*

b. Procedure:

1) Obtain a profile of the input of solar radiation for the photoperiod with a pyrheliometer.

2) Determine the depth of the euphotic zone (the region that receives 1% or more of surface illumination) with a submarine photometer. Select depth intervals for bottle placement. The photosynthesis-depth curve will be closely approximated by placing samples at intervals equal to one-tenth the depth of the euphotic zone. Productivity in relatively shallow water may be estimated adequately with fewer depth intervals.

3) Introduce samples taken from each preselected depth into duplicate clear, darkened, and initial-analysis bottles. Insert the delivery tube of the sampler to the bottom of the sample bottle and fill the bottle so that three volumes of water are allowed to overflow. Remove the tube slowly and close the bottle. Water used to fill a "set" (one light, one dark, and one initial bottle) should come from the same grab sample.

4) Immediately treat (fix) samples taken for the chemical determination of initial dissolved oxygen (see Dissolved Oxygen, Section 422) with manganous sulfate, alkaline iodide, and sulfuric acid, or check with an oxygen probe. Analyses may be delayed several hours if necessary, if samples are fixed or iced and stored in the dark.

5) Suspend the duplicate paired clear and darkened bottles at the depth from which the samples were taken and incubate for at least 2 hr, but never longer than it takes for oxygen-gas bubbles to form in the clear bottles or dissolved oxygen to be depleted in the dark bottles.

6) At the end of the exposure period, immediately fix the samples as described above and determine dissolved oxygen.

c. Calculations: The increase in oxygen concentration in the light bottle during incubation is a measure of net production which, because of the concurrent use of oxygen in respiration, is somewhat less than the total (or gross) production. The loss of oxygen in the dark bottle is used as an estimate of respiration. Thus:

Net photosynthesis = light bottle DO – initial DO

Respiration = initial DO – dark bottle DO

Gross photosynthesis = light bottle DO – dark bottle DO

Average results from duplicates.

1) Calculate the gross or net production for each incubation depth and plot:

mg carbon fixed/m^3 =
    mg oxygen released/l $\times$ 12/32 $\times$ 1,000

The factor 12/32 is used to convert oxygen to carbon; 1 mole of O_2 (32 g) is released for each mole of carbon (12 g) fixed.

2) Productivity is defined as the rate of production and generally is reported in grams of carbon fixed per square meter per day. Determine the productivity of a vertical column of water 1 m square by plotting the productivity value for each exposure depth and graphically integrating the area under the curve.

3) Using the solar radiation profile and photosynthetic rate during the incubation period, adjust the data to represent phytoplankton productivity for the entire photoperiod. Since photosynthetic rates vary widely during the daily cycle,[53,54] conversion of the data obtained from exposure periods other than those described may be difficult or completely impossible.

3. Productivity, Carbon 14 Method

A solution of radioactive carbonate ($^{14}CO_3^{2-}$) is added to light and dark bottles that have been filled with sample as described for the oxygen method. After in situ incubation, the plankton is collected on a membrane filter, treated with hydrochloric acid fumes to remove inorganic carbon 14, and assayed for radioactivity. The quantity of carbon fixed is proportional to the fraction of radioactive carbon assimilated.

This procedure differs from the oxygen method in that it affords a direct measurement of carbon uptake and measures only net photosynthesis.[55] It is basically more sensitive than the oxygen method, but fails to account for the organic materials that leach from the cells[56,57] during incubation.

a: Equipment and reagents:

1) *Pyrheliometer.*

2) *Submarine photometer.*

3) *BOD bottles and supporting apparatus* (see Oxygen Method above).

4) *Membrane-filtering device and 25-mm filters* with pore diameters of 0.22, 0.30, 0.45, 0.80, and 1.2 μm.

5) *Counting equipment* for measuring radioactivity: scaler with end-window tube, gas flow detector, or liquid scintillation counter (see Part 700). The thin-window tube is the least expensive detector and, when used with a small scaler, provides acceptable data at a modest cost.

6) *Fuming chamber.* Use a glass desiccator with about 1.5 cm of conc HCl in the desiccant chamber. The fuming chamber is recommended for filter decontamination.[58,59]

7) *A 2-ml hypodermic syringe* with 15-cm (6-in.) needle.

8) *Chemical reagents;* see Sections 407 (Carbon Dioxide) and 403 (Alkalinity).

9) *Radioactive carbonate solutions:*

a) *Sodium chloride dilution solution,* 5% w/v solution of sodium chloride in distilled water. Add 0.3 g of anhydrous sodium bicarbonate and one sodium hydroxide pellet to each liter of solution. Use for marine studies only.

b) *Carrier-free radioactive carbonate solution*, commercially available in sealed vials having approximately 5 μCi of carbon 14/ml.

c) *Working solutions* with activities of 1, 5, and 25 μCi ^{14}C/2 ml. For fresh-water studies use carrier-free radioactive carbonate and for marine studies prepare by diluting the carrier-free radioactive carbonate solution with the sodium chloride dilution solution.

d) *Stock ampuls.* Prepare ampuls containing 2 ml of the required working solution. Fill ampuls using hypodermic needles; autoclave sealed ampuls at 121 C for 20 min.[8]

b. Procedure:

1) Obtain a record of the incident solar radiation for the photoperiod with a pyrheliometer.

2) Determine the depth intervals for sampling and incubation as described for the Oxygen Method, above.

3) Use duplicate light and dark bottles at each depth. Fill the bottles with sample, add 2 ml of radioactive carbonate solution (using the syringe with needle) to the bottom of each bottle, and mix thoroughly by repeated inversion. The concentration of carbon 14 in the sample should be approximately 10 μCi/l. For statistical significance, there should be at least 1,000 cpm in the filtered sample. Take duplicate samples at each depth to determine the initial concentration of inorganic carbon (CO_2, HCO_3, and CO_3^{2-}) available for photosynthesis (see Carbon Dioxide, Section 407).

4) Incubate the samples for up to 4 hr. If measurements are required for the entire photoperiod, overlap 4-hr periods from dawn until dusk. A 4-hr incubation period may be sufficient provided energy input is used as the basis for integrating the incubation period into the entire photoperiod (incubation procedure, see Oxygen Method).

5) At the end of incubation, remove sample bottles and immediately place in the dark or preserve by adding 40 ml formalin/l. Filter unpreserved samples without delay.

6) Filter two portions of each sample through a membrane filter, taking care that the largest pore size is consistent with quantitative retention of the plankton. Although the 0.45- μm pore filter is usually adequate, the efficiency of sample retention should be determined immediately before the analysis, with a wide range of pore sizes.[60,61] Apply approximately 0.3 atm of vacuum during filtration. Excess vacuum may cause extensive cell rupture and loss of radioactivity through the membrane.[62] The volume of sample filtered should be the maximum amount consistent with rapid filtration (1 to 2 min).

7) After filtration, place the membranes in HCl fumes for 20 min. Count filters as soon as possible, although extended storage in a desiccator is acceptable.

8) Determine radioactivity by counting with an end-window tube, windowless gas flow detector, or liquid scintillation counter. The efficiency of the counting methods is approximately as follows: thin-window, 3%; windowless gas flow, 50%; liquid scintillation, 40%.

9) Determine counting geometry of thin-window and windowless gas flow detectors.[63] Using three ampuls of carbon 14, prepare a series of $BaCO_3$ pre-

cipitates on tared 0.45-μm membrane filters, each precipitate containing the same amount of carbon 14 activity but varying in thickness from 0.5 to 6.0 mg/cm^2. Dilute each ampul to 500 ml with a solution of 1.36 g Na_2CO_3/l of CO_2-free distilled water. Pipet 0.5-ml portions of this solution into each of seven conical flasks containing 0, 0.5, 1.5, 2.5, 3.5, 4.5, and 5.5 ml, respectively, of a solution of 1.36 g Na_2CO_3/l of CO_2-free distilled water. Add, respectively, 0.3, 0.6, 1.2, 1.8, 2.4, 3.0, and 3.6 ml of 1.04% $BaCl_2$ solution. Allow the $BaCO_3$ precipitate to stand 2 hr with gentle swirling every half hour. Collect each precipitate on a filter (using an apparatus with a filtration area comparable to that of the samples). With suction, dry the filters without washing; place in a desiccator for 24 hr, weigh, and count. The counting rate increases exponentially with decreasing precipitate thickness and is extrapolated graphically (or mathematically) to zero precipitate thickness. The zero-thickness counting rate is multiplied by 1,000 to correct for ampul dilution. This represents the amount of activity added to each sample bottle and is used to determine the fraction of carbon 14 taken up in the light and dark bottles.

c. Calculations:

1) Subtract the mean dark-bottle sample counts from the mean light-bottle counts for each replicate pair.

2) Determine the total dissolved inorganic carbon available for photosynthesis (carbonate, bicarbonate, and free CO_2) from pH and alkalinity measurements; make direct measurement of total carbon dioxide according to Section 407 or the methods described in the literature.[64,65,66,67]

3) Determine the quantity of carbon fixed by using the following relationship:

mg carbon fixed/l

$$= \frac{\text{counting rate of filtered sample}}{\text{total activity added to sample}}$$

$$= \times \frac{300}{\text{volume filtered}}$$

$$\times \text{mg/l initial inorganic carbon} \times 1.064*$$

4) Integrate the productivity for the entire depth of the euphotic zone and express as grams of carbon fixed per square meter per day (see Oxygen Method, preceding).

5) Using the solar radiation records and photosynthetic rates during the incubation period, adjust the data to represent phytoplankton productivity for the entire photoperiod. If the samples were incubated for less than the full photoperiod, apply a correction factor.

---

*Correction for isotope effect.

1002 J. References

1. PALMER, C.M. 1969. A composite rating of algae tolerating organic pollution. *J. Phycol.* 5:78.

2. PALMER, C.M. 1963. The effect of pollution on river algae. *Bull. N.Y. Acad. Sci.* 108:389.

3. RAWSON, D.S. 1956. Algal indicators of trophic lake types. *Limnol. Oceanogr.* 1:18.

4. STOERMER, E.F. & J.J. YANG. 1969. Plankton Diatom Assemblages in Lake Michigan. Spec. Rep. No. 47, Great Lakes Res. Div., Univ. of Michigan, Ann Arbor.

5. HOLLAND, R.E. 1968. Correlation of *Melosira* species with trophic conditions in Lake Michigan. *Limnol. Oceanogr.* 13:555.

6. PRESCOTT, G.W. 1968. The Algae: A Review. Houghton Mifflin Co., Boston, Mass.

7. WELCH, P.S. 1948. Limnological Methods. Blakiston Co., Philadelphia, Pa.

8. STRICKLAND, J.D.H. & T.R. PARSONS. 1968. A Practical Manual of Sea Water Analysis. Fish. Res. Board Can. Bull. No. 167. Queens Printer, Ottawa, Ont., Canada.

9. NANSEN, F. 1915. Closing nets for vertical hauls and for horizontal towing. *Publ. Circonst. Cons. Perma. Int. Explor. Mer.* 67:1.

10. MORTIMER, C.H. 1942. The exchange of dissolved substances between mud and water in lakes. *J. Ecol.* 30:147.

11. VOLLENWEIDER, R.A. 1969. A Manual on Methods for Measuring Primary Production in Aquatic Environments. IBP Handbook 12, Blackwell Sci. Publ., England.

12. MEYER, R.L. 1971. A study of phytoplankton dynamics in Lake Fayetteville as a means of assessing water quality. *Arkansas Water Res. Center*, Publ. 10.

13. WEBER, C.I. 1968. The preservation of phytoplankton grab samples. *Trans. Amer. Microsc. Soc.* 87:70.

14. JUDAY, C. 1916. Limnological apparatus. *Trans. Wis. Acad. Sci.* 18:566.

15. SCHWOERBEL, J. 1970. Methods of Hydrobiology. Pergamon Press, Toronto, Ont., Canada.

16. TRANTER, D.J., ed. 1968. Reviews on Zooplankton Sampling Methods. UNESCO, Switzerland.

17. CLARKE, G.L. & D.F. BUMPUS. 1940. The Plankton Sampler: An Instrument for Quantitative Plankton Investigations. Spec. Publ. No. 5, Limnol. Soc. Amer.

18. McNABB, C.D. 1960. Enumeration of freshwater phytoplankton concentrated on the membrane filter. *Limnol. Oceanogr.* 5:57.

19. PATRICK, R. & C.W. REIMER. 1967. The Diatoms of the United States. Vol. 1. Monogr. 13, Philadelphia Acad. Natur. Sci.

20. HOHN, M.H. & J. HELLERMAN. 1963. The taxonomy and structure of diatom populations for three eastern North American Rivers using three sampling methods. *Trans. Amer. Microsc. Soc.* 62:250.

21. LUND, J.W.G., C. KIPLING & E.D. LeCREN. 1958. The inverted microscope method of estimating algal numbers and the statistical basis of estimations by counting. *Hydrobiologia* 11:143.

22. JACKSON, H.W. & L.G. WILLIAMS. 1962. Calibration and use of certain plankton counting equipment. *Trans. Amer. Microsc. Soc.* 81:96.

23. INGRAM, W.M. & C.M. PALMER. 1952. Simplified procedures for collecting, examining, and recording plankton in water. *J. Amer. Water Works Ass.* 44:617.

24. PALMER, C.M. & T.E. MALONEY. 1954. A New Counting Slide for Nannoplankton. Spec. Publ. No. 21, Amer. Soc. Limnol. & Oceanogr.

25. LACKEY, J.B. 1938. The manipulation and counting of river plankton and changes in some organisms due to formalin preservation. *Pub. Health Rep.* 53:2080.

26. MADDUX, W.S. & J.W. KANWISCHER. 1965. An *in situ* particle counter. *Limnol. Oceanogr.* 10 (Suppl):R162.

27. LORENZEN, C.J. 1967. Determination of chlorophyll and pheo-pigments: spectrophotometric equations. *Limnol. Oceanogr.* 12:343.

28. FITZGERALD, G.P. & S.L. FAUST. 1967. A spectrophotometric method for the estimation of percentage degradation of chlorophylls to pheo-pigments in extracts of algae. *Limnol. Oceanogr.* 12:335.

29. YENTSCH, C.S. & D.W. MENZEL. 1963. A method for the determination of phytoplankton chlorophyll and phaeophytin by fluorescence. *Deep Sea Res.* 10:221.

30. LOFTUS, M.E. & J.H. CARPENTER. 1971. A fluorometric method for determining chlorophylls *a*, *b*, and *c*. *J. Mar. Res.* 29:319.

31. HOLM-HANSEN, O., C.J. LORENZEN, R.W. HOLMES & J.D.H. STRICKLAND. 1965. Fluorometric determination of chlorophyll. *J. Cons. Cons. Perma. Int. Explor. Mer* 30:3.

32. LORENZEN, C.J. 1966. A method for the continuous measurement of *in vivo* chlorophyll concentration. *Deep Sea Res.* 13:223.

33. PARSONS, T.R. 1963. A new method for the microdetermination of chlorophyll "c" in seawater. *J. Mar. Res.* 21:164.

34. PATTERSON, J. & T.R. PARSONS. 1963. Distribution of chlorophyll *a* and degradation products in various marine materials. *Limnol. Oceanogr.* 8:355.

35. VERNON, L.P. 1960. Spectrophotometric determination of chlorophyll and pheophytins in plant extracts. *Anal. Chem.* 32:1144.

36. WEBER, C.I. 1973. Recent developments in the measurement of the response of plankton and periphyton to changes in their environment. In: Bioassay Techniques and Environmental Chemistry (G. Glass, ed.). Ann Arbor Sci. Publ. Inc., Ann Arbor, Mich.

37. HOLM-HANSEN, O. & C.R. BOOTH. 1966. The measurement of adenosine triphosphate in the ocean and its ecological significance. *Limnol. Oceanogr.* 11:510.

38. HOLM-HANSEN, O., W.H. SUTCLIFFE, JR. & J. SHARP. 1968. Measurement of deoxyribonucleic acid in the ocean and its ecological significance. *Limnol. Oceanogr.* 13:507.

39. HOLM-HANSEN, O. 1969. Determination of microbial biomass in ocean profiles. *Limnol. Oceanogr.* 14:740.

40. CREITZ, G.I. & F.A. RICHARDS. 1955. The estimation and characterization of plankton populations by pigment analysis. *J. Mar. Res.* 14:211.

41. KUTKUHN, J.H. 1958. Notes on the precision of numerical and volumetric plankton estimates from small sample concentrations. *Limnol. Oceanogr.* 3:69.

42. NELSON, D.J. & D.C. SCOTT. 1962. Role of detritus in the productivity of a rock-outcrop community in a Piedmont stream. *Limnol. Oceanogr.* 7:396.

43. RUDD, J.W.M. & R.D. HAMILTON. 1973. Measurement of adenosine triphosphate (ATP) in two precambrian shield lakes of northwestern Ontario. *J. Fish. Res. Board Can.* 30:1537.

44. BURRIS, R.H., F.J. EPPLING, H.B. WAHLIN & P.W. WILSON. 1942. Studies of biological nitrogen fixation with isotopic nitrogen. *Proc. Soil Sci. Soc. Amer.* 7:258.

45. NEESS, J.C., R.C. DUGDALE, V.A. DUGDALE & J.J. GOERING. 1962. Nitrogen metabolism in lakes. I. Measurement of nitrogen fixation with N^{15}. *Limnol. Oceanogr.* 7:163.

46. STEWART, W.D.P., G.P. FITZGERALD & R.H. BURRIS. 1967. *In situ* studies on N_2 fixation using the acetylene reduction technique. *Proc. Nat. Acad. Sci.* 58:2071.

47. STEWART, W.D.P., G.P. FITZGERALD & R.H. BURRIS. 1970. Acetylene reduction assay for determination of phosphorus availability in Wisconsin lakes. *Proc. Nat. Acad. Sci.* 66:1104.

48. GOLDMAN, C.R. 1968. Aquatic primary production. *Amer. Zoologist* 8:31.

49. ODUM, H.T. 1957. Primary production measurements in eleven Florida springs and a marine turtle-grass community. *Limnol. Oceanogr.* 2:85.

50. BEYERS, R.J. & H.T. ODUM. 1959. The use of carbon dioxide to construct pH curves for the measurement of productivity. *Limnol. Oceanogr.* 4:499.

51. GAARDER, T. & H.H. GRAN. 1927. Investigations of the production of plankton in Oslo Fjord. *Rapp. Proces-Verbaux, Reunions Cons. Perma. Int. Explor. Mer.* 42:1.

52. STEEMAN-NIELSEN, E. 1952. The use of radioactive carbon (C-14) for measuring organic production in the sea. *J. Cons. Perma. Int. Explor. Mer.* 18:117.

53. RYTHER, J.H. 1956. Photosynthesis in the ocean as a function of light intensity. *Limnol. Oceanogr.* 1:61.

54. FEE, E.J. 1969. A numerical model for the estimation of photosynthetic production, integrated over time and depth, in natural waters. *Limnol. Oceanogr.* 14:906.

55. STEEMAN-NIELSEN, E. 1964. Recent advances in measuring and understanding marine primary production. *J. Ecol.* 52(Suppl.):119.

56. ALLEN, M.B. 1956. Excretion of organic compounds by *Chlamydomonas*. *Arch. Mikrobiol.* 24:163.

57. Fogg, G.E. & W.D. Watt. 1965. The kinetics of release of extracellular products of photosynthesis by phytoplankton. In: Primary Productivity in Aquatic Environments (C.R. Goldman, ed.). Suppl. 18, Univ. California Press, Berkeley.

58. Wetzel, R.G. 1965. Necessity for decontamination of filters in C^{14} measured rates of photosynthesis in fresh waters. *Ecology* 46:540.

59. McAllister, C.D. 1961. Decontamination of filters in the C^{14} method of measuring marine photosynthesis. *Limnol. Oceanogr.* 6:447.

60. Lasker, R. & R.W. Holmes. 1957. Variability in retention of marine phytoplankton by membrane filters. *Nature* 180:1295.

61. Holmes, R.W. & C.G. Anderson. 1963. Size fractionation of C^{14}- labelled natural phytoplankton communities. In: Symp. on Marine Microbiology (C.H. Oppenheimer, ed.). Charles C. Thomas, Springfield, Ill.

62. Arthur, C.R. & F.H. Rigler. 1967. A possible source of error in the C^{14} method of measuring primary productivity. *Limnol. Oceanogr.* 12:121.

63. Jitts, H.R. & B.D. Scott. 1961. The determination of zero-thickness activity in Geiger counting of C^{14} solutions used in marine productivity studies. *Limnol. Oceanogr.* 6:116.

64. Saunders, G.W., F.B. Trama & R.W. Bachmann. 1962. Inst. of Science and Technology, Univ. of Michigan, Great Lakes Res. Div. Publ. No. 8.

65. Dye, J.F. 1944. The calculation of alkalinities and free carbon dioxide in water by use of nomographs. *J. Amer. Water Works Ass.* 36:859.

66. Moore, E.W. 1939. Graphic determination of carbon dioxide and the three forms of alkalinity. *J. Amer. Water Works Ass.* 31:51.

67. Park, K., D.W. Hood & H.T. Odum. 1958. Diurnal pH variation in Texas bays and its application to primary production estimations. *Publ. Inst. Mar. Sci. Univ. Tex.* 5:47.

1003   PERIPHYTON

1003 A.   Introduction

Communities of microorganisms growing on stones, sticks, aquatic macrophytes, and other submerged surfaces are greatly influenced by water quality and are very useful in assessing the effects of pollutants on lakes and streams. Included in this group of organisms, here designated periphyton,[1,2] are the zoogleal and filamentous bacteria, attached protozoa, rotifers, and algae, and also the free-living microorganisms found swimming, creeping, or lodged among the attached forms.

Unlike the plankton, which often do not respond fully to the influence of pollution in rivers for a considerable distance downstream, the periphyton show dramatic effects immediately below pollution sources. Examples are the beds of *Sphaerotilus* and other "slime organisms" commonly observed in streams below discharges of organic wastes. Because the abundance and composition of the periphyton at a given location are governed by the water quality at that point, observations of their condition generally are very useful in assessing conditions in streams.

The use of periphyton in determining water quality is often hindered by the lack of suitable natural substrates at the desired sampling station. Furthermore, it is often difficult to collect quantitative samples from these surfaces. As a result, several artificial substrates have been used that can be located at will and that provide a uniform, controlled surface type, area, and orientation.[3]

1003 B. Sample Collection

1. Station Selection

In rivers, locate stations a short distance upstream and at one or more points downstream from the pollution source. In large rivers, sample both sides of the stream. Since the effects of a pollutant depend on the assimilative capacity of the stream and on the nature of the pollutant, progressive changes in water quality downstream from the pollution source may be caused entirely by dilution and cooling—as in the case of nutrients, toxic industrial wastes, and thermal pollution—or to gradual mineralization of degradable organics. In the case of domestic and some industrial wastes, cursory examination of shoreline and bottom periphyton growths downstream from the outfall may disclose conspicuous zones of biological response to water quality that will be useful in determining appropriate locations for the sampling stations. In this manner, the boundaries of various zones of pollution can be delineated and the length of the affected reach determined. Where an intensive sampling program is not feasible, a minimum of two sampling stations will provide data on both the periphyton community at a control point above the pollution source and changes in the periphyton induced by the wastes in the zone downstream from the outfall, where complete mixing with the receiving water has occurred.

In lakes, reservoirs, and other standing-water bodies where the zones of pollution may be arranged concentrically, locate stations in an area adjacent to the waste outfall and in an unaffected area.

2. Sample Collection

a. Natural substrates: Qualitative and semi-quantitative samples may be taken by scraping submerged stones, sticks, pilings, and other substrates available at the station. Although many devices have been developed for the collection of quantitative samples from irregular surfaces, success is rarely achieved.

b. Artificial substrates: The most widely used artificial substrate is the standard, plain, 25- by 75-mm (1- by 3-in.) glass microscope slide, but other materials such as Plexiglas also are suitable. Do not make changes in substrate type during a study since colonization varies with the substrate. In small, shallow streams and in the littoral regions of lakes, place slides in frames anchored to the bottom. In large, deep streams or standing-water bodies where turbidity varies widely, the slides are best placed vertically at the surface in a floating rack (Figure 1003:1). Expose several slides for each type of analysis to assure the collection of sufficient material and to determine the variability in results caused by normal differences in the colonization of individual slides. It also must be recognized that, in addition to the effects of the pollutants, the length of substrate exposure and seasonal changes in temperature and other natural environmental conditions may have a profound effect on the composition of the samples collected.

c. Exposure period: Colonization of clean slides proceeds at an exponential rate for the first 1 or 2 wk and then slows. Because exposures of less than 2 wk may result in very sparse collections, and exposures of more than 2 wk may result in the loss of material due to sloughing, this period generally constitutes the optimum sampling interval during the summer season. However, this exposure period will preclude collec-

tion of the adult thalli of the larger, slow-growing filamentous algae such as *Cladophora* and *Stigeoclonium*.

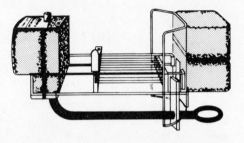

Figure 1003:1. Periphyton sampler. Floating slide rack constructed of Plexiglas and styrofoam. Used in streams and lakes. Source: PATRICK, R., M.H. HOHN and J.H. WALLACE. 1954. A new method for determining the pattern of the diatom flora. *Bull. Philadelphia Acad. Natur. Sci.* 259:1.

1003 C.   Sample Analysis

1. Sedgwick-Rafter Counts

Preserve samples that are taken for counting and identification in 5% formalin or other suitable material. Avoid solvents that remove the chlorophylls and other cell pigments.

The periphyton is easily removed from the slides with a razor blade and rubber policeman. Disperse the scrapings in the preservative (i.e., 100 ml) with vigorous shaking, transfer a 1-ml portion to a Sedgwick-Rafter cell, and make a strip count as described in Section 1002 F.2. If the material in the Sedgwick-Rafter cell is too dense to count directly, discard, and replace with a diluted sample.

Express the counts as cells per square millimeter of substrate area, calculated as follows:

1) Cells/ml of suspended scrapings

$$= \frac{\text{actual count/strip}}{\text{volume of 1 strip, ml}}$$

2) Cells/mm^2 of slide surface

$= $ cells/ml suspended scrapings

$$\times \frac{\text{total volume of scrapings}}{\text{area of slide or slides, mm}^2}$$

2. Diatom Species Proportional Counts

Correct preparation of permanent diatom mounts from periphyton samples usually differs from preparation of mounts from plankton samples because of the presence of large amounts of extracellular organic matter (such as the gelatinous attachment materials and formalin), which, if not removed, will lay down a thick brown or black carbonaceous deposit on the cover glass when the sample is incinerated. The organic substances can be decomposed by oxidation with ammonium persulfate or nitric acid and potassium dichromate (see Plankton, 1002 D.3) before mounting of the sample. Persulfate oxidation and cleanup are carried out as follows:

Place approximately 5 ml sample in a disposable 10-ml vial. Let stand 24 hr, withdraw supernatant liquid by aspiration, replace with a 5% solution of ammonium persulfate, and mix thoroughly. Do not exceed a total volume of 8 ml. Heat vial to approximately 90 C for 30 min. Let stand 24 hr, withdraw supernatant liquid, and replace with distilled water. After three changes of distilled water, transfer a drop of the diatom suspension to a cover glass with a disposable pipet, evaporate the water by warming, and prepare and count a mount as described for plankton (Section 1002).

3. Dry and Ash-free Weight

Collect several (at least three) replicate slides for weight determinations.[4] Obtain the weights from the material used for chlorophyll determinations or from separate slides exposed expressly for that purpose. In the latter case, air-dry the slides in the field; they can be stored indefinitely if protected from abrasion, moisture, and dust.

a. Equipment:

1) *Analytical balance*, with a sensitivity of 0.1 mg.

2) *Drying oven*, double-wall, thermostatically controlled to within ±1 C.

3) *Electric muffle furnace* with automatic temperature control.

4) *Crucibles*, porcelain, 30-ml capacity.

5) *Single-edge razor blades or rubber policeman.*

b. Procedure:

1) If the dry and ash-free weights are to be obtained from the material used for chlorophyll determinations, combine the particulate matter and the acetone extract from each slide, evaporate the acetone in a hood on a steam bath or in an explosion-proof oven; dry to constant weight at 105 C; and ignite for 1 hr at 500 C. If the weights are to be obtained from field-dried material, re-wet the

dried material with distilled water and remove from the slides with a razor blade or rubber policeman. Place scrapings from each slide in a separate crucible, dry to constant weight at 105 C, and ignite for 1 hr at 500 C.

2) Re-wet the ash with distilled water and dry to constant weight at 105 C. This step is taken to reintroduce the water of hydration of the clay (and other minerals), which is not driven off at 105 C but is lost during ashing. If not corrected for, this water loss will be recorded as volatile organic matter.[5]

c. *Calculations:* Calculate the mean weight from the several slides and report as grams dry weight and ash-free weight per square meter of exposed surface. If 25- by 75-mm (1- by 3-in.) slides are used, then

$$g/m^2 = \frac{g/\text{slide (average)}}{0.00375}$$

4. Chlorophyll and Pheophytin

The chlorophyll content of attached communities is a useful index of the biomass of the phytoperiphyton. Because quantitative chlorophyll determinations require the collection of periphyton from a known surface area, artificial substrates are well suited for this purpose. The pigments are extracted with aqueous acetone and the optical density of the extract is determined with a spectrophotometer. When immediate pigment extraction is not possible, the samples may be stored frozen for as long as 30 days if

kept in the dark.[6] The ease with which the chlorophylls are removed from the cells varies considerably with different algae. To achieve complete extraction of the pigments it is usually necessary to disrupt the cells mechanically with a grinder, blender, or sonic disintegrator, or to freeze them. Grinding is the most rigorous and effective of these methods.

a. *Equipment and reagents:* See Section 1002 G.

b. *Procedure:*

1) In the field, place the individual glass microscope slides used as substrates directly into 100-ml aqueous acetone in a wide-mouth bottle.

NOTE: Plexiglas is soluble in acetone. If Plexiglas is used as the substrate, scrape the periphyton from it before solvent extraction.

2) If extraction cannot be carried out immediately, freeze samples in the field and keep frozen until processed.

3) Rupture the cells by grinding and steep in acetone for 24 hr in the dark, at or near 4 C.

4) To determine the concentration of pigment, follow the procedures given in Section 1002 G.

c. *Calculations:* After the concentration of pigment in the extract has been determined, calculate the amount of pigment per unit surface area of sample as follows:

$$\text{mg chlorophyll } a/m^2 = \frac{C_a \times \text{volume of extract, l}}{\text{area of substrate, m}^2}$$

1003 D.   Productivity

The productivity of periphyton communities is a function of water quality, substrate, and seasonal patterns in temperature and solar illumination. It may be estimated from temporal changes in standing crop (biomass) or from the rate of oxygen evolution or carbon uptake.[7]

1. Biomass Accumulation

The rate of accumulation of organic matter on artificial substrates by the attachment, growth, and reproduction of colonizing organisms has been used widely to estimate the productivity of streams and reservoirs.[8, 9] In the application of this method, expose several replicate clean substrates for a predetermined period, scrape the accumulated material from the slides, and ash as described previously.

$$P = \frac{\text{mg ash-free weight/slide}}{TA}$$

where:

P = productivity, mg ash-free weight/m^2/day,

T = exposure time, days, and

A = area of a slide, m^2

Obtain estimates of the seasonal changes in the standing crop of established communities by placing many replicate substrates at a sampling point and then retrieving a few at a time at regular intervals, such as every 2 wk or every month, over the period of 1 yr or longer.[8] The gain in ash-free weight per unit area from one collection period to the next is a measure of net production.

2. Standing Water Productivity Measured by Oxygen Method

Hourly and daily rates of oxygen evolution and carbon uptake by periphyton growing in standing water can be studied by confining them briefly in bottles, bell jars, or other chambers. In contrast, the metabolism of organisms in flowing water is highly dependent on current velocity and cannot be determined accurately under static conditions. The measurement of productivity in flowing as opposed to standing waters presents somewhat different problems for each kind of water; therefore, procedures will be separated accordingly.

The productivity and respiration of the epilithic and epipelic periphyton in littoral regions of lakes and ponds can be determined by inserting transparent and opaque bell jars or open-ended plastic chambers into the substratum along transects perpendicular to the shoreline.[10, 11] The chambers are left in place for one-half the photoperiod. The concentration of dissolved oxygen in the chamber is determined at the beginning and end of the exposure period. The gross productivity is the sum of the net gain in dissolved oxygen in the transparent chamber and the oxygen used in respiration. The values obtained are doubled to determine the productivity for the entire photoperiod.

Failure to account for changes in dissolved oxygen in the chambers caused by the photosynthesis and respiration of the plankton may be the cause of serious errors in the estimates of periphyton metabolism. It is therefore essential that these values be obtained at the time the periphyton is studied. This can be done by using the light- and dark-bottle method discussed in Section 1002 I. for plankton.

a. Equipment and reagents:

1) Clear and darkened glass or Plexi-

glas chambers, approximately 20 cm in diameter and 30 cm high, with a median lateral port, sealed with a serum bottle stopper for removal of small samples of water for dissolved oxygen analyses or for the insertion of an oxygen probe. Fit the chamber with a small, manually operated, propeller-shaped stirring paddle.

2) *Dissolved oxygen probe, or equipment and reagents required for Winkler dissolved oxygen determinations* (see Section 422).

b. *Procedure:*

1) At each station place a transparent and opaque chamber over the substrate at sunrise or noon and leave in place for one-half the photoperiod. Determine the concentration of dissolved oxygen at the beginning of the incubation period.

2) At the end of the exposure period, carefully mix the water in the chambers and determine the concentration of dissolved oxygen.

c. *Calculations:* When the exposure period is one-half day, gross production is determined by

$$P_g = 2[V_L(L_F-L_I) + V_D(D_I-D_F)]$$

where:

$$P_g = \text{gross production, mg } O_2/m^2/\text{day,}$$

V_L = volume of clear chamber, l,

L_F and L_I = final and initial concentrations, respectively, of dissolved oxygen in the clear chamber, mg/l,

V_D = volume of opaque chamber, l.

D_I and D_F = initial and final concentrations, respectively, of dissolved oxygen in the opaque chamber, mg/l, and

A = substrate area, m².

The net production rate is determined by calculating the 24-hr uptake of oxygen in respiration and subtracting it from the gross production:

$$P_n = \frac{P_g - 24(D_I-D_F)}{T A}$$

where:

P_n = net production, mg $O_2/m^2/$day, and
T = length of exposure, hr.

3. Standing Water Productivity Measured by Carbon 14 Method

The approach is generally similar to that described above for the oxygen method. Transparent and opaque chambers are placed over the substrate. Carbon 14-labeled sodium carbonate is injected into the chamber by syringe, mixed well, and allowed to incubate with the periphyton for one-half the photoperiod. The concentration of dissolved inorganic carbon available for photosynthesis is determined by titration. At the end of the incubation period, the periphyton is removed from the substrate and assayed for carbon 14.[10, 12]

a. *Equipment and reagents:*

1) *Incubation chamber:* See above under Oxygen Method, Section 1003 D.2a.

2) *Special equipment and reagents:* See Section 1002 I.

3) *Carbon 14-labeled solution of sodium carbonate,* having a specific activity of approximately 10 μCi/ml.

4) *Other equipment and reagents:* See Section 407 on carbon dioxide.

b. *Procedure:*

1) At each station place a transparent and opaque chamber over the substrate and add approximately 10 μCi carbon 14/l of chamber volume. Mix water in the chambers well, taking

care to avoid disturbing the periphyton. Determine the concentration of dissolved inorganic carbon as described in Section 403, Alkalinity.

2) At end of exposure period, remove surface centimeter of periphyton enclosed in the chamber, freeze, and store frozen in a vacuum desiccator.

3) Immediately before the analysis, expose sample to fumes of HCl for 10 to 15 min to drive off all inorganic carbon 14 retained in the periphyton.

4) Combust sample (or portion) by the Van Slyke method[12] and assay the radioactivity by one of the following methods: (a) flush the carbon dioxide produced by combustion into a gas-flow counter or electrometer; (b) take it up in a 0.1N solution of sodium carbonate, precipitate as barium carbonate on a membrane filter, and count with an end-window tube; or (c) assay as the sodium carbonate solution by the liquid scintillation technic.

c. Calculations:

$$P_n = \frac{\text{(activity in sample)}}{\text{(activity added)}} \times \frac{\text{(dissolved inorganic carbon)}}{\text{(area of substrate)}} \times 1.064$$

where:

P_n = net productivity for the exposure period, and

1.064 = correction for the isotope effect.

4. Flowing Water Productivity Measured by Oxygen Method

Diurnal changes in the concentration of dissolved oxygen are the result of the integrated effects of the respiration and photosynthesis of the periphyton and plankton, water velocity and turbulence, turbidity, depth, organic waste loads, and accrual of groundwater and surface drainage. Daily fluctuations in the photosynthetic production of oxygen are imposed on the relatively steady oxygen demand of respiratory activity. Respiration rates also may vary diurnally under certain conditions, but the factors involved are not well understood. The effects of plankton photosynthesis and respiration on the overall oxygen balance can be estimated by the light- and dark-bottle method.

The rate of change in the concentration of dissolved oxygen (q) in grams per cubic meter, is the algebraic sum of the rates of photosynthesis (p), respiration (r), diffusion (d), and accrual in groundwater inflow and surface runoff (a).[13]

$$q = p - r + d_{in.} + a$$

If the equation is multiplied through by the depth in meters (z), the resulting values are in grams per square meter.

$$zq = Q = P - R + D_{in.} + A$$

The rate of diffusion of oxygen into the water per area (D) is a product of the gas transfer coefficient (K) based on the diffusion rate at 0% saturation, and the percent saturation deficit (S):

$$D (g/m^2/hr) = KS$$

a. Equipment and reagents:

1) BOD bottles, for light- and dark-bottle measurements. See sections on plankton productivity (1002 I).

2) DO probe, where applicable.

3) Bottom chamber, 60 by 20 by 10 cm, with 32-cm lengthwise dividing baffle, rheostat-controlled submersible pump, temperature thermistor, and DO probe or glass tube for removing water in oxygen determinations.[14]

4) Plastic dome, Plexiglas, approximately 22 cm in diameter, with float, temperature thermistor, and rubber-sealed port for removal of gas samples.[15]

b. Procedure: Make hourly or continuous measurements of the concentration of dissolved oxygen at one or two stations, depending on stream conditions, precision desired, and availability of equipment. If similar conditions have obtained for some distance upstream from the reach to be studied, diurnal measurements of dissolved oxygen at a single station are sufficient to determine productivity. However, where upstream conditions are significantly different from those in the reach to be studied, make measurements at the upstream and downstream limits of the reach.

1) Measure plankton photosynthesis and respiration rates by the light- and dark-bottle method described under plankton productivity (Section 1002 I.2).

2) Determine the gas transfer coefficient (K)—

a) Single-station method—Determine the K value from the measurements of dissolved oxygen taken shortly after sunset and just before sunrise. At sunset

$$q_e = \frac{KS_e}{z} - r \qquad (1)$$

where:

q_e = evening rate of change in dissolved oxygen, and
S_e = saturation deficit.

At sunrise

$$q_m = \frac{KS_m}{z} - r \qquad (2)$$

where:

q_m = morning rate of change in dissolved oxygen, and
S_m = saturation deficit.

Subtracting Equation 1 from Equation 2 and rearranging results in the following relationship:

$$K = z \frac{(q_m - q_e)}{(S_m - S_e)}$$

b) Two-station method—If the accrual is negligible, determine the diffusion rate (D) for a given saturation deficit by subtracting the respiration rate (R) from the upstream-downstream change in dissolved oxygen.

$$D = KS = z(C_1 - C_2) - R$$
$$K = \frac{z(C_1 - C_2) - R}{S}$$

where:

C_1 and C_2 = concentration of dissolved oxygen at the upstream and downstream stations, respectively.

c) Plastic dome method—Determine the diffusion rate directly by measuring the nighttime loss of oxygen from a plastic dome in contact with the water surface.[15] Fill the dome (diameter approximately 22 cm and a volume 2.5 l with atmospheric gases and float on the water. Every 2 to 3 hr, remove 5-ml samples of gas from the dome and analyze for oxygen content. Determine the concentration of dissolved oxygen in the water.

3) Determine the periphyton respiration—

a) Single-station method—If the diffusion rate is known, determine the respiration rate by subtracting the diffusion rate from the nighttime rate of change in oxygen concentration.

b) Two-station method—Nighttime upstream-downstream changes in dissolved oxygen (DO) observed at the time of 100% saturation are caused by respiration.

c) Chamber method (Thomas-O'Connell chamber)[14]—This chamber may be considered a modification of the bell jar. Measure current velocity of the stream with a meter and duplicate inside the chamber with the aid of a pump. This is the only chamber method expected to yield accurate estimates of periphyton respiration at all current velocities.

c. Calculations:

1) Determine hourly rates of change in stream DO by subtracting successive pairs of DO measurements.

2) Calculate the percent oxygen saturation and diffusion rates D for each sample and determine the average value for each sampling interval (If the plastic dome method is used, the D values are obtained directly).

3) Correct the q and r values for phytoplankton photosynthesis and respiration and plot on the same axes. Determine the area between the two curves graphically; this represents the gross productivity of the periphyton.[16]

4) Determine the daily productivity per square meter of surface by multiplying the daily productivity per cubic meter by the discharge in cubic meters and dividing by the average depth in meters.

5. Flowing Water Productivity Measured by Carbon 14 Method

The use of carbon 14 to measure periphyton photosynthesis in flowing waters is restricted to closed chambers with forced circulation. In this case, periphyton grown on natural or artificial substrates may be transferred to the chamber, which rests on the bottom of the stream, or a chamber that is open at the bottom is placed over a section of undisturbed stream bed. Labeled sodium carbonate is introduced into the chamber and the water in the chamber is circulated mechanically to provide a cur-

rent velocity comparable to that in the stream. The sample is incubated for one-half the photoperiod, removed, and analyzed as described previously. (See Section 1002 I.3).

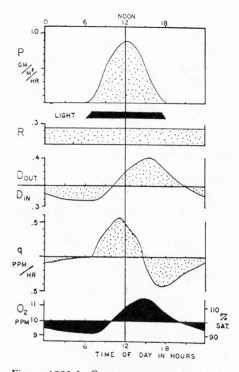

Figure 1003:2. Component processes in the oxygen metabolism of a section of a hypothetical stream during the course of a cloudless day. Production (P), respiration (R), and diffusion (D) are given on an areal basis. The combined effect of these rate processes for a stream 1 m deep is given in ppm/hr (q). The actual oxygen values that would result in a stream with a long homogeneous community are given in the lowermost curve. Source: ODUM, H.T. 1956. Primary production in flowing waters. *Limnol. Oceanogr.* 1:102.

1003 E.   Reporting Results

Although several systems have been developed to organize and interpret periphyton data, no single method has received universal acceptance. The methods may be qualitative or quantitative. The qualitative methods attempt to relate the taxonomic composition of the communities to zones of pollution, whereas the quantitative methods deal with numerical indices of saprobity, community diversity, and composition.

1. Qualitative Methods (Indicator Species and Communities)

The saprobity system developed by Kolkwitz and Marsson is probably the most widely used method of interpreting periphyton data. This scheme divides the polluted reaches of streams into polysaprobic, α and β mesosaprobic, and oligosaprobic zones, and lists the characteristic species found in each. The system has been refined[17, 18] and has been enlarged by Fjerdingstad[19, 20] and Sladecek.[21, 22]

2. Quantitative Methods

These methods incorporate the use of cell counts per unit area of substrate and numerical indices of pollution or water quality. Considerable data on cell densities and species composition of periphyton collected on glass slides in polluted rivers in England are available.[23] Other indices include those based on the saprobity system,[24] where code numbers assigned for the saprobial value and the abundance of individual species are used to calculate a Mean Saprobial Index; the truncated-log normal distribution of diatom species;[25, 26] indices of community diversity derived from information theory equations,[27] and the autotrophic index (AI).[28]

1003 F.   References

1. Roll, H. 1939. Zur terminologie des periphytons. *Arch. Hydrobiol.* 35:59.
2. Young, O.W. 1945. A limnological investigation of periphyton in Douglas Lake, Michigan. *Trans. Amer. Microsc. Soc.* 64:1.
3. Sladeckova, A. 1962. Limnological investigation methods for the periphyton community. *Bot. Rev.* 28:286.
4. Newcombe, C.L. 1950. A quantitative study of attachment materials in Sodon Lake, Michigan. *Ecology* 31:204.
5. Nelson, D.J. & D.C. Scott. 1962. Role of detritus in the productivity of a rock outcrop community in a piedmont stream. *Limnol. Oceanogr.* 7:396.
6. Grzenda, A.R. & M.L. Brehmer. 1960. A quantitative method for the collection and measurement of stream periphyton. *Limnol. Oceanogr.* 5:190.
7. Vollenweider, R.A., ed. 1969. A Manual on Methods for Measuring Primary Production in Aquatic Environments. IBP Handbook No. 12, F.A. Davis, Co., Philadelphia, Pa.
8. Sladecek, V. & A. Sladeckova. 1964. De-

termination of periphyton production by means of the glass slide method. *Hydrobiologia* 23:125.

9. KING, D.L. & R.C. BALL. 1966. A qualitative and quantitative measure of aufwuchs production. *Trans. Amer. Microsc. Soc.* 82:232.

10. WETZEL, R.G. 1963. Primary productivity of periphyton. *Nature* 197:1026.

11. WETZEL, R.G. 1964. A comparative study of the primary productivity of higher aquatic plants, periphyton, and phytoplankton in a large shallow lake. *Int. Rev. Ges. Hydrobiol.* 49:1.

12. ARONOFF, S. 1956. Techniques in Radiobiochemistry. Iowa State College Press, Ames.

13. ODUM, H.T. 1956. Primary production in flowing waters. *Limnol. Oceanogr.* 1:102.

14. THOMAS, N.A. & R.L. O'CONNELL. 1966. A method for measuring primary production by stream benthos. *Limnol. Oceanogr.* 11:386.

15. COPELAND, B.J. & W.R. DUFFER. 1964. Use of a clear plastic dome to measure gaseous diffusion rates in natural waters. *Limnol. Oceanogr.* 9:494.

16. ODUM, H.T. & C.M. HOSKIN. 1958. Comparative studies of the metabolism of marine water. *Publ. Inst. Mar. Sci. Univ. Tex.* 4:115.

17. KOLKWITZ, R. 1950. Oekologie der saprobien. *Ver Wasser-, Boden, Lufthyg. Schriftenreihe* (Berlin) 4:1.

18. LIEBMANN, H. 1951. Handbuch der Frischwasser und Abwasserbiologie. Bd. I. Oldenbourg, Munchen, Germany.

19. FJERDINGSTAD, E. 1964. Pollution of streams estimated by benthal phytomicroorganisms.

I. A saprobic system based on communities of organisms and ecological factors. *Int. Rev. Ges. Hydrobiol.* 49:63.

20. FJERDINGSTAD, E. 1965. Taxonomy and saprobic valency of benthic phytomicroorganisms. *Int. Rev. Ges. Hydrobiol.* 50:475.

21. SLADECEK, V. 1966. Water quality system. *Verh. Int. Ver. Limnol.* 16:809.

22. SLADECEK, V. 1973. System of water quality from the biological point of view. *Arch. Hydrobiol.* 7:1.

23. BUTCHER, R.W. 1946. Studies in the ecology of rivers. VI. The algal growth in certain highly calcareous streams. *J. Ecol.* 33:268.

24. PANTLE, R. & H. BUCK. 1955. Die biologische uberwachung der Gewasser und der Darstellung der Ergebnisse. *Gas- Wasserfach* 96:604.

25. PATRICK, R., M.H. HOHN & J.H. WALLACE. 1954. A new method for determining the pattern of the diatom flora. *Bull. Philadelphia Acad. Natur. Sci.* 259:1.

26. PATRICK, R. 1973. Use of algae, especially diatoms, in the assessment of water quality. In: Biological Methods for the Assessment of Water Quality (J. Cairns, Jr., ed.). ASTM STP 528, Amer. Soc. for Testing & Materials, pp. 76-95.

27. MARGALEF, R. 1956. Information y Diversidad Espicifia en las Communidades de Organismos. *Invest. Pesq.* 3:99.

28. WEBER, C. 1973. Recent developments in the measurement of the response of plankton and periphyton to changes in their environment. In: Bioassay Techniques and Environmental Chemistry (G. Glass, ed.). Ann Arbor Sci. Publ., Inc., Ann Arbor, Mich., pp. 119-138.

1003 G. Bibliography

KOLKWITZ, R. & M. MARSSON. 1908. Okologie der pflanzlichen Saprobien. *Berl. Deut. Bot. Ges.* 26(a):118.

FRITSCH, F.E. 1929. The encrusting algal communities of certain fast-flowing streams. *New Phytol.* 28:166.

BUTCHER, R.W. 1931. An apparatus for studying the growth of epiphytic algae with special relation to the river Tees. *Trans. N. Natur. Union* 1:1.

BUTCHER, R.W. 1932. Studies in the ecology of rivers. II. The microflora of rivers, with special reference to the algae on the river bed. *Ann. Bot.* 46:813.

BUTCHER, R.W. 1947. Studies in the ecology of rivers. VII. The algae of organically enriched waters. *J. Ecol.* 35:186.

MARGALEF, R. 1948. A new limnological method for the investigation of thin-layered epilithic communities. *Trans. Amer. Microsc. Soc.* 67:153.

FJERDINGSTAD, E. 1950. The microflora of the River Mølleaa, with special reference to the relation of the benthal algae to pollution. *Folia Limnol. Scand.* 5:1.

BLUM, J.L. 1956. The ecology of river algae. *Bot. Rev.* 22:291.

COOKE, W.B. 1956. Colonization of artificial bare areas by microorganisms. *Bot. Rev.* 22:613.

YOUNT, J.L. 1956. Factors that control species numbers in Silver Springs, Florida. *Limnol. Oceanogr.* 1:286.

BUTCHER, R.W. 1959. Biological assessment of river pollution. *Proc. Linnean Soc. London* 170:159.

HOHN, M.H. 1959. The use of diatom populations as a measure of water quality in selected areas of Galveston and Chocolate Bay, Texas. *Publ. Inst. Mar. Sci. Univ. Tex.* 5:206.

POMEROY, L.R. 1959. Algal productivity in salt marshes. *Limnol. Oceanogr.* 4:386.

CASTENHOLZ, R.W. 1961. An evaluation of a submerged glass method of estimating production of attached algae. *Verh. Int. Ver. Limnol.* 14:155.

HOHN, M.H. 1961. Determining the pattern of the diatom flora. *J. Water Pollut. Control Fed.* 33:48.

PATRICK, R. 1963. The structure of diatom communities under varying ecological conditions. *Ann. N.Y. Acad. Sci.* 108:359.

WHITFORD, L.A. & G.J. SCHUMACHER. 1964. Effect of a current on respiration and mineral uptake in *Spirogyra* and *Oedogonium. Ecology* 45:168.

WILLIAMS, L.G. & D.I. MOUNT. 1965. Influence of zinc on periphytic communities. *Amer. J. Bot.* 52:26.

DUFFER, W.R. & T.C. DORRIS. 1966. Primary productivity in a southern Great Plains stream. *Limnol. Oceanogr.* 11:143.

EATON, J.W. & B. MOSS. 1966. The estimation of numbers and pigment content in epipelic algal populations. *Limnol. Oceanogr.* 11:584.

HOHN, M.H. 1966. Artificial substrate for benthic diatoms—collection, analysis, and interpretation. In: Organism-Substrate Relationships in Streams (K.W. Cummings, C.A. Tryon, Jr., & R.T. Hartman, eds.). Pymatuning Lab. of Ecology, Spec. Publ. No. 4, pp. 87-97, Univ. of Pittsburgh.

KEVERN, N.R., J.L. WILHM & G.M. VAN DYNE. 1966. Use of artificial substrata to estimate the productivity of periphyton communities. *Limnol. Oceanogr.* 11:499.

KING, D.L. & R.C. BALL. 1966. A qualitative and quantitative measure of *aufwuchs* production. *Trans. Amer. Microsc. Soc.* 82:232.

McINTIRE, C.D. 1966. Some factors affecting respiration of periphyton communities in lotic environments. *Ecology* 47:918.

SCHLICHTING, H.E., JR. & R.A. GEARHEART. 1966. Some effects of sewage effluent upon phyco-periphyton in Lake Murray, Oklahoma. *Proc. Okla. Acad. Sci.* 46:19.

SLADECKOVA, A. & V. SLADECEK. 1966. Periphyton as indicator of reservoir water quality. *Technol. Water* (Czech). 7:507.

THOMAS, N.A. & R.L. O'CONNELL. 1966. A method for measuring primary production by stream benthos. *Limnol. Oceanogr.* 11:386.

CUSHING, C.E. 1967. Periphyton productivity and radionuclide accumulation in the Columbia River, Washington, USA. *Hydrobiologia* 29:125.

PHAUP, J.D. & J. GANNON. 1967. Ecology of *Sphaerotilus* in an experimental outdoor channel. *Water Res.* 1:523.

TAYLOR, M.P. 1967. Thermal effects on the periphyton community in the Green River. TVA, Div. Health & Safety, Water Qual. Br., Biol. Sect., Chattanooga, Tenn.

MOSS, B. 1968. The chlorophyll *a* content of some benthic algal communities. *Arch. Hydrobiol.* 65:51.

PATRICK, R. 1968. The structure of diatom communities in similar ecological conditions. *Amer. Natur.* 102:173.

ARTHUR, J.W. & W.B. HORNING. 1969. The use of artificial substrates in pollution surveys. *Amer. Midland Natur.* 82:83.

DICKMAN, M. 1969. A quantitative method for assessing the toxic effects of some water soluble substances, based on changes in periphyton community structure. *Water Res.* 3:963.

BESCH, W.K., M. RICARD & R. CANTIN. 1970. Use of benthic diatoms as indicators of mining pollution in the N.W. Miramichi River. *Tech. Rep. Fish. Res. Board Can.* 202:1.

NUSCH, E.A. 1970. Ecological and systematic studies of the Peritricha (Protozoa, Ciliata) in the periphyton community of reservoirs and dammed rivers with different degrees of saprobity. *Arch. Hydrobiol.* (Suppl.) 37:243.

ROSE, F.L. & C.D. MCINTIRE. 1970. Accumulation of dieldrin by benthic algae in laboratory streams. *Hydrobiologia* 35:481.

TIPPETT, R. 1970. Artificial surfaces as a method of studying populations of benthic micro-algae in fresh water. *Brit. Phycol. J.* 5:187.

WHITTON, B.A. 1970. Toxicity of zinc, copper and lead to Chlorophyta from flowing waters. *Arch. Mikrobiol.* 72:353.

BURROWS, E.M. 1971. Assessment of pollution effects by the use of algae. *Proc. Roy. Soc. Lond. Ser. B.* 177:295.

CURTIS, E.J.C. & C.R. CURDS. 1971. Sewage fungus in rivers in the United Kingdom: The slime community and its constituent organisms. *Water Res.* 5:1147.

ERTL, M. 1971. A quantitative method of sampling periphyton from rough substrates. *Limnol. Oceanogr.* 16:576.

HANSMANN, E.W., C.B. LANE & J.D. HALL. 1971. A direct method of measuring benthic primary production in streams. *Limnol. Oceanogr.* 16:822.

PATRICK, R. 1971. The effects of increasing light and temperature on the structure of diatom communities. *Limnol. Oceanogr.* 16:405.

ANDERSON, M.A. & S.L. PAULSON. 1972. A simple and inexpensive woodfloat periphyton sampler. *Progr. Fish-Cult.* 34:225.

ARCHIBALD, R.E.M. 1972. Diversity of some South African diatom associations and its relation to water quality. *Water Res.* 6:1229.

CAIRNS, J., JR., B.R. LANZA & B.C. PARKER. 1972. Pollution-related structural and functional changes in aquatic communities with emphasis on freshwater algae and protozoa. *Proc. Acad. Natur. Sci. Philadelphia* 124:79.

OLSON, T.A. & T.O. ODLAUG. 1972. Lake Superior Periphyton in Relation to Water Quality. Univ. Minn. Sch. Pub. Health, Minneapolis, Water Pollut. Control Res. Ser., 18080 DEM 02/72.

HANSMANN, E.W. 1973. Effects of logging on periphyton in coastal streams of Oregon. *Ecology* 54:194.

RUTHVEN, J.A. & J. CAIRNS, JR. 1973. Response of fresh-water protozoan artificial communities to metals. *J. Protozool.* 20:127.

SCHINDLER, D.W., V.E. FROST & R.V. SCHMIDT. 1973. Production of epilithiphyton in two lakes of the experimental lakes area, northwestern Ontario. *J. Fish. Res. Board Can.* 30:1511.

MIDWEST BENTHOLOGICAL SOCIETY. 1964-1973. (Annual) Current and Select Bibliographies on Benthic Biology. Springfield, Ill.

1004   MACROPHYTON

1004 A.   Introduction

The macrophyton consist principally of the aquatic flowering plants, but also include the aquatic mosses, liverworts, and ferns, and the larger marine algae. Freshwater forms range from the tiny watermeal (*Wolffia*), about the size of a pinhead, to plants such as the cattail (*Typha*), up to 4 m in height, and the water lily (*Nymphaea*), with large floating leaves. The higher aquatic plants often are found clustered in large numbers and covering extensive areas of shallow lakes, marshes, and canals. A few of the larger freshwater algae, among them *Chara* and *Cladophora*, resemble the higher plants in size, form and habit, but are not included with the macrophyton. In marine water, the intertidal rockweeds such as *Fucus* and *Ascophyllum* and offshore kelps such as *Fucus* and *Macrocystis* are conspicuous. Vascular marine or estuarine plants, such as the eel-grass *Zostera* and the marshgrass *Spartina*, are essential to the aquatic ecosystem.

Three types of macrophyton are recognized: floating, submersed, and emersed. The floating plants are not rooted: their principal foliage or crown floats on the water surface. All or most of the foliage of the submersed plants grows beneath the water surface; the plants may or may not have roots. The emersed plants are erect or spreading, with their principal foliage in the air above the water surface; they are attached by roots to the bottom mud. In some cases the same species may grow as either a floating or an emersed type, depending on the water level. Submersed and emersed vascular plants usually are rooted in the bottom. Most of the large marine algae are attached by special holdfasts.

1004 B.   Macrophyton Description

1. Identification

Identification of the plants should be carried out to species if possible. A reference collection of identified specimens, either preserved or dried, is helpful for comparison. Report percentage of areal coverage and amount of growth of each species.

2. Extent of Growth (Areal Coverage)

Report coverage either as marginal, occurring in patches, or extending continuously over all or a significant part of a body of water. Words often used to describe the growth coverage are: dense (abundant, excessive, heavy, profuse) when there is continuous coverage of the area being considered; medium (common to fairly common) when the growth covers approximately half the area; and sparse (rare) when the growth is seldom observed.

Particularly when growth is dense, report the areal coverage in hectares or as percentage of surface covered. For canals, ditches, and streams, coverage may be recorded as kilometers of the watercourse affected.

3. Depth of Growth

Report depth of solid growth as depth in meters. Actual measurements may range from 1 cm to 3 to 5 m or greater.

4. Volume of Growth

Although seldom used as a measure, the volume of growth may be reported in cubic meters.

5. Biomass

Estimate the wet or dry weight of the growth from representative samples.

6. Preliminary Area Survey

Subdivide the area of interest into a number of distinguishable geographic sections and plot on a map. During the period of maximum growth, conduct a reconnaissance by boat of the area to be surveyed. Record on the map the predominant genera or species of aquatic vegetation for each subarea and assign to each such genus or species a symbol of relative abundance. Using the map, determine the extent of plant growth with a planimeter. Aerial photographs, especially with infrared film, are a valuable supplement to other observations.

1004 C. Bibliography

MUENSCHER, W.C. 1944. Aquatic Plants of the United States. Comstock Publ. Co., Ithaca, N.Y.

MASON, H.L. 1957. A Flora of the Marshes of California. Univ. of California Press, Berkeley.

FASSETT, N.C. 1960. A Manual of Aquatic Plants (with a revised appendix by E.C. Ogden). Univ. of Wisconsin Press, Madison.

ARBER, A. 1963. Water Plants, A Study of Aquatic Angiosperms. Hafner Publ. Co., N.Y.

EYLES, D.E. & J.L. ROBERTSON, JR. 1963. A Guide and Key to the Aquatic Plants of the Southeastern United States. U.S. Fish & Wildlife Serv. Circ. 158.

KLUSSMAN, W.G. & F.G. LOWMAN. 1964. Common Aquatic Plants: Identification, Control. Texas A. & M. Univ., College Station, B-1018.

HOTCHKISS, N. 1964. Bulrushes and Bulrushlike Plants of Eastern North America. U.S. Fish & Wildlife Serv. Circ. 221.

LAWRENCE, J.M. & L.W. WELDON. 1965. Identification of aquatic weeds. *Hyacinth Control J.* 4:5.

OTTO, N.E. & T.R. BARTLEY. 1965. Aquatic Pests on Irrigation Systems. U.S. Dept. Interior, Bureau of Reclamation, Water Resour. Tech. Publ.

WINTERRINGER, G.S. & A.C. LOPINOT. 1966. Aquatic Plants of Illinois. Ill. State Museum Popular Sci. Ser. Vol. 6.

HOTCHKISS, N. 1967. Underwater and Floating-Leaved Plants of the United States and Canada. U.S. Fish & Wildlife Serv. Res. Publ. 44.

MACKENTHUN, K.E. & W.M. INGRAM. 1967. Recognizing some common higher aquatic plants. In: Biological Associated Problems in Freshwater Environments. FWPCA, Washington, D.C.

SCULTHROPE, C.D. 1967. The Biology of Aquatic Vascular Plants. St. Martins Press, N.Y.

WELDON, L.W., R.D. BLACKBURN & D.S. HARRISON. 1969. Common Aquatic Weeds. U.S. Dept. Agr. Handbook No. 352.

BRYANT, C.B. 1970. Aquatic weed harvesting—effects and costs. *Hyacinth Control J.* 8:37.

HOTCHKISS, N. 1970. Common Marsh Plants of the United States and Canada. Resource Publ., Bur. Sport Fish. & Wildlife, U.S. Dept. Interior, Washington, D.C.

PATTON, V.D. & W.E. STARNES. 1970. Aquatic weeds and water pollution. *Hyacinth Control J.* 8:48.

SHEFFIELD, C.W. 1970. Eutrophication and aquatic weeds. *Hyacinth Control J.* 8:26.

BOYD, C.E. 1971. The limnological role of aquatic macrophytes and their relationship to reservoir management. In: Reservoir Fisheries and Limnology (G.E. Hall, ed.). Amer. Fish. Soc. Spec. Publ. 8.

STUCKEY, R.L. 1971. Changes of vascular aquatic flowering plants during 70 years in Put-in-Bay harbor, Lake Erie, Ohio. *Ohio J. Sci.* 71:321.

KOEGEL, R.G., H.D. BRUHN & D.F. LIVERMORE. 1971. Improving Surface Water Conditions Through Control and Disposal of Aquatic Vegetation. Wis. Water Res. Cent., Madison.

CORRELL, D.S. & H.B. CORRELL. 1972. Aquatic and Wetland Plants of Southwestern United States. USEPA, 16030 DNL 01/72.

1005   BENTHIC MACROINVERTEBRATES

1005 A.   Introduction

Benthic macroinvertebrates are animals inhabiting the bottoms of lakes and streams or attached to stones or other submersed objects. Although immature forms may be very small, by definition, organisms collected for study are those that are retained on a U.S. Standard No. 30 sieve (0.595-mm openings). Macroinvertebrate communities are sampled to determine the species composition and abundance of organisms or to monitor long-term changes in community structure. A body of water of good quality usually supports a diverse benthic fauna with no overabundance of any one group. Organic pollution may restrict the variety of organisms in the water; it may also favor the development of large numbers of organisms that tolerate the pollution-associated physical and chemical conditions. On the other hand, pollution by toxic substances may eliminate almost all macroinvertebrates.

1005 B.   Sample Collection

1. General Considerations

Before conducting a survey, investigators must determine specific objectives and define clearly the information sought. For example, to determine whether the macroinvertebrate community downstream from a discharge is damaged, only a few sampling stations upstream and downstream from the discharge are needed. However, if the objective of the survey is to delimit the extent of damage from a discharge or series of discharges, it is necessary to have reference stations upstream from all discharges, to bracket each discharge with stations, and to establish stations downstream.

After gaining a thorough understanding of the factors involved with a particular body of water, the investigator must select specific areas to be sampled. There is no set number of sampling stations that will be sufficient to monitor all the possible types of waste discharges. No water quality survey is routine, nor can one be conducted on a "cookbook" basis. However, some basic rules, if carefully followed, will result in a basically sound survey design:

1. Always establish a reference station(s) upstream or at a point remote from all possible wastewater discharges. Because the usual purpose of a survey is to determine the damage that pollution causes to aquatic life, this will be the basis for comparison of the fauna in polluted and unpolluted areas. In practice, it is advisable to have at least two reference stations. One should be well away from, or upstream from, the discharge and one directly above or in the immediate vicinity of the effluent discharge, but not subject to influence from it.

2. Locate a station immediately downstream or in the affected area in the immediate vicinity of each discharge.

3. If the discharge does not mix completely on entering the water body but channels on one side or disperses in a specific direction, subdivide stations into left bank, mid-channel, and right bank in streams or into concentric arcs in lakes. Keep all data collected separate by substations.

4. Establish stations at various distances downstream from the last discharge to determine the linear extent of damage to the river.

5. To permit comparison of macroinvertebrate communities, be sure that all sampling stations are ecologically similar. For example, the stations should be similar with respect to bottom substrate (sand, gravel, rock, or mud), depth, presence of riffles and pools, stream width, flow velocity, and bank cover.

6. Collect samples for physical and chemical analyses close to biological sampling stations to assure correlation of findings.

7. Locate sampling stations for macroinvertebrates in an area not influenced by atypical habitats, such as those created in streams by road bridges.

8. In order to make comparisons among sampling stations, sample all during the same time period.

For a long-term biological monitoring program, macroinvertebrates should be collected at each station at least once during each of the annual seasons. More frequent sampling may be necessary if the characteristics of any effluents change or if spills occur. In general, the most critical period for macroinvertebrates in streams is during periods of high temperature and low flow. Therefore, if available time and funds limit the sampling frequency, then at least one survey during this time will produce useful information.

2. Sampling Design

A sample is a portion taken from some larger aggregate about which inferences are to be made. The problem in doing this arises from the variation usually encountered in successive samples. Without knowledge of sample variation sample data cannot be correctly inferred to represent the population. Simply stated, replicate samples of a population or aggregate must be taken and studied if correct inferences about the population are to be made.[1]

Sampling design should be standardized to the extent that the following requirements are met:

1. Define the set of all samples that can be selected (separate the population into sampling units).
2. Assign to each possible sample a known probability of selection (randomize to give every sample equal probability of being selected).
3. Select each sample by a process that assigns the correct probability of selection to all samples.
4. Choose a method for computation of estimates from the sample that provides a unique value for each sample.

Standardize acquisition and recording of data when practical. Record and report data in metric units; however, the U.S. equivalent may be noted in parentheses.

One of the most difficult decisions to make when collecting aquatic invertebrates is how many replicate samples to take at each station or substation in order to obtain reliable information. Organisms are not distributed randomly over the bottom of a river or lake. Different habitats (sand, mud, gravel, or organic material) support different densities and species of organisms. Even on a relatively homogeneous bottom, animals tend to occur in clusters. Therefore, it is mandatory to take replicate samples to evaluate this variability.

In most cases three or more replicate samples are required to describe the macroinvertebrate community. Often from 3 to 10 grab samples per station are collected. Of course, more may be necessary to achieve the desired level of accuracy. If a need exists for dividing a station into substations, then each substation should be sampled as described above. These numbers do not apply to all possible situations and should not be used as rigid criteria. Ideally, a base-line survey should be conducted to determine the number of samples necessary to achieve the desired level of accuracy in each pollution survey.

3. Sampling Devices, Quantitative

Quantitative and qualitative samplers have been designed to collect organisms from stream and lake bottoms. The most common quantitative sampling devices are the Ponar, Petersen, and Ekman grabs and the Surber or square-foot stream bottom sampler, all described below.

When sampling qualitatively, the collector searches for as many different organisms as possible. Samples can be taken by any method that will capture representative species.

a. The Ponar grab (Figure 1005:1) is increasingly used in deep lakes[2] and is capable of sampling the widest variety of substrates. It is similar to the Petersen grab in size, weight, lever system, and sample compartment, but has side plates and a screen on the top of the sample compartment to prevent loss of sample during closure. With one set of weights, the sampler weighs 20 kg (about 46 lb).

b. The Ekman grab (Figure 1005:2) is useful for sampling silt, muck, and sludge in water with little current. Do not use on rocky or sandy bottoms, because small pebbles or grit may prevent proper closing of the jaws. The grab is

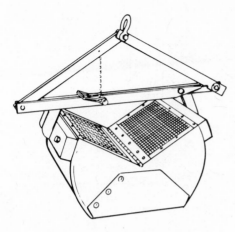

Figure 1005:1. Ponar grab.

wash due to clogging.) This net is held open by a square-foot metal frame (30.5 by 30.5 cm) hinged at one side to another frame of equal size.

In operation, the frame that supports the net is in a vertical position, while the other frame is locked into a horizontal position against the bottom. Triangular cloth sides fill half the side spaces between the horizontal and vertical frames. Place the net opening facing upstream, using the current to hold the net open. Push the horizontal frame into the stream bottom material. Within the

made of 12- to 20-gauge brass or stainless steel and weighs approximately 3.2 kg (7 lb). The box-like part holding the sample has spring-operated jaws on the bottom that must be manually cocked (exercise caution in cocking and handling the grab, which can cause injury if accidentally tripped). At the top of the grab are two hinged overlapping lids that are held partially open during descent by water passing through the sample compartment. These lids are held shut by water pressure when the sampler is being retrieved.

The grab is made in three sizes, 15 cm by 15 cm (6 in. by 6 in.), 23 cm by 23 cm (9 in. by 9 in.), and 30 cm by 30 cm (12 in. by 12 in.), but the smallest size is usually ·adequate and most desirable for taking replicate samples.

c. The Surber or square-foot stream bottom sampler (Figure 1005:3) is a lightweight device for procuring samples in water depths up to 0.6 m (2 ft) in fast-flowing streams. It consists of a strong, close-woven fabric (0.595-mm openings) approximately 69 cm (27 in.) long. (Smaller mesh sizes cause back-

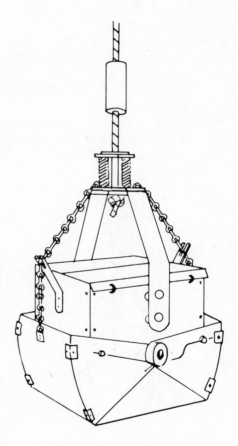

Figure 1005:2. Ekman grab.

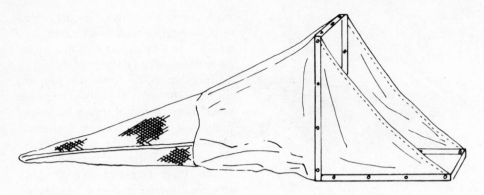

Figure 1005:3. Surber or square-foot sampler.

framed areas, dig up rocks and other bottom deposits by hand or with a tool to a depth of at least 5 cm (2 in.). The organisms dislodged drift into the open net.

d. Other quantitative sampling devices: In addition to those discussed above, many other quantitative samplers are available. Some of these have definite advantages for the sampling of particular habitats or macroinvertebrates. Welch, [3] Pennak,[4] and Barnes[5] have assembled information on several such samplers.

1) *The orange-peel grab* (Figure 1005:4) is a multijawed round grab with a canvas closure at the top serving as a portion of the sample compartment. The 1,600-cm³ (100-in.³) size is generally used, although larger sizes are available. The area sampled and the volume of material collected depend on the depth of penetration.[6] This grab is suited to marine waters and deep lakes, where it has advantages over other tools when sandy substrates are sampled.

2) *The Petersen grab* (Figure 1005: 5) is used widely for sampling hard bottoms such as sand, gravel, marl, and clay in swift currents and deep water. It is an iron, clam-type grab manufactured in various sizes that will sample an area of 0.06 to 0.09 m² (0.6 to 1.0 ft²). Therefore, each grab must be measured to determine its exact sampling area. It weighs approximately 13.7 kg (30 lb), but may weigh as much as 31.8 kg (70 lb) when auxiliary weights are bolted to its sides. Primary purposes of the extra

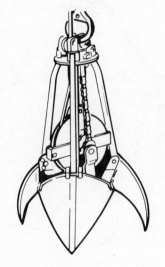

Figure 1005:4. Orange peel sampler.

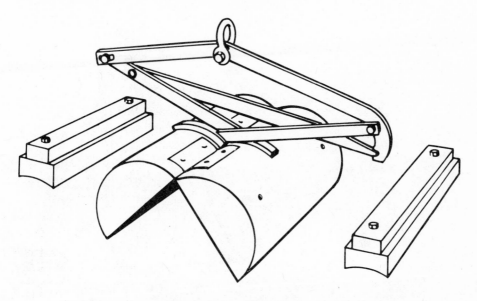

Figures 1005:5. Petersen grab.

weights are to make the grab stable in swift currents and to give additional cutting force in fibrous or firm bottom materials.

Set the grab and lower slowly to the bottom to avoid disturbing lighter bottom materials. Ease rope tension to release the catch. As the grab is raised the lever system closes the jaws.

3) *The Smith-McIntyre grab* (Figure 1005:6) has the heavy steel construction of the Petersen, but its jaws are closed by strong coil springs.[7] Chief advantages are its stability and easier control in rough water. Its bulk and heavy weight require operation from a large boat equipped with a winch. The 45.4-kg (100-lb) grab can sample an area of 0.20 m^2 (2.15 ft^2).

4) *The Shipek grab* (Figure 1005:7) is designed to take a sample 0.04 m^2

(approximately 8 in. by 8 in.) in surface area and approximately 10 cm (4 in.) deep at the center. The sample compartment is composed of two concentric half cylinders. When the grab touches bottom, inertia from a self-contained weight releases a catch and helical springs rotate the inner half cylinder 180 deg. The sample bucket may be disengaged from the upper semicylinder by release of two retaining latches. This grab is used primarily in marine waters and large inland bodies of water.

5) *Core samplers* are used to sample sediments in depth. The area collected at the mud-water interface, 13 to 26 cm^2 (2 to 4 in.^{2}), is small. Their efficient use as surface samplers requires dense animal populations. Core samplers vary from hand-pushed tubes to explosive-driven and automatic-surfacing models.[5]

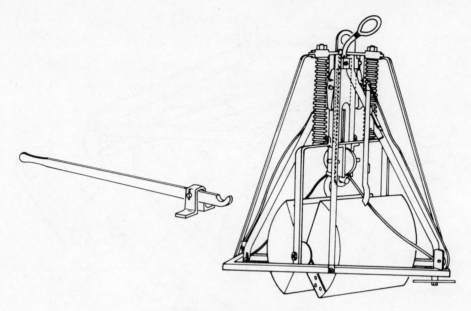

Figure 1005:6. Smith-McIntyre grab.

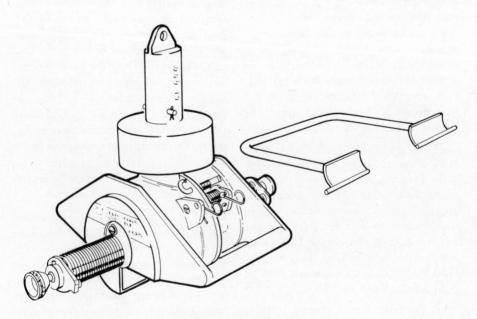

Figure 1005:7. Shipek grab.

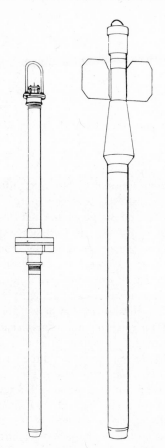

Figure 1005:8. Phleger core sampler.

A KB core sampler or a modification thereof known as the Kajak-Brinkhurst corer may be useful in obtaining estimates of the standing stock of benthic macroinvertebrates inhabiting soft sediments.[8]

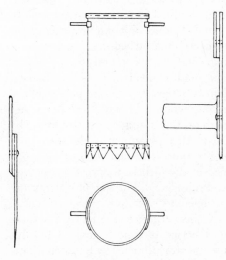

Figure 1005:9. Wilding or stovepipe sampler.

The Phleger type (Figure 1005:8) is widely used in water quality studies. It operates on the gravity principle. Styles and weights vary among manufacturers, some using interchangeable weights that allow variations between 7.7 and 35.0 kg (17 and 77 lb), while others, with fixed weights, weigh 41.0 kg (90 lb) or more. Length of the core taken will vary with substrate texture, but such cores are adequate for most physical, chemical, or fossil examinations to delineate recent environmental changes.

6) *The Wilding or stovepipe sampler* (Figure 1005:9) is made in various sizes and with many modifications. It is especially useful for quantitatively sampling a bottom with dense vascular plant growth. It may be used to sample the vegetation or the mud-water interface sediment, or both. Large volumes of vegetation, when sampled in this way, may require much time for laboratory processing.

e. *Drift nets* (Figure 1005:10) are anchored in flowing water for the capture of macroinvertebrates that have migrated or have been dislodged from the bottom substrates into the current. [9,10]

Drift organisms are vulnerable prey for stream fishes and thus should be considered in studies of fish populations. Benthic invertebrates may respond to pollutional stresses by increased drift from an affected area so that drift may be important in water quality investigations. Drift is also a factor in recolonization of denuded areas and thus contributes to recovery of disturbed streams. Nets having a 929 cm² (1 ft²) upstream opening and mesh equivalent to U.S. Standard No. 30 screen (0.595-mm pore size) are recommended. However, a Nitex net with a 0.471-mm pore size may be used. After placement in the water, the nets require frequent removal of organisms and debris to prevent clogging and subsequent diversion of water at the net opening.

Collect drift net samples for any specified period of time (usually 3 hr) but use the same time for each station. Sampling between dusk and 1:00 AM is optimum.

The total quantity (numbers or biomass) of organisms drifting past a given station per 24 hr divided by the total stream discharge is the best measure of drift intensity.[11] Report data in terms of (number/24 hr)/(m³/24 hr) or (biomass/24 hr)/(m³/24 hr).

4. Sampling Devices, Qualitative

a. Tow nets or trawls range from simple sled-mounted nets to complicated devices incorporating teeth that dig into the bottom. Some models feature special apparatus to hold the net open during towing and to close the net during descent and retrieval. Welch,[3] Barnes,[5] and Usinger[12] discuss some of the styles available.

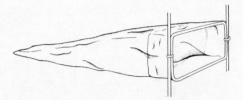

Figure 1005:10. Drift net sampler.

b. Dip nets are practical devices for sweeping animals from vegetation or other substrates near the shore. Select the size and shape of the net and the length of the pole to best suit requirements of a particular sampling situation.

c. Hand screens may be constructed of ordinary window screen, approximately 1 m square and attached on two parallel sides to wooden poles. They are useful for catching organisms in currents and near the shoreline. The poles permit holding or manipulating of the screen.

d. Miscellaneous devices such as garden rakes, pocket knives, buckets, or sieves are useful for collecting macroinvertebrates in a variety of situations. The extent of their use is determined by the type of substrate to be sampled and the collector's ingenuity.

5. Sampling Devices, Artificial Substrate Samplers

The use of artificial substrates to collect aquatic organisms is increasing because they offer a fairly simple way to sample at difficult stations and, to some extent, standardize the sampling procedure. They also eliminate some of the subjectivity required in the use of more traditional sampling devices by providing sites where bottom fauna can colonize. Although the same types of habitats are open for colonization by the organisms at each station, the substrates must be placed at physically similar stations. When it is practical, collect artificial substrates in situ in drawstring cotton bags or other devices to prevent escape of organisms.

a. The multiple-plate sampler[13] is constructed of eight large tempered hardboard plates separated by seven small plates exposing slightly more than 929 cm² (1 ft²) of surface for the attachment of organisms. A hole is bored through the center of each plate. The larger plates are 7.6 by 7.6 cm (3 in.

square) and 3.2 mm (1/8 in.) thick; the smaller plates are 2.5 by 2.5 cm (1 in. square) and 6.4 mm (1/4 in.) thick. The plates are placed alternately on an eyebolt or long threaded rod and held together by two nuts (Figure 1005:11). Instead of an iron or galvanized bolt, which may rust, a nylon cord may be looped through the plates to hold them together. The sampler may be used in streams or lakes, supported by any method that will hold it in the desired place. Depth and exposure should be consistent in a given study.

Begin the collection procedure by carefully placing a plastic bag or dip net (0.595-mm mesh openings) under the sampler. Take the organisms from the sampler in the field by disassembling the plates and scraping or brushing the organisms into a container, or take the entire sampler in the plastic bag to the laboratory for processing. Preserve the collected material in 10% formalin or 70% ethanol.

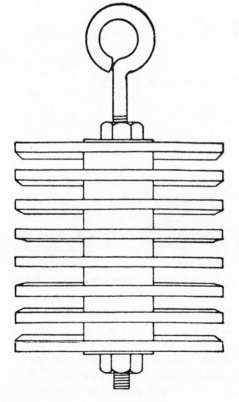

Figure 1005:11. Multiple-plate or Hester-Dendy sampler.

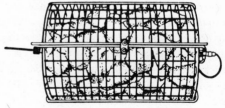

Figure 1005:12. Basket sampler.

b. The basket sampler[14] was developed for the collection of macroinvertebrates in large rivers and lakes. The sampler (Figure 1005:12) consists of a cylindrical chromium-plated basket 18 cm (7 in.) in diameter and 28 cm (11 in.) long, which is filled with 30 rocks 5 to 7.5 cm (2 to 3 in.) in diameter. It weighs approximately 7.8 kg (17 lb). The basket is sturdy, inexpensive, and commercially available.

Where possible, suspend the sampler within the euphotic zone (upper zone where light penetration permits growth of green plants) from stationary or floating structures at an approximate depth of 1.5 m (5 ft) for a 6-wk exposure period. If these conditions cannot be met, it is important that the depth and ex-posure period be standard in any study. The sampler collects immature insects, bryozoans, coelenterates, and other macroinvertebrates often not collected from the bottom sediments by grab and trawl.

Begin the collection procedure by carefully placing a plastic bag or dip net (0.595-mm mesh openings) under the sampler. Empty the rocks into a tub partially filled with water. Brush each rock with a stiff-bristle brush to remove the attached organisms and replace in the basket for another exposure period.

1005 C.   Sample Analysis

After collecting a bottom grab sample containing sand or organic material, empty it into a tub, dilute with water, and swirl the mixture. Pour this slurry through a U.S. Standard No. 30 sieve. Slurries that clog the screen require removal of the screened material. A series of one or two coarser screens (e.g., 1-cm and 0.5-cm mesh) will hold back leaves, sticks, etc., while permitting the smaller organisms to pass through to the No. 30 sieve. Carefully check rocks, sticks, and other artifacts for clinging organisms before discarding. Wash the screened material into a container and preserve in 10% formalin or 70% ethanol. (If ethanol is used, the screened material should not exceed one-half the volume of the container.) Label with the location, date, type of sampler used, name of collector, and other pertinent information.

Some macroinvertebrates such as oligo-chaetes, leeches, and turbellarians are more easily identified if they are relaxed to prevent constriction during preservation.[4]

For qualitative samples it is often desirable to place rocks, sticks, and other objects in a white pan partially filled with water. Many of the animals will float free from these objects and can be removed with forceps.

Concentrate organisms taken from artificial substrates in a U.S. Standard No. 30 sieve and preserve with 10% formalin or 70% ethanol.

Assign identification numbers either in the field or at the laboratory and transcribe information from the labels to a permanent ledger. The ledger provides a convenient reference in identifying the number of samples collected at various places, time of sampling, and characteristics of the water.

Whether the organisms are sorted from the sample detritus in the field or at the laboratory, follow the same procedures consistently. Before processing a sample, transfer information from the label to a data sheet that provides space for scientific names and the number of individuals. Place the sample directly in a shallow white tray with water for sorting. One method used to facilitate sorting organisms from detritus[15] is to stain the organisms red with a concentration of 200 mg/l of rose bengal in the formalin or ethanol preservative. Examine the entire sample and separate organisms unless they occur in very large numbers. If a subsample is sorted, take care that rare forms are not excluded. As the organisms are picked from the sample (a 2× scanning lens is useful), enumerate major taxonomic categories (e.g., Odonata, Coleoptera, and Ephemeroptera) on the data sheet. Place the animals in separate vials according to category and fill with 5% formalin or 70% ethanol. Label with sample number, date, sampling location, names of organisms, etc.

Identify the animals in each vial with the aid of stereoscopic and compound microscopes, according to needs, and available experience and resources. Additional references useful for laboratory technics and the identification of macroinvertebrates are included at the end of this section.

1005   D.   Data Evaluation and Presentation

There are two basic approaches used in evaluating the effects of pollutants on aquatic life. The first is to make a qualitative analysis of the fauna and flora "above and below" or "before and after," thereby determining the species that were present or absent. Then through an understanding of the responses of various species to specific pollutants, one makes an evaluation of the significance of damage or change. The second approach is to make a quantitative inventory of the number of specimens, species, and the structure of the aquatic community affected by the pollutant and to compare it to reference information. In most pollution surveys the two approaches are integrated since both provide valuable interpretative information.

1. Qualitative Data Evaluation

No two aquatic organisms react identically to a pollutant because of the complex interrelationships between genetic factors and environmental conditions. However, certain groups of organisms have been found to be intolerant of various types of pollution. For example, operculate snails, immature stages of certain mayflies, stoneflies, caddisflies, riffle beetles, and hellgrammites are quite sensitive to many pollutants. Pollution-tolerant macroinvertebrates such as sludgeworms, certain midge larvae (bloodworms), leeches, and pulmonate snails usually increase in number under organically enriched conditions. Facultative organisms, those that tolerate moderate amounts of pollution, include most snails, sowbugs, scuds, and black-fly larvae. Tolerant organisms may be found in either clean or polluted situations so that their presence does not mean a body of water is polluted. However, a population of tolerant organisms combined with an absence of intolerant organisms is a good indication of the presence of pollution.

Experienced aquatic biologists, through careful study of the types of fish and the macroinvertebrate, algal, and bacterial species present in a receiving system, can determine its "health". This qualitative evaluation approach, while subjective, does provide useful information.

2. Quantitative Data Evaluation

There is a strong trend toward greater use of statistical methods of data evaluation and mathematical expressions of community structure, partially in response to criticisms of subjectivity directed toward the more quantitative approaches. Statistical analyses of biological data commonly include determination of the mean and confidence interval and use tests such as chi-square, Student's t, regression, correlation, and one- and two-way analysis of variance. The use of mathematical expressions of community structure to derive numerical indices of the diversity of aquatic communities are based on the general, though not invariably true, assumption that the greater the diversity of aquatic life, the greater the structural and functional stability of the system, and therefore the greater the health of the system.

Diversity indices are useful because they condense considerable biological data into a single numerical value. Diversity indices in current use include $\bar{d}$ (diversity per individual), which follows concepts of information theory[16–18] and the SCI (Sequential Comparison Index).[19]

To evaluate statistically the data collected in a pollution survey, it is essential to separate out the sources of variability commonly found.[1] Variability in macroinvertebrate data collected to evaluate water quality comes from the methods of sampling and the distribution of the organisms. Perhaps the major source is sampling error. Distribution of organisms is generally clustered in relation to habitat distribution. Therefore, random samples often show high variability among replicates. In statistical analyses of quantitative data, large numbers of samples often are required to detect statistically significant differences. Care should be exercised in using parametric statistical methods because the basic assumption of normal distribution is often not true. A danger exists in relying on statistical evaluations to determine change because a statistically significant difference may or may not be ecologically significant.

3. Data Presentation

Presentation of data in reports may take as many forms as there are investigators; however, the basic technics most often used include tables, bar graphs (horizontal and vertical), pie diagrams, pictorial charts (ideographs), line graphs, frequency distribution tables and graphs, histograms, frequency polygons, and cumulative frequency polygons. Some of these may be superimposed on maps. Several reports that may be of use to the investigator in analyzing macroinvertebrate data have been included in the bibliography.

1005 E.   References

1. Snedecor, G.W. & W.G. Cochran. 1967. Statistical Methods. Iowa State Univ. Press, Ames.

2. Powers, C.F. & A. Robertson. 1967. Design and Evaluation of an All-Purpose Benthos Sampler. Spec. Rept. No. 30, Great Lakes Res. Div., Univ. of Michigan, Ann Arbor.

3. Welch, P.S. 1948. Limnological Methods. Blakiston Co., Philadelphia, Pa.

4. Pennak, R.W. 1953. Fresh-water Invertebrates of the United States. Ronald Press, New York, N.Y.

5. Barnes, H. 1959. Oceanographic and Marine Biology. George Allen and Unwin, Ltd., London, England.

6. Merna, J.W. 1962. Quantitative sampling with the orange peel dredge. *Limnol. Oceanogr.* 7:432.

7. Smith, W. & A.D. McIntyre. 1954. A spring-loaded bottom sampler. *J. Mar. Biol. Ass. U. K.* 33:257.

8. Brinkhurst, R.O., K.E. Chua & E. Batoosingh. 1969. Modifications in sampling procedures as applied to studies on the bacteria and tubificid oligochaetes inhabiting aquatic sedments. *J. Fish. Res. Board Can.* 26:2581.

9. Waters, T.F. 1961. Standing crop and drift of stream bottom organisms. *Ecology* 42:532.

10. Dimond, J.B. 1967. Pesticides and Stream Insects. Bull. No. 2, Maine Forest Service, Augusta, and Conservation Foundation, Washington, D. C.

11. Waters, T.F. 1972. The drift of stream insects. *Annu. Rev. Entomol.* 17:253.

12. Usinger, R.L. 1956. Aquatic Insects of California, with Keys to North American Genera and California Species. Univ. of California Press, Berkeley.

13. Hester, F.E. & J.B. Dendy. 1962. A multiple-plate sampler for aquatic macroinvertebrates. *Trans. Amer. Fish. Soc.* 91:420.

14. Anderson, J.B. & W.T. Mason, Jr. 1968. A comparison of benthic macroinvertebrates collected by dredge and basket sampler. *J. Water Pollut. Control Fed.* 40:252.

15. Mason, W.T., Jr. & P.P. Yevich. 1967. The use of phloxine B and rose bengal stains to facilitate sorting benthic samples. *Trans. Amer. Microsc. Soc.* 86:221.

16. Wilhm, J.L. 1967. Comparison of some diversity indices applied to populations of benthic macroinvertebrates in a stream receiving organic wastes. *J. Water Pollut. Control Fed.* 39:1673.

17. Wilhm, J.L. 1970. Range of diversity index in benthic macroinvertebrate populations. *J. Water Pollut. Control Fed.* 42:R221.

18. Wilhm, J.L. 1972. Graphic and mathematical analyses of biotic communities in polluted streams. *Annu. Rev. Entomol.* 17:223.

19. Cairns, J., Jr., D.W. Albaugh, F. Busey & M.D. Chaney. 1968. The sequential comparison index—A simplified method for non-biologists to estimate relative differences in biological diversity in stream pollution studies. *J. Water Pollut. Control Fed.* 40:1607.

1005 F. Bibliography

BAKER, F.C. 1928. The Freshwater Mollusca of Wisconsin Part I. Gastropoda and Part II. Pelecypoda. Wisconsin Acad. Science, Madison, Wisc.

FRISON, T.H. 1935. The stoneflies or Plecoptera of Illinois. *Bull. Ill. Natur. Hist. Surv.* 20:281.

NEEDHAM, J.G. & P.R. NEEDHAM. 1941. A Guide to the Study of Freshwater Biology. Comstock Pub. Co., Ithaca, N.Y.

ROSS, H.H. 1944. The caddisflies, or Trichoptera, of Illinois. *Bull. Ill. Natur. Hist. Surv.* 23:1.

CHU, H.F. 1949. How to Know the Immature Insects. William C. Brown Co., Dubuque, Ia.

BERNER, L. 1950. The Mayflies of Florida. Univ. of Florida Studies in Biol. Sci. Ser. 4:1.

PATRICK, R. 1950. Biological measure of stream conditions. *Sewage Ind. Wastes* 22:926.

PRATT, H.W. 1951. A Manual of the Common Invertebrate Animals Exclusive of Insects. The Blakiston Co., Philadelphia, Pa.

WIMMER, G.R. & E.W. SURBER. 1952. Bottom Fauna Studies in Pollution Surveys and Interpretation of the Data. 14th Mid. Wildlife Conf., Des Moines, Ia.

PENNAK, R.W. 1953. Freshwater Invertebrates of the United States. The Ronald Press, New York, N.Y.

BURKS, B.D. 1953. The mayflies or Ephemeroptera of Illinois. *Bull. Ill. Natur. Hist. Surv.* 26:1.

BECK, W.M. 1954. Studies in stream pollution biology. I. A simplified ecological classification of organisms. *Quart. J. Fla. Acad. Sci.* 17:211.

NEEDHAM, J.G. & M.J. WESTFALL, JR. 1954. Dragonflies of North America. Univ. of California Press, Berkeley.

BECK, W.M. 1955. Suggested method for reporting biotic data. *Sewage Ind. Wastes* 27:1193.

GAUFIN, A.R. & C.M. TARZWELL. 1956. Aquatic macroinvertebrate communities as indicators of organic pollution in Lytle Creek. *Sewage Ind. Wastes* 28:906.

HUTCHINSON, G.E. 1957. A Treatise on Limnology. John Wiley & Sons, New York, N.Y.

ROBACK, S.S. 1957. The Immature Tendipedids

of the Philadelphia Area. Philadelphia Acad. Natur. Sci. Monogr. No. 9.

WALKER, E.M. 1958. The Odonata of Canada and Alaska. Univ. of Toronto Press, Toronto. Vols. 1 and 2.

BOUSFIELD, E.L. 1958. I. Freshwater amphipod crustaceans of glaciated North America. *Can. Field Natur.* 72:55.

EDMONDSON, W.T., ed. 1959. Ward and Whipple's Freshwater Biology, 2nd ed. John Wiley & Sons, Inc., New York, N.Y.

INGRAM, W.M. 1960. Effective methods for collecting and recording data from water pollution surveys. In: Biological Problems in Water Pollution (C.M. Tarzwell, compiler). U.S. Dept. Health, Education & Welfare, Cincinnati, Ohio, pp. 260-263.

INGRAM, W.M. & A.F. BARTSCH. 1960. Graphic expression of biological data in water pollution reports. *J. Water Pollut. Control Fed.* 32:297.

EDDY, S. & A.C. HODSON. 1961. Taxonomic Keys to the Common Animals of the North Central States, 3rd ed. Burgess Publ. Co., Minneapolis, Minn.

HYNES, H.B.N. 1963. The Biology of Polluted Waters. Liverpool Univ. Press, England.

MACAN, T.T. 1963. Freshwater Ecology. John Wiley & Sons, New York, N.Y.

BRINKHURST, R.O. 1964. Studies on the North American aquatic oligochaeta. Part I. *Proc. Acad. Sci. Philadelphia* 116:195.

KING, D.L. & R.C. BALL. 1964. A quantitative biological measure of stream pollution. *J. Water Pollut. Control Fed.* 36:650.

SINCLAIR, R.M. 1964. Water Quality Requirements for Elmid Beetles. Tenn. Dep. Pub. Health, Nashville, Tenn.

BRINKHURST, R.O. 1965. Studies on the North American aquatic oligochaeta. Part II. *Proc. Acad. Sci. Philadelphia* 117:117.

SUBLETTE, J.E. & M.S. SUBLETTE. 1965. Family Chironomidae (Tendipedidae). A catalog of diptera of America north of Mexico. *Bull. U.S. Dep. Agr.* 276:143.

TACKETT, J.H. 1965. Biological Assessment of Water Quality. Roanoke River-Tinker Creek. (mimeograph). Virginia State Water Control Board.

RUTTNER, F. 1966. Fundamentals of Limnology. Univ. of Toronto Press, Canada.

HEARD, W.H. & J. BURCH. 1966. Keys to the Genera of Freshwater Pelecypods of Michigan. Univ. of Michigan Museum of Zoology Circ. No. 4, Ann Arbor.

BECK, W.M., JR. & E.C. BECK. 1966. Chironomidae (Diptera) of Florida. I. Pentaneurini (Tanypodinae). *Bull. Fla. State Museum* 10:305.

INGRAM, W., K.M. MACKENTHUN & A.F. BARTSCH. 1966. Biological Field Investigative Data for Water Pollution Surveys. FWPCA, U.S. Govt. Printing Off., Washington, D.C.

PIELOU, E.C. 1966. The measurement of diversity in different types of biological collections. *J. Theor. Biol.* 13:131.

MACKENTHUN, K.M. & W.M. INGRAM. 1967. Biological Associated Problems in Freshwater Environments. FWPCA, Washington, D.C.

LLOYD, M., J.H. ZAR & J.R. KARR. 1968. On the calculation of information—Theoretical measures of diversity. *Amer. Midland Natur.* 79:257.

MASON, W.T., JR. 1968. An Introduction to the Identification of Chironomid Larvae. Div. Pollut. Surveillance, FWPCA, Cincinnati, Ohio.

SURBER, E.W. 1969. Procedure in taking stream bottom samples with the stream square foot bottom sampler. *Proc. 23rd Annu. Conf. S.E. Ass. Game Fish Comm.* 587.

CAIRNS, J., JR., K.L. DICKSON, R.E. SPARKS & W.T. WALLER. 1970. A preliminary report on rapid biological information systems for water pollution control. *J. Water Pollut. Control Fed.* 45:685.

HYNES, H. B. N. 1970. The Ecology of Running Waters. Univ. of Toronto Press, Canada.

JACKSON, H.W. 1970. A controlled-depth volumetric bottom sampler. *Progr. Fish-Cult.* 32(2):113.

LARIMORE, R.W. 1970. Two shallow-water bottom samplers. *Progr. Fish-Cult.* 32(2).

CAIRNS, J., JR. 1971. A simple method for the biological assessment of the effects of waste discharges on aquatic bottom-dwelling organisms. *J. Water Pollut. Control Fed.* 43:755.

ERMAN, D.C. & W.T. HELM. 1971. Comparison of some species importance values and ordination techniques used to analyze benthic invertebrate communities. *Oikos* 22:240.

DICKSON, K.L., J. CAIRNS, JR. & J.C. ARNOLD. 1971. An evaluation of the use of a basket-type artificial substrate for sampling macroinvertebrate organisms. *Trans. Amer. Fish. Soc.* 100:553.

ODUM, E.P. 1971. Fundamentals of Ecology, 3d ed. Saunders Publ. Co., Philadelphia, Pa.

1006   FISHES

Information on the abundance and species composition of the fish is useful for assessing the quality of a body of water.[1] Fish occupy the peak of the aquatic food chain (barring predation by higher vertebrates); hence their condition constitutes a summation of the condition of lower biological forms and is a result of the total quality of the water. Water quality factors that alter the ecological balance of the periphyton, plankton, and macroinvertebrate populations also can alter the fish population. Because fish and invertebrates have differing susceptibilities to certain toxicants, the fish might be affected by certain pollutants that do not cause a demonstrable change in the invertebrate and plant communities. It becomes important to sample fish populations as the final or climax product of the aquatic community. Since fish as aquatic organisms are already well known and also have economic value, they are to the general public the most intelligible symbol of water quality and must be ranked high for public relations purposes as well as for technical interpretations.

Where commercial fisheries exist locally, the hiring of commercial fishermen and equipment should be considered, especially for studies of relatively short duration. Commercial catch data may also be useful in detecting certain long-term changes in water quality.

1006 A.   Sample Collection and Preservation

A fishery survey should secure information on the kinds of fish present and their relative abundance. A one-time study can provide information on the species of fish present in a given body of water. This may be sufficient, for example, when one is investigating a fish kill, but in many rivers and lakes, the changes in fish populations are subtle and should be determined through long-range studies.

State regulations on fish collection should be checked carefully when field operations are being planned. Scientific collecting permits issued by state fish and game agencies provide authorization for most cases. If the use of piscicides is contemplated, however, a thorough check must be made of Food and Drug Administration, Environmental Protection Agency, and state regulations, since the introduction of toxic substances into any water is stringently controlled.

Fish may be collected by a variety of methods such as seining, trapping, gill- or trawlnetting, electrofishing, or with chemicals.[2, 3, 4, 5] To obtain representative data, sample in the obscure and unlikely areas as well as at obvious locations. Early life states (eggs and larvae)

of many species may be found in the plankton. Trawl waterway bottoms for bottom fish; seine both riffles and pools of streams; fish for free-swimming open-water types with various nets; and take migrating or roving types with traps or gillnets. Sample all depths, not just surface and bottom. Brush, rock, and other types of obstructions are sometimes best sampled by using chemicals or by electrofishing.

Visual observations by a trained individual also are very useful. Various methods of fish sampling, such as electrofishing, trapping, and gillnetting, are best undertaken at night because many species of fish are sedentary during daylight hours.

1. Sampling Devices

Devices commonly used in fish sampling are as follows:

a. Haul seines are used to collect fish from shallow water. In small streams, seining is usually done with "straight" seines of various lengths, 1.2 m (4 ft) or longer, with square-mesh sizes of 3, 6, or 12 mm (1/8, 1/4, or 1/2 in.).

Shoreline seining of lakes and large rivers usually is most effective when a bag seine is used. There are two common sizes of bag seines: One is 7.5 m (25 ft) long and 1.8 m (6 ft) deep, with the main portion constructed of 12.6-mm (1/2-in.) square-mesh netting. The center 1.8-m-(6-ft-) long bag is made of 6-mm (1/4-in.) mesh netting. The second size, often used for larger fish, is 30 m (100 ft) long and 1.8 or 2.4 m (6 or 8 ft) deep, with 2.5-to 5-cm (1-to-2-in.) square-mesh netting in the main body and 12- to 25-mm (1/2- to 1-in.) netting in the center bag. A waterway free from snags is essential to successful seining. Although results are expressed as number of fish per unit area seined, quantitative seining is very difficult. The procedure is more useful in determining the variety of fish inhabiting the water than for quantitative sampling.

b. Gillnets (Figure 1006:1A) are used in estuaries, lakes, reservoirs, or large rivers where fish movement can be expected. The most versatile experimental gillnet is 38 m (125 ft) long; there are five 7.5-m (25-ft) sections with mesh sizes ranging from 19 mm (3/4 in.) to 62 mm (2-1/2 in.) square. Express results as number or weight of fish taken per length of net per day.

c. Trammel nets (Figure 1006:1B) have a layer of large mesh netting on each side of loosely hung smaller gillnetting. Small fish are captured in the gillnetting and larger fish are captured in a "bag" of the gillnetting that is formed in the larger mesh netting. Express results as number or weight of fish captured per length of net per day.

d. Traps range in size from small containers (minnow traps) with inverted cone entrances to semipermanent structures (weirs) (Figure 1006:1C). Traps and weir nets are used mainly in rivers and estuaries.

Trap nets, when properly located to intercept fish movements, may be used effectively to sample fish populations in lakes during certain seasons. The trap net most used in fishery studies is the square or round hoop net. This net may have leads or wings attached to the first frame. The second and third frames can each hold tunnel throats that prevent the escape of fishes entering each section in turn. The opposite (closed) end of the net may be tied with a slip cord to facilitate fish removal. Express results as fish per net-day. Most fish can be sampled when trap nets of varying mesh sizes are set in a variety of habitats.

e. Trawls are specialized gear used in large open water areas of reservoirs, lakes, large rivers, estuaries, and offshore marine areas (Figure 1006:1D). They are best used to gain information on a particular species of fish rather than on the overall fish population. Three basic types of trawls are: the fry trawl, with a permanent opening; the otter trawl, used to capture near-bottom and bottom fishes [6]; and the mid-water trawl, used to collect schooling fish at various depths.

f. Electrofishing devices are effective in collecting most sizes and species of fish from many different environments. These devices vary in size and complexity. Small streams can be surveyed by two men, one using a back-pack shocker, the other dipping fish. In large rivers and lakes, a generator and electrical control equipment are required to achieve satisfactory results. The survey of a large river may require several

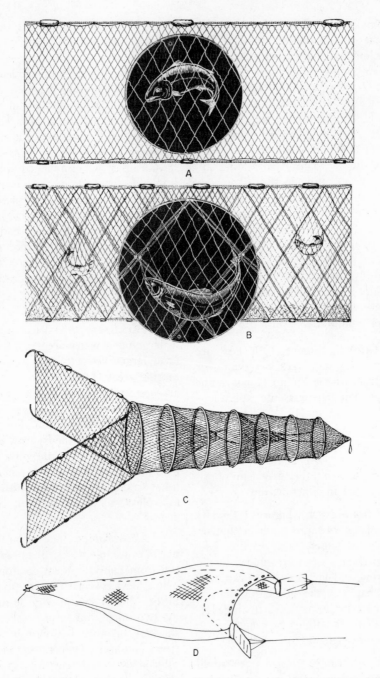

Figure 1006:1. Some types of nets: A—gillnet; B—trammel net; C—Fyke or hoop net; D—otter trawl.

men, but electrofishing offers the advantage of surveying a reach of water in a short time and does not entail leaving unattended, expensive, and pilferable equipment such as nets. Shockers can be installed on boats for sampling waters that cannot be effectively waded. Electrofishing may be limited by water conductance, turbidity, and depth. Sampling is more efficient at night, when underwater lights may be used. Block nets may be used to delineate the sampling area as well as to prevent the escape of fish from the electrical field.

g. Chemicals, such as rotenone, often are used to collect fish from a restricted area. This technic of sampling is usually used on a spot basis—for example, a short reach of river or an embayment of a lake. Results are expressed as fish per unit of surface area sampled.

h. Trotlines (or long lines) can be used to sample a limited segment of the fish population. These are used mainly to sample fish feeding at night. A trotline consists of a series of short drop lines with baited hooks attached to a long main line.

i. Suction tubes or hoses often are effective for the removal of eggs and fry from bottom nests. The study of fish egg viability is important because the egg stage is a most critical stage in the life cycle of the fish.

2. Procedures

Observations by experienced personnel can provide much information on fish habitats and populations. Such observations can be enhanced through the use of such equipment as underwater television or photographic cameras, underwater breathing equipment, or submersible vessels.

Preserve fish in the field as soon after collection as possible. If they are to be analyzed the same day, icing is sufficient; if not, preserve in 10% formalin, to which has been added 3 g borax and 50 ml glycerin/l of formalin. Open the body cavity of fish larger than 7.5 cm to enable the preservative to quickly reach the internal organs. Make a slit at least one-third as long as the body cavity on the right side of the fish.

After fixation (1 to 7 days depending on the size of the fish), wash the fish in running water or in several changes of water for 24 hr and place in 40% isopropyl alcohol.

Place labels on the inside and outside of the sample container. Use waterproof ink and paper for the inner label. Labels should bear information such as station location, date, collector, gear used, etc.

Field notes should be taken that describe the station and provide other information necessary to interpret the data obtained from the sample.

1006 B.   Sample Analysis

Identify all fish to species. In reports prepared for nonfisheries personnel, use the common names adopted by the American Fisheries Society.[7]

Determine the weight in grams and total length in centimeters of each fish. The total length is defined as the distance from the anterior end (with mouth closed) to the tip of the fins, when drawn together.[2]

Age and growth rates are very useful for determining the effects of water quality on fish populations. The methods for these measurements include[2] (a) the length-frequency method. (b) otolith and bone methods, and (c) the scale method. The lengths of young fish tend to cluster into groups (size classes), permitting separation into age classes. As the fish age, however, the year classes usually become less distinct. The age of fish also can be estimated by counting the annual growth rings in ear stones, vertebrae fin rays, opercles, and scales. The scale method is the most widely used.

The coefficient of condition is the length-weight relationship used to express the relative plumpness or robustness of fish, which is related to environmental conditions. The equation[8] generally used is:

$$K = \frac{W \times 10^5}{L^3}$$

where:

K = coefficient of condition (or condition factor),
W = weight, g, and
L = length, mm.

The general health and well-being of a fish influences its response to pollution; likewise, sublethal levels of pollution may affect the health of the fish and its ability to resist disease. Natural epidemics and debilities of many types occur among fishes as among all groups of organisms. Fish should be examined early in any water quality survey for their general condition, parasites, and other factors that might accentuate or mask the effects of pollution.

Parasites, particularly the larger attached external parasites such as copepods or leeches, usually can be detected by examining the surface of live or freshly killed fish under a wide-field dissecting microscope. Examination, under greater magnification, of slime scraped from the body surface or from areas of accumulation around the gills may reveal smaller external parasites. Scars from lamprey attacks may appear as round fresh red lesions or older healed areas up to 2 cm or more in diameter. Inflamed areas, swellings, frayed or eroded fins, or other gross indications of disability may be visible externally and should be reported. Internal parasites and other pathologies may be revealed by appropriate microtechnics. For the critical identification of pathological conditions, an established laboratory specializing in this field should be contacted.

When chronic toxicity is suspected or when a general weakness or poor condition of the fish is noted, histological, physiological, and/or biochemical tests should be made.[9-12]

Fish flesh is often unpalatable because of chemicals present in the water. Many of these taste-producing substances are from municipal or industrial wastes, although natural sources are also known to contribute.[13] Taste panels have been the most successful method for detecting tainted fish flesh. Test fish may be native fish from the stream, uncontaminated fish held in cages in the test area, or uncontaminated fish held in tanks, with the suspect chemical added. The taste panel should be trained in fish tasting and should be given acceptable samples for comparison.[14-17]

1006 C. Production and Productivity

Fish production in a given body of water is highly indicative of the quality of that water. The species composition of the entire fish community must be considered as well as the relative quantities of each species. Productivity in a fishery context includes the following concepts:[3]

PRODUCTIVITY: the rate at which a given body of water is capable of producing fish biomass (usually pounds/ acre/year).

PRODUCTION: the actual amount (weight) produced in a unit of time (pounds/year)

STANDING CROP: the quantity of fish present at any given time (usually pounds/acre). This quantity may be reported as the total for all species or may be broken down into the actual or relative (percentage) weights of each.

HARVEST OR YIELD: the quantity of fish actually removed by man (pounds/ year or pounds/acre/year).

1006 D. Investigation of Fish Kills

Fish kills vary in cause—from the individual fish that dies of old age to the catastrophic kill—from partial to complete, and from natural to man-caused. No single investigative procedure can be appropriate for all situations. The following brief description may serve as an aid in investigating kills. Too much emphasis cannot be given to the importance of getting to the scene promptly before the evidence has decomposed or drifted away. If surveillance of a particular body of water or area is involved, preset plans and equipment should be available on a standby basis.[18,19]

Fish kills may be caused by such natural events as acute temperature change, storms, ice and snow cover, decomposition of natural materials, salinity change, spawning mortalities, parasites, and bacterial and viral epidemics. Man-caused fish kills may be attributed to municipal or industrial wastes, agricultural activities, and water control activities.

One dead fish in a stream may be called a fish kill; however, in a practical sense, some minimal range in the number of dead fish observed, plus additional qualifications, should be adopted in reporting and classifying fish kills. Any fish kill is of significance if it affects fish of sport or commercial value, results from a suspected negligent discharge or malfunctioning waste treatment facility, or causes widespread environmental damage. The following definitions, based on a stream about 60 m (200 ft) wide and 2 m (6 ft) deep, are suggested as guidelines. For other size streams, adjustments should be made.

1. MINOR KILL: 1 to 100 dead or dying fish confined to a small area or stream stretch. If recurrent, it could be significant and should be investigated.

2. MODERATE KILL: 100 to 1,000 dead or dying fish of various species in a mile or so of stream or equivalent area of a lake or estuary.

3. MAJOR KILL: 1,000 or more dead or dying fish of many species in a reach of stream up to 16 km (10 miles) or greater, or equivalent area of a lake or estuary.

In preparation for a field investigation, study the area maps [1,20,21] and determine the kill area and access to it. Identify waste dischargers. Contact participating laboratories to discuss the number and size of samples that will be submitted, the types of analyses required, the dates of sample receipt, the method of sample shipment, the date by which results are needed, and to whom the results are to be reported.

Two information record forms are strongly recommended for fish kill investigations, an initial contact form and a field investigation form.

On all fish kill investigations take a thermometer, dissolved oxygen test kit, conductivity and pH meters; or a general chemical kit, biological sampling gear, sample bottles, and other specimen containers. The investigating team should include at least one person who is experienced in investigating fish kills.

The field investigation consists of visual observations, sampling of fish, water, and biota, and physical measurements of the environment. The first local observer of the kill makes a useful guide to the area, which should be reconnoitered initially to establish that a fish kill has actually occurred.

If a fish kill has taken place, immediately start fish sampling since the collection of dying or recently dead fish is critical. For purposes of comparison, collect healthy fish from an unaffected area.

Place individual fish in well-labeled plastic bags and preserve by freezing until the fish can be examined in a laboratory. Bleed dying or dead fish at collection time so as to obtain at least 1 g of blood. Collect the blood sample in a chemically clean, solvent-washed glass bottle with a teflon-lined screw cap.

Identify and count dead fish. In a large river an observer may count dead fish from a fixed station such as a bridge during a fixed period of time. Extrapolations may then be made to the total time involved. Alternatively, in a large river or lake, a shore count may be made and projected to the entire area of the kill. In smaller bodies of water traverse the entire area for enumeration of dead fish.

Collect water samples representative of unpolluted and polluted areas in accordance with the instruction given in Section 1002 (Plankton). As a minimum, measure temperature, pH, dissolved oxygen, and specific conductance. Additional tests may be performed, depending on suspected causes of the fish kill. Take samples for the examination of plankton, periphyton, macrophyton, and macroinvertebrates.

Record observations on water appearance, streamflow, and weather conditions. Color photographs are valuable in recording conditions.

1006 E. References

1. MACKENTHUN, K.M. 1973. Toward a Cleaner Environment. USEPA, Office of Air & Water Programs, Washington, D.C.

2. LAGLER, K.F., J.E. BARDACH & R.R. MILLER. 1962. Ichthyology. The Study of Fishes. John Wiley & Sons, New York, N. Y.

3. RICKER, W.E., ed. 1971. Methods for Assessment of Fish Production in Fresh Waters. IBP Handbook No. 3, 2nd ed., Blackwell Sci. Publ., Oxford, England.

4. DUMONT, W.H., & G.T. SUNDSTROM. 1961. Commercial Fishing Gear of the United States. U. S. Fish & Wildlife Circ. No. 109, U. S. Govt. Printing Off., Washington, D.C.

5. ROUNSEFELL, G.A. & W.H. EVERHART. 1953. Fishery Science—Its Methods and Applications. John Wiley & Sons, New York, N.Y.

6. STANSBY, M.E. 1963. Industrial Fishery Technology. Reinhold Publ. Co., New York, N.Y.

7. BAILEY, R.M., J.E. FITCH, E.S. HERALD, E.A. LACHNER, C.C. LINDSEY, C.R. ROBINS & W.B. SCOTT. 1970. A List of Common and Scientific Names of Fishes from the United States and Canada, 3rd ed. Spec. Publ. No. 6, Amer. Fish. Soc., Washington, D.C.

8. CARLANDER, K.D. 1969. Handbook of Freshwater Fishery Biology. Vol. I., Iowa State Univ. Press, Ames.

9. CAIRNS, J., JR. & A. SCHEIER. 1963. The acute and chronic effects of standard sodium alkyl benzene sulfonate on the pumpkin seed sunfish, *Lepomis gibbosus* (Linn.) and the bluegill sunfish. *L. macrochirus* Raf. *Proc. 17th Ind. Waste Conf.*, Eng. Ext. Serv. Ser. No. 112, Purdue Univ., Lafayette, Ind. pp. 14-28.

10. JACKIM, E., J.M. HAMLIN & S. SONIS. 1970. Effects of metal poisoning on five liver enzymes in the killfish (*Fundulus heteroclitus*). *J. Fish. Res. Board Can.* 27:383.

11. HINTON, D.E., R.L. SNIPES & M.W. KEN-DALL. 1972. Morphology and enzyme histochemistry in the liver of largemouth bass (*Micropterus salmoides*). *J. Fish. Res. Board Can.* 29:531.

12. OLSON, K.R. & P.O. FROMM. 1973. Mercury uptake and ion distribution in gills of rainbow trout (*Salmo gairdneri*): tissue scans with an electron microprobe. *J. Fish. Res. Board Can.* 30:1575.

13. NATIONAL TECHNICAL ADVISORY COMMITTEE. 1968. Water Quality Criteria. FWPCA, Washington, D.C.

14. WINSTON, A.W. 1959. Test for odor imparted to the flesh of fish. 2nd Seminar on Biological Problems in Water Pollution, Cincinnati, Ohio. USPHS, Div. Water Supply & Pollution Control.

15. BOYLE, H.W. 1967. Taste/odor contamination of fish from the Ohio River near Tell City, Indiana, Cincinnati Water Research Lab, FWPCA, Cincinnati, Ohio

16. THOMAS, N.A. 1969. Flavor of Ohio River channel catfish (*Ictalarus punctatus* Raf.). USEPA, Cincinnati, Ohio.

17. THOMAS, N.A. & D.B. HICKS. 1971. Effects of waste water discharge on the flavor of fishes in the Missouri River (Sioux Falls, Iowa, to Waverly, Missouri). In: Everyone Can't Live Upstream. USEPA Off. Water Programs, Kansas City, Mo.

18. BURDICK, G.E. 1965. Some problems in the determination of the cause of fish kills. In: Biological Problems in Water Pollution. USPHS Publ. No. 999-WP-25.

19. Pollution Caused Fish Kills. 1967. 1968. U.S. Dept. Interior, FWPCA Publ. No. CWA-7.

20. SMITH, L.L. JR., et al. 1956. Procedures for Investigation of Fish Kills. A Guide for Field Reconnaissance and Data Collection. ORSANCO, Cincinnati, Ohio.

21. Investigating Fish Mortalities. 1970. U.S. Dept. Interior, FWPCA Publ. No. CWT-5 (also available from U.S. Govt. Printing Off. as No. 0-380-257).

1007   IDENTIFICATION OF TYPES OF AQUATIC ORGANISMS

Experienced aquatic biologists will be familiar with most of the types of organisms illustrated in Plates 1 through 38, and will seldom need the assistance of keys to identify organisms to the level illustrated. Since these plates are not intended for critical identification, specific (species) names are not cited. Types most likely to be observed are illustrated in this group. For the convenience of those less familiar with the organisms referred to in preceding sections, a series of short keys is presented that should enable them to identify most unknown organisms to the level illustrated by the plates.

In conformity with preceding sections, organisms are arbitrarily divided into microscopic and macroscopic, depending on whether or not they pass through a U.S. Standard No. 30 sieve. For the study of microscopic forms, a compound microscope is needed. For examination of the smaller macroscopic organisms and to resolve the finer structures of larger forms, a wide-field stereoscopic microscope is required.

1007 A.   Procedure in Identification

Critical identification of an unknown specimen is often time-consuming, even for the experienced biologist. Before looking at any key or other aid to identification, allow from one to several minutes for carefully studying the specimen. If necessary, find other examples and compare them with the unknown.

It is often important to know where or under what conditions the subject organism lived before attempting to identify it. For example, did it come from fresh water—a lake or a stream? Is it marine—from the open ocean, shoreline, or estuary? Was it a free swimmer or floater in the water? Was it a bottom organism, attached, crawling, or burrowing? Finally, turn to the following key to major groups.

Only the more common types of aquatic organisms are illustrated here, with special attention to those most frequently used in water quality evaluation. When specimens do not fit obviously into one of the types listed, consult a professional biologist, a microbiologist for the bacteria and fungi, or some of the references provided. Descriptions of color and movement refer to freshly collected or living specimens, or, in the case of microscopic forms, to those preserved as described in Section 1002 (Plankton).

Sizes of the organisms illustrated in Plates 1 through 38 are given in metric units and shown in parenthesis in the legend. These are intended to represent *common* sizes, not absolute maxima or minima. Exceptional individuals and even whole localized populations may be encountered that are considerably larger or smaller than the sizes cited.

1007 B. Key to Major Groups of Aquatic Organisms, (Plates 1–38)

Beginning with couplet 1a and 1b of the Keys, compare the descriptions given with the subject specimen. A choice must be made between statement "a" and statement "b." Proceed to the couplet number indicated at the right and repeat the process. Continue until the name of a type of organism or a plate number is cited instead of another couplet number. Additional information is provided in many of the plate legends.

Refer to Couplet No.

1a. Macroscopic: The organism, mass, or colony is visible to the naked eye 13
1b. Microscopic: Not readily visible to the naked eye 2

1. Key to Microscopic Organisms

    2a. Specimen a single living cell or a mass or colony of relatively independent cells (shapeless, rounded, or threadlike) 3
    2b. Specimen a many-celled, highly organized plant or animal. 7
3a. Cells contain one or more pigments, including chlorophyll *a* (overall color may range through various shades of green, blue, red, brown, or yellow). ALGAE (for details, see Section 1007D following, "Key for Identification of Freshwater Algae") 4
3b. Cells typically colorless, lacking chlorophyll *a* 12
    4a. Nuclei present; pigment confined to chloroplasts 5
    4b. Nuclei, plastids, or vacuoles absent (pseudovacuoles may be present in certain filamentous forms). Pigment generally diffused throughout cytoplasm. BLUE-GREEN ALGAE, Plates 1 and 2.
5a. Cell wall permanently rigid, composed of SiO₂, geometrical in appearance, and with regular patterns of fine markings; composed of two essentially similar halves, one placed over the other as a cover. Golden brown to greenish in color. DIATOMS, Plates 5 and 6.
5b. Cell wall, if present, capable of sagging or bending, rigidity depending on internal pressure of cell contents. Cell walls usually of one piece 6
    6a. Cells or colonies nonmotile. Usually some shade of green. NONMOTILE GREEN ALGAE, Plates 3 and 4.
    6b. Cells or colony move by means of relatively long whiplike "flagella." PIGMENTED FLAGELLATES, Plates 11 and 12.
7a. Body with cilia (hairlike structures used for locomotion) 8
7b. Body without cilia. 9
    8a. Body generally covered with cilia, usually somewhat elongate or wormlike, bilaterally symmetrical. Minute FLATWORMS (Platyhelminthes), relatives of *Planaria*, Plate 19.
    8b. Cilia confined to one or two crowns at anterior end, which often present the illusion of rotating wheels. Internal jaws present. ROTIFERS (Rotifera), Plate 17.
9a. Long slender unsegmented worms that move by sinuous crawling or thrashing motion. ROUNDWORMS (Nemathelminthes), Plate 18.
9b. Possess external skeleton and jointed appendages. 10
    10a. Crawl about or swim by means of jointed appendages thrust out from between two clamlike shells. All appendages can be withdrawn entirely within shells when disturbed. OSTRACODS (Ostracoda), Plate 21.
    10b. Swim rapidly by means of a pair of enlarged jointed appendages (antennae) that cannot be withdrawn inside carapace or shell 11

Refer to
Couplet
No.

11a. Locomotor appendages (antennae) branched. Microcrustacea, CLADOCERA (Cladocera), Plate 20.

11b. Locomotor appendages (antennae) unbranched; body tapers toward rear. Microcrustacea, COPEPODS (Copepoda), Plate 21.

    12a. Ingest and digest food internally (ingested food of various colors may be visible through body wall). Single-celled or colonial, attached or free-living. PROTOZOANS (Protozoa), Plates 13, 14, and 15.

    12b. Digest food externally and adsorb products through cell wall. Often secrete masses of slime. BACTERIA and FUNGI, Plate 38.

2. Key to Macroscopic Organisms

13a. Specimen a mass of filaments or a glob of gelatinous or semisolid material containing many tiny units, requiring microscopic examination to determine details of structure. 2

13b. Specimen a well-organized unit or colony 14

    14a. Organism plantlike; flowerlike structures, if present, do not respond when touched, generally are colored some shade of green, brown, or red 16

    14b. Organism animal-like; usually responds rapidly when touched, whether attached or free-living 15

15a. Internal backbone present (vertebrates) 17

15b. No internal backbone present (macroinvertebrates)* 18

    16a. Plant structure relatively simple. Attachment structures may be present, but no true roots or fibrous tissue. Larger ALGAE, Plate 7 and Color Plates A (*Nitella*) and F (*Chara* and *Batrachospermum*).

    16b. Plant structure usually includes true roots, stems, and leaves. Fibers or vascular tissue usually present; flowers or seeds may be observed. (One atypical group, "water-meal," consists only of tiny roundish masses, 0.5 to 1 mm in diameter, often misidentified as algae.) HIGHER PLANTS. Plates 8, 9, and 10.

17a. Side appendages, if present, are flat fins. FISHES, Plate 36.

17b. Side appendages, if present, are footlike, with separate digits. AMPHIBIANS, Plate 37.

3. Key to Macroinvertebrates

    18a. Body bilaterally symmetrical (with right and left sides, but may be superficially coiled into a spiral); animal not attached but may live inside an attached cocoon or case, or crawl about; usually solitary 23

    18b. Symmetry not bilateral 19

19a. Body typically radially symmetrical 21

19b. Body or colony nonsymmetrical 20

    20a. Body mass generally porous; not a colony, sometimes finger- or antler-like. Freshwater representatives are generally fragile, colored green or brown; marine forms tougher, various colors. SPONGES (Porifera), Plate 16.

    20b. Body mass otherwise. 22

21a. Animals with soft smooth bodies and tentacles around a mouth; no anus. Solitary or colonial. Larger colonies usually have rigid limy skeleton of massive, branched, or fan-shaped form. HYDRAS, SEA ANEMONES, JELLYFISHES, CORALS, etc. (Coelenterata), Plate 35A, B.

---

*Invertebrates retained on a U.S. Standard No. 30 sieve.

21b. Body covering usually spiny, soft or rigid, flattened or elongate, typically having five radii, with or without spines or arms; anus present. Solitary. Marine only. STARFISHES and relatives (Echinodermata), Plate 34.

    22a. Colony a jellylike mass, a network of branching tubes, a plant-like tuft, or a lacy limy crust or mass. MOSS ANIMALS (Bryozoa), Plate 16.

    22b. Exclusively marine. Surface of body or colony relatively smooth but tough. Solitary forms, sac-like, with two external openings. Exhibit all degrees of colonialism. Compound forms range from thin slimy masses, with organisms arranged in tiny radial patterns to huge, shapeless masses resembling tough frozen gelatin. SEA SQUIRTS, SEA PORK (Ascidiacea, Urochorda, Chordata), not illustrated.

23a. Animal living within a hard limy shell, soft body (Mollusca). 29

23b. Animal without a limy shell. 24

    24a. Jointed legs present (may not be functional). Body may be hard or soft 30

    24b. Jointed legs absent, body covering mostly soft, animal pliable (a hardened head capsule may be present) 25

25a. Body girded by annulations or creases at regular intervals, dividing it into many small segments much wider than long 26

25b. Segments present or absent; if present, not much wider than they are long 27

    26a. Body with suction disk at one or both ends, in length usually less than 10 times its width. LEECHES (Annelida, Hirudinea), Plate 19.

    26b. Body without suction disks, in length usually more than 10 times its width; hairs or bristles often evident. SEGMENTED WORMS (Annelida), Plate 19.

27a. Body unsegmented, long and slender, appearing smooth, evenly tapered to a fine point at one end. ROUNDWORMS (Nematoda), Plate 18.

27b. Body otherwise 28

    28a. Body flat, elongate, or oblong; unsegmented head is spade-shaped. Pigmented spots on top of head often give the animal a cross-eyed appearance. FLATWORMS (Turbellaria), Plate 19.

    28b. Body segmented, cylindrical, oblong, or capsule-like; may or may not have a head capsule and thick fleshy knobs on underside. Larvae of TWO-WINGED FLIES (Diptera), Plate 29. 30

29a. Shell consisting of two hinged halves. BIVALVES (Pelecypoda), Plate 33.

29b. Shell entire, usually spiral but may be "coolie hat"-shaped. SNAILS (Gastropoda), Plate 32.

    30a. Body with functional legs 31

    30b. Body without functional legs, mummy- or capsule-like, living in a cocoon. PUPAE (Insecta), Plate 22 38

31a. Body with three pairs of legs. Larvae, nymphs, and some adults (Insecta) 42

31b. Body with more than three pair of legs 32

    32a. Body compact, spider-like, with four conspicuous pairs of legs (two other pairs of appendages present). WATER MITES (Acari), Plate 35.

    32b. Body with at least five conspicuous pairs of legs. CRUSTACEANS (Crustacea) 33

4. Key to Crustaceans

33a. Sides of body compressed 34

33b. Body flattened horizontally 36

    34a. Eyes on stalks 35

    34b. Eyes, if present, only seen as spots on sides of head. SCUDS (Amphipoda), Plate 21.

35a. Pincers on first pair of legs strong and large; other legs stout, cylindrical, and used for walking. CRAYFISH, also marine lobster (Decapoda), Plate 21.

35b. Pincers on first pair of legs weak and small; other legs, thin and flattened, are used for swimming. SHRIMPS (Mysidea and others), Plate 21.

    36a. Eyes on stalks, shells generally broad, various shapes (marine and brackish water). CRABS (Decapoda), not illustrated.

    36b. Eyes not on stalks 37

37a. Body covering hard; divided into broad head, truncate body, and sharp tail sections (marine). HORSESHOE CRABS (Arthropoda), Plate 35.

37b. Body with three or more joints. SOWBUGS (Isopoda), Plate 21.

5. Key to Insect Pupae

    38a. Back of pupa with small, paired, hook-bearing plates. CADDISFLIES (Trichoptera), Plate 27.

    38b. Back without paired hook-bearing plates but may have knobs or bristles 39

39a. Developing wings (pads) held free from body. BEETLES (Coleoptera), Plate 30.

39b. Wing pads closely appressed to body, mummy-like, or appendages not evident. 40

    40a. With one closely appressed pair of wing pads, but not fused to body; or capsule-like, appendages not evident. TWO-WINGED FLIES (Diptera), Plate 28.

    40b. Two pairs of wing pads 41

41a. First two or three abdominal segments with spiracles (holes for breathing) on each side; body without numerous projections. AQUATIC MOTHS (Lepidoptera), not illustrated.

41b. Body differing from above, may have numerous knobs or other projections on back. HELLGRAMMITES (Neuroptera and Megaloptera), Plate 26.

6. Key to Insect Larvae, Nymphs, and Some Adults

    42a. Animal flea-like, with a bifid projecting appendage on the underside. SPRINGTAILS (Collembola), Plate 35.

    42b. Animal otherwise 43

43a. Body ending in long segmented filaments 44

43b. Long filaments absent or, if present, not segmented 45

    44a. Two tail filaments, legs ending in two claws. STONEFLIES (Plecoptera), Plate 23.

    44b. Three tail filaments (with few exceptions); middle filament may be slightly smaller than laterals, legs ending in one claw. MAYFLIES (Ephemeroptera), Plate 24.

45a. Back of body covered with two hard wing covers, a pair of membranous wings underneath the covers. Adult BEETLES (Coleoptera), Plate 30.

45b. Back without hard wing covers 46

    46a. Body with exposed membranous wings or wing pads on back. 47

    46b. Body without membranous wings or wing pads (larvae) 49

47a. Membranous wings present; held flat and in a V-shape on back. Mouth parts formed into a long, sharply pointed beak folded underneath body. TRUE BUGS (Hemiptera), Plate 31.

47b. Membranous wings absent, wing pads present. Mouth parts formed into an extendable, scoop-like mask that covers face. (Odonata) 48

    48a. Body ending in three oblong, fan-like plates. DAMSELFLIES (Zygoptera), Plate 25.

    48b. Fan-like plates absent. DRAGONFLIES (Anisoptera), Plate 25.

49a. Mouth parts formed into slender curved rods nearly half as long as body (less than 10 mm). SPONGILLA FLIES (Neuroptera), not illustrated.

49b. Mouth parts adapted for biting or chewing *50*

    50a. Body with five paired knobs on underside of abdominal segments, legs on first three segments short and stubby. Often found on lily pads. Aquatic Moths (Lepidoptera), not illustrated.

    50b. Body without paired knobs on underside of abdomen *51*

51a. Sides of each abdominal segment with a slender, tapering process *52*

51b. Sides of each abdominal segment without a tapering process, but may have hair-like or tubular processes *53*

    52a. Body ending in a pair of hook-bearing fleshy legs or in a single tapering filament. Hellgrammites and relatives (Megaloptera), Plate 26.

    52b. Body otherwise. Beetles (Coleoptera), Plate 30.

53a. Body covering mostly hard; knobs, hairlike processes, or other special ornamentation may be present on back, or else body is entirely soft except for a hardened head capsule. Beetles (Coleoptera), Plate 30.

53b. Most of body soft except for a hardened head capsule and with one to three hard plates on the back of first body segments; tubular processes may be present on sides of the body in various arrangements. Body may end in a pair of hood-bearing legs. Most larvae living in portable cases made of bits of sticks, leaves, or sand or in attached fibrous cases. Caddis-flies (Trichoptera), Plate 27.

1007 C.   List of Common Types of Aquatic Organisms (Plates 1-38), by Trophic Level

ACKNOWLEDGMENTS

Plates 1 through 38, which follow on succeeding pages, present over 200 aquatic organisms commonly found in natural, polluted, and treated waters. These plates were drawn especially for this work by Eugene Schunk of the Cincinnati Art Service, Inc. In a number of instances, it would have been impossible to illustrate a certain organism for the purposes of this manual were it not for the courtesy of other publishers, who permitted illustrations from their publications to be incorporated. The following organisms were so reproduced:

Plate
  5: B—*Diatoma*,
     F—*Achnanthes*,
     G—*Gomphonema*,
     H—*Cymbella*, and
     K—*Surirella*, courtesy of Veb Gustav Fischer Verlag, Jena. Source: Die Susswasser—Flora Mitteleuropas, Heft 10, by F. Hustedt, 1930.
  6: C—*Coscinodiscus*, and
     D—*Melosira*, courtesy of E. Schweizerbart'sche Verlagsbuchhandlung, Stuttgart. Source: Das Phytoplankton des Susswassers, Die Binnengewasser, Band XVI, Teil II, Halfte II, by G. Huber-Pestalozzi and F. Hustedt, 1942. Plates CVIII-CXVI and CXXIII.
     F—*Skeletonema*, courtesy of Academische Verlagsgesellschaft, Leipzig. Source: Die Kieselalgen, by F. Hustedt. In: L. Rabenhorst, Kryptogamen-Flora von Deutschland, Osterreich und der Schweiz, Band VII, 1930.
 16: E—*Membranipora monostachys*, reprinted by permission of G. P. Putnam's Sons, Inc., New York. Source: Field Book of Seashore Life, by R. W. Miner. Copyright 1950 by the author. Plate 236, page 817.
 17: I—*Notholca* Robert W. Pennak, Fresh-Water Invertebrates of the United States, Copyright © 1953, The Ronald Press Company, New York. Figure 116*N*, page 190, adapted for Figure 171, courtesy of The Ronald Press.
 21: A—*Asellus* (sowbug),
     C—*Mysis* (shrimp),
     D—*Diaptomus* (copepod),
     E—*Cypridopsis* (ostracod),
     F—*Cyclops* (copepod), and
     G—*Cambarus* (crayfish, crawdad), courtesy of Holden-Day, Inc., San Francisco, California. Source: Needham & Needham's Guide to the Study of Freshwater Biology, 1951. Figures 1 and 10, Plate 14, page 37; Figures 16, 18 and 20, Plate 24, page 61; and Figure 9, Plate 14, page 37.
 22: Dr. Harold Walters
 32: A—*Pomacea* (apple snail),
     B—*Marisa*,
     E—*Tarebia*,
     I—*Lymnaea* (pond snail),
     J—*Helisoma* (orb snail), and
     M—*Lanx* (limpet) courtesy of John Wiley & Sons, Inc., New York. Source: Ward & Whipple, Fresh Water Biology (2nd ed.), W. T. Edmondson, Editor, 1959. Figures 43.31A (A), 43.31B (B), 43.62B (E), 43.13 (I), 43.20 (J) and 43.14 (M).
     C—*Campeloma*,
     D—*Bithynia* (faucet snail),
     F—*Pleurocera* (river snail),

Plate

    G—*Valvata,*

    H—*Littorina* (periwinkle),

    K—*Nassa* (mud snail),

    L—*Ferrissia* (limpet), and

    N—*Physa,* courtesy of R. M. Sinclair, Advisor for Biological Sampling and Analysis (American Public Health Association) 13th ed.

34: Connecticut State Geological and Natural History Survey: Echinoderms of Connecticut, by Wesley Roswell Coe, 1912.

35: C—*Limulus* (horseshoe crab) courtesy of Western Publishing Company, Inc., Golden Press Division, Racine, Wisconsin. Source: Seashores, a Golden Nature Guide, 1955. Page 79.

37: C—*Ambystoma* (terrestrial adult), courtesy of Dover Publications, Inc., New York. Source: Biology of the Amphibia, by G. K. Noble, 1931. Figure 147C, page 471.

    D—*Ambystoma* (aquatic larva), courtesy of the New York State Museum and Science Service, Albany, New York. Source: The Salamanders of New York, by Sherman C. Bishop, 1941. Figure 33b, page 166. [Bulletin 324, New York State Museum, Albany.]

    E—*Necturus,* courtesy of Dover Publications, Inc., New York. Source: Biology of the Amphibia, by G. K. Noble, 1931. Figure 35B, page 99.

    G—*Siren intermedia* (siren), reprinted from Sherman Bishop: Handbook of Salamanders. Copyright 1943 by Comstock Publishing Company, Inc. Used by permission of Cornell University Press.

38: A—(a) micrococcus, (b) streptococcus, (c) sarcina, (d) bacillus, (e) vibrio, (f) spirillum, courtesy of John Wiley & Sons, Inc., New York. Source: Ward & Whipple, Fresh Water Biology (2nd ed.), W. T. Edmondson, Editor, 1959. Figure 3.1

    (k) actinomycete growth form, Selman A. Waksman, The Actinomycetes. Copyright © 1957, The Ronald Press Company, New York. Figure 2-6, page 18, adapted for Figure 37A(k), courtesy The Ronald Press.

    B—*Tetracladium* and (e) (f), *Achlya,* courtesy of John Wiley & Sons, Inc., New York. Source: Ward & Whipple, Fresh Water Biology (2nd ed.), W. T. Edmondson, Editor, 1959. Figures 4.119 and 4.79.

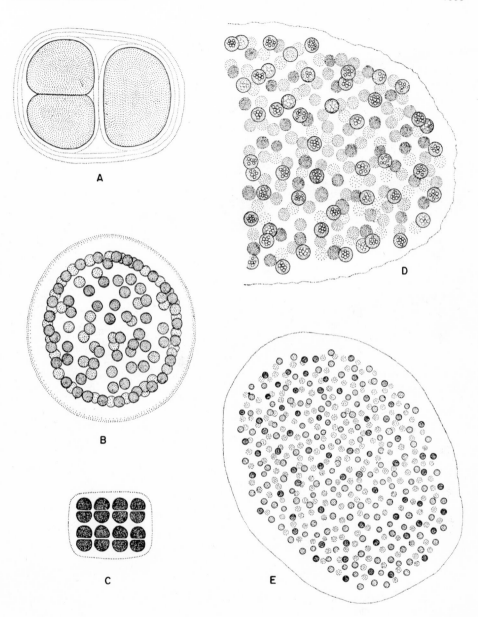

Plate 1. Blue-green algae: Coccoid (Phylum Cyanophyta). Dimensions refer to individual cells.

A—*Anacystis*   (4–20 μm)   D—*Anacystis* sp.   (4–6 μm)
B—*Gomphosphaeria*   (3–6 μm)   E—*Anacystis* sp.   (3–4 μm)
C—*Agmenellum*   (2–6 μm)

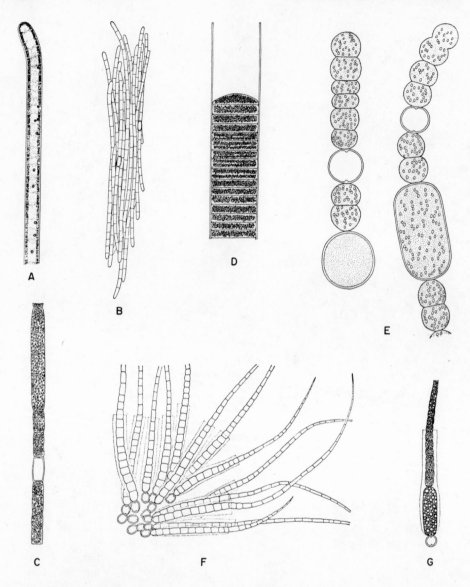

Plate 2. Blue-green algae: Filamentous (Phylum Cyanophyta). Most dimensions refer to diameter of individual filaments.

A—*Oscillatoria*	(4–20 μm)	E—*Anabaena*	(5–12 μm)
B—*Aphanizomenon,*	(5–6 μm)	F—*Gleotrichia,*	(Cells 7–9
aggregate of filaments		portion of colony	μm diameter
C—*Aphanizomenon,* detail			near akinete)
D—*Lyngbya*	(4–20 μm)	G—*Gleotrichia,* detail	

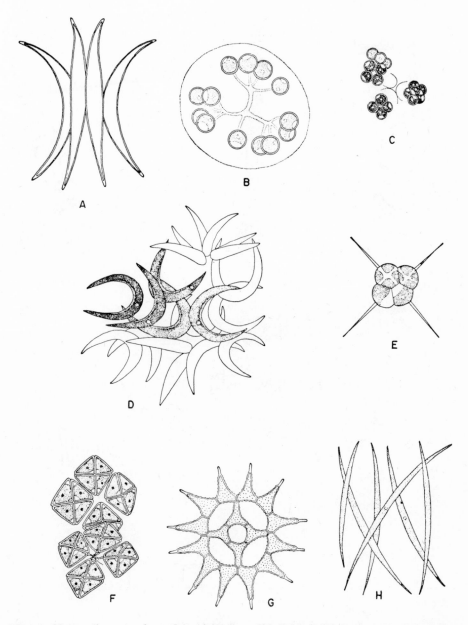

Plate 3. Nonmotile green algae: Coccoid (Phylum Chlorophyta). Dimensions refer to individual cells.

A—*Scenedesmus*	(4–6 μm diameter)	E—*Tetrastrum*	(5–9 μm)
B—*Dictyosphaerium*	(8–14 μm)	F—*Crucigenia*	(5–8 μm)
C—*Westella*	(5–7 μm)	G—*Pediastrum*	(10–20 μm)
D—*Selenastrum*	(6–7 μm)	H—*Ankistrodesmus*	(2–3 μm)

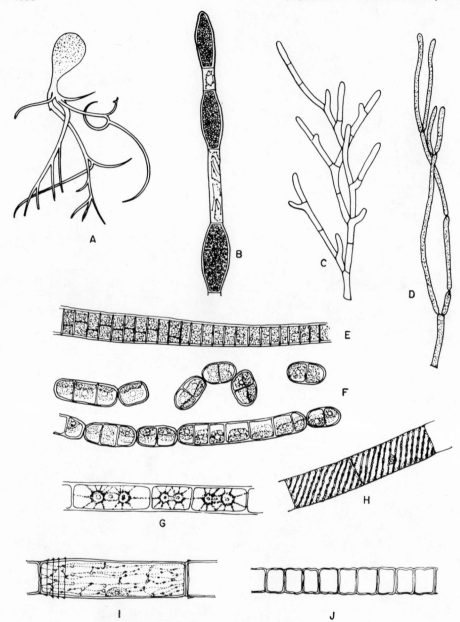

Plate 4. Nonmotile green algae: Filamentous (Phylum Chlorophyta). Dimensions refer to diameters of filaments or to mass.

A—*Botrydium*	(1000–2000 μm)	F—*Stichococcus*	(3 μm)
B—*Pithophora*	(50–100 μm)	G—*Zygnema*	(20–35 μm)
C—*Microthamnion*	(2–4 μm)	H—*Spirogyra*	(15–100 μm)
D—*Dichotomosiphon*	(50–100 μm)	I—*Oedogonium*	(6–40 μm)
E—*Schizomeris*	(12–18 μm)	J—*Hyalotheca*	(12–30 μm)

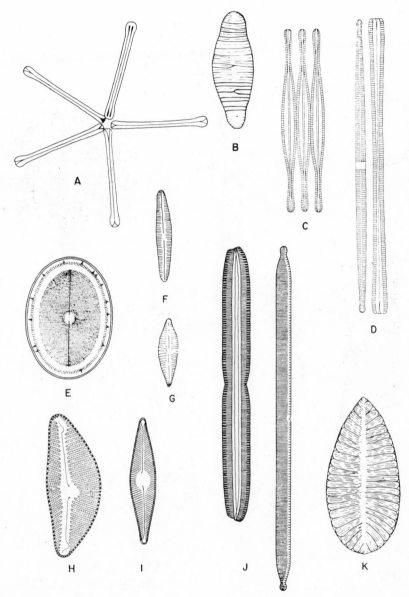

Plate 5. Diatoms: Pennate (Phylum Chrysophyta, Class Bacillariophyceae). Dimensions refer to length of cells unless otherwise specified.

A—*Asterionella*	(300 μm, entire colony)	G—*Gomphonema*	(20 μm)
B—*Diatoma*	(20 μm)	H—*Cymbella*	(15 μm)
C—*Fragilaria*	(100 μm)	I—*Navicula*	(30 μm)
D—*Synedra*	(200 μm)	J—*Nitzschia*	(100 μm)
E—*Cocconeis*	(10 μm)	K—*Surirella*	(20 μm)
F—*Achnanthes*	(10 μm)		

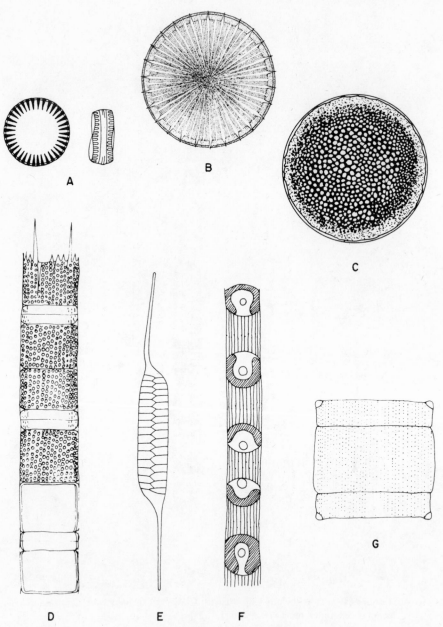

Plate 6. Diatoms: Centric (Phylum Chrysophyta, Class Bacillariophyceae). Dimensions refer to diameter.

A—*Cyclotella*   (10 μm)   E—*Rhizosolenia*   (5–15 μm)
B—*Stephanodiscus*   (30 μm)   F—*Skeletonema*   (3–18 μm)
C—*Coscinodiscus*   (20 μm)   G—*Biddulphia*   (100 μm)
D—*Melosira*   (3–12 μm)

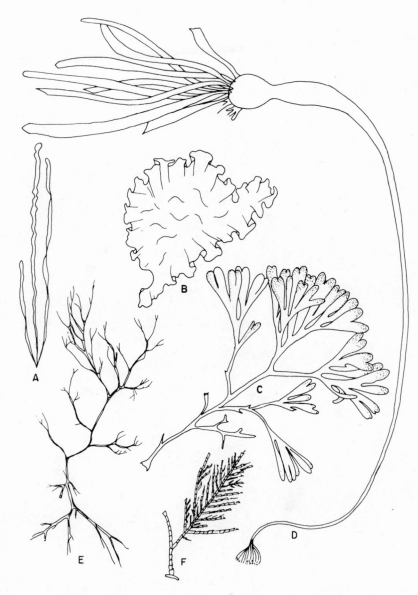

Plate 7. **Types of larger marine algae** (green, brown, and red).

Green algae (Phylum Chlorophyta):
A—*Enteromorpha* (40 cm)
B—Sea lettuce, *Ulva* (20 cm)
Brown algae (Phylum Phaeophyta):
C—Rockweed, *Fucus* (75 cm)
D—Giant kelp, *Nereocystis* (20 m)

Red algae (Phylum Rhodophyta):
E—*Gracilaria* (50 cm)
F—*Corallina* (4 cm)

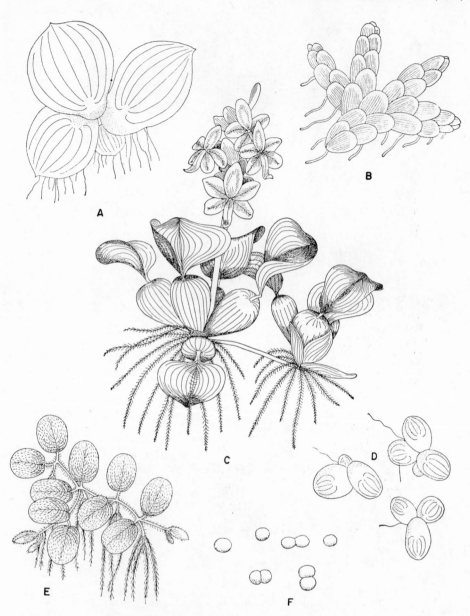

Plate 8. Higher plants: Floating plants.

A—Great duckweed, *Spirodela*
    (Phylum Spermatophyta, 8mm)
B—Water velvet, *Azolla*
    (Phylum Pteridophyta, 1 cm)
C—Water hyacinth, *Eichhornia*
    (Phylum Spermatophyta, 22 cm)

D—Lesser duckweed, *Lemna*
    (Phylum Spermatophyta, 5 mm)
E—Water fern, *Salvinia*
    (Phylum Pteridophyta, 4 cm)
F—Watermeal, *Wolffia*
    (Phylum Spermatophyta, 1–1.5 mm)

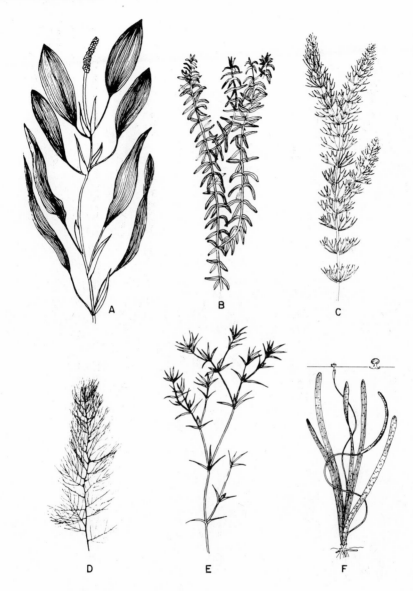

Plate 9. Higher plants: Submersed (all forms illustrated are Spermatophytes).

A—Pondweed, *Potamogeton*   (30–60 cm)   E—Naiad, *Najas*   (60 cm)
B—Waterweed, *Elodea*   (15 cm)   F—Eelgrass, *Vallisneria* (45 cm)
C—Coontail, *Ceratophyllum*   (30 cm)
D—Water milfoil,
     Myriophyllum   (30 cm)

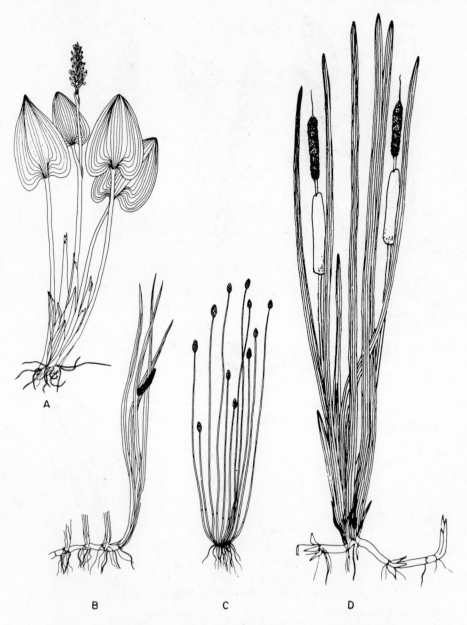

Plate 10. Higher plants: Emersed (all forms illustrated are Spermatophytes).

A—Pickerelweed, *Pontederia*   (60 cm) │ C—Spike rush, *Eleocharis*   (30 cm)
B—Sweetflag, *Acorus*   (30 cm) │ D—Cattail, *Typha*   (1–2 m)

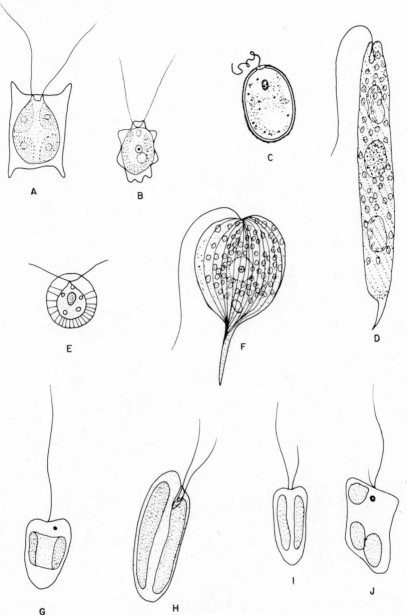

Plate 11. **Pigmented flagellates**: Single-celled (various phyla).

A—*Pteromonas*	(9–18 μm)	F—*Phacus*	(20–50 μm)
B—*Lobomonas*	(5–14 μm)	G—*Chromulina*	(4–10 μm)
C—*Trachelomonas*	(15–30 μm)	H—*Cryptomonas*	(6–12 μm)
D—*Euglena*	(10–25 μm)	I—*Ochromonas*	(7–14 μm)
E—*Haematococcus*	(40–45 μm)	J—*Chloramoeba*	(10–15 μm)

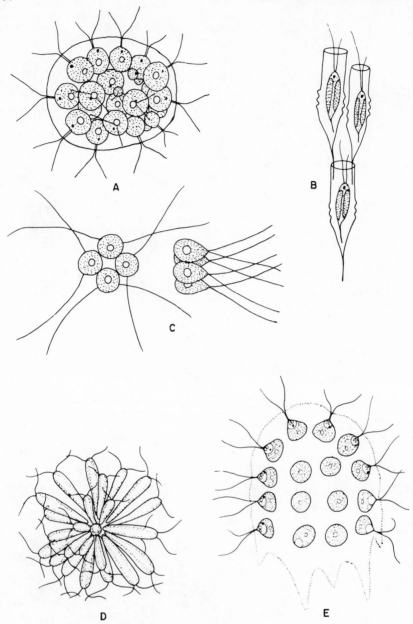

Plate 12. Pigmented flagellates: Colonial types (various phyla). Dimensions refer to individual cells unless otherwise specified.

A—*Pleodorina*	(8–10 μm)	D—*Synura*	(10–15 μm)
B—*Dinobryon*	(7–12 μm)	E—*Platydorina*	(66–70 μm
C—*Gonium*	(7–12 μm)		colony)

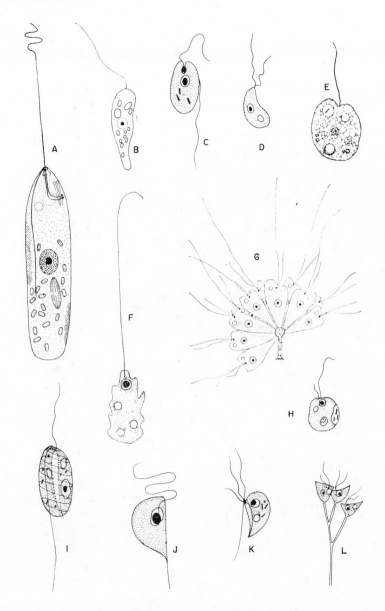

Plate 13. Nonpigmented flagellates (Phylum Protozoa).

A—*Peranema*	(40–70 μm)	G—*Anthophysa*	(5–6 μm)
B—*Astasia*	(40–50 μm)	H—*Monas*	(5–16 μm)
C—*Bodo*	(11–22 μm)	I—*Anisonema*	(14–60 μm)
D—*Dinomonas*	(15–16 μm)	J—*Cercomonas*	(10–36 μm)
E—*Oikomonas*	(5–20 μm)	K—*Tetramitus*	(11–30 μm)
F—*Mastigamoeba*	(28–200 μm)	L—*Dendromonas*	(8 μm)

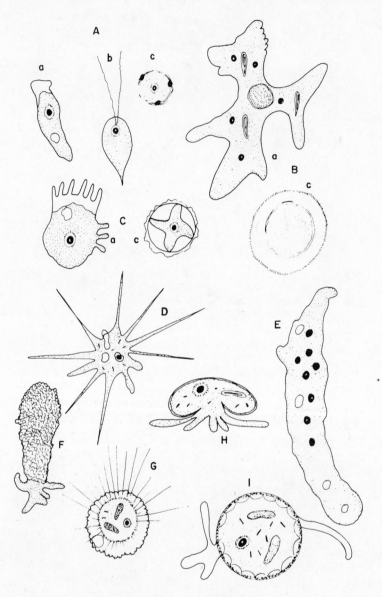

Plate 14. **Amoebas** (Phylum Protozoa). (a) Amoeboid stages, (b) flagellated stages, (c) cyst stages.

A—*Naegleria*	(10–36 μm)	E—*Pelomyxa*	(0.25–3 mm)
B—*Amoeba* sp.	(30–600 μm)	F—*Difflugia*	(40 μm)
C—*Acanthamoeba*		G—*Actinophrys*	(25–50 μm)
(*Hartmannella*)	(15–25 μm)	H—*Arcella* (side view)	(30–260 μm)
D—*Amoeba radiosa*	(30–120 μm)	I—*Arcella* (top view)	(30–260 μm)

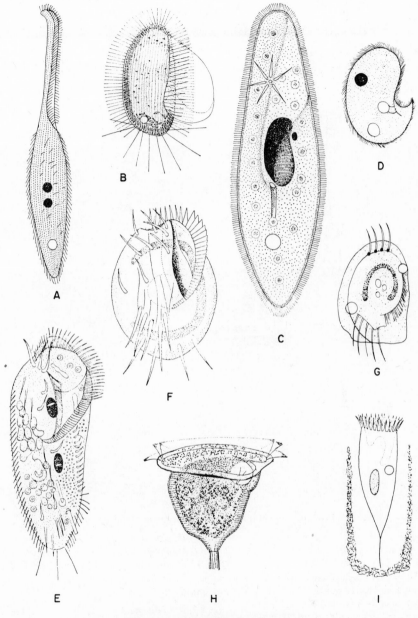

Plate 15. Ciliates (Phylum Protozoa).

A—*Lionotus*	(100 μm)	F—*Euplotes*	(70–195 μm)
B—*Pleuronema*	(38–120 μm)	G—*Aspidisca*	(30–50 μm)
C—*Paramoecium*	(50–330 μm)	H—*Vorticella*	(40–175 μm)
D—*Colpoda*	(12–110 μm)	I—*Tintinnidium*	(40–200 μm)
E—*Stylonychia*	(100–300 μm)		

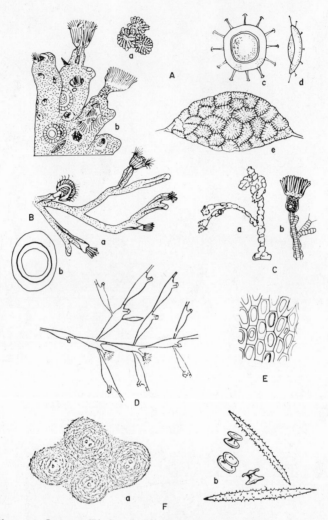

Plate 16. Sponges (Phylum Porifera) and Bryozoans (Phylum Bryozoa).

Bryozoa:

A—Jellyball, *Pectinatella*
    (a) Young colony (15 mm)
    (b) Section (highly magnified)
    (c) Statoblast (1 mm)
    (d) Statoblast (1 mm)
    (e) Colony on a plant stem (10 cm)

B—*Plumatella*
    (a) Colony (4 cm)
    (b) Statoblast (0.5 mm)

C—*Urnatella* (5 mm)
    (a) Colony (7 mm)
    (b) Individual zooid at tip of stalk (0.5 mm)

D—*Paludicella* (6 mm)

E—*Membranipora*, an encrusting marine form (individuals 1 mm, colonies unlimited)

Porifera:

F—*Trochospongilla*
    (a) Gemmules in a colony (1 mm)
    (b) Spicules (0.2 mm)

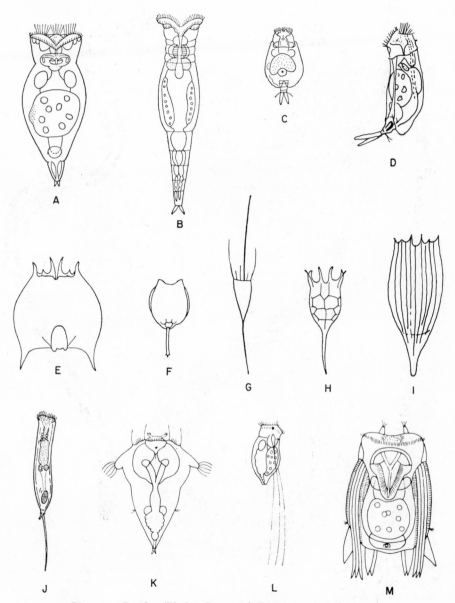

Plate 17. Rotifers (Phylum Rotatoria). Dimensions include spines.

A—*Epiphanes*	(600 μm)	H—*Keratella*	(200 μm)
B—*Philodina*	(400 μm)	I—*Notholca*	(200 μm)
C—*Euchlanis*	(250 μm)	J—*Trichocerca*	(600 μm)
D—*Proales*	(450 μm)	K—*Synchaeta*	(260 μm)
E—*Brachionus*	(200 μm)	L—*Filinia*	(150 μm)
F—*Monostyla*	(150 μm)	M—*Polyarthra*	(175 μm)
G—*Kellicottia*	(1 mm)		

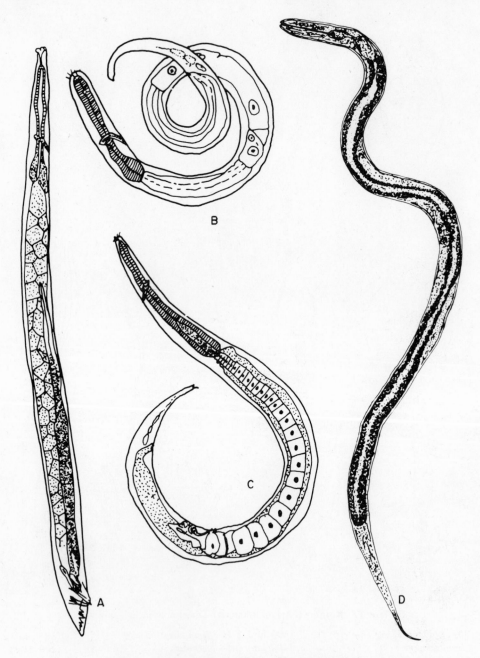

Plate 18. Roundworms (Phylum Nemathelminthes).

A—*Rhabditis* (male)   (1.6–1.9 mm) | D—*Diplogasteroides*
B—*Achromadora* (female)   (0.3–0.7 mm) | (female)
C—*Monhystera* (female)   (0.8–1.0 mm) | (1.5–1.85 mm)

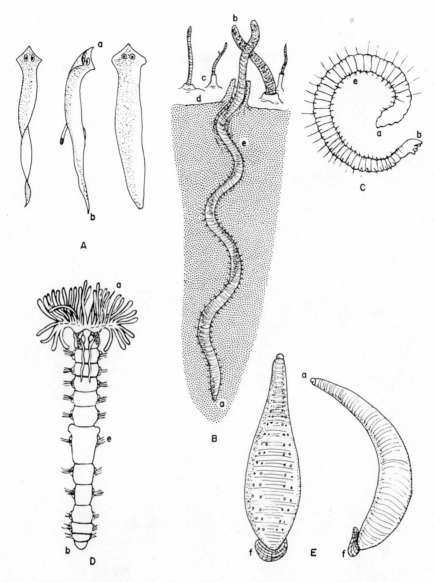

Plate 19. Flatworms (Phylum Platyhelminthes) **and segmented worms** (Phylum Annelida). (a) Anterior end, (b) posterior end, (c) tubes, (d) mud surface, (e) setae, (f) sucker disk.

Platyhelminthes:

A—*Planaria*, a free-living flatworm (5–13 mm)

Annelida:

B—*Tubifex*, a sludgeworm (25–50 mm)

C—*Dero*, a bristle worm (3–7 mm)

D—*Manayunkia*, a freshwater tube-building polychaet worm similar to certain common marine forms (5 mm)

E—Leech (50 mm)

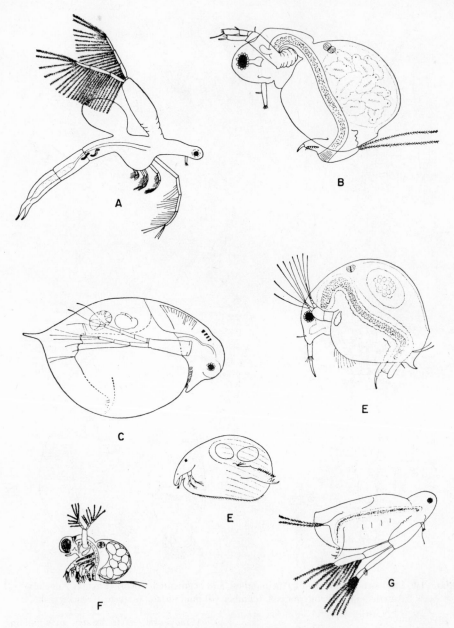

Plate 20. Crustaceans (Phylum Arthropoda, Class Crustacea): Types of cladocerans (Order Cladocera).

A—*Leptodora*	(9 mm)	E—*Bosmina*	(0.4 mm)
B—*Moina*	(1.5 mm)	F—*Polyphemus*	(1.5 mm)
C—*Daphnia*	(2 mm)	G—*Diaphanosoma*	(1.5 mm)
D—*Alona*	(0.4 mm)		

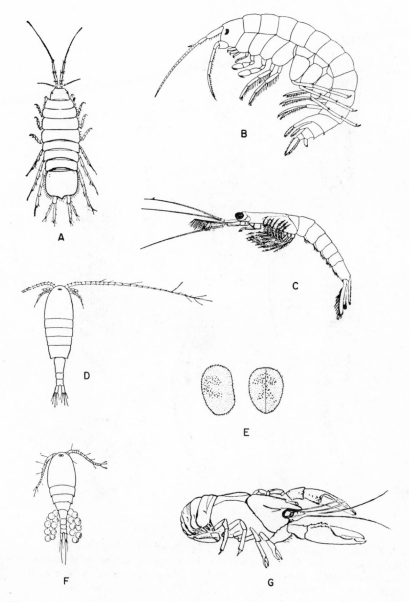

Plate 21. Crustaceans (Phylum Arthropoda, Class Crustacea): Selected common types.

A—Sowbug, *Asellus*, Order Isopoda (20 mm)
B—Scud, *Gammarus*, Order Amphipoda (15 mm)
C—Shrimp, *Mysis*, Order Decapoda (20 mm)
D—Copepod, *Diaptomus*, Order Copepoda (2 mm)

E—Ostracod, *Cypridopsis*, Order Ostracoda (1 mm)
F—Copepod, *Cyclops*, Order Copepoda (1 mm)
G—Crayfish, crawdad, *Cambarus*, Order Decapoda (150 cm)

Plate 22. Types of insect pupae.

A—Caddisfly, *Goera*, Order Trichoptera
B—Hellgrammite, *Corydalis*, Order Megaloptera
C—Beetle, *Cybister*, Order Coleoptera
D—Cranefly, *Antocha*, Tipulidae

E—Blowfly, *Tabanus*, Tabinidae
F—Sewage fly, *Limnophorus*, Anthomyidae
G—Midge, *Chironomus*, Chironomidae
H—Mosquito, *Culex*, Culicidae

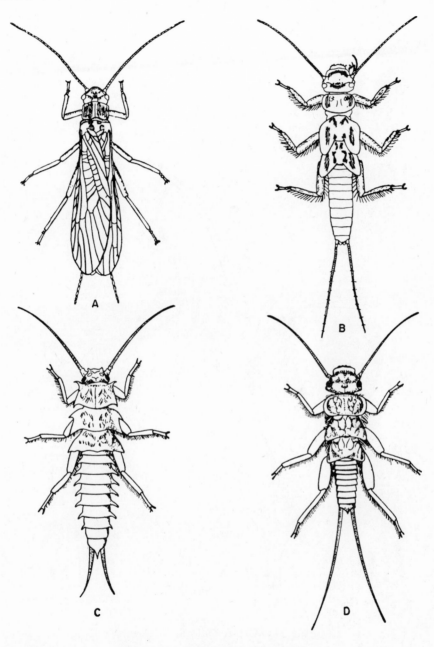

Plate 23. Stoneflies (Order Plecoptera).

A—Adult *Isoperla*, Isoperlidae (14–23 mm)
B—Nymph *Isoperla*,
   Isoperlidae (10–14 mm)

C—Nymph *Pteronarcys*,
   Pteronarcidae (10–40 mm)
D—Nymph *Acroneuria*, Perlidae (20–30 mm)

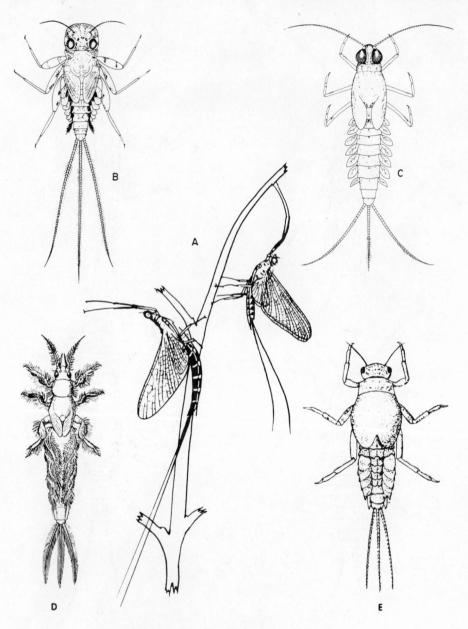

Plate 24. Mayflies (Order Ephemeroptera).

A—Adult mayfly, Heptageniidae (12–18 mm)

B—Nymph *Stenonema*, Heptageniidae (10–14 mm)

C—Nymph *Baetis*, Baetidae (7–14 mm)

D—Nymph *Hexagenia*, Ephemeridae (20–30 mm)

E—Nymph *Ephemerella*, Ephemerellidae (8–15 mm)

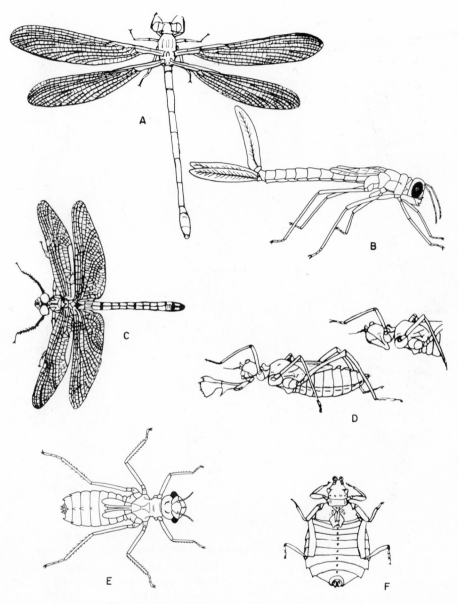

Plate 25. Damselflies, dragonflies (Order Odonata)

A—Adult damselfly (35–55 mm)
B—Damselfly nymph *Lestes*, Coenagrionidae (20–30 mm)
C—Adult dragonfly *Macromia*, Libellulidae (50–70 mm)
D—Dragonfly nymph *Macromia*, showing "mask" both extended and contracted, Libellulidae (15–45 mm)
E—Dragonfly nymph *Helocordulia*, Libellulidae (15–45 mm)
F—Dragonfly nymph *Hagenius*, Gomphidae (15–20 mm)

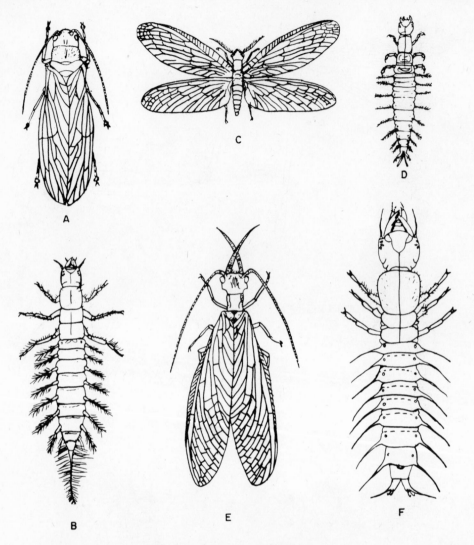

Plate 26. Hellgrammite and relatives.

A—Adult alderfly *Sialis*, Sialidae (9–15 mm)
B—Alderfly larva *Sialis*, Sialidae (15–30 mm)
C—Adult fishfly *Chauliodes*, Corydalidae (15–30 mm)
D—Fishfly larva *Chauliodes*, Corydalidae (20–40 mm)
E—Adult dobsonfly, *Corydalus* (25–70 mm)
F—Dobsonfly larva or hellgrammite, *Corydalus* (25–90 mm)

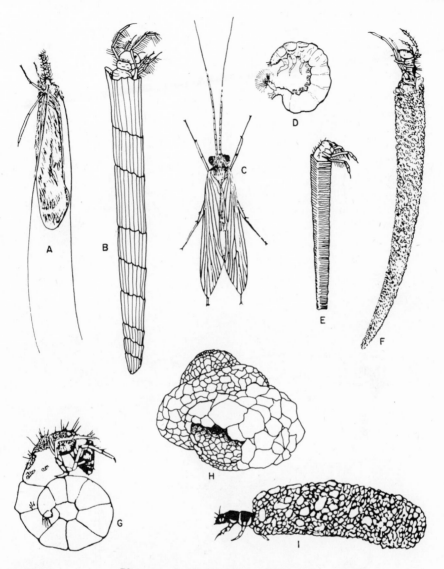

Plate 27. Caddisflies (Order Trichoptera).

A—Adult *Triaenodes*, Leptoceridae (10–20 mm)

B—Larva and case, *Triaenodes*, Leptoceridae (10–14 mm)

C—Adult *Hydropsyche*, Hydropsychidae (20–30 mm)

D—*Hydropsyche* larva, Hydropsychidae (20–30 mm)

E—Larva and case, *Brachycentrus*, Brachycentridae (12–16 mm)

F—Larva and case, *Leptocella*, Leptoceridae (14–18 mm)

G—*Helicopsyche* larva, Helicopsychidae (6–10 mm)

H—*Helicopsyche* case, Helicopsychidae (4–6 mm)

I—Larva and case, *Ochrotricha*, Hydroptilidae (4–6 mm)

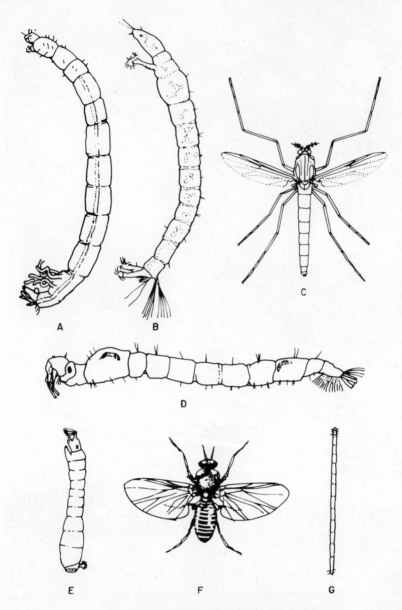

Plate 28. Two-winged flies (Order Diptera).

A—Larva midge *Chironomus*, Chironomidae (5–30 mm)

B—Larva midge *Ablabesmyia*, Chironomidae (5–10 mm)

C—Adult midge, Chironomidae (4–12 mm)

D—Larva phantom midge *Chaoborus*, Culicidae (8–12 mm)

E—Larva black fly *Simulium*, Simuliidae (3–8 mm)

F—Adult black fly *Simulium*, Simuliidae (2–6 mm)

G—Larva biting midge, Ceratopogonidae (3–12 mm)

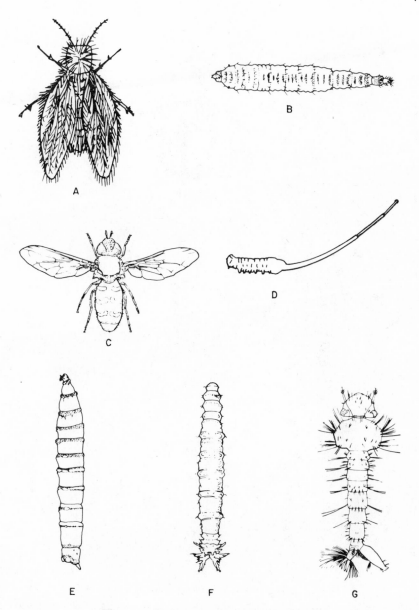

Plate 29. Two-winged flies (Order Diptera).

A—Adult sewage fly *Psychoda*, Psychodidae (2–5 mm)

B—Larva sewage fly *Psychoda*, Psychodidae (4–6 mm)

C—Adult drone fly, Syrphidae (10–15 mm)

D—Rat-tailed maggot *Eristalis*, Syrphidae (15–30 mm)

E—*Tabanus* larva, Tabanidae (30–40 mm)

F—Larva cranefly *Tipula*, Tipulidae (30–40 mm)

G—Larva mosquito *Aedes*, Culicidae (10–15 mm)

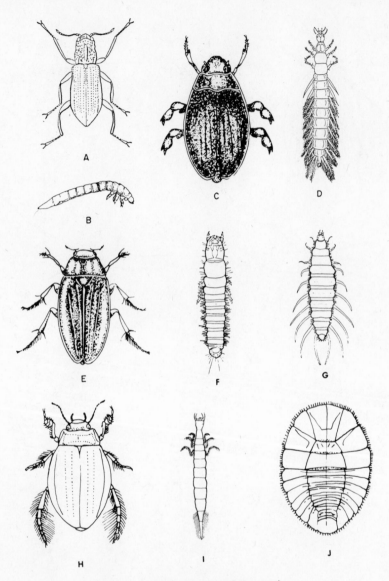

Plate 30. Beetles (Order Coleoptera).

A—Adult riffle beetle *Stenelmis*, Elmidae (2–5 mm)

B—Larva *Narpus*, Elmidae (4–10 mm)

C—Adult whirligig beetle *Dineutus*, Gyrinidae (7–15 mm)

D—Larva *Dineutus*, Gyrinidae (10–30 mm)

E—Adult water scavenger beetle *Hydrophilus*, Hydrophilidae (2–40 mm)

F—Larva *Berosus*, Hydrophilidae (5–20 mm)

G—Larva *Enochrus*, Hydrophilidae (10–25 mm)

H—Adult predacious diving beetle *Dytiscus*, Dytiscidae (2–40 mm)

I—Larva *Cybister*, Dytiscidae (10–25 mm)

J—Larva water penny *Psephenus*, Psephenidae (3–10 mm)

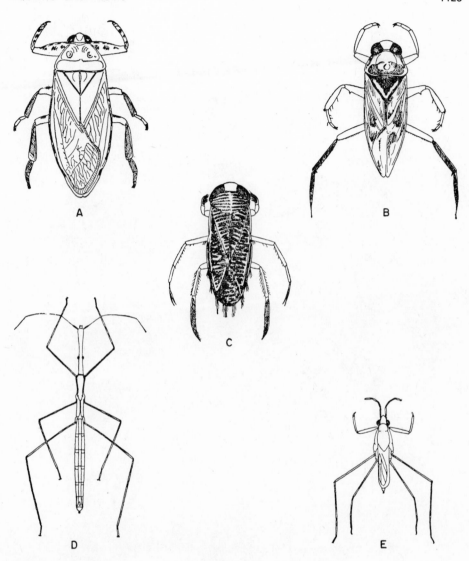

Plate 31. True bugs (Order Hemiptera, all adults).

A—Electric light bug, *Lethocerus*, Belostomidae (20–70 mm)

B—Backswimmer, *Notonecta*, Notonectidae (5–17 mm)

C—Water boatman *Sigara*, Corixidae (3–12 mm)

D—Marsh treader *Hydrometra*, Hydrometridae (8–11 mm)

E—Water strider *Gerris*, Gerridae (2–15 mm)

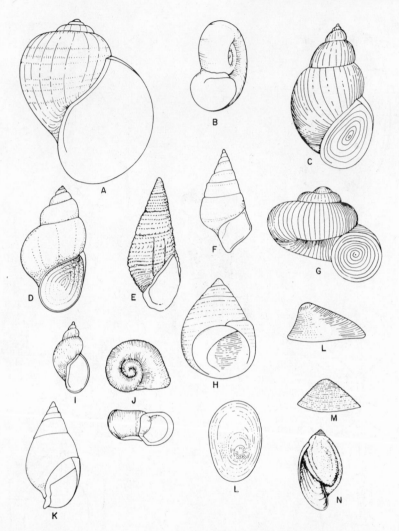

Plate 32. **Mollusks** (Phylum Mollusca): Snails (Class Gastropoda).

Gill-breathing families:

A—Apple snail *Pomacea*, Pilidae (5 cm)
B—*Marisa*, Pilidae (15 mm)
C—*Campeloma*, Viviparidae (4 cm)
D—Faucet snail *Bithynia*, Amnicolidae (2 cm)
E—*Tarebia*, Thiaridae (15 mm)
F—River snail *Pleurocera*, Pleuroceridae (3 cm)
G—*Valvata*, Valvatidae (1 cm)
H—Periwinkle *Littorina*, Littorinidae (marine, 2 cm)

Lung breathers:

I—Pond snail *Lymnaea*, Lymnaeidae (15 mm)
J—Orb snail *Helisoma*, Planorbidae (1 cm)
K—Mud snail *Nassa*, Nassidae (marine, 2 cm)
L—Limpet *Ferrissia*, Ancylidae (2 mm)
M—Limpet *Lanx*, Lancidae (10 mm)
N—Pouch snail *Physa*, Physidae (5 mm)

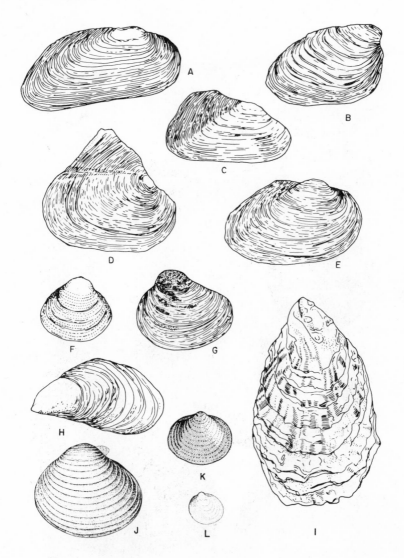

Plate 33. Mollusks (Phylum Mollusca): Bivalves (Class Pelecypoda)

A—Spectacle case *Margaritifera*, Margaritiferidae (10 cm)

B—Pearly mussel *Pleurobema*, Unionidae (10 cm)

C—Pearly mussel *Gonidea*, Unionidae (10 cm)

D—Winged lampshell *Proptera*, Lampsilinae (13 cm)

E—Papershell *Anodonta*, Anodontidae (14 cm)

F—Marsh clam *Polymesoda*, Corbiculidae (marine, 4 cm)

G—Rangia clam *Rangia*, Mactridae (marine, 5 cm)

H—Edible mussel *Mytilus*, Mytilidae (marine, 6 cm)

I—Oyster *Crassostrea*, Ostreidae (marine, 9 cm)

J—Asiatic clam *Corbicula*, Corbiculidae (4 cm)

K—Fingernail clam *Sphaerium*, Sphaeriidae (1 cm)

L—Peashell clam *Pisidium*, Sphaeriidae (5 mm)

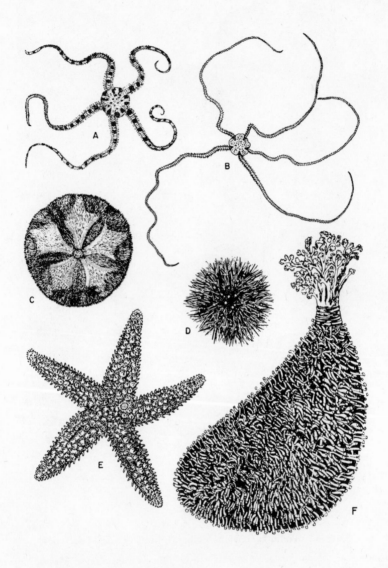

Plate 34. Echinoderm types (Phylum Echinodermata, all marine).

A—Brittle star, class Ophiuroidea: *Ophiopholis* (disc 15 mm)

B—Brittle star, class Ophiuroidea: *Amphioplus* (disc 5 mm)

C—Sand dollar, class Echinoidea: *Echinarachnius* (7 cm)

D—Sea urchin, class Echinoidea: *Strongylocentrotus* (6 cm)

E—Starfish, class Asteroidea: *Asterias* (15 cm)

F—Sea cucumber, class Holothuroidea: *Thyone* (10 cm)

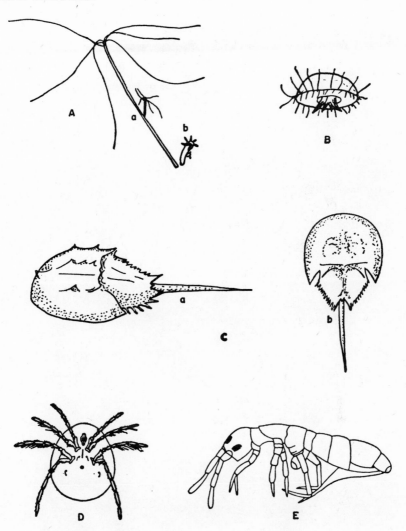

Plate 35. Miscellaneous invertebrates.

Freshwater coelenterates (Phylum Coelenterata):

A—*Hydra*, at (a) extended (2 cm) with bud, and at (b) contracted

B—Jellyfish (Medusa) stage of *Craspedacusta* (2 cm)

Arthropods (Phylum Arthropoda):

C—Horseshoe crab (Class Arachnoidea), marine: *Limulus* (30 cm); (a) shows side view and (b) top view.

D—Water mite (Class Arachnoidea): *Limnochares* (3 mm)

E—Springtail (Class Insecta, Order Collembola): *Orchesella* (2 mm)

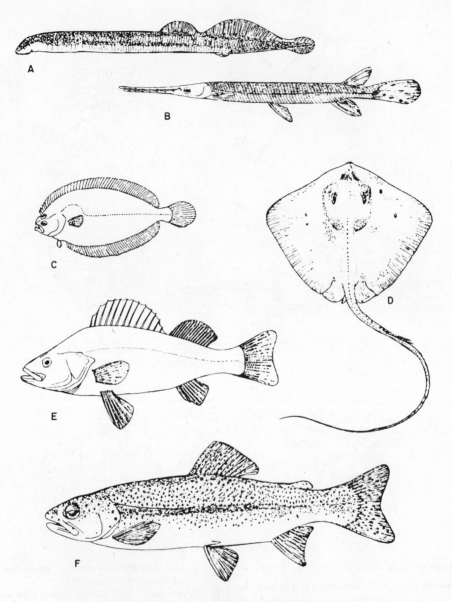

Plate 36. Some types of fishes (Phylum Chordata).

A—Jawless fish (Class Agnatha): lamprey, *Petromyzon* (750 cm)

B—Ganoid fish (Class Osteichthys, or Pisces): long-nosed gar, *Lepisosteus* (800 cm)

C—Flatfish (Class Osteichthys): flounder, *Paralichthys* (500 cm)

D—Cartilage fish (Class Chondrichthys): stingray, *Dasyatis* (2 m)

E—Spiny-rayed fish (Class Osteichthys): perch, *Perca* (30 cm)

F—Soft-rayed fish (Class Osteichthys): rainbow trout, *Salmo* (30 cm)

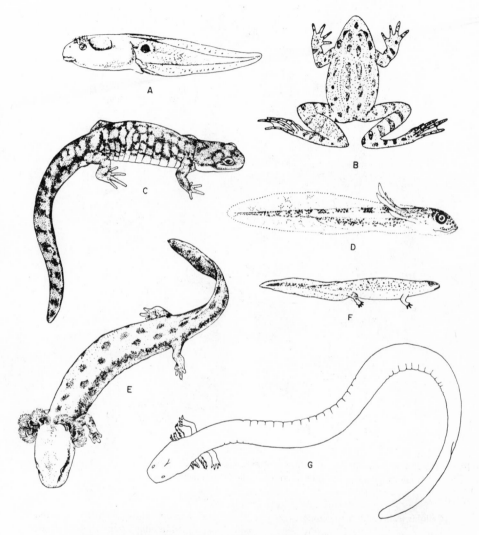

Plate 37. Types of amphibians (Phylum Chordata, Class Amphibia)

Frogs and toads (Order Salientia):

A—The "tadpole" larva (note the developing leg protruding from the body of the tadpole)

B—An adult frog, *Rana* (20 cm). Salientia with dry warty skins are usually called toads.

Salamanders (Order Caudata):

C—*Ambystoma* (20 cm). Adult is typically terrestrial.

D—*Ambystoma* larva is aquatic. Salamander larvae typically have gills.

E—Water dog or mud puppy, *Necturus* (to 60 cm). Larval gills are retained by the adult.

F—An adult aquatic salamander with a flat tail, *Diemictylus* (9 cm).

G—An aquatic salamander. The hind legs have been lost; *Siren* (1 m).

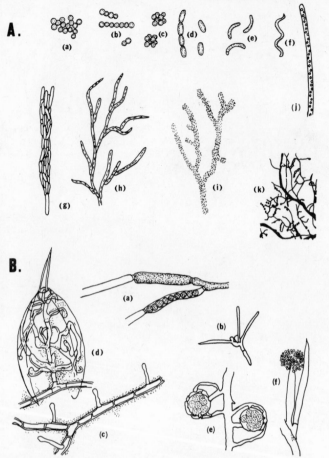

Plate 38. Bacteria and Fungi. (Diameter of most bacterial cells is less than 2 μm, though *Beggiatoa* may range up to 16 μm in diameter, and be of indefinite length.)

A—Bacteria:

  (Cellular forms and arrangements)

  (a) micrococcus
  (b) streptococcus
  (c) sarcina
  (d) bacillus
  (e) vibrio
  (f) spirillum

  (Sewage organisms)

  (g) *Sphaerotilus* ("sewage fungus") cells
  (h) A *Sphaerotilus* growth form
  (i) A growth form of *Zoogloea*
  (j) *Beggiatoa* (sulfur bacterium)
  (k) An actinomycete growth form from compost

B—Fungi:

  (a) *Leptomitus*, showing zoospores and cellulin plugs (diameter 8.5–16 μm)
  (b) *Tetracladium* (diameter 2.5–3.5 μm)
  (c) *Zoophagus*, showing mycelial pegs
  (d) *Zoophagus* with rotifer impaled on mycelial peg (diamter 3 μm)
  (e) *Achlya*, showing oospores
  (f) *Achlya*, showing extruded encysted zoospores (Oogonia 50–60 μm, oospores 18.5–22 μm, encysted zoospores 3–5 μm)

1007 D.   Key for Identification of Freshwater Algae Common in Water Supplies and Polluted Waters (Color Plates A-F)

By C. Mervin Palmer

Beginning with 1a and 1b, choose one of the two contrasting statements and follow this procedure with the "a" and "b" statements of the number given at the end of the chosen statement. Continue until the name of the alga is given instead of another key number. (Where recent changes in names of algae have been made, the new name is given followed by the old name in parenthesis.)

Refer to Couplet No.

1a. Plastid (separate color body) absent; complete protoplast pigmented; generally blue-green; iodine starch test* negative (blue-green algae)   4
1b. Plastid or plastids present; parts of protoplast free of some or all pigments; generally green, brown, red, etc., but not blue-green; iodine starch test* positive or negative   2
   2a. Cell wall permanently rigid (never showing evidence of collapse), and with regular pattern of fine markings (striations, etc.); plastids brown to green; iodine starch test* negative; flagella absent; wall of two essentially similar halves, one placed over the other as a cover (diatoms) 29
   2b. Cell wall, if present, capable of sagging, wrinkling, bulging, or rigidity, depending on existing turgor pressure of cell protoplast; regular pattern of fine markings on wall generally absent; plastids green, red, brown, etc; iodine starch test* positive or negative; flagella present or absent; cell wall continuous and generally not of two parts . .   3
3a. Cell or colony motile; flagella present (often not readily visible); anterior and posterior ends of cell different from one another in contents and often in shape (flagellate algae) . . . 51
3b. Nonmotile; true flagella absent; ends of cells often not differentiated (green algae and associated forms) 77

1. Blue-Green Algae

   4a. Cells in filaments (or much elongated to form a thread).   5
   4b. Cells not in (or as) filaments 23
5a. Heterocysts present   6
5b. Heterocysts absent. 14
   6a. Heterocyst located at one end of filament.   7
   6b. Heterocysts at various locations in filament.   9
7a. Filaments radially arranged in a gelatinous bead . . . . *Rivularia*
7b. Filaments isolated or irregularly grouped   8
   8a. Filament gradually narrowed to one end . . . . *Calothrix*
   8b. Filament not gradually narrowed to one end. . . . . *Cylindrospermum*
9a. Filament unbranched 10
9b. Filament with occasional (false) branches 13
   10a. Crosswalls in filament much closer together than width of filament. . . . . *Nodularia*
   10b. Crosswalls in filament at least as far apart as width of filament 11
11a. Filaments normally in tight parallel clusters; heterocysts and spores cylindric to long oval in shape . . . . *Aphanizomenon*

---

*Add 1 drop of Lugol's (iodine) solution, diluted 1 : 1 with distilled water. In about 1 min, if positive, starch is stained blue and later black. Other structures (such as nucleus, plastids, cell wall) may also stain, but turn brown to yellow.

11b. Filaments not in tight parallel clusters; heterocysts and spores often round to oval   12

    12a. Filaments in a common gelatinous mass. . . . .*Nostoc*

    12b. Filaments not in a common gelatinous mass . . . .*Anabaena*

13a. False branches in pairs. . . . .*Scytonema*

13b. False branches, single . . . .*Tolypothrix*

    14a. Filament or elongated cell attached at one end, with one or more round cells (spores)
        at the other . . . .*Entophysalis (Chamaesiphon)*

    14b. Filament generally not attached at one end; no terminal spores present   15

15a. Filament with regular spiral form throughout   16

15b. Filament not spiral, or with spiral form limited to a portion of filament   17

    16a. Filament septate. . . . .*Arthrospira*

    16b. Filament nonseptate . . . .*Spirulina*

17a. Filament very narrow, only 0.5 to 2.0 μm wide . . . .*Schizothrix*

17b. Filament 3 to 95 μm wide   18

    18a. Filaments loosely aggregated or not in clusters   19

    18b. Filaments tightly aggregated and surrounded by a common gelatinous secretion that
        may be invisible   22

19a. Filament surrounded by wall-like sheath that frequently extends beyond the ends of the fil-
    ament of cells; filament generally without movement   20

19b. Filament not surrounded by a wall-like sheath; filament may show movement.   21

    20a. Cells separated from one another by a space . . . .*Johannesbaptistia*

    20b. Cells in contact with adjacent cells. . . . .*Lyngbya*

21a. All filaments short, with less than 20 cells; one or both ends of filament sharply pointed
    . . . .*Raphidiopsis*

21b. Filaments long, with more than 20 cells; filaments commonly without sharp-pointed ends
    . . . .*Oscillatoria*

    22a. Filaments arranged in a tight, essentially parallel bundle. . . . .*Microcoleus*

    22b. Filaments arranged in irregular fashion, often forming a mat . . . . .*Phormidium*

23a. Cells in a regular pattern of parallel rows, forming a plate . . . .*Agmenellum*
                                             (Merismopedia)

23b. Cells not regularly arranged to form a plate   24

    24a. Cells regularly arranged near surface of a spherical gelatinous bead.   25

    24b. Gelatinous bead, if present, not spherical   26

25a. Cells ovate to heart-shaped, connected to center of bead by colorless stalks.*Gomphosphaeria*

25b. Cells round, without gelatinous stalks . . . . .*Gomphosphaeria* (*Coelosphaerium* type)

    26a. Cells cylindric-oval . . . .*Coccochloris (Aphanothece)*

    26b. Cells spherical   27

27a. Two or more distinct layers of gelatinous sheath around each cell or cell cluster
    . . . .*Anacystis (Gloeocapsa)*

27b. Gelatinous sheath around cells not distinctly layered   28

    28a. Cells isolated or in colonies of 2 to 32 cells . . . .*Anacystis (Chroococcus)*

    28b. Cells in colonies composed of many cells. . . . .*Anacystis (Microcystis,*
                                                 Polycystis)

2. Diatoms

29a. Front (valve) view circular in outline; markings radial in arrangement; cells may form a
    filament (centric diatoms)   30

29b. Front (valve) view elongate, not circular; transverse markings in one or two longitudinal rows; cells, if grouped, not forming a filament (pennate diatoms). 32

30a. Cells in persistent filaments with valve faces in contact; therefore, cells commonly seen in side (girdle) view . . . .*Melosira*

30b. Cells isolated or in fragile filaments, often seen in front (valve) view. 31

31a. Radial markings (striations), in valve view, extending from center to margin; short spines often present around margin (valve view) . . . .*Stephanodiscus*

31b. Area of prominent radial markings, in valve view, limited to approximately outer half of circle, marginal spines generally absent . . . .*Cyclotella*

32a. Cell longitudinally symmetrical in valve view 33

32b. Cell longitudinally unsymmetrical (two sides unequal in shape), at least in valve view 49

33a. Raphe at or near the edge of the valve 34

33b. Raphe or pseudoraphe median or submedian 35

34a. Marginal, keeled raphe areas lie opposite one another on the two valves. .*Hantzschia*

34b. Marginal, keeled raphe areas lie diagonal to one another on the two valves .*Nitzschia*

35a. Cell transversely symmetrical in valve view 36

35b. Cell transversely unsymmetrical (two ends unequal in shape or size), at least in valve view . 44

36a. Cell round-oval in valve view, not more than twice as long as it is wide . . . .*Cocconeis*

36b. Cell elongate, more than twice as long as it is wide 37

37a. Cell flat (girdle face wide, valve face narrow) . . . .*Tabellaria*

37b. Girdle and valve faces about equal in width 38

38a. Cell with several markings (septa) extending without interruption across the valve face; no marginal line of pores present. . . . .*Diatoma*

38b. Cross-markings (striations or costae) on valve surface, interrupted by either longitudinal space (pseudoraphe), or line (raphe), or line of pores (carinal dots) 39

39a. Cells attached side by side to form a ribbon of several to many cells. . . . .*Fragilaria*

39b. Cells isolated or in pairs 40

40a. Cell narrow, linear, often narrowed to both ends; true raphe absent . . . . .*Synedra*

40b. Cell commonly "boat-shape" in valve view; true raphe present. 41

41a. Cell longitudinally unsymmetrical in girdle view; sometimes with attachment stalk . . . .*Achnanthes*

41b. Cell symmetrical in girdle as well as valve view; generally not attached 42

42a. Area without striations extending as a transverse belt around middle of cell . . . .*Stauroneis*

42b. No continuous clear belt around middle of cell 43

43a. Cell with coarse transverse markings (costae), which appear as solid lines even under high magnification . . . .*Pinnularia*

43b. Cell with fine transverse markings (striae), which appear as lines of dots under high magnification. . . . .*Navicula*

44a. Cells attached together at one end only to form radiating colony . . . . .*Asterionella*

44b. Cell not forming a loose radiating colony. 45

45a. Cells in fan-shaped colonies . . . .*Meridion*

45b. Cells isolated or in pairs 46

46a. Prominent wall markings in addition to striations present just below lateral margins on valve surface of cell. . . . .*Surirella*

46b. Wall markings along sides of valve limited to striations 47

47a. Cell elongate, sides almost parallel except for terminal knobs. . . . .*Asterionella*

47b. Sides of cell converging toward one end   48
   48a. Cells bent in girdle view. . . . .*Rhoicosphenia*
   48b. Cells straight in girdle view . . . .*Gomphonema*
49a. Valves with transverse septa or costae. . . . .*Epithemia*
49b. Valves with no transverse septa or costae.   50
   50a. Raphe located almost through center of valve. . . . .*Cymbella*
   50b. Raphe excentric, near concave edge of valve . . . .*Amphora*

3. Flagellate Algae

51a. Cell in a loose, rigid conical sac (lorica); isolated or in a branching colony. . . .*Dinobryon*
51b. Case or sac, if present, not conical; colony, if present, not branching   52
   52a. Cells isolated or in pairs   53
   52b. Cells in a colony of four or more cells.   71
53a. Prominent transverse groove encircles cell   54
53b. Cell without transverse groove.   56
   54a. Cell with prominent rigid projections, one forward and two or three on posterior end
. . . .*Ceratium*
   54b. Cell without several rigid polar projections   55
55a. Portions above and below transverse groove about equal . . . .*Peridinium*
55b. Front portion distinctly larger than posterior portion. . . . .*Massartia*
   56a. Cell with long bristles extending from surface plates . . . .*Mallomonas*
   56b. Cell without bristles and surface plates   57
57a. Cell protoplast enclosed in loose rigid covering (lorica).   58
57b. Cell with tight membrane or wall but no loose rigid covering   60
   58a. Lorica flattened; cell with two flagella. . . . .*Phacotus*
   58b. Lorica not flattened; cell with one flagellum   59
59a. Lorica often opaque, generally dark brown to red; plastid green . . . . . .*Trachelomonas*
59b. Lorica often transparent, colorless to light brown; plastid light brown. . . . .*Chrysococcus*
   60a. Plastids brown to red to olive or blue-green.   61
   60b. Plastids grass green   64
61a. Plastids blue-green to blue . . . .*Chroomonas*
61b. Plastids brown to red to olive green   62
   62a. Plastid brown; one or two flagella   63
   62b. Plastids red, red-brown, or olive green; two flagella . . . . . .*Rhodomonas*
63a. Anterior end of cell oblique; two flagella. . . . .*Cryptomonas*
63b. Anterior end of cell rounded or pointed; one flagellum . . . .*Chromulina*
   64a. Cell with colorless rectangular wing . . . .*Pteromonas*
   64b. No wing extending from cell   65
65a. Cells flattened; margin rigid . . . .*Phacus*
65b. Cell not flattened; margin rigid or flexible   66
   66a. Pyrenoid present in the single plastid; no paramylon; margin not flexible; two or
more flagella per cell.   67
   66b. Pyrenoid absent; paramylon present; several plastids per cell; margin flexible or
rigid; one flagellum per cell   70
67a. Cells fusiform (tapering at each end). . . . .*Chlorogonium*
67b. Cells not fusiform, generally almost spherical   68
   68a. Plastids numerous . . . .*Vacuolaria*
   68b. Plastids few, commonly one   69
69a. Two flagella per cell . . . .*Chlamydomonas*

*Refer to
Couplet
No.*

69b. Four flagella per cell . . . . *Carteria*

    70a. Cell flexible in form; paramylon a capsule or disk; cell elongate . . . . . *Euglena*

    70b. Cell rigid in form; paramylon ring-shaped; cell almost spherical . . . *Lepocinclis*

71a. Plastids brown 72

71b. Plastids green 73

    72a. Cells in contact with one another . . . . *Synura*

    72b. Cells separated from one another by space. . . . . *Uroglenopsis*

73a. Colony flat, one cell thick. . . . . *Gonium*

73b. Colony rounded, more than one cell thick 74

    74a. Cells in contact with one another. 75

    74b. Cells separated from one another by space. 76

75a. Cells radially arranged . . . . *Pandorina*

75b. Cells all facing one direction . . . . *Pyrobotrys (Chlamydobotrys)*

    76a. Cells more than 400 per colony . . . . *Volvox*

    76b. Cells less than 75 per colony . . . . *Eudorina*

4. Green Algae and Associated Forms

77a. Cells jointed together to form a net . . . . *Hydrodictyon*

77b. Cells not forming a net 78

    78a. Cells attached side by side to form a plate or ribbon one cell wide and thick; number of cells commonly two, four, or eight . . . . *Scenedesmus*

    78b. Cells not attached side by side. 79

79a. Cells isolated or in nonfilamentous or nontubular thalli 80

79b. Cells in filaments or other tubular or threadlike thalli 111

    80a. Cells isolated and narrowest at the center because of incomplete fissure (desmids). 81

    80b. Cells isolated or in clusters but without central fissure. 84

81a. Each half of cell with three spinelike or pointed knobular extensions . . . . *Staurastrum*

81b. Cell margin with no such extensions 82

    82a. Semicells with a median incision or depression. 83

    82b. Semicells with no median incision or depression . . . . *Cosmarium*

83a. Margin with rounded lobes. . . . . *Euastrum*

83b. Margin with sharp-pointed teeth. *Micrasterias*

    84a. Cells elongate. 85

    84b. Cells round to oval or angular. 92

85a. Cell radiating from a central point . . . . *Actinastrum*

85b. Cells isolated or in irregular clusters. 86

    86a. Cells with terminal spines . . . . *Schroederia*

    86b. Cells without terminal spines. 87

87a. Cells with colorless attachment area at one end . . . . *Characium*

87b. No attachment area at one end of cell 88

    88a. Plastids two per cell; unpigmented area across center of cell . . . . . . *Closterium*

    88b. Cell with plastid that continues across the center. 89

89a. Cell 5 to 10 times as long as it is broad 90

89b. Cell 2 to 4 times as long as it is broad 91

    90a. Pyrenoid absent, or one per cell . . . . *Ankistrodesmus*

    90b. Pyrenoids several per cell . . . . *Closteriopsis*

91a. Cells semicircular; cell ends pointed but with no terminal spines . . . . . *Selenastrum*

91b. Cells arcuate but less than semicircular; cell ends pointed and each with a short spine . . . . *Closteridium*

1007 E.   Recent Changes in Names of Algae

Old Name	New Name
Aphanocapsa	*Anacystis*
Aphanothece	*Coccochloris*
Chamaesiphon	*Entophysalis*
Chantransia.	*Audouinella*
Chlamydobotrys	*Pyrobotrys*
Chroococcus	*Anacystis*
Clathrocystis	*Anacystis*
Coelosphaerium	*Gomphosphaeria*
Encyonema	*Cymbella*
Gloeocapsa	*Anacystis*
Gloeothece	*Coccochloris*
Merismopedia	*Agmenellum*
Microcystis	*Anacystis*
Odontidium	*Diatoma*
Polycystis	*Anacystis*
Protococcus	*Phytoconis*
Sphaerella	*Haematococcus*
Synechococcus	*Coccochloris*

ALGAE COLOR PLATES

A through F

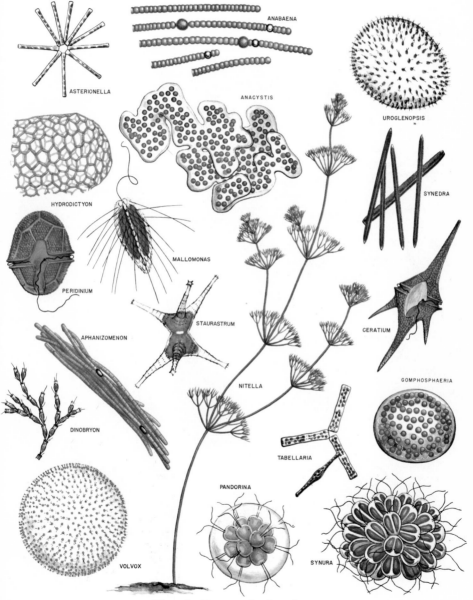

Plate A. Taste and odor algae

ASTERIONELLA

ANABAENA

ANACYSTIS

UROGLENOPSIS

HYDRODICTYON

SYNEDRA

PERIDINIUM

MALLOMONAS

APHANIZOMENON

STAURASTRUM

CERATIUM

NITELLA

GOMPHOSPHAERIA

DINOBRYON

TABELLARIA

VOLVOX

PANDORINA

SYNURA

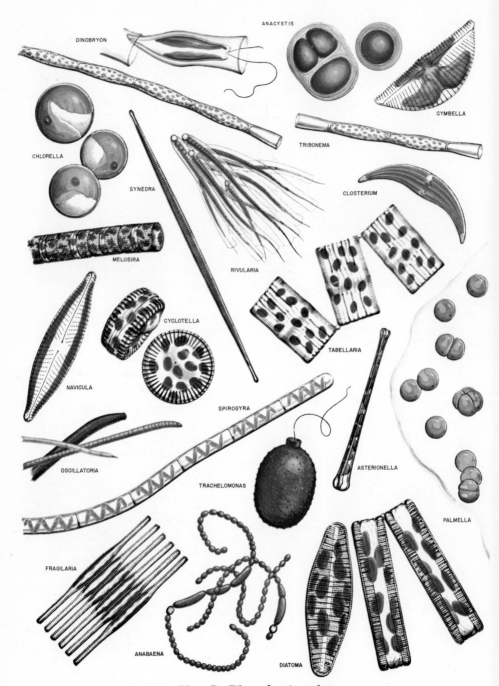

Plate B. Filter clogging algae

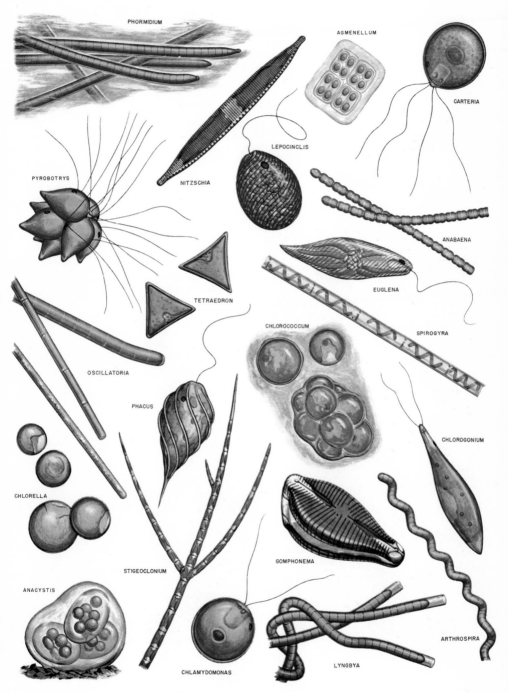

Plate C. Polluted water algae

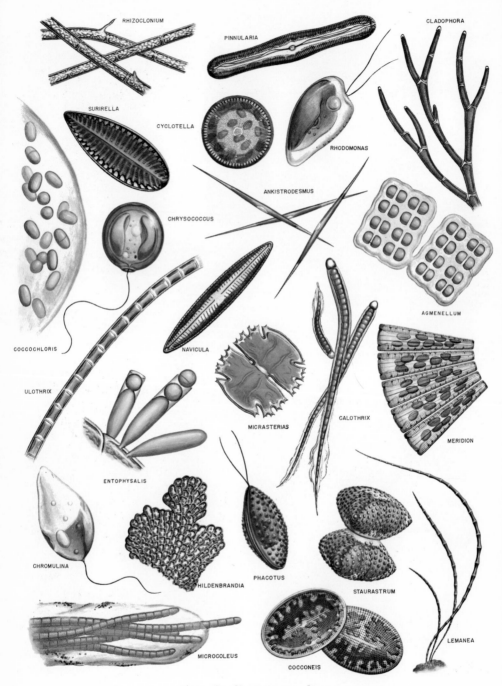

Plate D. Clean water algae

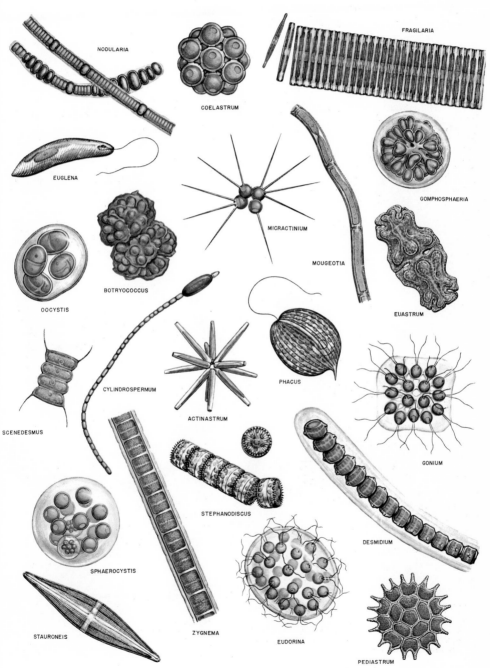

NODULARIA

COELASTRUM

FRAGILARIA

EUGLENA

MICRACTINIUM

MOUGEOTIA

GOMPHOSPHAERIA

BOTRYOCOCCUS

OOCYSTIS

EUASTRUM

SCENEDESMUS

CYLINDROSPERMUM

ACTINASTRUM

PHACUS

GONIUM

SPHAEROCYSTIS

STEPHANODISCUS

DESMIDIUM

STAURONEIS

ZYGNEMA

EUDORINA

PEDIASTRUM

Plate E. Plankton and other surface water algae

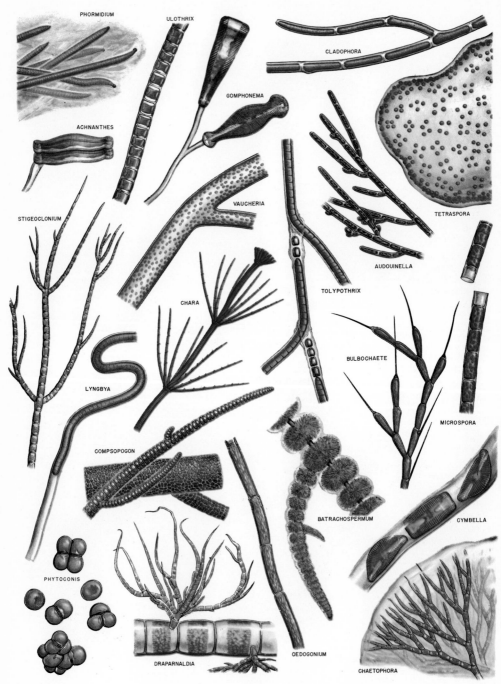

Plate F. Algae growing on reservoir walls

1007 F. Index to Illustrations

NOTE: Arabic numerals refer to black and white plate numbers, capital letters to color plates. See also "Recent Changes in Names of Algae," Section 1007 E, preceding. Family names are not generally included.

1007 G.   Selected Taxonomic References

1. General, Introductory

JAQUES, H.E. 1947. Living Things: How To Know Them. William C. Brown Co., Dubuque, Ia.

MINER, R.W. 1950. Field Book of Seashore Life. G.P. Putnam's Sons, N.Y.

DAVIS, C.C. 1955. The Marine and Fresh-Water Plankton. Michigan State Univ. Press, East Lansing.

EDDY, S. & A.C. HODSON. 1961. Taxonomic Keys to the Common Animals of the North Central States, Exclusive of the Parasite Worms, Insects, and Birds. Burgess Publ. Co., Minneapolis, Minn.

HEDGPETH, J. & S. HINTON. 1961. Common Seashore Life of Southern California. Naturegraph Co., Healdsburg, Calif.

NEEDHAM, J.G. & P.R. NEEDHAM. 1962. A Guide to the Study of Fresh-Water Biology, 5th ed. Holden-Day Inc., San Francisco, Calif.

RICKETTS, E.F. & J. CALVIN. 1963. Between Pacific Tides, 3d ed. Revised by Hedgpeth. Stanford Univ. Press, Calif.

KLOTS, E.B. 1966. New Field Book of Freshwater Life. G.P. Putnam's Sons, N.Y.

PIMENTEL, R.A. 1967. Invertebrate Identification Manual. Reinhold Publ. Corp., N.Y.

REID, G.K. 1967. Pond Life. A Guide to Common Plants and Animals of North American Ponds and Lakes. Golden Press, N.Y.

2. General, Advanced

PENNAK, R.W. 1953. Fresh-Water Invertebrates of the United States. The Ronald Press, N.Y.

EDMONDSON, W.T., ed. 1959. Ward and Whipple's Fresh Water Biology, 2nd ed. John Wiley & Sons, N.Y.

BLAIR, W.F. et al. 1968. Vertebrates of the United States. McGraw-Hill, N.Y.

3. Algae, General

BRANDT, K. & C. APSTEIN. 1908. Nordisches Plankton (Botanisher Teil). Asher & Co., Amsterdam, reprinted in 1964.

SETCHELL, W.A. & N.L. GARDNER. 1919–1925. The Marine Algae of the Pacific Coast of North America. Univ. of California Publ. in Botany No. 8 (Parts 1, 2, 3). J. Cramer, Weinheim, Germany. Reprinted in 1967.

DAWSON, E.Y. 1946. Marine algae of the Pacific Coast of North America. Mem. So. Calif. Acad. Sci. 3:2.

WHIPPLE, G.C. 1948. The Microscopy of Drinking Water. John Wiley & Sons, N.Y.

SMITH, G.M. 1950. The Fresh-Water Algae of the United States. McGraw-Hill, N.Y.

TIFFANY, L.H. & M.E. BRITTON. 1952. The Algae of Illinois. Univ. of Chicago Press, Chicago, Ill.

PRESCOTT, G.W. 1954. How To Know the Fresh Water Algae. Wm. C. Brown Co., Dubuque, Ia.

FRITSCH, F.E. 1956. The Structure and Reproduction of the Algae. Vol. I: Chlorophyceae, Xanthophyceae, Chrysophyceae, Bacillariophyceae, Cryptophyceae, Dinophyceae, Chloromonadineae, Euglenineae, and Colourless Flagellata. Cambridge Univ. Press, Cambridge, England.

TAYLOR, W.R. 1957. Marine Algae of the Northeastern Coast of North America, 2nd ed. Univ. of Michigan Press, Ann Arbor.

PALMER, C.M. 1959. Algae in Water Supplies. USPHS Publ. No. 657, Washington, D.C.

GRIFFITH, R.E. 1961. The Phytoplankton of Chesapeake Bay—An Illustrated Guide to the Genera. Chesapeake Biological Lab., College Park, Md., Contrib. No. 172.

PRESCOTT, G.W. 1962. Algae of the Western Great Lakes Area, rev. ed. Wm. C. Brown Co., Dubuque, Iowa.

FRITSCH, F.E. 1965. The Structure and Reproduction of the Algae. Vol. II: Phaeophyceae, Rhodophyceae, and Myxophyceae. Cambridge Univ. Press, Cambridge, England.

ROUND, F.E. 1965. The Biology of the Algae. Edward Arnold, Ltd., London.

DAWSON, E.Y. 1966. Marine Botany. Holt, Rinehart & Winston, N.Y.

PRESCOTT, G.W. 1968. The Algae: A Review. Houghton Mifflin, Boston, Mass.

WOOD, R.D. & J. LUTES. 1968. Guide to the Phytoplankton of Narragansett Bay, Rhode Island, rev. ed. Kingston Press, Kingston, R.I.

4. Blue-Green Algae

GEITLER, L. 1930. Cyanophyceae. In: Krypto-gamenflora von Deutschland, Osterreich, und der Schweiz (L. Rabenhorst, ed.). Akad. Verlags., Leipsig. Reprinted in 1961.

HUBER-PESTALOZZI, G. 1938. Blue-Green Algae, Bacteria and Aquatic Fungi. In: Die Binnengewasser. Part 1: Das Phytoplankton des Susswassers (A. Thienemann, ed.). E. Schweizerbart'sche Verlagsbuchhandlung, Stuttgart, Germany. Reprinted in 1962.

SMITH, G.W. 1950. The Fresh-Water Algae of the United States. McGraw-Hill, N.Y.

TIFFANY, L.H. & M.E. BRITTON. 1952. The Algae of Illinois. Univ. of Chicago Press, Chicago, Ill.

DROUET, F. & W.A. DAILY. 1956. Revision of the Coccoid Myxophyceae. Butler Univ. Bot. Studies XII. Indianapolis, Ind.

DESIKACHARY, T.V. 1959. Cyanophyta. Indian Coun. Agr. Res., New Delhi.

GEITLER, L. 1960. Schizophyzeen. In: Encyclopedia of Plant Anatomy (W. Zimmermann and P. Ozeuda, eds.). Gebruder Borntraeger, Berlin, Vol. 6, Part 1.

HUMM, H.J. 1962. Key to the Genera of Marine Bluegreen Algae of Southeastern North America. Virginia Fish. Lab. Spec. Sci. Rep. No. 28.

PRESCOTT, G.W. 1962. Algae of the Western Great Lakes Area, rev. ed. Wm. C. Brown Co., Dubuque, Ia.

WELCH, H. 1964. An introduction to the blue-green algae, with a dichotomous key to all the genera. *Limnol. Soc. S. Afr. News Letter* 1:25.

DROUET, F. 1968. Revision of the classification of the Oscillatoriaceae. Philadelphia Acad. Natur. Sci. Monogr. 15.

5. Green Algae

COLLINS, F.S. 1909. The Green Algae of North America. *Tufts College Studies, Sci. Ser.* 2:79.

TIFFANY, L.H. 1937. Oedogoniales, Oedogoniaceae. In: North American Flora (New York Botanical Gardens) Hafner Publ. Co., N.Y. 11(1):1.

SMITH, G.M. 1950. The Fresh-Water Algae of the United States. McGraw-Hill, N.Y.

TRANSEAU, E. N. 1951. The Zygnemataceae. Ohio State Univ. Press, Columbus.

TIFFANY, L.H. & M.E. BRITTON. 1952. The Algae of Illinois. Univ. of Chicago Press, Chicago, Ill.

RANDHAWA, M.S. 1959. Zygnemaceae. Indian Counc. Agr. Res. New Delhi.

HIRN, K.E. 1960. Monograph of the Oedogoniaceae. Hafner Publ. Co., N.Y.

PAL, B.P., B.C. KUNDU, U.S. SUNDARALINGAM & G.S. VENKATARAMAN. 1962. Charophyta. Indian Counc. Agr. Res., New Delhi.

PRESCOTT, G.W. 1962. Algae of the Western Great Lakes Area, rev. ed. Wm. C. Brown Co., Dubuque, Ia.

ISLAM, A.K.M. 1963. A revision of the genus *Stigeoclonium. Nova Hedwigia* (Supplement) 10:1.

SODERSTROM, J. 1963. Studies in Cladophora. Almquist Publ. Co., Uppsala, Sweden.

VAN DER HOEK, C. 1963. Revision of the European Species of Cladophora. Brill Publ. Co., Leiden, Netherlands.

RAMANATHAN, K.R. 1964. Ulotrichales. Indian Coun. Agr. Res. New Delhi.

WOOD, R.D. & K. IMAHARI. 1964. A Revision of the Characeae. Vols. I, II. Monograph and Iconograph. J. Cramer Publ. Co., Weinheim, Germany.

6. Flagellates

KOFOID, C.A. & O. SWEZY. 1921. The Free-Living Unarmored Dinoflagellata. Univ. of California Press, Berkeley.

SKVORTZOW, B.V. 1925. The euglenoid genus *Trachelomonas* Ehr. Systematic review. *Proc. Sungari River Sta.* 1:1.

DEFLANDRE, G. 1926. Monographie du genre Trachelomonas. Ehr. Nemours: Impremerie André Lesot.

HUBER-PESTALOZZI, G. 1938. Chrysophyceen. Farblose Flagellaten Heterokonten. In: Die Binnengewasser. Vol. 16. Das Phytoplankton des Susswassers, Part 2 (A. Thienemann, ed.). E. Schweizerbart'sche Verlagsbuchhandlung, Stuttgart, Germany. Reprinted in 1962.

ALLEGRE, C.F. & T.L. JAHN. 1943. A survey of the Genus *Phacus* Dumardin. *Trans. Amer. Microsc. Soc.* 62:233.

GRAHAM, H.W. & N. BRONIKOVSKY. 1944. The Genus Ceratium in the Pacific and North Atlantic Oceans. Publ. No. 565, Carnegie Inst., Washington, D.C.

HUBER-PESTALOZZI, G. 1950. Chryptophyceen, Chloromonadinen. Peridineen. In: Die Binnengewasser. Vol. 16. Das Phytoplankton des Susswassers, Part 3 (A. Thienemann, ed.). E. Schweizerbart'sche Verlagsbuchhandlung, Stuttgart, Germany. Reprinted in 1962.

SMITH, G.M. 1950. The Fresh-Water Algae of the United States. McGraw-Hill, N.Y.

TIFFANY, L.H. & M.E. BRITTON. 1952. The Algae of Illinois. Univ. of Chicago Press. Chicago, Ill.

GOJDICS, M. 1953. The Genus Euglena. Univ. of Wisconsin Press, Madison.

HUBER-PESTALOZZI, G. 1955. Euglenophyceen. In: Die Binnengewasser. Vol. 16. Das Phytoplankton des Susswassers, Part 4 (A. Thienemann, ed.). E. Schweizerbart'sche Verlagsbuchhandlung, Stuttgart, Germany. Reprinted in 1962.

HUBER-PESTALOZZI, G. 1938. Chlorophyceae; Ordnung Volvocales. In: Die Binnengewasser. Vol. 16. Part 5: Das Phytoplankton des Susswassers (A. Thienemann, ed.). E. Schweizerbart'sche Verlagsbuchhandlung, Stuttgart, Germany. Reprinted in 1962.

PRESCOTT, C.W. 1962. Algae of the Western Great Lakes Area, rev. ed. Wm. C. Brown Co., Dubuque, Ia.

7. Diatoms

CLEVE, P.T. 1894–1896. The Naviculoid Diatoms. Asher & Co., Amsterdam. Reprinted in 1965.

VAN HEURCH, H. 1896. A Treatise on the Diatomaceae. Weldon & Wesley, Ltd., Herts, England. Reprinted in 1962.

BOYER, C.S. 1916. The Diatomaceae of Philadelphia and Vicinity. Reproduced in Xerox by University Microfilms, Ann Arbor, Mich.

ELMORE, C.J. 1922. The Diatoms of Nebraska. Univ. of Nebraska Ser., Lincoln, 21(1–4).

BOYER, C.S. 1927. Synopsis of North American Diatomaceae. Proc. Acad. Natur. Sci. Philadelphia, 79 Supplement, Part 2: 229–583.

GRAN, H.H. & E.C. ANGST. 1930. Plankton Diatoms of Puget Sound. Univ. of Washington, Seattle.

HUSTEDT, F. 1930. The Diatoms. In: Krypto-gamenflora von Deutschland, Osterreich und der Schweiz (L. Rabenhorst, ed.). Geest and Partig K-G, Leipzig, Germany, Parts 1, 2, and 3.

HUSTEDT, F. 1930. Bacillariophyta (Diatomeae). In: Die Susswasserflora Mitteleuropas (A. Pascher, ed.). Vol. 10. Reproduced in Xerox by University Microfilms, Ann Arbor, Mich.

HUBER-PESTALOZZI, G. 1942. The Diatoms. In: Die Binnengewasser. Part 1: Das Phytoplankton des Susswassers (A. Thienemann, ed.). E. Schweizerbart'sche Verlagsbuchhandlung, Stuttgart, Germany. Reprinted in 1962.

CUPP, E.E. 1943. The Marine Plankton Diatoms of the West Coast of North America. Reproduced in Xerox by University Microfilms, Ann Arbor, Mich.

TIFFANY, L.H. & M.E. BRITTON. 1952. The Algae of Illinois. Univ. of Chicago Press, Chicago, Ill.

CLEVE-EULER, A. 1953. The Diatoms of Sweden and Finland. Almquest & Wiksells, Stockholm, Sweden.

HUSTEDT, F. 1955. Marine littoral diatoms, Beaufort, North Carolina. Duke Univ. Mar. Sta. Bull. 6:5.

VAN DER WERFF, A. & H. HULS. 1957–1966. Diatomenenflora van Nederlands, Parts 1–8. Published by the author, De Hoef, Netherlands.

MULFORD, R.A. 1962. Diatoms from Virginia Tidal Waters. Virginia Inst. Mar. Sci. Spec. Sci. Rep. No. 30, Gloucester Point, Va.

HENDY, N.I. 1964. An Introductory Account of the Smaller Algae of British Coastal Waters. Part V: Bacillariophyceae (Diatoms). Fishery Invest. Ser. IV, Her Majesty's Stationery Office, London.

CHOLNOKY, B.J. 1966. Diatomaceae, Vol. I. Krebs, Weinheim, Germany.

PATRICK, R. & C.W. REIMER. 1966. The Diatoms of the United States, Vol. I. Philadelphia Acad. Natur. Sci. Monogr. No. 13, Philadelphia, Pa.

WEBER, C.I. 1966. A Guide to the Common Diatoms at Water Pollution Surveillance Stations. U.S. Dept. Interior, FWPCA, Cincinnati, Ohio.

8. Higher Plants, Introductory

EYLES, D.E. & J.L. ROBERTSON. 1963. Guide and Key to the Aquatic Plants of the Southeastern United States. U.S. Fish & Wildlife Serv. Circ. 158.

HOTCHKISS, N. 1967. Underwater and Floating-Leaved Plants of the United States and Canada. U.S. Fish & Wildlife Serv. Resour. Publ. No. 44.

WELDON, L.W. 1969. Common Aquatic Weeds. U.S. Dep. Agr., Agr. Handbook No. 352.

9. Higher Plants, Advanced

MUENSCHER, W.C. 1944. Aquatic Plants of the United States. Comstock Publ. Co., Ithaca, N.Y.

OGDEN, E.C. 1953. Key to the North American species of *Potamogeton. Circ. N.Y. State Mus.* 31:1.

FASSETT, N.C. 1960. A Manual of Aquatic Plants (with a revision appendix by E.C. Ogden). Univ of Wisconsin Press, Madison.

SCULTHORPE, C.D. 1967. The Biology of Aquatic Vascular Plants. St. Martin's Press, N.Y.

10. General Invertebrates, Introductory

BUCHSBAUM, R.M. & L.J. MILNE. 1960. The Lower Animals, Living Invertebrates of the World. Chanticleer Press, Garden City, N.Y.

HICKMAN, C.P. 1967. Biology of the Invertebrates. C.V. Mosby, St. Louis, Mo.

11. General Invertebrates, Advanced

PRATT, H.S. 1951. A Manual of the Common Invertebrate Animals Exclusive of Insects. The Blakiston Co., Philadelphia, Pa.

PENNAK, R.W. 1953. Fresh-Water Invertebrates of the United States. The Ronald Press Co., N.Y.

LIGHT, S.F., R.I. SMITH, F.A. PITELKA, D.P. ABBOTT & F.M. WEESNER. 1961. Intertidal Invertebrates of the Central California Coast. Univ. of California Press, Berkeley.

12. Protozoa

JAHN, T.L. & F.F. JAHN. 1949. How To Know the Protozoa. Wm. C. Brown Co., Dubuque, Ia.

KUDO, R. 1950. Protozoology. Charles C Thomas, Springfield, Ill.

CORLISS, J.O. 1961. Ciliated Protozoa: Characterization, Classification, and Guide to the Literature. Pergamon Press, N.Y.

CALAWAY, W.T. & J.B. LACKEY. 1962. Waste Treatment Protozoa, Flagellata. Univ. of Florida, Fla. Eng. Ser. No. 3.

13. Sponges and Bryozoa

DELAUBENFELS, M.W. 1953. Guide to the Sponges of Eastern North America. Univ. of Miami, Coral Gables, Fla.

ROGICK, M.D. 1960. Ectoprocta. *McGraw-Hill Encyc. Sci. Technol.* 5:7.

ROGICK, M.D. 1960. Bryozoa. *McGraw-Hill Encyc. Sci. Technol.* 2:354.

BUSHNELL, J.H., JR. 1965. On the taxonomy and distribution of the freshwater Ectoprocta in Michigan (Parts I–III). *Trans. Amer. Microsc. Soc.* 84:231; 339; 529.

PENNEY, J.T. & A.A. RACEK. 1968. Comprehensive Revision of a Worldwide Collection of Freshwater Sponges. (Porifera: Spongillidae). USNM Bull. 272.

14. Rotifers

VOIGT, M. 1957. Rotataria—Die Radertiere. Mitteleuropas. Borntraeger, Berlin, Vols. I and II.

DONNER, J. 1966. Rotifers. Warne, London & N.Y.

15. Roundworms (Nemathelminthes)

CHITWOOD, B.G. 1951. North American marine nematodes. *Tex. J. Sci.* 3:617.

GOODEY, T. 1963. Soil and Freshwater Nematodes (revised by J. B. Goodey). John Wiley & Sons, N.Y.

WIESER, W. & B.E. HOPPER. 1967. Marine nematodes of the east coast of North America. 1. *Fla. Bull. Mus. Comp. Zool.* 135:239.

16. Segmented Worms (Annelids)

SPERBER, C. 1948. A Taxonomical Study of the Naididae. Zool. Bidrag Fran Uppsala, Sweden. Band. 28.

BRINKHURST, R.O. 1964–1966. Studies on the North American aquatic Oligochaeta: I. Naididae and Opistocystidae; II Tubificidae; III Lumbriculidae and additional notes and records of other families. *Proc. Acad. Natur. Sci. Philadelphia* 116:195; 117:117; 118:1.

BRINKHURST, R.O. 1966. Detection and assessment of water pollution using oligochaete worms. *Water Sewage Works* 113:398, 438, Parts I and II.

17. Flatworms (Platyhelminthes)

EDMONDSON, W.T., ed. 1959. Ward and Whipple's Fresh Water Biology, 2nd ed. John Wiley & Sons, N.Y.

18. Crustaceans

HOBBS, H.H., JR. 1942. The crayfishes of Florida. *Univ. Fla. Publ. Biol. Sci. Ser.* 3:1.

HUBRICHT, L. & J.G. MACKIN. 1949. The freshwater isopods of the genus *Lirceus* (Asellota, Asellidae). *Amer. Midland Natur.* 42:334.

BOUSFIELD, E.L. 1958. Freshwater amphipod crustaceans of glaciated North America. *Can. Field Natur.* 72:55.

WATERMAN, T.H. 1960. The Physiology of Crustacea. Vol. I. Metabolism and Growth. Academic Press, N.Y.

19. Insects, General and Introductory

LUTZ, P.E. 1927. Field Book of Insects. G.P. Putnam's Sons, N.Y.

CHU, H.F. 1949. How To Know the Immature Insects. Wm. C. Brown Co., Dubuque, Ia.

USINGER, R.L. 1956. Aquatic Insects of California, with Keys to North American Genera and California Species. Univ. of California Press, Berkeley.

20. Stoneflies (Plecoptera)

NEEDHAM, J.G. & P.W. CLAASEN. 1925. A Monograph of the Plecoptera or Stoneflies of America North of Mexico, Vol. 2. Thomas Say Foundation, Lafayette, Ind.

FRISON, T.H. 1935. The stoneflies, or Plecoptera, of Illinois. *Bull. Ill. Natur. Hist. Surv.* 20:281.

FRISON, T.H. 1942. Studies of North American Plecoptera, with special reference to the fauna of Illinois. *Bull. Ill. Natur. Hist. Surv.* 22:235.

JEWETT, S.G. 1960. The stoneflies (Plecoptera) of California. *Bull. Calif. Insect Surv.* 6:125.

21. Mayflies (Ephemeroptera)

NEEDHAM, J.G., J.R. TRAVER & Y. HSU. 1935. The Biology of Mayflies. Comstock Publ. Co., Ithaca, N.Y.

BERNER, L. 1950. The Mayflies of Florida. Univ. of Florida Press, Gainesville.

BURKS, B.D. 1953. The mayflies, or Ephemeroptera, of Illinois. *Bull. Ill. Natur. Hist. Surv.* 26:1.

BERNER, L. 1959. A tabular summary of the biology of North American mayfly nymphs (Ephemeroptera). *Bull. Fla. State Mus.* (Gainesville) 4:1.

EDMONDS, G.F., R.K. ALLEN & W.L. PETERS. 1963. An annotated key to the nymphs of the families and subfamilies of mayflies (Ephemeroptera). *Univ. Utah Biol. Ser.* 13:1.

22. Dragonflies and Damselflies (Odonata)

NEEDHAM, J.G. & M.J. WESTFALL, JR. 1955. A Manual of the Dragonflies of North America, Including the Greater Antilles and the Provinces of the Mexican Border. Univ. of California Press, Berkeley.

WALKER, E.M. 1958. The Odonata of Canada and Alaska, Vols. I and II. Univ. of Toronto Press, Toronto, Canada.

23. Hellgrammites and Relatives

PENNAK, R.W. 1953. Fresh-Water Invertebrates of the United States. The Ronald Press, N.Y.

EDMONDSON, W.T., ed. 1959. Ward and Whipple's Fresh Water Biology, 2nd ed. John Wiley & Sons, N.Y.

24. Caddisflies (Trichoptera)

ROSS, H.H. 1944. The caddis flies, or Trichoptera, of Illinois. *Bull. Ill. Natur. Hist. Surv.* 23:1.

FLINT, O.S., JR. 1962. Taxonomy and biology of nearctic limnephilid larvae (Trichoptera), with special reference to species found in eastern United States. *Entomol. Amer.* 40:1.

25. Two-Winged Flies (Diptera)

JOHANNSEN, O.A. 1933, 1935, 1936, 1937. Memoirs of the Cornell University Agricultural Experiment Station. Parts I–IV. (Part V by L.C. Thomsen.) Reproduced in 1969 by Ent. Reprint Specialists, East Lansing, Mich.

ROBACK, S.S. 1957. The Immature Tendipedids of the Philadelphia Area. Philadelphia Acad. Natur. Sci. Monogr. No. 9.

BECK, W.M., JR. & E.C. BECK. 1966. Chironomidae (Diptera) of Florida. I: Pentaneurini (Tanypodinae). *Bull. Fla. State Mus.* 10:305.

MASON, W.T. 1968. An Introduction to the Identification of Chironomid Larvae. FWPCA, Washington, D.C.

SNODDY, E.L. 1969. Simuliidae of Alabama. Ala. Agr. Exp. Sta. Bull. 390.

26. Beetles (Coleoptera)

JAQUES, H.E. 1951. How To Know the Beetles. Wm. C. Brown, Dubuque, Ia.

YOUNG, F.N. 1954. Water Beetles of Florida. Univ. of Florida Press, Gainesville.

DILLON, E.S. & L.S. DILLON. 1961. Manual of Common Beetles of Eastern North America. Harper and Row, N.Y.

27. True Bugs (Hemiptera)

PENNAK, R.W. 1953. Fresh-Water Invertebrates of the United States. The Ronald Press, N.Y.

EDMONDSON, W.T., ed. 1959. Ward and Whipple's Fresh Water Biology, 2nd ed. John Wiley & Sons, N.Y.

28. Mollusks, General and Introductory

PENNAK, R.W. 1953. Fresh-Water Invertebrates of the United States. The Ronald Press, N.Y.

EDMONDSON, W.T., ed. 1959. Ward and Whipple's Fresh Water Biology, 2nd ed. John Wiley & Sons, N.Y.

29. Snails (Gastropoda)

BAKER, F.C. 1928. The Fresh-Water Mollusca of Wisconsin. Part I. Gastropoda. Wisconsin Geol. Natur. Hist. Surv. Bull. No. 70.

KEEN, A.M. & J.C. PEARSON. 1952. Illustrated Key to West North American Gastropod Genera. Stanford Univ. Press, Stanford, Calif.

WALTER, H.J. & J.B. BURCH. 1957. Key to the Genera of Freshwater Gastropods (Snails and Limpets) Occurring in Michigan. Mus. Zool., Univ. Mich. Circ. No. 3.

LEONARD, A.B. 1959. Handbook of Gastropods in Kansas. Univ. Kans. Mus. Natur. Hist. Misc. Publ. No. 20.

LaROCQUE, A. 1968. Pleistocene mollusca of Ohio. *Ohio Geol. Surv. Bull.* 62:357.

30. Bivalves (Pelecypoda)

WALKER, B. 1918. A Synopsis of the Classification of Freshwater Mollusca of North America, North of Mexico, and a Catalogue of the More Recently Described Species, with Notes. Museum of Zoology, Univ. of Michigan Misc. Publ. No. 6.

BAKER, F.C. 1928. The Fresh-Water Mollusca of Wisconsin. Part II. Pelecypoda. Wis. Geol. Natur. Hist. Surv. Bull. No. 70.

KEEN, A.M. & D. FRIZZELL. 1946. Illustrated Key to West North American Pelecepod Genera. Stanford Univ. Press, Stanford, Calif.

MURRAY, H.D. & A.B. LEONARD. 1962. Handbook of Unionid Mussels in Kansas. Univ. Kans. Mus. Natur. Hist. Misc. Publ. No. 28.

HERRINGTON, H.B. 1962. A Revision of the Sphaeriidae of North America (Mollusca: Pelecypoda). Univ. Mich. Mus. Zool. Misc. Publ. No. 118.

NEEL, J.K. & W.R. ALLEN. 1963. The mussel fauna of the Upper Cumberland Basin before its impoundment. *Malacologia* 1:427.

HEARD, W.H. & J. BURCH. 1966. Keys to the Genera of Freshwater Pelecypods of Michigan. Museum of Zoology, Univ. Mich. Circ. No. 4.

LaROCQUE, A. 1967. Pleistocene mollusca of Ohio. Ohio Geol. Surv. Bull. No. 62.

31. Echinoderms

COE, W.R. 1912. Echinoderms of Connecticut, Conn. State Geol. Natur. Hist. Surv. Bull. No. 19.

MINER, R.W. 1950. Field Book of Seashore Life. G.P. Putnam's Sons, N.Y.

Harvey, E.B. 1956. The American Arbacia and Other Sea Urchins. Princeton Univ. Press, Princeton, N.J.

32. Fishes

Walford, L.A. 1937. Marine Game Fishes of the Pacific Coast from Alaska to the Equator. Univ. Calif. Press, Berkeley.

Breder, C.M. 1948. Fieldbook of Marine Fishes. G.P. Putnam's Sons, N.Y.

Eddy, S. 1957. How To Know the Freshwater Fishes. Wm. C. Brown Co., Dubuque, Ia.

Trautman, M.B. 1957. The Fishes of Ohio. Ohio State Univ. Press, Columbus.

Bailey, R.M., et al. 1960. A List of Common and Scientific Names of Fishes from the United States and Canada. Amer. Fish. Soc. Spec. Publ. No. 2.

Perlmutter, A. 1961. Guide to Marine Fishes. N.Y. Univ. Press, N.Y.

Hubbs, C.L. & K.F. Lagler. 1964. Fishes of the Great Lakes Region. Univ. Mich. Press, Ann Arbor.

Cross, F.B. 1967. Handbook of Fishes of Kansas. Univ. Kans. Mus. Natur. Hist., Lawrence, Kans.

Blair, W.F. & G.A. Moore. 1968. Fishes. In: Vertebrates of the United States, 2d ed. McGraw-Hill, N.Y.

33. Amphibians

Bishop, S.C. 1943. Handbook of Salamanders. Comstock Publ. Co., Ithaca, N.Y.

Conant, R. 1958. Field Guide to the Reptiles and Amphibians of Eastern North America. Houghton-Mifflin, N.Y.

Brandon, R.A. 1961. A comparison of the larvae of five northeastern species of *Ambystoma* (Amphibia, Caudata). *Copeia* 4:377.

Brandon, R.A. 1964. An annotated and illustrated key to multistage larvae of Ohio salamanders. *Ohio J. Sci.* 64:252.

Blair, W.F. et al. 1968. Vertebrates of the United States. McGraw-Hill, N.Y.

34. Bacteria and Fungi

Breed, R.S., E.G.D. Murray & N.R. Smith. 1957. Bergey's Manual of Determinative Bacteriology, 7th ed. Williams & Wilkins, Baltimore, Md.

Cooke, W.B. 1963. A Laboratory Guide to Fungi in Polluted Waters. USPHS, Cincinnati, Ohio.

Johnson, T.W., Jr. 1968. Saprobic Marine Fungi. In: The Fungi, Vol. III. (G.C. Ainsworth & A.S. Sussman, eds.). Academic Press, N.Y.

INDEX

M

NOTES

NOTES

NOTES

NOTES

NOTES

NOTES

ABBREVIATIONS

The following symbols and abbreviations are used throughout this book:

Abbreviation	Referent	Abbreviation	Referent
A or amp	ampere(s)	F	degree(s) Fahrenheit
AC	alternating current	ft	foot (feet)
ACS	American Chemical Society	ft-c	foot-candle(s)
APHA	American Public Health Association	g	gram(s)
		g	gravity, unit acceleration of
ASTM	American Society for Testing and Materials	gal	gallon(s)
atm	atmosphere(s)	gph	gallons per hour
AWWA	American Water Works Association	gpm	gallons per minute
		hr	hour
BOD	biochemical oxygen demand	ID	inside diameter
		IDOD	immediate dissolved oxygen demand
C	degree(s) Celsius	in	inch(es)
c	count(s)		
CAE	carbon alcohol extract	K	degree(s) Kelvin
CCE	carbon chloroform extract	KeV	kiloelectron volt(s)
Ci	curie(s)	kg	kilogram(s)
cm, cm², cm³	centimeter(s), square centimeter(s), cubic centimeter(s)	l	liter(s)
		LAS	linear alkylate sulfonate
COD	chemical oxygen demand	lb	pound(s)
Col.	column	LC	lethal concentration
conc	concentrated	M	molar
cpm	counts per minute	m, m², m³	meter(s), square meter(s), cubic meter(s)
cps	counts per second	MATC	maximum allowable toxicant concentration
DC	direct current	me	milliequivalent(s)
diam	diameter	MeV	megaelectron volt(s)
DO	dissolved oxygen	mg	milligram(s)
dpm	disintegrations per minute	min	minute(s)
		ml	milliliter(s)
EC	effective concentration	mm, mm², mm³	millimeter(s), square millimeter(s), cubic millimeter(s)
EDTA	ethylenediamine tetraacetic acid (or its salts)		